S0-AXK-755

Scott Foresman - Addison Wesley
MIDDLE SCHOOL MATH
Course 1

Randall I. Charles John A. Dossey Steven J. Leinwand
Cathy L. Seeley Charles B. Vonder Embse

L. Carey Bolster • Janet H. Caldwell • Dwight A. Cooley • Warren D. Crown
Linda Proudfit • Alma B. Ramírez • Jeanne F. Ramos • Freddie Lee Renfro
David F. Robitaille • Jane Swafford

Teacher's Edition

Volume 1

Chapters 1–6

Scott Foresman
Addison Wesley

Editorial Offices: Menlo Park, California • Glenview, Illinois
Sales Offices: Reading, Massachusetts • Atlanta, Georgia • Glenview, Illinois
Carrollton, Texas • Menlo Park, California

http://www.sf.aw.com

Math

that Makes Sense...

"I learn best when math is interesting to me."

The Student's Perspective

Student

"If we are to reach all students, we must strive for meaningful, challenging, and relevant learning in the classroom."

The Research Perspective

Re

Printed in the United States of America

ISBN 0-201-69026-8

1 2 3 4 5 6 7 8 9 10-DOW-01 00 99 98 97

Teacher

The Teacher's Perspective

*"My primary concern in teaching is to help **all** my students succeed."*

from **EVERY** *Perspective*

What kind of a math program are you looking for? What about your students? And how about mathematics education research? Can one program really satisfy *all* points of view? Through its content, features, and format, *Scott Foresman - Addison Wesley Middle School MATH* recognizes the real-life needs and concerns specific to middle school—supported by research but grounded in real classroom experience.

Welcome to a math program that excels from every perspective—especially yours!

search

Math that Connects to the Student's World

Middle school students have a perspective all their own. We've tapped into their world with experiences and information that grab their attention and don't let go.

"I want to know when I'll use this."

Real, age-appropriate data
Data based on what middle school students buy, eat, study in school, and enjoy permeate every lesson.

Cool themes like *Spiders, Disasters, Food,* and *Whales*
Student-friendly topics blend learning with what kids love.

MathSURF Internet Site
MathSURF's up and so is student interest! Kids can go online to explore text content of every chapter in safe and exciting destinations around the world.

Interactive CD-ROM
Interactive lessons for every chapter provide an exciting environment for learning.

Math that Promotes High School Success

Teachers in today's middle schools need a program that prepares their students for high school math. That means rigorous content, including preparation for algebra and geometry, NTCM content and process standards—PLUS practical strategies for taking tests and problem solving.

*"My students need to be prepared for high school math. And let's face it, how they perform is a reflection of how **I** perform!"*

Performance

The building blocks of algebra

Prepare students for success in high school math with instruction in mathematical reasoning.

Course 1—focuses on *numerical reasoning.*

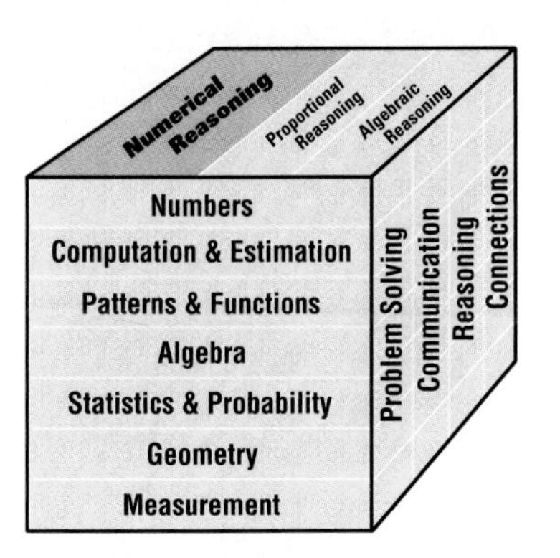

Course 2—focuses on *proportional reasoning.*

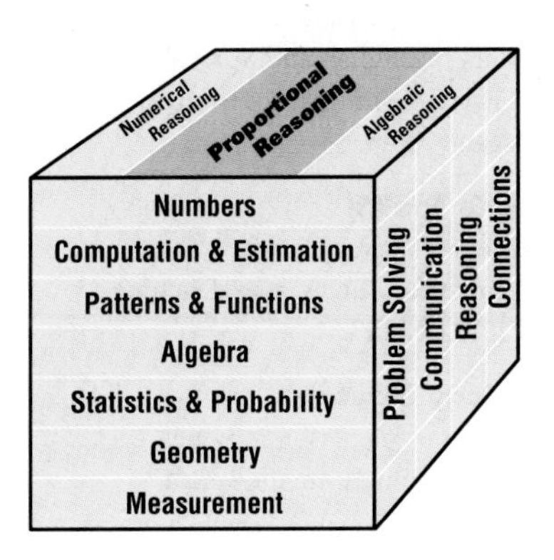

Course 3—focuses on *algebraic reasoning.*

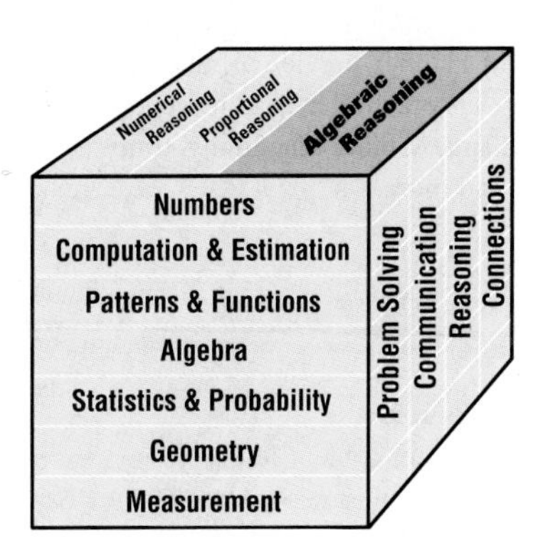

Test prep strategies

The next step in strategies! Helping students be smart about how they take standardized tests builds confidence and leads to success.

Problem solving that's no problem

Sharpen students' problem-solving skills with numerous opportunities to analyze and use the problem-solving process.

A Program that Supports Teaching Success

Teachers in today's middle schools face unique challenges—from improving student performance to adapting to each student's unique learning needs. This program is designed to help you meet those challenges. You'll find help for every teaching need—including *block scheduling* and *interdisciplinary team teaching,* PLUS *outstanding technology,* and more!

Student Edition

Colorful lessons, filled with student-oriented data, have a unique "middle school" look.

Teacher's Edition

(with Teacher's Resource Planner CD-ROM)

Two hardbound volumes, packaged with a CD-ROM Planner, provide complete lesson plans plus practical help to meet your every challenge—block scheduling, team teaching, and more.

Teacher's Resource Package

Practice Masters

Exercises reinforce content of every lesson. Also available as a workbook.

Alternative Lessons (Reteaching Masters)

Masters for every lesson offer another look at skills and concepts.

Extend Your Thinking (Enrichment Masters)

Masters enhance thinking skills and creativity in every lesson.

Problem-Solving Masters (for Guided Problem Solving)

Masters guide students step-by-step through one problem from every Student Edition exercise set. Also available as a workbook.

Assessment Sourcebook

Options to help profile students as learners. Includes multiple-choice, short-response, performance, and mixed-format chapter tests, as well as section quizzes and record forms.

Home and Community Connections

Make math a family affair! Booklet with letters in English and Spanish, also provides classroom tips, community projects, and more.

Teacher's Toolkit

Saves time with a variety of Management Resources, plus Teaching Tool Transparencies.

Technology Masters

Computer and calculator activities energize lessons with the power of technology.

Chapter Project Masters

Masters support the on-going project in each Student Edition chapter.

Interdisciplinary Team Teaching

Math across the curriculum! Masters provide an engaging 2-page interdisciplinary lesson for each section.

Resources to Customize Instruction

Print Resources

Block Scheduling Handbook
Practical suggestions let you tailor the program to various block scheduling formats.

Overhead Transparency Package
Daily Transparencies (for Problem of the Day, Review, and Quick Quiz) and Lesson Enhancement Transparencies help enliven class presentations.

Multilingual Handbook
Enhanced math glossary with examples in multiple languages provides a valuable resource for teaching. Especially useful with ESL students.

Mathematics Dictionary
Handy reference tool of middle school math terms.

Solutions Manual
Manual includes convenient solutions to Student Edition exercises.

Technology

Teacher's Resource Planner CD-ROM
The entire Teacher's Resource Package on CD-ROM! Includes an electronic planning guide which allows you to set criteria when planning lessons, customize worksheets, correlate your curriculum to specific objectives, and more!

Interactive CD-ROM
Interactive, multimedia lessons with built-in math tools help students explore concepts in enjoyable and involving ways.

MathSURF Internet Site (for Students)
Math on the Web! Provides links to other sites, project ideas, interactive surveys and more.

MathSURF Internet Site (for Teachers)
Offers exciting opportunities for in-service ideas and sharing.

MathSURF Internet Site (for Parents)
This Web site offers a variety of practical tips to parents.

TestWorks: Test and Practice CD-ROM
CD-ROM saves hours of test-prep time by generating and customizing tests and worksheets.

Manipulative Kits

Student Manipulative Kit
Quantities of angle rulers, Power Polygons, and other items help students grasp mathematics concepts on a concrete level.

Teacher's Overhead Manipulative Kit
Kit makes demonstrating concepts from an overhead projector easy and convenient.

Authors with Middle School Expertise!

Math that makes sense from every perspective—it's a commitment we've kept in all aspects of this program, including our outstanding team of authors. Their expertise in mathematics education brings to the program extensive knowledge of how middle school students learn math and how best to teach them.

Expertise

"Students learn and perform better when they are taught in ways that match their own strengths."

Charles B. Vonder Embse

Professor of Mathematics Education and Mathematics

Central Michigan University
Mt. Pleasant, Michigan

Member of NCTM Instructional Issues Advisory Committee

Member of the Advisory Board of Teachers Teaching with Technology (T^3)

Jane Swafford

Professor of Mathematics

Illinois State University
Normal, Illinois

Randall I. Charles

Professor, Department of Mathematics and Computer Science

San Jose State University
San Jose, California

Past Vice-President, National Council of Supervisors of Mathematics

Co-author of two NCTM publications on teaching and evaluating progress in problem solving

Dwight A. Cooley

Assistant Principal

Mary Louise Phillips
Elementary School
Fort Worth, Texas

Member, NCTM Board of Directors

John A. Dossey

Distinguished University
Professor of Mathematics

Illinois State University
Normal, Illinois

Past President, NCTM

Guided development of NCTM Standards

Recipient, NCTM Lifetime Achievement Award

Chairman, Conference Board of the Mathematical Sciences

"A program that asks real-life questions provides rich possibilities for students."

Steven J. Leinwand

Mathematics Consultant

Connecticut Department
of Education
Hartford, Connecticut

Member, NCTM Board of Directors

Past President, National Council of Supervisors of Mathematics

Cathy L. Seeley

Director of Policy and Professional
Development for Texas SSI

University of Texas
Austin, Texas

Texas State Mathematics Supervisor

Writer, Curriculum and Evaluation Standards for School Mathematics

Member, NCTM Board of Directors

Turn the page, for more authors!

More Authors with Middle School Expertise!

Freddie Lee Renfro
Coordinator of Mathematics
Fort Bend Independent
School District
Sugarland, Texas

L. Carey Bolster
Director, K–12 Math Projects
Public Broadcasting Service
MATHLINE
Alexandria, Virginia

More

"Students construct new learning from a basis of prior knowledge and experience."

Linda Proudfit
University Professor of Mathematics and Computer Education
Governors State University
University Park, Illinois

Janet H. Caldwell
Professor of Mathematics
Rowan University
Glassboro, New Jersey

David F. Robitaille

Professor of Mathematics Education

University of British Columbia
Vancouver, British Columbia,
Canada

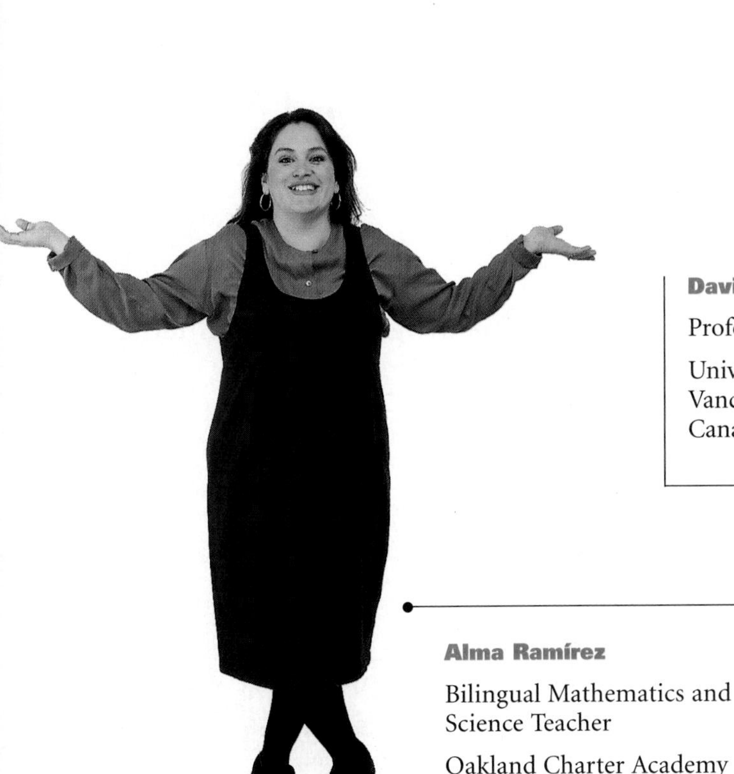

Alma Ramírez

Bilingual Mathematics and Science Teacher

Oakland Charter Academy
Oakland, California

"To be successful in high school, students need a solid foundation in mathematical reasoning."

Jeanne F. Ramos

Assistant Principal

Nobel Middle School
Los Angeles, California

Warren D. Crown

Professor of Mathematics Education

Rutgers, The State University of New Jersey
New Brunswick, New Jersey

Expertise

Contributors from Across the Country!

A Nationwide Perspective

Educators from across the country helped shape this program with valuable input about local needs and concerns.

Contributing Writers

Phillip E. Duren
California State University
Hayward, CA

Kathy A. Ross
Loyola University (LaSIP)
New Orleans, LA

Sheryl M. Yamada
Beverly Hills High School
Beverly Hills, CA

Content Reviewers

Ann Boltz
Coldwater, MI

John David Bridges
Greenville, SC

Glenn Bruckhart
Fort Collins, CO

Sharon Bourgeois Butler
Spring, TX

Carol Cameron
Seattle, WA

Steven T. Cottrell
Farmington, UT

Patricia Creel
Lawrenceville, GA

Wendi M. Cyford
New Market, MD

Scott Firkins
Owensboro, KY

Madelaine Gallin
New York, NY

Roy E. Griggs
Boise, ID

Lucy Hahn
Boise, ID

Allison Harris
Seattle, WA

Clay Hutson
Kingsport, TN

Beryl W. Jackson
Alexandria, VA

Janet Jomp
Wilson, NC

Ann P. Lawrence
Marietta, GA

Cheryl McCormack
Indianapolis, IN

Gary McCracken
Tuscaloosa, AL

Allison McNaughton
Marstons Mills, MA

Sandra A. Nagy
Mesa, AZ

Kent Novak
Greene, RI

Jeff C. Nusbaum
Rock Island, IL

Vince O'Connor
Milwaukee, WI

Mary Lynn Raith
Pittsburgh, PA

Kathleen Rieke
Zionsville, IN

Ellen G. Robertson
Norwich, NY

Nancy Rolsen
Worthington, OH

Edith Roos
Helena, MT

Lynn A. Sandro
Cedar Springs, MI

Carol Sims
Arcadia, CA

Paul E. Smith
Newburgh, IN

Donald M. Smyton
Kenmore, NY

Stella M. Turner
Indianapolis, IN

Tommie Walsh
Lubbock, TX

Terri Weaver
Houston, TX

Jacqueline Weilmuenster
Colleyville, TX

Multicultural Reviewers

Mary Margaret Capraro
Hialeah, FL

Robert Capraro
Miami, FL

Bettye Forte
Fort Worth, TX

Hector Hirigoyen
Miami, FL

James E. Hopkins
Auburn, WA

Patricia Locke
Mobridge, SD

Jimmie Rios
Fort Worth, TX

Linda Skinner
Edmond, OK

ESL Reviewers

Anna Uhl Chamot
Washington, DC

Jimmie Rios
Fort Worth, TX

Inclusion Reviewers

Lucy Blood
Amesbury, MA

Janett Borg
Monroe, UT

John David Bridges
Greenville, SC

Edith Roos
Helena, MT

Cross-Curricular Reviewers

Janett Borg
Monroe, UT

Kurt Brorson
Bethesda, MD

Geoffrey Chester
Washington, DC

Trudi Hammel Garland
Orinda, CA

M. Frank Watt Ireton
Washington, DC

Donna Krasnow
Carmel, CA

Chelcie Liu
San Francisco, CA

Edith Roos
Helena, MT

Technology Reviewers

Kurt Brorson
Bethesda, MD

Beverly W. Nichols
Overland Park, KS

Susan Rhodes
Springfield, IL

David L. Stout
Pensacola, FL

TABLE OF CONTENTS

Teacher's Edition

VOLUME 1: CHAPTERS 1–6

VOLUME 2: CHAPTERS 7–12

FROM THE AUTHORS

FROM THE AUTHORS

Dear Student,

We have designed a unique mathematics program that answers the question students your age have been asking for years about their math lessons: "When am I ever going to use this?"

In *Scott Foresman - Addison Wesley Middle School Math,* you'll learn about math in your own world and develop problem-solving techniques that will work for you in everyday life. The chapters have two or three sections, each with a useful math topic and an interesting theme. For example, you'll relate fractions to floods, algebra to the Oregon Trail, and geometry to origami.

Each section begins with an opportunity to explore new topics and make your own conjectures. Lessons are presented clearly with examples and chances to try the math yourself. Then, real kids like you and your friends say what they think about each concept and show how they understand it. And every section contains links to the World Wide Web, making your math book a dynamic link to an ever-expanding universe of knowledge.

You will soon realize how mathematics is not only useful, but also connected to you and your life as you continue to experience the real world. We trust that each of you will gain the knowledge necessary to be successful and to be everything you want to be.

Randall I. Charles *John A. Dossey* *Steven J. Leinwand*
Cathy L. Seeley *Charles B. Vonder Embse*

L. Carey Bolster *Janet H. Caldwell* *Dwight A. Cooley* *Warren D. Crown* *Linda Proudfit*
Alma B. Ramirez *Jeanne F. Ramos* *Freddie Lee Renfro* *David Robitaille* *Jane Swafford*

CHAPTER 1

Statistics—Real World Use of Whole Numbers

Problem Solving in Chapter 1

Search for patterns in data concerning shark habits, Presidential candidates, and top-ranked athletes.

TECHNOLOGY

- Spreadsheet
- Calculator
- World Wide Web
- Interactive CD-ROM

Algebra

See how to plot points and interpret algebraic information in different types of graphs.

CHAPTER 2

Connecting Arithmetic to Algebra

Problem Solving in Chapter 2

Present information concerning space probes, collections, and deep-sea diving to demonstrate your decision-making skills.

TECHNOLOGY

- Spreadsheet
- Calculator
- World Wide Web
- Interactive CD-ROM

Algebra

See how to use one of the basic units of algebra — the variable.

CHAPTER

1 2 3 4 5 6 7 8 9 10 11 12

CHAPTER 3

Decimals

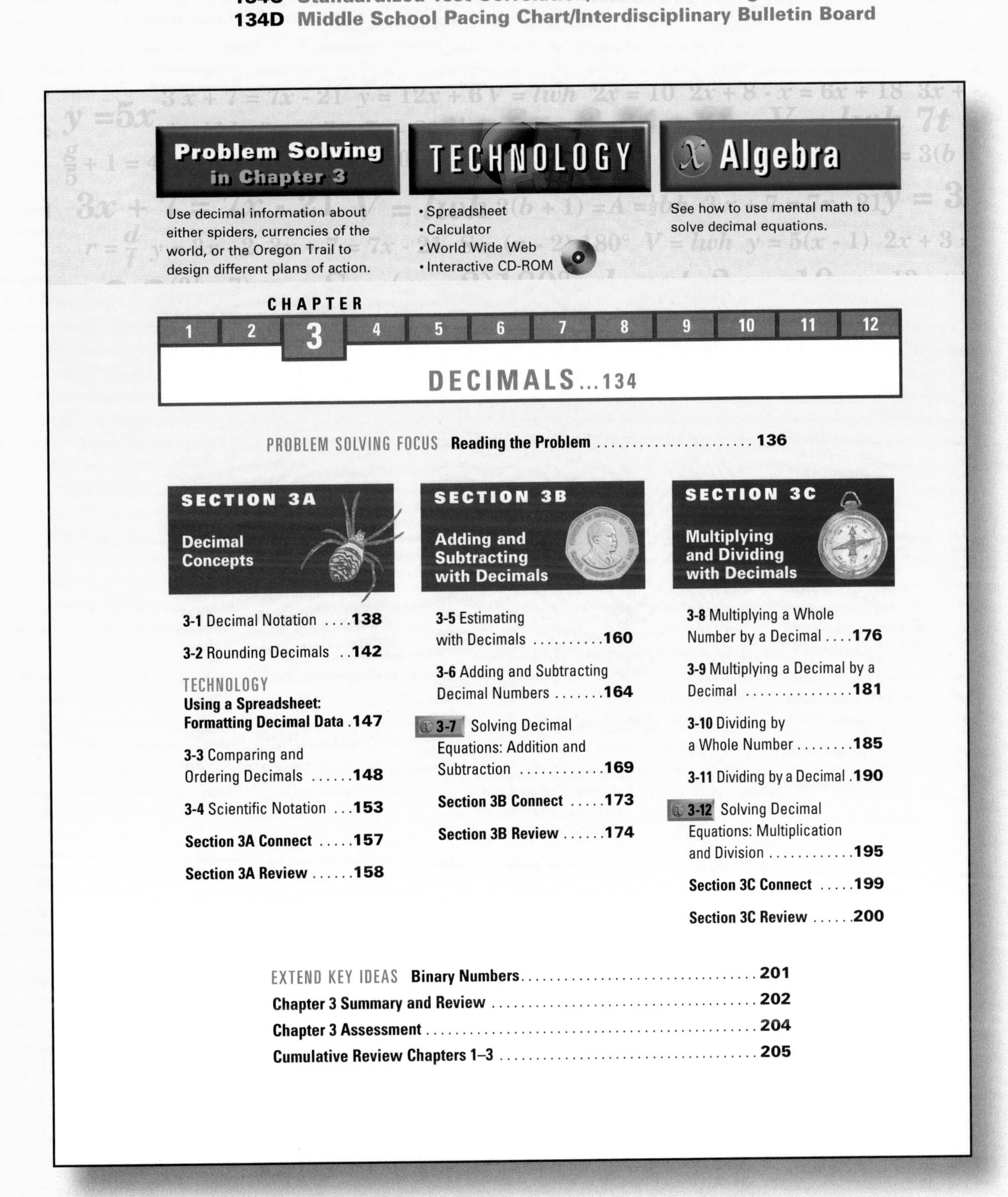

Problem Solving in Chapter 3

Use decimal information about either spiders, currencies of the world, or the Oregon Trail to design different plans of action.

TECHNOLOGY

- Spreadsheet
- Calculator
- World Wide Web
- Interactive CD-ROM

Algebra

See how to use mental math to solve decimal equations.

CHAPTER 1 2 **3** 4 5 6 7 8 9 10 11 12

CHAPTER 4

Measurement

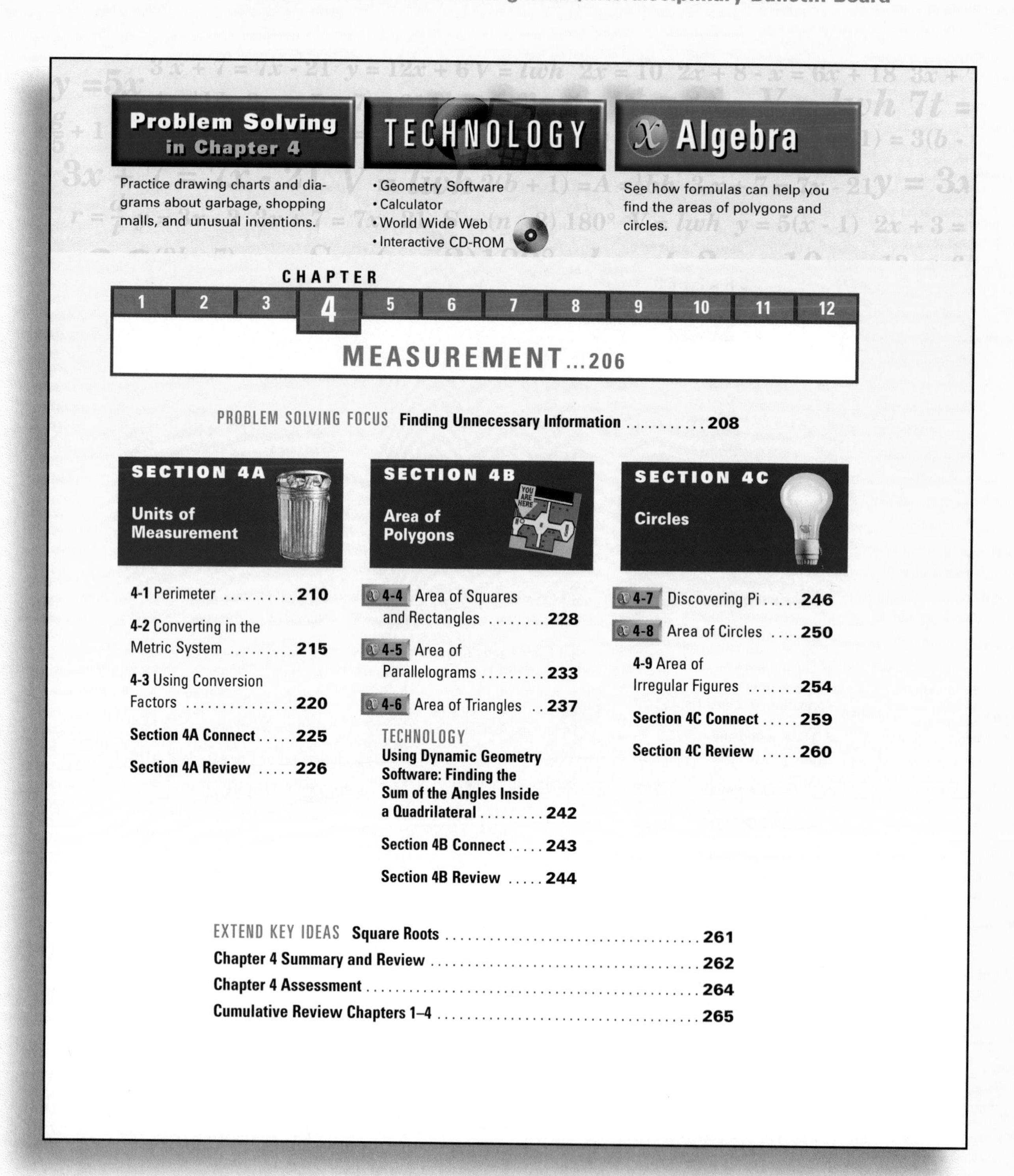

CHAPTER 5

Patterns and Number Theory

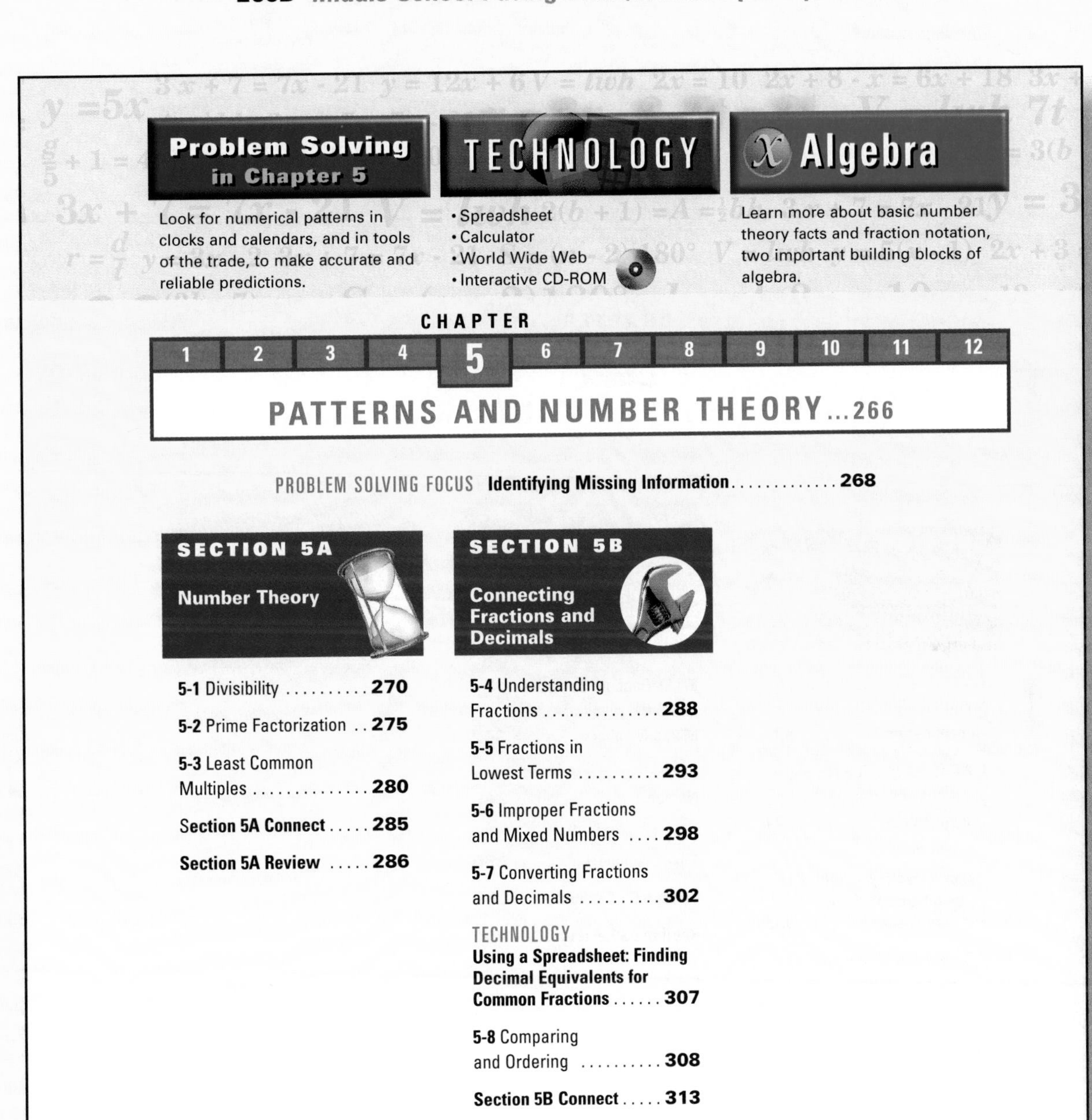

Problem Solving in Chapter 5

Look for numerical patterns in clocks and calendars, and in tools of the trade, to make accurate and reliable predictions.

TECHNOLOGY

- Spreadsheet
- Calculator
- World Wide Web
- Interactive CD-ROM

Algebra

Learn more about basic number theory facts and fraction notation, two important building blocks of algebra.

CHAPTER 1 2 3 4 **5** 6 7 8 9 10 11 12

CHAPTER 6

Adding and Subtracting Fractions

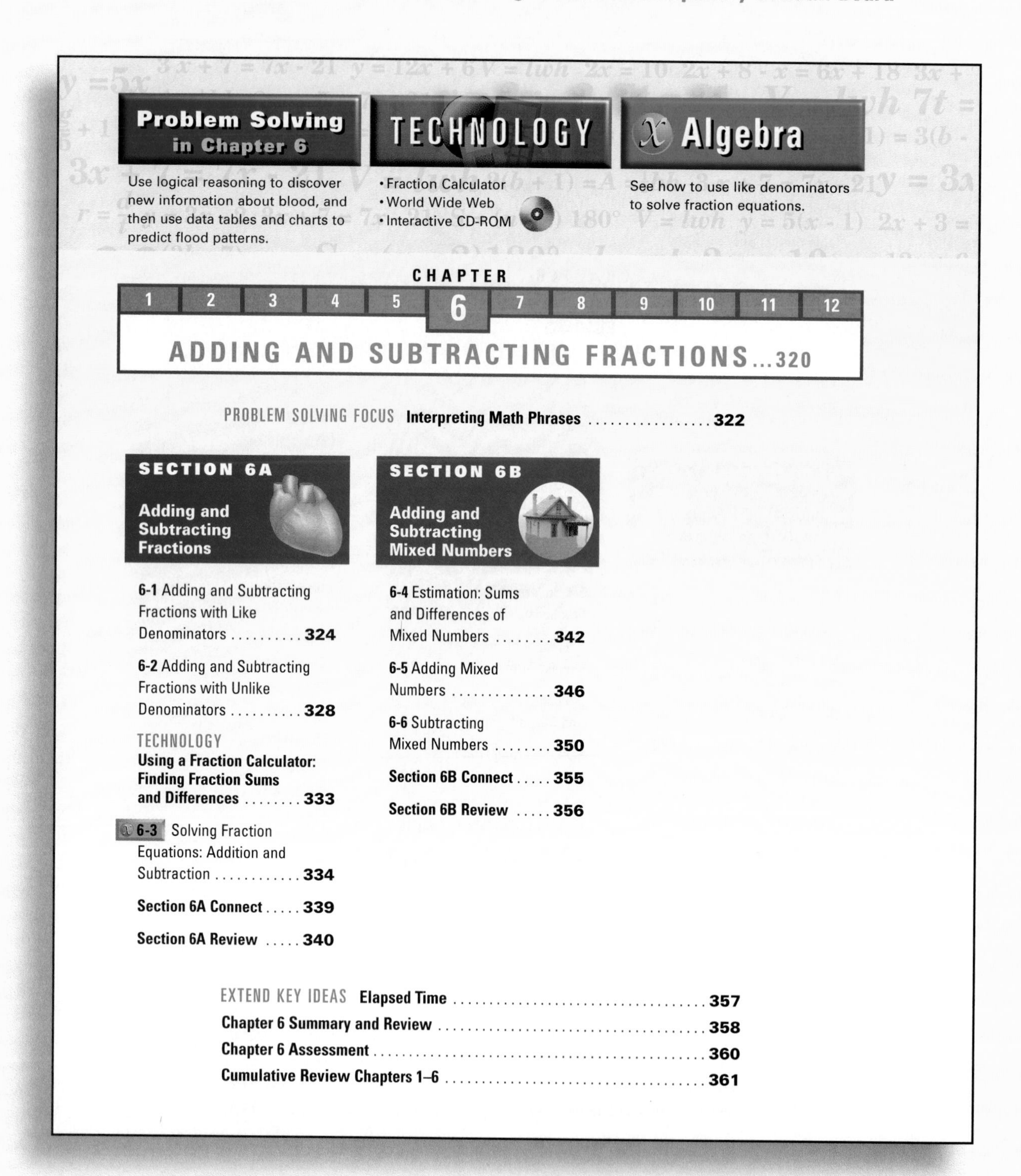

Problem Solving in Chapter 6

Use logical reasoning to discover new information about blood, and then use data tables and charts to predict flood patterns.

TECHNOLOGY

- Fraction Calculator
- World Wide Web
- Interactive CD-ROM

Algebra

See how to use like denominators to solve fraction equations.

CHAPTER 1 2 3 4 5 6 7 8 9 10 11 12

CHAPTER 7

Multiplying and Dividing Fractions

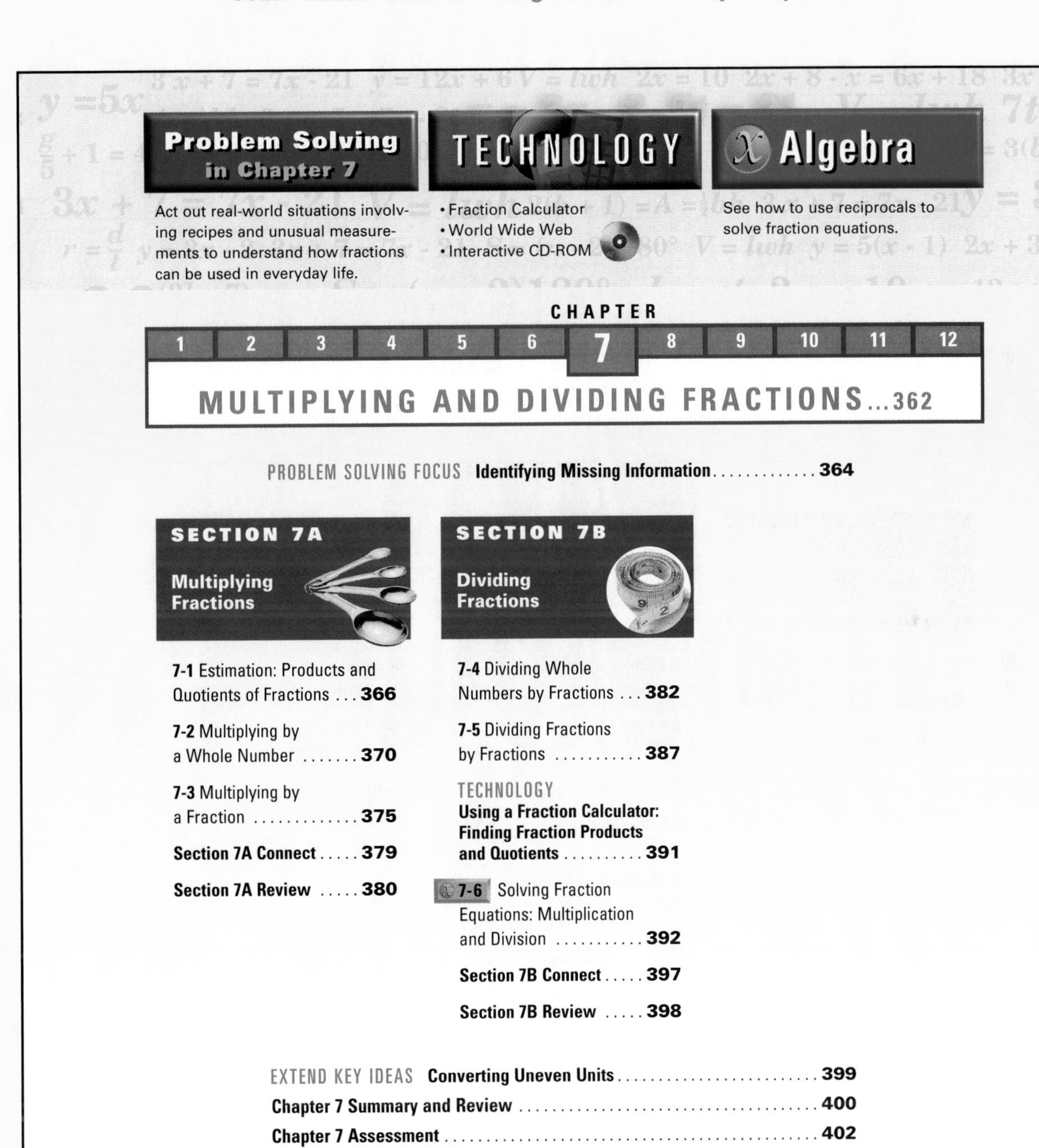

Problem Solving in Chapter 7

Act out real-world situations involving recipes and unusual measurements to understand how fractions can be used in everyday life.

TECHNOLOGY

- Fraction Calculator
- World Wide Web
- Interactive CD-ROM

Algebra

See how to use reciprocals to solve fraction equations.

CHAPTER 1 2 3 4 5 6 7 8 9 10 11 12

CHAPTER 8

The Geometry of Polygons

Problem Solving in Chapter 8

Draw diagrams and build models to communicate important geometry concepts in origami, crystals, and Islamic art.

TECHNOLOGY

- Geometry Software
- Calculator
- World Wide Web
- Interactive CD-ROM

Algebra

Use algebraic thinking as you classify polygons and look for numerical relationships within polygons.

CHAPTER

1 2 3 4 5 6 7 **8** 9 10 11 12

CHAPTER 9

Integers and the Coordinate Plane

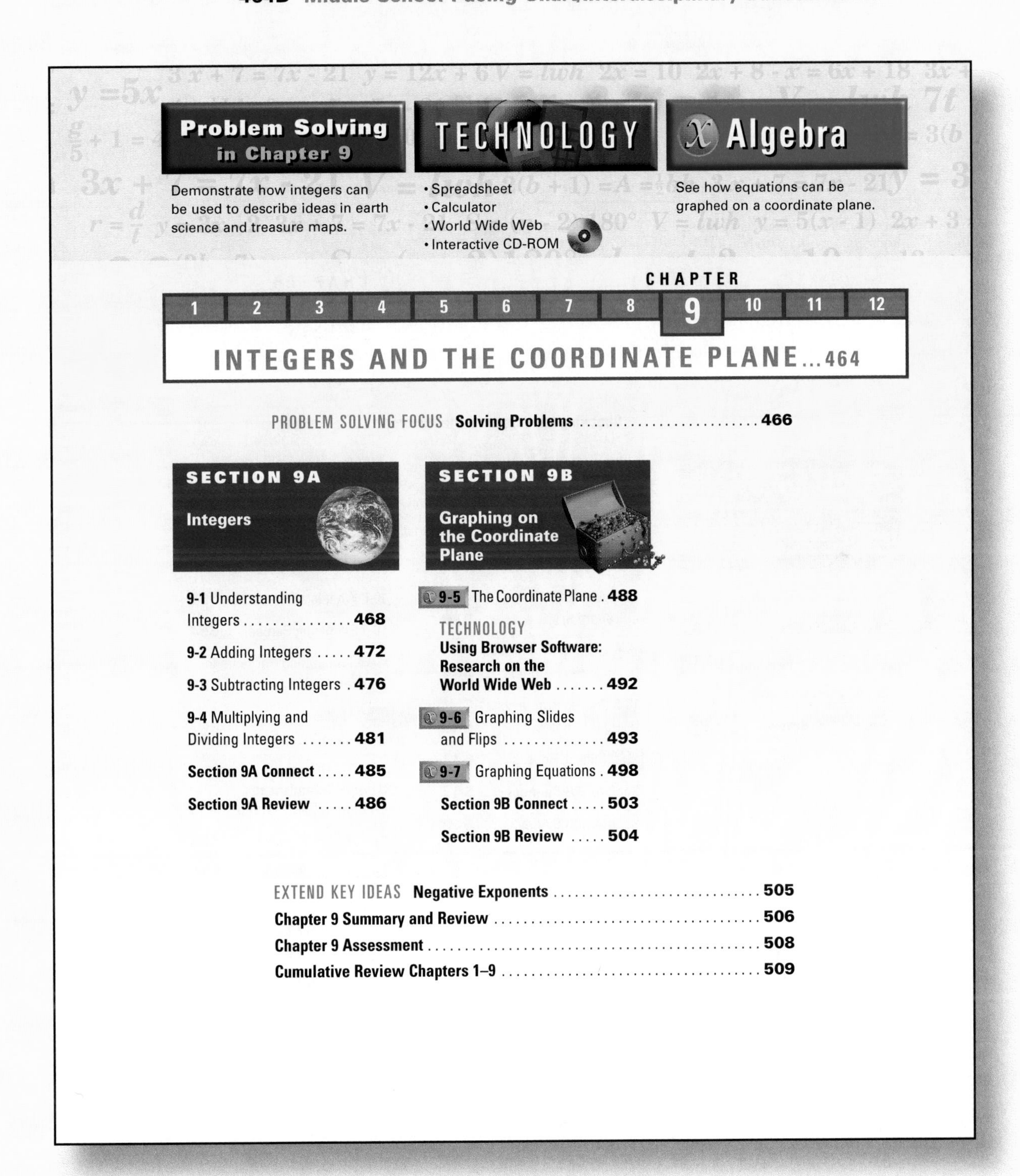

CHAPTER 10

Ratio, Proportion, and Percent

Problem Solving in Chapter 10

Determine how information about fire prevention, statues, and rain forests can help you make predictions and identify patterns.

TECHNOLOGY

- Spreadsheet
- Calculator
- World Wide Web
- Interactive CD-ROM

Algebra

See how proportions can be solved using algebra.

CHAPTER 1 2 3 4 5 6 7 8 9 10 11 12

CHAPTER 11

Solids and Measurement

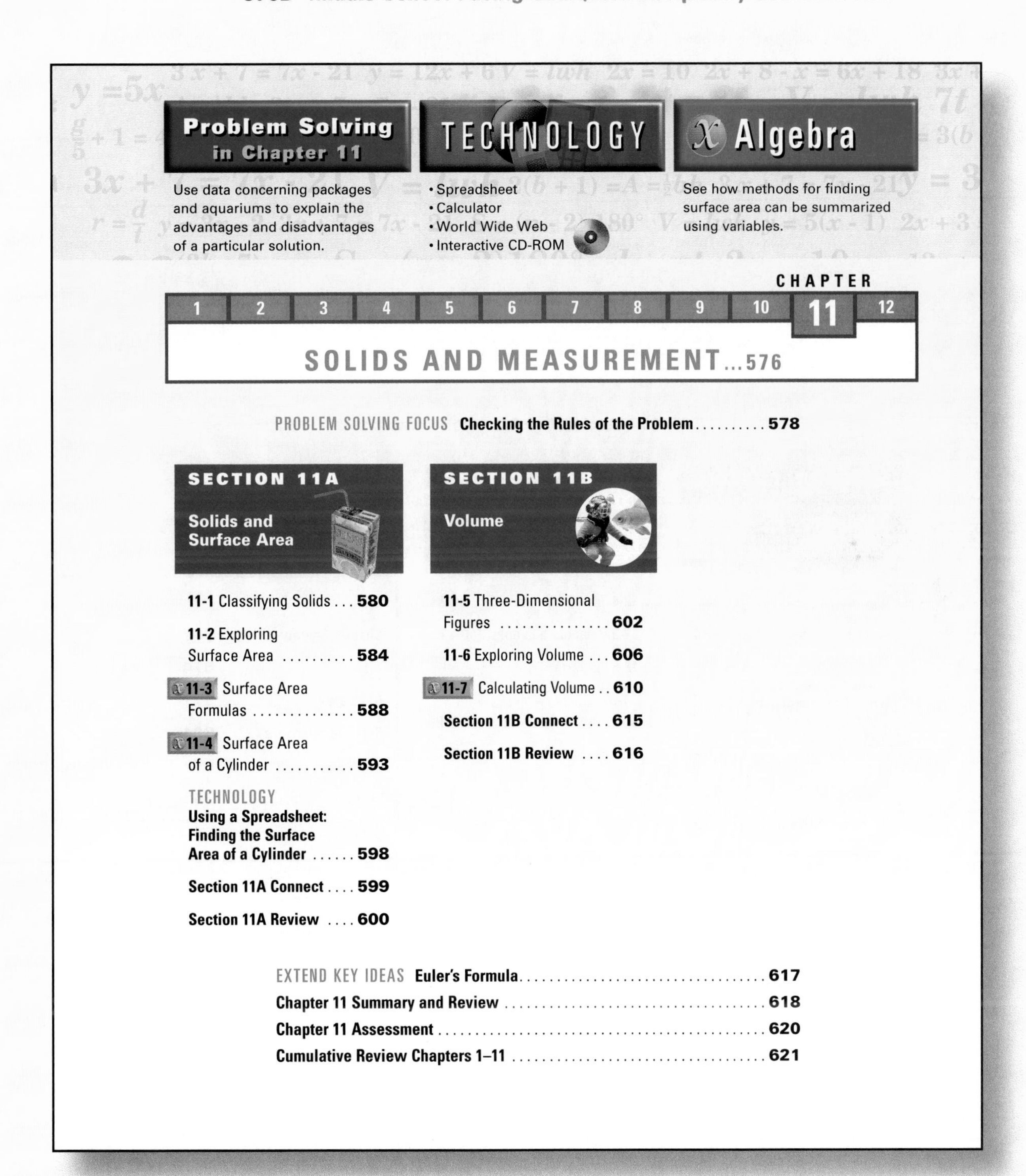

Problem Solving in Chapter 11
Use data concerning packages and aquariums to explain the advantages and disadvantages of a particular solution.

TECHNOLOGY
- Spreadsheet
- Calculator
- World Wide Web
- Interactive CD-ROM

Algebra
See how methods for finding surface area can be summarized using variables.

CHAPTER 1 2 3 4 5 6 7 8 9 10 11 12

CHAPTER 12

Probability

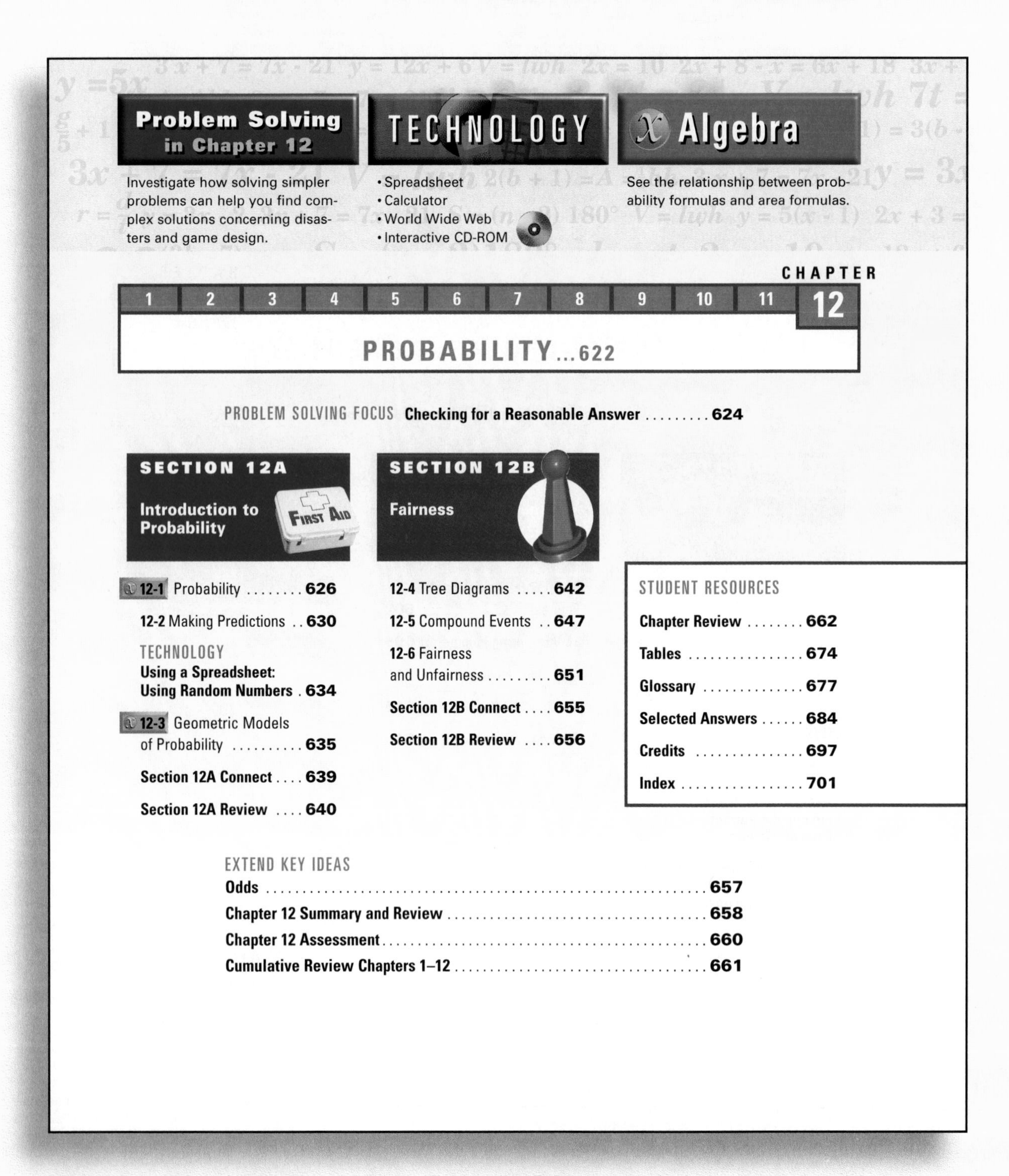

Pacing Guide

The pacing suggested in the chart at the right assumes one day for most lessons, one day for end-of-section Connect and Review, and two days for end-of-chapter Summary, Review, and Assessment. The same number of days per chapter is used for the block scheduling options. For example, see page 2D.

You may need to adjust pacing to meet the needs of your students and your district curriculum.

	CHAPTER	PAGES	NUMBER OF DAYS
1	Statistics—Real World Use of Whole Numbers	2–61	15
2	Connecting Arithmetic to Algebra	62–133	19
3	Decimals	134–205	18
4	Measurement	206–265	15
5	Patterns and Number Theory	266–319	13
6	Adding and Subtracting Fractions	320–361	11
7	Multiplying and Dividing Fractions	362–403	11
8	The Geometry of Polygons	404–463	16
9	Integers and the Coordinate Plane	464–509	12
10	Ratio, Proportion, and Percent	510–575	17
11	Solids and Measurement	576–621	12
12	Probability	622–661	11
	Total Days		**170**

Materials List

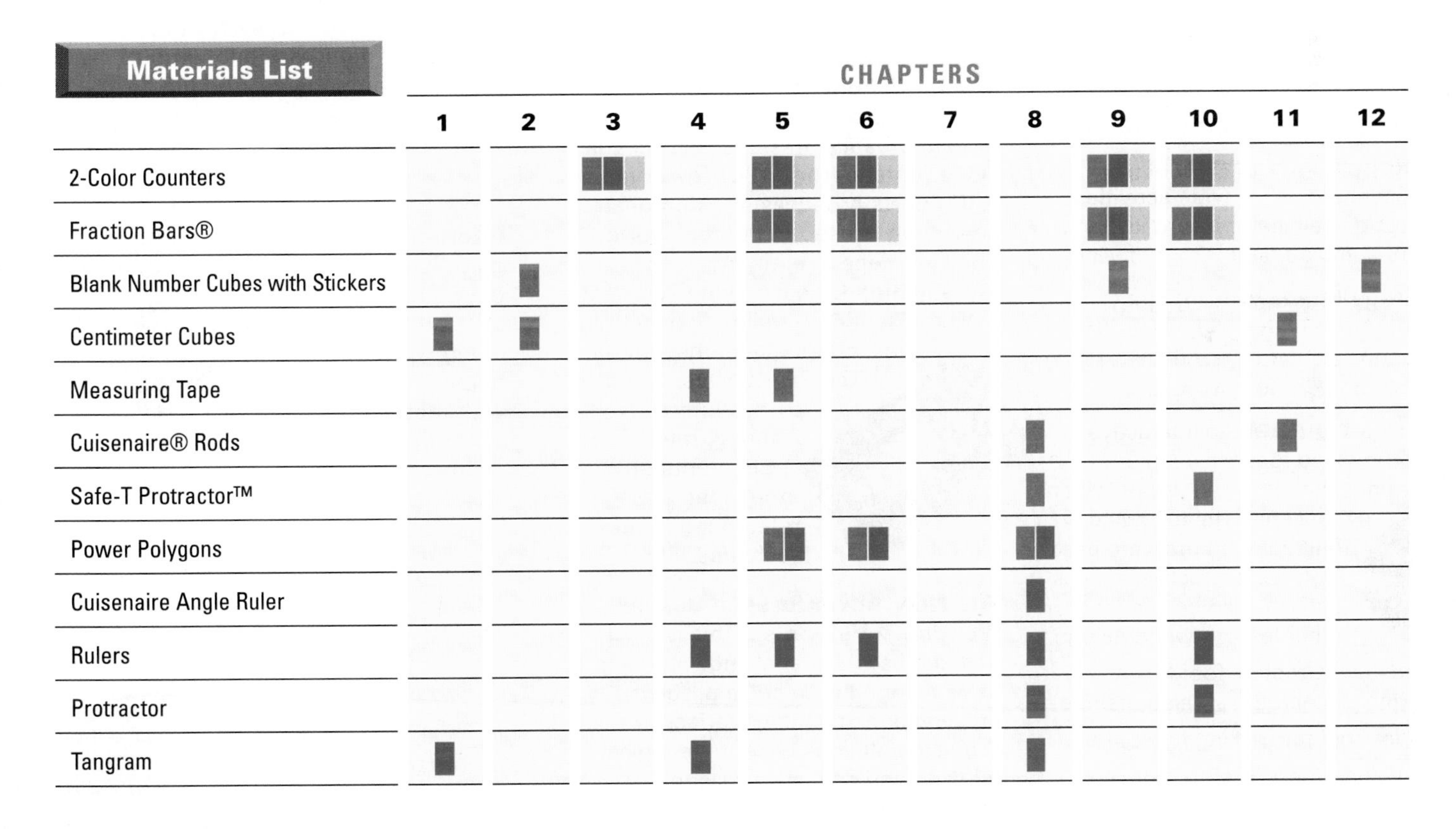

	CHAPTERS											
	1	2	3	4	5	6	7	8	9	10	11	12
2-Color Counters			■■□		■■□	■■□			■■□	■■□		
Fraction Bars®					■■□	■■□			■■□	■■□		
Blank Number Cubes with Stickers		■							■			■
Centimeter Cubes	■	■									■	
Measuring Tape				■	■							
Cuisenaire® Rods								■			■	
Safe-T Protractor™								■		■		
Power Polygons					■■	■■		■■				
Cuisenaire Angle Ruler								■				
Rulers				■	■	■		■		■		
Protractor								■		■		
Tangram	■			■				■				

Student Manipulative Kit **Teacher's Overhead Manipulative Kit** **Transparencies in Teacher's Toolkit**

Technology in Course 1

TECHNOLOGY FOR STUDENTS

Technology Used in Lessons Students should have access to scientific calculators for appropriate use as needed. In lessons, calculators are used to develop concepts involving exponents, order of operations, algebraic relationships, scientific notation, pi, and divisibility. Calculators are also used to solve problems involving large numbers or real-world data requiring tedious computation. Emphasize that it is not appropriate to use calculators instead of mental computation or simple paper-pencil computation. Emphasize the importance of estimating to check if answers are reasonable. Options for using spreadsheets appear at times in the Explore part of lesson development.

Calculator Hint and Technology Link These features appear in lesson development to offer tips about calculator key sequences and displays.

Technology Pages Feature pages called "Technology" provide activities using fraction calculators, spreadsheets, geometry software, and Web browsers.

Technology Masters Technology Masters offer activities with scientific and fraction calculators, spreadsheets, graphers, and geometry software.

Interactive CD-ROM An interactive lesson is provided for each chapter to enhance understanding and use of lesson concepts. The following built-in math tools are used with the interactive lessons and can also be used with other lessons when helpful.

- Spreadsheet/Grapher Tool for exploring mathematical relationships
- Line Plot Tool for making line plots
- Place Value Blocks Tool for concept development involving whole numbers, decimals, and integers.
- Fraction Tool for fraction models used to learn concepts and computation
- Geometry Tool for work with two-dimensional figures
- 3D Blocks Tool for work with solids
- Probability Tool for doing simulations
- Journal for student writing and for preparing written presentations that can include graphics

Mathsurf Internet Site Students go to the Scott Foresman - Addison Wesley Web site www.mathsurf.com using references given in the Student Book on chapter and section openers. Once at the site, students are given data and questions, or sent to other sites worldwide to gather and share data, or directed to use a search engine to research a specific term.

Wide World of Mathematics for Middle School on CD-ROM, Videodisc, or Videotape *Wide World of Mathematics* presents reports and video footage from ABC News and ABC Sports broadcasts to demonstrate how math is used in the real world. The videotape version includes an investigation for each video segment. The videodisc version also includes on-screen questions and data. The CD-ROM version also provides interactive math games. Segments on the video are referenced in the Teacher's Edition.

The New Adventures of Jasper Woodbury Videodisc This is a set of videodiscs that challenge students to work together to solve problems presented in engaging stories. Problem solutions encourage logical thinking and deductive reasoning. Episodes on the videodiscs are referenced in the Teacher's Edition.

TECHNOLOGY FOR TEACHERS

Teacher's Resource Planner CD-ROM The planner lets you preview and customize blackline masters in the program. It also offers an interactive planner that lets you map out a plan for the year or month as well as generate either default or customized daily lesson plans. Lesson plans include resources, correlations, assignment guides, space to write notes, and more.

TestWorks: Test and Practice Software This software lets you generate default as well as customized tests and worksheets in free response, multiple choice, or mixed formats. The software is packaged on a CD-ROM.

Internet Site for Teachers Go online at www.teacher.mathsurf.com to hear new ideas, get information about program components, and link to other Internet sites.

TECHNOLOGY FOR PARENTS

Internet Site for Parents Parents can go online at www.parent.mathsurf.com to get information about the program along with ideas for helping their children with math at home.

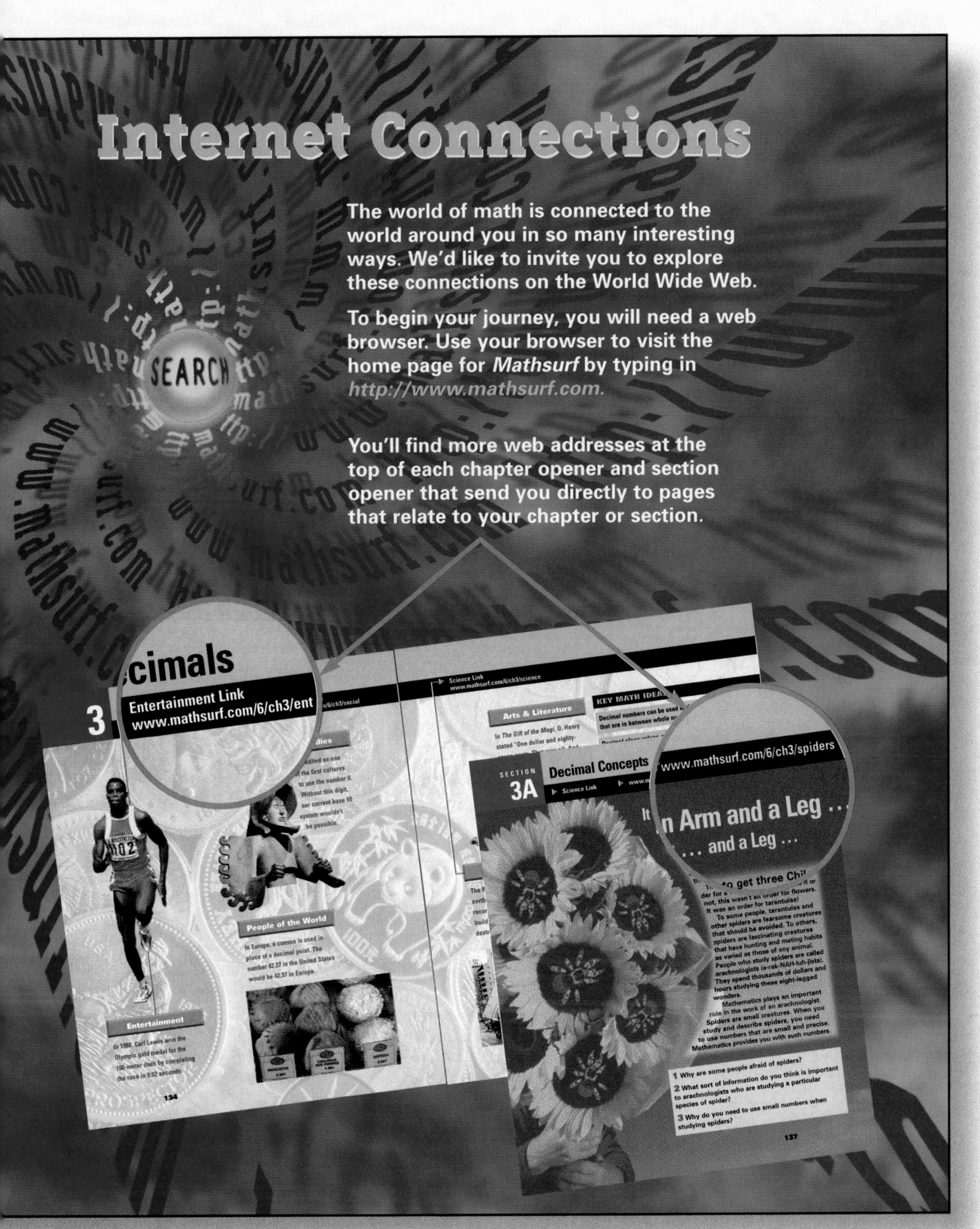

INTERNET CONNECTIONS

If your school or students have access to the World Wide Web point out the Web site addresses across the top of the chapter and section openers. Then show students how they can use the Web site addresses given to find interdisciplinary links for the topics discussed in the chapter. Let students work in small groups to browse the Web; tell them to note interesting information that they find and share it with the class.

You might want to discuss with students some advantages of researching on the Internet.

- Information may provide more complete details on recently recorded facts than newspapers, magazines, or reference books.
- It is often possible to find information about obscure topics that might be difficult to find elsewhere.
- It is easy to interact with the person who created a Web site.

You might also note some of the disadvantages.

- Information might remain at a Web site for only a short period of time.
- There is little or no regulation of what information does or does not appear on the Internet.
- Fact-checking is not required for information on the Internet; facts may be incorrect.

You may want to use the Teacher's Edition notes found on the chapter and section openers. These notes provide an activity for each link which does not require access to the World Wide Web.

PROBLEM SOLVING AND APPLICATIONS

"Problem solving is the process by which students experience the power and usefulness of mathematics in the world around them."

from The NCTM Standards

Scott Foresman-Addison Wesley Middle School Math is a problem solving based program that provides students with a wide range of problem-solving tools. When you teach mathematics from a problem-solving viewpoint, you provide students with the key skills and attitudes needed to be successful in mathematics.

Point out the logos at the top of this page. These logos are used throughout the book help students analyze the problem-solving process.

- The Problem Solving Guidelines logo lists the four steps students should consider when solving a problem: understand, plan, solve, and look back.
- The Problem Solving Strategies logo reminds students of strategies they can use in problem solving.
- Problem Solving Tips provide helpful hints for specific problems students are asked to solve.
- In **What Do You Think?** students see two ways to solve a problem. Then they discuss how they might solve the problem.

Students will encounter a diverse selection of problem-solving applications in the program. Discuss the six examples given on this page. Ask students if they can think of other uses of mathematics.

Throughout the book students will see connections to different disciplines, as well as to business, industry, career, and consumer topics. You might have groups of students page through their books to find references to connections other than those named at the bottom of this page.

Problem Solving and Applications

Math is all around you. Having good math skills can help you solve problems every day. What kinds of problems can you solve using mathematics?

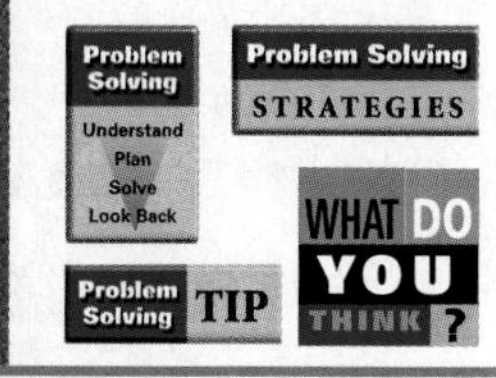

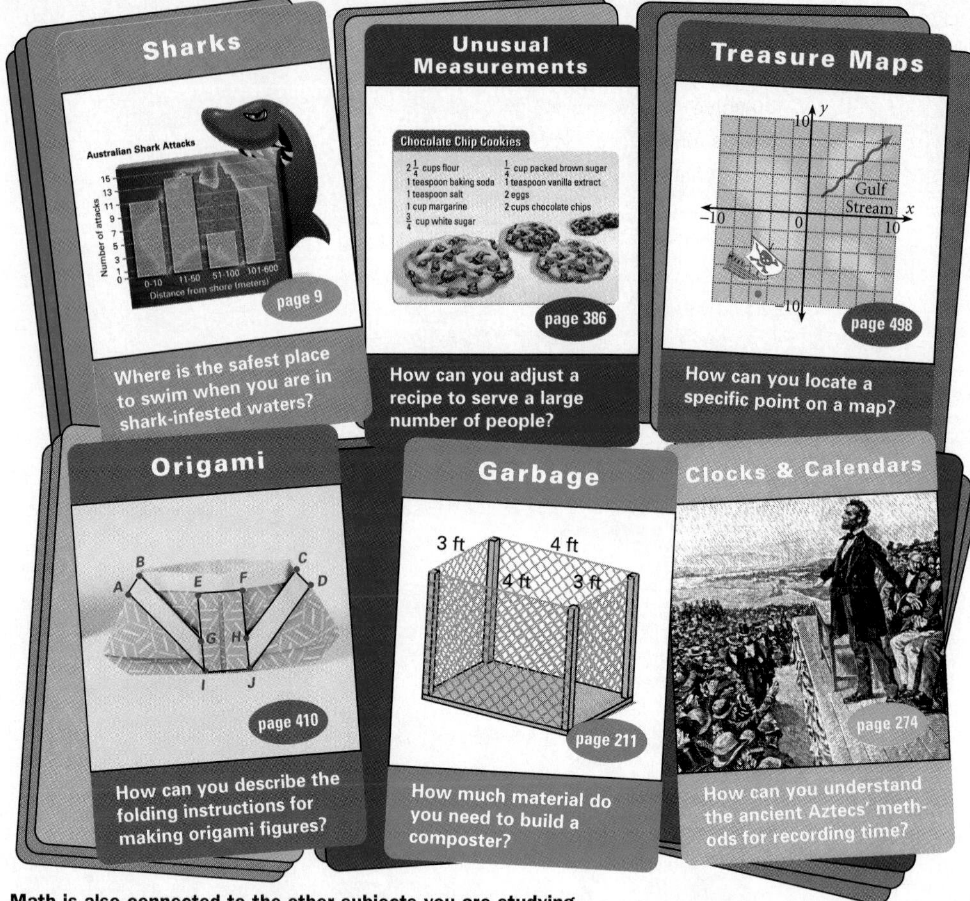

Math is also connected to the other subjects you are studying. Look here to find some examples of how math is connected to:

Science				History				Geography			
p. 14	p. 116	p. 331	p. 522	p. 27	p. 180	p. 297	p. 430	p. 32	p. 128	p. 240	p. 548
p. 72	p. 145	p. 385	p. 541	p. 37	p. 225	p. 368	p. 438	p. 76	p. 179	p. 258	p. 557
p. 88	p. 155	p. 455	p. 628	p. 113	p. 244	p. 374	p. 536	p. 92	p. 183	p. 439	p. 567
p.113	p. 253	p. 480	p. 649	p. 140	p. 274	p. 395	p. 629	p. 120	p. 235	p. 541	p. 613

PROBLEM SOLVING HANDBOOK

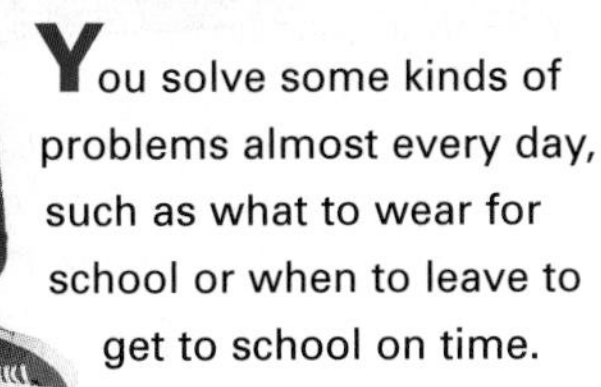

You solve some kinds of problems almost every day, such as what to wear for school or when to leave to get to school on time. You solve these problems so often that you don't even have to think to come up with an answer.

Other problems are more difficult to solve. How do you get home if you missed the bus? How can you earn enough money to buy a new bicycle? Finding solutions to these kinds of problems requires good problem-solving skills.

Learning mathematics is an excellent way to practice and improve your problem-solving skills. Mathematics gives you the chance to solve problems alone and with groups. It can help you learn more about how to use data and technology. It also helps you to think in a logical, step-by-step way.

Keep in mind that some problems in math have a "right" answer, but many have more than one answer. People may disagree about which answer is the best, and they may ask you, "What do YOU think?" Answering this question can help you develop a wide range of strategies to use when faced with challenging problems.

The students shown here will share their thinking with you throughout this book. But the key question will always be

"What do you think?"

1. What kinds of problems do you solve almost every day?
2. For what kinds of problems do you need to understand and use mathematics?
3. How can a problem have more than one answer?

PROBLEM SOLVING HANDBOOK

This Problem Solving Handbook provides students with an opportunity to focus on the problem-solving process and to preview the problem-solving strategies used throughout this book. The following strategies are included in the Handbook.

- Look for a Pattern
- Make an Organized List
- Make a Table
- Guess and Check
- Work Backward
- Use Logical Reasoning
- Draw a Diagram
- Solve a Simpler Problem

About What Do You Think?

It is important for students to understand that there is no single right way to solve a problem. In **What Do You Think?** students have the opportunity to see how other students solve a problem. This feature is designed to help create an atmosphere that allows your students to discuss strategies with classmates, and to explain their thinking. It encourages them to be flexible.

Ask ...

- Why would working in groups be helpful when solving a problem?
- Have you ever known the answer to a problem but did not give it because you were afraid you might be wrong?
- Have you ever known the answer to a problem but could not explain how you arrived at the answer?
- Do you know that many problems have been solved only after people have pursued false leads—sometimes for many years?

Answers for What Do You Think?

1–3. Answers may vary.

About Problem Solving

Throughout this book, students will use the following four steps to guide them through solving a problem:

- Understand
- Plan
- Solve
- Look Back

These Problem-Solving Guidelines appear on both Teaching Tool Transparencies 2 and 3: Guided Problem Solving, and on Teaching Tool Transparency 18: Problem-Solving Guidelines.

- On Transparencies 2 and 3, each guideline is followed by questions and space to write the solution to the problem. You may want to use these transparencies when you discuss a strategy; they are referenced in the Teacher's Edition with *Choose a Strategy* problems.
- Transparency 18 is similar to Transparencies 2 and 3. It presents the Problem-Solving Guidelines in a one-page format that can be used at any time.

You may wish to use these transparencies as you discuss the strategies on the following pages.

Solving Problems

You've solved many problems in your previous math classes. Now you'll look more closely at some methods that can help you solve problems. ◄

Problem Solving Getting Started

Problem solving can be complicated. Some problems include lots of information. Sometimes information is missing. There might be several ways to solve a problem. Your first answer might be unreasonable, or it might not even answer the question.

A good understanding of mathematics can help when solving problems. But you need to know more than just how to do math. You need to decide what math to do. Should you add the numbers or subtract them? Would the problem be easier to do with decimals or with fractions? Math is a tool for problem solving. As with any tool, you need to make good choices about how to use it.

You need a plan or a strategy to solve any problem. A plan or strategy will help you to understand the problem, to decide on a good approach, to work out a creative solution, and to see if your solution makes sense.

Problem Solving

Understand
Plan
Solve
Look Back

PROBLEM-SOLVING GUIDELINES

1 UNDERSTAND the Problem
- What do you know?
- What do you need to find out?

2 Develop a PLAN
- Have you ever solved a similar problem?
- What strategies can you use?
- Estimate an answer.

3 SOLVE the Problem
- Do you need to try another strategy?
- What is the solution?

4 LOOK BACK
- Did you answer the right question?
- Does your answer make sense?

Example

How many ways can you make 25¢ using only dimes, nickels, and pennies?

1 UNDERSTAND the Problem

You *know* that the problem uses only dimes, nickels and pennies. You *need to find* the number of ways you can make 25¢ with these coins.

2 Develop a PLAN

You've *solved similar problems* involving making a total amount of money. One *strategy* is to list possible combinations as they come to mind.

3 SOLVE the Problem

#1: 2 dimes, 5 pennies #2: 2 dimes, 1 nickel

#3: 5 pennies, 2 nickels, 1 dime #4: 5 pennies, 2 dimes

Notice that the list is not very organized. Some possibilities, such as 25 pennies, are missing. Also, combination #1 and combination #4 are the same.

So *try another strategy.* The number of pennies will always have to be a multiple of 5. So list all of the possible combinations with 0, 5, 10, 15, 20, and 25 pennies.

(0 pennies) #1: 2 dimes, 1 nickel #2: 1 dime, 3 nickels #3: 5 nickels

(5 pennies) #4: 2 dimes, 5 pennies #5: 1 dime, 2 nickels, 5 pennies #6: 4 nickels, 5 pennies

(10 pennies) #7: 1 dime, 1 nickel, 10 pennies #8: 3 nickels, 10 pennies

(15 pennies) #9: 1 dime, 15 pennies #10: 2 nickels, 15 pennies

(20 pennies) #11: 1 nickel, 20 pennies (25 pennies) #12: 25 pennies

The solution is that there are 12 combinations.

4 LOOK BACK

The *right question was answered.* The list is organized and does not have any repeated combinations, so *the answer makes sense.*

Check Your Understanding

1. Would the problem be harder or easier if you were not allowed to use pennies? Explain.
2. Describe a problem that you could solve using a similar method.
3. Why is it important to have a plan before you begin a solution?

About the Example

The example shows students how to use the Problem-Solving Guidelines.

Ask ...

- In the Example, what does it mean to understand the problem? Possible answer: To decide what question the problem is asking and to determine what information is given to solve the problem.
- How do you develop a plan? Possible answer: Think about what is involved in solving the problem. This problem says "How many ways" which suggests making a list and counting.
- What is the difference between the first and second strategy suggested in *Solve?* Possible answer: Making the second list is done in an organized way so that all of the possibilities are considered.
- Why is *Look Back* important? Possible answer: It is a check to see if the question in the problem has been answered.

About Check Your Understanding

Following the examples, in each lesson you will find **Check Your Understanding** questions. These questions may be used for class discussion; they provide an opportunity to clarify the examples and to pinpoint areas that need more explanation.

Answers for Check Your Understanding

1. The problem would be easier because there would be fewer kinds of coins to look at.
2. Answers may vary.
3. Answers may vary.

Problem-Solving Strategy: Look for a Pattern

Many problems that can be solved by looking for a pattern involve interpreting numerical or geometric relationships. Finding patterns allows students to find solutions to otherwise difficult or tedious problems.

- This strategy is often used in conjunction with Make a Table.
- Using concrete materials or drawing pictures can help students identify patterns.
- In real life, finding trends often involves looking for patterns in data.

About the Page

Students find a pattern that relates salary increases, and then use the pattern to solve the problem.

Ask ...

- What pattern is shown in the example? How is the pattern found? Marsha's wage increase forms a pattern; It is found by subtracting her first-year wage from her second-year wage.
- How do you know that this pattern holds for subsequent years after the first year? The problem states that Marsha's hourly wage increases by a fixed amount each year.
- Do you think that Marsha's wages will continue to increase in this way indefinitely? Possible answer: No, there may be a point when she reaches a maximum salary.

Try It

Ask students to state the rule they used to continue the patterns in these problems. Possible answers: Part a: Add 14; Part b: Subtract $1.46.

Answers for Try It

a. 84 pounds

b. $11.03

Problem Solving STRATEGIES

- Look for a Pattern
- Make an Organized List
- Make a Table
- Guess and Check
- Work Backward
- Use Logical Reasoning
- Draw a Diagram
- Solve a Simpler Problem

Look for a Pattern

Sometimes the numbers in a problem form a pattern. To solve the problem, find the rule that creates the pattern. Then use the rule to find the answer. ◄

Example

Marsha's hourly wage as a dog groomer increases by a fixed amount each year. She earned $4.75 per hour her first year on the job and $5.60 per hour her second year. Find her hourly wage during her fifth year of work.

Second-year wage:	$5.60
First-year wage:	– 4.75
Wage increase:	$0.85

The rule is that Marsha's wages increase by $0.85 each year.

Use the rule to continue the pattern:

Third-year wage:	$5.60 + $0.85 = $6.45
Fourth-year wage:	$6.45 + $0.85 = $7.30
Fifth-year wage:	$7.30 + $0.85 = $8.15

During her fifth year, she earned $8.15 per hour.

Try It

a. During their first year of life, swordfish increase in weight at a regular rate. A swordfish weighed 14 pounds at age 1 month and 28 pounds at age 2 months. How much did it weigh at age 6 months?

b. This year, the average price of Concert File CDs went from $13.95 to $12.49. If the price continues to change at the same rate, how much will they cost next year?

Make an Organized List

Problem Solving
STRATEGIES

- Look for a Pattern
- Make an Organized List
- Make a Table
- Guess and Check
- Work Backward
- Use Logical Reasoning
- Draw a Diagram
- Solve a Simpler Problem

Sometimes you need to find the number of ways in which something can be done. To solve the problem, make a list of all the ways and count them. It is important to organize your list so that you don't miss any possibilities, or repeat any of them. ◄

Example

At the Healthy Bowl Restaurant, you can order a garden salad with or without dressing, with or without croutons, and with or without bacon bits. If the manager wants to list all the possible combinations in the menu, how many combinations must she list?

One way to organize a list is to pick one item and list all the combinations that include that one item. Then, pick a second item and list all the combinations that include the second item but not the first.

First list the dressing choices: D

DC DB

DCB

Now, list the crouton choices without dressing:

C

CB

Now, list the bacon bit choices without dressing or croutons:

B

Finally, list any choices without dressing, croutons, or bacon bits:

no toppings

There are 8 combinations.

Try It

a. There are 5 pitchers and 3 catchers on the Middle School baseball team. How many pitcher-catcher pairs can the coach choose from?

b. Flavor-Filled Ice Cream has four flavors of soft-serve ice cream. How many ways could you choose two different flavors?

Problem-Solving Strategy: Make an Organized List

Many problems that require finding all possibilities or finding the number of combinations of things can be solved by making an organized list.

- This strategy is often used in conjunction with Make a Table or Find a Pattern.
- Often the same data can be organized in different ways.
- In real life, data or information must be organized before it can be interpreted.

About the Page

Given various choices, students find the number of different combinations of salads that can be made.

Ask ...

- Would you get the same result if you started with listing croutons choices rather than dressing choices? Yes: C, CB, CD, CDB, D, DB, B, no toppings
- Suppose that once a salad is served, a diner is offered fresh ground pepper. How many combinations are possible when pepper or no pepper are added to the list of choices? 16 choices: D, DC, DB, DP, DCB, DCP, DBP, DCBP, C, CB, CP, CBP, B, BP, P, no toppings

Try It

You might suggest that students give the names of the pitchers and catchers and choose four ice cream flavors. If the names and flavors start with different letters, only the first letters need to be used in the list.

Answers for Try It

a. 15

b. 6

PROBLEM SOLVING HANDBOOK

Problem-Solving Strategy Make a Table

By making a table, students can organize information in a way that may help them recognize patterns that lead to generalizations.

- This strategy is often used in conjunction with Make an Organized List and Look for a Pattern.
- Students need to decide column and row headings before making a table.
- Students will encounter tables in many places, such as newspapers, magazines, textbooks, almanacs, and the Internet.

About the Page

Students organize data in a table to help them see a relationship between numbers.

Ask ...

- If this pattern continues, how many ads would go out on the tenth mailing? 59,049
- Do you think that after six mailings 729 different people would get the ad? Explain. Possible answer: No; The same person might get more than one ad and some people may not send the ad to three friends.

Try It

- If students are having difficulty with Part a, you might suggest that they consider themselves Generation 0, their parents Generation 1, their grandparents Generation 2, and so on.
- You might ask students to describe the patterns they used to complete their tables for these problems. Possible answers: Part a: Multiply 2 by itself the number of times given by the generation number; Part b: Multiply the number of bald eagles by $\frac{7}{2}$ or divide the number of golden eagles by $\frac{7}{2}$.

Problem Solving STRATEGIES

- Look for a Pattern
- Make an Organized List
- Make a Table
- Guess and Check
- Work Backward
- Use Logical Reasoning
- Draw a Diagram
- Solve a Simpler Problem

Make a Table

A problem involving a relationship between two sets of numbers can often be solved by making a table. A table helps you organize data so that you can see the numerical relationship and find the answer. ◄

Example

Carl mailed ads for his new craft business to three friends. He asked each friend to mail three copies to friends. Each friend was then to mail ads to three of *their* friends, and so on. How many ads were sent in the sixth mailing?

Make a table to organize data about the mailings.

Mailing	1	2	3
Number sent	3	$3 \times 3 = 9$	$3 \times 3 \times 3 = 27$

The table helps you see the relationship between the number of a mailing and the number of ads sent. In mailing **1,** 3 is multiplied by itself **one time.** In mailing **2,** 3 is multiplied by itself **two times.** In mailing **3,** 3 is multiplied by itself **three times.**

So, to find the number of ads in mailing **6** multiply 3 by itself **six times.**

$3 \times 3 \times 3 \times 3 \times 3 \times 3 = 729$

In the sixth mailing, 729 ads were sent.

Try It

a. Every person has 2 parents, 4 grandparents, 8 great-grandparents, and so on. Record this information in a table. Then find how many great-great-great-great-great-great grandparents everyone has.

b. For every 2 bald eagles seen by visitors to the Audubon Eagle Sanctuary, 7 golden eagles are seen. Make a table showing the number of golden eagles seen when 2, 4, and 6 bald eagles are seen. Then find the number of bald eagles seen for 56 golden eagles.

Answers for Try It

a. 256

b. 16 bald eagles

Bald Eagles	Golden Eagles
2	7
4	14
6	21
8	28
10	35
12	42
14	49
16	56

Guess and Check

Problem Solving
STRATEGIES

- Look for a Pattern
- Make an Organized List
- Make a Table
- Guess and Check
- Work Backward
- Use Logical Reasoning
- Draw a Diagram
- Solve a Simpler Problem

If you're not sure how to solve a problem, make an educated guess at the answer. Check your guess. If it's wrong, use what you've learned in checking your guess to make a better guess. Continue to guess, check, and revise until you find the answer. ◄

Example

Twenty-five dolphins and killer whales perform at Sea Circus. There are 13 more dolphins than killer whales. How many of each animal are there?

	Dolphins	Killer Whales
Guess: Make an educated guess: 15 + 10 = 25	15	10
Check: There should be 13 more dolphins.	15 – 10 = 5	
Think: The difference isn't big enough. I need more dolphins.		
Revise: 20 + 5 = 25	20	5
Check:	20 – 5 = 15	
Think: I'm closer, but now I have slightly too many dolphins.		
Revise: 19 + 6 = 25	19	6
Check:	19 – 6 = 13 ✔	

There are 19 dolphins and 6 killer whales.

Try It

a. Before going on vacation, Vanessa bought 21 rolls of film. She bought twice as many rolls of print film as slide film. How many rolls of each type did she buy?

b. One weekend, Allan worked a total of 17 hours helping his uncle paint his cabin. They worked 3 hours more on Saturday than they worked on Sunday. How many hours did they work each day?

Problem-Solving Strategy: Guess and Check

The Guess-and-Check Strategy is a systematic process of making reasonable guesses. It is an especially useful tool when the number of possible solutions is small and when it is relatively easy to determine if a guess is reasonable. Many of the problems that students solve now using Guess and Check will be solved later using algebra.

- This strategy is often used in conjunction with Look for a Pattern and Use Logical Reasoning.
- To be able to make good guesses, students must understand the problem.
- In real life, many important discoveries have been made using Guess and Check, which is also called Trial and Error.

About the Page

Students use a given relationship between two numbers and make educated guesses until they find the answer to the problem.

Ask ...

- After making the first guess of 15 dolphins, how do you know that the next guess must be greater than 15? This guess only gives a difference of 5 dolphins while the problem says there is a difference of 13.
- Do you think 15 was a good first choice? Answers may vary.

Try It

After students complete the problems, you might invite several students to share their series of guesses with the class.

Answers for Try It

a. 7 rolls of slide film; 14 rolls of print film

b. Saturday: 10 hours; Sunday: 7 hours

PROBLEM SOLVING HANDBOOK

Problem-Solving Strategy: Work Backward

The Work Backward Strategy involves beginning with a final result and examining, in reverse order, the steps leading to this result; thus discovering the initial conditions of the problem.

- Students may use this strategy in conjunction with other strategies such as Make an Organized List, Make a Table, and Look for a Pattern.
- Students can use inverse operations when they work backward.
- In real life, this strategy is used to solve puzzles and develop ways to win games.

About the Page

Students are given an ending time and they work backward to find a starting time.

Ask ...

- Why do you think the solution shown demonstrates working backward? The answer is found by starting with the end result and working back to the beginning.
- How might you check the answer? Possible answer: Begin at 7:00. Add 45 min (7:45), 25 min (8:05), and 20 min (8:30). The answer checks.

Try It

If students are having trouble with a problem, suggest they follow the example. For each step, have them tell what happened and what they can conclude from this step.

Answers for Try It

a. 25° F

b. 116 miles wide

Problem Solving STRATEGIES

- Look for a Pattern
- Make an Organized List
- Make a Table
- Guess and Check
- Work Backward
- Use Logical Reasoning
- Draw a Diagram
- Solve a Simpler Problem

Work Backward

A problem may tell you what happened at the end of a series of steps and ask you to find what happened at the beginning. To solve the problem, work backward step-by-step to the beginning. ◄

Example

Ed was deciding when to get up in the morning. He needed 45 minutes to get ready for school. His bus ride took 25 minutes. He wanted to get to school 20 minutes early to do some library research. If school starts at 8:30, what time should he get up?

The problem describes three steps occurring in order (getting ready, riding the bus, doing research). It also tells you the end result (school starts at 8:30). To solve the problem, work backward to the beginning.

Step	What Happened	Conclusion
3	Ed did research for 20 minutes. Then it was 8:30.	Before this step, the time was 20 minutes before 8:30, or 8:10.
2	He rode the bus for 25 minutes. Then it was 8:10.	Before this step, the time was 25 minutes before 8:10, or 7:45.
1	He spent 45 minutes getting ready. Then it was 7:45.	Before this step, the time was 45 minutes before 7:45, or 7:00.

Ed should get up at 7:00.

Try It

a. One winter night, the temperature fell 14 degrees between midnight and 6 A.M. Between 6 A.M. and 10 A.M., the temperature doubled. By noon it had risen another 11 degrees, to 33°F. Find the midnight temperature.

b. Lake Erie is half as wide as Lake Michigan. Lake Erie is 5 miles wider than Lake Ontario. Lake Superior is 3 times as wide as Lake Ontario. Lake Superior is 159 miles wide. How wide is Lake Michigan?

Use Logical Reasoning

Problem Solving

STRATEGIES

- Look for a Pattern
- Make an Organized List
- Make a Table
- Guess and Check
- Work Backward
- Use Logical Reasoning
- Draw a Diagram
- Solve a Simpler Problem

To solve a problem using logical reasoning, decide how the facts of the problem relate to each other. Then work your way step-by-step from the given facts to a sensible solution. Along the way, avoid making false assumptions or drawing unreasonable conclusions. ◄

Example

Arnie, Becca, and Chad collect stamps, coins, and rocks, though not necessarily in that order. Becca is the sister of the rock collector. Chad once had lunch with both the rock collector and the stamp collector. Match each person with his or her hobby.

Take clues one at a time. Use a grid to keep track of your conclusions.

1. Becca is the sister of the rock collector. So she is not the rock collector.

	Stamps	Coins	Rocks
Arnie			
Becca			no
Chad			

2. Chad once had lunch with the rock collector and the stamp collector.

	Stamps	Coins	Rocks
Arnie			
Becca			no
Chad	no		no

Chad must collect coins.

Arnie must collect rocks.

That means Becca collects stamps.

	Stamps	Coins	Rocks
Arnie	no	no	yes
Becca	yes	no	no
Chad	no	yes	no

Try It

a. Tim, Mei, and Jamal are in 6th, 7th, and 8th grades, though not necessarily in that order. Mei is not in 8th grade. The 6th grader is in chorus with Tim and band with Mei. Match the students with their grades.

b. Sid, Todd, and Maria play soccer, baseball, and tennis, though not necessarily in that order. Maria doesn't play tennis. Sid rides the bus with the baseball and tennis players. Match the students and their sports.

Problem-Solving Strategy: Use Logical Reasoning

Many problems that can be solved with logical reasoning involve more than simply using basic mathematical operations. They involve thinking clearly, organizing information, and drawing conclusions.

- This strategy is often used in conjunction with Make a Table or Draw a Diagram.
- In a logic table, students list all possibilities and eliminate those that do not fit the problem.
- In real life, many puzzle problems involve logical thinking.

About the Page

Students work their way step-by-step through a logic puzzle.

Ask ...

- How do you know that Becca is not the rock collector? The rock collector is her sister.
- How do you know that Chad is not the rock collector or stamp collector? He had lunch with these people.
- How can you tell that Chad collects coins? The chart shows that he does not collect stamps or rocks. The only choice left is coins.
- How does knowing that Chad collects coins help you fill in the chart? You can write "no" in the coins column for Arnie and Becca.

Try It

You might want to help students set up their tables.

Answers for Try It

a. 6th: Jamal; 7th: Mei; 8th: Tim

b. Sid: soccer; Todd: tennis; Maria: baseball

PROBLEM SOLVING HANDBOOK

Problem-Solving Strategy
Draw a Diagram

Representing the information in a problem in the form of a picture or diagram may help students see the conditions of the problem more clearly.

- Sometimes a diagram is more appropriate than a table when information overlaps.
- Sometimes diagrams can be sketches. Other times a more accurate drawing is necessary.
- In real life, instructions are often given with diagrams to clarify a procedure.

About the Page

Students are given travel directions from a starting point. They draw a diagram to determine how far the end point is from the starting point.

Ask ...

- Could you solve this problem without drawing a picture? Does drawing a diagram make it easier? Answers may vary.
- Suppose that after Geena finishes her route she goes 4 blocks north and 7 blocks east to visit a friend. Then how far is she from her starting point? 4 blocks north

Try It

Students may not make the same diagrams to solve a problem. Invite students to share their work with classmates.

Answers for Try It

a. 15 miles

b. 22 feet

Problem Solving STRATEGIES

- Look for a Pattern
- Make an Organized List
- Make a Table
- Guess and Check
- Work Backward
- Use Logical Reasoning
- Draw a Diagram
- Solve a Simpler Problem

Draw a Diagram

Some problems are visual. They may involve objects, places, or physical situations. To solve such a problem, draw a diagram to help you see relationships among the given data. Then use the relationships to find the answer. ◂

Example

All the city blocks in Sunnyville are the same size. Geena starts her paper route at the corner of two streets. She goes 8 blocks south, 13 blocks west, 8 blocks north, and 6 blocks east. How far is she from her starting point when she is done?

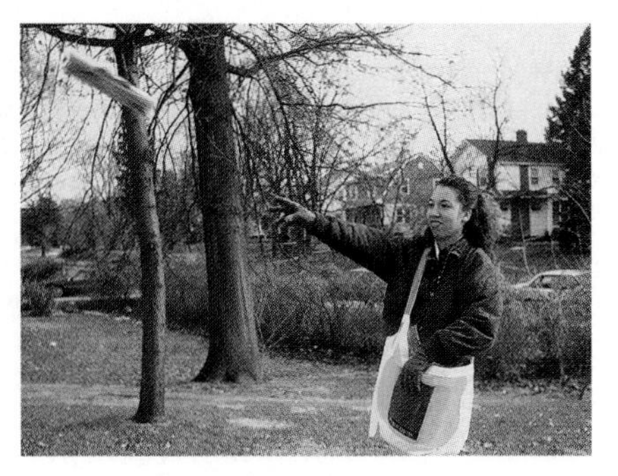

To get a clearer picture of what is happening, draw a diagram of Geena's route.

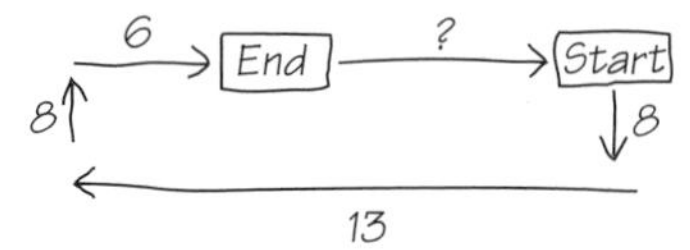

The diagram shows that at the end of her route, Geena is 13 – 6 blocks from her starting point.

13 – 6 = 7

When she finishes, Geena is 7 blocks from her starting point.

Try It

a. After leaving a warehouse, a trucker drove 28 miles south to make a delivery. The trucker then made three more deliveries, driving 13 miles west, 43 miles north, and 13 miles east. How far was the trucker from the warehouse?

b. The roots of an elm tree reach 17 feet into the ground. A robin's nest is 13 feet from the top of the tree. From treetop to root-bottom, the tree measures 52 feet. How far above the ground is the nest?

Solve a Simpler Problem

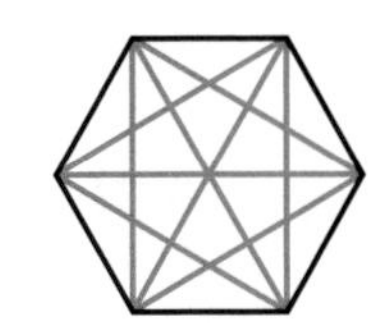

A problem may seem very complex. It may contain large numbers or appear to require many steps to solve. Instead of solving the given problem, solve a similar but simpler problem. Look for shortcuts, patterns, and relationships. Then use what you've learned to solve the original problem. ◄

Example

A diagonal is a line that connects two points in a figure that are not already connected by a side. For example, you can draw nine diagonals inside a 6-sided figure. How many diagonals can you draw inside an 8-sided figure?

You could draw an 8-sided figure and draw and count the number of diagonals. But that could be very complicated.

Instead, look at some very simple figures.

3-sided figure: 0 diagonals

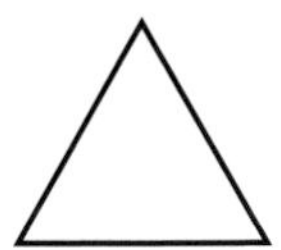

4-sided figure: 2 diagonals

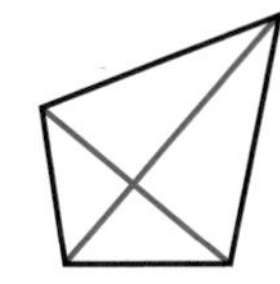

5-sided figure: 5 diagonals

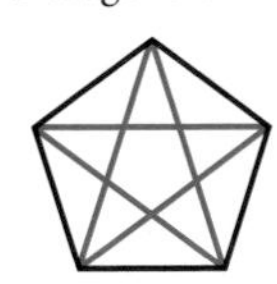

Notice that from a 3-sided to a 4-sided figure, 2 diagonals are added. From a 4-sided to a 5-sided figure, 3 diagonals are added. From a 5-sided to a 6-sided figure, 4 diagonals are added.

A 7-sided figure would have 14 diagonals (9 + 5). An 8-sided figure would have 20 diagonals (14 + 6). A 9-sided figure would have 27 diagonals (20 + 7).

Try It

a. Each side of each triangle is 1 in. long. If there were 42 triangles in a row, what would the combined length of all of their sides be?

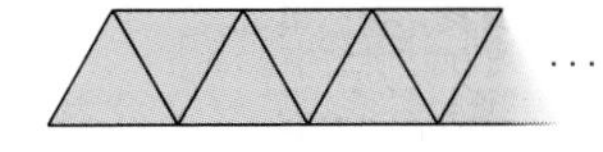

b. A bell rang 22 times. Each ring lasted 4 seconds. Two seconds elapsed between rings. How long did the ringing last?

Problem-Solving Strategy: Solve a Simpler Problem

Using smaller numbers or temporarily ignoring some conditions often helps students develop a method they can use to solve a multiple-step problem. This strategy often proves useful with more complex problems.

- Solve a Simpler Problem can be used with one or more of the other strategies discussed in this Problem Solving Handbook.
- Initially, students may need help determining an appropriate simpler problem.
- Solve a Simpler Problem is especially helpful in finding geometric patterns.

About the Page

Students solve simpler problems to help them find the number of diagonals in an octagon.

Ask ...

- Does every 3-sided figure have 0 diagonals? Does every 4-sided figure have only 2 diagonals? Draw different figures to find out. Yes; Yes
- Do you think drawing the diagonals in an 8-sided figure and counting them is complicated? You might want to try it. Possible answer: Yes; It is hard to determine if all diagonals have all been drawn and it is hard to count them.
- How many diagonals would there be in a 12-sided figure? 60 diagonals

Try It

- You might ask students to describe the pattern they found for Part a. Possible answer: Length (in.) = number of triangles + 2.
- Ask students to describe the pattern they found for Part b. Possible answer: Ringing time (sec.) = 6 × number of rings − 2.

Answers for Try It

a. 44 inches

b. 130 seconds

Chapter 1

Statistics— Real-World Use of Whole Numbers

▶ OVERVIEW

Section 1A

Reading and Interpreting Graphs: Students read and interpret bar graphs, pictographs, and line graphs. They also identify trends suggested by scatterplots.

1-1 Reading Graphs

1-2 Misleading Graphs

1-3 Scatterplots and Trends

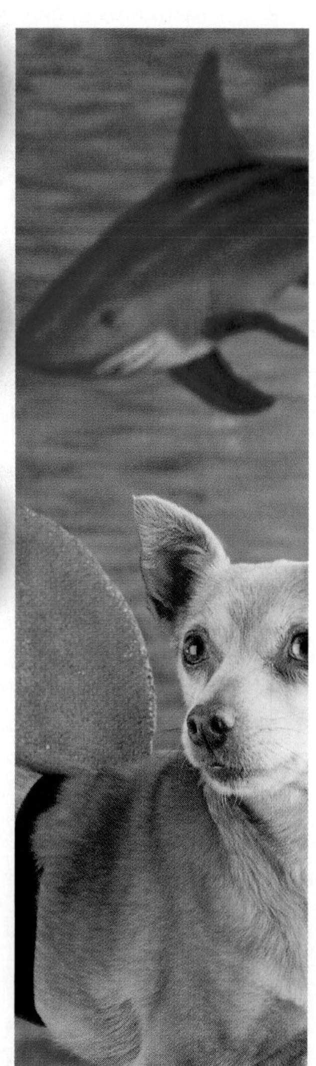

Section 1B

Displaying Data: Students organize data and determine its shape. Students construct bar graphs and stem-and-leaf diagrams to display information.

1-4 Tallies, Frequency Charts, and Line Plots

1-5 Scales and Bar Graphs

1-6 Stem-and-Leaf Diagrams

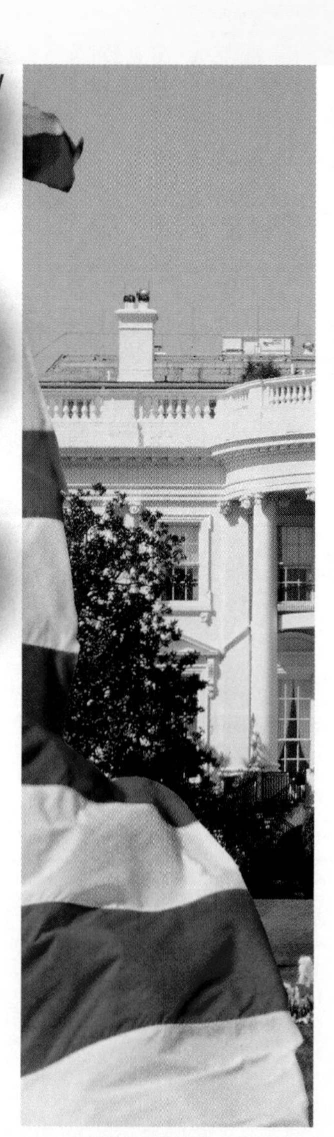

Section 1C

Describing Data: Students determine the mean, median, and mode to describe a set of data. They also determine if outliers affect the analysis of the data set.

1-7 Median and Mode

1-8 The Meaning of Mean

1-9 The Effects of Outliers

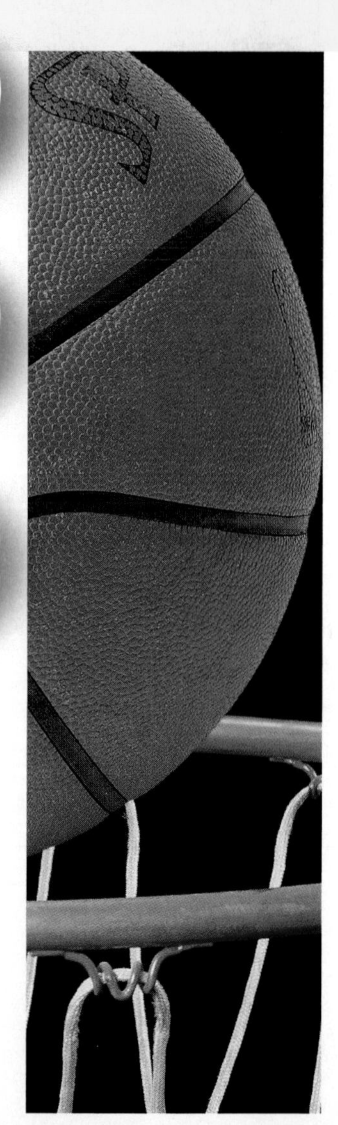

Meeting NCTM Standards

Curriculum Standards

STANDARD			pages
1	**Problem Solving**	Skills and Strategies	4, 25, 26, 35, 49
		Applications	9–10, 14–15, 19–20, 21, 27–28, 32–33, 37–38, 39, 44–45, 48–49, 53–54, 55
		Exploration	6, 11, 15, 16, 24, 28, 29, 34, 42, 46, 51, 54
2	**Communication**	Oral	5, 8, *10,* 13, 18, 23, 26, 31, 36, 41, 43, *45,* 47, 52
		Written	*4,* 10, 14, 15, 20, 22, 28, 33, 38, 45, *49,* 54, 56
		Cooperative Learning	*6, 11, 13, 16, 24, 26, 29, 31, 34, 36, 42, 46, 51, 57*
3	**Reasoning**	Critical Thinking	10, 15, 20, 28, 33, 38, 45, 49, 54
4	**Connections**	Mathematical	See Standards 5, 7, 8, 10, 13 below.
		Interdisciplinary	Science 2, *5, 8,* 12, *13, 14,* 17, *18,* 21, *33,* 37; Consumer 11, 48; Language 12; Medicine 16; Industry 22; Career 23; History *23,* 26, 27, 28, *31,* 35, *36,* 37; Geography 5, 27, 44, 61; Social Studies 3, *6, 26, 31,* 32; Civics 23; Health *41,* 48; Literature 3, *23;* Sports 54
		Technology	29, 50
		Cultural	2, *18*
5	**Number and Number Relationships**		10, 34
7	**Computation and Estimation**		7, 19, *20, 25,* 30, *35,* 47
8	**Patterns and Functions**		16–20, 24
10	**Statistics**		6–60
13	**Measurement**		46

Italic type indicates Teacher Edition reference.

Teaching Standards

Focus on Flexibility

A prime requirement for successful teaching is flexibility. Teachers should be willing to

- extend or shorten time frames of activities if necessary.
- adapt or change activities while teaching if it seems appropriate.

Assessment Standards

Focus on Mathematics

Projects "Mathematical Power," is defined in the Mathematics Standard, as the ability of students to apply their understanding of mathematical concepts to new situations. The project in Chapter 1 gives students the opportunity to

- collect data.
- organize collected data.
- display organized data on an appropriate graph.

TECHNOLOGY

For the Teacher

- **Teacher Resource Planner CD-ROM**
  Use the teacher planning CD-ROM to view resources available for Chapter 1. You can prepare custom lesson plans or use the default lesson plans provided.

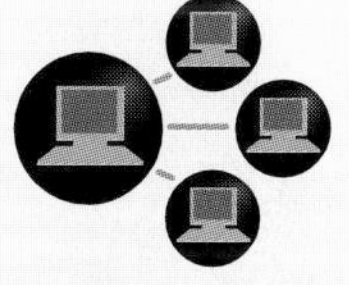

- **World Wide Web**
  Visit **www.teacher.mathsurf.com** for links to lesson plans from teachers and other professionals, NCTM information, and other sites.

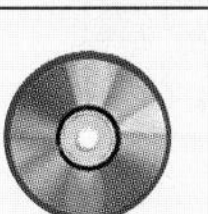

- **TestWorks**
  TestWorks provides ready-made tests and can create custom tests and practice worksheets.

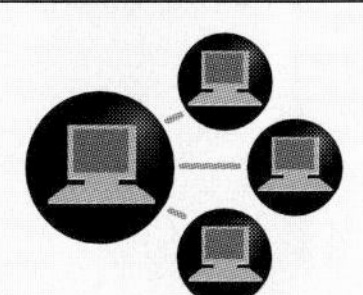

For the Parent

- **World Wide Web**
  Parents can use the Web site at **www.parent.mathsurf.com.**

For the Student

- **Interactive CD-ROM**
  Lesson 1-7 has an *Interactive CD-ROM Lesson.* The *Interactive CD-ROM Journal* and *Interactive CD-ROM Spreadsheet/Grapher Tool* are also used in Chapter 1.

- **Wide World of Mathematics™**
  Lesson 1-5 Middle School: Graphs in the News

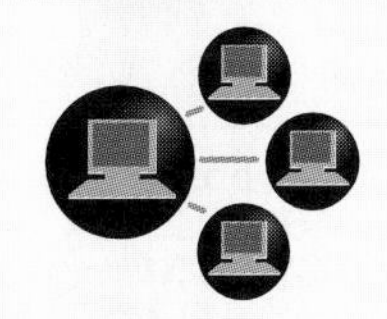

- **World Wide Web**
  Use with Chapter and Section Openers;
  Students can go online to the Scott Foresman-Addison Wesley Web site at **www.mathsurf.com/6/ch1** to collect information about chapter themes.

- **Jasper Woodbury Videodisc**
  Lesson 1-8: A Capital Idea

STANDARDIZED - TEST CORRELATION

SECTION 1A

LESSON	OBJECTIVE	ITBS Form M	CTBS 4th Ed.	CAT 5th Ed.	SAT 9th Ed.	MAT 7th Ed.	Your Form
1-1	• Read numbers from different types of graphs.	✘	✘	✘	✘	✘	
	• Compare numbers within the same graph.	✘	✘	✘		✘	
1-2	• Identify common ways that a graph can suggest misleading relationships.						
1-3	• Identify the two pieces of data represented by points in a scatterplot.						
	• Determine if a scatterplot suggests a trend.	✘					

SECTION 1B

LESSON	OBJECTIVE	ITBS Form M	CTBS 4th Ed.	CAT 5th Ed.	SAT 9th Ed.	MAT 7th Ed.	Your Form
1-4	• Organize data using tallies and frequency charts.		✘		✘	✘	
	• Use a line plot to show the shape of a data set.						
1-5	• Make a bar graph.						
1-6	• Organize large sets of data into stem-and-leaf diagrams.						

SECTION 1C

LESSON	OBJECTIVE	ITBS Form M	CTBS 4th Ed.	CAT 5th Ed.	SAT 9th Ed.	MAT 7th Ed.	Your Form
1-7	• Calculate the median and the mode for a set of data.				✘	✘	
1-8	• Calculate the mean for a set of data.			✘	✘	✘	
1-9	• Determine if an outlier affects the analysis of a data set.				✘		

Key: ITBS - Iowa Test of Basic Skills; CTBS - Comprehensive Test of Basic Skills; CAT - California Achievement Test; SAT - Stanford Achievement Test; MAT - Metropolitan Achievement Test

ASSESSMENT PROGRAM

Traditional Assessment

QUICK QUIZZES	SECTION REVIEW	CHAPTER REVIEW	CHAPTER ASSESSMENT FREE RESPONSE	CHAPTER ASSESSMENT MULTIPLE CHOICE	CUMULATIVE REVIEW
TE: pp. 10, 15, 20, 28, 33, 38, 45, 49, 54	SE: pp. 22, 40, 56 *Quiz 1A, 1B, 1C	SE: 58–59	SE: p. 60 *Ch. 1 Tests Forms A, B, E	*Ch. 1 Tests Forms C, E	SE: p. 61 *Ch. 1 Test Form F

Alternate Assessment

INTERVIEW	JOURNAL	ONGOING	PERFORMANCE	PORTFOLIO	PROJECT	SELF
TE: pp. 10, 45	SE: pp. 20, 22, 28, 38, 45 TE: pp. 4, 15, 38, 54	TE: pp. 6, 11, 16, 24, 29, 34, 42, 46, 51	SE: pp. 60, 61 TE: pp. 20, 49 *Ch. 1 Tests Forms D, E	TE: p. 28	SE: pp. 15, 28, 54 TE: p. 3	TE: p. 33

*Tests and quizzes are in *Assessment Sourcebook.* Test Form E is a mixed response test. Forms for Alternate Assessment are also available in *Assessment Sourcebook.*

TestWorks: Test and Practice Software

MIDDLE SCHOOL PACING CHART

REGULAR PACING

Day	5 classes per week
1	Chapter 1 Opener; Problem Solving Focus
2	Section **1A** Opener; Lesson **1-1**
3	Lesson **1-2**
4	Lesson **1-3**
5	**1A** Connect; **1A** Review
6	Section **1B** Opener; Lesson **1-4**
7	Lesson **1-5**
8	Lesson **1-6**
9	**1B** Connect; **1B** Review
10	Section **1C** Opener; Lesson **1-7**
11	Lesson **1-8**; Technology
12	Lesson **1-9**
13	**1C** Connect; **1C** Review; Extend Key Ideas
14	Chapter 1 Summary and Review
15	Chapter 1 Assessment Cumulative Review, Chapter 1

BLOCK SCHEDULING OPTIONS

Block Scheduling for Complete Course

Chapter 1 may be presented in

- nine 90-minute blocks
- twelve 75-minute blocks

Each block consists of a combination of

- Chapter and Section Openers
- Explores
- Lesson Development
- Problem Solving Focus
- Technology
- Extend Key Ideas
- Connect
- Review
- Assessment

For details, see *Block Scheduling Handbook*.

Block Scheduling for Interdisciplinary Course

Each block integrates math with another subject area.

In Chapter 1, interdisciplinary topics include

- Sharks
- Presidents
- Sports

Themes for Interdisciplinary Team Teaching 1A, 1B, and 1C are

- Marine Life
- Voting
- Deserts

For details, see *Block Scheduling Handbook*.

Block Scheduling for Lab-Based Course

In each block, 30–40 minutes is devoted to lab activities including

- Explores in the Student Edition
- Connect pages in the Student Edition
- Technology options in the Student Edition
- Reteaching Activities in the Teacher Edition

For details, see *Block Scheduling Handbook*.

Block Scheduling for Course with *Connected Mathematics*

In each block, investigations from **Connected Mathematics** replace or enhance the lessons in Chapter 1.

Connected Mathematics topics for Chapter 1 can be found in

- *Data About Us*

For details, see *Block Scheduling Handbook*.

INTERDISCIPLINARY BULLETIN BOARD

Set Up

Prepare a bulletin board with axes for a bar graph. The *y*-axis has a list of names of different kinds of whales, such as humpback, finback, blue, and gray. The *x*-axis indicates the number of meters from 0 to 30.

Procedure

- Have small groups of students choose a kind of whale, research its appearance, and the greatest length it is known to attain.
- Groups should draw the whales on the graph so that their lengths indicate the actual length of the whale in meters.

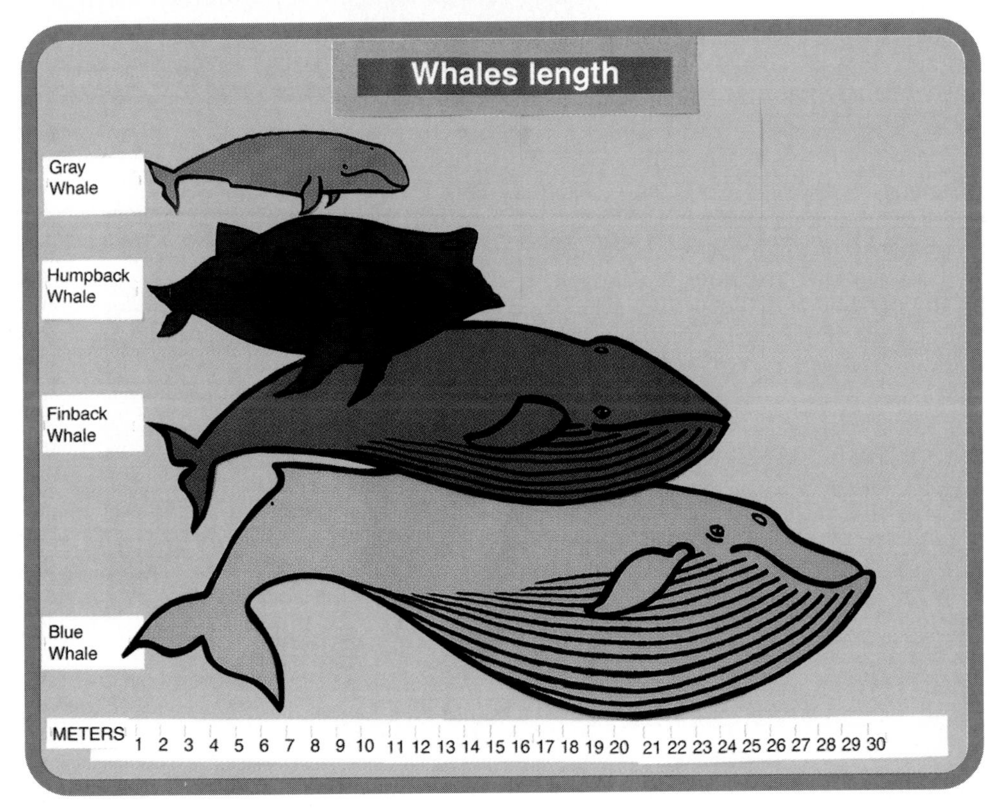

Chapter 1

The information on these pages shows how statistics are used in real-life situations.

World Wide Web

If your class has access to the World Wide Web, you might want to use the information found at the Web site addresses given.

Extensions

The following activities do not require access to the World Wide Web.

People of the World
Have students find a chart or graph that displays information about another country. Ask students to summarize the information for the class.

Science
Ask students to investigate the temperatures on various planets. Ask how a planet's distance from the sun affects its temperature. The closer a planet is to the sun, the warmer its temperature.

Entertainment
Suggest that students investigate the impact cable TV networks and satellite dishes have on a viewer's choices.

Arts & Literature
Have students write a sentence that contains no *e*'s. To make the task more interesting, suggest that they try to use every other letter except *e*.

Social Studies
Ask students to locate Norilsk, Russia, on a map and to investigate housing, type of heat, and other living conditions in that city.

1 Statistics – Real-World Use of Whole

Science Link
www.mathsurf.com/6/ch1/science

Entertainment

When it comes to houses with televisions, China is an outlier. 227,500,000 homes in China have televisions. The country with the next greatest number of televisions, the United States, has only 94,200,000.

People of the World

Charts and graphs in Japan's *Asahi Shimbun* newspaper are seen by over 7,000,000 people every day. That's four times the population of the state of Texas.

Science

If a bar graph showed the planets' distances from the Sun, and the bar representing Mercury's distance was one inch tall, the bar for Pluto's distance would be 9 feet tall.

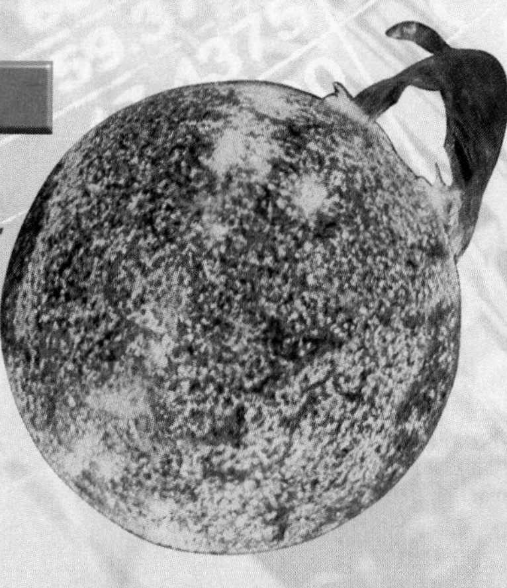

2

TEACHER TALK

Meet Ann Boltz

Legg Middle School
Coldwater, Michigan

Early in the school year, I have students start a folder in which they record the results of their quizzes and tests. This record allows them to evaluate their weekly progress and to apply the mathematics they are learning in this chapter. At the end of each month, I have them display their data using line plots, bar graphs, and stem-and-leaf diagrams. They find their average scores and look for patterns and trends in their data. Students become aware of the impact missed quizzes or tests have on their grade.

I require that students show their folders to their parents. I find parents enjoy seeing the student's data presented in a variety of visual ways.

Numbers

Social Studies Link
www.mathsurf.com/6/ch1/social

Arts & Literature

The letter that appears most often in English writings is "e." It is followed by "t," "a," "i," and "n."

KEY MATH IDEAS

Graphs can be used to compare numbers to each other, to compare numbers over time, and to compare numbers as part of a whole.

A scatterplot is a graph that can help determine if there is a relationship between two sets of data.

You can use stem-and-leaf diagrams to display data in intervals.

A large set of data can be described by listing the value that falls in the exact middle of the data, as well as the value that appears most often.

The mean, or average, of a set of data can also describe the data.

Social Studies

The mean temperature in Norilsk, Russia, is 12.4 °F. Water freezes at temperatures below 32 °F.

CHAPTER PROJECT

Problem Solving: Understand, Plan, Solve, Look Back

In this project, you will collect data about an interesting location somewhere in the world. Other students will have to guess the location you chose based on your data. Begin by thinking of a place in the world that you find interesting and want to learn more about.

3

Chapter Project

Students collect data about an interesting location somewhere in the world. Based on their data, other students will try to guess the location chosen.

Resources

Chapter 1 Project Master

Introduce the Project

- Discuss types of information about a location that might help someone identify the location, such as climate, landmarks, tourist attractions, and so on.
- Talk about where students might find information about selected locations, such as encyclopedias, travel magazines and guides, and the Internet.

Project Progress

Section A, page 15 Students may read and interpret various types of graphs to analyze data and statistics or to identify a trend about a specific location.

Section B, page 28 Students may use charts and tables to organize information they gathered, and then display this information in an appropriate graph.

Section C, page 54 Students calculate the mean, median, and mode of collected data to provide a hint that may be used to identify their chosen location.

Community Project

A community project for Chapter 1 is available in *Home and Community Connections.*

Cooperative Learning

You may want to use Teaching Tool Transparency 1: Cooperative Learning Checklist with **Explore** and other group activities in this chapter.

PROJECT ASSESSMENT

You may choose to use this project as a performance assessment for the chapter.

Performance Assessment Key

Level 4 Full Accomplishment

Level 3 Substantial Accomplishment

Level 2 Partial Accomplishment

Level 1 Little Accomplishment

Suggested Scoring Rubric

Level	Criteria
4	• Collected data is detailed, organized, and clearly presented in displays. • Statistics are accurate and correctly calculated.
3	• Collected data is informative, organized, and presented in displays. • Included statistics are accurate.
2	• Collected data provides little information and few displays are included. • Few statistics are included.
1	• Collected data provides little information and no displays are included. • Few statistics are included.

Problem Solving Focus

Reading the Problem

The Point
Students focus on reading and understanding a problem.

Resources
Teaching Tool Transparency 18: Problem-Solving Guidelines

 *Interactive CD-ROM Journal*

About the Page

Using the Problem-Solving Process
Discuss these three suggestions for reading a problem:

- Read the problem several times before beginning.
- Determine what the problem is about.
- Determine what the problem is asking.

Ask ...
- How would you organize the information in the problem?
- If you made a time line for Question 1, what would be the order of the eruptions? Explain. Mount Etna, Kratatoa, Nevado del Ruiz; Mount Etna erupted 316 years before Nevado del Ruiz and Kratatoa erupted 102 years before Nevado del Ruiz.

Answers for Problems

1. Krakatoa erupted in 1883.
   a. When the volcanoes erupted.
   b. In what year was Krakatoa's loud eruption.
   c. 1669
   d. Mount Etna
   e. Possible answers: Question: When did Nevado del Ruiz erupt? Answer: 1985.
2. Kilauea: 4,000 ft; Canlaon: 8,000 ft; On-Take: 10,000 ft.
   a. The height of volcanoes.
   b. How tall are Kilauea, Canlaon, and On-Take.
   c. Half
   d. On-Take
   e. Possible answer: Question: How much taller is On-Take than Canlaon? Answer: 2,000 ft.

Journal

Ask students to write about a problem that requires solving. Suggest they formulate questions to help solve the problem.

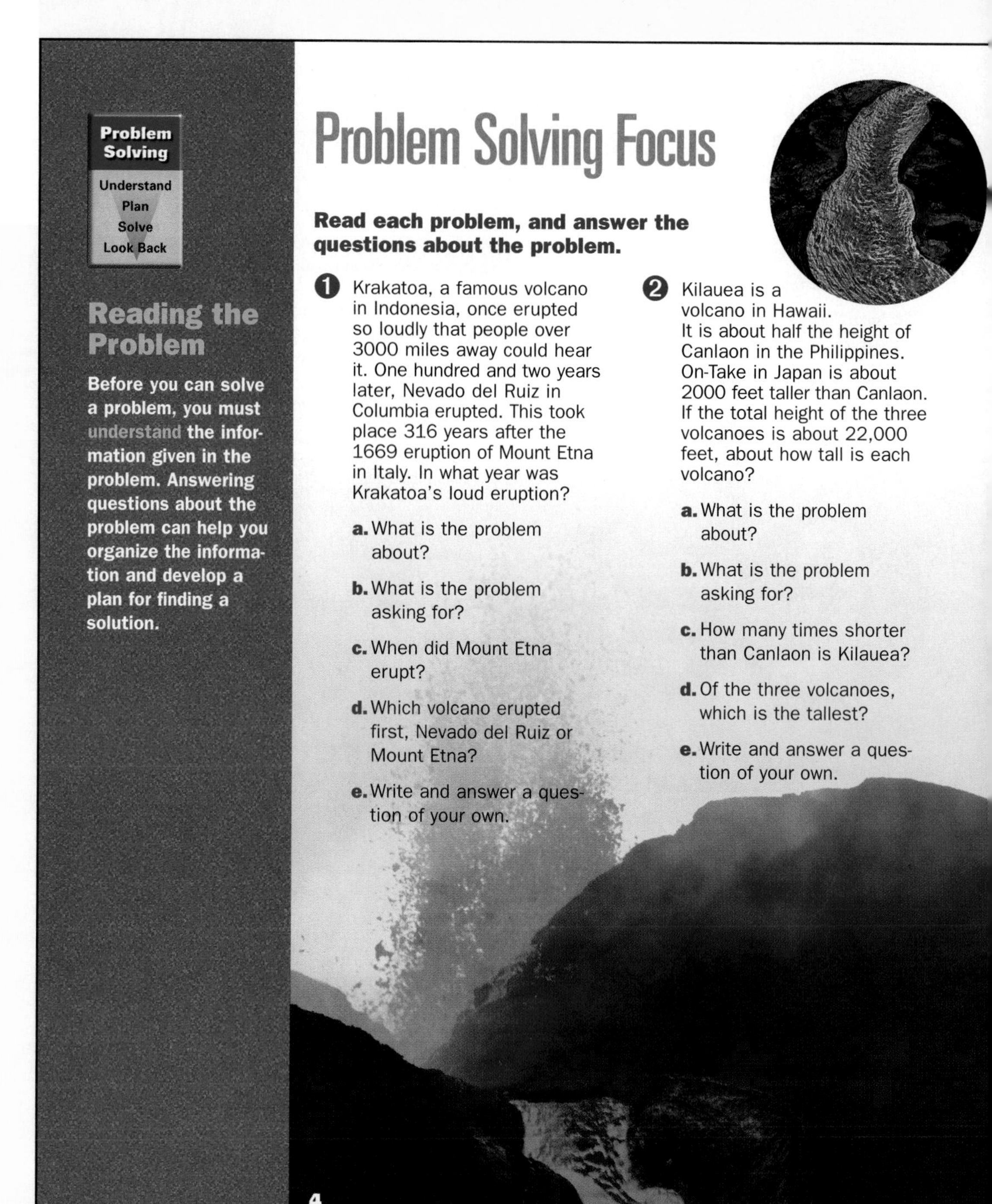

Problem Solving
Understand
Plan
Solve
Look Back

Reading the Problem

Before you can solve a problem, you must understand the information given in the problem. Answering questions about the problem can help you organize the information and develop a plan for finding a solution.

Problem Solving Focus

Read each problem, and answer the questions about the problem.

1 Krakatoa, a famous volcano in Indonesia, once erupted so loudly that people over 3000 miles away could hear it. One hundred and two years later, Nevado del Ruiz in Columbia erupted. This took place 316 years after the 1669 eruption of Mount Etna in Italy. In what year was Krakatoa's loud eruption?

a. What is the problem about?

b. What is the problem asking for?

c. When did Mount Etna erupt?

d. Which volcano erupted first, Nevado del Ruiz or Mount Etna?

e. Write and answer a question of your own.

2 Kilauea is a volcano in Hawaii. It is about half the height of Canlaon in the Philippines. On-Take in Japan is about 2000 feet taller than Canlaon. If the total height of the three volcanoes is about 22,000 feet, about how tall is each volcano?

a. What is the problem about?

b. What is the problem asking for?

c. How many times shorter than Canlaon is Kilauea?

d. Of the three volcanoes, which is the tallest?

e. Write and answer a question of your own.

4

Additional Problem

Maryanne collected $350 in pledges for the walkathon at her school. Robert collected $100 less in pledges than Maryanne, and Rachel collected half as much in pledges as Maryanne. Altogether, the students raised $8450 for playground equipment. They walked 65 miles in all. How much in pledges did Rachel raise? $175

1. What is the problem about? The amount of money raised in pledges for a walkathon.
2. What is the problem asking? The amount of pledges Rachel raised.
3. Who raised more in pledges, Robert or Rachel? Robert

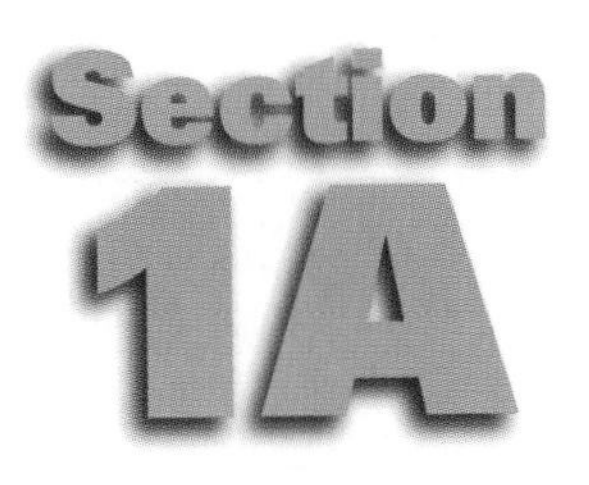

Reading and Interpreting Graphs

Visit www.teacher.mathsurf.com for links to lesson plans from teachers and other professionals, NCTM information, and other sites.

LESSON PLANNING GUIDE

Student Edition				Ancillaries*	
LESSON		**MATERIALS**	**VOCABULARY**	**DAILY**	**OTHER**
	Chapter 1 Opener				Teaching Tool Trans. 1 Ch. 1 Project Master Ch. 1 Community Project
	Problem Solving Focus				Teaching Tool Trans. 18 *Interactive CD-ROM Journal*
	Section 1A Opener				
1-1	**Reading Graphs**		bar graph, pictograph, line graph, circle graph	1-1	Lesson Enhancement Trans. 1
1-2	**Misleading Graphs**			1-2	Lesson Enhancement Trans. 2 Technology Master 1 Ch. 1 Project Master
1-3	**Scatterplots and Trends**		scatterplot, trend	1-3	Technology Master 2
	Connect				Lesson Enhancement Trans. 3 Interdisc. Team Teaching 1A
	Review				Practice 1A; Quiz 1A; *TestWorks*

* Daily Ancillaries include Practice, Reteaching, Problem Solving, Enrichment, and Daily Transparency. Teaching Tool Transparencies are in *Teacher's Toolkits*. Lesson Enhancement Transparencies are in *Overhead Transparency Package*.

SKILLS TRACE

LESSON	SKILL	FIRST INTRODUCED GR. 4	GR. 5	GR. 6	DEVELOP	PRACTICE/APPLY	REVIEW
1-1	**Reading graphs.**	✗			pp. 6–8	pp. 9–10	pp. 45, 58, 198, 214, 241, 297
1-2	**Identifying misleading relationships on graphs.**			✗ p. 11	pp. 11–13	pp. 14–15	pp. 49, 58
1-3	**Identifying trends on a scatterplot.**			✗ p. 16	pp. 16–18	pp. 19–20	pp. 54, 58, 224, 253, 297

CONNECTED MATHEMATICS

The unit *Data About Us (Statistics)*, from the **Connected Mathematics** series, can be used with Section 1A.

INTERDISCIPLINARY TEAM TEACHING

Math and Science/Technology

(Worksheet pages 01–02: Teacher pages T1–T2)

In this lesson, students read and interpret graphs.

Name ______________________ ***Math and Science/Technology***

Marine Monsters

Read and interpret graphs.

Imagine that you are deep-sea fishing for bluefish. You and your friends are happily hauling in one bluefish after another. Each fish is about 3 feet long and weighs about 10 pounds. Then, suddenly, someone in your group shouts, "Look! Over there! I think it's a whale shark!" Everyone turns their attention in the direction of a huge fish that has just broken the water's surface. It is enormous! You estimate its length at around 40 feet, about the size of a school bus. In seconds the shark is gone. You go back to fishing with a new appreciation for the size of animals that live in the sea.

Often, the largest and most frightening ocean animals are the ones that humans rarely, if ever, see. Here are a few of the most impressive ones:

Whale shark: This animal got its name from the fact that it is as big as some whales. It is so big that it has earned the title of the largest fish in the sea. The whale shark weighs around 40,000 pounds. In spite of its size, it is not a threat to people because it has very tiny teeth. It feeds on small fish and even smaller living things that float in the sea.

Giant squid: Weighing more than 4000 pounds, the giant squid is the biggest of the squids and lives in the depths of all the oceans.

Arctic lion's mane jellyfish: This creature, which lives in northern ocean waters, is the largest jellyfish in the world. About 1200 tentacles, 120 feet in length, hang from its bell-shaped body, which can be more than 7 feet in diameter. Each tentacle has poisonous stinging cells.

Giant spider crab: Found in the waters around Japan, the giant spider crab's legs are about 5 feet long. Each leg is tipped with five-inch pincers that are used for catching prey, fighting, and digging.

Blue whale: Found in all the oceans, this mammal is the heaviest known animal ever to have lived on Earth. Weighing more than 6000 pounds at birth, the blue whale can weigh an amazing 500,000 pounds as an adult.

It is often not the weight of the animal that amazes us. It is the creature's incredible length. Study the following graph. It allows you to compare the lengths of the animals mentioned above.

Called a whale shark, this animal is not a mammal like the whale, but a fish.

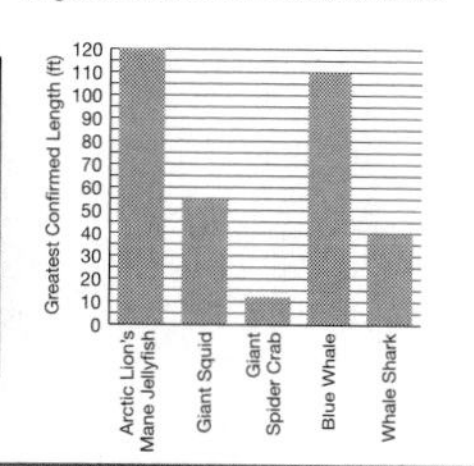

Name ______________________ ***Math and Science/Technology***

1. When the Arctic lion's mane jellyfish spreads out its long tentacles, it covers an area of more than 45,000 square feet. How does this ability help the jellyfish satisfy its need for large amounts of food?

   The larger the area covered by the jellyfish's tentacles, the larger the area in which it can catch the animals that are swimming in the sea.

2. Rank the giant sea creatures from the shortest to longest.

   giant spider crab, whale shark, giant squid, blue whale, Arctic lion's mane jellyfish

3. About how many times as long is the blue whale than the giant squid?

   twice as long

4. A bluefish is about 3 feet long. How many times longer are the other animals in the graph than the bluefish?

   crab: about 4 times as long; shark: 13 times as long; squid: 15 times as long; whale: 37 times as long; jellyfish: 40 times as long.

5. It's sometimes hard to appreciate the size of objects from numbers alone. You can get a more realistic idea of the sizes of the sea creatures described on page one by drawing pictures of them to actual size. Do research to find pictures of the animals and use chalk to draw them in a large open area on your school grounds. As an alternative, you could use string to outline them on an athletic field. How many times longer is each animal than you?

   Answers will vary depending on the height of the student.

6. As big as it is, the blue whale feeds on very tiny creatures. These tiny creatures feed on even tinier green living things. As these green things live, they give off oxygen into the air, which all animals including humans breathe. Identify the living things in the blue whale's food chain and tell what you think might happen if the world's blue whales became extinct.

   krill; phytoplankton; krill population might explode, phytoplankton population might go down, and oxygen concentration in air might fall

BIBLIOGRAPHY

FOR TEACHERS

Haven, Kendall. *Marvels of Science.* Englewood, CO: Libraries Unlimited, 1994.

Spangler, David. *Math for Real Kids.* Glenview, IL: Good Year Books, 1997.

Welton, Ann. *Explorers and Exploration.* Phoenix, AZ: Oryx Press, 1993.

The World Almanac and Book of Facts. Mahwah, NJ: Funk & Wagnalls, 1996.

FOR STUDENTS

Bramwell, Martyn. *Volcanoes and Earthquakes.* Chicago, IL: Watts, 1994.

Macquitty, Miranda. *Shark.* New York, NY: Knopf, 1992.

Ridpath, Ian. *The Facts on File Atlas of Stars and Planets.* New York, NY: Facts on File, 1993.

SECTION 1A

Reading and Interpreting Graphs

▶ Science Link ▶ Geography Link ▶ www.mathsurf.com/6/ch1/sharks

DANGER! SHARK ATTACK!

You walk alone on the beach, the water splashing against your feet. Suddenly, you feel a presence. A single animal that threatens your very life. As it approaches, you turn around. You scream in horror at the sight of … a dog!

Silly, maybe, but it's statistically sound. Each year, more people in the United States are killed by dogs than have been killed by sharks in the past 100 years. There are 350 species of sharks, but only 10 of them are known to have attacked humans.

Sharks are fascinating and often misunderstood. Suppose you were a marine biologist who wanted to study sharks to better understand them. How would you decide the best places to go and the best sharks to study? One way would be to refer to graphs that display data on shark attacks. Graphs allow you to compare numerical data, display it visually, and look for patterns and trends.

1 Why do you think more people are killed by dogs than by sharks?

2 Why might a graph of data be better than a list of data?

5

Where are we now?

In Grade 5, students explored the use of graphs to describe data.

They learned how to

- read bar and line graphs.
- make bar and line graphs.
- determine range, median, and mode.
- use information on graphs to make decisions.

Where are we going?

In Grade 6, Section 1A, students will

- use graphs to organize and display information.
- identify graphs that display misleading information.
- compare values in two sets of data using scatterplots.

Theme: Sharks

World Wide Web

If your class has access to the World Wide Web, you might want to use the information found at the Web site address given. The interdisciplinary links relate to topics discussed in this section.

About the Page

This page introduces the theme of the section, sharks, and discusses the number of people killed by sharks.

Ask …

- Have you ever seen a shark? Where? When?
- Can you suggest ways in which scientists determine the number and variety of sharks that exist? How is data gathered about animals that live in the ocean?

Extensions

The following activities do not require access to the World Wide Web.

Science

Sharks are large fish that some people confuse with whales. Have students list ways in which sharks and whales differ.

Geography

Many countries fish for sharks, including the U.S. Sharks form the basis of several industries in Norway. The Chinese consider dried shark fins a delicacy. Have students research the products made from shark. Fertilizer, food products, cod-liver oil, leather, glue.

Answers for Questions

1. More people encounter dogs than encounter sharks, so the chance that someone would get bitten by a rabid dog is greater than the chance that someone would get eaten by a shark.
2. Referring to graphs makes it easier to compare data and find possible patterns.

Connect

On page 21, students will analyze data given on graphs about shark attacks.

Lesson Organizer

Objectives

- Read numbers from different types of graphs.
- Compare numbers within the same graph.

Vocabulary

- Bar graph, pictograph, line graph, circle graph

NCTM Standards

- 1–5, 7, 10

▶ Review

Perform each operation.

1. 56 + 49 105
2. 4.5 × 50 225
3. 88 × 50 4400
4. 107 − 39 68
5. 7 × 50 350

Available on Daily Transparency 1-1

▶ Lesson Link

Discuss the four types of graphs with the class. Ask students to describe graphs they have seen in magazines, newspapers, and textbooks.

1 Introduce

Explore

You may wish to use Lesson Enhancement Transparency 1 with **Explore**.

The Point

Students make decisions about which graphs contain data they need.

Ongoing Assessment

Check that students are able to translate symbols to numbers in the pictograph and that they can relate points on the graphs to the scales.

1-1 Reading Graphs

You'll Learn ...

- to read numbers from different types of graphs
- to compare numbers within the same graph

... How It's Used

Marine biologists use graphs to find relationships between marine life and factors in their environment when developing research plans.

Vocabulary

bar graph

pictograph

line graph

circle graph

▶ Lesson Link In the past, you've learned the importance of using information to make decisions. Graphs are a useful way to organize information. ◀

Explore Graphs of Data

Attacking the Data

Use the graphs to answer the questions.

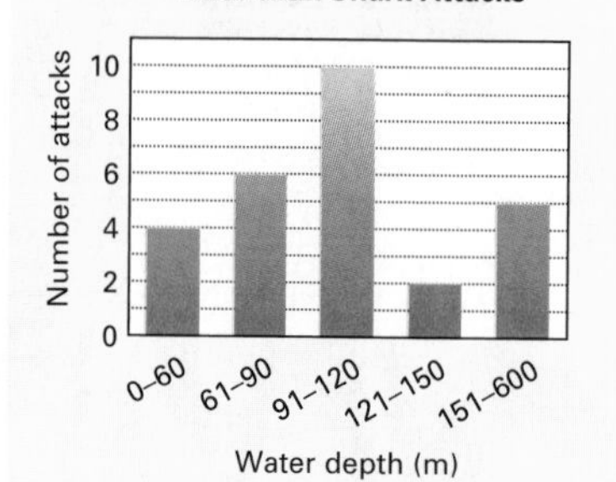

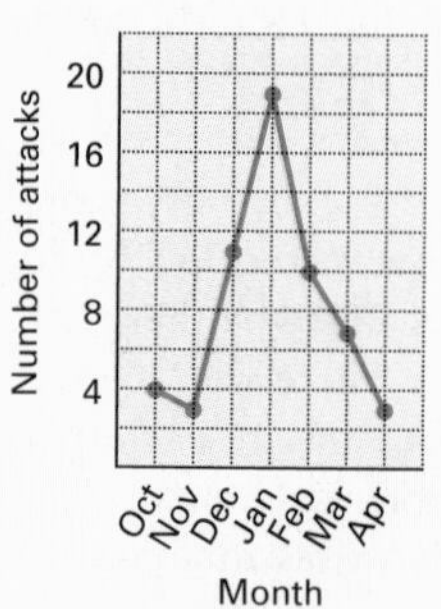

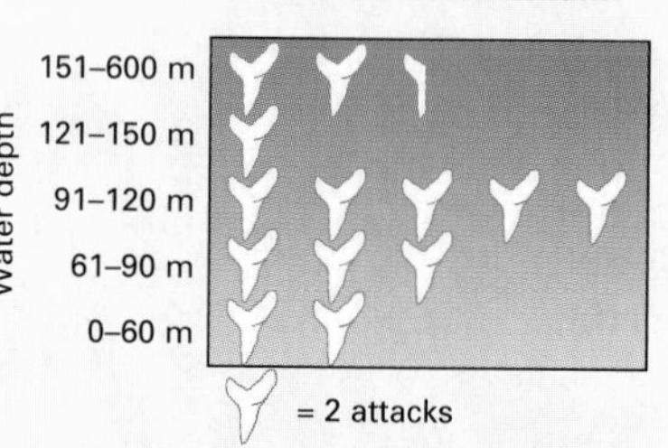

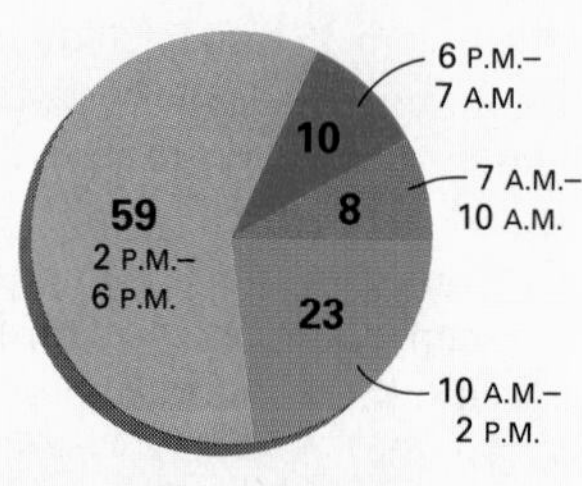

1. At what depth do most shark attacks occur? Name the graph(s) you can use to determine this.
2. In which month do the fewest attacks occur? The most attacks?
3. At what time of day do most shark attacks occur?
4. How many attacks were studied to produce each graph? Explain how you found your answers.

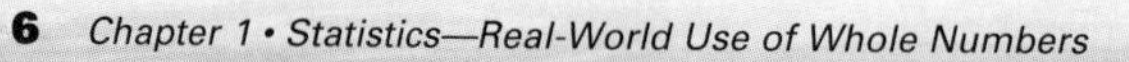

MEETING INDIVIDUAL NEEDS

Resources

- **1-1** Practice
- **1-1** Reteaching
- **1-1** Problem Solving
- **1-1** Enrichment
- **1-1** Daily Transparency
  - Problem of the Day
  - Review
  - Quick Quiz
- Lesson Enhancement Transparency 1

Learning Modalities

Visual When discussing the pictographs, you could use two pennies to represent each shark's-tooth symbol or two quarters to represent each animal species.

Kinesthetic If students experience difficulty reading the values in the bar graphs or line graphs, encourage them to use a ruler or the edge of an index card to align the top of the bar or the point with the appropriate axis.

Social Students could work in pairs to answer the questions in **Explore**.

Inclusion

Graphs presented to students should be clear and simple. Do not overwhelm the student by presenting too much information in one graph. Be certain that the legends are clearly labeled.

Students could make a math vocabulary reference notebook for learning new words.

Learn Getting Information from Graphs

A **bar graph** uses vertical or horizontal bars to display numerical information. The length of the bar tells you the number it represents.

Example 1

How much deeper than a free diver can a scuba diver dive?

Look at the bar for the free diver. It represents a depth of about 15 meters. The scuba diver bar represents 50 meters. Since $50 - 15 = 35$, the scuba diver can dive about 35 meters deeper.

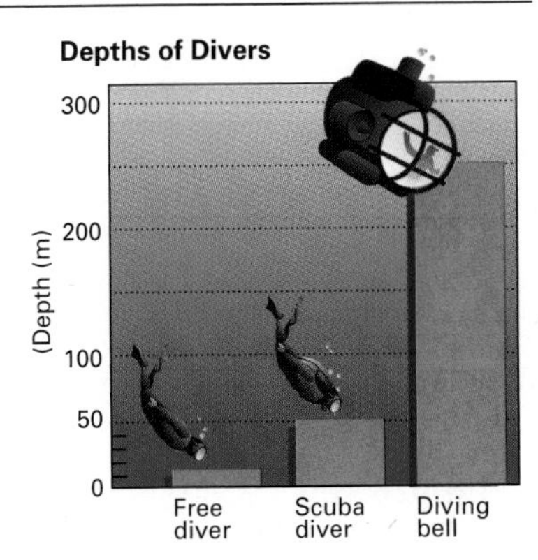

DID YOU KNOW?

SCUBA is an acronym. It stands for "self-contained underwater breathing apparatus."

A **pictograph** uses symbols to represent data. All of the symbols have the same value. To determine the measure of an item in a pictograph, count the number of symbols and multiply by the value of the symbol.

Example 2

About how many species of animals are there in the San Antonio Zoo?

In the pictograph, the number of species of animals in the San Antonio Zoo is represented by 7 symbols. Each symbol equals 100 species.

$7 \times 100 = 700$

There are about 700 species.

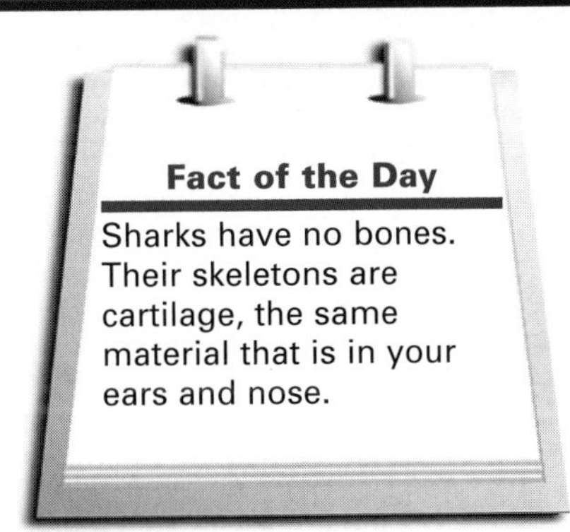

MENTAL MATH

A simple way to compute 7×100 is to compute 7×1 and annex two zeros to the end of the answer.

Try It

Use the bar graph or the pictograph to answer each question.

a. How much deeper can a diver in a diving bell dive than a scuba diver? 200 m

b. About how many species of animals are in the San Diego Zoo? 800

MATH EVERY DAY

Problem of the Day

Two corners of a square are at (8, 16) and (16, 8) Name some other possible corners.
Three possible pairs are (16, 16) and (8, 8); (0, 8) and (8, 0); (16, 24) and (24, 16).

Available on Daily Transparency 1-1

An Extension is provided in the transparency package.

Fact of the Day

Sharks have no bones. Their skeletons are cartilage, the same material that is in your ears and nose.

Mental Math

Find each product mentally.

1. 5×50 250
2. 8×50 400
3. 11×50 550
4. 14×50 700

For Groups That Finish Early

Which of the graphs showing shark attacks in Australia was easier for you to interpret? Why?
Answers may vary.

Answers for Explore

1. 91–120 m, using either of the two graphs on the left.
2. Apr. and Nov; Jan.
3. 2 P.M.–6 P.M.
4. Bar graph: 27 (total of bars); Pictograph: 27 (total of symbols × 2); Line graph: 57 (total of number of attacks for each point); Circle graph: 100 (total of numbers in the wedges).

2 Teach

Learn

Alternate Examples

1. How much deeper than a free diver can a diving bell dive?

   The bar for the diving bell represents 250 meters and the bar for the free diver represents 15 meters. Since $250 - 15 = 235$, the diving bell can dive 235 meters deeper.

2. How many species of animals are in the Cincinnati Zoo?

   There are $7\frac{1}{2}$ animal symbols in the pictograph for the Cincinnati Zoo. Each symbol represents 100 species.

   $7\frac{1}{2} \times 100 = 750$

   There are 750 species of animals in the Cincinnati Zoo.

Alternate Examples

3. Find the value of a Rickey Henderson baseball card in 1993.

   Find the dot for 1993 on the year line. The dot is to the right of the value 100.

   The card was worth $100 in 1993.

4. Which technology was second in popularity for advertising purposes?

   The second-largest wedge, not including "undecided," represents PC/Online Service, so it is second in popularity.

3 Practice and Assess

Check

Be sure that students understand how to read the values from the axes in both the bar and line graphs. They must translate numbers of symbols into actual numbers in the pictograph, while the actual percent values are given in the circle graph.

Answers for Check Your Understanding

1. A bar graph shows the value by the height (or length) of the bar. A pictograph shows it by the number of symbols. A circle graph shows it by the width of the wedge. A line graph shows it by the distance of the point from the horizontal axis.
2. Bar graph: Highest bar, lowest bar; Pictograph: Most symbols, least symbols; Circle graph: Widest wedge, narrowest wedge; Line graph: Highest point, lowest point.

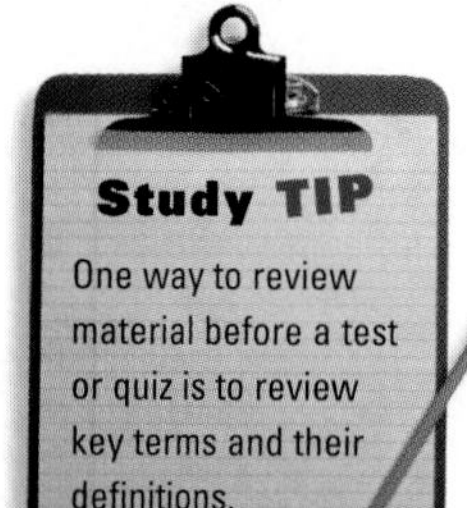

Study TIP

One way to review material before a test or quiz is to review key terms and their definitions.

A **line graph** often shows how data changes over time. Each dot represents an item of data. The height of the dot represents the value of the data. The time is shown by how far to the right the dot is.

Example 3

Find the value of a 1980 Rickey Henderson baseball card in 1992.

Find the dot above the 1992 on the year line. The dot is directly to the right of the value 150.

A card was worth $150 in 1992.

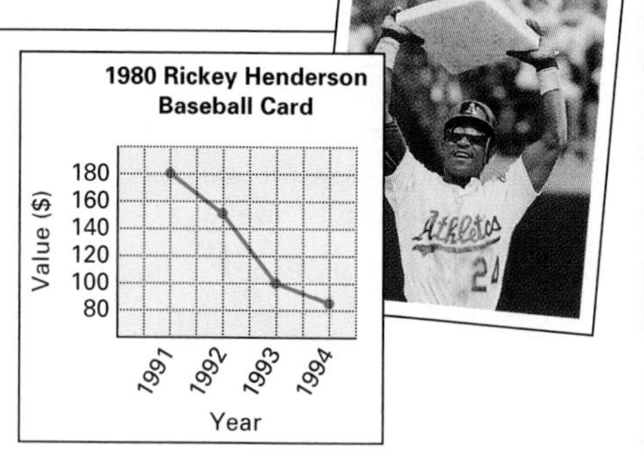

A **circle graph** shows how portions of a set of data compare with the whole set. The larger the value of the data, the wider the wedge that represents the value.

Example 4

Retailers were asked to name the technology they preferred for advertising. Which technology was most favored?

The largest wedge in the graph represents the Internet. It was the most favored technology.

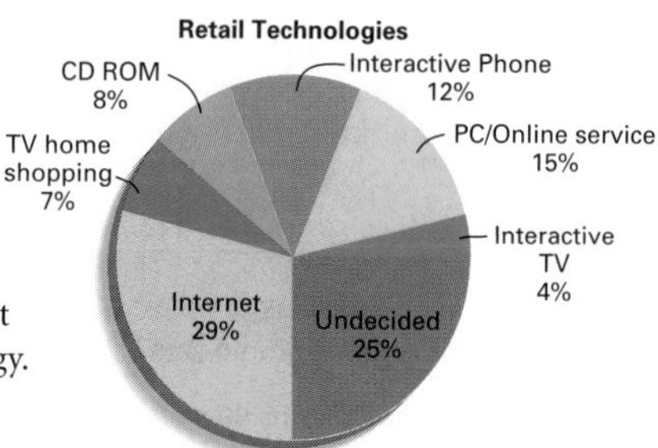

Science Link

Many retailers advertise on a part of the Internet known as the World Wide Web. On the Web, advertisers can use video, sound clips, and animation to advertise their products.

Try It

Use the line graph or the circle graph to answer each question.

a. In what year was a Rickey Henderson card worth about $100? **1993**

b. Which technology was the least preferred for advertising? **Interactive TV**

Check Your Understanding

1. How does each type of graph show the value of a data item?
2. For each graph, how can you tell which value is the highest number? The lowest number?

MEETING MIDDLE SCHOOL CLASSROOM NEEDS

Tips from Middle School Teachers

At the beginning of a chapter dealing with statistics, I have students begin to collect and record weather data for our area. They are responsible for weekends as well as school days. We culminate the chapter by representing the collected data in all the formats studied in the chapter.

Team Teaching

Have the other teachers on your team point out examples of various types of graphs in their texts and reference books.

Science Connection

A shark's teeth are larger, sharper versions of the hook-like scales that cover its body. In most kinds of sharks, the mouth is lined with five or six rows of teeth that curve inward. This makes escape harder for the shark's prey.

1-1 Exercises and Applications

Practice and Apply

Getting Started **Fill in the blank with the name of the graph described.**

1. A _____ uses symbols to represent data and a key to show the value of each symbol. Pictograph

2. A _____ shows data as a set of connected points. Line graph

3. In a _____, the data is broken into parts of a whole. Circle graph

Science Use the Shark Attack graph to answer each question.

4. What is the total number of shark attacks shown in the data? 41

5. Which bar represents the most shark attacks? The fewest shark attacks? 11–50 m; 51–100 m

6. Do more shark attacks take place within 50 m from shore or 51–600 m from shore? Within 50 m

7. How many bars represent a number of attacks that is greater than 10? 3

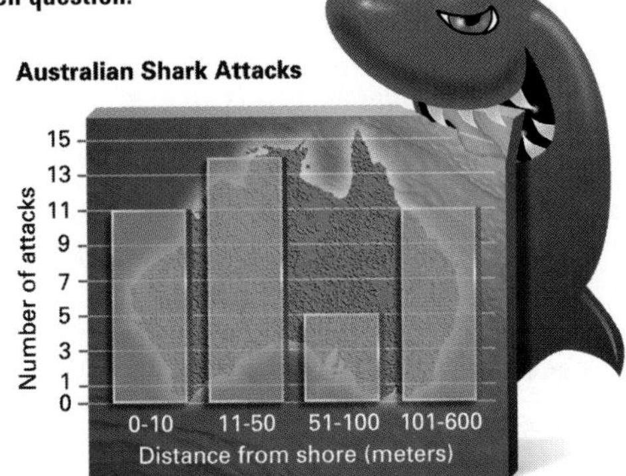

Use the Cost of Raising a Child graph for Exercises 8–11.

8. What is the cost of transportation? $15

9. For each $100 a parent spends on raising a child to age 18, how much more is spent on housing and clothes than on education? $37

10. **Test Prep** For each $300 spent, estimate how much is spent for food and clothes. B

Ⓐ $329 Ⓑ $90

Ⓒ $29 Ⓓ $130

11. Which costs are about twice as much as the cost of education? Five times as much? Eleven times as much? Medical, clothes; other, transportation; housing

Cost of Raising a Child to Age 18 (for each $100)

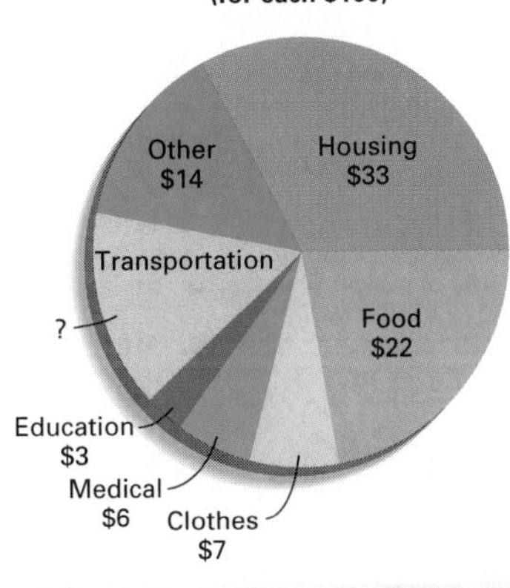

PRACTICE

Name ____________

Practice 1-1

Reading Graphs

Use the Disney Park Attendance pictograph to answer Exercises 1–5.

Disney Park Attendance, 1993

Disneyland
EPCOT at Disneyworld
Magic Kingdom at Disneyworld
Disney-MGM Studios
= 1 million visitors

1. Which park had the fewest visitors? Disney-MGM Studios
2. Which park had the most visitors? Magic Kingdom at Disneyworld
3. How many visitors did EPCOT have? 10,000,000
4. Which park had more visitors, Disneyland or EPCOT? Disneyland
5. What is the total number of visitors to the four parks? 41,000,000

Use the Children in U.S. families graph to answer Exercises 6–7.

Children in U.S. Families

No children, 51%
1 child, 20%
2 children, 19%
3 children, 7%
4 or more children, 3%

6. What percent of families include exactly 2 children? 19%
7. Of the categories shown, which is the largest? No children

Use the graph of the Five Best-selling Motorcycle Brands to answer Exercises 8–11.

The Five Best-selling Motorcycle Brands, 1993

Number sold (thousands): 0, 20, 40, 60, 80, 100
Brand: Honda, Suzuki, Yamaha, Harley-Davidson, Kawasaki

8. Which brand sold the most motorcycles? Harley-Davidson
9. Which brand (of the five shown) sold the fewest? Yamaha
10. About how many Honda motorcycles were sold? 44,000
11. Which brand sold more motorcycles, Suzuki or Kawasaki? Suzuki

RETEACHING

Name ____________

Alternative Lesson 1-1

Reading Graphs

A **pictograph** uses symbols to represent data. A **bar graph** uses vertical or horizontal bars to display numerical information. The two graphs below show the same data.

Australian Shark Attacks

Water Depth
151–600 cm
121–150 cm
91–120 cm
61–90 cm
0–60 cm
Key: = 2 attacks

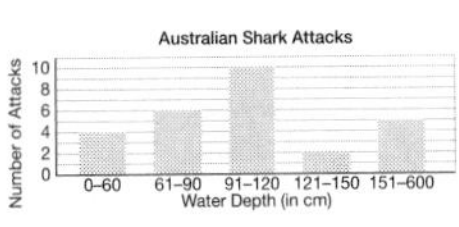

Example 1

Use the pictograph to decide how many shark attacks occur at a water depth of 61–90 cm.

Step 1: Count the number of symbols beside the bar marked 61–90 cm. There are 3 symbols.

Step 2: Multiply the number of symbols and the number each symbol represents. The key shows that each symbol equals 2 shark attacks, so find $3 \times 2 = 6$.

Six shark attacks occur at a water depth of 61–90 cm.

Example 2

Use the bar graph to decide how many shark attacks occur at a water depth of 61–90 cm.

Step 1: Find the bar labeled 61–90 cm on the horizontal scale showing water depths.

Step 2: Find the number on the vertical scale that matches the top of the bar: 6.

Six shark attacks occur at a water depth of 91–120 cm.

Try It Use the pictograph to answer each question. Then use the bar graph to verify each answer.

a. How many shark attacks occur at a water depth of 0–60 cm? 4 attacks.

b. How many shark attacks occur at a water depth of 151–600 cm? 5 attacks.

c. At what water depth did the least number of attacks occur? 121–150 cm

d. How many more attacks occur at a depth of 61–90 cm than occur at a depth of 0–60 cm? 2 attacks.

e. Which graph did you find easier to use? Why?
Possible answer: Pictograph, because one can count by 2s.

PRACTICE 1-1

1-1 Exercises and Applications

Assignment Guide

- Basic
  1–18, 20–42 evens
- Average
  1–19, 21–43 odds
- Enriched
  1–19, 22–42 evens

Exercise Notes

Exercise 9

Error Prevention Watch for students who neglect to consider both housing and clothes. Remind them to read each problem carefully before they solve it.

Reteaching

Activity

Class Animals

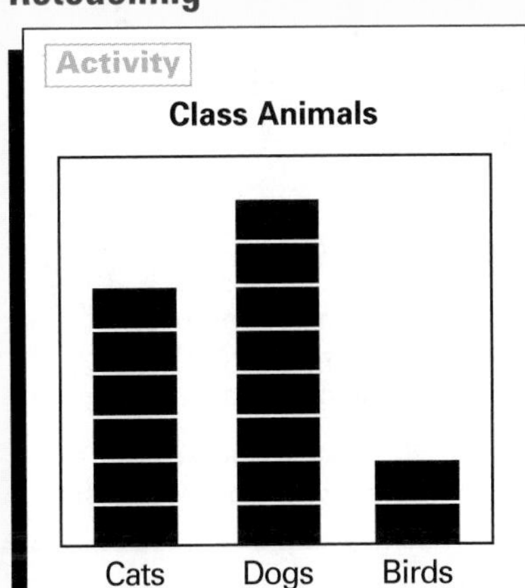

- Use the graph above and think of this as a bar graph where each rectangle represents one animal How many cats are there? 6 cats Dogs? 8 dogs Birds? 2 birds
- Now think of the graph as a pictograph where each symbol represents two animals. How many cats are there? 12 cats Dogs? 16 dogs Birds? 4 birds
- If you connect the tops of the bars, what kind of graph is represented by your line segments? Line graph

Exercise Notes

■ Exercises 12–14

Error Prevention Watch for students who merely count the symbols and do not multiply by 4,000,000. Suggest that students write the pictograph key on their papers to help them remember.

■ Exercise 16

Error Prevention Students may not realize the vertical scale starts at 1 million rather than 0 million. Remind them to carefully examine the vertical and horizontal scales before answering the question.

Exercise Answers

15. A steady increase: 4 million for 1991–1992, 12 million for 1992–1993, 6 million for 1993–1994.

19. Answers may vary.

Alternate Assessment

Interview Ask each student to explain which type of graph would be best suited to display the set of data.

1. Numbers of students participating in various school sports. Possible answer: Bar graphs or pictographs.
2. Amounts of allowance spent by a student for entertainment, food, clothes, and so on. Possible answer: Circle graph.
3. Monthly sales figures for a bakery. Possible answer: Line graph.

► Quick Quiz

Complete each sentence with *bar graph, circle graph, line graph,* or *pictograph.*

1. A ___ compares parts of a data set with the whole set. circle graph
2. A ___ shows data points connected. line graph
3. A ___ uses symbols to represent data. pictograph
4. A ___ is useful in showing comparisons. bar graph

Available on Daily Transparency 1-1

PROBLEM SOLVING 1-1

Problem Solving and Reasoning

Ocean sizes are often measured in square miles. Use this measurement and the graph to answer each question.

12. Number Sense What is the size of the Arctic Ocean? 6,000,000 sq mi

13. Operation Sense GPS The total area of the Pacific, Atlantic, and Indian Oceans is 124,000,000 square miles. How many square miles is the Pacific Ocean? 64,000,000 sq mi

14. Critical Thinking What's the difference in square miles between the sizes of the Indian Ocean and the Atlantic Ocean? 4,000,000 sq mi

Ocean Sizes

Atlantic
Indian
Arctic
Key = 4,000,000 sq. mi

Use the CD-ROM Sales graph to answer each question.

15. Communicate Describe the change(s) in the data overall and from year to year.

16. How many CD-ROMs were sold in 1992? 5 million

17. What's the difference between the number of CD-ROMs sold in 1993 and the number sold in 1994? 6 million

18. What year showed the biggest increase in CD-ROM sales? 1993

19. Critical Thinking How many CD-ROM sales would you expect in the year 2000?

CD-ROM Sales

Number of sales (millions): 5, 11, 17, 23
Year: 1991, 1992, 1993, 1994

Mixed Review

Write each as a number. *[Previous course]*

20. four hundred thirty-seven 437
21. five thousand one hundred six 5106
22. two thousand six hundred eleven 2611
23. eight thousand twenty-two 8022

Add. *[Previous course]*

24. 23 + 35 58 **25.** 61 + 29 90 **26.** 456 + 43 499 **27.** 712 + 94 806 **28.** 888 + 612 1500

29. 272 + 422 694 **30.** 510 + 501 **31.** 348 + 282 **32.** 638 + 804 **33.** 135 + 298 433

34. 429 + 316 745 **35.** 612 + 178 **36.** 543 + 799 **37.** 702 + 298 **38.** 941 + 62 1003

39. 667 + 919 1586 **40.** 52 + 452 504 **41.** 300 + 300 600 **42.** 185 + 468 653 **43.** 472 + 584 1056

30. 1011 31. 630 32. 1442
35. 790 36. 1342 37. 1000

PROBLEM SOLVING

Name ____________

Guided Problem Solving 1-1

GPS PROBLEM 13, STUDENT PAGE 10

Ocean sizes are often measured in square miles. Use this measurement and the graph to answer the question.

The total area of the Pacific, Atlantic, and Indian Oceans is 124,000,000 square miles. How many square miles is the Pacific Ocean?

Ocean Sizes
Atlantic
Indian
Arctic
Key = 4,000,000 sq. mi

— Understand —

1. What does the problem ask you to find? The area in square miles of the Pacific Ocean.
2. Which oceans have a combined area of 124,000,000 square miles? Pacific Ocean, Atlantic Ocean, and Indian Ocean.

— Plan —

3. Use the graph. What is the area of
   a. the Atlantic Ocean? 32,000,000 b. the Indian Ocean? 28,000,000
4. What is the combined area of the Atlantic and Indian Oceans? 60,000,000 square miles.

— Solve —

5. Write a number sentence to find the area of the Pacific Ocean. Possible answer: 124,000,000 – 60,000,000 = x
6. What is the area of the Pacific Ocean? 64,000,000 square miles.

— Look Back —

7. How can you use addition to check your answer? Add the square miles for the Pacific, Atlantic, and Indian Oceans and compare. The sum should be 124,000,000 square miles.

SOLVE ANOTHER PROBLEM

The total area of the Arctic and Indian Oceans, and the South China Sea is 35,000,000 square miles. How many square miles is the South China Sea? 1,000,000 sq. mi.

ENRICHMENT

Name ____________

Extend Your Thinking 1-1

Decision Making

You are the proprietor of a fast food restaurant. You need to make some decisions about product sales, hours of operation, and worker staffing. Use the data in these graphs to help you make these decisions.

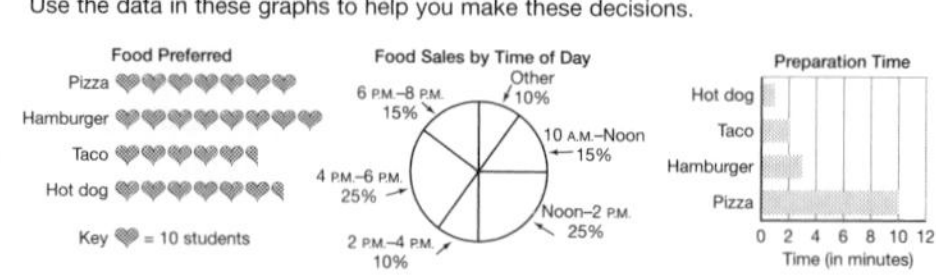

1. What will your hours of operation be? How did you decide which hours to be open? Possible answer: 10 A.M. to 8 P.M., because these are the hours when most fast foods are sold.
2. During which hours will you need the largest crew of workers? Why did you choose these times? Noon to 2 P.M. and 4 P.M. to 6 P.M., because one-half of all sales occur during these time periods.
3. If food preparation time was your only concern, which foods would you have on your menu? Explain. Hot dogs, tacos, and hamburgers because they all take 3 minutes or less to prepare.
4. If customer preference was your only concern, which foods would you have on your menu? Explain. Possible answer: Pizza, hot dogs, and hamburgers because more than half of the students surveyed prefer these foods.
5. Which food would you decide to have on your menu, taking into consideration both preparation time and customer preferences? Explain. Possible answer: Hamburgers, because they take little time to prepare and are a favorite of a large number of students.

Misleading Graphs

1-2

▶ Lesson Link In the last lesson, you learned some of the ways that a graph can give you a better understanding of data. Now you will see how a graph can *mis*lead you. ◀

You'll Learn ...

- to identify common ways that a graph can suggest misleading relationships

... How It's Used

Consumers have to check graphs to see if they could be misleading before deciding which product to buy or which service to use.

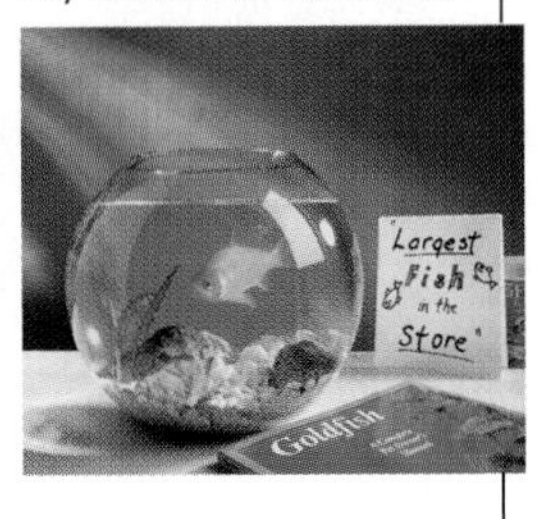

Explore Misleading Graphs

Monstro and Mighty

Monstro is a blue shark who lives at the Oceanside Aquarium. Mighty is another blue shark who lives at the Deep Sea Aquarium. Each aquarium created a graph showing the weights of the two sharks. An independent marine biologist also drew a graph. The three graphs are shown below.

Graph A: Weight (lb) axis: 0, 2000, 4000; bars: Mighty, Monstro

Graph B: Weight (lb) axis: 0, 2000, 4000; bars: Mighty, Monstro

Graph C: Weight (lb) axis: 0, 2000, 4000; bars: Mighty, Monstro

1. Which graph do you think was made by the owners of Monstro at the Oceanside Aquarium? Why?
2. Which graph do you think was made by the owners of Mighty at the Deep Sea Aquarium? Why?
3. Which graph shows that Monstro weighs 4000 pounds and Mighty weighs 2000 pounds?
4. If you were writing a newspaper article about Monstro and Mighty, which graph do you think would be the best one to use? Why?

MEETING INDIVIDUAL NEEDS

Resources
1-2 Practice
1-2 Reteaching
1-2 Problem Solving
1-2 Enrichment
1-2 Daily Transparency
Problem of the Day
Review
Quick Quiz
Lesson Enhancement Transparency 2
Technology Master 1
Chapter 1 Project Master

Learning Modalities

Verbal Encourage students to discuss the reasons people use misleading graphs.

Social Students can work in groups of four to answer the questions in **Explore.**

Challenge

The *Daily Bugle* sales of daily newspapers for the first six months of the year were as follows: Jan., 100,000; Feb., 100,100; Mar., 100,200; Apr., 100,250; May, 100,350; June, 100,500. Have students describe a graph that would convince people that *Bugle* sales are booming. Then ask students to describe a graph that a competitor might use to convince people that *Bugle* sales are not doing all that well. Possible answer: The graph showing booming sales could be labeled starting at a number other than zero, but not indicate any skipped numbers. The graph showing poor sales could be labeled using unequal number intervals.

1-2 Lesson Organizer

Objective

- Identify common ways that a graph can suggest misleading relationships.

NCTM Standards

- 1–4, 10

▶ Review

Find each quotient.

1. 56 ÷ 14 4
2. 84 ÷ 6 14
3. 72 ÷ 4 18
4. 96 ÷ 16 6
5. 85 ÷ 5 17

Available on Daily Transparency 1-2

1 Introduce

Explore

The Point

Students investigate how graphs can show the same numerical information but suggest different relationships.

Ongoing Assessment

Check that students are not basing their judgments on the widths of the bars in the misleading graphs. Also be sure that students perceive the errors in the vertical scales of the misleading graphs.

For Groups That Finish Early

Which other type of graph(s) could be used to correctly compare the weights of Monstro and Mighty? Possible answer: Pictographs.

Answers for Explore

1. Graph C; Because it shows the Monstro bar to be bigger.
2. Graph A; Because it shows the Mighty bar to be close to the Monstro bar.
3. A, B, and C.
4. Graph B; Because it gives an accurate picture of the data.

2 Teach

Learn

You may wish to use Lesson Enhancement Transparency 2 with **Try It**.

Students should become accustomed to seeing both horizontal and vertical bar graphs.

Alternate Examples

1. The great white shark is about how many times as long as the mako shark?

   Divide the length of the great white shark by the length of the mako shark: $16 \div 13 \approx 1.2$. The great white shark is about 1.2 times as long as the mako shark.

2. How could you correct the Breath-Holding Ability graph?

   Make all the time intervals equal. Change 15 to 10, and 25 to 15. Extend bar for Hippo accordingly.

Learn Misleading Graphs

There are many ways to make a graph that can mislead a careless reader. One way is to start labeling the graph at a number other than zero without indicating that some numbers have been skipped.

▶ Science Link

Great white sharks are known to attack humans, but they usually don't eat them. Great white sharks usually prey on seals, sea lions, whales, and other sharks.

Example 1

Is the great white shark twice as long as the mako shark?

In graph Ⓐ, the top bar is twice as long as the bottom bar. But the value for the great white shark, 16, is not twice the value for the mako shark, 13.

In graph Ⓑ, the great white shark is clearly not twice as long. When the bar graph starts at 0, the graph is not as misleading.

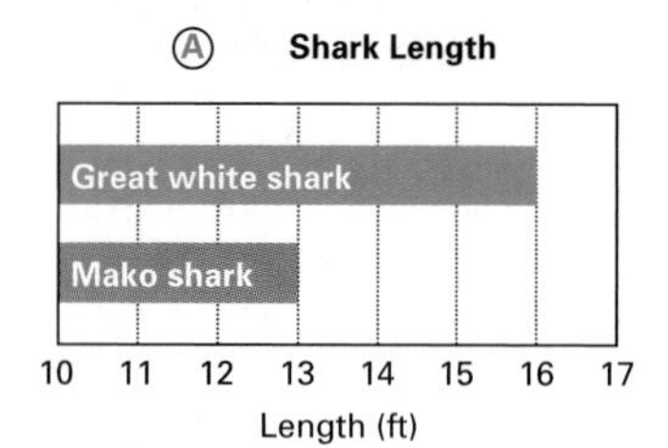

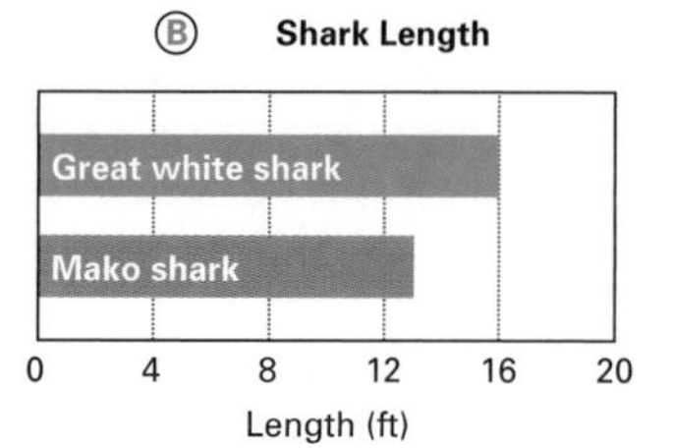

Example 2

▶ Language Link

Ichthyology (ik-thee-AHL-uh-gee) is the study of the structure and classification of fish.

Is the hippo able to hold its breath for twice as long as the sea otter?

Both bars start at zero, and the hippo bar is twice as tall as the sea otter bar. But the data values show that a sea otter can hold its breath for 5 minutes and the hippo for 15 minutes—three times as long as a sea otter.

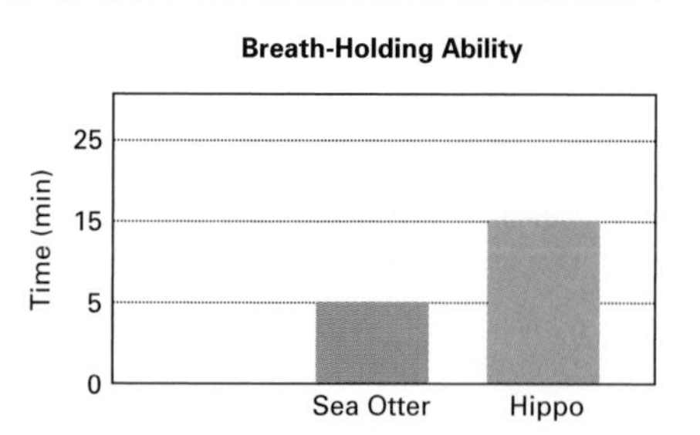

A misleading impression is created because the 5–15 space covers more values than the 0–5 space, but both spaces have equal heights.

MATH EVERY DAY

▶ Problem of the Day

Draw the figures without taking your pencil off the paper or retracing.

Possible answer:

Start

Start

Available on Daily Transparency 1-2

An Extension is provided in the transparency package.

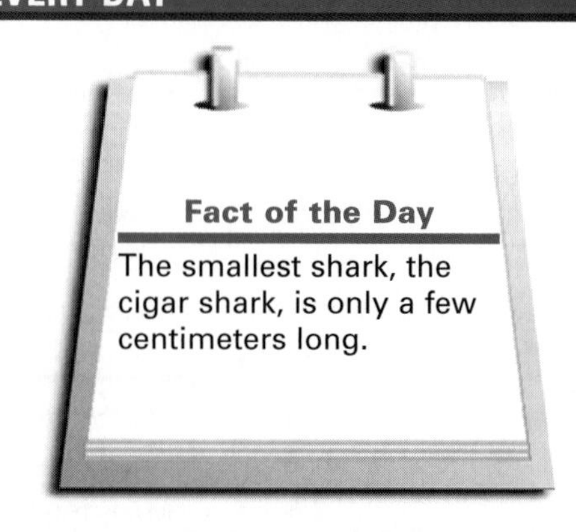

Fact of the Day

The smallest shark, the cigar shark, is only a few centimeters long.

Mental Math

Find each quotient mentally.

1. $180 \div 9$ 20
2. $120 \div 12$ 10
3. $360 \div 3$ 120
4. $600 \div 5$ 120

A graph can mislead by lengthening or shortening the spaces between data values in order to give a certain impression.

Example 3

Which admission price went up more quickly?

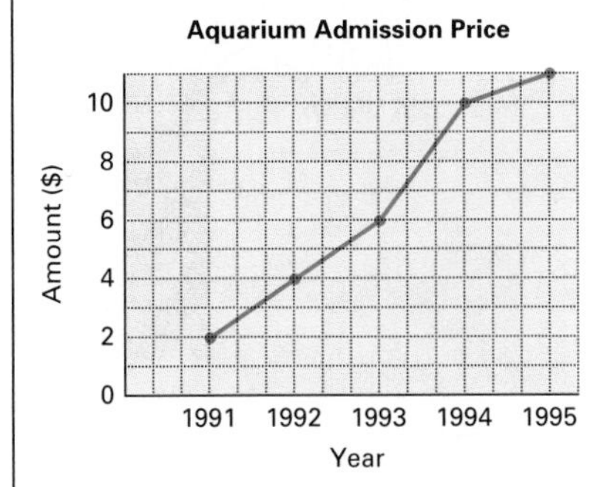

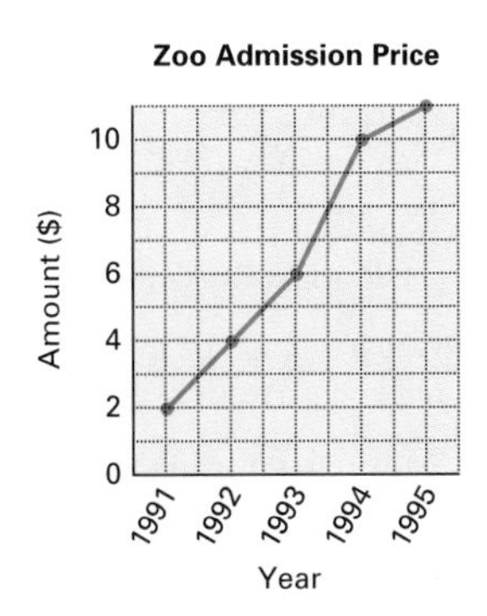

In the right graph, the years are much closer together, so the line appears to climb more rapidly. But both graphs show exactly the same data. Neither admission price went up more quickly.

Try It

Explain how each graph could create a misleading impression.

a.

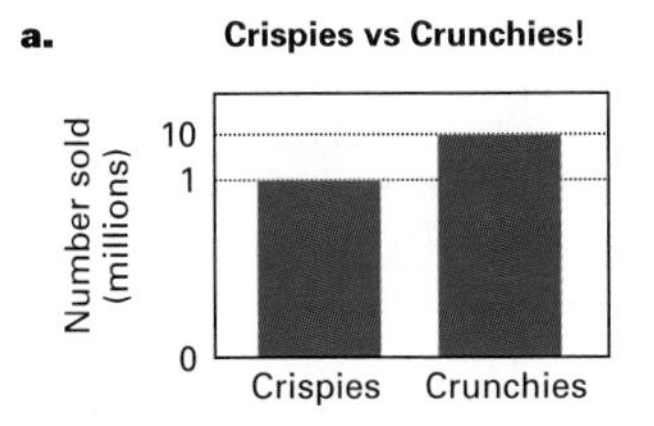

b.

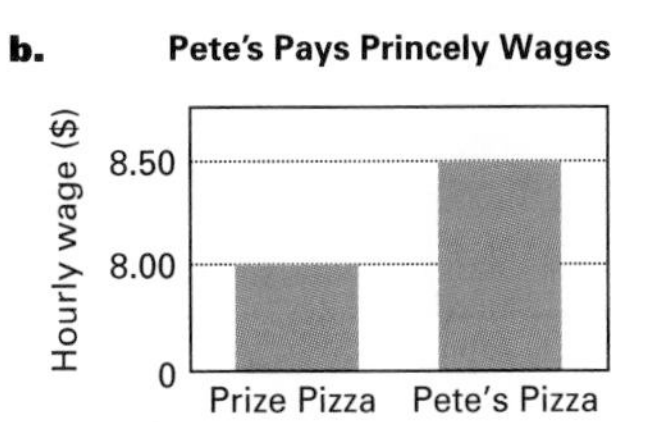

Test Prep

Many graphs can be misleading because the vertical scale has been drawn incorrectly. When evaluating a graph for misleading impressions, check the vertical scale first.

Check Your Understanding

1. What should you look at to determine if a graph is misleading?
2. Why might someone want to create a misleading graph? Give examples from everyday life.

Alternate Examples

3. Find the total increase in the admission price to the aquarium and the zoo between the years 1991 and 1994.

   The admission price for the aquarium and the zoo in 1991 was $2 and in 1994 each was $10. So, the increase was $8, even though it appears that the aquarium admission price had a greater increase.

Answers for Try It

a. Possible answer: The graph minimizes the apparent difference in sales by making the 0–1 space taller than the 1–10 space.

b. Possible answer: The graph exaggerates the wage difference by giving the 0–8.00 and 8.00–8.50 spaces equal heights.

3 Practice and Assess

Check

Be sure that students check that the scales for the graphs begin at zero and that the numbers along the axes are spaced to give the correct intervals.

Answers for Check Your Understanding

1. Possible answers: The height of the bars and the corresponding numbers; The space between data values on the graph.
2. Possible answer: To lead you toward a certain conclusion that the pure data doesn't suggest. For example, a cereal advertiser might want to suggest that people prefer the cereal, even when they don't. A misleading graph could be used to give this impression.

MEETING MIDDLE SCHOOL CLASSROOM NEEDS

Tips from Middle School Teachers

I have students find examples of misleading graphs and display them on the classroom bulletin board. Students should include short descriptions of the graphs and explain what is misleading.

Cooperative Learning

Each student should locate a misleading graph in a newspaper or magazine. Then have the students work in groups of three or four and analyze the graphs. Their discussion should include identifying the audience to whom the graph is directed, as well as how the graph is misleading.

Science Connection

The largest shark, the whale shark, can grow to more than 45 feet long. Its kite-shaped relative, the manta ray, can measure nearly 20 feet across. Neither of these fishes has teeth. The organisms they eat are so small you can hardly see them. A bony mesh inside the mouth filters the organisms out of the water.

1-2 Exercises and Applications

Assignment Guide

- **Basic**
  1–9, 11, 16–19, 22–25
- **Average**
  1–13, 18–29
- **Enriched**
  1–13, 20–25

Exercise Notes

Exercise 2

Science Manatees are large water mammals that can eat as much as 100 pounds of water plants a day. Ask students to estimate how many tons of water plants a manatee can eat in one year. About 18 tons.

Exercise Answers

1. Maximum life span of whale sharks and American manatees.
4. Yes; The vertical scale should start at zero.
6. 10; 20
7. 2 for the left graph, $1\frac{1}{2}$ for the right graph.
8. Yes; The right graph minimizes the difference in calorie needs by making the 0–10 space taller than the 10–20 space.
9. Mouse: 300; Robin: 600.
10. 37

Reteaching

Activity

Materials: Pennies, centimeter cubes

- Suppose a tuna is 8 feet long and a shark is 16 feet long. Use pennies and centimeter cubes to create a misleading "graph" for these data.
- Stack 8 pennies to represent the tuna's length and 16 cubes to represent the shark's length. From your graph, how many times as long as the tuna does the shark appear to be? About 12 times as long.
- Actually how many times as long as the tuna is the shark? 2 times as long

PRACTICE 1-2

1-2 Exercises and Applications

Practice and Apply

Getting Started Use the Life Span graph for Exercises 1–5.

1. What is the information in the graph about?
2. How many times taller does the shark's life span bar appear to be than the manatee's? 5
3. Read the graph. What is the approximate life span of the manatee? The shark? 30 yr; 70 yr
4. **Communicate** Could the bar graph be misleading? If so, how would you correct the graph?
5. **Test Prep** What is the difference in the life spans of the shark and the manatee? B

   Ⓐ about 4 yr Ⓑ about 40 yr
   Ⓒ about 50 yr Ⓓ about 100 yr

Maximum Life Span

Years: 20, 40, 60, 80

Whale shark; American manatee

Use the Calories Needed graphs for Exercises 6–10.

Daily Calories Needed

Number of calories: 0, 5, 10, 15, 20

mouse; robin

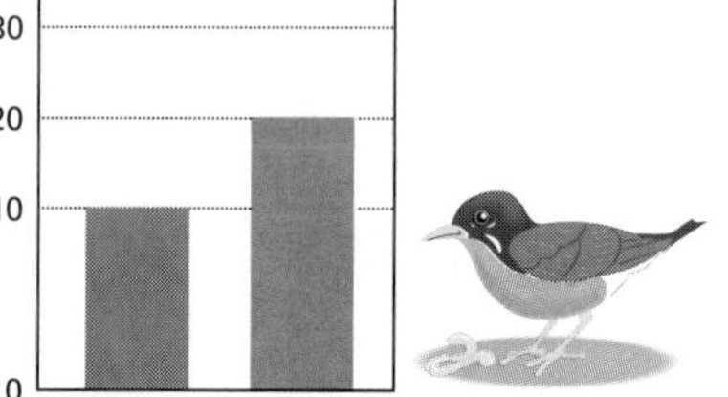

6. **Science** How many calories a day does a mouse need? A robin?
7. For each graph, the robin's calorie bar appears to be how many times greater than the mouse's calorie bar?
8. **Communicate** Do you think either graph is misleading? Explain.
9. How many calories does each animal need in a month that has 30 days?
10. **Science** If a cat needs 370 calories a day, how many days would it take for a mouse to eat the number of calories a cat needs each day?

PRACTICE

Name ______________

Practice 1-2

Misleading Graphs

Use the Number of Jobs in the U.S. graph for Exercises 1–4.

Number of Jobs in the U.S., 1990-1992

Number of jobs (millions): 106, 107, 108, 109, 110, 111

July 1990; July 1991; July 1992

1. About how many times taller does the July 1990 bar appear to be than the July 1991 bar?
   About twice as tall
2. Read the graph. How many jobs were there
   in July 1990? About 110.3 million
   in July 1991? About 108.2 million
3. Compare your answers to Exercises 1 and 2. Could the bar graph be misleading? If so, how would you correct the graph?
   Yes. Use a scale that starts at 0, or show a break to indicate missing numbers.
4. How many more jobs were there in July 1990 than in July 1992?
   About 1.7 million

Use the Endangered Birds graph for Exercises 5–8.

Endangered Birds

Number of species: 0, 10, 20, 30

State: Texas; Hawaii

5. The number of endangered bird species in Hawaii appears to be how many times greater than the number of endangered bird species in Texas?
   About 2
6. Texas has how many endangered bird species?
   10
7. Hawaii has how many endangered bird species?
   About 29
8. Could the bar graph be misleading? If so, how would you correct the graph?
   Yes. The numbers on the vertical axis should be evenly spaced, and start at zero.

RETEACHING

Name ______________

Alternative Lesson 1-2

Misleading Graphs

There are many ways to make a graph that can mislead a careless reader. One way is to start labeling the graph at a number other than zero without indicating that some numbers have been skipped. A graph can mislead by lengthening or shortening the space between data values in order to give a certain impression.

Example

Does *Sports Action* cost 4 times as much as *In Fashion?* Explain.

The bar showing the cost of *Sports Action* is about 4 times the length of the bar showing the cost of *In Fashion.* Look carefully at the scale along the left axis of the graph. Notice that the scale starts at $50 so the first $50 of each magazine subscription has been skipped. The graph is misleading.

The *Sports Action* subscription is $90 per year. *In Fashion* costs $60 per year. Since 90 is not 4 times as much as 60, *Sports Action* does not cost 4 times as much as *In Fashion.*

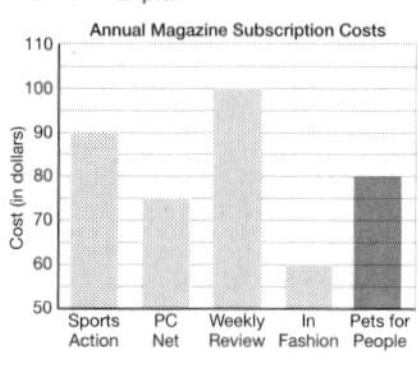

Try It

a. *Weekly Review* looks like it costs 5 times as much as *In Fashion.*
   What is the yearly cost for *Weekly Review?* $100 For *In Fashion?* $60
   Does *Weekly Review* cost 5 times as much as *In Fashion?* Explain.
   No, because $100 is not 5 times as much as $60.
b. *Weekly Review* looks like it costs 2 times as much as *PC Net.*
   What is the yearly cost for *Weekly Review?* $100 For *PC Net?* $75
   Is this a true or false impression? False
c. Add a bar to the graph to show that a new magazine, *Pets for People,* costs $80 for a year's subscription.
d. *Pets for People* looks like it costs 3 times as much as *In Fashion.*
   Is this a true or false impression? False
e. What can you do to the graph so that it is not misleading?
   Use a vertical scale that starts at 0.

Problem Solving and Reasoning

Use the Population graphs to answer Exercises 11–13.

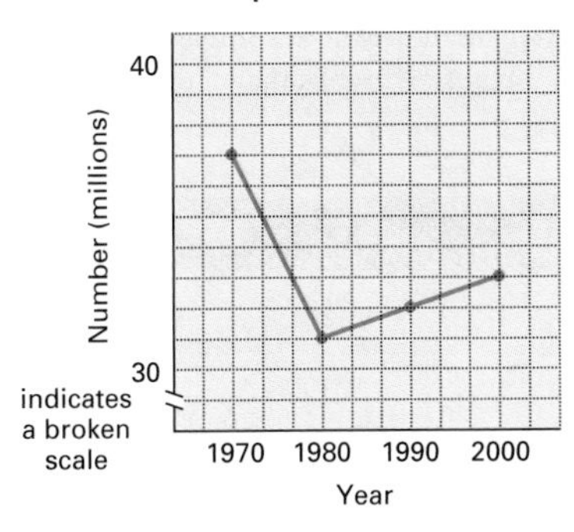

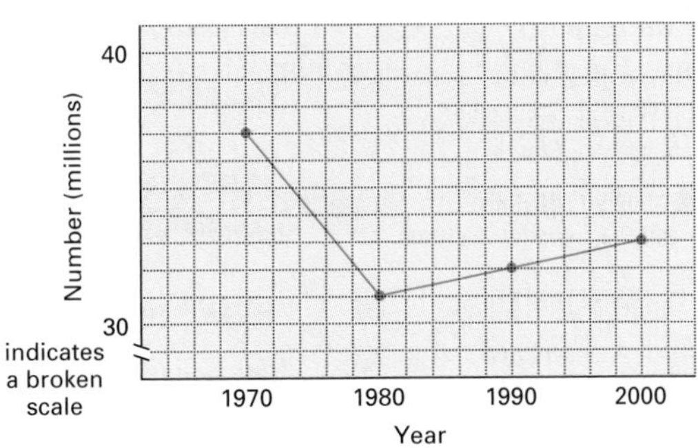

11. Critical Thinking How many more 5–13 year-olds will there be in the year 2000 than there were in the year when their population was the smallest?

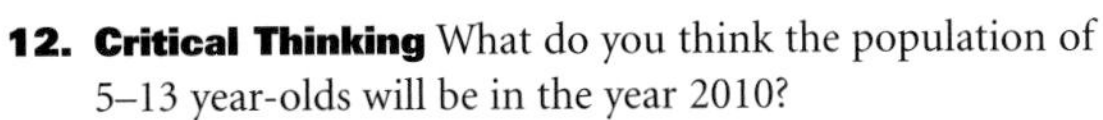

12. Critical Thinking What do you think the population of 5–13 year-olds will be in the year 2010?

13. Communicate Why might someone want to represent the information with the second graph?

Mixed Review

Write each number in words. *[Previous course]*

14. 639 **15.** 204 **16.** 883 **17.** 913

18. 6728 **19.** 8912 **20.** 2856 **21.** 1045

Subtract. *[Previous course]*

22. 239 − 51 188 **23.** 681 − 67 614 **24.** 714 − 80 634 **25.** 809 − 37 772

26. 489 − 211 278 **27.** 503 − 432 71 **28.** 932 − 601 331 **29.** 883 − 577 306

Project Progress

Start to collect data about the location you have chosen. Try to find data that has lots of numbers in it. You may want to look for data in your school library, your local public library, a travel agency, and the newspaper.

Problem Solving
Understand
Plan
Solve
Look Back

PROBLEM SOLVING

Name ____________ **Guided Problem Solving 1-2**

GPS PROBLEM 11, STUDENT PAGE 15

Use the population graph.
How many more 5–13 year-olds will there be in the year 2000 than there were in the year when their population was the smallest?

U.S. Population of 5–13 Year-Olds

— Understand —

1. Circle the question.
2. How do you find the number of 5–13 year-olds for 1970? Locate the point above 1970. Then find the number on the vertical scale directly to the left of the point.
3. What does the jagged line represent on the vertical scale? The jagged line represents a break in the vertical scale.

— Plan —

4. What year was the population of 5-13 year-olds the smallest? 1980
5. How many 5-13 year-olds were there in the year the population was the smallest? 31 million
6. How many 5-13 year-olds will there be in the year 2000? 33 million

— Solve —

7. Choose the number sentence you will use to solve the problem. b
   a. 33 + 31 = 64 b. 33 − 31 = 2 c. 37 − 31 = 6
8. Write your answer in a complete sentence. There will be 2 million more 5–13 year-olds in the year 2000.

— Look Back —

9. How could you have solved the problem in another way? Possible answer: Find the number in millions for both points and count how many spaces between the numbers.

SOLVE ANOTHER PROBLEM

How many more 5–13 year-olds were there in the year 1990 than in the year 1980? 1 million

ENRICHMENT

Name ____________ **Extend Your Thinking 1-2**

Visual Thinking

Without drawing a path through the maze, write the letter of the exit. Then draw the path.

1. A

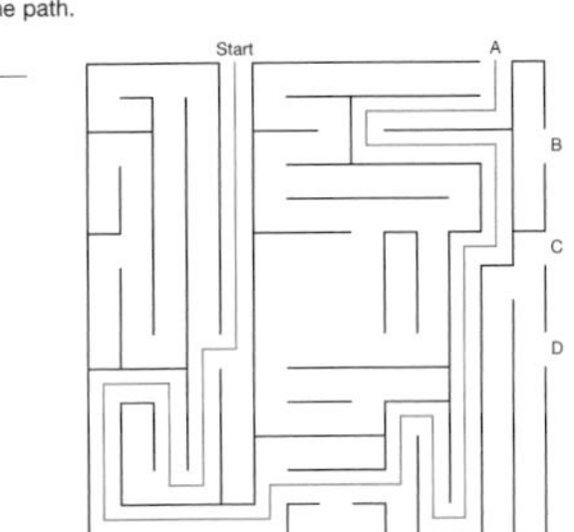

2. C

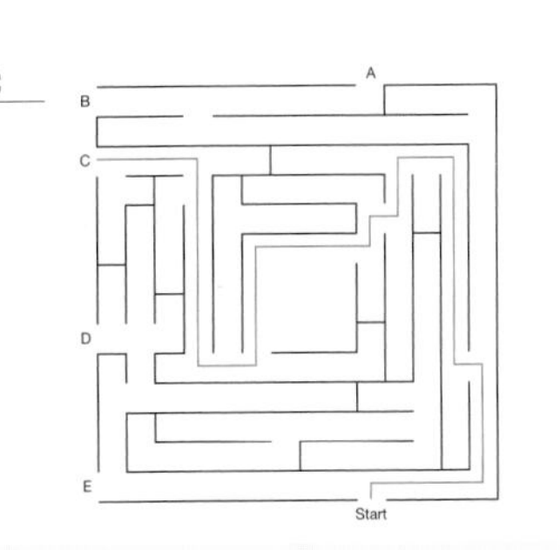

Exercise Notes

Exercises 11–13

Error Prevention Watch for students who do not notice that the vertical scale represents *millions* of children. Also, make students aware that the tick marks on the vertical axis indicate that not all the numbers from 0–30 are included on the scale.

Project Progress

You may want to have students use Chapter 1 Project Master.

Exercise Answers

11. 2 million
12. 34 million
13. To minimize the apparent changes in population size.
14. Six hundred thirty-nine
15. Two hundred four
16. Eight hundred eighty-three
17. Nine hundred thirteen
18. Six thousand seven hundred twenty-eight
19. Eight thousand nine hundred twelve
20. Two thousand eight hundred fifty-six
21. One thousand forty-five

Alternate Assessment

You may want to use the *Interactive CD-ROM Journal* with this assessment.

Journal Have students write a list of the ways that they can tell if a graph is misleading.

Quick Quiz

Refer to the graphs on pages 11 and 13.

1. Monstro is how many times as heavy as Mighty? 2 times
2. Sales of Crunchies are how many times greater than the sales of Crispies? 10 times
3. How much more per hour does Pete's Pizza pay than Prize Pizza? $0.50

Available on Daily Transparency 1-2

1-3 Lesson Organizer

Objectives

- Identify the two pieces of data represented by points in a scatterplot.
- Determine if a scatterplot suggests a trend.

Vocabulary

- Scatterplot, trend

NCTM Standards

- 1–4, 7, 8, 10

Review

For each point in the graph, tell how many units it is to the right of the left edge and up from the bottom edge.

1. *A* 4 to the right, 5 up.
2. *B* 2 to the right, 3 up.
3. *C* 0 to the right, 4 up.
4. *D* 5 to the right, 0 up.
5. *E* 2 to the right, 6 up.

Available on Daily Transparency 1-3

1 Introduce

Explore

The Point
Students develop an intuitive understanding of how to describe locations of scatterplot points.

Ongoing Assessment
Check that all students are able to read the positions of the points in relation to the scales on the axes.

1-3 Scatterplots and Trends

You'll Learn ...

- to identify the two pieces of data represented by points in a scatterplot
- to determine if a scatterplot suggests a trend

... How It's Used

Medical researchers use scatterplots to find relationships between data from medical tests and the health of patients.

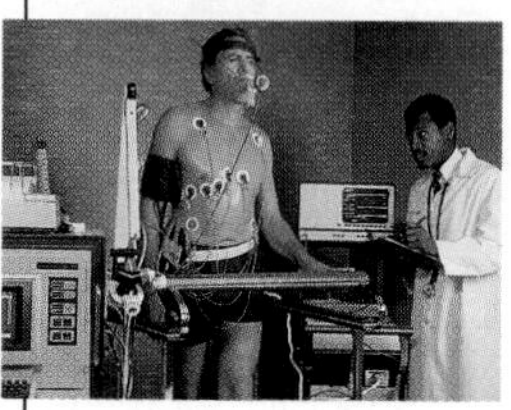

Vocabulary

scatterplot

trend

▶ Lesson Link The graphs you have seen so far allow you to compare values in a single set of numerical data. This lesson focuses on graphs that allow you to compare two sets of data. ◀

Explore Graphing Points

I've Been Framed!

1. Nine points labeled *A* through *I* are plotted on the graph. Each of the frames shows one of the nine points plotted by itself. For each frame, determine which of the nine points is shown.

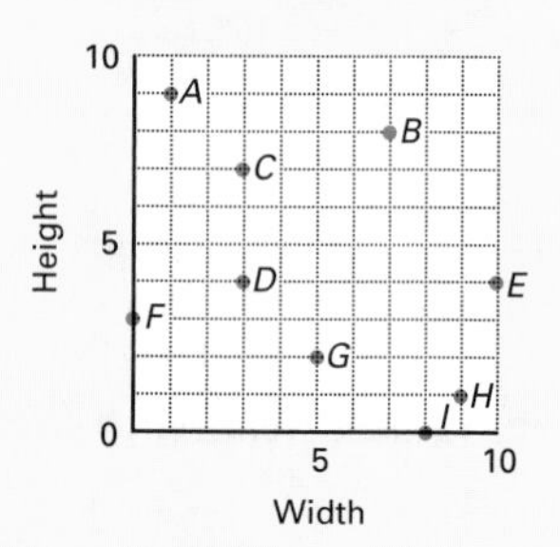

Frame 1 Frame 2 Frame 3

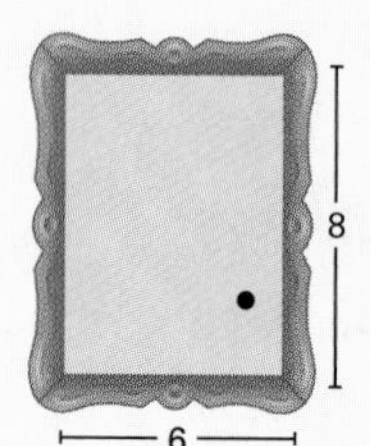

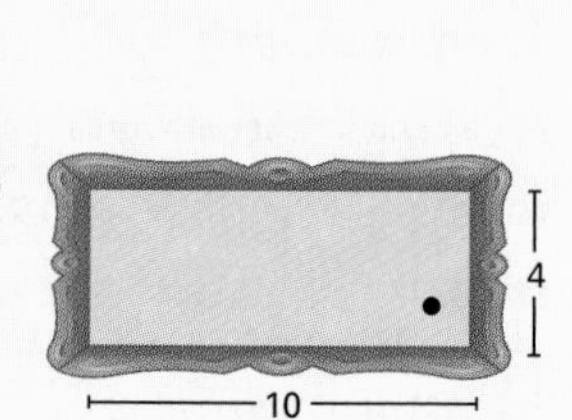

2. How did you decide which point appeared in each frame?
3. Choose a point that didn't appear in one of the three frames and draw a frame for it. Have another student decide which point you framed.
4. Give directions for how to get from the lower left corner of the graph to one of the points on the graph. Use words like "Go to the right so many squares" and "Go up so many squares."

MEETING INDIVIDUAL NEEDS

Resources

- **1-3** Practice
- **1-3** Reteaching
- **1-3** Problem Solving
- **1-3** Enrichment
- **1-3** Daily Transparency
  - Problem of the Day
  - Review
  - Quick Quiz
- Technology Master 2

Learning Modalities

Kinesthetic If your classroom desks are arranged in rows and columns, position yourself at the left corner of the last row of students. Give positions relative to yours, such as "4 right, 5 up," and have the student in that position stand up.

Social Students should work with a partner and exchange points and frames in Step 3 of **Explore**.

English Language Development

To help students understand the term "scatterplot," use a grid labeled like the one on this page and "scatter" a dozen or so grains of rice, dried peas, or beans over it. This scatterplot can be likened to that in the text, and students can identify positions of individual grains of rice, peas, or beans.

The *Multilingual Handbook* with its glossary of math terms, illustrations, and worked-out examples, can help you with students who have limited English language skill. The glossary is provided in multiple languages.

Learn Scatterplots and Trends

The graphs you have studied so far display individual items of data. For example, each bar in a bar graph represents one number. Sometimes data occurs in pairs. A graph that shows paired data is called a **scatterplot**.

Each point on a scatterplot represents *two* data values. To find the two values, start in the lower left corner. Find one value by counting how far *right* you must go until you are under the point. Find the second value by counting how far *up* you must go to reach the point.

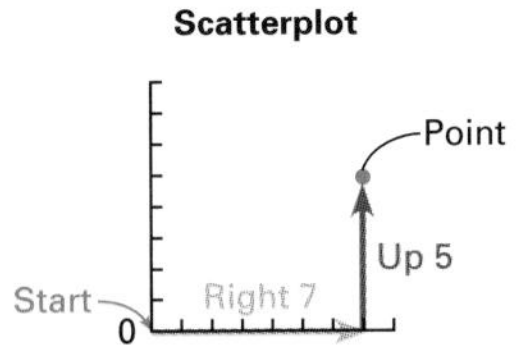

Example 1

The scatterplot compares the speeds of a mako shark (M) and two great blue sharks (GBS 1 and GBS 2) to their lengths. Give the length and speed of each shark.

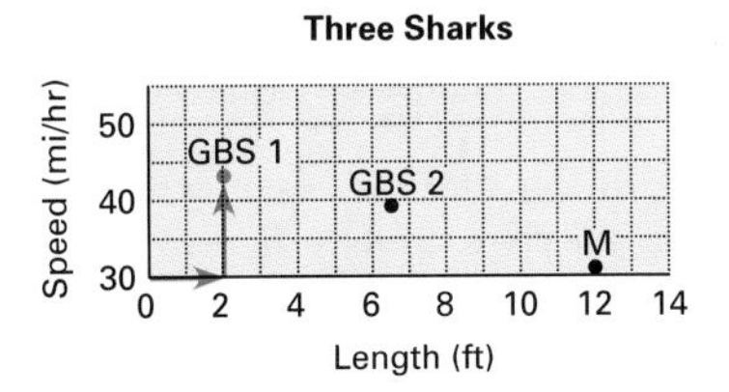

To reach data point GBS 1, go right to 2 feet and up to about 43 mi/hr. This means that the first great blue shark was 2 feet long and traveled 43 mi/hr.

Second great blue shark:	Length: $6\frac{1}{2}$ feet	Speed: 39 mi/hr
Mako shark:	Length: 12 feet	Speed: 31 mi/hr

Try It

For each point in the graph, estimate the data represented by the point.

a. *A* (80, 40)
b. *B* (100, 45)
c. *C* (125, 32)
d. *D* (160, 22)
e. *E* (200, 20)

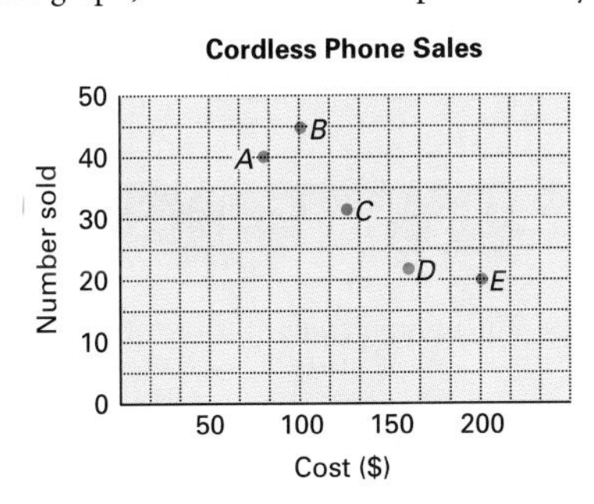

Science Link

The male mako shark usually grows to $6\frac{1}{2}$ feet long. The female shark grows to $8\frac{1}{2}$ feet long. Mako sharks have been known to grow up to 12 feet long.

MATH EVERY DAY

Problem of the Day

Shania has 4 more CDs than Carlos has. Neka has two more CDs than Shania has. They have 100 CDs in all. How many CDs does each person have? Shania, 34 CDs; Carlos, 30 CDs; Neka, 36 CDs

Available on Daily Transparency 1-3

An Extension is provided in the transparency package.

Fact of the Day

A shark's skin is like sandpaper. Small, tooth-like scales in the skin form a tough protective covering.

Mental Math

1. Multiply 12 by 1, 2, 3, 4, 6, and 12. What happens to the product? 12, 24, 36, 48, 72, 144; It increases.
2. Divide 12 by 1, 2, 3, 4, 6, and 12. What happens to the quotient? 12, 6, 4, 3, 2, and 1; It decreases.

For Groups That Finish Early

Is the point 5 squares to the right and 4 squares up the same as the point 5 squares up and 4 squares to the right? Why or why not? Students should be able to locate both points to verify that they are not the same.

Follow Up

Before continuing, be sure that all students are able to give directions for locating points.

Answers for Explore

1. 1 is point *G;* 2 is point *C;* 3 is point *H.*
2. By comparing about how far over and how far up you need to go from the lower left corner of the graph to get to the point in question.
3. Answers may vary.
4. Possible answer: For Point *A,* "Go to the right 1 square and then go up 9 squares."

2 Teach

Learn

Relate the points in a scatterplot to the points in a line graph. In each type of graph, positions along both the vertical and horizontal scales must be considered.

Alternate Examples

1. The scatterplot compares the length at birth to the maximum length of the nurse shark *N*, the whale shark *W*, and the sand tiger shark *S*. Give the length at birth and the maximum length of each shark.

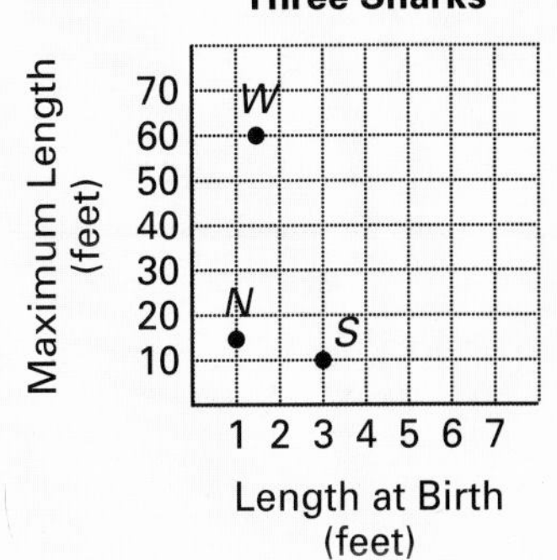

Nurse shark: length at birth, 1 ft; maximum length, 15 ft; Whale shark: length at birth, 1.5 ft; maximum length: 60 ft; Sand tiger shark: length at birth, 3 ft; maximum length: 10 ft.

Alternate Examples

2. Does the Cordless Phone Sales scatterplot on page 17 show a trend between the cost of the phones and the number sold?

   Yes, the farther to the right a point is, the lower it is. This suggests that as the price of the phones increases, there are fewer sales.

3. Refer to the scatterplot on page 16. Do the nine data points show a trend?

   No, the points are scattered at random over the graph.

3 Practice and Assess

Check

Students should recognize that bar graphs, pictographs, and line graphs relate two items, while circle graphs relate parts of something to the whole.

Answers for Check Your Understanding

1. Possible answers: Similarities: Both are graphs of numerical data, both use points, points in both signify two numbers; Differences: A line graph shows points connected, but a scatterplot does not.
2. Possible answers: Height and shoe size; Number of hours you're awake and number of hours you're asleep in a 24-hour period.

Sometimes the points in a scatterplot suggest a relationship between the two measured quantities. Look again at the scatterplot in Example 1. Notice that the farther to the right a point is, the farther down it is. This suggests that for the sharks in the experiment, the longer a shark was, the slower it swam. A relationship between two sets of data that shows a pattern like this is called a **trend**.

Study TIP

When you have a hard time with homework, check the Examples. They often show step-by-step how to do the homework problems.

Examples

For each graph, determine if there is a trend.

2

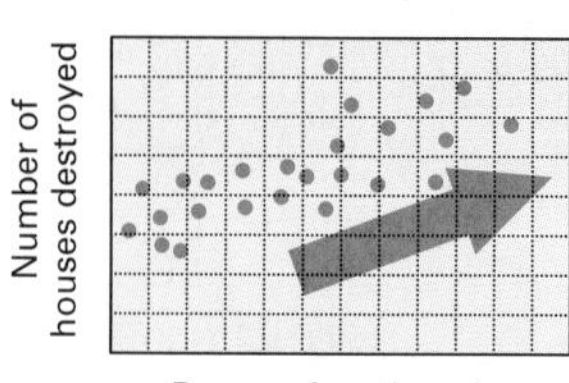

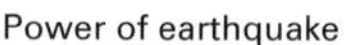

The farther to the right a point is, the farther up it is. This suggests that the greater the power of an earthquake, the greater the number of houses that are destroyed.

3

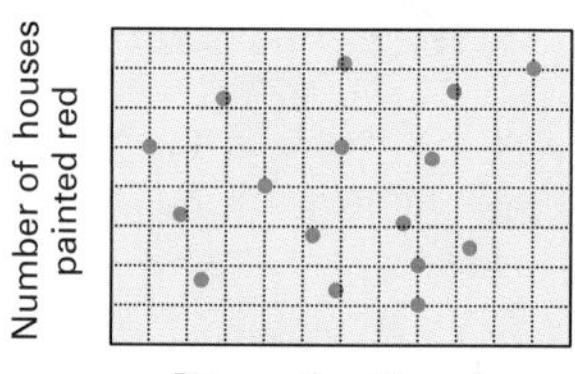

The points don't fall into any particular pattern. This suggests that there is no trend between the power of an earthquake and the number of red houses.

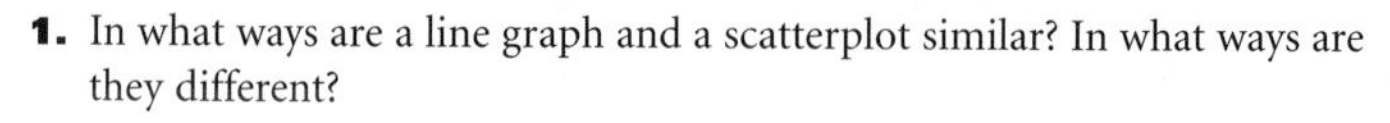

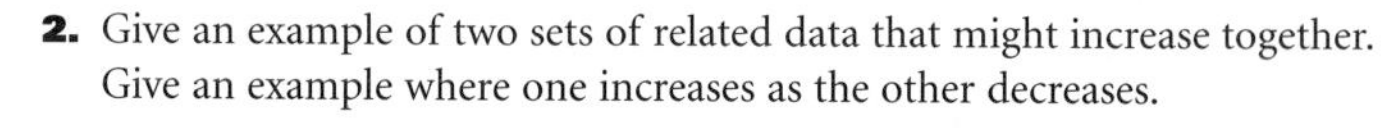

1. In what ways are a line graph and a scatterplot similar? In what ways are they different?
2. Give an example of two sets of related data that might increase together. Give an example where one increases as the other decreases.

MEETING MIDDLE SCHOOL CLASSROOM NEEDS

Tips from Middle School Teachers

Have students try to find examples of scatterplots and display them on your classroom bulletin board. Have them write brief descriptions of the graphs, including whether or not the graphs display trends.

Cultural Connection

Shark meat is used for food in many countries throughout the world. Shark-fin soup, which is considered a delicacy, is made in China. Fish 'n' chips served in England is often made with shark meat.

Science Connection

The power of an earthquake is usually measured on the Richter scale. An earthquake of 6 is ten times as strong as an earthquake of 5. The Mercalli scale classifies earthquakes by the damage they do at particular places. A quake may have an intensity of IX in one place and only II in another.

1-3 Exercises and Applications

Practice and Apply

Getting Started For each point on the graph, describe:

a. How far to the right and how far up on the graph it is.

b. The weight and the length the point represents.

1. *A* **2.** *B* **3.** *C*

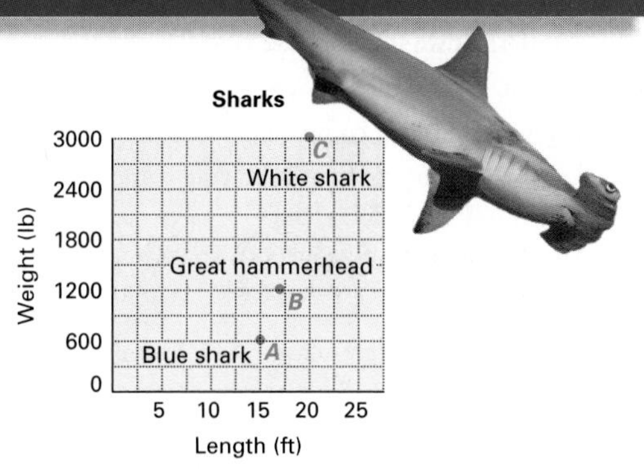

For each scatterplot, determine if there is a trend. If there is, describe the pattern of the data.

4. Age and Height

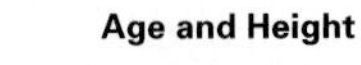

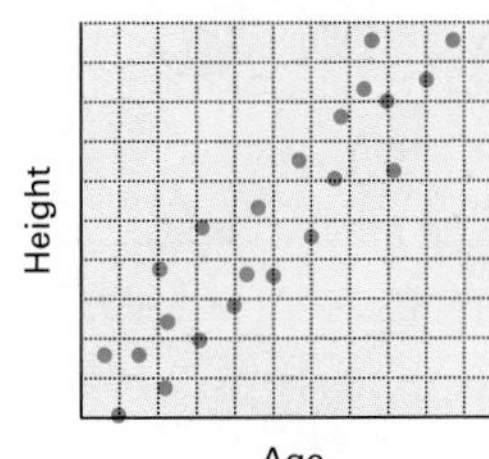

5. Exercise and Height

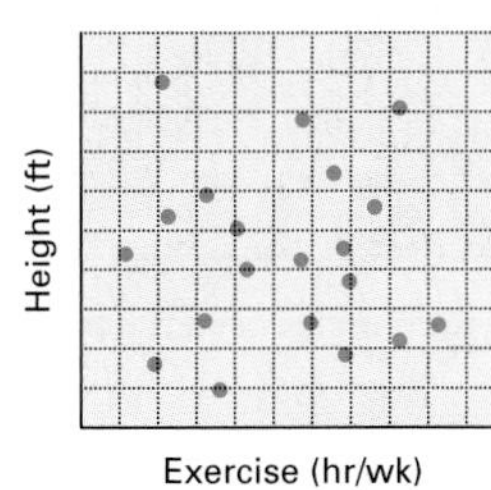

6. Sleep and Scores

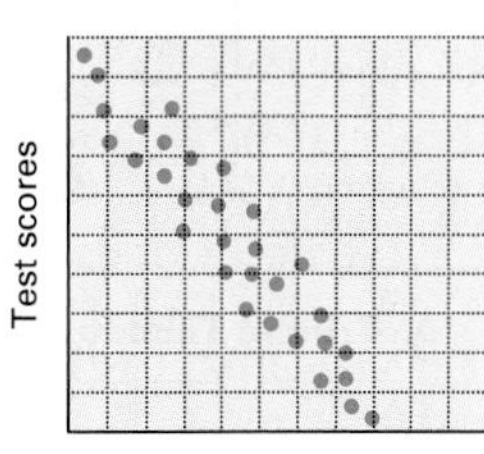

Use the Olympics graph to answer Exercises 7 and 8.

7. **Test Prep** Which two points represent the same values for number of postal stamps? A

Ⓐ *A* and *C* Ⓑ *C* and *E*

Ⓒ *B* and *D* Ⓓ *A* and *D*

8. Estimation Which point represents a number of events that is about four times greater than the number of stamps? About how many events and how many stamps does this point represent?

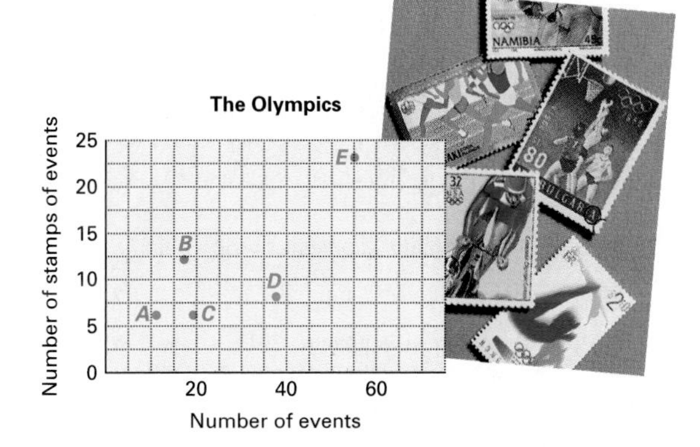

PRACTICE

Name ______________________

Practice 1-3

Scatterplots and Trends

For each scatterplot, determine if there is a trend. If there is, describe the pattern of the data.

1. Yes. As the price increases, there tend to be fewer sold.

2. No

Number sold / Price ($)

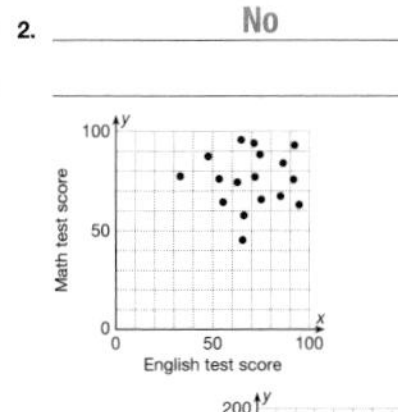

Use the scatterplot for Exercises 3–8.

Height (cm) / Age

3. Is there a trend? If so, describe the pattern of the data. Yes. As age increases, height tends to increase.

4. Name two points that represent people who are the same age. A and G How old are they? 10 yr

5. Which point represents the youngest person? D the oldest person? C

6. Which point represents the shortest person? D the tallest person? H

7. a. Name two points that represent people who are the same height. B and G

b. How tall are they? About 130 cm

8. Give the approximate age and height represented by each point.

a. *A*	b. *B*	c. *C*	d. *D*
age 10 yr	age 12 yr	age 16 yr	age 5 yr
height 110 cm	height 130 cm	height 160 cm	height 80 cm

RETEACHING

Name ______________________

Alternative Lesson 1-3

Scatterplots and Trends

A **scatterplot** shows paired data. Each point on a scatterplot represents *two* data values. Sometimes the points in a scatterplot suggest a relationship between two sets of data that shows a pattern. This relationship is called a **trend**.

Example

How long does it take Product *A* to cook in the microwave? How long does it take to cook in the oven?

Step 1: Find *A*. Go right to 3 minutes. This is the point on the horizontal axis that is below Point *A*.

Step 2: Find *A*. Go up to 25 minutes. This is the point on the vertical axis that is to the left of Point *A*.

Product *A* cooks for 3 minutes in the microwave and 25 minutes in the oven.

Cooking Times — Oven (in minutes) / Microwave (in minutes)

Try It

Using the scatterplot, find the following information.

a. The time it takes Product *B* to cook in a microwave 3 minutes.

b. The time it takes Product *B* to cook in an oven 30 minutes.

c. The product that cooks for 15 minutes in the oven Product *D*.

d. The time it takes Product *C* to cook in a microwave 4 minutes.

e. The time it takes Product *E* to cook in an oven 35 minutes.

f. The product that cooks for 45 minutes in the oven Product *C*.

g. How much longer it takes Product *G* than Product *D* to cook in an oven 15 minutes.

h. A product takes 40 minutes to cook in an oven. Do you think it would take more or less time to cook in the microwave? Explain. Possible answer: Less, because all products on the graph take less time to cook in a microwave than in an oven.

1-3 Exercises and Applications

Assignment Guide

- **Basic** 1–5, 7, 9–11, 13–15, 18–19
- **Average** 1, 4–9, 11–13, 16–19
- **Enriched** 1, 5–13, 16–17, 20–21

Exercise Notes

Exercise 4

Extension Ask students whether the trend in the data will continue indefinitely. Students should realize that most people reach maximum height in their late teens and that the data points will be positioned in a horizontal pattern after those years.

Exercise Answers

1. a. 15 right, 600 up; b. 15 ft, 600 lb.
2. a. 17 right, 1200 up; b. 17 ft, 1200 lb.
3. a. 20 right, 3000 up; b. 20 ft, 3000 lb.
4. Yes; The greater the age, the greater the height.
5. No trend.
6. Yes; The greater the hours without sleep, the lower the test score.
8. D; 37 events and 8 stamps.

Reteaching

Activity

- If the desks in your classroom are arranged in rows and columns, think of this arrangement as a grid.
- Use the desk in the last row farthest to your left as you face the front of the room as the starting point. Tell how many places right and up from the back your desk is located in relation to this point.
- Choose several students and tell where their desks are located in relation to this point. Students should be able to identify the positions.

Exercise Notes

■ Exercise 9a

Extension If students have indicated that there is a trend that the more hours worked, the greater the salary, discuss persons receiving monthly or annual salaries.

■ Exercises 18–21

Estimation Have students estimate the products to check if their answers are reasonable.

Exercise Answers

9. Possible answers are given:
   a. Points forming an upward trend; As hours worked per week increases, so does salary.
   b. Points forming a downward trend; The younger the person, the more sleep needed.
   c. Answers may vary. d. Points forming an upward trend. As the number of people in a family increases, so does amount spent on groceries.
10. 25–50; 30–50
11. 24; 14; Possible answer: Look at the vertical distance between the points for males and females at a given age.
12. For both genders, there is a gradual rise then a leveling off, then a steep drop after age 50.
13. Answers may vary.

Alternate Assessment

Performance Have students work in groups of four and produce examples of scatterplots that show a trend and those that do not. Students should be able to sketch the graph, label it correctly, and share their information with the class.

▶ Quick Quiz

Describe the scatterplot of data related to each situation.

1. Length of hair compared to height. Points will be scattered randomly, indicating no trend.
2. Shoe size compared to height. Points will show a trend that as height increases, shoe size increases.
3. Shoe size compared to age. Points will show a trend that as age increases, shoe size increases until shoe size reaches a maximum even though age continues to increase.

Available on Daily Transparency 1-3

PROBLEM SOLVING 1-3

Problem Solving and Reasoning

9. **Critical Thinking** For each situation, describe what the pattern in a scatterplot would look like.
   a. The hours you work per week compared to your weekly salary
   b. A person's age compared to the amount of sleep needed
   c. The number of books you read compared to the scores on your math tests
   d. The number of people in a family compared to the amount they spend on groceries each week

Use the Calorie Requirements graph for Exercises 10–12.

Calorie Requirements by Age

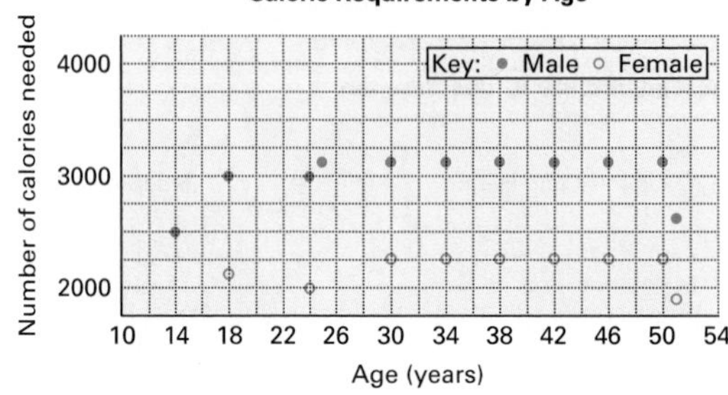

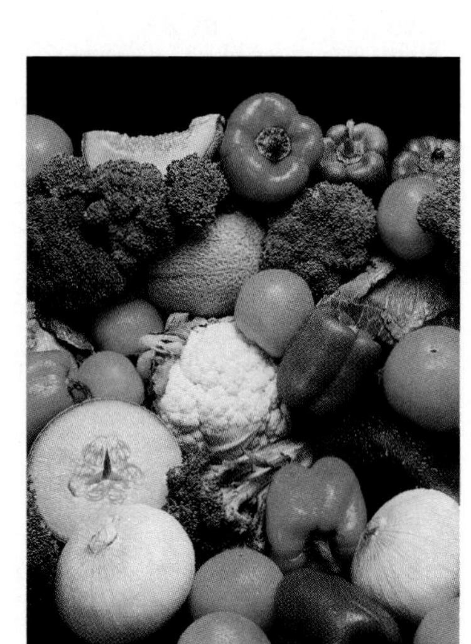

10. **Critical Thinking** At what age(s) do males need the most calories? Females?
11. **Communicate** At what age is the difference in calorie needs the greatest between males and females? The smallest? How can you tell?
12. **Critical Thinking** What pattern is shown in the data for males? For females? For males and females?
13. **Journal** In your own words, describe and sketch the kinds of patterns you have seen in scatterplots.

Mixed Review

Write each as a number. *[Previous course]*

14. nine hundred twenty-nine 929
15. six thousand six hundred six 6606
16. four thousand ninety-eight 4098
17. eight thousand nine hundred 8900

Multiply. *[Previous course]*

18. 6×425 2550 **19.** 9×481 4329 **20.** 2×804 1608 **21.** 8×236 1888

PROBLEM SOLVING

Name ______

Guided Problem Solving 1-3

GPS PROBLEM 11, STUDENT PAGE 20

Use the Calorie Requirements graph. At what age is the difference in calorie needs the greatest between males and females? The smallest? How can you tell?

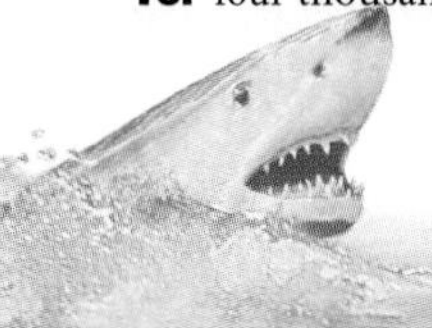

— Understand —

1. What do these points represent?
   a. solid Males' calorie needs.
   b. open Females' calorie needs.
2. What does the distance between two points at any age represent?
   The difference in calorie needs between males and females.

— Plan —

3. The greatest distance between two points for any age is at age 24.
4. The smallest distance between two points for any age is at age 51.

— Solve —

5. At what age is the difference in calorie needs the greatest between males and females? How can you tell? 24, because the greatest distance between two points occurs at this age.
6. At what age is the difference in calorie needs the smallest between males and females? How can you tell? 51, because the smallest distance between two points occurs at this age.

— Look Back —

7. How can you use subtraction to verify your answer? Find the difference in calorie requirements between males and females and then compare differences to find the least and the greatest number.

SOLVE ANOTHER PROBLEM

At what ages is the difference in calorie needs about the same?
18, 30, 34, 38, 42, 46, 50

ENRICHMENT

Name ______

Extend Your Thinking 1-3

Patterns in Data

The scatterplots show some data representing how many hours some students spend watching television and how many hours they spend doing homework. Their math scores are also recorded. Use the information in the scatterplots to answer the following questions.

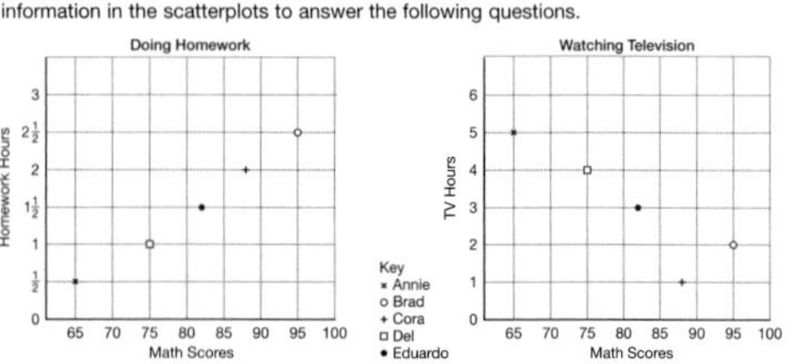

1. Do you see any relationship (trend) between hours spent watching television and math scores?
   Possible answer: Math scores increase when fewer hours are spent watching television.
2. What is the relationship between hours spent doing homework and math scores?
   Possible answer: Math scores increase when more hours are spent doing homework.
3. Which activity seems to affect math scores the most?
   Possible answer: Although both activities have some effect on math scores, it appears that doing more homework is a better way to assure better math scores.
4. If you wanted to tell Annie how to improve her math scores, what advice would you give her?
   Possible answer: Spend more time doing homework and watch less television.

Section 1A Connect

At the beginning of this section, you saw how information from graphs can help you make sensible decisions. Now you will have an opportunity to use graphs to make some decisions of your own.

Danger! Shark Attack!

Shark attacks are extremely rare. Millions of people swim in the ocean each year without fear of sharks. The graphs give information on some of the very few attacks that have actually occurred.

U.S. Shark Attacks

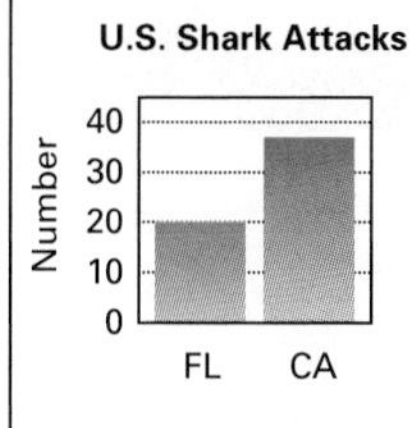

Twelve Florida Attacks

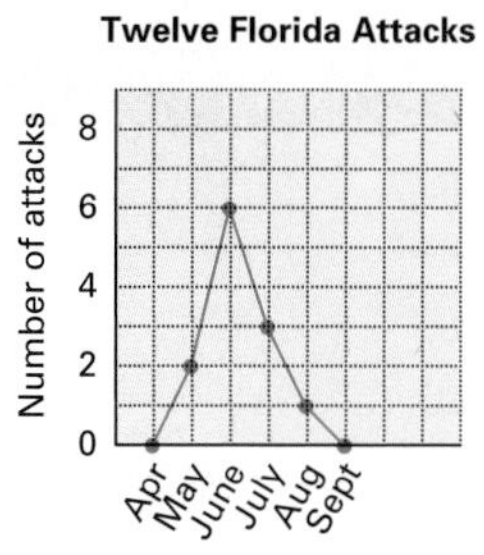

Twenty California Attacks

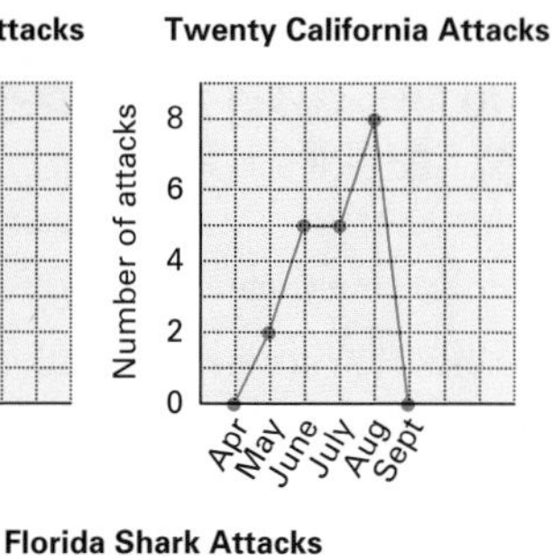

California Shark Attacks

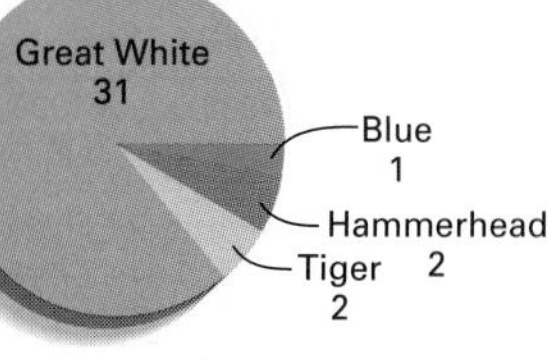

Florida Shark Attacks

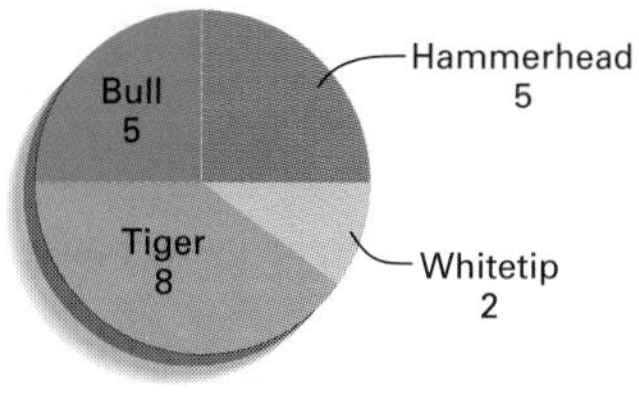

You are a scientist who wants to study shark attacks during June.

1. Which species appears to attack humans the most?
2. Which state has more attacks during the entire year? How many more? How did you determine this?
3. During the month of May, which state has more shark attacks? How did you determine this?
4. If you can study only one species in the month of June, which state should you go to? Explain how you made your decision.

21

Danger! Shark Attack!

The Point

In *Danger! Shark Attack!* on page 5, students learned about dangers posed by sharks and dogs. Now the will interpret information from various types of graphs in order to decide how to study shark attacks.

Resources

Lesson Enhancement Transparency 3

About the Page

- Review the graphs to be sure students understand the information each graph is displaying.
- Discuss with students the facts they would need to know before they decided whether or not it was safe to swim in the ocean.

Ongoing Assessment

To determine whether students are correctly interpreting the graphs, check their answers for Question 2.

Extension

Using the information in the graphs, have students determine which sharks appear to be the most dangerous and the least dangerous in California. Great white; Blue. Have them also determine which sharks appear to be the most dangerous and the least dangerous in Florida. Tiger; Whitetip.

Answers for Connect

1. The great white shark; It has 31 attacks, more than any other shark.
2. California; 16 more; The bar graph shows California had 36 attacks, and Florida had only 20.
3. They're the same; The line graphs show both states at 2 attacks in May.
4. Florida; There are more attacks in June.

1A Review

Review Correlation

Item(s)	Lesson(s)
1–4	1-1
5	1-2
6–8	1-1
9	1-3
10	1-1

Test Prep

Test-Taking Tip

Tell students that sometimes information given in a test problem is unnecessary. In this case, you do not need to know the number of green apples to answer the question.

Answers for Review

1. All the symbols have the same value, so count the number of symbols and multiply by the value in the key.
2. *The Sharks*
3. 3 million
4. *Great Moments*
5. Yes; The data values do not start at 0.
6. 3.6 lb; 14.4 lb.
7. The daily garbage per person increases.
8. Possible answers: Similarities: Both are line graphs, both show same data, both use same data values and spaces between data values; Difference: Spaces between years are wider in the second graph.
9. Possible answers should be a scatterplot showing a trend and a description of the trend.
10. C

Section 1A Review

REVIEW 1A

1. Communicate Explain how it is possible to read the symbols in a pictograph and determine their number values.

Most-Watched Nature TV Specials

Viewers (millions): 15, 20, 25

The Sharks, *Land of the Tiger*, *The Grizzlies*, *Great Moments*

WINNER

Use the bar graph for Exercises 2–5.

2. Which special had the most viewers?

3. How many more viewers watched *The Sharks* than watched *Great Moments?*

4. What was the least watched show?

5. Could the graph be misleading? Explain.

Industry Use the line graphs for Exercises 6–8.

6. In 1980, how much garbage did each person generate in a day? A family of four in a day?

7. Describe the change in the data over time.

8. How are the two graphs alike? How are they different?

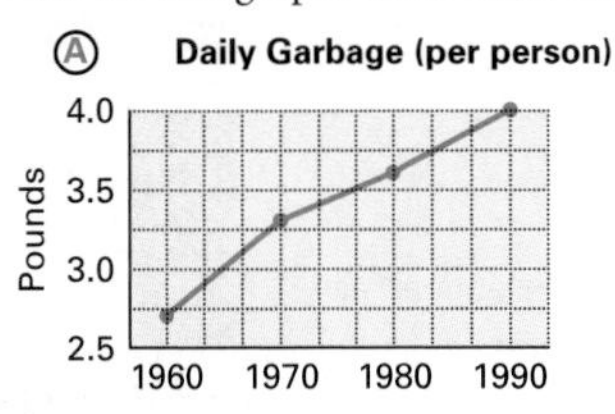

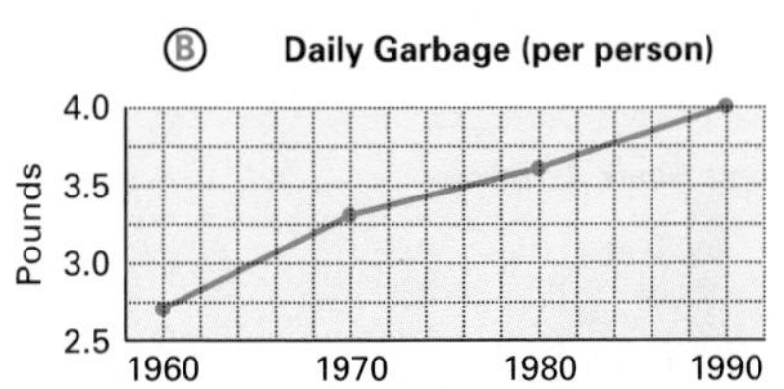

9. Journal Sketch an example of a scatterplot pattern that shows a trend and describe the trend.

Test Prep

You can compare two kinds of data on a circle graph by finding their differences or stating how many times larger one appears than another.

10. Which statement accurately compares the red apples to the yellow apples?

Ⓐ There are four times more red apples than yellow apples.

Ⓑ There are about half as many red apples as yellow apples.

Ⓒ There are 38 more red apples than yellow apples.

Ⓓ There are 48 fewer yellow apples than red apples.

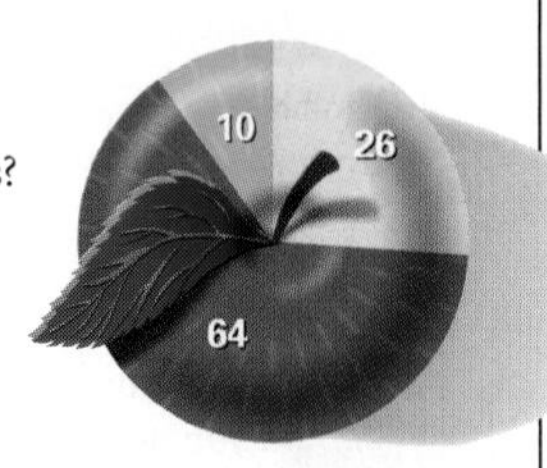

Resources

Practice Masters
Section 1A Review

Assessment Sourcebook
Quiz 1A

Test Works
Test and Practice Software

PRACTICE

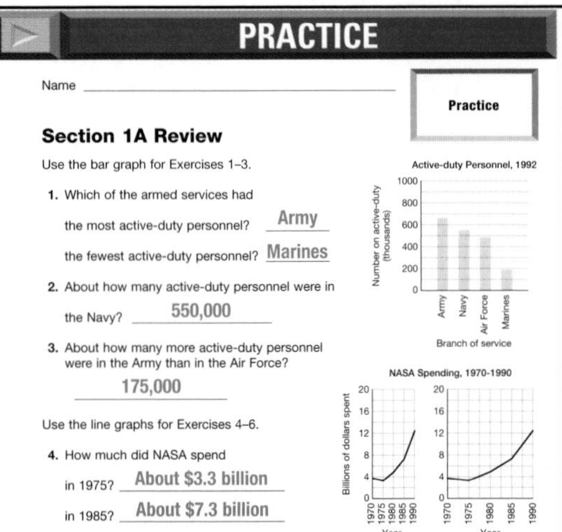

Name ______________

Practice

Section 1A Review

Use the bar graph for Exercises 1–3.

1. Which of the armed services had the most active-duty personnel? Army
 the fewest active-duty personnel? Marines

2. About how many active-duty personnel were in the Navy? 550,000

3. About how many more active-duty personnel were in the Army than in the Air Force? 175,000

Active-duty Personnel, 1992

Number on active-duty (thousands): 0, 200, 400, 600, 800, 1000

Army, Navy, Air Force, Marines

Branch of service

Use the line graphs for Exercises 4–6.

4. How much did NASA spend
 in 1975? About $3.3 billion
 in 1985? About $7.3 billion

NASA Spending, 1970-1990

Billions of dollars spent: 0, 4, 8, 12, 16, 20

Year: 1970, 1975, 1980, 1985, 1990

5. Describe the change in the data over time.
 The spending decreased slightly from 1970 to 1975, then increased rapidly.

6. How are the two graphs alike? How are they different?
 They show the same data. The spending *appears* to increase faster in the graph on the left.

7. **Consumer** A clock radio sells for $26.00. If a customer pays $30.00 for the radio, how much change should be given? Assume there is no tax. *[Previous Course]* $4.00

8. Last summer Rolando read 17 books. If each book had 236 pages, how many pages did Rolando read all together? 4012 pages

Displaying Data

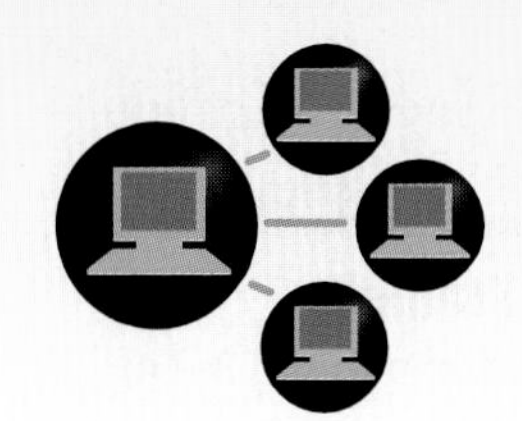

Visit www.teacher.mathsurf.com for links to lesson plans from teachers and other professionals, NCTM information, and other sites.

LESSON PLANNING GUIDE

Student Edition				Ancillaries*	
LESSON		MATERIALS	VOCABULARY	DAILY	OTHER
	Section 1B Opener				
1-4	**Tallies, Frequency Charts, and Line Plots**		tally, frequency chart, line plot	1-4	Teaching Tool Trans. 22 Lesson Enhancement Trans. 4 Ch. 1 Project Master
1-5	**Scales and Bar Graphs**	spreadsheet software for making bar graphs	scale, interval, horizontal axis, vertical axis, range	1-5	Technology Master 3 *Interactive CD-ROM Spreadsheet/Grapher Tool* *WW Math*–Middle School
1-6	**Stem-and-Leaf-Diagrams**		stem-and-leaf-diagram	1-6	
	Connect				Interdisc. Team Teaching 1B
	Review				Practice 1B; Quiz 1B; *TestWorks*

* Daily Ancillaries include Practice, Reteaching, Problem Solving, Enrichment, and Daily Transparency. Teaching Tool Transparencies are in *Teacher's Toolkits*. Lesson Enhancement Transparencies are in *Overhead Transparency Package*.

SKILLS TRACE

LESSON	SKILL	FIRST INTRODUCED			DEVELOP	PRACTICE/ APPLY	REVIEW
		GR. 4	GR. 5	GR. 6			
1-4	**Organizing data using tallies, frequency charts, line plots.**		✗		pp. 24–26	pp. 27–28	pp. 59, 73, 141
1-5	**Making bar graphs.**		✗		pp. 29–31	pp. 32–33	pp. 59, 146, 306
1-6	**Making stem-and-leaf diagrams.**		✗		pp. 34–36	pp. 37–38	pp. 59, 69, 152, 232, 312

CONNECTED MATHEMATICS

The unit *Data About Us (Statistics)*, from the **Connected Mathematics** series, can be used with Section 1B.

INTERDISCIPLINARY TEAM TEACHING

Math and Social Studies

(Worksheet pages 03–04: Teacher pages T3–T4)

In this lesson, students display data to represent voter activity.

Name ______________________ *Math and Social Studies*

A Duty, a Privilege, and a Right

Display data to represent voter activity.

When you turn 18, you will reach an important milestone. You will be able to vote in local, state, and national elections. Before 1970, most states required a person to be 21 to vote. In that year, the U.S. Supreme Court ruled that 18-year-olds from all states had the right to vote in national elections. The 26th Amendment to the Constitution was ratified in 1971 and extended the right to vote to 18-year-olds in all elections.

Before a person can vote, however, he or she must register to vote. Registration is a process that determines whether a person is qualified to vote. For example, when you register to vote, you will have to prove that you are 18. You must also show that you are a U.S. citizen and where you live. Only U.S. citizens can vote in U.S. elections.

As you can see, there are few limits on the right to vote. Yet, as you will discover in this activity, not everyone who has the right to vote, registers or votes.

Americans have fought a long and hard battle to earn the right to participate in elections. It is every citizen's duty, privilege, and right to cast his or her vote in local, state, and national elections.

Table of Voter Activity in Four Recent Presidential Elections

	1980	1984	1988	1992
Voting-Age Population (millions)	157	170	178	186
Number Reporting They Registered (millions)	105	116	119	127
Number Reporting They Voted (millions)	93	102	102	114

1. In addition to the year of each presidential election, what other information is provided in the table?
   the voting-age population, the number of people who registered to vote, and the number of people who voted
2. Use the information from the table to create four bar graphs, one for each of the years shown. Use the graphs on the next page. Each graph should show the voting-age population, number of people that registered to vote, and number that voted. Then answer questions 3–5.
3. Study the completed bar graphs. How are the patterns in the four graphs similar?
   The patterns show that if people register to vote, then they usually vote.
4. What is unexpected about the patterns of the bar graphs?
   Students may say that they would have expected the second and third bars to be taller, as more of the voting-age population should have registered and voted.

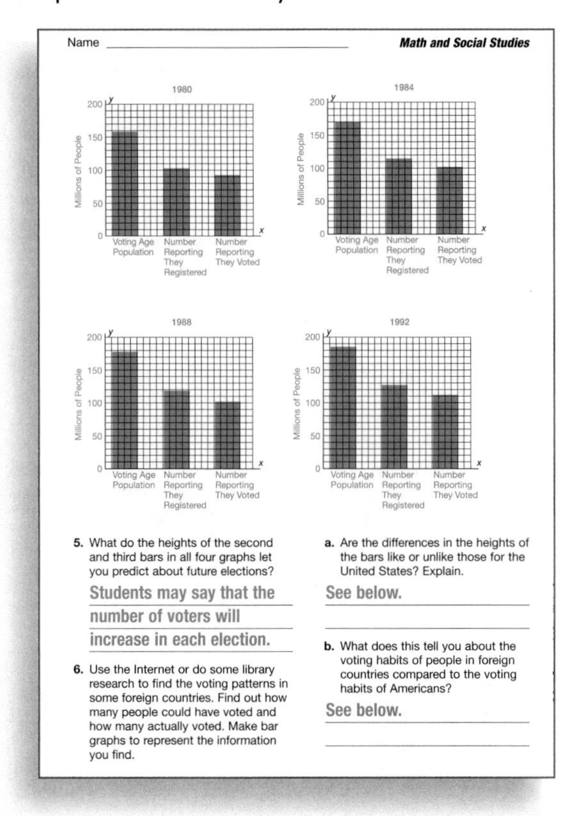

Name ______________________ *Math and Social Studies*

5. What do the heights of the second and third bars in all four graphs let you predict about future elections?
   Students may say that the number of voters will increase in each election.
6. Use the Internet or do some library research to find the voting patterns in some foreign countries. Find out how many people could have voted and how many actually voted. Make bar graphs to represent the information you find.
   a. Are the differences in the heights of the bars like or unlike those for the United States? Explain.
      See below.
   b. What does this tell you about the voting habits of people in foreign countries compared to the voting habits of Americans?
      See below.

Answers

6. a. Probably unlike and closer in height
   b. In foreign countries, more eligible voters actually vote than in the United States.

BIBLIOGRAPHY

FOR TEACHERS

Haven, Kendall. *Marvels of Science*. Englewood, CO: Libraries Unlimited, 1994.

Spangler, David. *Math for Real Kids*. Glenview, IL: Good Year Books, 1997.

Welton, Ann. *Explorers and Exploration*. Phoenix, AZ: Oryx Press, 1993.

The World Almanac and Book of Facts. Mahwah, NJ: Funk & Wagnalls, 1996.

FOR STUDENTS

Career Discovery Encyclopedia. Chicago, IL: J. G. Ferguson Publishing Company, 1993, Vol. 5.

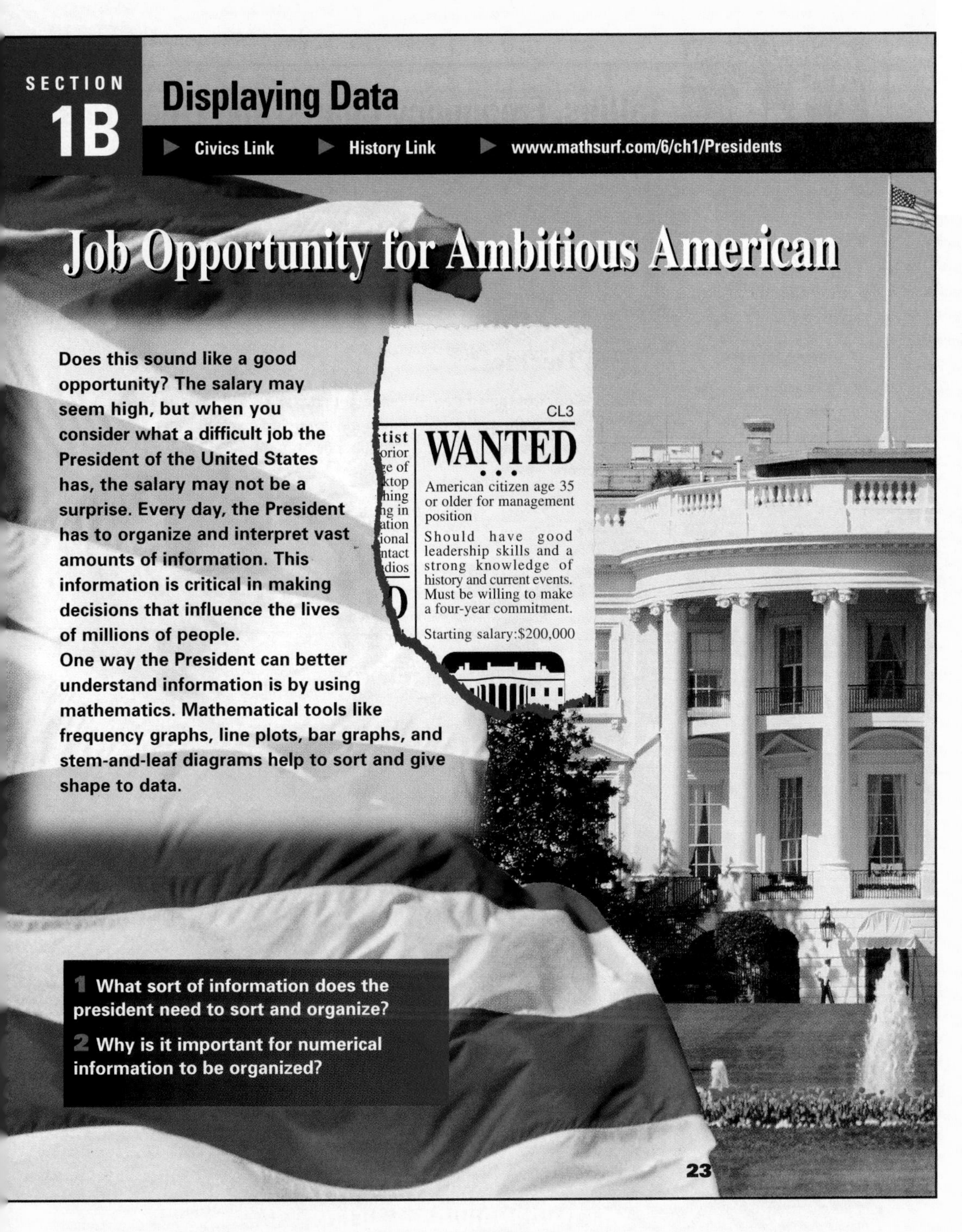

SECTION 1B

Displaying Data

▶ Civics Link ▶ History Link ▶ www.mathsurf.com/6/ch1/Presidents

Job Opportunity for Ambitious American

Does this sound like a good opportunity? The salary may seem high, but when you consider what a difficult job the President of the United States has, the salary may not be a surprise. Every day, the President has to organize and interpret vast amounts of information. This information is critical in making decisions that influence the lives of millions of people.

One way the President can better understand information is by using mathematics. Mathematical tools like frequency graphs, line plots, bar graphs, and stem-and-leaf diagrams help to sort and give shape to data.

1 What sort of information does the president need to sort and organize?

2 Why is it important for numerical information to be organized?

23

Where are we now?

In Section 1A, students used graphs to compare values.

They learned how to

- use graphs to organize and display information.
- identify graphs that display misleading information.
- compare values in two sets of data using scatterplots.

Where are we going?

In Section 1B, students will

- organize data using frequency charts.
- determine the shape of a set of data.
- construct bar graphs.
- determine the range of the data.
- organize data into stem-and-leaf diagrams.

Section 1B

Theme: Presidents

World Wide Web

If your class has access to the World Wide Web, you might want to use the information found at the Web site address given. The interdisciplinary links relate to topics discussed in this section.

About the Page

This page introduces the theme of the section, Presidents, and discusses the vast amount of information the President must read and interpret to do his job.

Ask ...

- Would you like to be President? Why?
- What information do you think the President receives each day? How does he get this information?

Extensions

The following activities do not require access to the World Wide Web.

Civics

Books have been written about our Presidents and some of our Presidents have written books. Have students read a book by or about one of the Presidents. Have them list the important accomplishments of that President.

History

Presidential elections are held every four years. Ask students to research the last election. Have them determine who the candidates were, what party they represented, what the issues were, and the number of popular and electoral votes. Ask students to report their findings to the class.

Answers for Questions

1. Possible answers: The President must organize statistics on crime, unemployment, taxes, and so on.
2. Numerical information needs to be organized so that it is clear what the information is about.

Connect

On page 39, students will graph data about the Presidents that is shown in a table.

1-4 Lesson Organizer

Objectives

- Organize data using tallies and frequency charts.
- Use a line plot to show the shape of a data set.

Vocabulary

- Tally marks, frequency chart, line plot

NCTM Standards

- 1–4, 7, 8, 10

Review

Order the numbers from least to greatest.

1. 18, 30, 23, 12, 16, 25
   12, 16 18, 23, 25, 30
2. 34, 6, 22, 10, 63, 48, 9
   6, 9, 10, 22, 34, 48, 63
3. 178, 134, 189, 200, 106, 145
   106, 134, 145, 178, 189, 200

Available on Daily Transparency 1-4

1 Introduce

Explore

You may wish to use Teaching Tool Transparency 22: Map of the United States and Lesson Enhancement Transparency 4 with **Explore.**

The Point
Students construct their own method for organizing data to explore the value of having data organized.

Ongoing Assessment
You may want to involve the students in listing the information on an overhead projector to facilitate discussion of the questions. It would be helpful to cross off the states as students list them.

For Groups That Finish Early
Which state has the greatest number of electors? California The least number of electors? Alaska, Delaware, Montana, North Dakota, South Dakota, Vermont, Washington, D.C., Wyoming.

1-4 Tallies, Frequency Charts, and Line Plots

You'll Learn ...

- to organize data using tallies and frequency charts
- to use a line plot to show the shape of a data set

... How It's Used

Advertising executives use frequency charts and line plots to organize and communicate about data on public opinion.

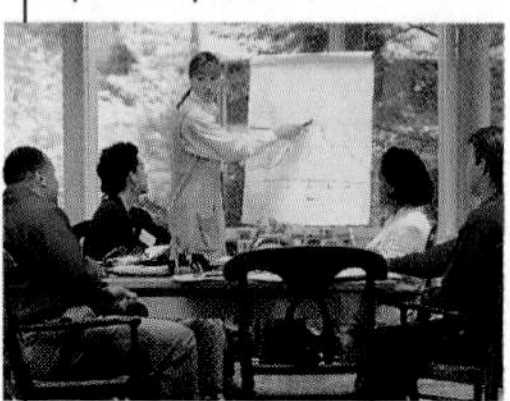

Vocabulary

tally marks
frequency chart
line plot

▶ Lesson Link In the last section, you saw various ways to display data on graphs. Before data can be displayed, it must be carefully organized. ◀

Explore — Organizing Data

Who Decides?

The President of the United States is not chosen directly by the voters. Instead, voters choose people called *electors.* The electors meet after the election to elect the President. The table lists the number of electors for each state.

Number Of Electors For Each State

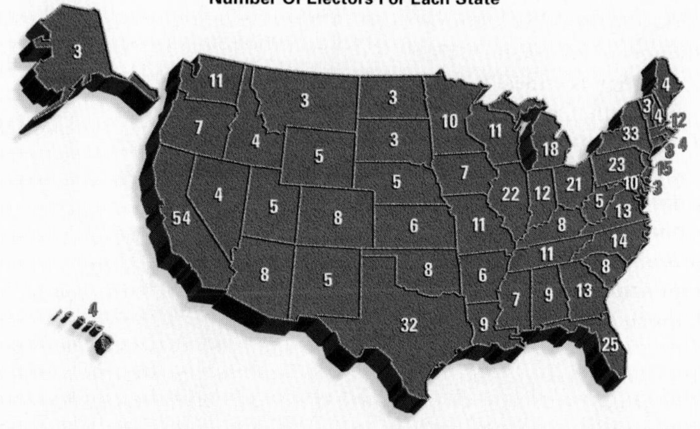

1. Organize the data so that you can quickly tell how many states have 3 electoral vote, how many have 4, how many have 5, and so on.
2. What is the most common number of electors? Second most common?
3. Why do you think different states have different numbers of electors?
4. What patterns can you see in the organized data that you can't easily see from the table?

MEETING INDIVIDUAL NEEDS

Resources

- **1-4** Practice
- **1-4** Reteaching
- **1-4** Problem Solving
- **1-4** Enrichment
- **1-4** Daily Transparency
  - Problem of the Day
  - Review
  - Quick Quiz
- Teaching Tool Transparency 22
- Lesson Enhancement Transparency 4
- Chapter 1 Project Master

Learning Modalities

Visual Create a line plot of the students' favorite colors. Write the names of six or seven colors in a row across the chalkboard. Have each student come to the board and mark an x above his or her favorite color, keeping the x's for each color in a column.

Social When doing **Explore,** students can work with a partner to prepare the list, with one student finding the numbers and the other recording the names and numbers.

English Language Development

Pair limited English speakers with those proficient in the language and have them work together to construct a frequency chart and a line plot for some data, such as the numbers of cousins or pets in his or her family.

Learn Tallies, Frequency Charts, and Line Plots

Tally marks are used to organize a large set of data. Each tally mark indicates one time that the value appeared in the data.

A **frequency chart** can help you list the data quickly. Each value that appeared in the data is followed by the number of times it appeared.

Example 1

Use the data to make a frequency chart. For each age, how many states specify that age in their law?

Ages at Which State Laws Require Children to Be in School

State	Age	State	Age	State	Age	State	Age	State	Age
CA	6	KS	7	MO	7	NH	6	UT	6
DE	5	MA	6	MT	7	OH	5	VA	5
FL	6	MD	5	NC	7	PA	8	WA	8
ID	6	ME	7	ND	7	TN	7	WI	6
IN	7	MN	6	NE	7	TX	6	WY	7

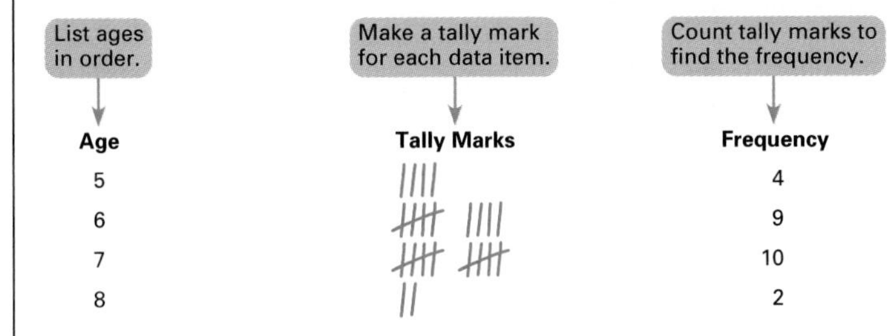

Age	Tally Marks	Frequency
5	////	4
6	𝍸 ////	9
7	𝍸 𝍸	10
8	//	2

Four states require children to be in school at age 5, nine states at age 6, ten states at age 7, and two at age 8.

Try It

a. Make a frequency chart of the test scores. Use these groups: under 60; 60–69; 70–79; 80–89; 90–100.

b. How many students scored 80–89? Less than 70?

History Test Scores

81	95	77	64	85
62	79	92	100	61
83	55	84	83	91
75	83	72	84	95

Problem Solving TIP

Some data sets are more easily organized if you put the data into groups. This way, you have fewer categories, and more data per category.

MATH EVERY DAY

▶ Problem of the Day

Which five letters do you think are used least often in written English? Check your predictions by picking several paragraphs at random in a book. Make a frequency chart to tally the results.

Answer:

Student predictions and tallies may vary. Based on counting the letters in thousands of sentences, the following five letters are used least often: K, X, J, Q, Z.

Available on Daily Transparency 1-4

An Extension is provided in the transparency package.

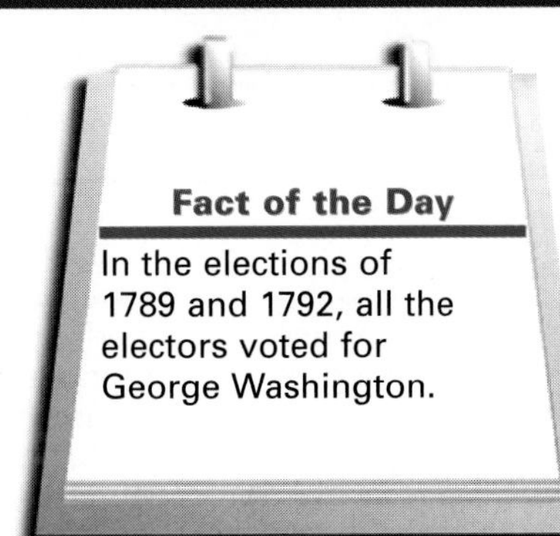

Estimation

Estimate.

1. 68 + 34 100
2. 173 + 89 300
3. 420 + 398 800

Answers for Explore

1.

Number of Electoral Votes	Number of States with That Many Votes
3	6
4	6
5	5
6	2
7	3
8	6
9	2
10	2
11	4
12	2
13	2
14	1
15	1
18	1
21	1
22	1
23	1
25	1
32	1
33	1
54	1

2. 3, 4, and 8 are the most common numbers of electors; 5 is the second most common.
3. Different states have different numbers of people.
4. Possible answers: About half of the states have 8 or fewer votes, and about half have 8 or more. There are very few states with more than 20 votes, and only one in the 50s.

2 Teach

Learn

Alternate Examples

1. Use your answer to **Explore** Step 1 to construct a frequency chart of states with 7 or fewer electors.

Number of Electors	Tally Marks	Frequency Chart
3	𝍸 I	6
4	𝍸 I	6
5	𝍸	5
6	II	2
7	III	3

Answers for Try It

a.

History Test Scores	Frequency
Under 60	1
60–69	3
70–79	4
80–89	7
90–100	5

b. 7; 4

Alternate Examples

2. Use your answer to **Explore** Step 1 to construct a line plot of states with 10 or fewer electors. What picture of the data does the line plot show?

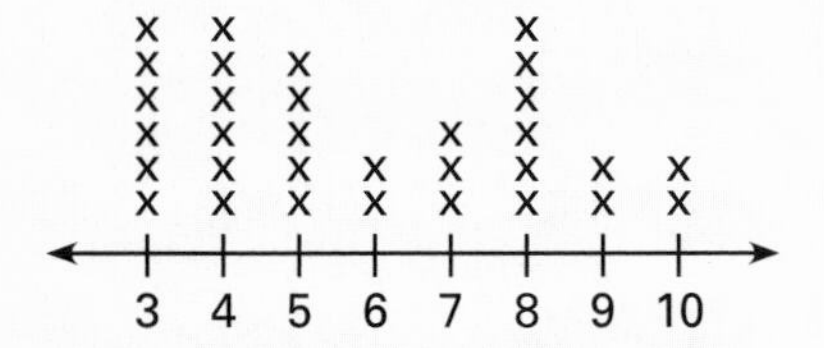

The line plot shows that 3, 4, and 8 are the most common number of electors, that 5 states have 5 electors, and that 3 states have 7 electors.

Answers for Try It

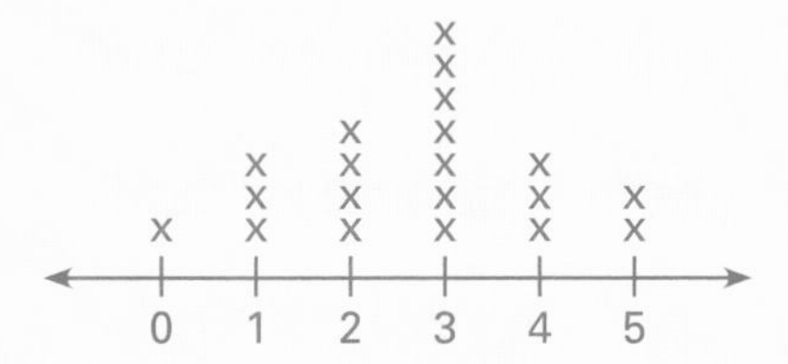

The line plot shows that 3 is the most common number of phone calls, 0 is the least common, and 1 and 4 appear with the same frequency.

3 Practice and Assess

Check

Be sure that students understand that each x in a line plot represents a single tally mark in the corresponding frequency chart.

Answers for Check Your Understanding

1. Possible answers: Similarities: Both give you an idea of how often each value occurred in the data; Differences: A frequency chart is easier to write but it doesn't give the data any shape, whereas a line plot gives shape to the data but it takes longer to write.
2. Yes; They both show the same information, they just show it in different ways. A frequency chart uses tally marks while a line plot uses an x for each mark.

A **line plot** shows the shape of a set of data. It is similar to a set of tally marks that has been turned onto its side. Instead of tally marks, a line plot uses ×'s.

Age	Tally
5	||||
6	~~||||~~ ||||
7	~~||||~~ ~~||||~~
8	||

Example 2

Make a line plot of the data. What does the line plot show?

Number of Children of 20th-Century Presidents and First Ladies					
2	5	3	3	0	2
2	5	1	1	2	2
2	4	4	2	6	1

The line plot shows that 2 is the most common number of children, 0 and 6 are the least common, and 3, 4, and 5 all appear with the same frequency.

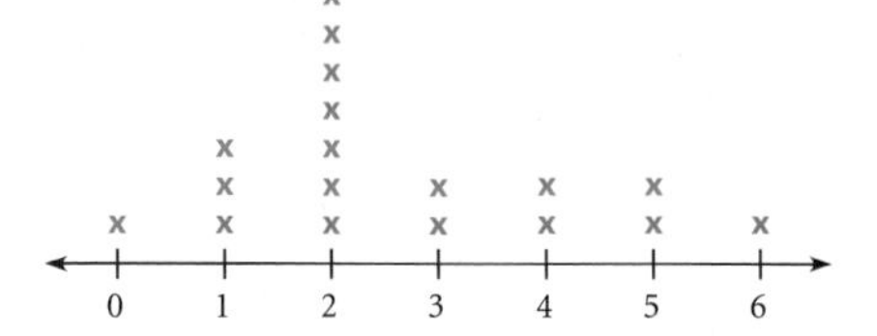

History Link

James Buchanan (1791–1868) was the only U.S. President who never married.

Try It

The table gives the results of a survey of 20 middle school students. Make a line plot of the data. What picture of the data does the line plot show?

Average Phone Calls Made (daily)				
2	3	5	2	3
1	0	3	4	2
1	5	3	4	3
2	3	1	4	3

Problem Solving TIP

It may be useful to scan the data before you start to tally it. This gives you an idea of how high and how low the numbers will be.

Check Your Understanding

1. How are frequency charts and line plots similar? How are they different?
2. Can the same information be shown in a frequency chart and a line plot? Explain.

MEETING MIDDLE SCHOOL CLASSROOM NEEDS

Tips from Middle School Teachers

When working with frequency tables, I have students describe games they have played in which they have kept score using a tally system.

Team Teaching

Have the other teachers on your team describe any situations when information might be recorded using a frequency chart.

Social Studies Connection

In addresses, state names are shortened to two capital letters. These abbreviations were authorized by the United States Postal Service. Have students use the map on page 24 to identify as many states as they can and write their abbreviations. Students should use an almanac to help them.

1-4 Exercises and Applications

Practice and Apply

1. **Getting Started** Record each data set in a tally chart.
   - **a.** 5, 4, 1, 3, 3, 6, 10, 4, 7, 3, 1, 1, 2, 1, 4
   - **b.** 23, 21, 18, 20, 19, 22, 17, 22, 21, 20, 19, 20, 13, 20
   - **c.** 2000, 4000, 5000, 2500, 2000, 1500, 6500, 6000, 4000, 3500

Make a frequency chart for each set of tally marks.

2. Hours spent doing homework each week

Hours	Tally
4	||||
5	𝍸 ||
6	𝍸 𝍸 |||
7	𝍸 ||||
8	𝍸 𝍸 𝍸 |
9	𝍸 𝍸 |
10	𝍸 ||

3. Shoes in your closet

Shoes	Tally
2	𝍸
4	𝍸 |
6	𝍸 ||||
8	𝍸 𝍸 |||
10	𝍸 𝍸 𝍸 |
12	𝍸 𝍸 𝍸 |||

4. Hair length

Length (in)	Tally
1	|
2	𝍸 |||
3	𝍸 𝍸
4	𝍸
5	|||
6	||
7	|

5. History Draw a line plot of the ages of the first ten Presidents when they took office.

GPS

Age of First Ten Presidents

Age	Frequency
49	1
54	1
57	4
58	1
61	2
68	1

6. Geography Draw a line plot of the number of states bordering each state in the United States.

Borders	Frequency
0	2
1	2
2	4
3	8
4	12
5	11
6	8
7	1
8	2

PRACTICE 1-4

1-4 Exercises and Applications

Assignment Guide

- **Basic** 1–5, 7–8, 11–31 odds
- **Average** 1–5, 7–10, 12–32 evens
- **Enriched** 1, 3–10, 12–32 evens

Exercise Answers

1.

a.		b.		c.	
1	||||	13	|	1500	|
2	|	17	|	2000	||
3	|||	18	|	2500	|
4	|||	19	||	3500	|
5	|	20	||||	4000	||
6	|	21	||	5000	|
7	|	22	||	6000	|
10	|	23	|	6500	|

2.

No. Hours Doing Homework	Frequency
4	4
5	7
6	13
7	9
8	16
9	11
10	7

3–6. See page C1.

PRACTICE

Name ______________________

Practice 1-4

Tallies, Frequency Charts, and Line Plots

Make a frequency chart for each set of tally marks in Exercises 1–2.

1. Number of hours of television watched yesterday

Hours	Tally
0	|||
1	𝍸 ||
2	𝍸
3	𝍸 |||
4	|||
5	||

Frequency Chart

Hours	Frequency
0	3
1	7
2	5
3	8
4	3
5	2

2. Number of pets at home

Pets	Tally
0	𝍸 𝍸 𝍸 ||
1	𝍸 𝍸 ||
2	𝍸 |||
3	𝍸 |
4	|||
5	|

Frequency Chart

Pets	Frequency
0	17
1	12
2	8
3	6
4	3
5	1

3. Make a line plot of the number of books read last month.

Books	Frequency
0	4
1	6
2	3
3	2
4	1

4. The following data set shows the answers people gave when asked how many hours they slept last night: 8, 7, 8, 6, 8, 7, 5, 6, 9, 7, 6, 8, 7, 9, 7

   a. Make a frequency chart for the data. **b.** Make a line plot for the data.

Hours	Frequency
5	1
6	3
7	5
8	4
9	2

RETEACHING

Name ______________________

Alternative Lesson 1-4

Tallies, Frequency Charts, and Line Plots

Tallies are marks that help to organize a large set of data. Each tally mark indicates one time that the value appeared in the data.

A **frequency chart** can help you list the data quickly. Each value that appeared in the data is followed by the number of times it appeared.

Example

Use the data to make a frequency chart.
How many words have 4 letters?

Number of Letters in Each Word in a Given Paragraph
8, 3, 4, 2, 3, 2, 3, 5, 4, 1, 9, 5, 3, 1, 4, 4

Step 1: List the number of letters in order from 1 to 9.

Step 2: Record a tally mark for each item. Place a tally mark next to 8. Do this for each of the data.

Step 3: Count the tally marks to find the frequency of each item. There are two tallies next to 1, so the frequency is 2. Do this for every item.

Since there are 4 tallies for words with 4 letters, there are 4 words that contained 4 letters.

Number of Words

Number of letters	Tally marks	Frequency
1	||	2
2	||	2
3	||||	4
4	||||	4
5	||	2
6		0
7		0
8	|	1
9	|	1

Try It Use the data to make a frequency chart. How many sentences in the short story have 13 words?

Number of Words in 12 Sentences
12, 11, 10, 13, 8, 13, 10, 9, 7, 8, 7, 10

Number of Sentences

Number of words	Tally marks	Frequency
7	||	2
8	||	2
9	|	1
10	|||	3
11	|	1
12	|	1
13	||	2

a. Record a tally mark for the number of words in each sentence.

b. Total the tallies and write the frequency for each sentence length.

c. How many sentences have 13 words? Two sentences.

Reteaching

Activity

Make a frequency chart of the hair length represented by the students in your class.

- Use these lengths: very short, short, medium, long.
- The columns should be labeled "Hair Length," "Tally," and "Frequency."
- Under Hair Length list the lengths. Then in the next column make a tally mark for each student with that length hair. Each time you get to 5, make that tally mark across the preceding 4.
- Count the tally marks for each length and record that number in the last column.

Project Progress

You may want to have students use Chapter 1 Project Master.

Exercise Answers

7. a.

No. of Vetoes	Frequency
0	6
2	2
3	1
7	1
10	1
12	1

b.

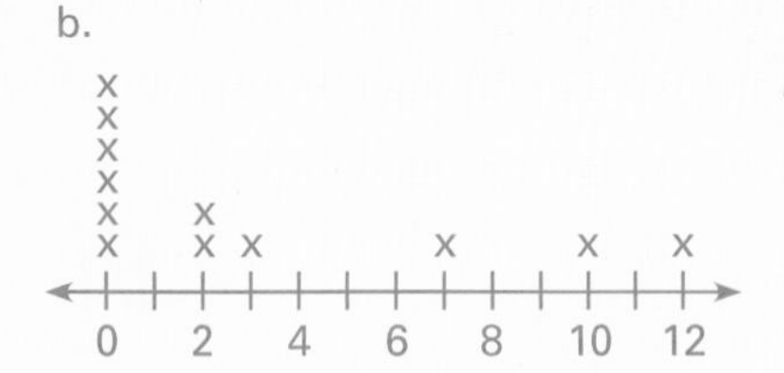

8. Odd numbers; There are 8 odd numbers and 5 even numbers.
9. Possible answer: The number that occurs most frequently has the tallest stack of x's.
10. Possible answers: To summarize a data set in a chart; To summarize a data set in a graph.
11. Two hundred seventeen
12. Three hundred fifty-six
13. Six hundred sixteen
14. Four hundred ninety-one
15. Six hundred nine
16. Seven hundred seventy-three

17–22. See page C1.

Alternate Assessment

Portfolio Have students select one frequency chart and one line plot that they made as an exercise answer and add these samples to their portfolio.

Quick Quiz

1. Use a tally chart to record the number of siblings each student in your class has in his or her family.
   Answers may vary.
2. Draw a line plot of the tally chart from Question 1.
   Answers may vary.

Available on Daily Transparency 1-4

PROBLEM SOLVING 1-4

7. History If the President signs a bill from the Congress, that bill becomes a law. If the President doesn't think it should become a law, he or she can veto the bill.

a. Make a frequency chart for the data in the table.

b. Make a line plot for the data in the table.

President	Number of Vetoes	President	Number of Vetoes
Washington	2	Jackson	12
J. Adams	0	Van Buren	0
Jefferson	0	W. Harrison	0
Madison	7	Tyler	10
Monroe	2	Polk	3
J. Q. Adams	0	Taylor	0

from HERBLOCK: A CARTOONIST'S LIFE (Macmillan Publishing, 1993)

Problem Solving and Reasoning

8. Critical Thinking Does the frequency chart show a data set with mostly even numbers or mostly odd numbers? Explain.

Age	Frequency
5	2
6	5
7	6

9. Communicate How does a line plot show the shape of a data set?

10. Journal What is the purpose of a frequency chart? A line plot?

Mixed Review

Write each number in words. *[Previous course]*

11. 217 **12.** 356 **13.** 616 **14.** 491 **15.** 609 **16.** 773

17. 2143 **18.** 3781 **19.** 9611 **20.** 5505 **21.** 4302 **22.** 9933

Divide. *[Previous course]*

23. 50 ÷ 2 25 **24.** 66 ÷ 3 22 **25.** 84 ÷ 4 21 **26.** 96 ÷ 6 16 **27.** 88 ÷ 8 11

28. 98 ÷ 7 14 **29.** 95 ÷ 5 19 **30.** 87 ÷ 2 43 R 1 or 43.5 **31.** 74 ÷ 3 24 R 2 or 24.7 **32.** 57 ÷ 1 57

Project Progress

After you have collected numerical data about your location, think about the best way to display your data. You might want to consider using frequency charts, line plots, or bar graphs.

Problem Solving: Understand, Plan, Solve, Look Back

PROBLEM SOLVING

Name ________

Guided Problem Solving 1-4

GPS PROBLEM 5, STUDENT PAGE 27

Draw a line plot of the ages of the first ten presidents when they took office.

Age of First Ten Presidents

Age	Frequency
49	1
54	1
57	4
58	1
61	2
68	1

Understand

1. What are you asked to do? Draw a line plot of the ages of the first ten presidents when they took office.
2. What mark do you use to record an item of data on a line plot? X

Plan

3. List the president's ages. 49, 54, 57, 58, 61, 68
4. The smallest number you record is 49.
5. The largest number you record is 68.
6. How many marks will you write for one president's age? One mark.

Solve

7. Write the ages in order from youngest to oldest on the line plot. Include all ages between the youngest and oldest.
8. Record the data.

46 48 50 52 54 56 58 60 62 64 66 68

Look Back

9. How can you make sure that you have recorded each data item in the line plot? Possible answer: Count the number of marks and check to see if there are the same number of data items.

SOLVE ANOTHER PROBLEM

Make a line plot to represent the value of the coins in this data set: dime, nickel, dime, penny, nickel, penny, dime, dime, penny, nickel, nickel, penny, penny, dime, dime, nickel, penny, nickel, dime, dime

Penny Nickel Dime

ENRICHMENT

Name ________

Extend Your Thinking 1-4

Patterns in Data

Business, Inc. opened for business in 1990. Their sales are shown in the bar graph at the right. Executives also graphed monthly sales for two years. That graph is shown below.

Yearly Sales: Sales (in dollars) 0, 100,000, 200,000, 300,000, 400,000; Year 1990 1991 1992 1993 1994 1995

Monthly Sales: Sales (in dollars) 0, 20,000, 40,000, 60,000, 80,000; Year Jan '94 Apr '94 Jul '94 Oct '94 Jan '95 Apr '95 Jul '95 Oct '95

1. What pattern, or trend, do you see in the yearly sales graph? What does it mean?
   Possible answer: Bars become taller each year, meaning sales are increasing.
2. If the pattern continues, what do you think sales might be in the year 2000? Explain.
   Possible answer: Since the growth in sales each year is about $50,000, the sales in the year 2000 will be about $550,000.
3. If executives wanted sales to appear steady over the years, how would they change the graph?
   Possible answer: They could use larger intervals.
4. What pattern do you see in the monthly sales graph? What does it mean?
   Possible answer: The same month in both years shows about the same number of sales. In both years, sales are higher in May, June, October, November, and December.
5. Why do you think the pattern of monthly sales occurs?
   Possible answer: Sales increase in May and June is influenced by gifts bought for Mother's and Father's Days. Sales increase in October, November, and December is influenced by holiday shopping.

Scales and Bar Graphs

1-5

▶ Lesson Link You know how to read and interpret a bar graph. Now you will construct a bar graph. ◀

A bar graph is a way to visually display and compare numerical data. The **scale** of a bar graph is the "ruler" that measures the heights of the bars. The **intervals** are the equal divisions marked on the scale to make it easier to read. The lines on which a bar graph is built are the **horizontal axis** and the **vertical axis**.

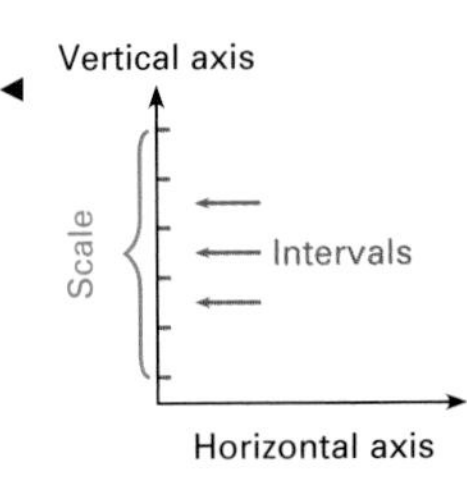

You'll Learn ...

■ to make a bar graph

... How It's Used

Political analysts use bar graphs to communicate the popularity of presidential candidates.

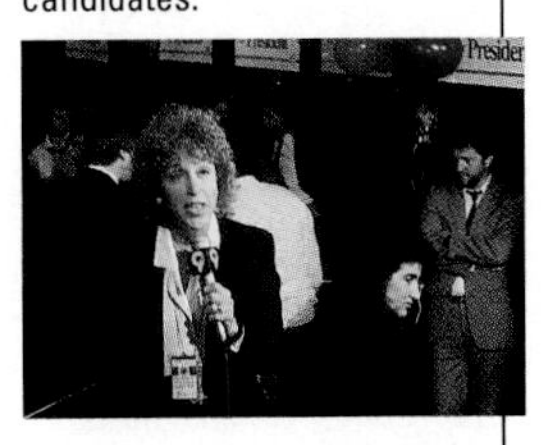

Vocabulary

scale
interval
horizontal axis
vertical axis
range

Explore | Scales on Bar Graphs

Tipping the Scales for Victory!

Materials: Spreadsheet software

The map shows five regions of the country and the number of electoral votes each region casts for President. Presidential candidates often try to attract voters regionally rather than nationwide. A candidate who can win great popularity in three regions is likely to win the election.

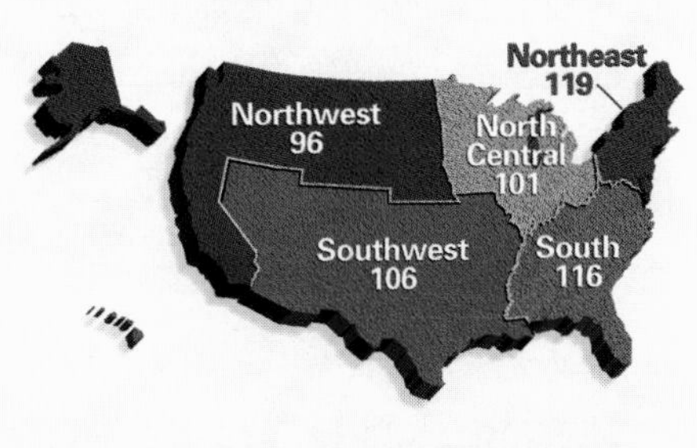

1. On a blank spreadsheet, enter the names of each region in column A. Enter the electoral vote totals in column B.
2. Using the data in the spreadsheet, draw a bar graph.
3. Using the data in the spreadsheet, draw a second bar graph. This time, use a small number for the scale.
4. Using the data in the spreadsheet, draw a third bar graph. This time, use a large number for the scale.
5. Explain how the choice of scale affects the look of a bar graph.

1-5 Lesson Organizer

Objective

■ Make a bar graph.

Vocabulary

■ Scale, interval, horizontal axis, vertical axis, range

Materials

■ Explore: Spreadsheet software

NCTM Standards

■ 1–4, 10

▶ Review

Find each difference.

1. 33 − 15 18
2. 68 − 39 29
3. 80 − 27 53
4. 104 − 28 76

Available on Daily Transparency 1-5

1 Introduce

Explore

The Point
Students investigate how changing the scale of a bar graph can change the perception of the differences between the values in the graph.

Ongoing Assessment
Check that students understand how to enter data into the spreadsheet program and that they can vary the scale intervals.

For Groups That Finish Early
A President must have 270 electoral votes to be elected. Calculate the totals for all combinations of three regions to verify that winning three regions basically guarantees victory.

Answers for Explore on next page.

MEETING INDIVIDUAL NEEDS

Resources

1-5 Practice
1-5 Reteaching
1-5 Problem Solving
1-5 Enrichment
1-5 Daily Transparency
Problem of the Day
Review
Quick Quiz
Technology Master 3

Interactive CD-ROM Spreadsheet/ Grapher Tool

Wide World of Mathematics Middle School: Graphs in the News

Learning Modalities

Visual Students may find it easier to make more accurate graphs if they use grid paper with rather large squares, as they can make the bars the same width and the same distance apart, and the heights of the bars are easy to determine.

Social Students can work with a partner to construct the bar graphs in **Explore**.

Inclusion

Be aware that learning-disabled students may be confused by data displayed on graphs with different scales. Use stacking cubes to help these students work with bar graphs.

Answers for Explore

1. Northwest 96; Southwest 106; North Central 101; South 116; Northeast 119.
2. Possible answer:

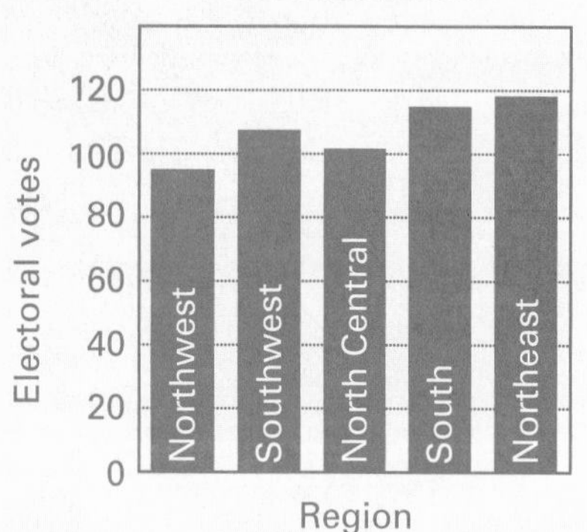

3. Possible answer: Bar graph with smaller scales than student's graph in Step 2.
4. Possible answer: Bar graph with larger scales than student's graph in Step 2.
5. The size of intervals used does not affect the final look of the bar graph.

2 Teach

Learn

Alternate Examples

1. Use the data in Example 1 to make a bar graph with intervals of 2. Label the graph and give the graph a title.

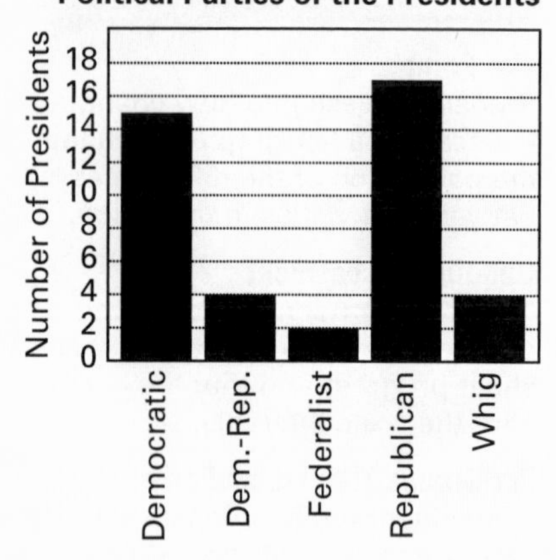

DID YOU KNOW?

Sometimes people define a range by saying "from (the lowest number) to (the highest number)." You could say this data set has a range "from 28 to 31."

Learn Scales and Bar Graphs

The **range** of a data set refers to the difference between the highest value and the lowest value. For this data set, the highest value is 31, and the lowest is 28. The difference, 31 – 28, is 3. The range is 3.

Number of Days in Month			
31	28	31	30
31	30	31	31
30	31	30	31

When data in a set are spread fairly evenly from low values to high values, it is often best to start the scale on a bar graph at 0.

Example 1

A political party is a group of citizens who want to influence the government by having their members elected to government offices. The first 42 U.S. Presidents came from five political parties. Use the data to make a bar graph.

Party	Number of Presidents
Democratic	15
Democratic-Republican	4
Federalist	2
Republican	17
Whig	4

Top value of scale must be greater than 17. Numbers ending in zero are easy to understand and to divide into intervals. Therefore 20 is a good choice for the top of the scale.

The lowest number in the data is 2. Data are spread fairly evenly across the range from 2 to 17, so zero is a convenient choice for the bottom of the scale.

20
15
10
5
0

← It is easy to divide 20 into intervals of 5, but you could also use intervals of 2, 4, or 10.

Represent each party with vertical bars of the same width. Label the bars and give the graph a title.

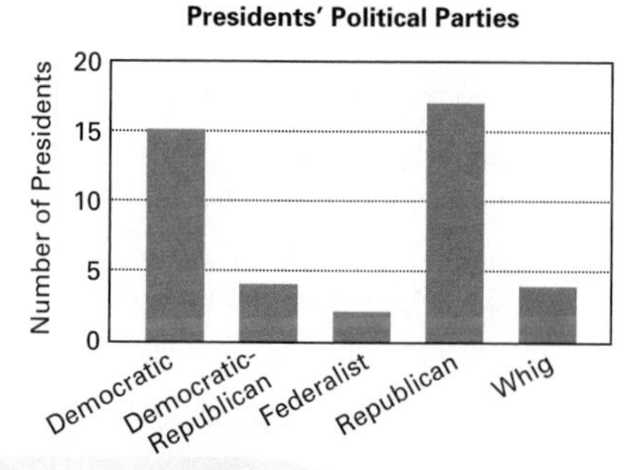

Mental Math

Every number that ends in 0 or 5 can be evenly broken into groups of 5.

MATH EVERY DAY

Problem of the Day

Copy the problem and fill in the missing digits.

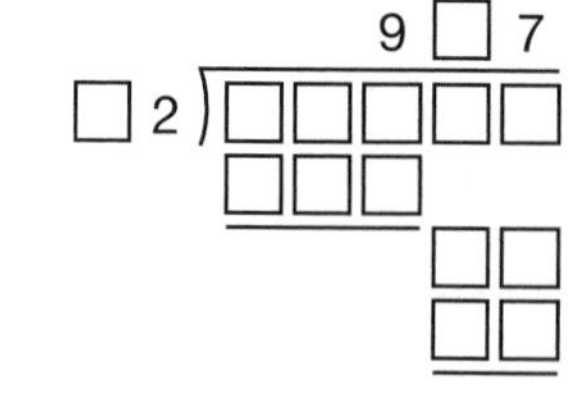

$$\begin{array}{r} 907 \\ 12\overline{)10884} \\ \underline{108} \\ 84 \\ \underline{84} \end{array}$$

Available on Daily Transparency 1-5

An Extension is provided in the transparency package.

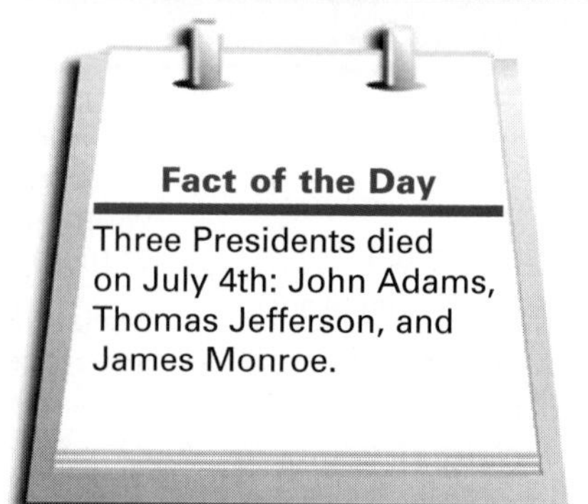

Mental Math

Find each difference mentally.

1. 350 − 250 100
2. 87 − 47 40
3. 57 − 23 34
4. 225 − 25 200
5. 809 − 502 307

Sometimes all of the data are crowded at the top end of the range. Sometimes a wide part of the range has no data. In these situations, you may want to "break" the scale.

Example 2

Make a bar graph of the data.

Lengths of the Great Lakes (through widest point)					
Lake	Erie	Huron	Michigan	Ontario	Superior
Length (mi)	241	206	307	193	350

Since all of the data are 193 or greater, you may want to skip over the values between 0 and 193 by breaking the scale, in order to save space. If you want to show the actual heights of all the bars, however, use the entire scale beginning at 0, as in the right-hand graph.

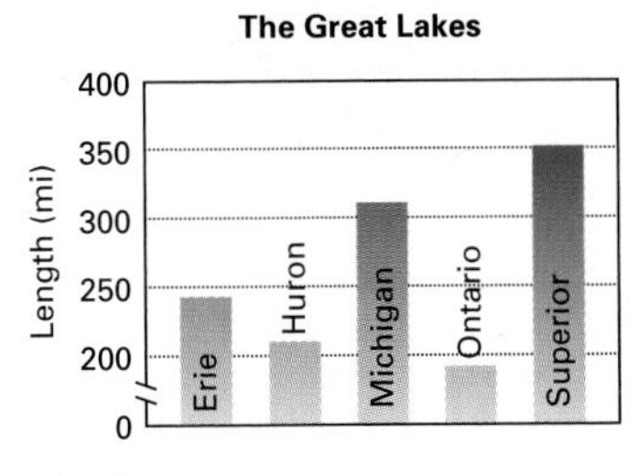

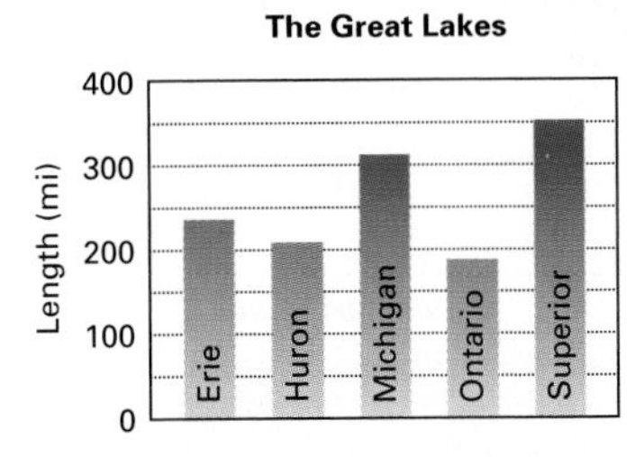

Try It

Make a bar graph of the data showing female Prime Ministers years in office.

Years in Office	5	18	11	13

Check Your Understanding

1. How does the range affect the scale and intervals of a bar graph?
2. When should you use a broken scale on a bar graph? Give an example.
3. Is only one scale possible for a given bar graph? Explain.

Alternate Examples

2. Make a bar graph of the widths of the Great Lakes: Erie: 57 mi; Huron: 183 mi; Michigan: 118 mi; Ontario: 53 mi; Superior: 160 mi.

   Skip the values between 0 and 50. Use intervals of 10 or 20, and 190 as the greatest value

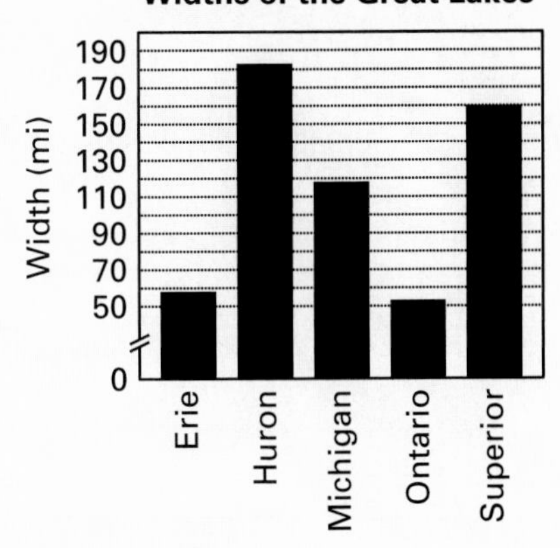

Answers for Try It

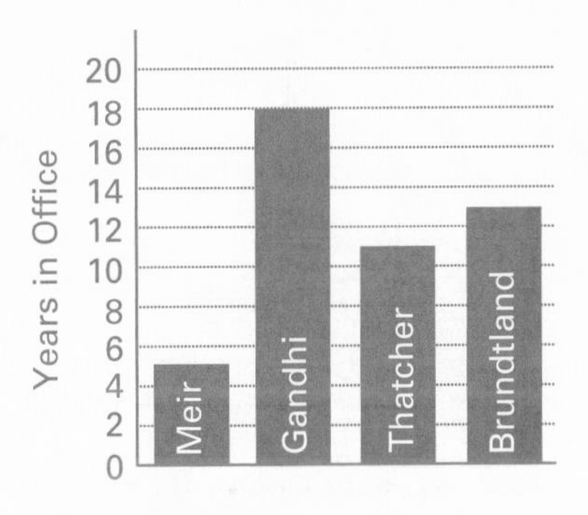

3 Practice and Assess

Check

Answers for Check Your Understanding

1. Data with a large range usually has large intervals to fit the scale. Data with a small range usually has small intervals within the scale for the range.
2. A broken scale is used when all of the data clusters are in a small range but the range is not near zero. For example, height in inches of basketball players would be numbers that are somewhat close together, but none of them would be close to zero.
3. No; There are several different possible scales for a graph. It depends on how much space you want the graph to take.

MEETING MIDDLE SCHOOL CLASSROOM NEEDS

Tips from Middle School Teachers

I have students keep a record of temperatures, game scores for a sports team, or other relevant data and then have them make bar graphs to be displayed on the class bulletin board.

Cooperative Learning

The three graphs constructed in **Explore** were vertical bar graphs. Have students work in groups of three or four to use the same data and draw a horizontal bar graph using paper and pencil.

History Connection

Grover Cleveland is both the twenty-second and the twenty-fourth President! He served a term from 1885 to 1889 and another from 1893 to 1897. He lost the election of 1888 to Benjamin Harrison. Cleveland got a bigger popular vote, but Harrison had more votes from the electors.

1-5 Exercises and Applications

Assignment Guide

- **Basic** 1–5, 7–17 odds
- **Average** 1–6, 8–18 evens
- **Enriched** 1–6, 10–18 evens

Exercise Answers

1. a. Range 13, interval 2.
   b. Range 90, interval 25.
2. a. 4; b.

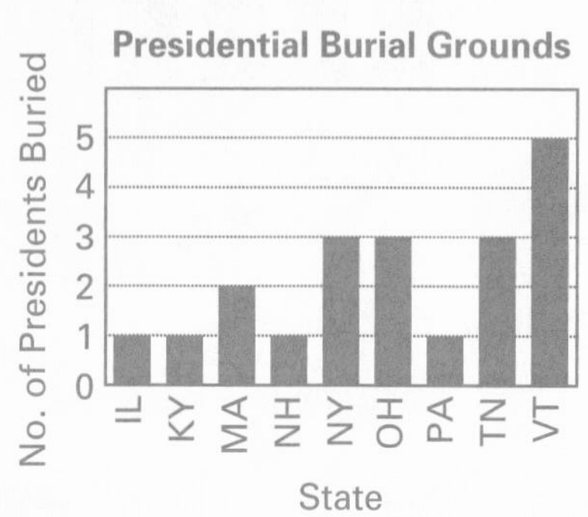

3.

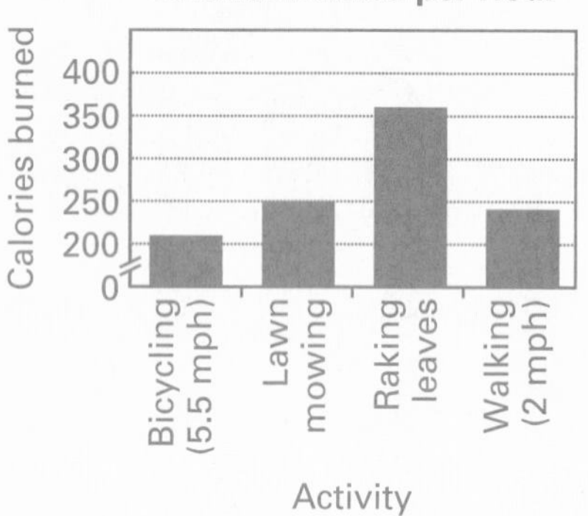

Reteaching

Activity

- Make a bar graph using the data for electoral votes given on page 29.
- Choose a convenient scale. Use equal intervals of 5 along the vertical scale.
- Place region names at the bottom.

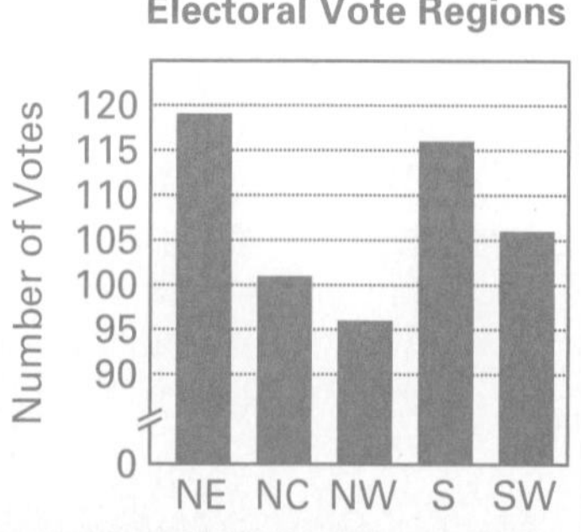

1-5 Exercises and Applications

PRACTICE 1-5

Practice and Apply

Lincoln's burial site

1. **Getting Started** For each data set, give the range and choose the better interval to use for a bar graph.
   a. Data: 3, 6, 9, 12, 15, 16; interval of 2 or 10?
   b. Data: 55, 101, 120, 145; interval of 10 or 25?

2. **Social Studies** Many people consider Presidential burial grounds to be of important historical value. The first 20 Presidents were buried in the following states: Illinois (1), Kentucky (1), Massachusetts (2), New Hampshire (1), New York (3), Ohio (3), Pennsylvania (1), Tennessee (3), Vermont (5).
   a. What is the range of values in this set of data?
   b. Make a bar graph of the data.

3. **Science** Make a bar graph to show the calories burned each hour by a 150-pound person while doing an activity. Use a broken scale, if appropriate.

Bicycling

Mowing the Lawn

Raking Leaves

360 calories

Walking

4. **Test Prep** What interval is used on this bar graph's scale? A
   Ⓐ 5 Ⓑ 0
   Ⓒ 10 Ⓓ 15

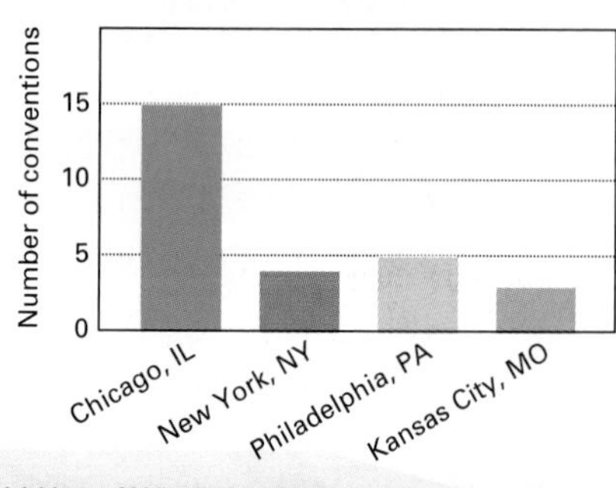

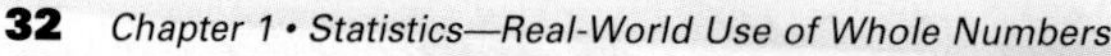

PRACTICE

Name ______________________ **Practice 1-5**

Scales and Bar Graphs

1. Make a bar graph from the data showing the number of answering machines sold from 1989 to 1993.

Year	Millions of machines
1989	3.7
1990	5.6
1991	8.0
1992	11.1
1993	13.6

Answering Machines Sold

2. **Social Science** The data shows the average size of U.S. households from 1960 to 1990. Make a bar graph of the data.

Year	Average household size
1960	3.33
1970	3.14
1980	2.76
1990	2.63

Average Household Size

3. What is the range of the data for the average household size in Exercise 2?
   0.70

4. **Career** The data shows the 1990 average weekly earnings of workers in several industries. Make a bar graph of the data. Use a broken scale, if appropriate.

Industry	Earnings
Iron and steel foundries	484.99
Electric and electric equipment	420.65
Machinery, non-electrical	494.34
Hardware, cutlery, hand tools	440.08
Fabricated metal products	447.28

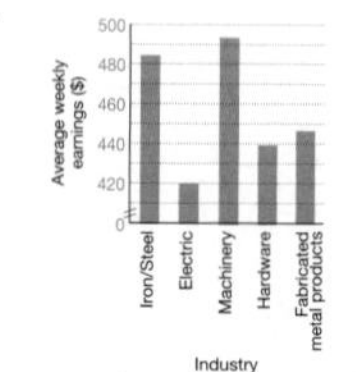

RETEACHING

Name ______________________ **Alternative Lesson 1-5**

Scales and Bar Graphs

A bar graph is a way to visually display and compare numerical data. The **scale** of a bar graph is the "ruler" that measures the heights of the bars. The **intervals** are the equal divisions marked on the scale to make it easier to read. The lines on which a bar graph is built are the **horizontal axis** and the **vertical axis**. The **range** of a data set refers to the difference between the highest value and the lowest value.

Example

Sam followed these steps to make a bar graph using the data on mountain heights.

Step 1: He used a scale from 0 to 30,000 since the highest mountain was 29,000 feet. The range of data is 25,000. He used intervals of 5,000 because 30,000 is divisible by 5,000.

Step 2: He drew bars to represent the data and labeled the bars.

Step 3: He wrote a title for the graph.

Mountain Heights

Try It Use the data to complete the bar graph.

Ocean Depths (to nearest thousand meters)

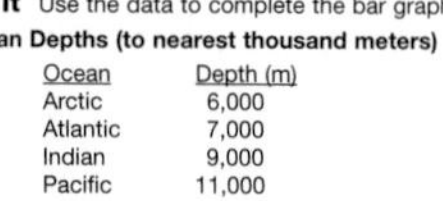

Ocean	Depth (m)
Arctic	6,000
Atlantic	7,000
Indian	9,000
Pacific	11,000

Ocean Depths

a. What is the range of the data? 5000 meters.

b. What interval was used on the vertical scales? 2000

c. Would it be reasonable to use an interval of 20,000? Explain.
No. Since the data will be graphed in one interval, it would be hard to read and interpret.

d. Draw bars that represent the depths of the Indian, Pacific, and Atlantic oceans.

e. Label and shade the bars. Give the graph a title.

f. Write a problem that can be solved using the data in the graph.
Possible answer: How much deeper is the Pacific Ocean than the Atlantic Ocean?

Problem Solving and Reasoning

5. Geography The graphs show the average temperatures of two of the coldest and two of the warmest cities in the United States.

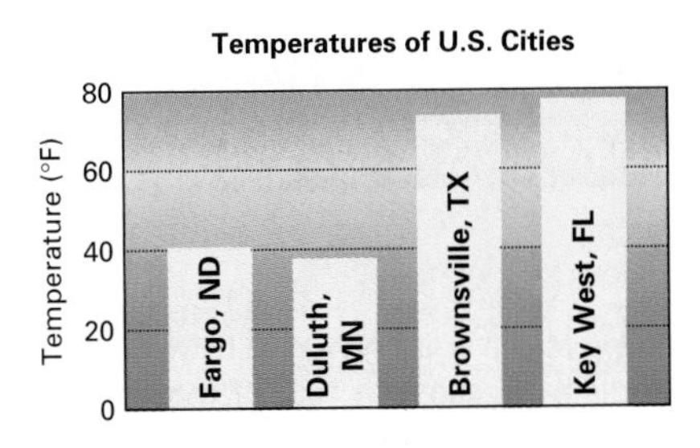

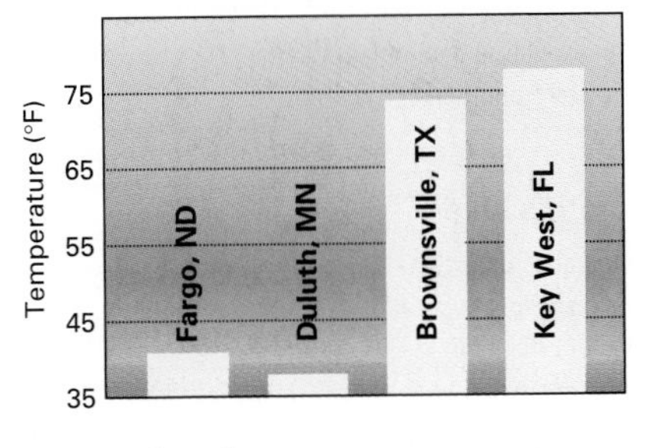

a. For each graph, give the range of values and the interval used on the scale.

b. Critical Thinking Compare the appearance of the two graphs. Could either graph be misleading? Explain.

c. Communicate Describe the shape of the data shown in the bar graphs.

6. Critical Thinking The bar graph was made from the following data.

a. Two of the bars have been drawn incorrectly. Which two have been drawn wrong? What is wrong about them?

b. The scale used in the graph is not convenient. What would be a better scale for this data?

Sandal Prices

Price ($): 30, 24, 18, 12, 6

Shop n' Spend, Shoe String Budgets, Max's Fine Footwear, The Retread

Price of a Pair of Sandals	
Shop'n'Spend	$10
Shoe String Budgets	$12
Max's Fine Footwear	$23
The Retread	$15

7. 8587 8. 70,441 9. 718,530
10. 26,070 11. 32,717 12. 981,599
13. 3594 14. 13,006 15. 153,885
16. 6375 17. 13,991 18. 565,994

Mixed Review

Perform the appropriate operation. *[Previous course]*

7. 4678 + 3909 **8.** 12,439 + 58,002 **9.** 536,092 + 182,438

10. 9,346 + 16,724 **11.** 25,392 + 7,325 **12.** 36,382 + 945,217

13. 6329 − 2735 **14.** 51,027 − 38,021 **15.** 837,327 − 683,442

16. 7003 − 628 **17.** 23,422 − 9,431 **18.** 603,288 − 37,294

Exercise Notes

Exercise 5

Geography One of the lowest temperatures ever recorded in North Dakota was −60°F and one of the highest temperatures ever recorded in Texas was 120°F.

Exercise Answers

5. a. The first graph has range 40, interval 20. The second graph has range 40, interval 10.
   b. Possible answer: Yes; The second graph could be misleading because the vertical axis does not begin at 0.
   c. Possible answer: The two cold cities are approximately the same and the two warm cities are approximately the same. The two warm cities have temperatures approximately double the temperatures of the cold cities.
6. a. The bar for Shop 'n' Spend should have a height of $10. The bar for Max's Fine Footwear should have a height of $23.
   b. 5

Alternate Assessment

Self Assessment Ask students to describe what they like best about making a bar graph and also what they find most difficult about making a bar graph.

Quick Quiz

Find the range and choose the better interval for a bar graph of the given data.

1. 5, 8, 12, 16, 20; interval of 2 or 5. Range, 15; Interval, 2.
2. 25, 75, 125, 150, 200; interval of 10 or 25. Range, 175; Interval, 25.

Available on Daily Transparency 1-5

PROBLEM SOLVING

Name ____________

Guided Problem Solving 1-5

GPS PROBLEM 2, STUDENT PAGE 32

Many people consider Presidential burial grounds to be of important historical value. The first 20 presidents were buried in the following states: Illinois (1), Kentucky (1), Massachusetts (2), New Hampshire (1), New York (3), Ohio (3), Pennsylvania (1), Tennessee (3), Vermont (5).

a. What is the range of values in this set of data?

b. Make a bar graph of the data.

Understand

1. How can you find the range? Subtract the least number from the greatest number.

Plan

2. What will each axis on your graph will represent? One axis will be the number of presidents, and the other axis will be the states.

3. What interval will you use on the axis showing the number of presidents buried in each state? Explain. One, because the data is represented by one-digit numbers.

Solve

4. What is the range of values? 4

5. Draw and shade the bars that represent the number of burial grounds for each state. The one for Illinois is completed for you. Give the graph a title.

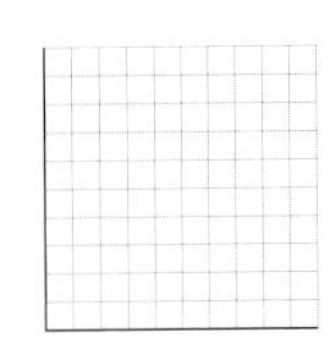

Look Back

6. How can you make sure you have graphed the data accurately? Check each bar to make sure its height reflects the correct number of presidents.

SOLVE ANOTHER PROBLEM

The next three presidents were buried in New York, New Jersey, and Indiana. Use a different color pencil to add this information to your graph. How does this affect the range? The range remains the same.

ENRICHMENT

Name ____________

Extend Your Thinking 1-5

Decision Making

Make a bar graph of the topic of your choice. You might want to find data such as climate in your social studies book, or the amount of calcium in your health book. You can use the questions below to help you organize your work.

1. Write the data about your topic in these spaces. Check students' work.

2. Write a number sentence to show the range of your data. Check students' work.

3. What interval will you use on your scale? How did you decide which interval to use? Check students' work.

4. Use the information in Questions 1, 2, and 3 to construct your bar graph. Check students' work.

5. Which way is easier to use when analyzing the data—a list or a bar graph? Explain. Possible answer: A bar graph because it is easier to compare the data visually and make generalizations.

1-6 Lesson Organizer

Objective

- Organize large sets of data into stem-and-leaf diagrams.

Vocabulary

- Stem-and-leaf diagram

NCTM Standards

- 1–5, 7, 10

Review

Order from least to greatest.

1. 352, 389, 362, 304, 321
   304, 321, 352, 362, 389
2. 1923, 1920, 1900, 1953
   1900, 1920, 1923, 1953
3. 56, 52, 54, 56, 59, 57
   52, 54, 56, 56, 57, 59

Available on Daily Transparency 1-6

1 Introduce

Explore

The Point
Students explore how a set of data can have a shape.

Ongoing Assessment
Check that students are able to order the numbers within each thousands interval. Remind them to order by the hundreds digits, and if those are the same to order by the tens digits, and so on.

For Groups That Finish Early
In how many cities did Bill Clinton lead both George Bush and Ross Perot? 15 cities

Follow Up
After interpreting the numbers in the three lists, students should welcome strategies for making the work easier.

1-6 Stem-and-Leaf Diagrams

You'll Learn ...

■ to organize large sets of data into stem-and-leaf diagrams

... How It's Used

Paleontologists use stem-and-leaf diagrams to study the sizes of groups of dinosaurs.

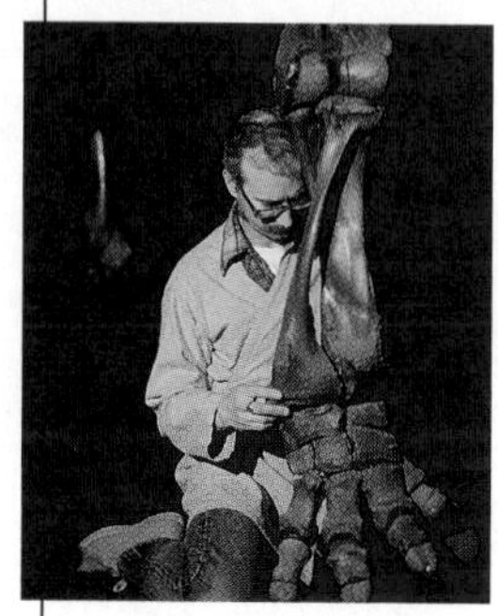

Vocabulary

stem-and-leaf diagram

▶ Lesson Link You've seen how a line plot helps to organize individual pieces of data. Sometimes, you need to organize data in intervals.◄

Explore Ordering Data

The Maine Event

The 1992 Presidential election in Maine was a tight race between three candidates—Bill Clinton, George Bush, and Ross Perot. The table shows the total votes for each candidate in the 16 largest cities in Maine.

1992 Maine Election Results

City	Clinton	Bush	Perot	City	Clinton	Bush	Perot
Auburn	5,025	3,653	3,964	Old Town	2,272	1,173	1,302
Augusta	4,657	3,003	3,002	Portland	19,510	8,660	6,910
Bangor	6,826	5,185	4,689	Rockland	1,192	1,081	1,059
Bath	1,988	1,630	1,458	Saco	4,000	2,769	2,303
Biddeford	4,945	2,533	2,717	Sanford	3,854	3,030	3,215
Brewer	1,788	1,907	1,625	So. Portland	5,933	3,999	2,734
Gardiner	1,391	1,054	1,115	Waterville	3,868	1,832	2,257
Lewiston	9,265	4,372	6,180	Westbrook	3,665	2,904	2,512

1. Order each candidate's 16 totals from greatest to least.
2. For each candidate, determine the strongest city and the weakest city.
3. Describe any voting patterns you see in the table.

George Bush (left), Ross Perot (center), and Bill Clinton (right)

MEETING INDIVIDUAL NEEDS

Resources

1-6 Practice
1-6 Reteaching
1-6 Problem Solving
1-6 Enrichment
1-6 Daily Transparency
  Problem of the Day
  Review
  Quick Quiz

Learning Modalities

Logical Have students round each total in **Explore** lists to the nearest thousand and find the totals for the 16 cities. Ask: "According to the data for these 16 cities, was the race really close?" No; Bush's and Perot's totals were relatively close, at 50,000 and 47,000, but Clinton's total was much greater, 81,000.

Social Have students work in groups of three or four to organize **Explore** lists. In groups of three, each student can organize one candidate's totals. In groups of four, each student can be assigned a different interval for all three lists.

English Language Development

Write the numbers 10, 12, 13, 14, 14, 16, and 18 on the chalkboard. Then draw a diagram of a stem with seven leaves. Label the stem "1" and write the ones digits of the seven numbers on the leaves, one to each leaf. It might be helpful to bring in a real stem with leaves and label them with masking-tape numbers.

Learn Stem-and-Leaf Diagrams

A **stem-and-leaf diagram** is a graph that shows the shape of the data according to the data place values. The "leaf" of a number is usually the right-hand digit. The "stem" is the portion of the number to the left of the leaf.

Number		Stem	Leaf
47	→	4	7
710	→	71	0
8802	→	880	2
6	→	0	6

Example 1

Analyze the shape of the data in the table by making a stem-and-leaf diagram.

Ages of 20th-Century Presidents at Inauguration

42	51	56	55
51	54	51	60
62	43	55	56
61	52	69	64
46			

Draw two columns, and write the stems in the left column. Since all of the data are in the 40s, 50s, and 60s, you need only three stems: 4, 5, and 6. For every number, write the last digit (the leaf) in the right column on the same line as the matching stem.

Stem	Leaf
4	2 3 6
5	1 6 5 1 4 1 5 6 2
6	0 2 1 9 4

Kennedy was inaugurated at age 43.

Now redraw the diagram, ordering the leaves from least to greatest.

Stem	Leaf
4	2 3 6
5	1 1 1 2 4 5 5 6 6
6	0 1 2 4 9

The diagram shows that the data range from 42 to 69, that the most frequent age is 51, and that most Presidents were in their 50s when they took office. Note that, unlike most bar graphs and tally charts, a stem-and-leaf diagram groups data in intervals.

Try It

Make a stem-and-leaf diagram of the bowling scores.

130	90	141	128	133	142	113	148	105	93
118	130	133	100	124	146	97	108	126	115
136	144	114	101	93	108	95	143	128	141

DID YOU KNOW?

Sometimes the numbers in a set of data are so large that the last two digits are used as the leaf.

History Link

Three Presidents have been elected even though they didn't receive the highest number of votes from the people: John Quincy Adams in 1824, Rutherford Hayes in 1876, and Benjamin Harrison in 1888.

Stem	Leaf
9	0 3 3 5 7
10	0 1 5 8 8
11	3 4 5 8
12	4 6 8 8
13	0 0 3 3 6
14	1 1 2 3 4 6 8

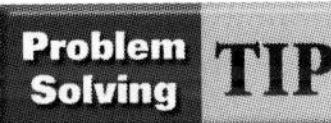

It may be helpful to write down all of the stems before you begin to plot the leaves.

Answers for Explore

1. Clinton: 19,510; 9265; 6826; 5933; 5025; 4945; 4657; 4000; 3868; 3854; 3665; 2272; 1988; 1788; 1391; 1192
   Bush: 8660; 5185; 4372; 3999; 3653; 3030; 3003; 2904; 2769; 2533; 1907; 1832; 1630; 1173; 1081; 1054
   Perot: 6910; 6180; 4689; 3964; 3215; 3002; 2734; 2717; 2512; 2303; 2257; 1625; 1458; 1302; 1115; 1059
2. Clinton: Strongest, Portland; Weakest, Rockland.
   Bush: Strongest, Portland; Weakest, Gardiner.
   Perot: Strongest, Portland; Weakest, Rockland.
3. Possible answers: About half of the data were below 3000. Clinton has the one data number bigger than 10,000.

2 Teach

Learn

Alternate Examples

The ages of the 18th- and 19th-century United States Presidents at their inaugurations are given below. Analyze the data by making a stem-and-leaf diagram.

57, 57, 49, 52, 51, 61, 61, 64, 56, 47, 57, 54, 50, 46, 55, 57, 68, 48, 54, 55, 58, 51, 65, 49, 54

Stem	Leaf
4	6 7 8 9 9
5	0 1 1 2 4 4 4 5 5 6 7 7 7 7 8
6	1 1 4 5 8

The diagram shows that the data range from 46 to 68, that the most frequent age is 57, and that most Presidents were in their 50s when they took office.

MATH EVERY DAY

Problem of the Day

Move three straws to make 5 squares that are the same size.

Available on Daily Transparency 1-6

An Extension is provided in the transparency package.

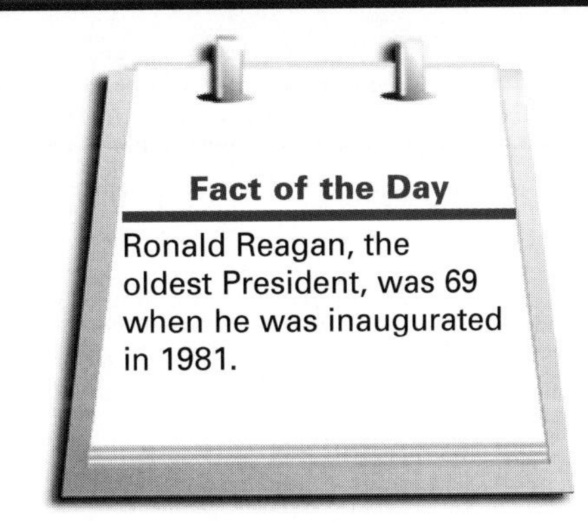

Estimation

Estimate.

1. 3 × 21 60
2. 24 × 6 150
3. 12 × 45 450
4. 710 × 8 5600
5. 5 × 8400 40,000

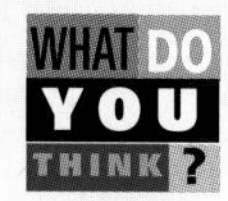

Students see a frequency chart and a stem-and-leaf diagram for the same data. They are asked to describe advantages and disadvantages for both representations.

Answers for What Do You Think?

1. Possible answers: Catherine: Most members have ages from 11 to 30 Jamar: Most members are in their twenties; the youngest member is 9; the oldest is 59; the middle age is 22.5; the most common age is 21; the range is 50.
2. Possible answers: Both displays show the interval from 11 to 30 is most common; Jamar's shows the exact range of the ages; Catherine's graph is good if you don't need to know exact ages.

3 Practice and Assess

Check

Ask students how many different numbers would be needed for the scale of a line plot for the information in **What Do You Think?** 20 They should recognize that a line plot of a large set of data is cumbersome and inefficient.

Answers for Check Your Understanding

1. Similarities: Both diagrams show the shape of the data. Differences: A line plot shows a picture of the data for each value, whereas a stem-and-leaf diagram shows a picture of the data by intervals.
2. A stem-and-leaf diagram is helpful because you can store a large amount of data in a smaller space. Also, sometimes a stem-and-leaf diagram can be drawn and filled in more quickly than a line plot.

Catherine and Jamar need to plan a party for their community band. Before they decide on what kind of party to have, they want to see how the ages of the band members are distributed.

Community Band Member Ages									
21	34	16	26	41	21	9	34	19	11
20	39	24	18	21	59	32	14	32	41
14	21	36	43	27	26	16	28	13	20

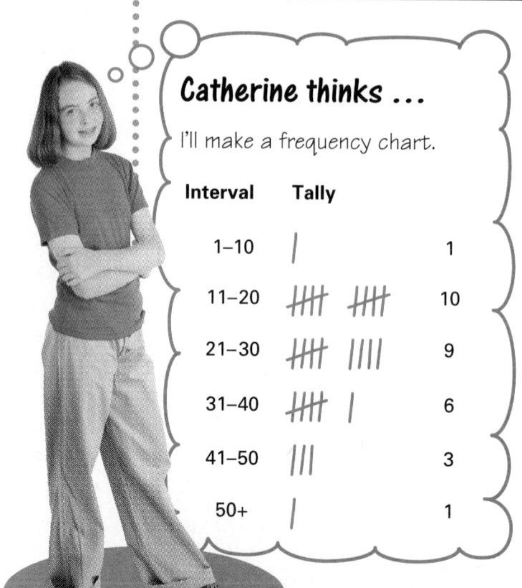

Catherine thinks . . .

I'll make a frequency chart.

Interval	Tally	
1–10	|	1
11–20	𝍸 𝍸	10
21–30	𝍸 ||||	9
31–40	𝍸 |	6
41–50	|||	3
50+	|	1

Jamar thinks . . .

I'll make a stem-and-leaf diagram.

Stem	Leaf
0	9
1	1 3 4 4 6 6 8 9
2	0 0 1 1 1 1 4 6 6 7 8
3	2 2 4 4 6 9
4	1 1 3
5	9

What do you think?

1. What conclusions can Catherine and Jamar draw from their displays?
2. For what purposes could you use either display equally well? When might Jamar's display have an advantage over Catherine's? When might Catherine's display have an advantage over Jamar's?

Check Your Understanding

1. How is a stem-and-leaf diagram like a line plot? How is it different?
2. Why is a stem-and-leaf diagram helpful when trying to organize a large set of data?

MEETING MIDDLE SCHOOL CLASSROOM NEEDS

Tips from Middle School Teachers

I find that it helps students to be able to read and interpret graphs before they try to construct them. So I provide many opportunities for them to study and talk about a great variety of graphical representations.

Cooperative Learning

- Students should work in groups of three or four and write down fifteen two-digit numbers
- Each group should sort the numbers and create a stem-and-leaf diagram.
- Have the groups exchange their set of numbers with other groups and then create a stem-and-leaf diagram for the new set of numbers.
- Finally, select one student from each group to write the group's stem-and-leaf diagram on the chalkboard so that all groups can check their work.

History Connection

Eight Presidents died in office. Four were assassinated: Abraham Lincoln, James Garfield, William McKinley, and John F. Kennedy. Four died of natural causes: William Henry Harrison, Zachary Taylor, Warren G. Harding, and Franklin D. Roosevelt.

1-6 Exercises and Applications

Practice and Apply

1. **Getting Started** Follow the steps to make a stem-and-leaf diagram of the data.

   27, 38, 42, 18, 29, 40, 19, 10, 32, 47, 19, 36, 42

   a. Use two columns. Write the stems from least to greatest. Write each leaf to the right of its stem.

Stem	Leaf
1	
2	
?	
?	

   b. Redraw the stem-and-leaf diagram, with the leaves in order from least to greatest.

Stem	Leaf
1	
2	
?	
?	

2. **Science** Make a stem-and-leaf diagram from the data.

   GPS The ten fastest fish in the world (in miles per hour) include the following: sailfish, 68; blue shark, 43; swordfish, 40; marlin, 50; bluefin tuna, 46; wahoo, 41; tarpon, 35; bonefish, 40; yellowfin tuna, 44; tiger shark, 33.

3. **History** Make a stem-and-leaf diagram from the ages of the first 20 Presidents at death.

Presidents	Age	Presidents	Age	Presidents	Age
Washington	67	Van Buren	79	Buchanan	77
J. Adams	90	W. Harrison	68	Lincoln	56
Jefferson	83	Tyler	71	A. Johnson	66
Madison	85	Polk	53	Grant	63
Monroe	73	Taylor	65	Hayes	70
J. Q. Adams	80	Fillmore	74	Garfield	49
Jackson	78	Pierce	64		

The Lincoln assassination

Use the stem-and-leaf diagram for Exercises 4–7.

Stem	Leaf
2	1
3	0 0 4 4 7 8
5	0 2 2 2 2 3 3

4. What is the range of the values? 32
5. What value appears most often? 52
6. What's the largest number in the data that's less than 50? 38
7. **Test Prep** How many times was 53 a data item? A

   Ⓐ two Ⓑ three Ⓒ five Ⓓ thirty-three

PRACTICE 1-6

PRACTICE

Name ____________

Practice 1-6

Stem-and-Leaf Diagrams

Use the stem-and-leaf diagram for Exercises 1–4.

stem	leaf
6	7 8 8
7	0 1 2 3 4 9 9
8	1 3 3 3 4 7
9	0 2 5

1. What is the range of the values? 28
2. What value appears most often? 83
3. How many times does the value 79 appear? 2 times
4. What is the largest number in the data that is less than 90? 87
5. Make a stem-and-leaf diagram of the data showing scores on a history test.

   84, 93, 72, 87, 75, 86, 97, 68, 74, 86, 91, 64, 83, 79, 80, 72, 83, 76, 90, 77

stem	leaf
6	48
7	2245679
8	0334667
9	0137

6. Make a stem-and-leaf diagram of the data showing the number of badges earned by local scouts.

   7, 12, 9, 2, 17, 24, 0, 3, 10, 20, 12, 3, 6, 4, 9, 15

stem	leaf
0	023346799
1	02257
2	04

7. Make a stem-and-leaf diagram of the data showing the number of compact discs owned by some students.

   17, 36, 0, 64, 5, 0, 39, 12, 7, 19, 67, 42, 0, 3, 12, 4, 9, 13, 17, 31, 0

stem	leaf
0	000034579
1	223779
3	169
4	2
6	47

8. **History** The data shows the number of individuals who served as cabinet members for each of the first 21 Presidents. Make a stem-and-leaf plot of the data.

Washington: 11	J. Adams: 8	Jefferson: 10
Madison: 16	Monroe: 8	J.Q. Adams: 6
Jackson: 19	Van Buren: 10	W. Harrison: 6
Tyler: 21	Polk: 9	Taylor: 7
Fillmore: 11	Pierce: 7	Buchanan: 14
Lincoln: 13	A. Johnson: 13	Grant: 23
Hayes: 10	Garfield: 7	Arthur: 17

stem	leaf
0	66777889
1	00011334679
2	13

RETEACHING

Name ____________

Alternative Lesson 1-6

Stem-and-Leaf Diagrams

A **stem-and-leaf diagram** is a graph that shows the shape of the data according to the data place values. The **"leaf"** of a number is usually the right-hand digit. The leaf is one digit. The **"stem"** is the portion of the number to the left of the leaf. The stem can be one or more digits.

— Example —

Make a stem-and-leaf diagram using the data showing minutes spent eating lunch.

Minutes Spent Eating Lunch
46, 35, 12, 37, 28, 10, 22, 54, 19, 13, 46, 51

Step 1: Decide what the stem of the diagram will represent. Since these data are two-digit numbers, the stem will be the tens digits and the leaves will be the ones digits.

Step 2: Write the tens digits in order in the left-hand column of the diagram. Then write each leaf at the right of its stem as they occur in the problem.

Step 3: Complete the second stem-and-leaf diagram, with the leaves in order from least to greatest.

Step 2

Stem	Leaf
1	2 0 9 3
2	8 2
3	5 7
4	6 6
5	4 1

Step 3

Stem	Leaf
1	0 2 3 9
2	2 8
3	5 7
4	6 6
5	1 4

Try It

a. Make a stem-and-leaf diagram of the data showing the monthly attendance at the teen club.

Attendance at Teen Club
489, 527, 479, 519, 514, 480, 493, 523, 508, 504

1. Write the stems in the left column. Since all of the data are in the 47s, 48s, 49s, 50s, 51s, and 52s, you need six stems.
2. For each number, write the last digit (the leaf) in the right column on the same line as the matching stem.

Step 2

Stem	Leaf
47	9
48	9 0
49	3
50	8 4
51	9 4
52	7 3

Step 3

Stem	Leaf
47	9
48	0 9
49	3
50	4 8
51	4 9
52	3 7

b. Make a stem-and-leaf diagram to show the data in this chart. Remember to put the leaves in order.

Sit-ups in One Minute
35, 28, 52, 58, 12, 29, 41, 37, 19, 23, 26, 45

Step 2

Stem	Leaf
1	2 9
2	8 9 3 6
3	5 7
4	1 5
5	2 8

Step 3

Stem	Leaf
1	2 9
2	3 6 8 9
3	5 7
4	1 5
5	2 8

1-6 Exercises and Applications

Assignment Guide

- **Basic** 1–2, 4–8, 10–11, 14–20 evens
- **Average** 1–10, 13–19 odds
- **Enriched** 2–4, 7–12, 14–20 evens

Exercise Notes

Exercises 2–3

The data leaves for each stem can be listed either from least to greatest or vice versa.

Exercise Answers

1. a.

Stem	Leaf
1	8 9 0 9
2	7 9
3	8 2 6
4	2 0 7 2

   b.

Stem	Leaf
1	0 8 9 9
2	7 9
3	2 6 8
4	0 2 2 7

2.

Stem	Leaf
3	3 5
4	0 0 1 3 4 6
5	0
6	8

3.

Stem	Leaf
4	9
5	3 6
6	3 4 5 6 7 8
7	0 1 3 4 7 8 9
8	0 3 5
9	0

Reteaching

Activity

Materials: Cards with the numbers 15, 17, 19, 22, 22, 27, 28, 30, 33, 35; scissors.

- Place the cards in 3 piles, using their tens digits.
- Keep the cards in groups, and cut them apart between the tens and ones digits. Put the tens digits to the left and the ones to the right.
- In the tens pile, stack the 1's, 2's, and 3's into separate piles. Then, for each tens group, arrange the ones digits from least to greatest, placing them to the right of the 1, 2, or 3.
- Name the stems. 1, 2, and 3 Name the leaves. 5, 7, 9, 2, 2, 7, 8, 0, 3, and 5

Exercise Notes

■ Exercise 8

Extension Ask how many numbers appear only once in the data. 6 What numbers are they? 7, 17, 69, 82, 91, and 92

■ Exercises 13–20

Estimation Have students estimate their answers before computing as a check for reasonableness.

Exercise Answers

8. Three; 8, 20, 96; Possible answer: Look at how many times a number appears on a row.
9. There are no data values in the 70s.
10. Possible answer: Most of the values are in the teens, the second most in the 90s, 13 is the most common value. The data can help give consumers an idea of how many cars have a certain amount of room.
11. There will be more leaves with the 5 stem because there are more ages in the 50s than in the 40s.
12. Frances Cleveland was only 21 when she became First Lady, 10 years younger than the next youngest First Lady.

Alternate Assessment

You may want to use the *Interactive CD-ROM Journal* with this assessment.

Journal Have students give examples of information that is suitable for a stem-and-leaf diagram, and examples of information that is not.

► Quick Quiz

Make a stem-and-leaf diagram of the data.

1. 42, 57, 56, 48, 42, 33

Stem	Leaf
3	3
4	2 2 8
5	6 7

2. 28, 19, 15, 23, 15, 16, 15

Stem	Leaf
1	5 5 5 6 9
2	3 8

Available on Daily Transparency 1-6

PROBLEM SOLVING 1-6

Problem Solving and Reasoning

Use the stem-and-leaf diagram for Exercises 8–10.

This stem-and-leaf diagram is based on the available amount of room in cubic feet in the car models of one manufacturer.

Stem	Leaf
0	7 8 8 8
1	3 3 3 3 3 3 3 3 3 3 6 6 7
2	0 0 0
3	3 3 3 3
6	9
8	2
9	1 2 6 6 6 8 8 9 9

8. **Communicate** How many numbers appear three times in the data? How can you tell?
9. **Critical Thinking** Why is there no 7 in the stem column?
10. Journal Describe the shape of the data. Explain how this graph could help consumers narrow their search for the best car.

This is a list of First Ladies and their ages when they became First Ladies. Use this list for Exercises 11–12.

First Ladies	Age	First Ladies	Age
Grace Coolidge	44	Lady Bird Johnson	50
Lou Hoover	53	Patricia Nixon	56
Eleanor Roosevelt	48	Betty Ford	53
Bess Truman	60	Rosalynn Carter	49
Frances Cleveland	21	Nancy Reagan	59
Mamie Eisenhower	56	Barbara Bush	64
Jacqueline Kennedy	31	Hillary Clinton	46

Frances Cleveland

11. **Critical Thinking** If you make a stem-and-leaf diagram of the data, will there be more leaves after the 4 stem or the 5 stem? Explain.
12. **Communicate** Why is the data for Frances Cleveland so unusual?

Mixed Review

Perform the appropriate operation. *[Previous course]*

13. 16×72 1152 **14.** 35×28 980 **15.** 68×20 1360 **16.** 44×91 4004

17. $386 \div 2$ 193 **18.** $483 \div 3$ 161 **19.** $790 \div 5$ 158 **20.** $987 \div 7$ 141

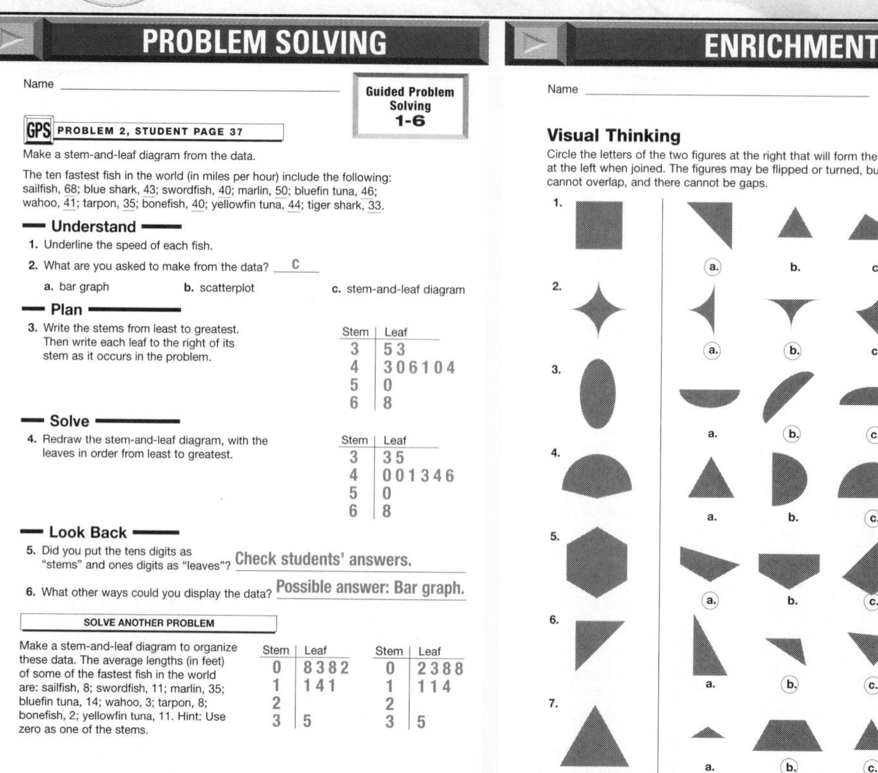

PROBLEM SOLVING

Name

Guided Problem Solving 1-6

GPS PROBLEM 2, STUDENT PAGE 37

Make a stem-and-leaf diagram from the data.

The ten fastest fish in the world (in miles per hour) include the following: sailfish, 68; blue shark, 43; swordfish, 40; marlin, 50; bluefin tuna, 46; wahoo, 41; tarpon, 35; bonefish, 40; yellowfin tuna, 44; tiger shark, 33.

— Understand —

1. Underline the speed of each fish.
2. What are you asked to make from the data? c

a. bar graph b. scatterplot c. stem-and-leaf diagram

— Plan —

3. Write the stems from least to greatest. Then write each leaf to the right of its stem as it occurs in the problem.

Stem	Leaf
3	5 3
4	3 0 6 1 0 4
5	0
6	8

— Solve —

4. Redraw the stem-and-leaf diagram, with the leaves in order from least to greatest.

Stem	Leaf
3	3 5
4	0 0 1 3 4 6
5	0
6	8

— Look Back —

5. Did you put the tens digits as "stems" and ones digits as "leaves"? Check students' answers.
6. What other ways could you display the data? Possible answer: Bar graph.

SOLVE ANOTHER PROBLEM

Make a stem-and-leaf diagram to organize these data. The average lengths (in feet) of some of the fastest fish in the world are: sailfish, 8; swordfish, 11; marlin, 35; bluefin tuna, 14; wahoo, 3; tarpon, 8; bonefish, 2; yellowfin tuna, 11. Hint: Use zero as one of the stems.

Stem	Leaf
0	8 3 8 2
1	1 4 1
2	
3	5

Stem	Leaf
0	2 3 8 8
1	1 1 4
2	
3	5

ENRICHMENT

Name

Extend Your Thinking 1-6

Visual Thinking

Circle the letters of the two figures at the right that will form the figure at the left when joined. The figures may be flipped or turned, but they cannot overlap, and there cannot be gaps.

1. a. b. c. d.
2. a. b. c. d.
3. a. b. c. d.
4. a. b. c. d.
5. a. b. c. d.
6. a. b. c. d.
7. a. b. c. d.

Section 1B Connect

At the beginning of this section, you read about a few of the shared characteristics of our presidents. The following exploration asks you to make decisions about how to display data about presidential characteristics.

Job Opportunity for Ambitious American!

The table gives data on the winners of presidential elections from 1900 to 1992 (Rep = Republican, Dem = Democrat).

President	Age	Party	Birth Month	Age of Vice President	Years in Office	Birth State
McKinley	54	Rep	January	43	4	OH
T. Roosevelt	42	Rep	October	53	7	NY
Taft	51	Rep	September	54	4	OH
Wilson	56	Dem	December	59	8	VA
Harding	55	Rep	November	49	2	OH
Coolidge	51	Rep	July	60	6	VT
Hoover	54	Rep	August	69	4	IA
F. Roosevelt	51	Dem	January	65	12	NY
Truman	60	Dem	May	72	8	MO
Eisenhower	62	Rep	October	40	8	TX
Kennedy	43	Dem	May	53	3	MA
Johnson	55	Dem	August	54	5	TX
Nixon	56	Rep	January	51	6	CA
Ford	61	Rep	July	66	2	NE
Carter	52	Dem	October	49	4	GA
Reagan	69	Rep	February	57	8	IL
Bush	64	Rep	June	42	4	MA
Clinton	46	Dem	August	45	4	AR

1. In addition to the presidents' last names, there are six sets of data. Chose three of the six sets. For each set, make either a frequency chart or a stem-and-leaf diagram. Explain why you chose the type of graph you used.

2. Choose one of your frequency charts or stem-and-leaf diagrams. If you drew a bar graph of this data, would your scale start at zero? Would it show any breaks? How large would each interval be?

3. Make the bar graph that you described for the previous question.

39

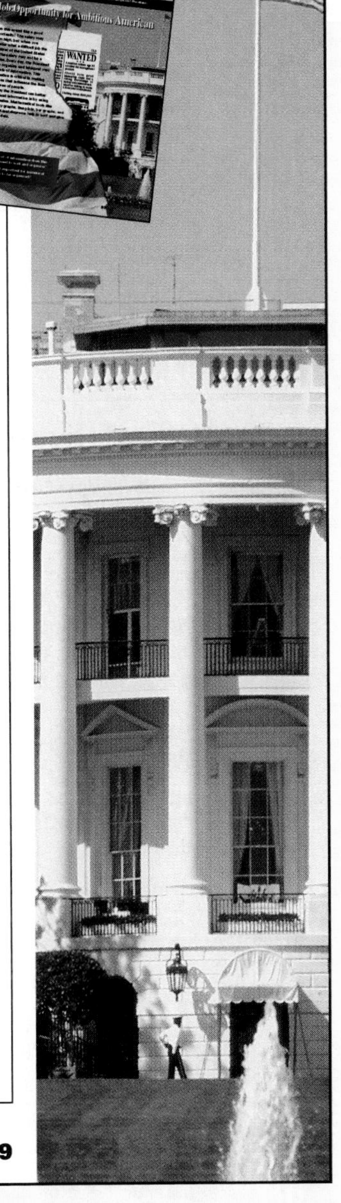

Job Opportunity for Ambitious American!

The Point

In *Job Opportunity for Ambitious American!* on page 23, students choose which type of graph is the best graph for displaying a set of data. Now they will make decisions about how to display data about presidential characteristics.

About the Page

- Discuss the frequency with which each of the items in the sets of data appears.
- Suggest that students tally the information given in the table before they make their graph or diagram.
- Discuss ways in which students might group the data.
- Ask students why the scale would not start at zero if they were graphing the age of the Presidents.

Ongoing Assessment

Check that students have made the frequency charts or stem-and-leaf diagrams correctly before they continue with Questions 2 and 3.

Extension

Using the data presented, have students determine which state(s) and which birth month(s) produced the most Presidents in the 20th century. Ohio; January, August, October.

Answers for Connect

1. Possible answers will be three of the following:

President's Age

Stem	Leaf
4	2 3 6
5	1 1 1 2 4 4 5 5 6 6
6	0 1 2 4 9

Vice-Pres. Age

Stem	Leaf
4	0 2 3 5 9 9
5	1 3 3 4 4 7 9
6	0 5 6 9
7	2

No. of Years in Office	Freq
2	2
3	1
4	6
5	1
6	2
7	1
8	4
12	1

Party	Freq
Republican	11
Democrat	7

Birth State	Freq
OH	3
NY	2
VA	1
VT	1
IA	1
MO	1
TX	2
MA	2
CA	1
NE	1
GA	1
IL	1
AR	1

Birthmonth	Freq
Jan	3
Feb	1
Mar	0
Apr	0
May	2
June	1
July	2
Aug	3
Sep	1
Oct	3
Nov	1
Dec	1

2. Possible answers: Scale could start at 0 for all graphs; The scales of the ages graphs could start at 40 and then the scale would be broken; Intervals should be appropriate to the graph (1, 5, or 10).

3. Bar graph should incorporate answers to Question 2.

1B Review

Review Correlation

Item(s)	Lesson(s)
1	1-4
2	1-5
3, 4	1-6

Test Prep

Test-Taking Tip

Tell students that sometimes, when taking a test, they might momentarily forget a definition. Suggest that they skip the problem and come back to it later. Some other question on the test may help them recall the definition.

Answers for Review

1.

No. of Elections Lost	Frequency
1	13
2	3
3	2

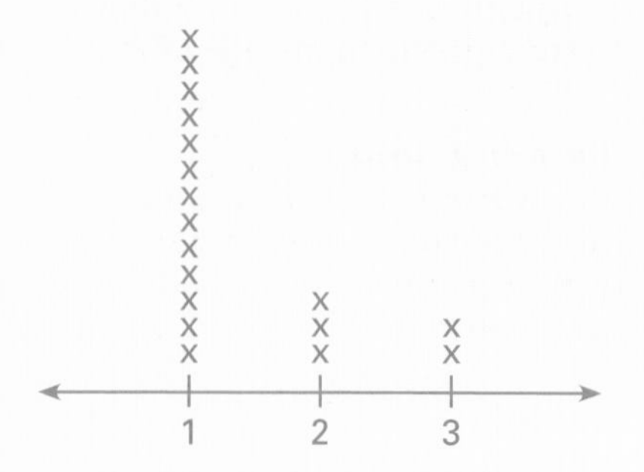

Possible answer: Most of the 18 candidates lost one election; the maximum number of attempts was three times by two candidates.

2.

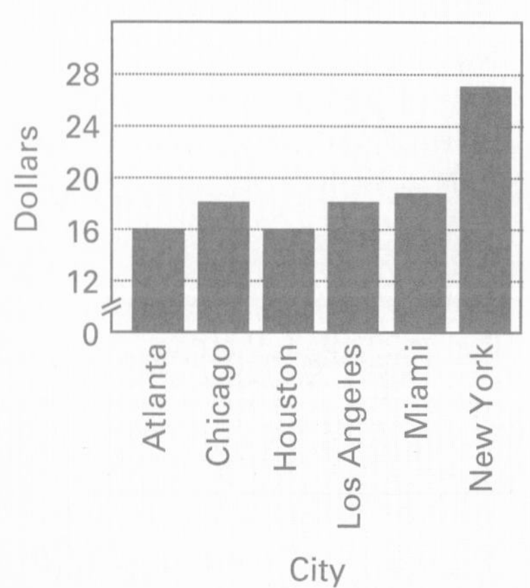

3–4. See page C1.

Section 1B Review

REVIEW 1B

1. The data lists several people who ran for President and the number of Presidential elections they lost. Make a frequency chart and a line plot of the data. Describe the shape of the data.

Name	Elections Lost	Name	Elections Lost
William Bryan	2	Adlai Stevenson	2
Alton Parker	1	Richard Nixon	1
Eugene Debs	3	Gerald Ford	1
William Taft	1	Jimmy Carter	1
Theodore Roosevelt	1	John Anderson	1
Alfred Smith	1	Walter Mondale	1
Norman Thomas	3	Michael Dukakis	1
Herbert Hoover	1	George Bush	1
Thomas Dewey	2	Bob Dole	1

2. Make a bar graph of the data.

Cost of Private Piano Lessons (30 min—rounded to nearest $)			
Atlanta, GA	$16.00	Los Angeles, CA	$18.00
Chicago, IL	$18.00	Miami, FL	$19.00
Houston, TX	$16.00	New York, NY	$27.00

3. Make a stem-and-leaf diagram of the lengths of water birds in inches. Describe the shape of the data.
15, 22, 15, 32, 23, 17, 18, 23, 19, 23, 23, 32, 24

Test Prep

On a multiple-choice test, you may need to match a set of data to a stem-and-leaf diagram. It may be helpful to first draw your own stem-and-leaf diagram, and then match that diagram to the choices provided.

4. Which stem-and-leaf diagram accurately represents the data set?
47, 42, 59, 43, 53, 42, 38, 53, 55, 50, 61, 42, 41, 60, 57

Ⓐ

Stem	Leaf
3	8
4	1 2 2 2 3 7
5	0 3 3 5 7 9
6	0 1

Ⓑ

Stem	Leaf
3	8
4	1 2 2 3 3 7
5	0 3 3 5 7 9
6	0 1

Ⓒ

Stem	Leaf
3	8
4	1 2 2 2 3 7
5	0 3 3 3 7 9
6	0 1

Resources

Practice Masters
Section 1B Review
Assessment Sourcebook
Quiz 1B

TestWorks
Test and Practice Software

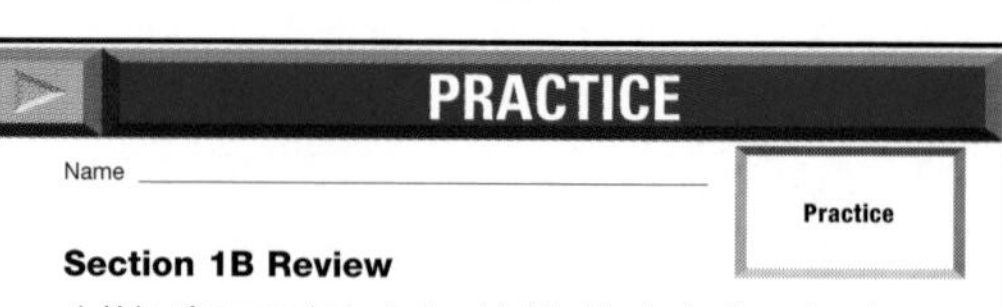

Section 1B Review

1. Make a frequency chart and a line plot of the data showing the number of teachers that a set of students have at Monroe Middle School.

3, 7, 4, 7, 3, 5, 6, 4, 6, 4, 5, 6, 4, 7, 5, 6

Frequency Chart

Number of Teachers	Frequency
3	2
4	4
5	3
6	4
7	3

Line Plot

2. **Geography** Make a bar graph of the data showing the five longest rivers in America. Use a broken scale, if appropriate.

River	Length (mi)
Missouri	2540
Mississippi	2340
Yukon	1980
St. Lawrence	1900
Arkansas	1460

Longest U.S. Rivers

3. Make a stem-and-leaf diagram of the data showing the scores that some students received in a spelling bee.

23, 36, 17, 21, 42, 19, 30, 22, 61, 20, 19, 24, 18, 26, 21, 19, 20

stem	leaf
1	78999
2	00112346
3	06
4	2
6	1

4. Give the approximate weight and price for the package of cereal represented by each point in the scatterplot. *[Lesson 1-3]*

A: weight 12 oz price $3.00
B: weight 16 oz price $2.25
C: weight 20 oz price $2.75
D: weight 15 oz price $2.00
E: weight 24 oz price $4.25
F: weight 18 oz price $3.00

Describing Data

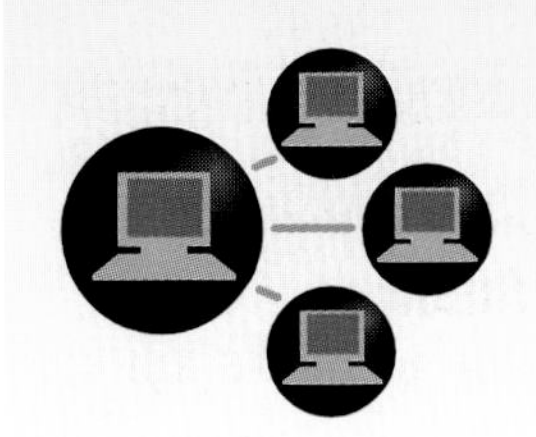

Visit **www.teacher.mathsurf.com** for links to lesson plans from teachers and other professionals, NCTM information, and other sites.

LESSON PLANNING GUIDE

Student Edition			Ancillaries*	
LESSON	MATERIALS	VOCABULARY	DAILY	OTHER
Section 1C Opener				
1-7 Median and Mode		median, mode	1-7	*Interactive CD-ROM Lesson*
1-8 The Meaning of Mean	string, scissors, meter stick or yardstick	mean	1-8	Teaching Tool Trans. 2, 3 Technology Master 4
Technology	spreadsheet software			*Interactive CD-ROM Spreadsheet/Grapher Tool*
1-9 The Effects of Outliers		outlier	1-9	Technology Master 5 Ch. 1 Project Master
Connect				Interdisc. Team Teaching 1C
Review				Practice 1C; Quiz 1C; *TestWorks*
Extend Key Ideas				
Chapter 1 Summary and Review				
Chapter 1 Assessment				Ch. 1 Tests Forms A–F *TestWorks*; Ch. 1 Letter Home
Cumulative Review, Chapter 1	watch or clock with second hand			Cumulative Review Ch. 1

* Daily Ancillaries include Practice, Reteaching, Problem Solving, Enrichment, and Daily Transparency. Teaching Tool Transparencies are in *Teacher's Toolkits*. Lesson Enhancement Transparencies are in *Overhead Transparency Package*.

SKILLS TRACE

LESSON	SKILL	FIRST INTRODUCED GR. 4	GR. 5	GR. 6	DEVELOP	PRACTICE/ APPLY	REVIEW
1-7	**Calculating median and mode.**	✘			pp. 42–43	pp. 44–45	pp. 59, 73, 156
1-8	**Calculating mean.**			✘ p. 46	pp. 46–47	pp. 48–49	pp. 59, 69, 77, 163
1-9	**Assessing the effects of outliers.**			✘ p. 51	pp. 51–52	pp. 53–54	pp. 59, 168, 301

CONNECTED MATHEMATICS

The unit *Data About Us (Statistics)*, from the **Connected Mathematics** series, can be used with Section 1C.

INTERDISCIPLINARY TEAM TEACHING

Math and Social Studies

(Worksheet pages 05–06: Teacher pages T5–T6)

In this lesson, students interpret desert weather data.

Name ______________________ *Math and Social Studies*

Dry as Dust

Interpreting desert weather data.

Deserts are regions of the Earth that get less than 10 inches (254 mm) of precipitation (rain, snow, hail, sleet, drizzle) per year. They are also places where water evaporates so fast that almost none of it remains for long as a liquid.

There are four kinds of desert:

1. Hot deserts—These deserts are found close to the equator. An example is the Sahara Desert in northern Africa.
2. Semi-deserts—These deserts have short, unpredictable rainy seasons. An example is the Sahel region of western Africa.
3. Deserts with a hot and cold season—These deserts are located in the central areas of large continents. An example is the Gobi desert in Central Asia.
4. Cold deserts—These lie in the icy polar and near-polar regions of the Earth. They are located in such places as Greenland, Alaska, Siberia, and the continent of Antarctica.

Living in the desert is hard. Moisture, which must be replaced, leaves the body through a person's skin and lungs. Because deserts are so difficult to live on, they support less than 5% of the world's population, but some people, such as the Bedouins of the Middle East have adapted well to desert life. Bedouins move from place to place in search of water, together with herds of sheep, goats, and camels which provide meat and milk. People who live in the hottest deserts survive by resting during the hottest times of the day. This conserves body fluids. Many desert dwellers and travelers cover themselves from head to foot with loose clothing to protect their bodies from the sun.

Some people live in permanent desert towns and cities located near water.

1. Deserts are defined by their low amount of precipitation. Complete the table below by calculating the mean monthly rainfall of each city. Round to the nearest whole number.
2. Find the median monthly rainfall for Alice Springs.
   16.5 mm
3. Which city has the most months of zero rainfall? What are you determining to answer this question?
   Antofagasta; mode

Monthly Rainfall (mm)													
City	J	F	M	A	M	J	J	A	S	O	N	D	Mean Monthly Rainfall (mm)
Alice Springs, Australia	43	33	28	10	15	13	8	8	8	18	31	38	21
In Salah, Algeria	3	3	0	0	0	0	0	3	0	0	5	3	1
Kashgar, China	15	3	13	5	8	5	10	8	3	3	5	8	7
Antofagasta, Chile	0	0	0	0	0	3	5	3	0	3	0	0	1
Phoenix, United States	20	20	18	10	3	3	25	25	18	10	15	23	16

Name ______________________ *Math and Social Studies*

4. The desert cities listed in the chart below developed near sources of water. For many years, the weather in these cities has been recorded, studied, and compared. Complete each part of the chart by calculating the mean high and low monthly temperatures for each city. Round to whole numbers.
5. Examine the difference between the mean highs and lows for each city (bottom row). What is interesting about this data?
   All but Antofagasta have a range between 24 and 29 degrees. Antofagasta's range is only 12°.
6. What advice would you have for American troops who are going to be stationed in a desert area?
   Students' responses will vary. Students may suggest that the soldiers do their work at night and sleep during the day, that they keep their level of activity low, that they drink plenty of fluids at all times, and that they cover their bodies with loose-fitting clothing while in the sun.

	Mean High Temperature (°F)					Mean Low Temperature (°F)				
Month	Alice Springs	In Salah	Kashgar	Anto-fagasta	Phoenix	Alice Springs	In Salah	Kashgar	Anto-fagasta	Phoenix
January	97	69	33	76	65	70	43	12	63	39
February	95	75	43	76	69	69	47	19	63	43
March	90	83	56	74	75	63	53	35	61	47
April	81	92	71	70	82	54	62	48	58	53
May	73	99	81	67	91	46	69	58	55	60
June	67	110	89	65	101	41	80	64	52	69
July	67	113	92	63	104	39	83	68	51	77
August	73	111	90	62	101	43	82	66	52	76
September	81	105	83	64	97	49	77	57	53	69
October	88	94	71	66	86	58	66	43	55	56
November	93	80	54	69	75	64	53	29	58	45
December	96	71	38	72	66	68	45	17	60	40
Mean Temp.	83	92	67	69	84	55	63	43	57	56

BIBLIOGRAPHY

FOR TEACHERS

Haven, Kendall. *Marvels of Science*. Englewood, CO: Libraries Unlimited, 1994.

Spangler, David. *Math for Real Kids*. Glenview, IL: Good Year Books, 1997.

Welton, Ann. *Explorers and Exploration*. Phoenix, AZ: Oryx Press, 1993.

The World Almanac and Book of Facts. Mahwah, NJ: Funk & Wagnalls, 1996.

FOR STUDENTS

Thomas, Ron. *The Grolier Student Encyclopedia of the Olympic Games*. Danbury, CT: Grolier Educational Press, 1996.

SECTION 1C Describing Data

▶ Health Link ▶ www.mathsurf.com/6/ch1/sports

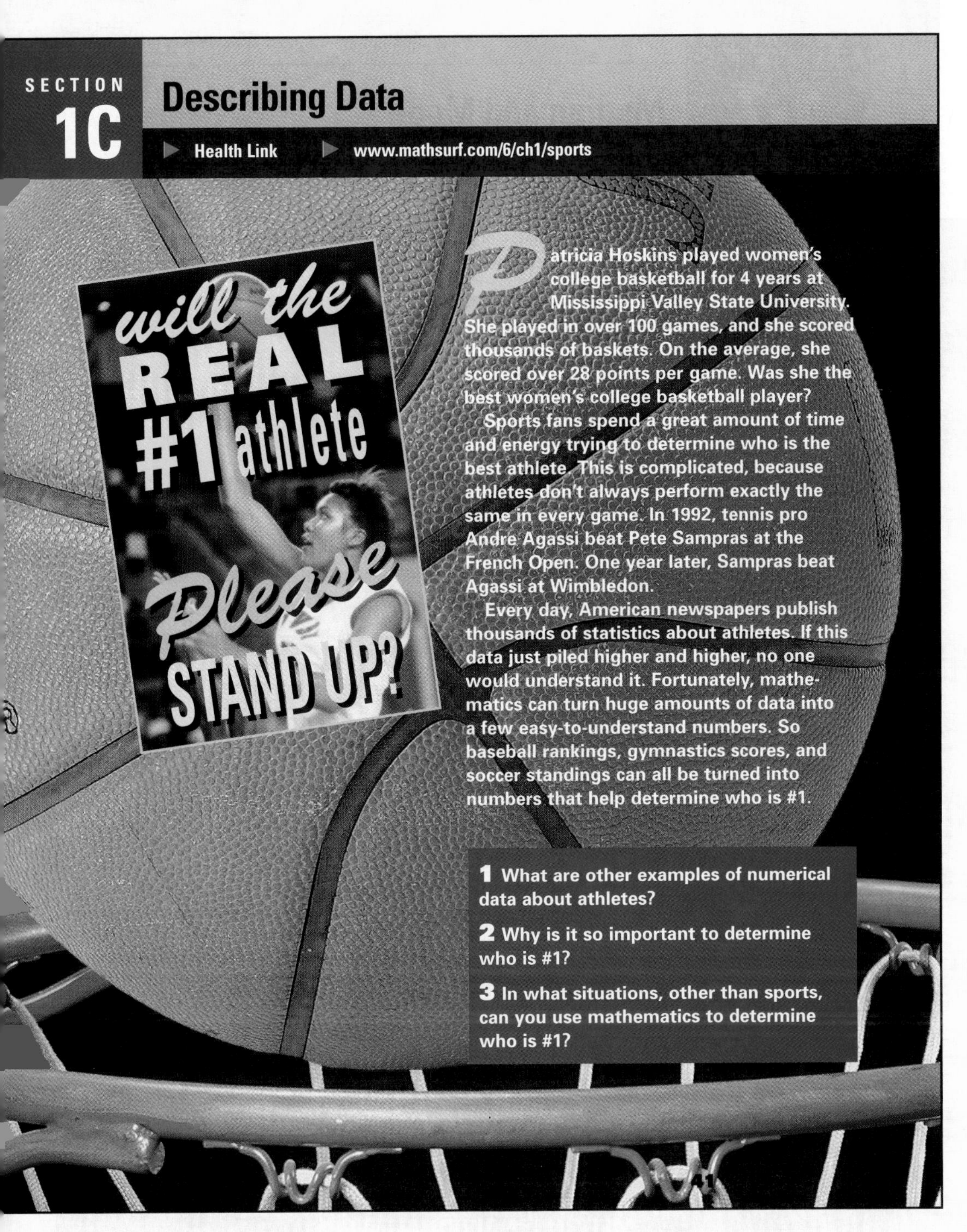

Patricia Hoskins played women's college basketball for 4 years at Mississippi Valley State University. She played in over 100 games, and she scored thousands of baskets. On the average, she scored over 28 points per game. Was she the best women's college basketball player?

Sports fans spend a great amount of time and energy trying to determine who is the best athlete. This is complicated, because athletes don't always perform exactly the same in every game. In 1992, tennis pro Andre Agassi beat Pete Sampras at the French Open. One year later, Sampras beat Agassi at Wimbledon.

Every day, American newspapers publish thousands of statistics about athletes. If this data just piled higher and higher, no one would understand it. Fortunately, mathematics can turn huge amounts of data into a few easy-to-understand numbers. So baseball rankings, gymnastics scores, and soccer standings can all be turned into numbers that help determine who is #1.

1 What are other examples of numerical data about athletes?

2 Why is it so important to determine who is #1?

3 In what situations, other than sports, can you use mathematics to determine who is #1?

Where are we now?

In Section 1B, students organized and compared data using graphs.

They learned how to

- use graphs to organize and display information.
- identify graphs that display misleading information.
- compare values in two sets of data using scatterplots.

Where are we going?

In Section 1C, students will

- calculate the mean, median, and mode for a set of data.
- identify outliers in a set of data.
- determine the effect of an outlier on a data set.

Section 1C

Theme: Sports

World Wide Web

If your class has access to the World Wide Web, you might want to use the information found at the Web site addresses given. The interdisciplinary link relates to topics discussed in this section.

About the Page

This page introduces the theme of the section, sports, and discusses how compiled statistics are used to rank athletic performance.

Ask ...

- How is the best baseball player chosen? Best pitcher? Best hitter?
- How are the statistics organized so they can be interpreted?

Extension

The following activity does not require access to the World Wide Web.

Health

Every year, the #1 athlete in each sport is decided by analyzing the players skills during athletic competitions and interpreting the statistics. Have each student select an athlete and research his or her nutrition and training plans.

Answers for Questions

1. Possible answers: Baseball records: Runs, stolen bases, home runs, runs batted in. Football records: Passes, interceptions, yards gained, points scored. Gymnastics records: Scores by judges.
2. Possible answers: The #1 athlete is often recognized with a special award, such as Most Valuable Player. Being #1 can mean more endorsements and celebrity appearances.
3. Possible answers: Ranking of colleges, movie ticket sales, speeds of cars, and presidential elections.

Connect

On page 55, students will graph data compare the performances of Babe Ruth and Hank Aaron.

INTERACTIVE LESSON

1-7 Lesson Organizer

Objective

- Calculate the median and the mode for a set of data.

Vocabulary

- Median, mode

NCTM Standards

- 1–4, 10

▶ Review

Order from least to greatest.

1. 32, 20, 8, 16, 41, 33, 20, 3, 12 3, 8, 12, 16, 20, 20, 32, 33, 41
2. 1.8, 0.2, 3.1, 2.4, 0.9, 2.0, 1.4 0.2, 0.9, 1.4, 1.8, 2.0, 2.4, 3.1
3. 23, 9, 12, 45, 9, 16, 8, 40, 38 8, 9, 9, 12, 16, 23, 38, 40, 45

Available on Daily Transparency 1-7

▶ Lesson Link

Students learn to calculate the median and the mode for a set of data and apply the skills to analyzing sports statistics and other types of information.

1 Introduce

Explore

The Point

Students develop an intuitive sense of the middle number and the number appearing most often in a data set.

Ongoing Assessment

Check that students are able to judge whether to choose a greater or lesser number after being given hints by their partners.

For Groups That Finish Early

What is the middle number in the list of pitching wins? 342 What number(s) appear most often? 373 and 361 each appear twice.

1-7 Median and Mode

You'll Learn ...

- to calculate the median and the mode for a set of data

... How It's Used

Real estate agents use medians and modes when comparing the costs of houses for sale.

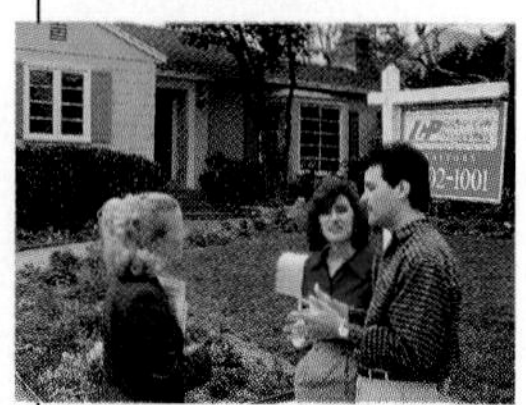

Vocabulary

median

mode

▶ Lesson Link You know how to organize data using a frequency chart, and how to show the shape of a data set using a line plot or a stem-and-leaf diagram. Now you will learn how to find single numbers that describe entire sets of data. ◀

Explore The Middle and the Most

The Winning Pitch

The table gives the totals of the top 15 major league pitchers according to career wins.

Cy Young	511	Kid Nichols	361	John Clarkson	326
Walter Johnson	416	Pud Galvin	361	Don Sutton	324
Christy Mathewson	373	Tim Keefe	342	Nolan Ryan	319
Grover Alexander	373	Steve Carlton	329	Phil Niekro	318
Warren Spahn	363	Eddie Plank	327	Gaylord Perry	314

1. Get together with a partner. One person chooses a number from the data. The other person tries to guess which number the first person chose in as few guesses as possible. After each guess, the first person should say "too high," "too low," or "correct."
2. Play the game twice. Switch roles after the first game.
3. Which number is the best first number to guess? Why?
4. If your partner chose a number at random and you could only make one guess, which guess would be the best guess to make? Why?

Learn Median and Mode

The **median** of a data set is the middle number when the data are listed from lowest to highest. If a set has two middle numbers, the median is the value halfway between the two middle numbers.

The **mode** of a data set is the item that occurs most often. If all items occur once, there is no mode. If several items occur "most often," each is a mode.

MEETING INDIVIDUAL NEEDS

Resources

- 1-7 Practice
- 1-7 Reteaching
- 1-7 Problem Solving
- 1-7 Enrichment
- 1-7 Daily Transparency
  - Problem of the Day
  - Review
  - Quick Quiz

Interactive CD-ROM Lesson

Learning Modalities

Visual Draw a number line on the chalkboard and list the numbers 1–9.

- Have students identify the middle number. 5
- Have students explain if there is a mode. No mode, because no number appears more than once.
- Add 10 to the number line and ask for the middle number(s). There are two, 5 and 6.
- Ask students to find the actual middle number. The point halfway between 5 and 6, 5.5.

Individual Students of this age enjoy working with data that are important to them. Try to use examples dealing with sports or other relevant topics, such as popular music, videos, or family.

English Language Development

To help students, relate the term "median" to a highway median and the term "mode" to a mode in fashion, a style that appears often.

Example 1

The Long Beach State women's basketball team has won more games than any other major college women's basketball team. Find the median number of wins and the mode number of wins.

Long Beach State Win Totals (for 1986–1996)										
29	33	28	30	25	24	21	9	11	13	15

9 11 13 15 21 24 25 28 29 30 33 — Order the totals.

9 11 13 15 21 [24] 25 28 29 30 33 — Find the middle number.

The median is 24 wins. Since each number appears once, there is no mode.

DID YOU KNOW?

The first National College Athletic Association basketball championship for men was held in 1939. The first national championship for women was held in 1982.

Example 2

Twelve Houston babysitters were surveyed to find their hourly rates. Find the median and the mode of the data.

Babysitter Hourly Rates ($)		
4.00	3.30	3.25
3.00	3.75	3.25
3.15	3.50	3.00
3.75	3.75	3.60

To find the median, list the numbers in order.

3.00, 3.00, 3.15, 3.25, 3.25, 3.30, 3.50, 3.60, 3.75, 3.75, 3.75, 4.00

There are two middle numbers, $3.30 and $3.50. The median is the value halfway between, which is $3.40.

The mode is $3.75 because it appears more times than any other number.

Try It

Number of Stations on Longest Commuter Rail Systems in the United States								
134	108	18	126	62	101	181	27	158

a. Find the median of the data. 108 **b.** Find the mode of the data. No mode

Check Your Understanding

1. For any data set, which is bigger, the median or the mode? Explain.

2. Is the median of a data set always one of the numbers in the set? Is the mode? Explain.

MATH EVERY DAY

Problem of the Day

Edward stacked 4 cubes on his desk. A red cube is above a blue cube. A green cube is on a pink cube. The blue cube is above the pink cube. Draw the stack. The cubes are stacked in this order from top to bottom: red, blue, green, pink.

Available on Daily Transparency 1-7

An Extension is provided in the transparency package.

Fact of the Day

On September 5, 1995, Cal Ripken, Jr., played his 2131st consecutive baseball game. He broke a record set in 1939 by Lou Gehrig.

Mental Math

Do these mentally.

1. Find a number halfway between 5 and 9. 7
2. Find a number halfway between 12 and 13. 12.5
3. Find a number halfway between 46 and 52. 49

Follow Up

Be sure that students understand the reasoning in the strategies used in guessing the numbers.

Answers for Explore

3. 342, because it's in the exact middle; By guessing that, you'll eliminate half of the guesses, regardless of whether you're too high or too low.
4. 373 or 361, because each appears twice; All the rest of the numbers appear only once.

2 Teach

Learn

Alternate Examples

1. Find the median and the mode of the list in **Explore**.

   314 318 319 324 326 327 329 342 361 361 363 373 373 416 511

   The median is 342. Both 361 and 373 appear two times and no number appears more than that, so 361 and 373 are both modes.

2. Find the median and the mode of these numbers: 3.9, 5.2, 3.6, 4.8, 2.3, 2.8, 4.2, 3.7

   First list the numbers from least to greatest: 2.3 2.8 3.6 3.7 3.9 4.2 4.8 5.2 There are two middle numbers, 3.7 and 3.9. The median is the value halfway between, 3.8. There is no mode.

3 Practice and Assess

Check

Answers for Check Your Understanding

1. It depends on the data set. Data with several identical low numbers may have a higher median. Data with several identical high numbers may have a higher mode.
2. The median is not always a number in the set. Sometimes it's the midpoint between the middle two numbers. The mode is always a number in the set, unless all the numbers appear exactly once and there is no mode.

Assignment Guide

- **Basic**
  1–3, 5–8, 10–18 evens, 24–38 evens
- **Average**
  1–8, 9–17 odds, 19, 23–37 odds
- **Enriched**
  2–8, 10–18 evens, 19, 24–38 evens

Exercise Notes

Exercise 6

Error Prevention Remind students to consider numbers that appear more than once and to to include the stem part of the numbers.

Exercises 9–14

Extension Have students find the range for each set of points.

9. 48
10. 6
11. 8
12. 10
13. 2
14. 11

Reteaching

Activity

Work with a large group or the whole class to find the median and the mode of your heights.

- Arrange yourselves in a straight line according to height.
- If there is an odd number of students, identify the middle person. That person's height is the median height. If there is an even number of students, identify the two middle students. The median is the height halfway between those students' heights.

1-7 Exercises and Applications

PRACTICE 1-7

Practice and Apply

1. **Getting Started** Find the median and the mode for each data set. The data are ordered from lowest to highest.
   a. $1, $2, $3, $4, $4, $5, $10, $10, $10 **Median $4, mode $10**
   b. 12, 12, 18, 19, 54, 54, 102 **Median 19, modes 12 and 54**
   c. 82, 82, 84, 85, 87, 88, 95, 98 **Median 86, mode 82**
   d. 300, 301, 302, 310, 313, 318 **Median 306, no mode**

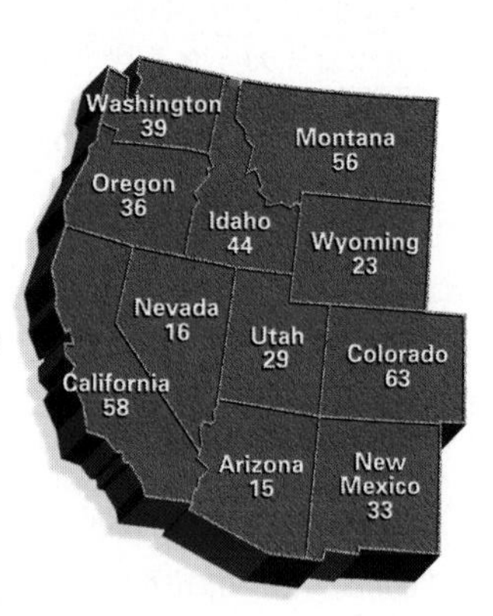

2. **Geography** Find the median and mode number of counties for the 11 western states shown in the map. **Median 36, no mode**
   GPS
3. **Geography** Find the median number of counties for the 5 states surrounding Nevada. **36**
4. **Geography** Find the median number of counties for the 6 states surrounding Utah. **28**

Find the median and mode.

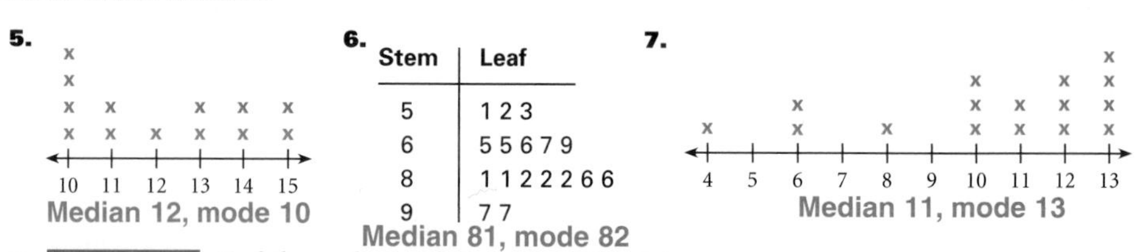

5. **Median 12, mode 10**

6.

Stem	Leaf
5	1 2 3
6	5 5 6 7 9
8	1 1 2 2 2 6 6
9	7 7

Median 81, mode 82

7. **Median 11, mode 13**

8. **Test Prep** Find the median and the mode of this data set: 25, 31, 28, 25, 21, 21, 32, 25, 32. **D**
   Ⓐ 21 and 25 Ⓑ 25 and 32 Ⓒ 21 and 32 Ⓓ 25 and 25

Find the median and mode.

9. 15, 31, 45, 61, 13, 21, 31, 13, 20 **Median 21, modes 13 and 31**
10. 25, 26, 24, 21, 25, 21, 23, 21, 26, 21, 20 **Median 23, mode 21**
11. 9, 13, 7, 11, 12, 6, 8, 14 **Median 10, no mode**
12. 20, 25, 21, 23, 22, 30, 28, 20, 23, 22, 21, 30, 29, 28, 28, 28, 30, 29, 20 **Median 25, mode 28**
13. 25, 16, 18, 20, 21, 24, 23, 28, 27, 26, 17, 18, 18, 28, 28, 27, 28, 27, 26 **Median 25, mode 28**
14. 23, 24, 24, 34, 30, 31, 32, 23, 24, 26, 27, 23, 23, 24, 24, 24, 34, 34 **Median 24, mode 24**

PRACTICE

Name ______________________

Practice 1-7

Median and Mode

Find the median and mode(s).

1. median 25
   mode(s) 24
2. median 7.5
   mode(s) 7
3. median 27
   mode(s) 18 and 25

stem	leaf
1	8 8 9
2	0 3 5 5 7 9
3	1 3 8
4	2 3 5

4. median 57.5
   mode(s) None

stem	leaf
3	4 6 9
5	0 2 3 7 8
6	1 4 6 7
7	2 3

5. 13, 19, 20, 22, 24, 19, 14, 18, 20, 19, 32, 17, 40, 27, 25, 35, 28.
   median 23.1 mode(s) 19

In Exercises 6–7, make a line plot for each data set, and then find the median and mode(s).

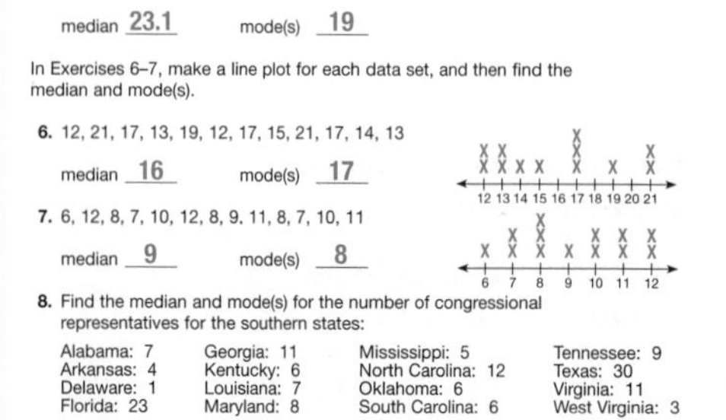

6. 12, 21, 17, 13, 19, 12, 17, 15, 21, 17, 14, 13
   median 16 mode(s) 17
7. 6, 12, 8, 7, 10, 12, 8, 9. 11, 8, 7, 10, 11
   median 9 mode(s) 8
8. Find the median and mode(s) for the number of congressional representatives for the southern states:

Alabama: 7	Georgia: 11	Mississippi: 5	Tennessee: 9
Arkansas: 4	Kentucky: 6	North Carolina: 12	Texas: 30
Delaware: 1	Louisiana: 7	Oklahoma: 6	Virginia: 11
Florida: 23	Maryland: 8	South Carolina: 6	West Virginia: 3

median 7 mode(s) 6

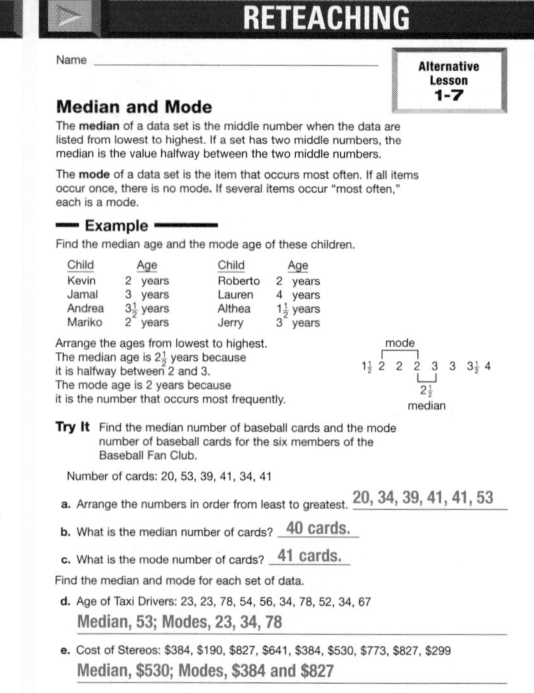

RETEACHING

Name ______________________

Alternative Lesson 1-7

Median and Mode

The **median** of a data set is the middle number when the data are listed from lowest to highest. If a set has two middle numbers, the median is the value halfway between the two middle numbers.

The **mode** of a data set is the item that occurs most often. If all items occur once, there is no mode. If several items occur "most often," each is a mode.

Example

Find the median age and the mode age of these children.

Child	Age	Child	Age
Kevin	2 years	Roberto	2 years
Jamal	3 years	Lauren	4 years
Andrea	$3\frac{1}{2}$ years	Althea	$1\frac{1}{2}$ years
Mariko	2 years	Jerry	3 years

Arrange the ages from lowest to highest.
The median age is $2\frac{1}{2}$ years because it is halfway between 2 and 3.
The mode age is 2 years because it is the number that occurs most frequently.

mode
$1\frac{1}{2}$ 2 2 2 3 3 $3\frac{1}{2}$ 4
$2\frac{1}{2}$
median

Try It Find the median number of baseball cards and the mode number of baseball cards for the six members of the Baseball Fan Club.

Number of cards: 20, 53, 39, 41, 34, 41

a. Arrange the numbers in order from least to greatest. **20, 34, 39, 41, 41, 53**
b. What is the median number of cards? **40 cards.**
c. What is the mode number of cards? **41 cards.**

Find the median and mode for each set of data.

d. Age of Taxi Drivers: 23, 23, 78, 54, 56, 34, 78, 52, 34, 67
   Median, 53; Modes, 23, 34, 78
e. Cost of Stereos: $384, $190, $827, $641, $384, $530, $773, $827, $299
   Median, $530; Modes, $384 and $827

Make a line plot for each and then find the median and mode.

15. 6, 11, 12, 5, 7, 11, 6, 6, 10

16. 3, 0, 1, 0, 1, 3, 2, 2, 3, 1, 0, 3

PROBLEM SOLVING 1-7

Problem Solving and Reasoning

17. Critical Thinking Create a data set of 10 numbers with a median of 8 and a mode of 10.

18. Critical Thinking The following data lists the tennis players with the most Wimbledon titles. Laurence Doherty's data is missing. If the median of the data set is 13 and the modes are 10 and 13, what's the missing data?

Louise Brough	13	Suzanne Longlen	15
Margaret Court	10	Martina Navratilova	18
Laurence Doherty	???	William Renshaw	14
Doris Hart	10	Elizabeth Ryan	19
Billie Jean King	7	Helen Wills-Moody	12

Martina Navratilova

19. 

Describe how to find the median of a set of data. Your description should explain what to do if the data set contains either an even or an odd number of values.

Mixed Review

Multiply. *[Previous course]*

20. 83 × 54 4482 **21.** 29 × 76 2204 **22.** 80 × 32 2560 **23.** 91 × 98 8918 **24.** 42 × 76 3192

25. 302 × 18 5436 **26.** 412 × 43 17,716 **27.** 520 × 63 32,760 **28.** 622 × 22 13,684 **29.** 928 × 52 48,256

30. 816 × 102 83,232 **31.** 792 × 653 517,176 **32.** 140 × 339 47,460 **33.** 469 × 203 95,207 **34** 515 × 934 481,010

35. What's the second highest selling type of shoe? *[Lesson 1-1]* Basketball

36. What's the difference between the sales in running shoes and golf shoes? *[Lesson 1-1]* 20 pairs

37. If the total sales equals 100 pairs, what's the number of sales for tennis shoes? *[Lesson 1-1]* 15 pairs

38. If each symbol represented 7 pairs of shoes, how many running shoes would have been sold? 42 pairs

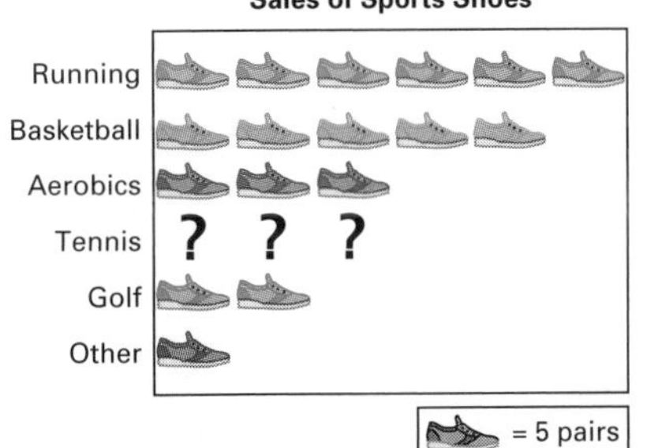

PROBLEM SOLVING

Name ______________________

Guided Problem Solving 1-7

GPS PROBLEM 2, STUDENT PAGE 44

Find the median and mode number of counties for the 11 western states shown in the map.

Washington 39, Idaho 44, Oregon 36, Nevada 16, California 58, Montana 56, Wyoming 23, Utah 29, Colorado 63, New Mexico 33, Arizona 15

Understand

1. What are you asked to find? The median and mode number of counties for 11 western states.

Plan

2. Explain what you need to do to find the median or the mode. To find the median, order the numbers and identify the middle number. To find the mode, identify the number or numbers that occur most often.

Solve

3. Write the numbers in order from least to greatest. 15, 16, 23, 29, 33, 36, 39, 44, 56, 58, 63

4. Write the median. 36

5. Write the mode. There is no mode.

Look Back

6. What are some different ways you can organize the information given in the problem? Possible answer: Make a line plot; make a stem-and-leaf diagram.

SOLVE ANOTHER PROBLEM

Find the median and mode number of counties or parishes for these 16 southern states: Alabama, 67; Arkansas, 75; Delaware, 3; Florida, 67; Georgia, 159; Kentucky, 120; Louisiana, 64; Maryland, 23; Mississippi, 82; North Carolina, 100; Oklahoma, 77, South Carolina, 46, Tennessee, 95, Texas, 254, Virginia, 95, and West Virginia, 55.

The median is 76. The modes are 67 and 95.

ENRICHMENT

Name ______________________

Extend Your Thinking 1-7

Decision Making

Karel and her family have just moved into a new neighborhood. Karel wants to earn money by baby-sitting for families with young children. She asked other students her age how much they charged for baby-sitting. The results are listed in the chart at the right.

Hourly Baby-sitting Charges	
Stephanie	$2.75
Jessica	$2.00
Michael	$3.00
Raoul	$2.50
Rolanda	$2.75
Harry	$2.25
Samuel	$2.25
Anita	$2.75

1. Suppose Karel wants to be the least expensive baby-sitter in the neighborhood. How much should she charge? Less than $2 per hour.

2. Suppose Karel wants to charge the same hourly rate as most of the other baby-sitters. How much should she charge? Explain. $2.75 per hour, because this is the fee charged by more babysitters than any other fee.

3. Suppose Karel wants her hourly rate to be higher than the rate of half of other baby-sitters, but lower than the hourly rate of the rest of the baby-sitters. How much should she charge? Explain. She will set her fee between $2.50 and $2.75 because half of the girls charge less than $2.50 and half charge more than $2.75.

4. In addition to the baby-sitting rates charged by others, what might Karel consider when she sets her rates? Possible answer: How often she plans to babysit, when the parents need her to babysit, how long each job will last, how close to her home the parents live, and so on.

5. Find out how much six people in your school charge for baby-sitting. Organize the information and find the median and mode. If you were going to baby-sit, how much would you charge? Why? Check students' work.

Exercise Notes

■ Exercises 20–34

Estimation Have students estimate their answers before computing as a check on reasonableness.

Exercise Answers

15.

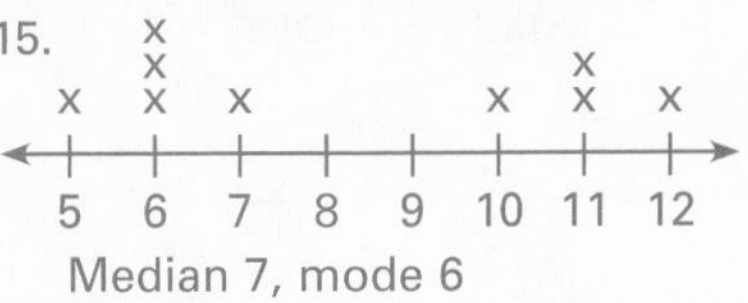

Median 7, mode 6

16.

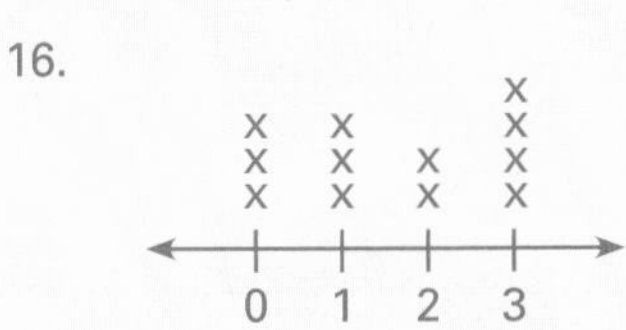

Median 1.5, mode 3

17. Possible answer: 1 2 3 6 7 9 10 10 10 11

18. 13

19. Possible answer: Order the values from least to greatest. If there are an odd number of values, the median is the middle value. If there are an even number of values, the median is the average of the two middle values.

Alternate Assessment

Interview Ask students to give an example of a data set that has a mode and a data set that does not have a mode.

► Quick Quiz

Find the median and the mode for each set of data.

1. 8, 10, 7, 6, 5, 7, 9
   Median: 7; Mode: 7
2. 12, 18, 10, 13, 15, 19, 22, 24
   Median: 16.5; Mode: none

Available on Daily Transparency 1-7

1-8 Lesson Organizer

Objective

- **Calculate the mean for a set of data.**

Vocabulary

- **Mean**

Materials

- **Explore: String, scissors, meter stick or yard stick**

NCTM Standards

- **1–4, 7, 10, 13**

Review

Find each sum or quotient.

1. 32 + 49 + 52 + 48 + 35 + 56 272
2. 1.8 + 2.2 + 3.1 + 2.4 + 1.9 + 1.4 12.8
3. 270 ÷ 6 45
4. 434 ÷ 7 62
5. 76 ÷ 8 9.5

Available on Daily Transparency 1-8

Lesson Link

Ask students to list uses and meanings of the word *average*. They might suggest "average grades," "average student," "average ball player," and so on. Explain that an average is a number which helps to describe a set of data.

1 Introduce

Explore

The Point
Students explore how changes in the people in their group would change the group's average arm length.

Ongoing Assessment
Check that students are able to measure accurately.

For Groups That Finish Early
Use the same method you used in **Explore** to find the average shoe length of the members in your group.

1-8 The Meaning of Mean

You'll Learn ...

- to calculate the mean for a set of data

... How It's Used

Automobile manufacturers examine the mean dimensions of a person's body when designing an automobile.

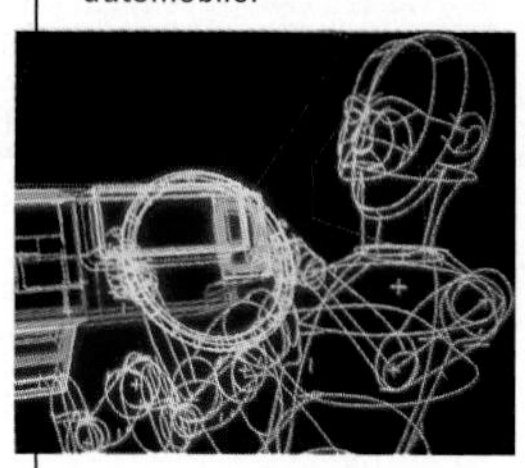

Vocabulary

mean

Lesson Link You've learned to use the median and the mode of a data set to describe the data. Now you'll learn to find another such number that is often referred to as the *average*. ◄

Explore The Mean

Let's Cut a Record

Materials: String, Scissors, Meter stick or Yard stick

Work in a group of at least four students.

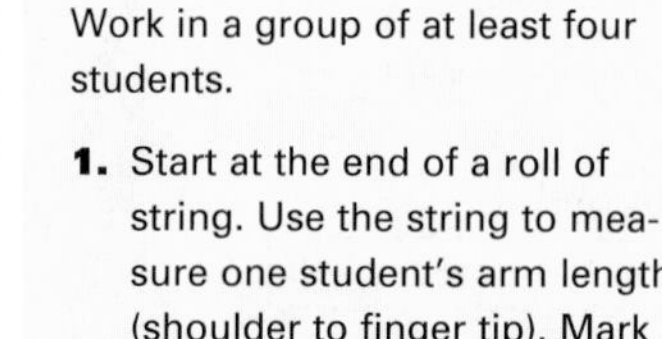

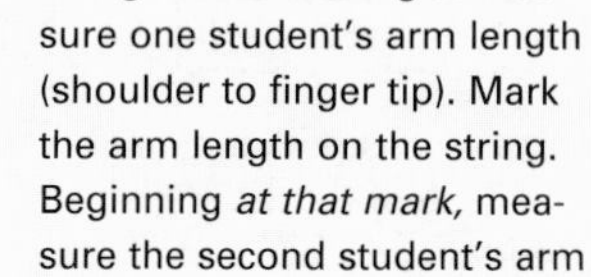

1. Start at the end of a roll of string. Use the string to measure one student's arm length (shoulder to finger tip). Mark the arm length on the string. Beginning *at that mark,* measure the second student's arm length and mark that. Continue until all arms have been measured on the same string.
2. Cut the string at the last mark. You should now have a single length of string equal to the combined lengths of all the arms. Measure and record the total length of the string.

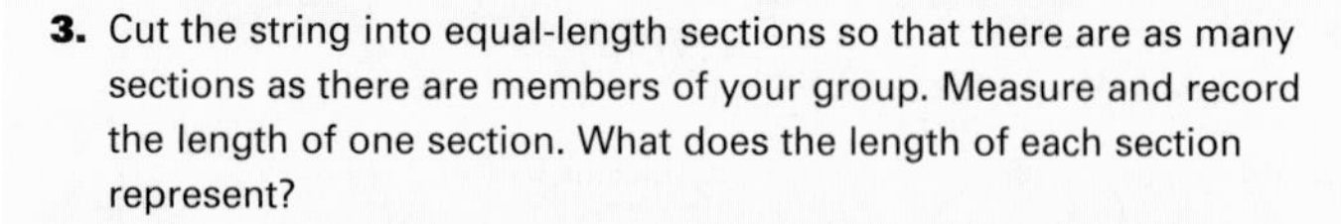

3. Cut the string into equal-length sections so that there are as many sections as there are members of your group. Measure and record the length of one section. What does the length of each section represent?
4. Does it make a difference which student gets measured first and which student gets measured last? Explain.
5. If you add a new person to your group and repeat Steps 1 through 3, will your final section be longer or shorter than the final section for your original group?

MEETING INDIVIDUAL NEEDS

Resources

- **1-8** Practice
- **1-8** Reteaching
- **1-8** Problem Solving
- **1-8** Enrichment
- **1-8** Daily Transparency
  - Problem of the Day
  - Review
  - Quick Quiz
- Teaching Tool Transparencies 2, 3
- Technology Master 4

Learning Modalities

Logical After discussing **Check Your Understanding,** ask students which measure—the median, the mode, or the mean— is the best number to describe a set of data. Ask students to explain their reasoning.

Individual Now that students have studied the three major measures of central tendency, the mean, the median, and the mode, offer to let them decide which measure should be used to figure their weekly grade. Have them write a paragraph explaining their choice.

Challenge

Have students solve the following problem. For a set of five numbers, the mean is 28, the mode is 24, the median is 28, and the range is 10. Find the five numbers. 24, 24, 28, 30, 34

Learn The Mean

The **mean** of a data set is the sum of the items in the set divided by the number of items. The mean can also be called the *average.* To find the mean, add all the data values and divide by the number of values.

Remember

The sum of a set of numbers is the result of adding the numbers together. **[Previous course]**

Example 1

The Iditarod dogsled race crosses the Alaskan wilderness from Anchorage to Nome. Susan Butcher has won the race four times. Here are her 1983–1994 finishing positions. (She wasn't in the race in 1985.) Find the mean.

9, 2, 1, 1, 1, 2, 1, 3, 2, 4, 10

9 + 2 + 1 + 1 + 1 + 2 + 1 + 3 + 2 + 4 + 10 = 36 Add the items.

36 ÷ 11 = 3.272727... Divide the sum by the number of items.

Susan Butcher's mean finishing position was 3.272727.... Sometimes the mean is a decimal value with several digits after the decimal point. Since real-world measurements aren't usually written with so many decimals, it's reasonable to use just the first two digits after the decimal. So, Susan Butcher's mean finishing position was 3.27.

Try It

a. Find the mean soccer ball price. $12.50, $16.00, $14.95, $19.00, $9.50 $14.39

b. Find the mean number of soccer goals scored. 2, 3, 0, 1, 1, 2, 5, 0, 2, 1, 1, 0 1.5

The mean is sometimes referred to as the *equal sharing* number. If all the values in a data set are evened out so that they are all equal to each other and their total is still the same, then each value will be equal to the mean.

Check Your Understanding

1. How is the mean different from the median? The mode?

2. Is the mean of a data set a member of the set? Explain.

MATH EVERY DAY

Problem of the Day

Martha has a 7-ounce glass and a 4-ounce glass. How can she use these glasses and another container to measure exactly 6 ounces of water?

Possible answer: Martha fills the 7-ounce glass and pours 4 ounces into the 4-ounce glass. She then pours the remaining 3 ounces into another container and empties the 4-ounce glass. She repeats the process. When she adds the 3 ounces to the container already containing 3 ounces, she has 6 ounces in all.

Available on Daily Transparency 1-8

An Extension is provided in the transparency package.

Fact of the Day

Ty Cobb was the American League batting champion 12 times in the early 1900s. His average ranged from .324 to .420.

Estimation

Estimate.

1. 421 ÷ 4 100
2. 483 ÷ 6 80
3. 7218 ÷ 71 100
4. 4624 ÷ 54 90

Answers for Explore

1–2. Answers may vary.

3. It represents one arm length if all group members had exactly the same length arm.
4. No; The total will be the same regardless of the order.
5. It depends on the person added. If the person's arm length is shorter than the arm length from Step 3, the new group arm length will go down. If the person's arm length is longer, the group arm length will go up.

2 Teach

Learn

Alternate Examples

In the 1996 NBA championship playoff games, Michael Jordan scored the following number of points: 28, 29, 36, 23, 26, and 22.

Find the mean number of points. First add the points: 28 + 29 + 36 + 23 + 26 + 22 = 164

Since there were 6 games, divide the sum by 6.
164 ÷ 6 = 27.333333...

The mean number of points is 27.33.

3 Practice and Assess

Check

Be sure that students understand that the mean is not necessarily the middle number.

Answers for Check Your Understanding

1. The mean is the measure of how much each would have if all the values are shared equally. The median is the middle value, regardless of equal sharing. The mode is the value occurring most often, regardless of equal sharing.
2. Not necessarily. The mean is a quotient that may not turn out to be a number in the data set.

1-8 Exercises and Applications

Assignment Guide

- **Basic**
  1, 3–4, 6–12, 14–26 evens
- **Average**
  2–4, 6–13, 16–28 evens
- **Enriched**
  2, 5–13, 20–28 evens

Exercise Notes

Exercise 6

Error Prevention If students do not get the correct answers, remind them to include the stem when they consider the data.

Exercise 9

Test Prep Students can answer this question without actually finding the mean, median, and mode of the data set. Explain that the mode is a number in the data set. and that the median and mean will be less than 7, the largest number. Therefore, D cannot be the mean, median, or mode.

Reteaching

Activity

Materials: Centimeter cubes

Use centimeter cubes to represent this set of numbers as a bar graph: 8, 3, 9, 4, 1. Arrange the bars in order from least to greatest.

- What is the median number? 4
- How can you tell? It's in the middle.
- What is the range? 8
- How did you find the range? The greatest number is 9 and the least number is 1; 9 − 1 = 8.
- Try to make 5 equal-length bars with these cubes. How many cubes are in each bar? 5: The number 5 is the mean, or the average, number of cubes.

PRACTICE 1-8

1-8 Exercises and Applications

Practice and Apply

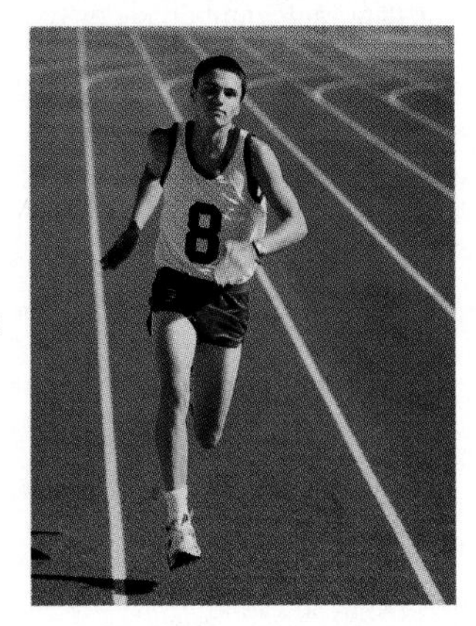

Getting Started For each data set, find the mean by adding the numbers and then dividing the sum by the number of items.

1. $10, $10, $5, $1, $2, $5, $4, $3 $5
2. 100, 85, 88, 98, 95, 87, 82, 83, 84 89.11
3. 5, 5, 5, 5, 5, 5, 5, 5 5
4. **Consumer** Find the mean amount of money spent by patrons at theaters. $8.43
   $8, $7, $10, $12, $8, $11, $8, $6, $9, $8, $10, $7, $7, $7
5. **Health** The data is the number of seconds it took Manuel to run the 100-meter dash. Find his mean time. 11.81 seconds
   10, 12, 15, 10, 11, 14, 13, 16, 10, 12, 10, 9, 13, 12, 11, 11

Find the mean of each set of data.

6. 32.29

Stem	Leaf
1	3 4 5
2	1 2 2 5 6
4	2 4 6 6
5	7 9

7. 3.63

```
            x
      x     x     x     x
      x     x     x     x     x
x     x     x     x     x     x
1     2     3     4     5     6
```

8. Find the mean, median, and mode. Mean 37.2, median 35, mode 33

NFL Teams That Have Played the Most Postseason Games (through 1995)

Team	Games	Team	Games
Cowboys	49	Rams	33
'49ers	33	Raiders	36
Redskins	35		

9. **Test Prep** Which number is **not** the mean, median, or mode for the following data? D
   6, 7, 7, 6, 4, 4, 7, 2, 0
   Ⓐ 7 Ⓑ 5 Ⓒ 6 Ⓓ 50

PRACTICE

Name ____________

Practice 1-8

The Meaning of Mean

Find the mean of each set of data.

1. mean About 9.18
2. mean 22.7

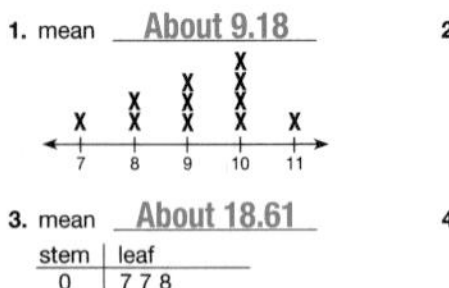

3. mean About 18.61

stem	leaf
0	7 7 8
1	0 1 3 8 9 9
2	0 0 1 1 4 6 9
3	0 2

4. mean 47

stem	leaf
3	4 7 8
4	0 1 3 3 7 9
5	1 1 4 6
6	0 1

Find the mean, median, and mode(s) of each data set.

5. 8, 10, 10, 12, 14, 18, 21, 35
   mean 16
   median 13
   mode(s) 10
6. 23, 28, 36, 36, 42, 49, 64, 83, 94
   mean About 50.56
   median 42
   mode(s) 36
7. 41, 18, 63, 24, 37, 72, 84
   mean About 48.43
   median 41
   mode(s) None
8. 6, 3, 8, 7, 5, 7, 6, 2, 9, 9, 4, 3, 9, 4
   mean About 5.86
   median 6
   mode(s) 9
9. Find the mean, median, and mode(s) of the data showing the number of members of local scout troops.
   41, 75, 32, 115, 75, 68, 81, 93, 102, 53, 49, 71
   mean 71.25 median 73 mode(s) 75
10. Find the mean, median, and mode(s) of the data showing the number of points scored by the Hooping Cranes basketball team in their last 12 games.
    87, 112, 98, 93, 79, 80, 89, 83, 91, 93, 86, 101
    mean 91 median 90 mode(s) 93

RETEACHING

Name ____________

Alternative Lesson 1-8

The Meaning of Mean

The **mean** of a data set is the sum of the items in the set divided by the number of items. The mean can also be called the *average*. To find the mean, add all the data values and divide by the number of values.

Example

The weekly allowances for a group of children are: $5.00, $4.00, $3.50, $6.00, $5.00, $2.50, $2.00, $7.00, $6.50, $4.50, $3.50, $5.50. What is the mean allowance? Round your answer to the nearest cent.

Step 1: Add all of the amounts.
The total is $55.00.

Step 2: There are 12 items.
Divide the total dollar amount by this number.
$55.00 ÷ 12 = $4.5833...

The mean allowance is $4.58 when rounded to the nearest cent.

Try It Find the mean price of these six boxes of crackers: $3.25, $2.75, $2.00, $3.25, $2.50, $2.75.

a. Add all of the prices together. What is the sum? $16.50
b. How many boxes of crackers are there all together? 6 boxes.
c. Divide the sum of the prices by the number of boxes of crackers.
   Show your number sentence. 16.50 ÷ 6 = 2.75
d. Write the mean price. $2.75

Find the mean weight of these cats: Frisky, 6 lb; Mittens, 8 lb; Tiger, 12 lb; Baby Kitty, 7 lb; Patches, 10 lb; Kissy, 9 lb; Tripod, 14 lb; Angel, 9 lb. Round your answer to the nearest whole number.

e. Step 1: 6 + 8 + 12 + 7 + 10 + 9 + 14 + 9 = 75
f. Step 2: 75 ÷ 8 = 9.375
g. Mean weight: 9 lb

Find the mean of each set of data.

h. Length of these six pencils:
   12 cm, 15 cm, 16 cm, 10 cm, 11 cm, 14 cm 13 cm
i. Score of these eight tests:
   78, 69, 82, 75, 90, 88, 72, 86 80

Problem Solving and Reasoning

10. Critical Thinking Find the mean, median, and mode. Which one best describes the tennis players? Mean 75.5 in., median 76 in., mode 76 in. Possible answer: Mode, because 4 of the 6 are the same.

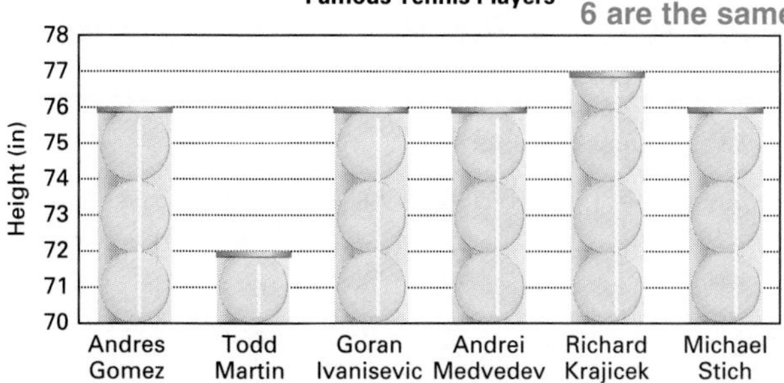

11. Critical Thinking Create a data set of five different numbers whose mean is 10. Explain your method.

12. Choose a Strategy GPS Suppose you have test scores of 92, 85, 86, and 90. What would you need to score on the next test to have a mean score of 90? 97

13. Critical Thinking How does the mean of a data set change if you add a number to the data and the new number is exactly equal to the mean? It does not change.

Problem Solving STRATEGIES

- Look for a Pattern
- Make an Organized List
- Make a Table
- Guess and Check
- Work Backward
- Use Logical Reasoning
- Draw a Diagram
- Solve a Simpler Problem

Mixed Review

Divide. *[Previous course]*

14. 275 ÷ 5 **15.** 361 ÷ 7 **16.** 834 ÷ 9 **17.** 709 ÷ 8

18. 396 ÷ 11 **19.** 522 ÷ 13 **20.** 618 ÷ 15 **21.** 980 ÷ 20

22 384 ÷ 24 **23.** 616 ÷ 56 **24.** 996 ÷ 83 **25.** 736 ÷ 32

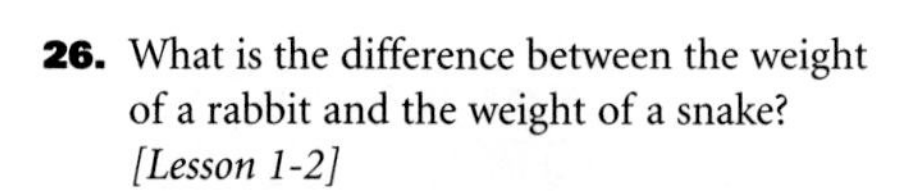

26. What is the difference between the weight of a rabbit and the weight of a snake? *[Lesson 1-2]*

27. About how many times taller than the snake bar does the elephant bar appear to be? *[Lesson 1-2]*

28. Do you think the graph is misleading? Explain. *[Lesson 1-2]*

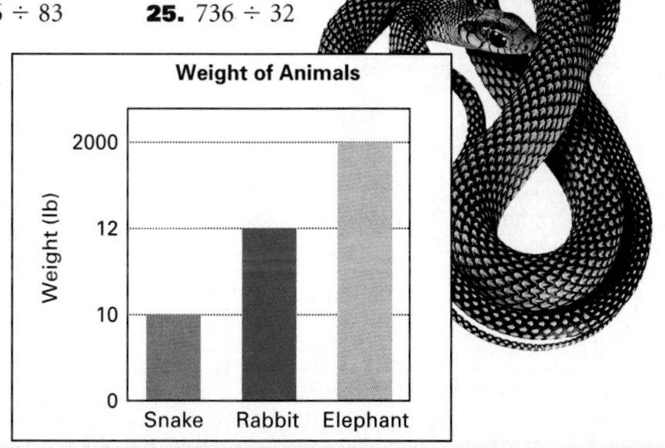

PROBLEM SOLVING 1-8

PROBLEM SOLVING

Name ______ Guided Problem Solving 1-8

GPS PROBLEM 12, STUDENT PAGE 49

Suppose you have test scores of 92, 85, 86, and 90. What would you need to score on the next test to have a mean score of 90?

— Understand —

1. What are the scores on the first four tests? 92, 85, 86, 90
2. What is the mean score you want after five tests? 90
3. How do you find the mean of a set of data? Add the data and divide by the number of items.

— Plan —

4. Which operation will you use to find the total score of four tests. Addition.
5. Which operation will you use to find the total score you should have on five tests if the mean score is 90? Multiplication.
6. Which operation will you use to find the score you need on the fifth test? Subtraction.

— Solve —

7. What is the total of the first four test scores? 353
8. What is the total you would need on five tests to have a mean score of 90 points? 450
9. What do you need to score on the fifth test? 97

— Look Back —

10. How can you check to see if your answer is reasonable? Add 97 to the four scores, and divide by 5 to see if the answer is 90.

SOLVE ANOTHER PROBLEM

Suppose you are on a trip. You have traveled 50 miles, 60 miles, 140 miles, 200 miles, and 10 miles. How far must you travel tomorrow to have a mean distance of 100 miles? 140 miles.

ENRICHMENT

Name ______ Extend Your Thinking 1-8

Critical Thinking

The box below shows some prices students paid for mountain and ten-speed bikes. Organize this information and use it to answer the questions below.

Bicycle Prices
$180, $275, $675, $420, $385, $450, $610, $295, $450, $145, $395, $265, $515, $495, $235

1. What is the **median** price for a bicycle? How do you know? $395, because it is the middle number.
2. What is the **mode** price for a bicycle? How do you know? $450, because it occurs most often.
3. What is the **mean** price for a bicycle? How do you know? $386, because the sum of the data, $5790, divided by the number of items, 15, is 386.
4. Would you use the median, mode, or mean price as your savings goal if you wanted to buy a bicycle? Explain. Accept any reasonable answer. Possible answer: Use the median because half of the bicycles are priced above it and half are priced below it.
5. Suppose you add bicycles that cost $435 and $565 to the data set. Will the median, mode, and mean change? If so, what are they now? New, median, $420; new mean, $399.41; mode remains the same, $450.
6. Would the addition of the new data affect your decision in Question 4? Why or why not? Possible answer: Yes, The median increases from $395 to $420, so I need to save $25 more.

Exercise Notes

■ Exercise 12

Problem-Solving Tip You may wish to use Teaching Tool Transparencies 2 and 3: Guided Problem Solving, pages 1–2.

Exercise Answers

11. Possible answer: 8, 9, 10, 11, 12; Choose five numbers that add to 50, because 50 divided by 5 is 10.
14. 55
15. 51 R 4 or 51.57
16. 92 R 6 or 92.67
17. 88 R 5 or 88.63
18. 36
19. 40 R 2 or 40.15
20. 41 R 3 or 41.2
21. 49
22. 16
23. 11
24. 12
25. 23
26. 2 pounds
27. 3 times
28. Possible answer: Yes, because an elephant weighs 200 times as much as a snake, but it looks as if it weighs only 3 times as much.

Alternate Assessment

Performance Have students work in groups of three to prepare a presentation directed to younger students in 4th or 5th grade. Students should choose data that is of interest to the younger students and use the data to demonstrate the meaning of mean, median, and mode.

➤ Quick Quiz

Find the mean, the median, and the mode for each set of data.

1. 8, 10, 7, 6, 5, 7, 13 Mean: 8; Median: 7; Mode: 7.
2. 12, 18, 10, 13, 15, 19, 22, 27 Mean: 17; Median: 16.5; Mode: none.

Available on Daily Transparency 1-8

Technology

Using a Spreadsheet • Finding the Median

The Point
Students use spreadsheets to find the median of a set of data.

Materials
Spreadsheet software

Resources

Interactive CD-ROM Spreadsheet/Grapher Tool.

About the Page

If students are not familiar with spreadsheets:

- Point out the columns, rows, and cells.
- Identify cell locations by column letter and row number.
- Discuss how to enter data.
- Discuss how to use the sort function.

Ask ...

- How is the median found for an odd number of data values? Order the data; determine the middle number.
- How is the median found for an even number of data values? Order the data; find the average of the two middle numbers.

Answers for Try It
a. 81.5
b. 81.5

On Your Own
Students will have to collect data to answer these questions. You might suggest that they do this as a class. For the second question, be sure students understand the definition of mode.

Answers for On Your Own

- Answers may vary.
- The sort command will order the numbers so you can easily see how many of each number there are.
- Yes; Possible answer: The user could input the wrong data. Using technology doesn't mean that the user won't make a mistake.

TECHNOLOGY

Using a Spreadsheet • Finding the median

Problem: What is the median for the given set of data?

You can use your spreadsheet to sort the data. This will help you find the median.

90	80	88	58	78	93	93	93	75	88	90	70
78	95	83	75	78	50	88	78	93	43	93	48
60	93	83	78	48	70	65	73	85	85	88	

1 Type the data into column A. Check to make sure you have 35 numbers in the spreadsheet.

	A	B
1	90	
2	80	
3	88	
4	58	
5	78	
6	93	
7	93	
8	93	

2 Use the sort command to arrange the data from least to greatest. To do this, first highlight the data then select the sort command.

3 Using what you know about computing the median, find the median of the data.

Solution: The median of the data is 80.

TRY IT

a. What is the median of the first four columns of data?

b. What is the median of the top two rows of data?

ON YOUR OWN

- ▶ Use a spreadsheet to determine the median number of brothers and sisters your classmates have.
- ▶ How can the sort function of a spreadsheet help you find the mode?
- ▶ Is it possible to get a wrong answer when using a spreadsheet to find the median? Explain.

50

The Effects of Outliers

1-9

▶ Lesson Link You've learned about three numbers that you can use to describe a data set—the median, the mode, and the mean. Now you'll see how data items that are much different from the other items in the set can affect the median, the mean, and the mode. ◀

You'll Learn ...

■ to determine if an outlier affects the analysis of a data set

... How It's Used

Exercise researchers must check whether their data has been affected by outliers before they can use it to recommend new training procedures.

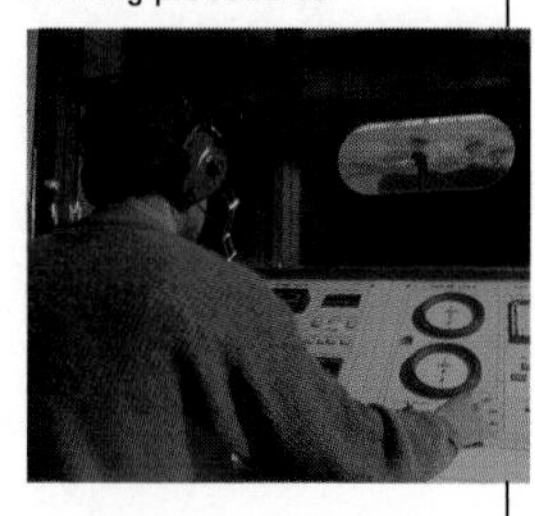

Vocabulary

outlier

Explore Outliers

Wayne's World

The Hart Trophy is awarded each year to the professional hockey player who is voted the most valuable in the National Hockey League. The table lists all but one of the players who won the Hart Trophy from 1974 to 1995.

1. Find the median, the mode, and the mean of the data.
2. The player who is not listed in the table is hockey legend Wayne Gretsky. Gretsky won the Hart Trophy nine times. Add Gretsky's data to the data set and recalculate the median, the mode, and the mean.
3. How does Gretsky's total affect the median? The mode? The mean?

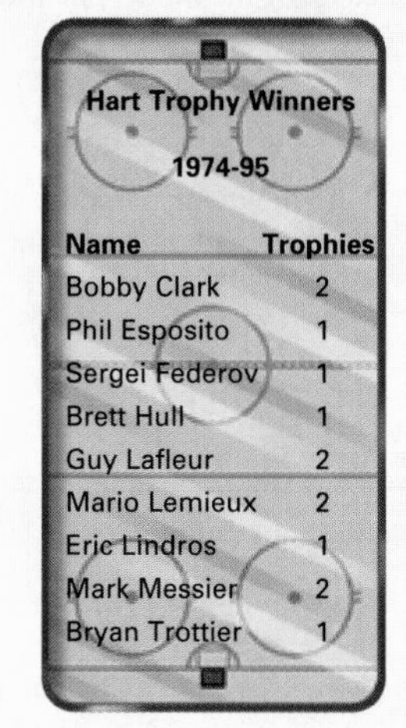

Hart Trophy Winners 1974-95

Name	Trophies
Bobby Clark	2
Phil Esposito	1
Sergei Federov	1
Brett Hull	1
Guy Lafleur	2
Mario Lemieux	2
Eric Lindros	1
Mark Messier	2
Bryan Trottier	1

Learn The Effects of Outliers

An **outlier** is a number in a data set that is very different from the rest of the numbers. Outliers can have a big effect on the mean.

In the last lesson, you saw that the mean of a data set may represent the set well. For example, the mean of the daily high temperatures shown here is 91°F. Because the mean is close to all of the data, it represents the set well.

Daily High Temperatures (°F)	
Monday	88
Tuesday	94
Wednesday	94
Thursday	92
Friday	87

1-9 Lesson Organizer

Objective

- Determine if an outlier affects the analysis of a data set.

Vocabulary

- Outlier

NCTM Standards

- 1–4, 7, 10

▶ Review

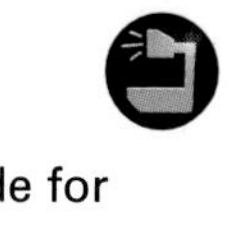

Find the mean, the median, and the mode for each set of data.

1. 24, 12, 16, 18, 16, 22 18, 17, 16
2. 1.6, 2.2, 3.1, 2.4, 1.7, 2.2, 2.2 2.2, 2.2, 2.2
3. 8, 7, 40, 9, 8, 6 13, 8, 8

Available on Daily Transparency 1-9

1 Introduce

Explore

The Point

Students learn how one or two data items which are very different from most of the data affect the other measures of central tendency they have studied.

Ongoing Assessment

Check that all students can find the mean, the median, and the mode for a set of data.

Answers for Explore

1. Median: 1; Mode: 1; Mean: 1.44.
2. Median: 1.5; Mode: 1; Mean: 2.2.
3. It changes the median only slightly, and it doesn't affect the mode at all. The mean changes most of all.

MEETING INDIVIDUAL NEEDS

Resources

- **1-9** Practice
- **1-9** Reteaching
- **1-9** Problem Solving
- **1-9** Enrichment
- **1-9** Daily Transparency
  - Problem of the Day
  - Review
  - Quick Quiz
- Technology Master 5
- Chapter 1 Project Master

Learning Modalities

Kinesthetic Have five students line up at the left end of the front of the room. Have the rest of the class estimate the mean and the median distances of the five students from the left end. Then position one more student at the far right end of the room. Have the rest of the class recalculate the mean and the median.

Social Have students work in groups of three or four to share the tasks of ordering **Explore** data and finding the mean, the median, and the mode for Step 1. They can trade roles and work on Step 2.

English Language Development

You can relate the term *outlier,* a number which is far away from the rest of the numbers in a data set, to the baseball term *outfielder,* a player whose position is well away from the baseball diamond. Both terms indicate something that is away from the others. If some students are not familiar with baseball, ask other students to give a brief explanation of the game.

2 Teach

Learn

Alternate Examples

The four tallest structures in Toronto, Canada, are the CN Tower at 1821 feet, First Canadian Place at 952 feet, Bay/Adelaide Center at 945 feet, and Scotia Plaza at 902 feet. Find the median, the mode, and the mean of the data with and without the outlier.

Since it is so much greater than the other values, 1821 is the outlier.

Without outlier

Median = 945.
No mode.
Mean: 952 + 945 + 902 = 2799.
2799 ÷ 3 = 933.

With outlier

Median: 952 + 945 = 1897
1897 ÷ 2 = 948.5.
No mode.
Mean:
1821 + 952 + 945 + 902 = 4620
4620 ÷ 4 = 1155.

3 Practice and Assess

Check

Discuss with students how an outlier might affect the median of a set of data.

Answers for Check Your Understanding

1. The mode doesn't change because the one outlier is a new value of data, and it doesn't change which number appears most often.
2. Yes; A high outlier will pull the mean up, and a low outlier will pull it down. The median and the mode are usually not profoundly affected either way.

Suppose that on Saturday the temperature plunges to 55°F. Look what happens to the mean: 88 + 94 + 94 + 92 + 87 + 55 = 510
510 ÷ 6 = 85

The mean temperature of 85°F is *less than* five of the six data items. It has been pulled downward by the outlier, 55°F.

The table shows that the median is affected only slightly by the addition of the Saturday outlier. The mode hasn't changed.

	Mon–Fri	Mon–Sat
Mean	91	85
Median	92	90
Mode	94	94

You can see that a data set with an outlier is usually better represented by the median or the mode. The mean is often pulled too much toward the outlier to represent the set well.

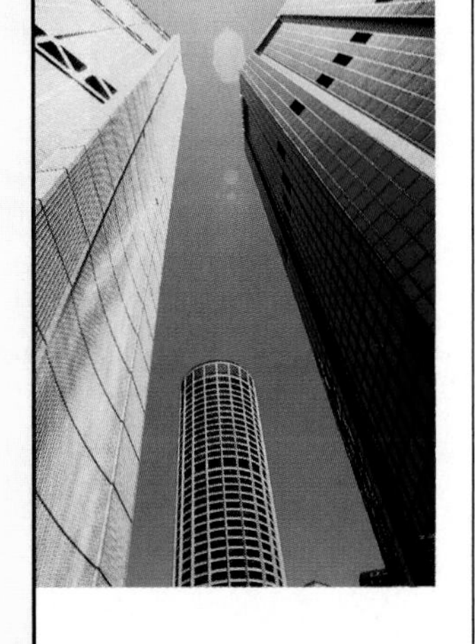

Example 1

Find the median, mode, and mean of the data with and without the outlier.

Tallest Buildings in Las Vegas	
Building	**Height (ft)**
Vegas World Tower	1012
Fitzgerald Hotel	400
Landmark Hotel	356
Las Vegas Hilton	345

Without outlier

Median = 356
No mode
Mean: 400 + 356 + 345 = 1101
1101 ÷ 3 = 367

With outlier

Median: 400 + 356 = 756
756 ÷ 2 = 378
No mode
Mean: 400 + 356 + 345 + 1012 = 2113
2113 ÷ 4 = 528.25

Try It With the outlier: Median 21, no mode, mean 28
Without the outlier: Median 19, no mode, mean 18.29

Find the median, mode, and mean with and without the outlier.

States with Most Indian Reservations								
State	AZ	CA	MN	NV	NM	WA	WI	SD
Number	23	96	14	19	25	27	11	9

Check Your Understanding

1. Why doesn't the mode change when an outlier is added to a data set?
2. Would a high outlier and a low outlier affect a data set differently? Explain.

MATH EVERY DAY

Problem of the Day

The tangram puzzle is believed to have its origin in China and is over 4000 years old. Draw a diagram showing how to use the tangram pieces to make these designs.

Possible answer:

Available on Daily Transparency 1-9

An Extension is provided in the transparency package.

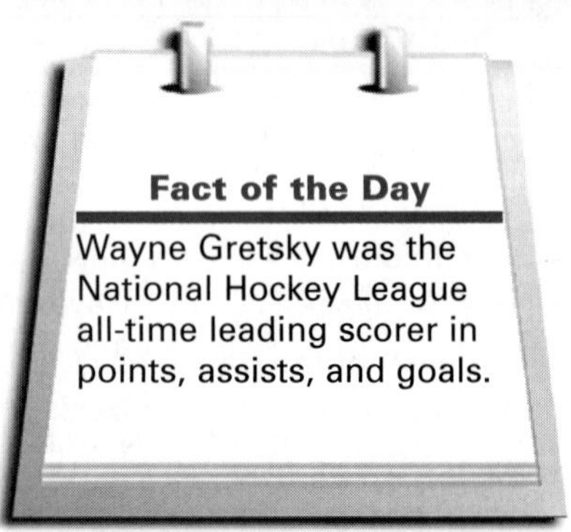

Mental Math

Do these mentally.

1. Find the mean of 4, 6, 8, 10, 12, 14 9
2. Find the mean of 5, 10, 15, 20, 25 15
3. Find the mean of 5, 10, 5, 10, 5, 10 7.5

1-9 Exercises and Applications

Practice and Apply

Getting Started **Identify the outlier in each data set.**

1. 24, 24, 18, 56, 25, 12, 15, 22 56 **2.** 34, 28, 31, 34, 37, 2, 29, 21 2

3. 7, 6, 9, 10, 11, 6, 8, 11, 0, 10, 7, 8 0 **4.** 200, 225, 3000, 500, 325, 311 3000

Identify the outliers in each data set.

5. 3

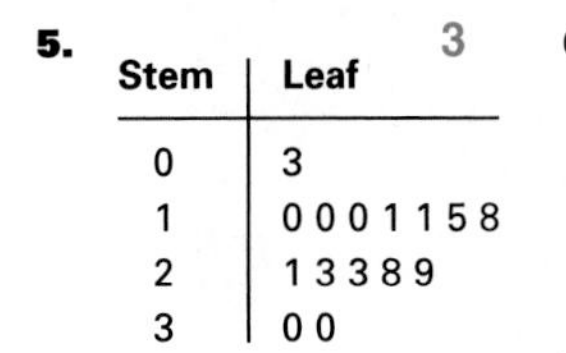

6. 9

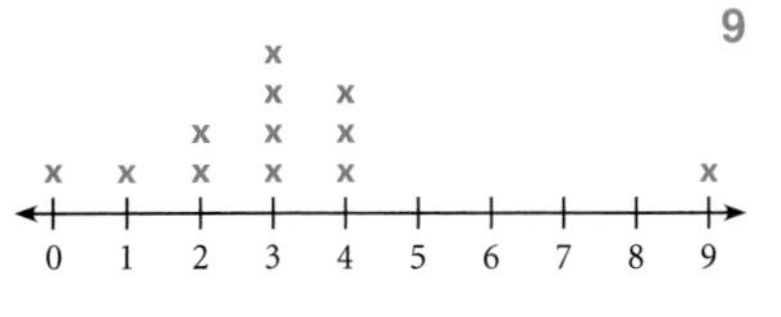

7. 70

Stem	Leaf
1	0 0 2 2 5
2	0 2 6 7
3	0 3 4 6
7	0

8. a. Find the mean, median, and mode with and without the outlier.

b. Did the outlier affect the mode? The mean? The median? Which did it affect the most?

British Open Tournament Scores (1996)	
John Daly	282
Costantino Rocca	282
Michael Campbell	283
Steven Bottomley	283
Barry Lane	288

9. a. GPS Find the mean, median, and mode with and without the outlier.

b. Did the outlier affect the mode? The mean? The median? Which did it affect the most?

Dinah Shore Tournament Scores (1996)	
Nanci Bowen	285
Susie Redman	286
Brandie Burton	287
Sherri Turner	287
Meg Mallon	292

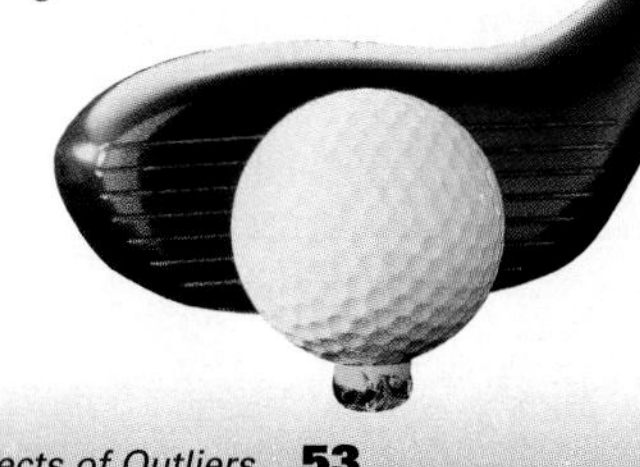

10. **Test Prep** Which has the greatest value for the following set of data, the mean, the median, the mode, or the outlier? C

94, 88, 11, 90, 94, 92

Ⓐ mean Ⓑ median

Ⓒ mode Ⓓ outlier

PRACTICE

Name ________________

Practice 1-9

The Effects of Outliers

Identify the outlier in each data set.

1. 84

23, 32, 21, 36, 84, 27, 32, 29

2. 11

90, 87, 112, 96, 11, 107, 93, 85

3. 69 **4.** 14 **5.** 82

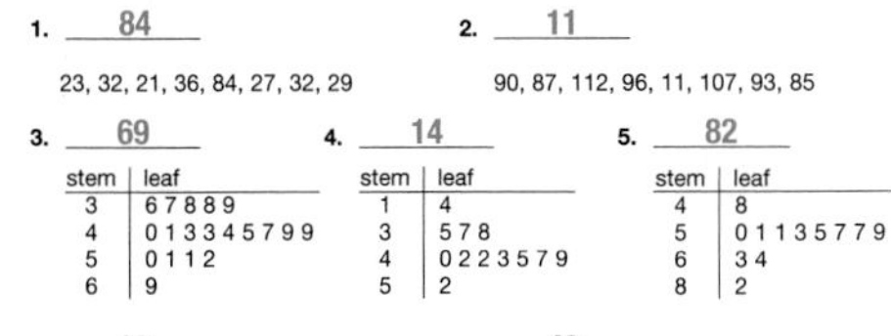

6. 13

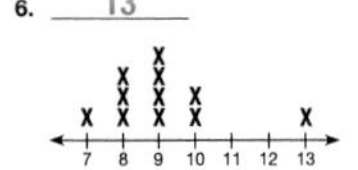

7. 43

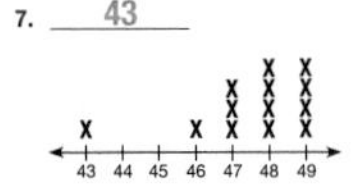

8. a. Find the mean, median, and mode(s) with and without the outliers.

With

mean About 134.62

median 104

mode(s) 82

Without

mean About 106.64

median 104

mode(s) 82

Areas of States (thousands of square miles)	
AK	571
AZ	114
CA	156
CO	104
HI	6
ID	82
MT	145
NV	110
NM	121
OR	96
UT	82
WA	66
WY	97

b. Did the outlier(s) affect the mode(s)? No

the mean? Yes

the median? No

Which did it affect the most? Mean

RETEACHING

Name ________________

Alternative Lesson 1-9

The Effects of Outliers

An **outlier** is a number in a data set that is very different from the rest of the data. Outliers can have a big effect on the mean.

Example

Find the mean, median, and mode with and without the outlier for this set of data about the number of days 6 people exercised in one month: 4, 23, 21, 22, 21, 23.

Identify the outlier. Since most of data is in the low twenties, the outlier of the data set is 4.

Find the mean of the data set. The mean is 19. — Think: $4 + 23 + 21 + 22 + 21 + 23 = 114$; $114 \div 6 = 19$

Without the outlier, 4, the mean of the data set is 22. — Think: $23 + 21 + 22 + 21 + 23 = 110$; $110 \div 5 = 22$

Find the median of the data set. The median is 21.5. — Think: 4, 21, 21, 22, 23, 23 → 21.5

Without the outlier, 4, the median of the data is 22. — Think: 21, 21, 22, 23, 23

Find the mode of the data set. The modes are 21 and 23. — Think: 4, 21, 21, 22, 23, 23

Without the outlier, 4, the modes of the data remain the same, 21 and 23. — Think: 21, 21, 22, 23, 23

Try It Find the mean, median, and mode, with and without outliers for this set of data: 450, 420, 435, 450, 5500, 440, 425, 460.

a. Identify the outlier. 5500

b. Organize your results in the table.

Miles Traveled Last Week		
	With Outlier	Without Outlier
Mean	1072.5	440
Median	445	440
Mode	450	450

1-9 Exercises and Applications

Assignment Guide

- **Basic** 1–7, 9–15, 20, 22
- **Average** 3–8, 9–11, 16–22
- **Enriched** 4–7, 9–11, 16–22

Exercise Notes

Exercise 10

Test Prep Point out that in this exercise the outlier is *less* than the rest of the data.

Exercise Answers

8. a. With outlier: Mean 283.6, median 283, modes 282 and 283; Without outlier: Mean 282.5, median 282.5, modes 282 and 283.

   b. Modes didn't change; Mean and median did change; Mean changed the most.

9. a. With outlier: Mean 287.4, median 287, mode 287; Without the outlier: Mean 286.25, median 286.5, mode 287.

   b. Mode didn't change; Mean and median did change; Mean changed the most.

Reteaching

Activity

Materials: Centimeter cubes

Use centimeter cubes to model a bar graph of the Hart Trophy winners listed on page 51. Arrange the columns in order from least to greatest, but do not include Wayne Gretzky.

- How many cubes are in the middle bar? 1 cube
- What number of cubes appears most? 1 cube
- What division gives the mean number of cubes? $13 \div 9 = 1.4$
- Add a bar of cubes for Wayne Gretzky's awards. What is the median? 1.5 cubes What is the mode? 1 cube What division gives the average number of cubes? $22 \div 9 \approx 2.4$

Exercise Notes

■ **Exercise 11**

Sports Patricia Hoskins played basketball for four years at Mississippi Valley College. She is the all-time leading scorer in women's college basketball.

■ **Exercises 12–19**

Estimation Have students first estimate their answers to check for reasonableness.

Project Progress

You may want to have students use Chapter 1 Project Master.

Exercise Answers

11. a. Mean 74.8, median 82, mode 82; b. Mean 69.64, median 82, mode 82; c. Mean is decreased; Median and mode are unchanged; d. Possible answers: The median or mode, which aren't affected by the outliers.

Alternate Assessment

You may want to use the *Interactive CD-ROM Journal* with this assessment.

Journal Have students create a data set of ten values, with an outlier. With and without the outlier, have them find the mean, median, and mode of their data set. Then, they should write a paragraph explaining which value the outlier affected the most.

► Quick Quiz

Find the mean, the median, and the mode for each set of data with and without the outlier.

1. 4, 17, 7, 6, 5, 7, 10
   With outlier 17: Mean, 8; median, 7; mode, 7
   Without outlier 17: Mean, 6.5; median, 6.5; mode, 7.
2. 12, 18, 10, 34, 13, 15
   With outlier 34: Mean, 17; median, 14; mode, none.
   Without outlier 34: mean, 13.6; median, 13; mode, none.

Available on Daily Transparency 1-9

PROBLEM SOLVING 1-9

Problem Solving and Reasoning

11. The following table shows the number of games Michael Jordan has played with the Chicago Bulls.

Year	Games Played	Year	Games Played	Year	Games Played
1984–85	82	1988–89	81	1993–94	78
1985–86	???	1989–90	82	1994–95	17
1986–87	82	1991–92	82	1995–96	82
1987–88	82	1992–93	80		

a. Find the mean, median, and mode of the data provided. Ignore the entry for 1985–86.

b. During the 1985–86 season, Michael had an injury and played only 18 games. Add this outlier to the data and recompute the mean, median, and mode.

c. Communicate How do the outliers affect the mean? The median? The mode? Explain.

d. Critical Thinking Which number (the median, the mode, or the mean) is the best measure to use when describing the number of games Michael played each year? Explain.

12. 5512 13. 1687 14. 1352
15. 34 R 1 or 34.11 16. 46,019 17. 83,210
18. 28,294 19. 30 R 14 or 30.47

Mixed Review

Perform the appropriate operation. *[Previous course]*

12. 234 + 5278 **13.** 5678 − 3991 **14.** 26 × 52 **15.** 307 ÷ 9

16. 43,675 + 2,344 **17.** 89,021 − 5,811 **18.** 329 × 86 **19.** 914 ÷ 30

20. How many women played in exactly three games? *[Lesson 1-3]* 3

21. One woman played in six games. How many hits did she get? *[Lesson 1-3]* 5

22. Does there appear to be a trend in the scatterplot? Explain. *[Lesson 1-3]*
The more games played, the more hits made.

Hits For Women's Softball Players

Number of hits: 1 2 3 4 5 6
Number of games played: 1 2 3 4 5 6

Project Progress

Continue to work on the graphs and charts that show your data. If you find a large set of data about a single topic, you may want to calculate the median, the mode, and the mean of the data and include that in your report.

Problem Solving
Understand
Plan
Solve
Look Back

54 *Chapter 1 • Statistics—Real-World Use of Whole Numbers*

PROBLEM SOLVING

Name ______

Guided Problem Solving 1-9

GPS PROBLEM 9, STUDENT PAGE 53

a. Find the mean, median, and mode with and without the outlier.

b. Did the outlier affect the mode? The mean? The median? Which did it affect the most?

Dinah Shore Tournament Scores (1996)	
Nanci Bowen	285
Susie Redman	286
Brandie Burton	287
Sherri Turner	287
Meg Mallon	292

— Understand —

1. How many times will you need to find the mean, median, and mode for this set of data? Two times.

— Plan —

2. Write the data in order from least to greatest. Underline the outlier. 285, 286, 287, 287, 292

— Solve —

3. Complete the table to find the means, medians, and modes.

	With outlier	Without outlier
Mean	287.4	286.25
Median	287	286.5
Mode	287	287

4. How did the outlier affect the mean, median, and mode?
The mean increased by more than one. The median increased by 0.5. The mode remained the same.

5. Which did the outlier affect the most? Mean.

— Look Back —

6. How can you tell if your answer to Item 4 is reasonable? Because the outlier was greater than the other data, logically it will increase the mean and median but have little effect on the mode.

SOLVE ANOTHER PROBLEM

For these scores, calculate the mean, median, and mode, with and without the outlier: 35, 82, 85, 85, 90, 93.
Mean: With, 78.3; Without, 87; Median: With, 85; Without, 85;
Mode: With, 85; Without 85.

ENRICHMENT

Name ______

Extend Your Thinking 1-9

Critical Thinking

Here is some information about the heights of several different dog breeds.

Breed	Average Height (in centimeters)	Breed	Average Height (in centimeters)
Collie	63	Labrador Retriever	58
Doberman	66	Chihuahua	20
Poodle	31	Cocker Spaniel	34
German Shepherd	63	Bull Mastiff	65
Beagle	36	Shih Tzu	24
Golden Retriever	59		

1. Organize the data into two groups—breeds shorter than 40 cm and breeds taller than 40 cm. What is the mean, median, and mode of each group?
Less than 40: mean, 29; median, 31; mode, no mode;
Greater than 40: mean; 62.33; median 63; mode, 63.

2. What happens to the mean, median, and mode of the tallest group if you include the shortest breed's height as an outlier?
Median and mode remain the same. Mean (56.29) is less than all heights other than the shortest breed's height.

3. What generalization can you make about the effect on the median and the mean if the outlier is less than the other data?
The mean will not be as great if the outlier is included.

4. What happens to the mean, median, and mode of the shortest group if you include the tallest breed's height as an outlier?
No mode. Median increases from 31 to 32.5. Mean (35.17) is greater than 4 of the 6 items in the data set.

5. What generalization can you make about the effect on the median and the mean if the outlier is greater than the other data?
Mean will be greater if the outlier is included. In many cases, most of the data will be less than the mean. The median is affected only slightly; however, it will usually increase.

Section 1C Connect

The article at the beginning of this section stated that "mathematics can turn huge amounts of data into a few easy-to-understand numbers." Since then, you've learned about three measures that can do this: the median, the mode, and the mean. Now you'll have a chance to use those numbers to decide which athlete is #1.

Will the Real #1 Athlete Please Stand Up?

Babe Ruth and Hank Aaron are two of baseball's most famous athletes. Both played for different teams and at different times. Is it possible to use statistics to determine who was the better athlete?

The following data represent the hits and home runs made by each player during the years he played for the teams shown.

Babe Ruth	New York Yankees (1920–1934)														
Hits	172	204	128	205	200	104	184	192	173	172	186	199	156	138	105
Home Runs	54	59	35	41	46	25	47	60	54	46	49	46	41	34	22

Hank Aaron	Milwaukee Braves (1954–1965)											
Hits	131	189	200	198	196	223	172	197	191	201	187	181
Home Runs	13	27	26	44	30	39	40	34	45	44	24	32

1. For each player, find the median, mode, and mean for both hits and home runs.
2. According to the statistics, who do you think was the better athlete? Write a paragraph explaining your reasoning.
3. Choose either the hits data or the home runs data. Draw a graph comparing the athletes' means, medians, and modes. The graph should help justify your decision of who is the better athlete.

55

Will the Real #1 Athlete Please Stand Up?

The Point

In *Will the Real #1 Athlete Please Stand Up?* on page 41, students discussed how compiled statistics are used to rank athletic performance. Now they will interpret data to determine if Babe Ruth or Hank Aaron is the #1 Athlete.

About the Page

- Review the meaning of hits and home runs for students who may not be familiar with the game of baseball.
- Remind students to list the numbers given in order to help them determine the median and the mode.
- Remind students that the mean is the average of the data presented.
- Ask students which numbers might be outliers in the data.
- Ask students if mean, median, or mode best represents the data given.
- Discuss whether hits, home runs, or a combination of both best determines who is #1.

Ongoing Assessment

Check that students have determined the mean, median, and mode correctly.

Extension

Have students choose the best hitter on their favorite baseball team and determine his total number of career hits and home runs. Have students compare that data with the information given about Babe Ruth and Hank Aaron. How do today's players measure up to these baseball legends?

Answers for Connect

1.

Babe Ruth Hits	Babe Ruth Home Runs	Hank Aaron Hits	Hank Aaron Home Runs
104	22	131	13
105	25	172	24
128	34	181	26
138	35	187	27
156	41	189	30
172	41	191	32
172	46	196	34
173	46	197	39
184	46	198	40
186	47	200	44
192	49	201	44
199	54	223	45
200	54		
204	59		
205	60		
Median		Median	
173	46	193.5	33
Mode		Mode	
172	46	None	44
Mean		Mean	
167.87	43.93	188.83	33.17

2. Possible answer: Hank Aaron was a better athlete, because although his mean number of home runs was less, his mean number of hits was higher.

3. Possible answer: There should be one graph that compares mean, median, and mode about hits or home runs for both Hank Aaron and Babe Ruth.

1C Review

Review Correlation

Item(s)	Lesson(s)
1–3	1-7, 1-8
4	1-2, 1-5
5	1-7, 1-8, 1-9
6	1-5
7	1-7

Test Prep

Test-Taking Tip

Point out to students that time on a test is limited, so they should not do more than what is required. Here, they need not find the mean since none of the answers involve this number.

Answers for Review

1. Mean: 4.81; Median: 5; Modes: 5 and 1.
2. Mean: 3.2; Median: 3; Mode: 3.
3. Mean: 15.07; Median: 12; Modes: 10 and 25.
4. a. 32; b. 14; c. Yes; Possible answer: The bar graph could be misleading because the intervals on the vertical scale are not equal.
5. The mean; Possible answer: The mean is often pulled too much toward the outlier to represent the set well.
6. Length of School Year

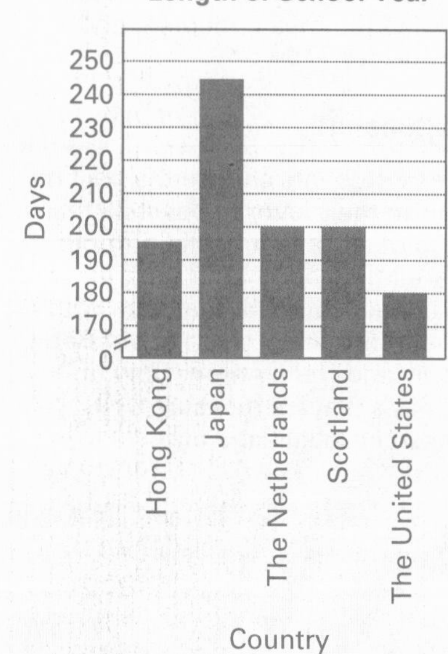

7. C

Section 1C Review

REVIEW 1C

Find the mean, median, and mode of each set of data.

1. 1, 1, 5, 5, 7, 7, 9, 9, 8, 1, 1, 3, 4, 5, 5, 6

2.

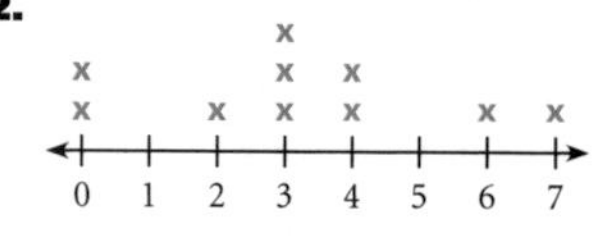

3.

Stem	Leaf
1	0 0 0 0 1 1 2 2 3 3 4
2	5 5 5 5

4. These graphs display data about female athletes in the Winter Olympics.

Female Competitors in Winter Olympics

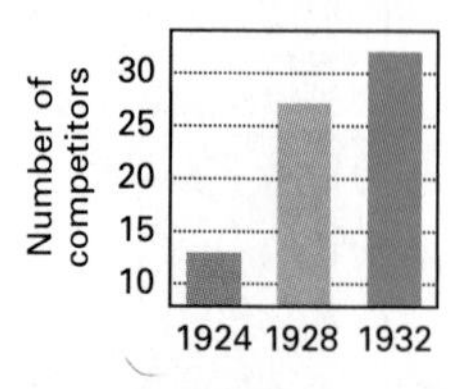

Female Competitors in Winter Olympics

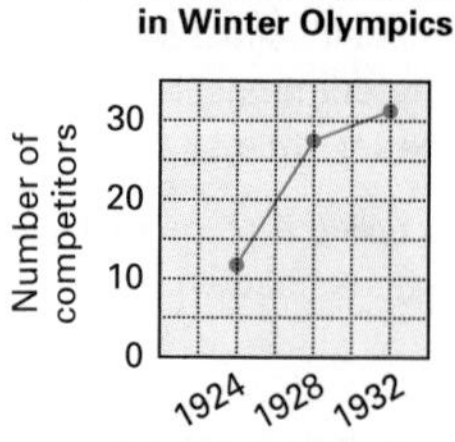

a. How many women competed in the 1932 Winter Olympics?

b. The number of females increased between 1924 and 1928. By how much did it increase?

c. Communicate Could either graph be misleading? Explain.

5. Communicate Which measure—the mean, the median, or the mode—can be most affected by an outlier? Why?

6. Draw a bar graph for the data about the length in days of each country's school year: Hong Kong, 195; Japan, 244; Netherlands, 200; Scotland, 200; United States, 180.

Test Prep

When you need to find the median and mode of a large set of data, a line plot can help you keep track of the data.

7. Which value is greater for the following set of data, the median or the mode?

9, 10, 12, 11, 9, 13, 12, 10, 11, 10, 12, 11, 11, 10, 12, 11, 13, 15

Ⓐ Median Ⓑ Mode Ⓒ The two are equal.

Resources

Practice Masters
Section 1C Review

Assessment Sourcebook
Quiz 1C

TestWorks
Test and Practice Software

PRACTICE

Name ____________________ Practice

Section 1C Review

Find the mean, median, and mode(s) of each set of data in Exercises 1–3.

1. mean About 29.92 median 29.5 mode(s) 25
2. mean About 84.29 median 84.5 mode(s) 85
3. mean 39.8 median 40 mode(s) 33

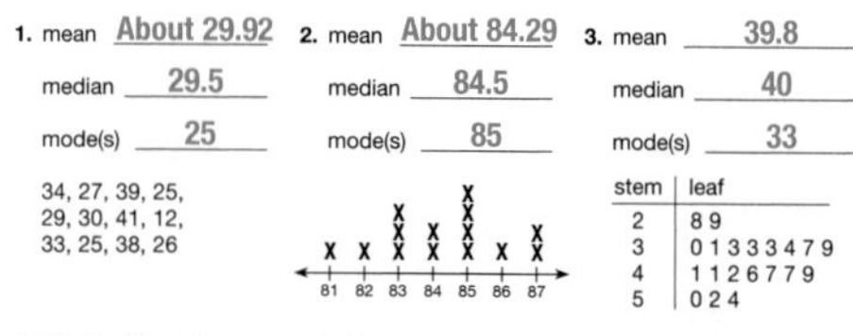

4. Use the Wheat Exports graph. *[Lesson 1-2]*

a. About how many times taller does the U.S. bar appear to be than the bar for France? Almost twice as tall

b. Read the graph. What was the dollar value of French wheat exports? $2.8 billion of American wheat exports? $3.4 billion

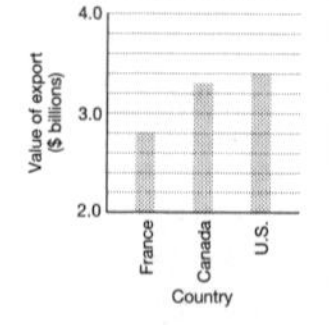

c. Could the bar graph be misleading? If so, how would you correct the graph? Yes. Use a scale that starts at 0, or show a break to indicate missing numbers.

5. Make a bar graph of the data showing the number of American households with various pets in 1993.

Pet	Millions of Households
Birds	5.4
Cats	29.2
Dogs	34.6
Fish	2.7
Rabbits	2.3

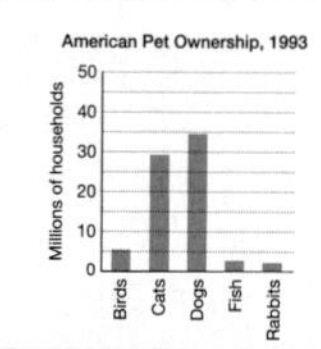

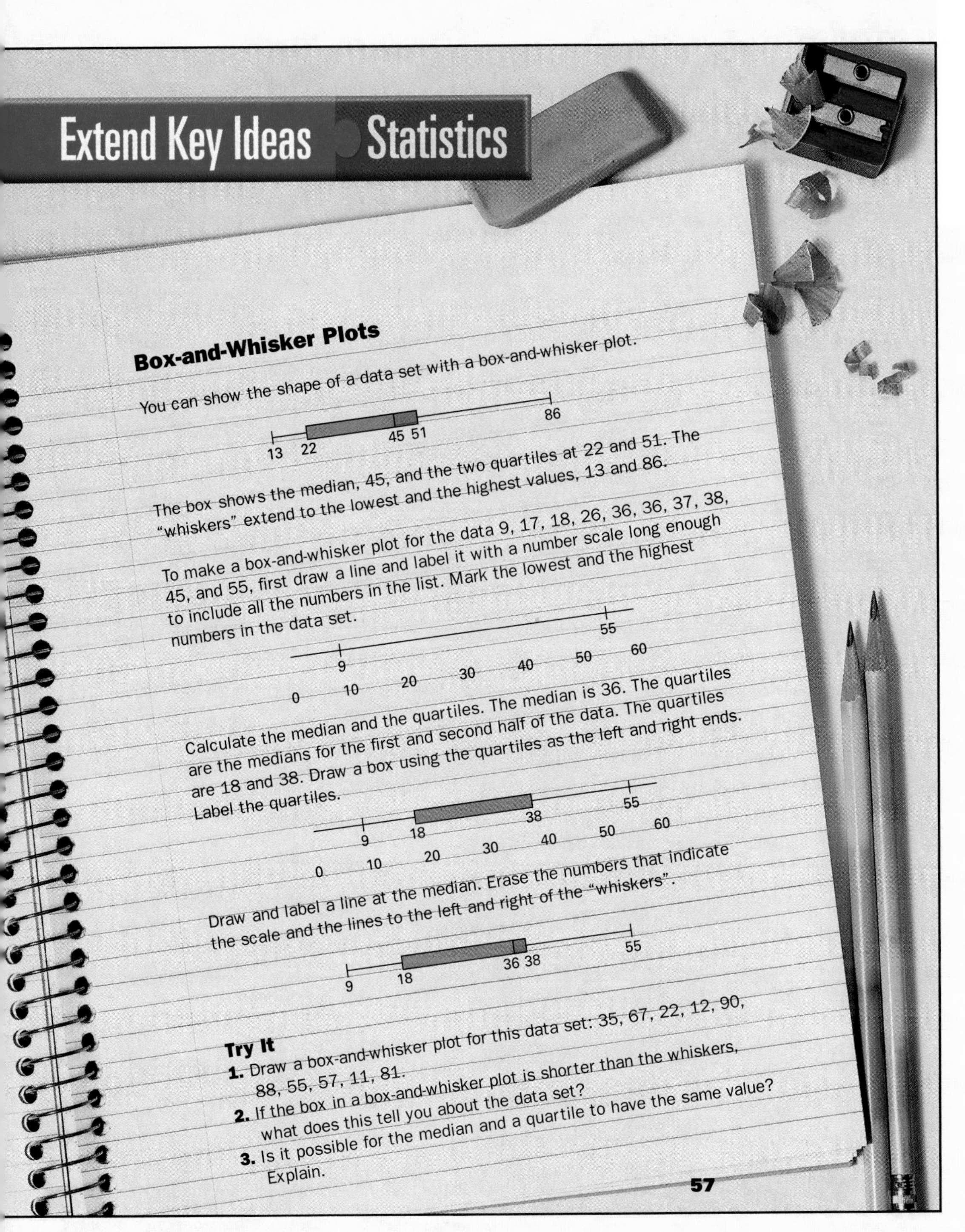

Extend Key Ideas • Statistics

Box-and-Whisker Plots

You can show the shape of a data set with a box-and-whisker plot.

The box shows the median, 45, and the two quartiles at 22 and 51. The "whiskers" extend to the lowest and the highest values, 13 and 86.

To make a box-and-whisker plot for the data 9, 17, 18, 26, 36, 36, 37, 38, 45, and 55, first draw a line and label it with a number scale long enough to include all the numbers in the list. Mark the lowest and the highest numbers in the data set.

Calculate the median and the quartiles. The median is 36. The quartiles are the medians for the first and second half of the data. The quartiles are 18 and 38. Draw a box using the quartiles as the left and right ends. Label the quartiles.

Draw and label a line at the median. Erase the numbers that indicate the scale and the lines to the left and right of the "whiskers".

Try It

1. Draw a box-and-whisker plot for this data set: 35, 67, 22, 12, 90, 88, 55, 57, 11, 81.
2. If the box in a box-and-whisker plot is shorter than the whiskers, what does this tell you about the data set?
3. Is it possible for the median and a quartile to have the same value? Explain.

57

Box-and-Whisker Plots

The Point

Students investigate how a box-and-whisker plot represents a set of data.

About the Page

- Remind students that, although the data in the example is ordered, they will probably have to order the data themselves when constructing a box-and-whisker plot.
- Box-and-whisker plots visually represent the entire set of data, rather than using only one value to represent all the data.

Ask ...

- How are the quartiles determined? The median of the lower half of the data; The median of the upper half of the data.
- What does the box represent? The box represents the part of the data between the upper and lower quartiles.
- What do the whiskers represent? The difference between the least data value and the lower quartile; The difference between the greatest data value and the upper quartile.

Extension

Have students work in groups of four. Suggest that each group find two sets of related data, such as the points scored per game by their school's basketball team during each of two consecutive seasons. Then have the students represent each set of data in a box-and-whisker plot. Each group should share its work with the class. Encourage students to draw conclusions and to suggest reasons for any differences that may occur between the two sets of data.

Answers for Try It

1. 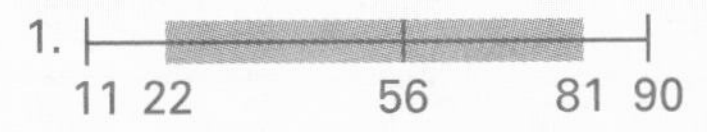

2. A lot of the data clusters around the median; There could be outliers.
3. Yes; If there are repeated values in the data.

Chapter 1 Summary and Review

Review Correlation

Item(s)	Lesson(s)
1, 2	1-1
3, 4	1-4
5	1-5
6	1-6
7	1-7, 1-8
8	1-9

For additional review, see page 662.

Answers for Review

1. 80 blue jackets
2. 270 mi
3.

Box of Souvenirs	Tally Marks	Frequency
Flags	𝍸	5
White House models	III	3
Posters	IIII	4
Uncle Sam hats	I	1

4.

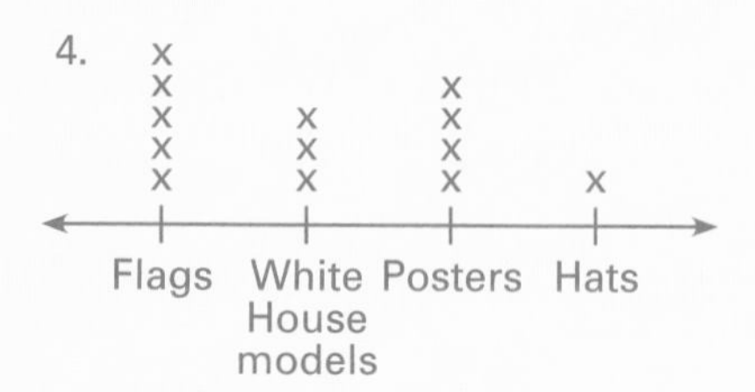

5.

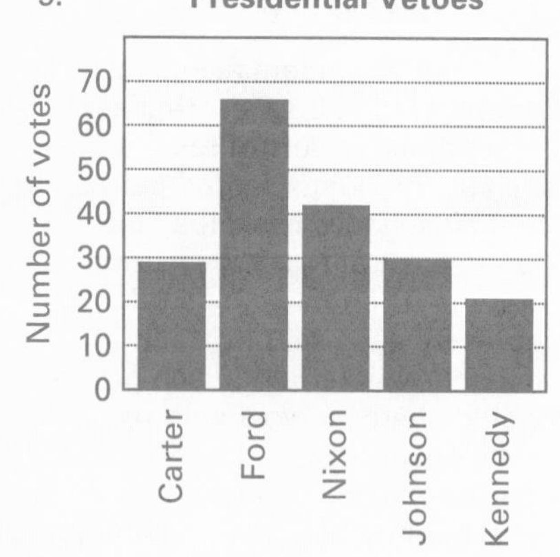

Chapter 1 Summary and Review

Graphic Organizer

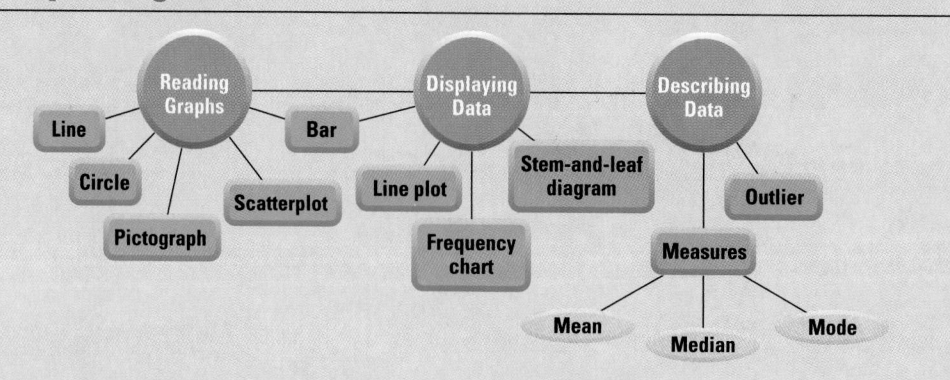

Section 1A Reading and Interpreting Graphs

Summary

- Data is represented in a **bar graph** by the height of each bar.
- In a **pictograph**, data is shown by symbols. A key tells the value of each symbol.
- Data is represented in a **line graph** by the heights of points on a line.
- In a **circle graph**, data is represented as parts of a whole circle.
- You can graph two sets of data as points on a **scatterplot**. If the points fall in a line, the scatterplot shows a **trend**.

Review

1. How many blue jackets were sold?

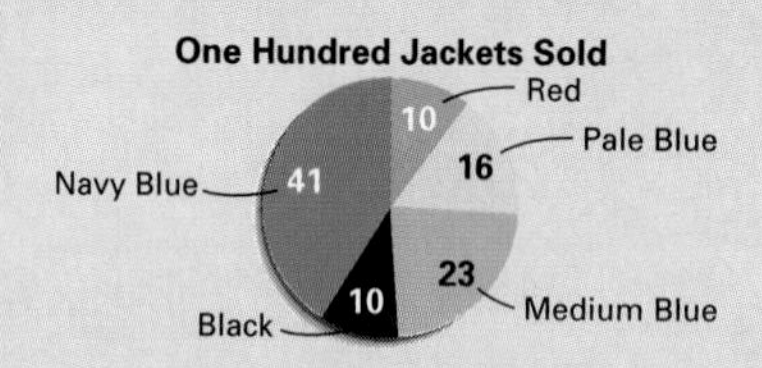

2. About how far did the train travel in the first 3 hours?

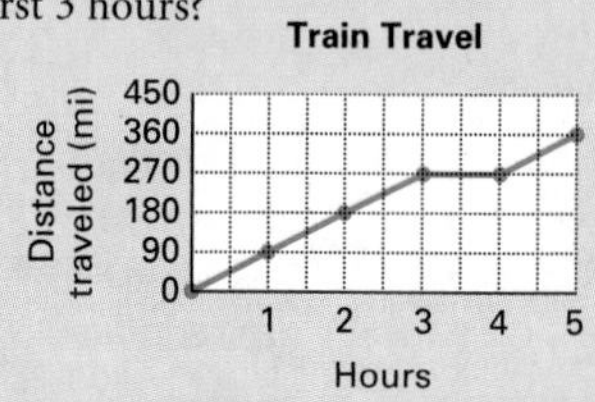

Resources

Practice Masters
Cumulative Review Chapter 1

PRACTICE

Name ____________

Practice

Cumulative Review Chapter 1

Add, subtract, multiply, or divide. *[Previous Course]*

1. 38 + 84 = 122
2. 837 − 123 = 714
3. 387 × 3 = 1161
4. 6)2322 = 387
5. 8)1552 = 194
6. 13)2171 = 167

Social Science Use the American Grandparents graph to answer each question. *[Lesson 1-1]*

American Grandparents

Millions of grandparents: 0, 4, 8, 12, 16, 20

Age: 44 and under, 45-54, 55-64, 65 and over

7. Which age group includes the most grandparents? 65 and over
   the fewest grandparents? 44 and under
8. About how many are in the 45 to 54 age group? 10.3 million
9. Estimate the total number of grandparents shown in the data. 47.1 million

The circle graph shows the results of a poll in which people were asked to name the most important factor in sleeping well. Use it to answer each question. *[Lesson 1-1]*

Factors Promoting Good Sleep

Other 29%; Good mattress 32%; Exercise 20%; Diet 11%; Pillow 8%

10. What percent of those surveyed said exercise was the most important factor? 20%
11. What was the most common response? Good mattress

Find the mean of each set of data. *[Lesson 1-1]*

12. mean 26.75
    12, 17, 23, 42, 37, 21, 15, 45, 18, 31, 25, 38, 17, 24, 34, 29
13. mean About 46.89

stem	leaf
3	4 7 7 8
4	0 0 2 3 3 4 7 8
5	1 3 3 5 9
6	2 5

14. mean About 84.29

Section 1B Displaying Data

Summary

- Use **tally marks** to count data by type. Then organize them into a **frequency chart**.
- Use columns of ×'s to show the shape of the data in a **line plot**.
- Use **range** to help decide the **scale** and **intervals** needed to mark the **horizontal** and **vertical axes** of a bar graph.
- Use a **stem-and-leaf diagram** to see the distribution or shape of data in intervals.

Review

3. Use tally marks to make a frequency chart of boxes of campaign souvenirs.

4. Use the souvenir data to make a line plot.

5. Make a bar graph using the veto data for these presidents: Carter, 29; Ford, 66; Nixon, 42; L. B. Johnson, 30; and Kennedy, 21.

6. Describe the stems and leaves for a set of data containing all the even whole numbers less than 100.

Section 1C Describing Data

Summary

Three measures can help you describe a set of data.

- The **median** is the middle value of an ordered set of data.
- A **mode** is the number or numbers that appear most often in a set of data.
- The **mean** is the sum of the numbers in a data set divided by the number of numbers.
- An **outlier** is a data value that is far from the other data in the set.

Review

7. Find the median, mode, and mean for these home-run records: Aaron, 755; Williams, 521; Foxx, 534; Ruth, 714; Jackson, 563; Mays, 660; Robinson, 586; Killebrew, 573; Mantle, 536; Schmidt, 548; and McCovey, 521.

8. For any data set, which of the three measures is likely to be most affected by an outlier?

Answers for Review

6. Stems will be 0 through 9. Leaves will be 2, 4, 6, and 8 for the row opposite the zero stem and leaves of 0, 2, 4, 6, and 8 for each row opposite the 1 through 9 stems.
7. Median: 563; Mode: 521; Mean: 591.91 or ≈ 592.
8. The mean.

Chapter 1 Assessment

Assessment Correlation

Item(s)	Lesson(s)
1, 9	1-9
2	1-8
3, 8	1-3
4, 12, 13	1-6
5, 12, 13	1-7
6	1-4
7	1-5
10,11	1-1

Answers for Assessment

1. d
2. b
3. c
4. g
5. e
6. a
7.

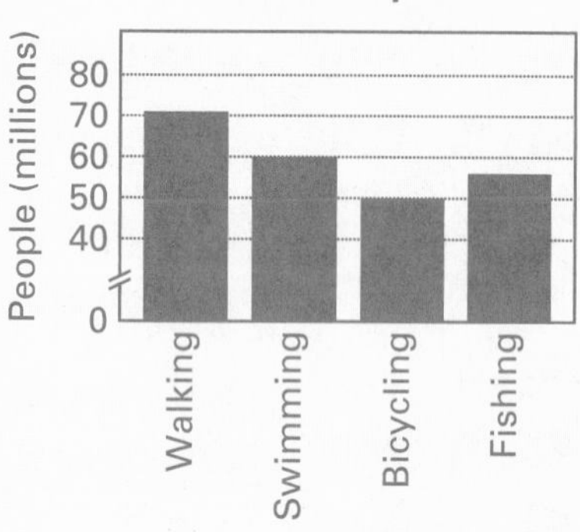

   b. Mean, 59.25 or ≈ 59 million
8. Yes; Overall, the pattern of points shows that the more jumps a frog makes, the farther he is from the starting point.
9. No outlier.
10. Each symbol represents 6 washed cars.
11. 120 cars were washed.
12. Median: 13.
13. No mode.

Chapter 1 Assessment

For Problems 1–6, match each description with a vocabulary word.

1. A number that is much larger or much smaller than any other number in a data set

2. A measure found by adding the data values and dividing by the number of values

3. A graph that shows a trend between two sets of data

4. A graph that is often used to see the shape of large sets of data in intervals

5. The middle value of a data set

6. A graph that usually shows change over time

a. Line graph
b. Mean
c. Scatterplot
d. Outlier
e. Median
f. Range
g. Stem-and-leaf diagram
h. Circle graph

7. Favorite sports and the number of millions of people who engaged in them in 1995: Walking, 71; Swimming, 60; Bicycling, 50; and Fishing, 56.

a. Use the data to draw and label a bar graph.

b. Find the mean of the data.

Use the data shown on the graphs to answer Exercises 8–13.

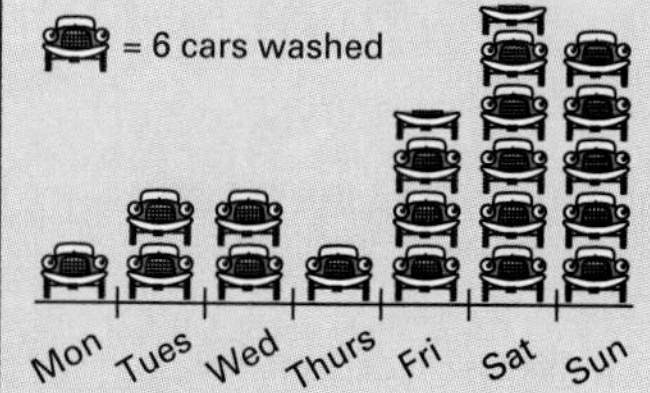

Stem	Leaf
0	2 5
1	2 3 5 6
2	2

8. Does the data show a trend? Explain.

9. Is there an outlier? If so, where?

10. What is the value of each symbol?

11. How many cars were washed?

12. What is the median value?

13. What is the mode?

Performance Task

At the end of the 1994–95 season, these colleges had the most bowl wins: Alabama, 27; University of Southern California, 24; Oklahoma, 20; Penn State, 19; and Tennessee, 19. Name the types of data displays you could use to show this information. Make at least two of these displays and explain how each helps you understand the data.

Answer for Performance Task

Answer may vary, but might include: A bar graph showing the bowl wins of each team; a pictograph with each symbol representing 2 bowl wins; a stem-and-leaf diagram; or a line plot.

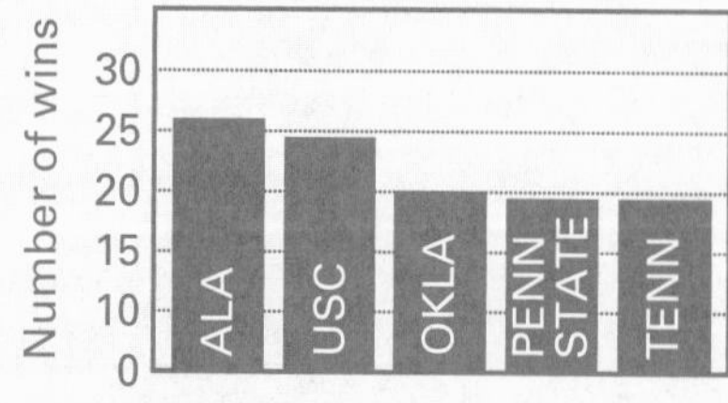

Stem	Leaf
1	9 9
2	0 4 7

Resources

Assessment Sourcebook

Chapter 1 Tests
- Forms A and B (free response)
- Form C (multiple choice)
- Form D (performance assessment)
- Form E (mixed response)
- Form F (cumulative chapter test)

TestWorks
Test and Practice Software

Home and Community Connections
- Letter Home for Chapter 1 in English and Spanish

Cumulative Review Chapter 1

Test Prep

Performance Assessment

Choose one problem.

State of Recall

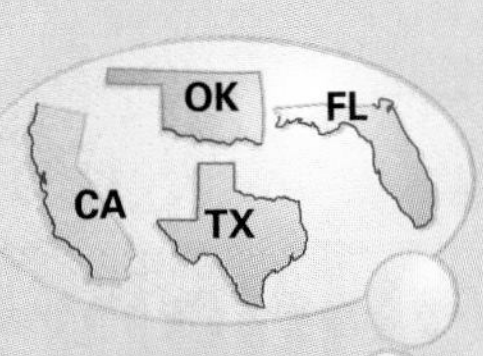

Use a watch or clock with a second hand. Ask at least 20 people to name as many states in the United States as they can in 30 seconds. Collect and record your data in a table. Make a line plot and a stem-and-leaf diagram of the data. Explain which chart gives a better picture of the data.

Let's Go Fly a Kite!

Here are the results from the Lakeside Kite Flying Contest.

Contestant	Height (m)	Contestant	Height (m)
Greg	233	Hassan	360
Tyron	212	Bill	274
Ku	272	Cassie	501
Manny	319	Ali	124
Charlene	275	Maria	286

Create a bar graph from this data. List five things that you can interpret from the bar graph.

It's My Party

Pizza Party

Large, one topping	4 pizza symbols
Large, two toppings	2½ pizza symbols
Medium, one topping	3 pizza symbols
Small, one topping	1½ pizza symbols

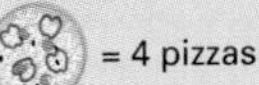 = 4 pizzas

The pictograph shows the number of pizzas a youth group needs for a pizza party. Call or visit a pizza restaurant and find out how much each pizza would cost. Determine the cost for the entire order. Explain how you determined the total cost.

As Time Goes By

Use a watch or clock with a second hand. Ask at least 20 people to estimate a minute. Record the data and find the mode, median, and mean. Explain which measure best describes the data, and discuss any outliers.

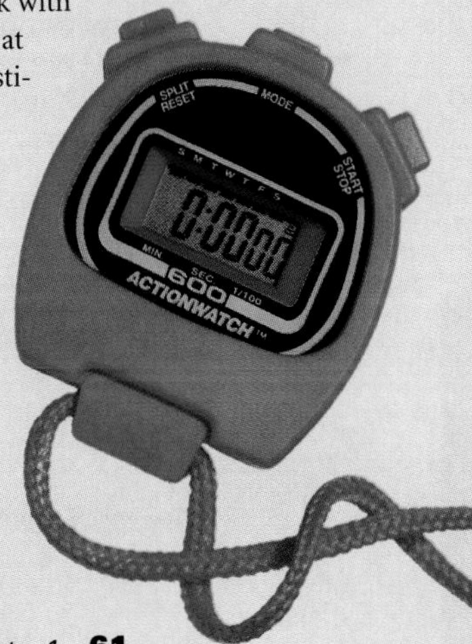

Cumulative Review Test Prep

About Performance Assessment

The Performance Assessment options ...

- provide teachers with an alternate means of assessing students.
- address different learning modalities.
- allow students to choose one problem.

Teachers may encourage students to choose the most challenging problem.

Learning Modalities
State of Recall **Visual** Students select chart that is best visual representation.
Let's Go Fly a Kite **Verbal** Students write interpretations of a bar graph.
As Time Goes By **Logical** Students experiment to gather and then interpret data.
It's My Party **Individual** Students contact restaurants to gather the information to price a party order.

Performance Assessment Key

See key on page 3.

Suggested Scoring Rubric

State of Recall

4
- Accurately records all data.
- Makes detailed line plot and stem-and-leaf diagram.
- Provides clear explanation.

3
- Records most data.
- Makes adequate line plot and a stem-and-leaf diagram.
- Provides adequate explanation.

2
- Records some data.
- Makes one graph and attempts to give explanation.

1
- Records less than 10 data items in a table.
- Poor explanation.

Rubric for **It's My Party** on page C1.

Let's Go Fly a Kite!

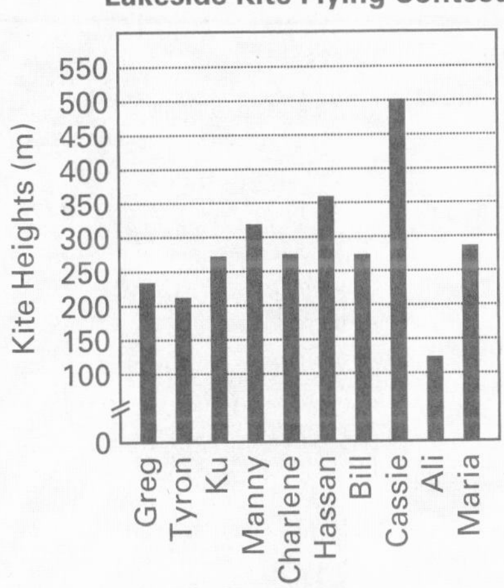

Possible answers: Tallest kite height; the median, mean, or mode of the heights; an outlier of the height data, and the lowest kite.

As Time Goes By

4
- Finds correct mean, median, and mode for all data.
- Clearly explains which measure best describes the data and the effect of an outlier.

3
- Finds mean, median, and mode for most data.
- Explains which measure best describes the data and the effect of an outlier.

2
- Finds correct mean, median, and mode for some data.
- Attempts to explain either which measure best describes the data or the effect of an outlier.

1
- Cannot identify an outlier or explain its effect.
- Unable to calculate mean, median, or mode.
- Cannot identify an outlier or explain its effect.

Chapter 2

Connecting Arithmetic to Algebra

OVERVIEW

Section 2A

Making Sense of Large Numbers: Students learn to write numbers in word form, number-word form, and with exponents. They also learn the rules for rounding, comparing, and ordering large numbers.

2-1 Reading and Writing Large Numbers

2-2 Rounding Large Numbers

2-3 Comparing and Ordering Numbers

2-4 Exponents

Section 2B

Number Sense and Operation Sense: Mental math, estimation, and the rules for order of operations are presented to students as the tools necessary to solve many problems.

2-5 Mental Math

2-6 Estimating Sums and Differences

2-7 Estimating Products and Quotients

2-8 Order of Operations

2-9 Numerical Patterns

Section 2C

Introduction to Algebra: Students work with variables and variable expressions and are introduced to equations.

2-10 Variables and Expressions

2-11 Writing Expressions

2-12 Using Equations

2-13 Solving Equations

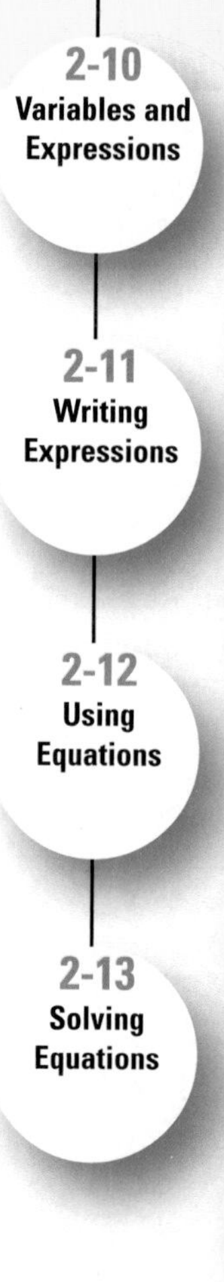

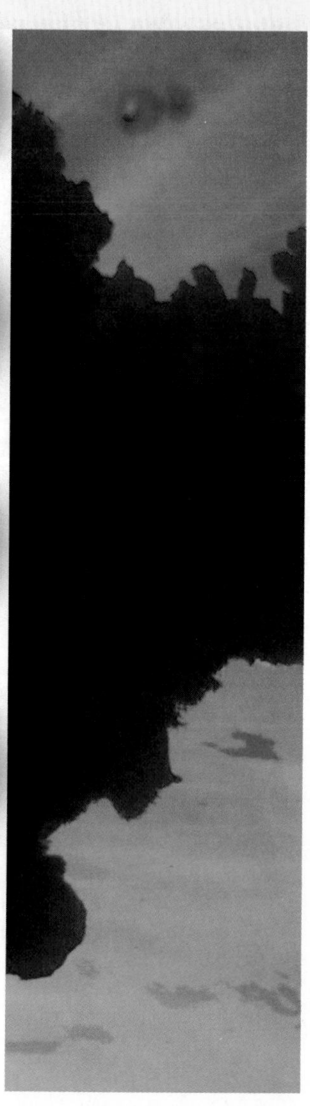

Meeting NCTM Standards

Curriculum Standards

STANDARD			pages
1	**Problem Solving**	Skills and Strategies	64, 82, 97, 121
		Applications	68–69, 72–73, 76–77, 81–82, 83, 88–89, 92–93, 96–97, 100–101, 105–106, 107, 112–113, 116–117, 120–121, 124–125, 127
		Exploration	66, 70, 74, 78, 82, 86, 90, 94, 98, 102, 110, 114, 118, 122
2	**Communication**	Oral	65, 68, 72, 75, *77*, 80, 85, 88, 92, 95, 97, 99, 104, 109, 112, 119, 123
		Written	69, 73, 77, *82*, 84, 89, *93*, 97, *101*, 106, 113, 117, 121, 125
		Cooperative Learning	*66*, *70*, *74*, *78*, 82, *86*, *90*, *94*, *98*, *102*, *110*, *114*, *118*, *122*
3	**Reasoning**	Critical Thinking	69, 73, 77, 82, 89, 93, 97, 101, 106, 113, 117, 121, 125
4	**Connections**	Mathematical	See Standards 5–10 and 13 below.
		Interdisciplinary	Science 62, *65*, 67, 68, 69, 72, *74*, 75, 77, *80*, 81, 88, *104*, 106, 110, 113, 116, 118, 119; History 65, 113, 115; Fine Arts 62, 103, 116; Health 116; Language 67, *78*, 103, 115; Geography 76, 92, 117, 120, 125, 128; Literature 93, 117; Industry 96; Social Sciences 96, 106; Social Studies 63, *96*; Music 62; Consumer *85*
		Technology	*80*, 98, 111, 126
		Cultural	63, 68, 77
5	**Number and Number Relationships**		66–73, 78–82, 100, 105
6	**Number Systems and Number Theory**		74–77, 91, 98–101
7	**Computation and Estimation**		73, 75, 79, 86–97
8	**Patterns and Functions**		87, 102–106, 129
9	**Algebra**		110–125
10	**Statistics**		68, 89
13	**Measurement**		76, 96

Italic type indicates Teacher Edition reference.

Teaching Standards

Focus on Respect

An important ingredient for a successful learning environment is respect of teachers for students. A successful teacher

- respects conventional and nonconventional ideas of students.
- refrains from the use of ridicule of students.

Assessment Standards

Focus on Learning

Portfolios The Learning Standard encourages teachers to provide students with the opportunity to reflect on their own learning, and to participate in the assessment process. Selecting portfolio entries requires that students develop criteria by which to measure their progress. In Chapter 2, students

- select examples that illustrate their understanding of a particular skill.
- select a problem and explain what they learned from doing the problem.

TECHNOLOGY

For the Teacher

- **Teacher Resource Planner CD-ROM**
  Use the teacher planning CD-ROM to view resources available for Chapter 2. You can prepare custom lesson plans or use the default lesson plans provided.

- **World Wide Web**
  Visit **www.teacher.mathsurf.com** for links to lesson plans from teachers and other professionals, NCTM information, and other sites.

- **TestWorks**
  TestWorks provides ready-made tests and can create custom tests and practice worksheets.

For the Parent

- **World Wide Web**
  Parents can use the Web site at **www.parent.mathsurf.com.**

For the Student

- **Interactive CD-ROM**
  Lesson 2-12 has an *Interactive CD-ROM Lesson*. The *Interactive CD-ROM Journal* and *Interactive CD-ROM Spreadsheet/Grapher Tool* are also used in Chapter 2.

- **Wide World of Mathematics**
  Lesson 2-13 Middle School: The Census

- **World Wide Web**
  Use with Chapter and Section Openers; Students can go online to the Scott Foresman-Addison Wesley Web site at **www.mathsurf.com/6/ch2** to collect information about chapter themes.

STANDARDIZED - TEST CORRELATION

SECTION 2A

LESSON	OBJECTIVE	ITBS Form M	CTBS 4th Ed.	CAT 5th Ed.	SAT 9th Ed.	MAT 7th Ed.	Your Form
2–1	• Identify the place values of digits.	✘	✘	✘	✘	✘	
	• Write numbers in standard, word, and number-word form.	✘		✘	✘	✘	
2–2	• Round numbers using rules for rounding.	✘	✘	✘		✘	
	• Use common sense to round numbers in real-life situations.			✘			
2–3	• Compare and order large numbers.	✘	✘	✘		✘	
2–4	• Use exponents to express numbers.		✘			✘	
	• Write expressions containing exponents in standard form.						

SECTION 2B

LESSON	OBJECTIVE	ITBS Form M	CTBS 4th Ed.	CAT 5th Ed.	SAT 9th Ed.	MAT 7th Ed.	Your Form
2–5	• Solve problems mentally using patterns, the Distributive Property, compatible numbers, and compensation.	✘		✘		✘	
2–6	• Estimate sums and differences using front-end estimation and clustering.	✘			✘	✘	
2–7	• Estimate products and quotients using rounding and compatible numbers.	✘	✘		✘	✘	
2–8	• Use order of operation rules to solve arithmetic problems.		✘	✘		✘	
2–9	• Continue numerical patterns based on addition and subtraction.	✘		✘	✘	✘	

SECTION 2C

LESSON	OBJECTIVE	ITBS Form M	CTBS 4th Ed.	CAT 5th Ed.	SAT 9th Ed.	MAT 7th Ed.	Your Form
2–10	• Recognize the difference between a variable and a constant.		✘	✘		✘	
	• Evaluate expressions.			✘	✘	✘	
2–11	• Translate phrases and situations into mathematical expressions.			✘	✘	✘	
2–12	• Know what an equation is.	✘				✘	
	• Determine if an equation is true or false.	✘		✘		✘	
2–13	• Find the value of the variable that makes an equation true.	✘		✘		✘	

Key: ITBS - Iowa Test of Basic Skills; CTBS - Comprehensive Test of Basic Skills; CAT - California Achievement Test; SAT - Stanford Achievement Test; MAT - Metropolitan Achievement Test

ASSESSMENT PROGRAM

Traditional Assessment

QUICK QUIZZES	SECTION REVIEW	CHAPTER REVIEW	CHAPTER ASSESSMENT FREE RESPONSE	CHAPTER ASSESSMENT MULTIPLE CHOICE	CUMULATIVE REVIEW
TE: pp. 69, 73, 77, 82, 89, 93, 97, 101, 106, 113, 117, 121, 125	SE: pp. 84, 108, 128 *Quiz 2A, 2B, 2C	SE: pp. 130–131	SE: p. 132 *Ch. 2 Tests Forms A, B, E	*Ch. 2 Tests Forms C, E	SE: p. 133 *Ch. 2 Test Form F

Alternate Assessment

INTERVIEW	JOURNAL	ONGOING	PERFORMANCE	PORTFOLIO	PROJECT	SELF
TE: pp. 69, 73, 97	SE: pp. 73, 84, 89, 93, 97, 106, 113, 117, 121 TE: pp. 64, 89, 93, 121	TE: pp. 66, 70, 74, 78, 86, 90, 94, 98, 102, 110, 114, 118, 122	SE: p. 132 TE: pp. 82, 113, 125 *Ch. 2 Tests Forms D, E	TE: pp. 106, 117	SE: pp. 82, 101, 125 TE: p. 63	TE: pp. 77, 101

*Tests and quizzes are in *Assessment Sourcebook.* Test Form E is a mixed response test. Forms for Alternate Assessment are also available in *Assessment Sourcebook.*

TestWorks: Test and Practice Software

MIDDLE SCHOOL PACING CHART

REGULAR PACING

Day	5 classes per week
1	Chapter 2 Opener; Problem Solving Focus
2	Section **2A** Opener; Lesson **2-1**
3	Lesson **2-2**
4	Lesson **2-3**
5	Lesson **2-4**
6	**2A** Connect; **2A** Review
7	Section **2B** Opener; Lesson **2-5**
8	Lesson **2-6**
9	Lesson **2-7**
10	Lesson **2-8**
11	Lesson **2-9**
12	**2B** Connect; **2B** Review
13	Section **2C** Opener; Lesson **2-10**
14	Lesson **2-11**
15	Lesson **2-12**
16	Lesson **2-13**; Technology
17	**2C** Connect; **2C** Review; Extend Key Ideas
18	Chapter 2 Summary and Review
19	Chapter 2 Assessment Cumulative Review, Chapters 1–2

BLOCK SCHEDULING OPTIONS

Block Scheduling for Complete Course

Chapter 2 may be presented in

- fourteen 90-minute blocks
- seventeen 75-minute blocks

Each block consists of a combination of

- Chapter and Section Openers
- Explores
- Lesson Development
- Problem Solving Focus
- Technology
- Extend Key Ideas
- Connect
- Review
- Assessment

For details, see *Block Scheduling Handbook.*

Block Scheduling for Interdisciplinary Course

Each block integrates math with another subject area.

In Chapter 2, interdisciplinary topics include

- Space
- Collections
- Oceans

Themes for Interdisciplinary Team Teaching 2A, 2B, and 2C are

- Comets
- Literature
- SCUBA Diving

For details, see *Block Scheduling Handbook.*

Block Scheduling for Lab-Based Course

In each block, 30–40 minutes is devoted to lab activities including

- Explores in the Student Edition
- Connect pages in the Student Edition
- Technology options in the Student Edition
- Reteaching Activities in the Teacher Edition

For details, see *Block Scheduling Handbook.*

Block Scheduling for Course with *Connected Mathematics*

In each block, investigations from **Connected Mathematics** replace or enhance the lessons in Chapter 2.

Connected Mathematics topics for Chapter 2 can be found in

- *Prime Time*

For details, see *Block Scheduling Handbook.*

INTERDISCIPLINARY BULLETIN BOARD

Set Up

Prepare a bulletin board with a display of the solar system and a blank table on which students can fill in the distance of each planet from the Sun.

Procedure

- Have students research the sizes of the planets and their distances from the Sun.
- Have students copy drawings of the planets.
- Assign one student to place an outline of the solar system on the bulletin board. Have other students add planets at the appropriate distance from the Sun.

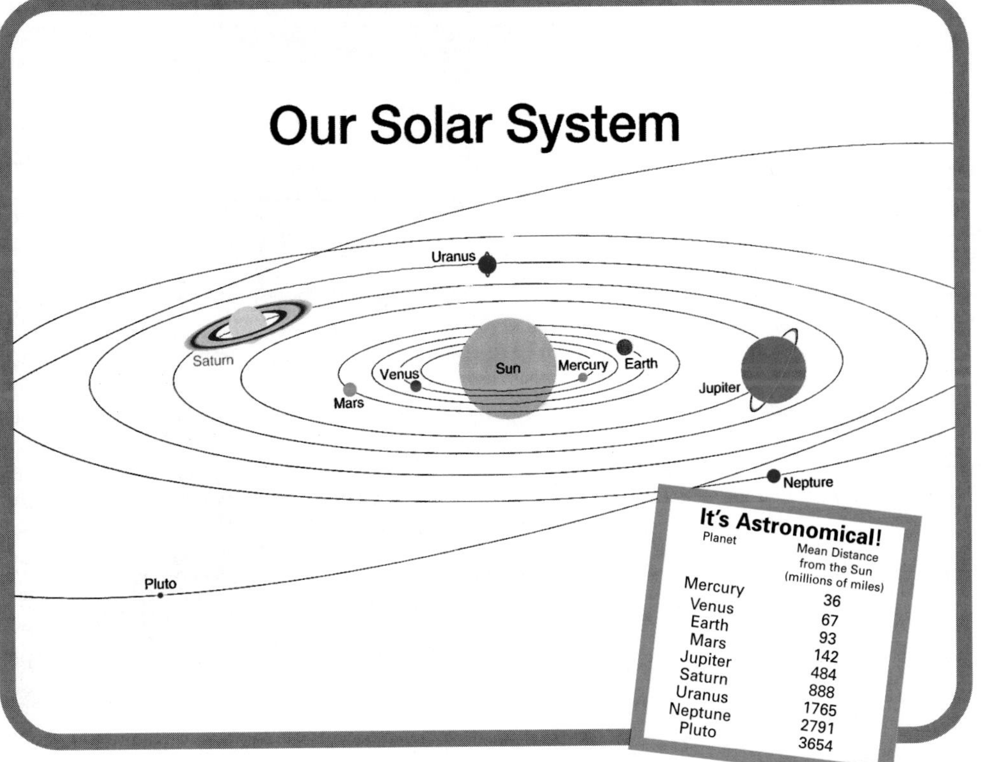

Chapter 2

The information on these pages shows how large and small numbers and equations are used in real-life situations.

World Wide Web

If your class has access to the World Wide Web, you might want to use the information found at the Web site addresses given.

Extensions

The following activities do not require access to the World Wide Web.

Arts & Literature
Show students several pictures of Van Gogh's work and ask them to write a paragraph describing his painting style.

Science
Ask students why there is a difference between the time they see lightning and the time they hear the thunder. Light travels faster than sound, so you will see the lightning first.

Entertainment
Have students take a survey to identify their classmates' favorite songs. Choose the five most popular songs identified by the survey and find out how these songs rank on the charts.

Social Studies
Have students write a short essay about the contribution to the development of algebra made by the Greek mathematician Diophantus of Alexandria or the Arab mathematician Al-Khowarizmi.

People of the World
Have groups of students research how to use an abacus to perform the four basic operations and prepare a demonstration for the class. Ask students to compare the abacus to their calculator.

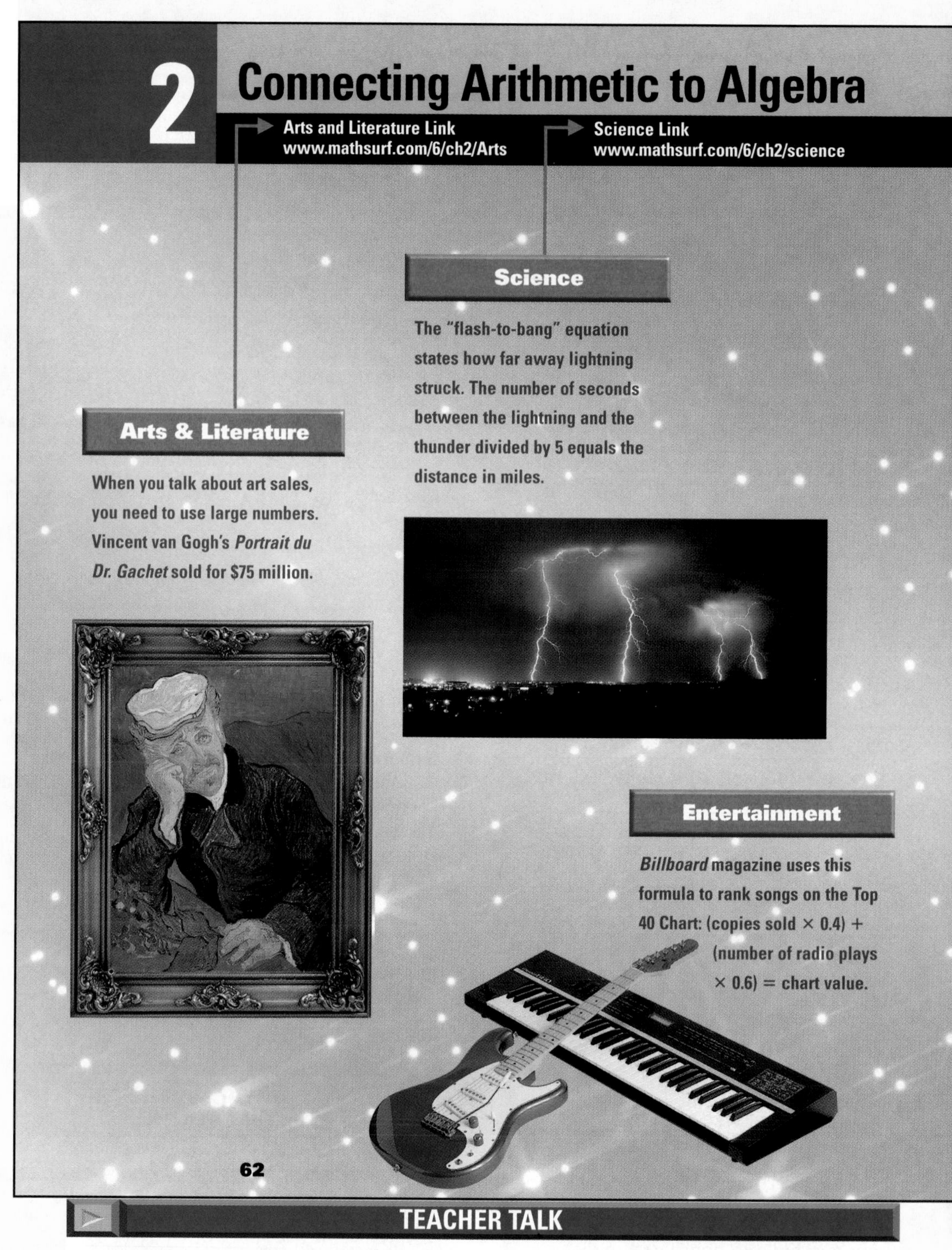

2 Connecting Arithmetic to Algebra

Arts and Literature Link
www.mathsurf.com/6/ch2/Arts

Science Link
www.mathsurf.com/6/ch2/science

Science

The "flash-to-bang" equation states how far away lightning struck. The number of seconds between the lightning and the thunder divided by 5 equals the distance in miles.

Arts & Literature

When you talk about art sales, you need to use large numbers. Vincent van Gogh's *Portrait du Dr. Gachet* sold for $75 million.

Entertainment

Billboard magazine uses this formula to rank songs on the Top 40 Chart: (copies sold × 0.4) + (number of radio plays × 0.6) = chart value.

62

TEACHER TALK

Meet Sharon Butler

Twin Creeks Middle School
Spring, Texas

I use the following activity to provide additional practice evaluating expressions. I have students find a simple picture to duplicate from a coloring or comic book, or, if they wish, draw their own picture. Then I have them write expressions in the spaces to be colored, such as $a + 2$, $a - 2$, $56 \div a$, $4a$, $\frac{a}{4}$, and $12 - a$. Next, I have them assign a value for the variable and create a coloring key. For example, if they assign a value of 8 to a, the coloring key could be: red = 6; yellow = 2; blue = 8; green = 7; purple = 10; brown = 4; and black = 32. Any space with a different solution can be colored any other color.

Students exchange their pictures, evaluate the expressions, and color the picture according to the key.

This activity can be repeated throughout the year, using fractions, decimals, or integers for the value of a.

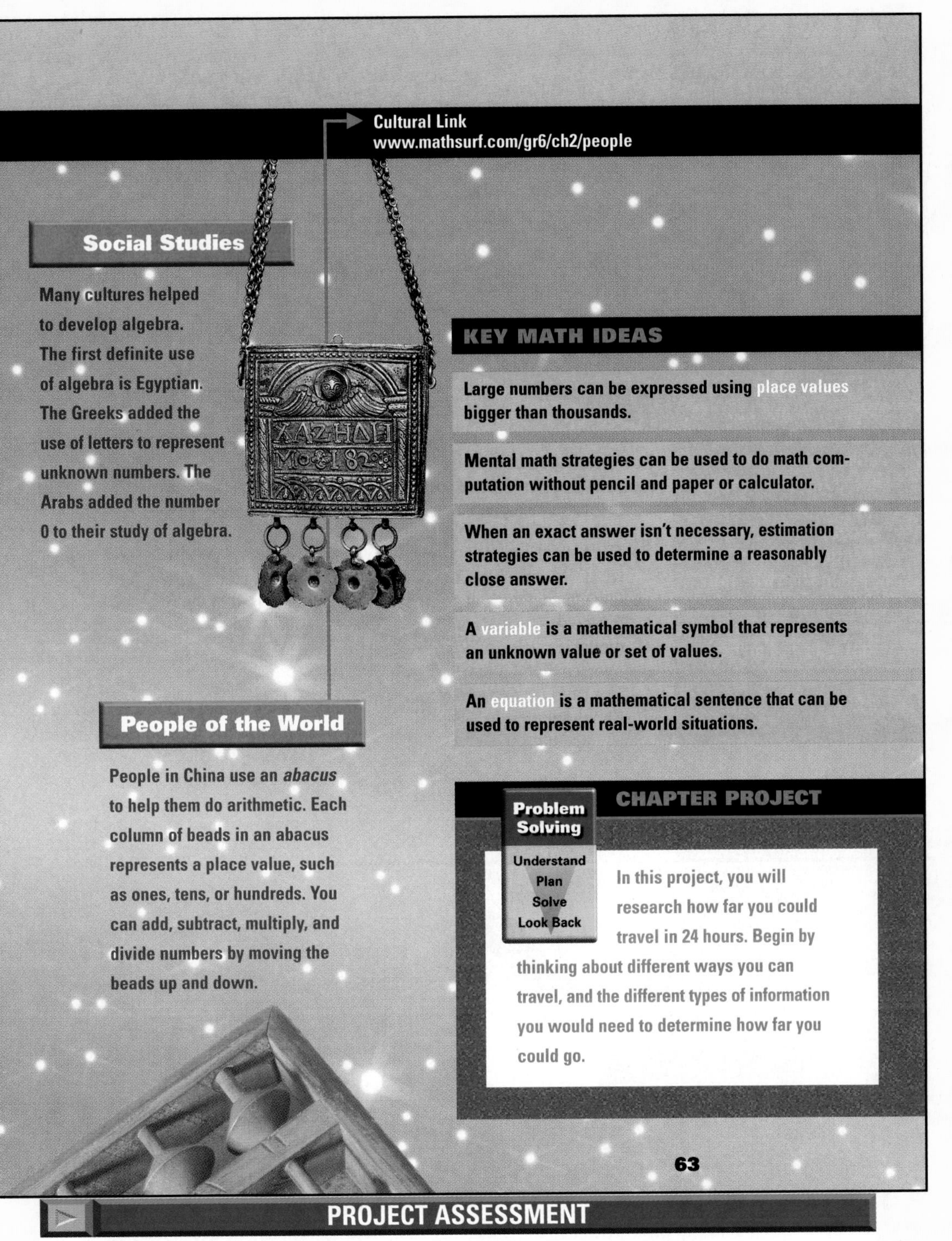

Cultural Link
www.mathsurf.com/gr6/ch2/people

Social Studies

Many cultures helped to develop algebra. The first definite use of algebra is Egyptian. The Greeks added the use of letters to represent unknown numbers. The Arabs added the number 0 to their study of algebra.

KEY MATH IDEAS

Large numbers can be expressed using place values bigger than thousands.

Mental math strategies can be used to do math computation without pencil and paper or calculator.

When an exact answer isn't necessary, estimation strategies can be used to determine a reasonably close answer.

A variable is a mathematical symbol that represents an unknown value or set of values.

An equation is a mathematical sentence that can be used to represent real-world situations.

People of the World

People in China use an *abacus* to help them do arithmetic. Each column of beads in an abacus represents a place value, such as ones, tens, or hundreds. You can add, subtract, multiply, and divide numbers by moving the beads up and down.

CHAPTER PROJECT

Problem Solving: Understand, Plan, Solve, Look Back

In this project, you will research how far you could travel in 24 hours. Begin by thinking about different ways you can travel, and the different types of information you would need to determine how far you could go.

63

Chapter Project

Students will collect data about methods of travel and then use the information to project how far they could travel in 24 hours.

Resources
Chapter 2 Project Master

Introduce the Project

- Ask students to guess how far they think they could travel in 24 hours.
- Discuss different methods of travel.
- Discuss where students might find information about different means of transportation.

Project Progress

Section A, page 82 Students may organize the data they collect by comparing and ordering the various distances.

Section B, page 101 Students may use mental math or estimation to determine the distance they can travel in 24 hours. Suggest that students identify patterns between travel times and distances.

Section C, page 125 Students may write a variable expression to represent the distance they could travel using a specific means of transportation.

Community Project

A community project for Chapter 2 is available in *Home and Community Connections.*

Cooperative Learning

You may want to use Teaching Tool Transparency 1: Cooperative Learning Checklist with **Explore** and other group activities in this chapter.

PROJECT ASSESSMENT

You may choose to use this project as a performance assessment for the chapter.

Performance Assessment Key

Level 4 Full Accomplishment

Level 3 Substantial Accomplishment

Level 2 Partial Accomplishment

Level 1 Little Accomplishment

Suggested Scoring Rubric

Level	Criteria
4	•Gathers accurate information about various means of transportation. •Distances for a 24-hour period are accurately calculated.
3	•Gathers adequate information about several means of transportation. •Distances for a 24-hour period are calculated.
2	•Gathers minimum information about different means of transportation. •Errors occur in calculation of distances.
1	•No research is done on any means of transportation. •Calculated distances are not reasonable.

Problem Solving Focus

Finding Unnecessary Information

The Point
Students learn to evaluate which given numerical information is necessary and which is unnecessary.

Resources
Teaching Tool Transparency 18: Problem-Solving Guidelines

 *Interactive CD-ROM Journal*

About the Page

Using the Problem-Solving Process
A critical skill of a successful problem solver is to be able to identify information which is not needed to solve the problem. Discuss these suggestions:

- Read the problem several times.
- Determine what the problem is asking.
- Identify unnecessary information.
- Identify and organize necessary information.

Ask ...
- What information is needed to answer Question 1? The height of Mount Everest is needed to find the height of K2; The height of Kanchenjunga.
- What information is not needed to answer Question 2? The number of the mountains higher than 16,000 feet; The names of the mountains.
- Refer to Question 3. How many pounds of garbage is left on Mount Everest? 100,000 lb

Answers for Problems
1. 42 ft
2. Five
3. 33 tons

Journal
Have students write a short essay explaining why they would or would not want to climb Mount Everest.

Problem Solving
Understand
Plan
Solve
Look Back

Finding Unnecessary Information

To solve real-life problems, you need to understand the available data. Some of the data is needed to find the answer, but usually not all of it. Identifying the information that will not help you answer the question is an important step in finding a solution.

Problem Solving Focus

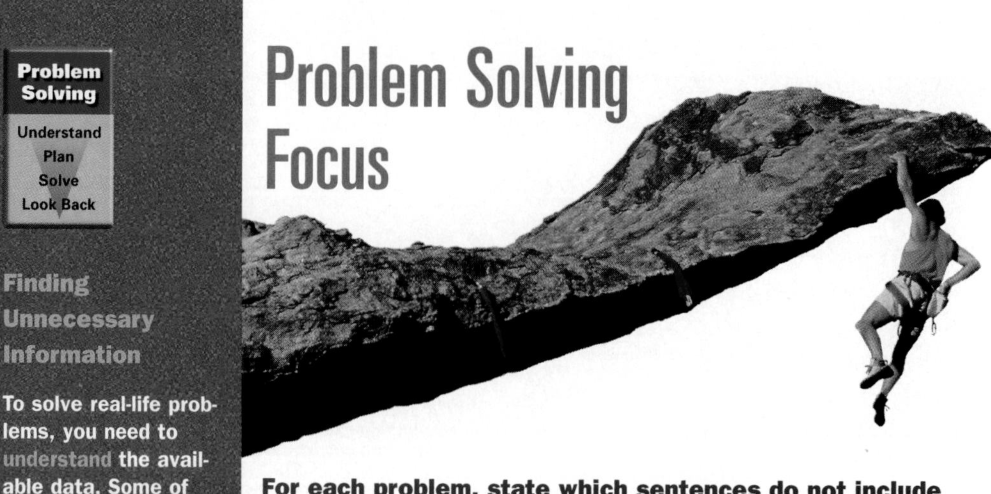

For each problem, state which sentences do not include necessary information. For some problems, all the sentences may have necessary information.

1. The tallest mountain in the world, Mount Everest, is 29,028 feet high. It is located in Nepal. The second largest mountain, K2, is 778 feet shorter than Mount Everest. The third largest mountain, Kanchenjunga, is 28,208 feet high. What's the difference in elevation between K2 and Kanchenjunga?

2. In Antarctica, there are two mountains higher than 16,000 feet. There are ten mountains taller than 14,000 feet. There are exactly three mountains whose heights are between 15,000 and 16,000 feet. Their names are Shinn, Gardner, and Epperly. How many mountains are between 14,000 and 15,000 feet?

3. There are 50 tons of garbage on Mount Everest left by people who have climbed the mountain. 17 tons can be found in the South Col area, just below the summit. How many tons can be found on the rest of Mount Everest?

64

Additional Problem

Indoor ice skating rinks opened for the first time in Philadelphia 40 years before ice skating became an Olympic sport in 1908. Dick Button won the first gold medal for the United States in 1948. Since then, the United States has won 11 gold medals in singles ice skating. Winter Olympics are held every 4 years. How many years after the first indoor rinks opened did Dick Button win the first gold medal for the United States in skating? 80 years

1. What is the problem asking? How many years after the first indoor ice skating rinks opened did Dick Button win a gold medal?
2. Is the year the first indoor rinks opened given in the problem? No; You find the year by subtracting 40 from 1908.
3. Identify any unnecessary information in the problem. The number of gold medals the United States has won; How often Winter Olympics are held.

Section 2A

Making Sense of Large Numbers

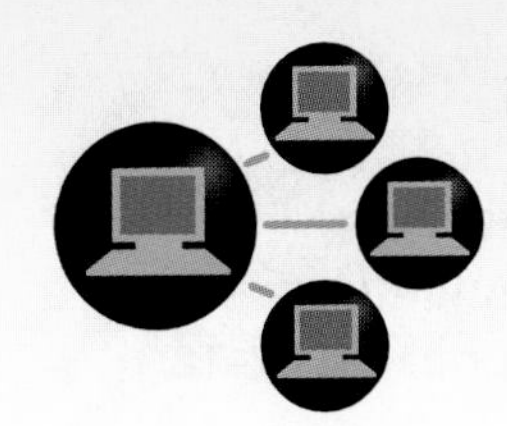

Visit www.teacher.mathsurf.com for links to lesson plans from teachers and other professionals, NCTM information, and other sites.

LESSON PLANNING GUIDE

Student Edition | **Ancillaries***

LESSON		MATERIALS	VOCABULARY	DAILY	OTHER
	Chapter 2 Opener				Ch. 2 Project Master Ch. 2 Community Project Teaching Tool Trans. 1
	Problem Solving Focus				Teaching Tool Trans. 18 *Interactive CD-ROM Journal*
	Section 2A Opener				
2-1	**Reading and Writing Large Numbers**		place value	2-1	Teaching Tool Trans. 4 Lesson Enhancement Trans. 5
2-2	**Rounding Large Numbers**		rounding	2-2	Teaching Tool Trans. 4
2-3	**Comparing and Ordering Numbers**			2-3	Lesson Enhancement Trans. 6
2-4	**Exponents**	scientific calculator	factor, base, exponent, power, squared, cubed	2-4	Teaching Tool Trans. 2, 3, 23 Technology Masters 6, 7 Ch. 2 Project Master
	Connect				Interdisc. Team Teaching 2A
	Review				Practice 2A; Quiz 2A; *TestWorks*

* Daily Ancillaries include Practice, Reteaching, Problem Solving, Enrichment, and Daily Transparency. Teaching Tool Transparencies are in *Teacher's Toolkits.* Lesson Enhancement Transparencies are in *Overhead Transparency Package.*

SKILLS TRACE

LESSON	SKILL	FIRST INTRODUCED GR. 4	GR. 5	GR. 6	DEVELOP	PRACTICE/ APPLY	REVIEW
2-1	**Identifying place value. Writing numbers in standard form.**	✘			pp. 66–67	pp. 68–69	pp. 89, 130, 172, 219, 274
2-2	**Rounding numbers.**	✘			pp. 70–71	pp. 72–73	pp. 93, 130, 279
2-3	**Comparing and ordering large numbers.**	✘			pp. 74–75	pp. 76–77	pp. 97, 130, 180, 284
2-4	**Using exponents.**			✘ p. 78	pp. 78–80	pp. 81–82	pp. 101, 130, 194, 236, 241, 249

CONNECTED MATHEMATICS

Investigation 5 in the unit *Prime Time (Factors and Multiples)*, from the **Connected Mathematics** series, can be used with Section 2A.

INTERDISCIPLINARY TEAM TEACHING

Math and Science/Technology

(Worksheet pages 7–8: Teacher pages T7–T8)

In this lesson, students make sense of large numbers used to describe close approaches of comets to Earth.

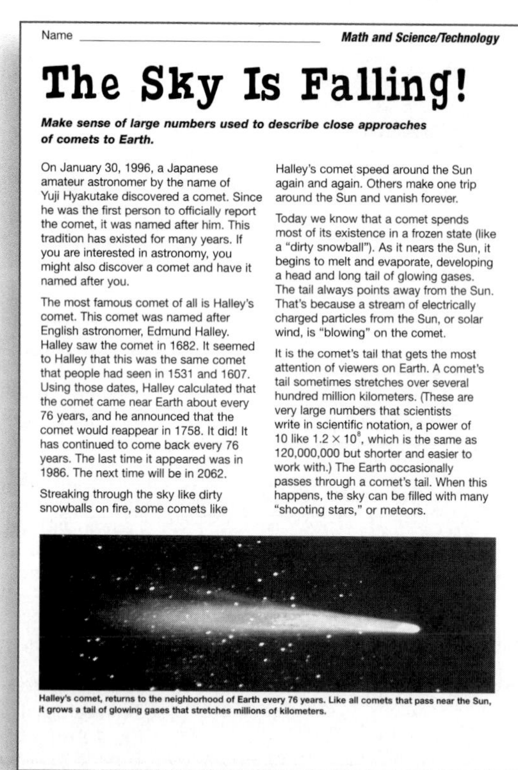

Name ______________ *Math and Science/Technology*

The Sky Is Falling!

Make sense of large numbers used to describe close approaches of comets to Earth.

On January 30, 1996, a Japanese amateur astronomer by the name of Yuji Hyakutake discovered a comet. Since he was the first person to officially report the comet, it was named after him. This tradition has existed for many years. If you are interested in astronomy, you might also discover a comet and have it named after you.

The most famous comet of all is Halley's comet. This comet was named after English astronomer, Edmund Halley. Halley saw the comet in 1682. It seemed to Halley that this was the same comet that people had seen in 1531 and 1607. Using those dates, Halley calculated that the comet came near Earth about every 76 years, and he announced that the comet would reappear in 1758. It did! It has continued to come back every 76 years. The last time it appeared was in 1986. The next time will be in 2062.

Streaking through the sky like dirty snowballs on fire, some comets like Halley's comet speed around the Sun again and again. Others make one trip around the Sun and vanish forever.

Today we know that a comet spends most of its existence in a frozen state (like a "dirty snowball"). As it nears the Sun, it begins to melt and evaporate, developing a head and long tail of glowing gases. The tail always points away from the Sun. That's because a stream of electrically charged particles from the Sun, or solar wind, is "blowing" on the comet.

It is the comet's tail that gets the most attention of viewers on Earth. A comet's tail sometimes stretches over several hundred million kilometers. (These are very large numbers that scientists write in scientific notation, a power of 10 like 1.2×10^8, which is the same as 120,000,000 but shorter and easier to work with.) The Earth occasionally passes through a comet's tail. When this happens, the sky can be filled with many "shooting stars," or meteors.

Halley's comet, returns to the neighborhood of Earth every 76 years. Like all comets that pass near the Sun, it grows a tail of glowing gases that stretches millions of kilometers.

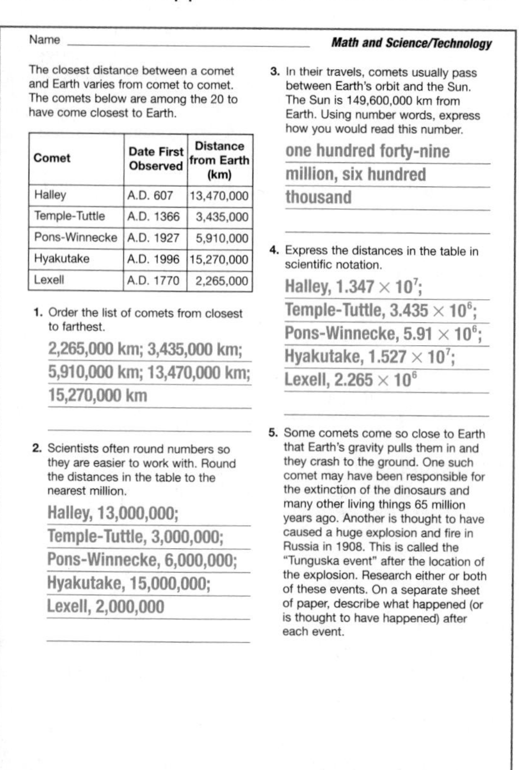

Name ______________ *Math and Science/Technology*

The closest distance between a comet and Earth varies from comet to comet. The comets below are among the 20 to have come closest to Earth.

Comet	Date First Observed	Distance from Earth (km)
Halley	A.D. 607	13,470,000
Temple-Tuttle	A.D. 1366	3,435,000
Pons-Winnecke	A.D. 1927	5,910,000
Hyakutake	A.D. 1996	15,270,000
Lexell	A.D. 1770	2,265,000

1. Order the list of comets from closest to farthest.
   2,265,000 km; 3,435,000 km; 5,910,000 km; 13,470,000 km; 15,270,000 km

2. Scientists often round numbers so they are easier to work with. Round the distances in the table to the nearest million.
   Halley, 13,000,000; Temple-Tuttle, 3,000,000; Pons-Winnecke, 6,000,000; Hyakutake, 15,000,000; Lexell, 2,000,000

3. In their travels, comets usually pass between Earth's orbit and the Sun. The Sun is 149,600,000 km from Earth. Using number words, express how you would read this number.
   one hundred forty-nine million, six hundred thousand

4. Express the distances in the table in scientific notation.
   Halley, 1.347×10^7; Temple-Tuttle, 3.435×10^6; Pons-Winnecke, 5.91×10^6; Hyakutake, 1.527×10^7; Lexell, 2.265×10^6

5. Some comets come so close to Earth that Earth's gravity pulls them in and they crash to the ground. One such comet may have been responsible for the extinction of the dinosaurs and many other living things 65 million years ago. Another is thought to have caused a huge explosion and fire in Russia in 1908. This is called the "Tunguska event" after the location of the explosion. Research either or both of these events. On a separate sheet of paper, describe what happened (or is thought to have happened) after each event.

BIBLIOGRAPHY

FOR TEACHERS

Mount, Ellis and List, Barbara A. *Milestones in Science and Technology*. Phoenix, AZ: Oryx Press, 1994.

Discovery Box Series: Planets. New York, NY: Scholastic, 1996.

The Reader's Digest Illustrated Book of Dogs. Pleasantville, NY: Reader's Digest Association, 1993.

Spangler, David. *Math for Real Kids*. Glenview, IL: Good Year Books, 1997.

FOR STUDENTS

Rand McNally World Facts & Maps. Chicago, IL: Rand McNally, 1996.

Schraff, Anne. *American Heroes of Exploration and Flight*. Bloomington, IL: Library Book Selection Service, 1996.

The Statesman's Year-Book. New York, NY: St. Martin's Press, 1996.

SECTION 2A

Making Sense of Large Numbers

▶ Science Link ▶ History Link ▶ www.mathsurf.com/6/ch2/space

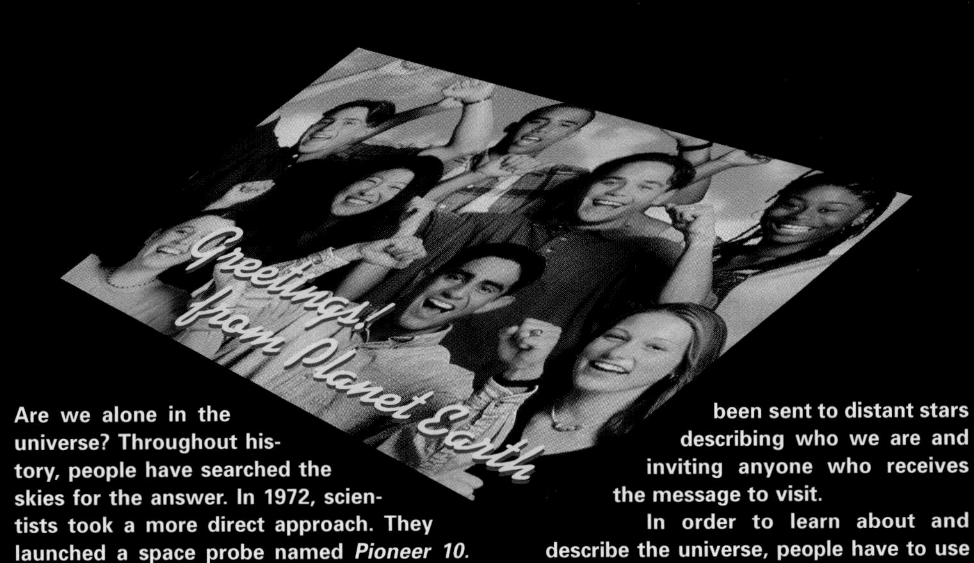

Are we alone in the universe? Throughout history, people have searched the skies for the answer. In 1972, scientists took a more direct approach. They launched a space probe named *Pioneer 10.* Fourteen years later, *Pioneer 10* crossed the orbit of Pluto and became the first human-made object to leave our solar system.

Scientists use a variety of technologies to study the universe. Astronauts orbit Earth and land on the moon. Space stations and orbiting telescopes provide information that is impossible to get from Earth. Signals have been sent to distant stars describing who we are and inviting anyone who receives the message to visit.

In order to learn about and describe the universe, people have to use numbers much larger than hundreds, thousands, or even millions. Mathematics provides people with several tools for talking about large numbers conveniently and effectively. Meanwhile, *Pioneer 10* speeds toward a distant star called Ross 248. It should arrive in the year 34,600 unless it encounters something else first. Something, or someone ...

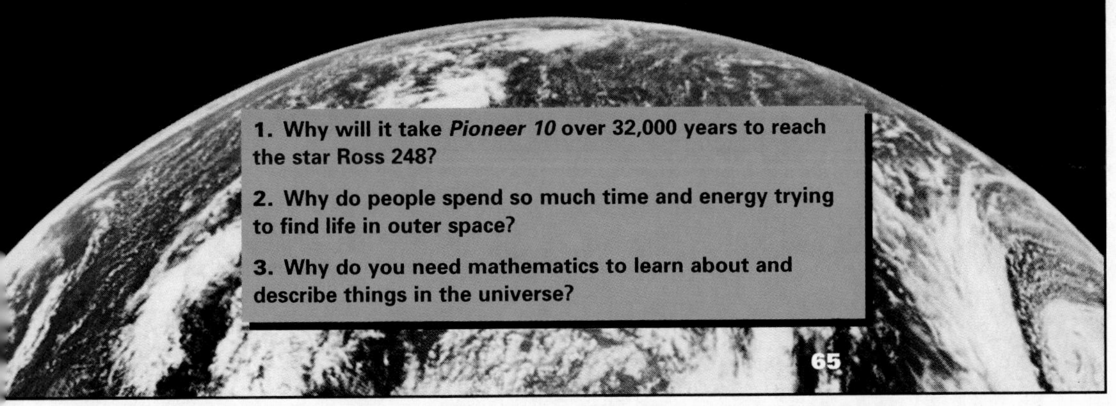

1. Why will it take *Pioneer 10* over 32,000 years to reach the star Ross 248?
2. Why do people spend so much time and energy trying to find life in outer space?
3. Why do you need mathematics to learn about and describe things in the universe?

65

Where are we now?

In Grade 5, students learned about large numbers.

They learned how to

- identify place values.
- compare and order large numbers.
- round large numbers.

Where are we going?

In Grade 6 Section 2A, students will

- read and write large numbers.
- round numbers in real-life situations.
- compare and order large numbers.
- use exponents to express numbers and write expressions containing exponents in standard form.

Theme: Space

World Wide Web

If your class has access to the World Wide Web, you might want to use the information found at the Web site address given. The interdisciplinary links relate to topics discussed in this section.

About the Page

This page introduces the theme of the section, space, and discusses the technology and mathematics needed to study the universe.

Ask ...

- Have you ever wondered if there is anyone living on other planets?
- Would you like to be an astronaut?
- What are some ways in which scientists are studying the universe?

Extensions

The following activities do not require access to the World Wide Web.

Science
Ask students to research and report on the discoveries made about space through the use of such space vehicles as Sputnik, Apollo, Challenger, Explorer, Orbiter, and Mir.

History
Have students create a time line showing the progress of space research since the launch of Sputnik in 1957.

Answers for Questions

1. Possible answer: Because the star is so far away.
2. Possible answer: They are curious about what is out there.
3. Possible answer: People need to use large numbers to talk about space.

Connect

On page 83, students will compare and order large numbers describing distances from a star to the planets.

2-1 Lesson Organizer

Objectives

- Understand place values of digits in numbers.
- Write numbers in standard form, word form, and number-word form.

Vocabulary

- Place value

NCTM Standards

- 1–5, 10

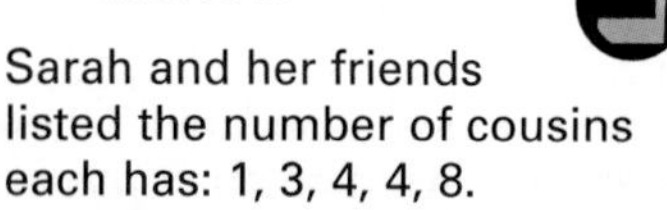

Review

Sarah and her friends listed the number of cousins each has: 1, 3, 4, 4, 8.

1. Find the mean number of cousins. 4
2. Find the median. 4
3. Find the mode. 4
4. Find the range. 7

Available on Daily Transparency 2-1

1 Introduce

Explore

You may wish to use Teaching Tool Transparency 4: Place-Value Charts or Lesson Enhancement Transparency 5 with this lesson.

The Point
Students explore why it is useful to have names for numbers such as hundreds, thousands, and millions.

Ongoing Assessment
Students should be able to read large numbers, not just the digits.

For Groups That Finish Early
Try other strategies and see which one your group likes best.

2-1 Reading and Writing Large Numbers

You'll Learn ...

- the place values of digits in numbers
- to write numbers in standard form, word form, and number-word form

... How It's Used

Astronomers must be able to read and write huge numbers when studying the distance between planets.

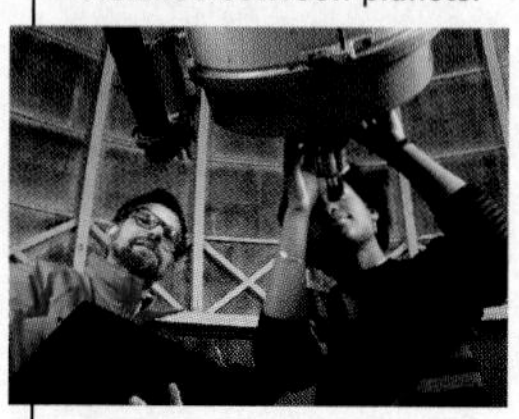

Vocabulary

place value

▶ Lesson Link In the last chapter, you learned to display and interpret data. To display and interpret some kinds of data, you must be able to read and write extremely large numbers. ◀

Explore Large Numbers

Mission Control, Do You Read Me?

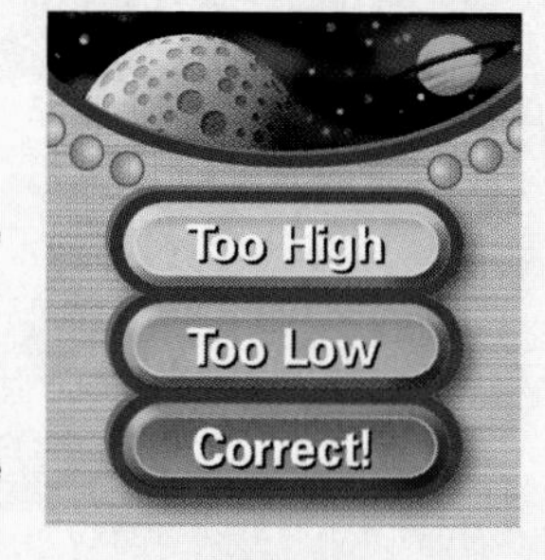

You are the commander of a disabled spacecraft. Mission Control in Houston wants to know how far you are from Earth. Although you can hear Mission Control, they cannot hear you. Each time Mission Control guesses a distance, you must press one of the signal buttons.

Work with a partner. One of you should play the Spacecraft Commander, and the other, Mission Control.

1. The Spacecraft Commander should secretly pick a distance from 1 to 100 miles. Mission Control should try to guess the distance in as few guesses as possible. After each guess, the Spacecraft Commander should say "Too high," "Too low," or "Correct."
2. Switch roles. This time, the Spacecraft Commander should pick a distance from 1 to 1,000,000 miles.
3. Which game was easier? Why?
4. Which game would go faster, a game from 20 thousand to 50 thousand or a game from 20 million to 50 million? Why?

Learn Reading and Writing Large Numbers

Every digit of a number has a **place value**. The place value tells you how much that digit represents. In 2364, the digit 3 represents 3 hundreds (or 300) because the 3 is in the hundreds place. In order to use large numbers, you need to know the names of large place values.

MEETING INDIVIDUAL NEEDS

Resources

- 2-1 Practice
- 2-1 Problem Solving
- 2-1 Reteaching
- 2-1 Enrichment
- 2-1 Daily Transparency
  - Problem of the Day
  - Review
  - Quick Quiz
- Teaching Tool Transparency 4
- Lesson Enhancement Transparency 5

Learning Modalities

Verbal Working in pairs, have one student say a number aloud and the other write the number or enter it into a calculator.

Musical Students could write a rap or jingle that illustrates place value reading large numbers.

Visual Have students write numbers with spaces instead of commas between each group of three digits to help students read the numbers.

English Language Development

Students may be overwhelmed by all the words in Exercises 23–36. Suggest that students make a list of the words and corresponding numbers, such as thousand = 1000, which they can use while working on these exercises. You may also ask students if they know the names of large numbers in their native language. If so, have them write them next to their English equivalents.

Place Value

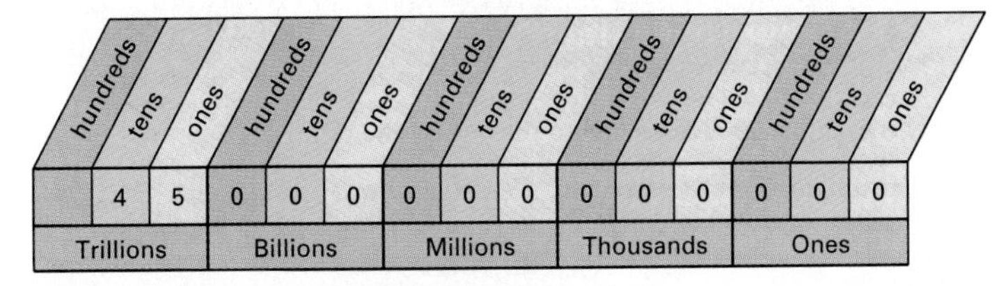

Numbers can be written in three different forms.

Standard form: 45,000,000,000,000
Word form: forty-five trillion
Number-word form: 45 trillion

Examples

1 Find the place value of the 9 in Vega's diameter.

Vega's diameter is 2,5[9]4,200 miles.

The 9 is in the ten-thousands place. It represents 9 ten-thousands, or 90,000.

2 Write Alpha Centauri's diameter in word form.

Write each number of trillions, billions, millions, thousands, and ones.

1 million	37 thousands	700 ones
1,	037,	700
one million,	thirty-seven thousand,	seven hundred

3 Write seven billion, forty thousand, two in standard form.

billions	millions	thousands	ones	
7	000	040	002	= 7,000,040,002

4 Write 36,000,000,000 in number-word form.

36,000,000,000 = 36 billion

Diameters of Six Brightest Stars

Name	Diameter (mi)
Sun	864,730
Sirius	1,556,500
Canopus	25,941,900
Alpha Centauri	1,037,700
Arcturus	19,888,800
Vega	2,594,200

Science Link

The largest known star is Betelgeuse (BEE-tuhl-joos) in the constellation of Orion. Betelgeuse has a diameter of approximately 400,000,000 miles, about 500 times the diameter of the sun.

Try It

a. Find the place value of the digit 1 in Arcturus's diameter. ten-millions

b. Write the diameter of Arcturus in words.

c. Write five trillion, twenty billion, three hundred in standard form. 5,020,000,000,300

b. Nineteen million, eight hundred eighty-eight thousand, eight hundred

Language Link

Scientists use the prefix *mega-* to indicate 1 million (as in *megabyte*) and the prefix *giga-* to indicate 1 billion (as in *gigabyte*).

Answers for Explore

3. The game from 1 to 100 is easier because there are fewer numbers to choose from.
4. The game from 20 thousand to 50 thousand would be faster because there are fewer numbers to choose from.

2 Teach

Learn

Have students identify parts of the place-value chart they already know and parts that are new to them. Point out that each group of three places in the place-value chart is called a *period*.

Alternate Examples

1. Find the place value of the 4 in the Sun's diameter, 864,730 miles.

   The 4 is in the thousands place. It represents 4 thousands, or 4000.

2. Write Sirius's diameter in word form.

   One million, five hundred fifty-six thousand, five hundred

3. Write seven billion, twenty-one thousand, three in standard form. 7,000,021,003

4. Write 9,000,045,000 in number-word form.

   9,000,045,000 = 9 billion 45 thousand

MATH EVERY DAY

Problem of the Day

Put four + signs between the following digits so that the answer is 1000.

8 8 8 8 8 8 8 8 Possible answer: 888 + 88 + 8 + 8 + 8

Available on Daily Transparency 2-1

An Extension is provided in the transparency package.

Fact of the Day

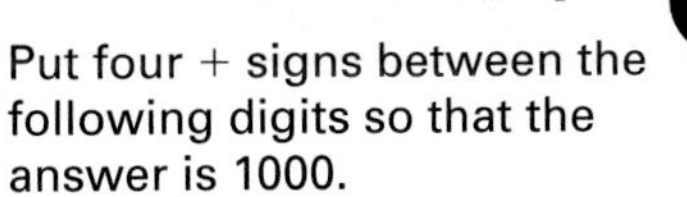

Pioneer 10 traveled 620,000,000 miles to provide, in 1973, the first close-up view of the planet Jupiter.

Mental Math

Find the mean of each set of data.

1. 20, 25, 30, 35, 40 30
2. 70, 70, 70, 30 60
3. 65, 65, 65, 65, 65, 65 65

2-1 Exercises and Applications

Assignment Guide

- **Basic**
  1–8, 11–19, 26–43, 45–46, 49–50
- **Average**
  2–30 evens, 31–47, 49–51
- **Enriched**
  2–36 evens, 37–51

3 Practice and Assess

Check

Answers for Check Your Understanding

1. Each place value is ten times larger than the one to its right.
2. No; Some numbers are so large, they've never been named.

Exercise Notes

Exercises 9–16

Cultural The numbers we use today are known as Arabic numerals. However, they originated in India and are really called Indian-Hindu numbers.

Exercise Answers

9. Thirty million, eighty thousand, seven hundred five
10. Five billion, one hundred eleven million, two hundred ninety-three thousand, twenty-six

11–22. See page C1.

Reteaching

Activity

Materials: Number cubes

- Toss a number cube 10 times and write down each toss as a digit in a number, from left to right.
- Write the number in word form.
- Repeat the process for 8 tosses and 14 tosses.

Check Your Understanding

1. How is each place value related to the one on the right?
2. Is there a name for every number, no matter how large? Explain.

2-1 Exercises and Applications

PRACTICE 2-1

Practice and Apply

Getting Started Name the place-value position of the given digit in the number 31,480,725.

1. 5 Ones **2.** 7 Hundreds **3.** 8 Ten-thousands **4.** 3 Ten-millions

5. 1 Millions **6.** 4 Hundred-thousands **7.** 0 Thousands **8.** 2 Tens

Write the number in words.

9. 30,080,705 **10.** 5,111,293,026 **11.** 8235 **12.** 9,303,946

13. 7098 **14.** 222 **15.** 56,056,560 **16.** 8,000,969,152,001

Science Write each planet's average distance from Earth in number-word form.

17. Mercury **18.** Venus

19. Saturn **20.** Uranus

21. Neptune **22.** Pluto

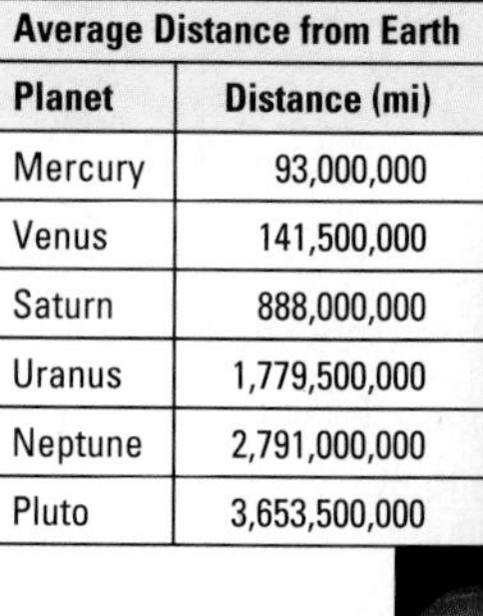

Average Distance from Earth	
Planet	**Distance (mi)**
Mercury	93,000,000
Venus	141,500,000
Saturn	888,000,000
Uranus	1,779,500,000
Neptune	2,791,000,000
Pluto	3,653,500,000

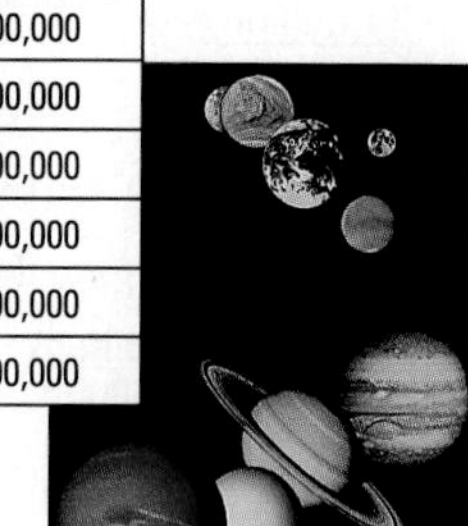

Write each number in standard form.

23. 52 million 52,000,000 **24.** 38 thousand 38,000

25. 560 million 560,000,000 **26.** 7 trillion 7,000,000,000,000

27. 9 thousand 9000 **28.** 4 hundred 400

29. 321 thousand 321,000 **30.** 26 million 26,000,000

31. forty-two million, six thousand 42,006,000 **32.** eight hundred four thousand, two 804,002

33. nine trillion, twenty billion, thirty 9,020,000,000,030 **34.** four thousand, seven hundred five 4705

35. eighty-one thousand, five hundred 81,500 **36.** three million, nine hundred 3,000,900

PRACTICE

Name ______

Practice 2-1

Reading and Writing Large Numbers

Write the number in words.

1. 3784 Three thousand, seven hundred eighty-four
2. 842,630 Eight hundred forty-two thousand, six hundred thirty
3. 7,308,060 Seven million, three hundred eight thousand, sixty

Write each state's 1990 population in number-word form.

4. Delaware 700 thousand
5. Pennsylvania 12 million
6. Texas 18 million

State	1990 Population
Delaware	700,000
Pennsylvania	12,000,000
Texas	18,000,000

Write each number in standard form.

7. 2 million 2,000,000 8. 63 thousand 63,000
9. 42 billion 42,000,000,000 10. 15 trillion 15,000,000,000,000
11. Five billion, six hundred fifty thousand, three hundred twenty 5,000,650,320
12. Eight million, seven hundred twenty thousand, two hundred five 8,720,205

For each number, fill in the blank. Give your answers in standard form.

13. 93,000,000,000 = 93 billion 14. 2,000,000,000,000 = 2 trillion
15. 23,000,000 = 23 million 16. 24,000 = 24 thousand

For each fact, write the number in word form and in number-word form.

17. In 1990, Pepsico had sales of $18,000,000,000.
word form Eighteen billion
number-word form 18 billion

18. In 1990, the population of New York City was 7,000,000.
word form Seven million
number-word form 7 million

RETEACHING

Name ______

Alternative Lesson 2-1

Reading and Writing Large Numbers

Every digit of a number has a **place value.** The place value tells you how much that digit represents.

Example 1

Write 72,152,295 in word form.

Think:

Place Value

Trillions			Billions			Millions			Thousands			Ones		
H	T	O	H	T	O	H	T	O	H	T	O	H	T	O
							7	2	1	5	2	2	9	5

Write: seventy-two million, one hundred fifty-two thousand, two hundred ninety-five

So, 72,152,295 can be written as seventy-two million, one hundred fifty-two thousand, two hundred ninety-five.

Try It Write in word form.

a. 8,039,183,702
eight billion, thirty-nine million, one hundred eighty-three thousand, seven hundred two

b. 754,031,590,344,601
seven hundred fifty-four trillion, thirty-one billion, five hundred ninety million, three hundred forty-four thousand, six hundred one

Example 2

Write two hundred six billion, twelve thousand, fifty-six in standard form.

Think:

Place Value

Trillions			Billions			Millions			Thousands			Ones		
H	T	O	H	T	O	H	T	O	H	T	O	H	T	O
			2	0	6	0	0	0	0	1	2	0	5	6

Write: 206,000,012,056

So, two hundred six billion, twelve thousand, fifty-six can be written as 206,000,012,056.

Try It Write in standard form.

c. thirty-seven billion, six hundred four million, one hundred fifteen 37,604,000,115
d. four hundred trillion, nine hundred fifty-six billion, forty-four million, six hundred thousand. 400,956,044,600,000
e. two hundred million, five thousand, four 200,005,004

Complete.

37. 36,000 = 36 Thousand

38. 42,000,000 = 42 million

39. 67,000,000,000 = 67 Billion

40. 5,000,000,000,000 = 5 trillion

Science **For each fact, write the number in word form and in number-word form.**

41. The Cassini orbiter, designed to carry a probe, science instruments, and fuel into space, weighs 5655 kg.

42. Scientists can see more than 100,000,000,000 galaxies in the universe.

43. GPS Neptune's mean distance from the sun is 2,798,800,000 miles.

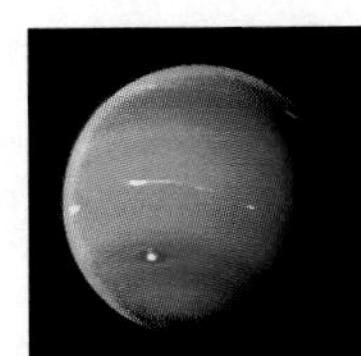

44. As of 1995, American astronauts have spent over 17,715 hours in space.

Shannon Lucid.

45. **Test Prep** Select the standard form for four hundred thirty thousand, four hundred seven. D

Ⓐ 43,047 Ⓑ 403,407 Ⓒ 430,047 Ⓓ 430,407

Problem Solving and Reasoning

46. **Communicate** Explain the difference between the two 7's in the number 737,459.

47. **Critical Thinking** When the planets are aligned, Earth has an approximate distance of 92,960,000 miles from the sun. Pluto has an approximate distance of 3,573,240,000 miles from Earth. What is the approximate distance between Pluto and the sun? Explain.

48. **Critical Thinking** Make a bar graph of a student's budget: $4 for bus, $5 for lunch, $3 for games. Then make a bar graph of a city's budget: $4 million for road maintenance, $5 million for salaries, $3 million for construction. How are the graphs similar? How are they different?

Mixed Review

Use the stem-and-leaf diagram for Exercises 49–50. *[Lesson 1-6]*

Stem	Leaf
1	4
2	8 8 9
3	2 6 6 7
4	1 2 4 4 4 9

49. Identify the outlier. 14

50. How many digits are in each number of the data? 2

51. Find the mean of the data. Round to the nearest tenth. *[Lesson 1-8]* 1.9

1, 2, 7, 0, 3, 1, 0, 4, 2, 1, 0

PROBLEM SOLVING

Name ______ Guided Problem Solving 2-1

GPS PROBLEM 43, STUDENT PAGE 69

For the fact, write the number in word form and in number-word form.

Neptune's mean distance from the sun is 2,798,800,000 miles.

— Understand —

1. How many digits are there in the number? 10 digits.
2. In which forms will you write the number? Word and number-word forms.

— Plan —

3. Write each number of trillions, billions, millions, thousands, and ones.
   a. Trillions 0 b. Billions 2 c. Millions 798
   d. Thousands 800 e. Ones 0
4. Which places have zeros? What is the greatest place value you will use when you write the number in number-word form? Trillions and ones; billions.

— Solve —

5. Write the number in number-word form. 2 billion, 798 million, 800 thousand.
6. Write the entire number in words. two billion, seven hundred ninety-eight million, eight hundred thousand.

— Look Back —

7. How can you check your work by reading each number aloud? Possible answer: The answers to Items 5 and 6 should sound the same when read aloud.

SOLVE ANOTHER PROBLEM

For the fact, write the number in word form and in number-word form.

Light travels 5,880,000,000,000 miles in one year.

five trillion, eight hundred eighty billion; 5 trillion, 880 billion

ENRICHMENT

Name ______ Extend Your Thinking 2-1

Visual Thinking

Estimate how many birds are in this picture without counting all of them. Explain how you made your estimate.

Possible answer: About 136 birds. Count birds in small square and multiply by 4.

Exercise Notes

■ Exercise 43

Science The fastest winds in the Solar System are on Neptune with speeds of 1,243 mph.

Exercise Answers

41. Five thousand, six hundred fifty-five; 5 thousand, 655
42. One hundred billion; 100 billion
43. Two billion, seven hundred ninety-eight million, eight hundred thousand; 2 billion, 798 million, 800 thousand
44. Seventeen thousand, seven hundred fifteen; 17 thousand, 715
46. The first 7 is in the hundred-thousands place. The second 7 is in the thousands place.
47. 3,666,200,000 miles; Add the distance from the Sun to the Earth to the distance from the Earth to Pluto to find the distance between Pluto and the Sun.
48. See page C1.

Alternate Assessment

Interview Have students explain why 200,800 is different from 280,000.

➤ Quick Quiz

1. Write 3,042,001 in word form. Three million, forty-two thousand, one
2. Write 32 billion, 34 thousand, six in standard form. 32,000,034,006
3. Write five hundred three thousand, four hundred twenty-nine in standard form. 503,429

Available on Daily Transparency 2-1

2-2 Lesson Organizer

Objectives

- Round numbers using rules for rounding.
- Use common sense to round numbers in real-life situations.

Vocabulary

- Rounding

NCTM Standards

- 1–5, 7

▶ Review

Find each product.

1. 7 × 90 630
2. 800 × 6 4800
3. 90 × 6 540
4. 8 × 700 5600

Available on Daily Transparency 2-2

1 Introduce

Explore

You may wish to use Teaching Tool Transparency 4: Place-Value Charts with this lesson.

The Point
Students compare how a given value can be expressed with exact and rounded numbers.

Ongoing Assessment
Some students may be able to recognize where the numbers came from yet not remember the term *rounding*. Others may need hints such as "How did they change 26,725 to get 27,000?"

For Groups That Finish Early
Would it be appropriate to say that *Pioneer 11* passed Jupiter at a distance of more than 20,000 miles? Explain. Although the statement is correct, it is misleading. It suggests that the actual distance was between 20,000 and 25,000 miles.

2-2 Rounding Large Numbers

You'll Learn ...

- to round numbers using rules for rounding
- to use common sense to round numbers in real-life situations

... How It's Used

Reporters round scientific data to make the stories accurate but easier to read.

Vocabulary

rounding

▶ Lesson Link In the last lesson, you learned how to read and write large numbers. Now you'll learn how to make large numbers easier to use. ◀

Explore Rounding

Round and Round and Round It Goes

Pioneer 11 was launched on April 5, 1973. Twenty months later, three reports described the spacecraft's closest encounter with Jupiter.

1. Do any of the reported distances give *Pioneer 11*'s exact distance from Jupiter? How can you tell?
2. Why do the reports give three different distances?
3. Earlier in 1973, *Pioneer 10* came within 81,000 miles of Jupiter. To compare *Pioneer 11*'s performance with *Pioneer 10*'s, which of the three reported distances would you use?
4. A *Pioneer 11* engineer explained why there should be another Jupiter project: "We're getting closer each time. This time we were down to almost 25,000 miles." Why did the engineer use 25,000 miles instead of one of the distances in the reports?

NASA Press Release
Dateline: 12/2/74
Contact: J.P. Richards
NASA Public Relations
Today, December 2, 1974, the space probe Pioneer 11 bypassed Jupiter at an altitude of 26,725 miles.

10A
Pioneer 11 Close to Jupiter
(UPI) — The Planetary explorer Pioneer 11 was nearly 27,000 miles from Jupiter when it flew by yesterday.

Pioneer 11
Late in 1974, Pioneer 11 passed within 30,000 miles of the planet Jupiter.

Learn Rounding Large Numbers

Large numbers can be difficult to work with. You don't always need to use the *exact* value of large numbers. You can often use numbers that are close to the exact value but easier to work with.

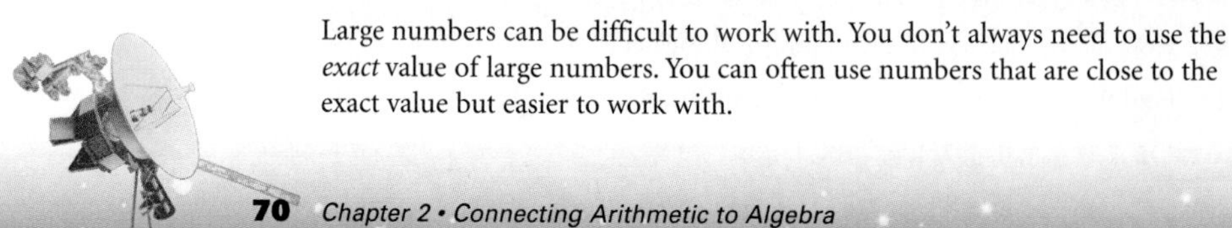

MEETING INDIVIDUAL NEEDS

Resources

2-2 Practice
2-2 Problem Solving
2-2 Reteaching
2-2 Enrichment
2-2 Daily Transparency
Problem of the Day
Review
Quick Quiz
Teaching Tool Transparency 4

Learning Modalities

Visual Show students how using a number line can help them determine whether to round a number up or down. For example, to round 268 to the nearest hundred, use a number line with 200 through 300 marked with intervals of 10. Students should be able to see that 268 is closer to 300.

Social Have students bring in examples of approximations of large numbers found in newspapers or magazines and work together to create a wall display.

Kinesthetic Have students model numbers using base-ten blocks. Rounding to a certain place means that the given place is the smallest size block that can be used.

Inclusion

Students with perceptual difficulties may not be able to easily identify the digit in the given place for rounding. Have them use graph paper with large grids to write numbers or highlight the digit to make it stand out.

Rounding is one way to find a number that's more convenient. Rounding will give you the closest convenient number according to a given place value.

There are four steps involved in the rounding process.

67,683 to thousands		2,341 to hundreds
6[7],683	Find the place value.	2,[3]41
6[7],683	Look at the digit to the right.	2,[3]41
6[7],683 ↑ Add one	If this digit is 5 or greater, add 1 to the place-value digit. If it's less than 5, leave the place-value digit alone.	2,[3]41 ↑ Leave alone
68,000	Change the digits to the right to zeros.	2,300

Examples

According to the 1990 U.S. Census, there were 45,249,989 people in the 5-to-17 age group. Round the population to the given place.

1 millions — millions | Leave the millions digit unchanged.

4 5, 2 4 9, 9 8 9 → round to 45,000,000

2 ten-millions — ten-millions | Add 1 to the ten-millions digit.

4 5, 2 4 9, 9 8 9 → round to 50,000,000

Try It

Round 73,952 to the given place.

a. ten-thousands 70,000 **b.** thousands 74,000 **c.** hundreds 74,000

DID YOU KNOW?

The 1990 census counted about 41 million students in public schools. At an average of about $4700 per student per year, the United States spends about $200 billion annually on public education.

Sometimes it makes more sense to round up or round down, even if it means rounding to a number that's not the closest number.

Example 3

Danielle thinks her diving tank contains enough air for about a 47-minute dive. Since 47 rounds to 50, can she make a 50-minute dive?

No. Danielle can't afford to run out of air under water. Rounding up gives her a closer number, but common sense says she should round *down* to estimate the length of her dive.

Answers for Explore

1. The distance in the NASA press release might be an exact number because it has exact digits in every place.
2. Each report uses a different amount of exactness.
3. The newspaper article.
4. He said "almost" and 25,000 is close enough to the actual distance.

2 Teach

Learn

Alternate Examples

According to Tom Heymann's *In An Average Lifetime*, the average American sees 136,692,500 advertisements and commercial messages in a lifetime. Round this number to the given place in Alternate Examples 1–2.

1. Millions

   137,000,000

2. Ten-millions

   140,000,000

3. Hal forgot his money, so you bought him a notebook for $0.74. He paid you back $0.70, since 74 rounds to 70. Is this acceptable?

   No; $0.70 does not cover the cost of the notebook.

MATH EVERY DAY

Problem of the Day

Brooke uses 12 scallop shells and 4 snail shells to decorate one side of a square picture frame. Draw how the picture frame might look if she repeats the same pattern on each side.

Possible answer:

NSSSSNSSSSNSSSSN (each side of the square)

N → Snail
S → Scallop

Available on Daily Transparency 2-2

An Extension is provided in the transparency package.

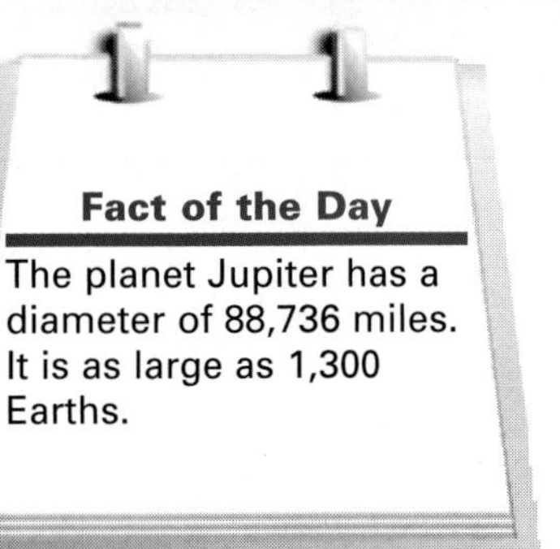

Fact of the Day

The planet Jupiter has a diameter of 88,736 miles. It is as large as 1,300 Earths.

Mental Math

Do these mentally.

1. 5 + 17 + 25 47
2. 30 + 70 + 5 105
3. 200 − 140 60
4. 325 − 50 275

2-2 Exercises and Applications

Assignment Guide

- Basic
  1–7, 11–13, 16–20, 22, 24
- Average
  1, 2–8 evens, 9–15, 17–21 odds, 22–27
- Enriched
  2–10 evens, 11–18, 19–27 odds

3 Practice and Assess

Check

Answers for Check Your Understanding

1. The rounded number might have many zeros in it, which are easy to add or subtract.
2. Answers may vary.

Exercise Answers

1. a. 4
   b. Less than 5.
   c. Leave it the same because the next digit is less than 5.
   d. 1,370,000

10. a. 84,226,499,400
    b. 84,226,500,000
    c. 84,226,500,000
    d. 80,000,000,000

11. Two billion, seven hundred fifty-eight million, five hundred thirty thousand, nine hundred twenty-eight

12. a. 2,758,500,000
    b. 2,760,000,000
    c. 2,800,000,000
    d. 3,000,000,000

Reteaching

Activity

Materials: Catalogs

- Find several items that have a total cost of $50, $100, $500, and $1000 when the cost of each item is rounded to the nearest 10 dollars.
- Use a calculator to find the actual total costs and see how close you came.

Check Your Understanding

1. Why is a rounded number easier to work with?
2. Describe one situation when you might purposely round up, and one when you might purposely round down.

2-2 Exercises and Applications

PRACTICE 2-2

Practice and Apply

1. **Getting Started** Answer these questions to round 1,374,692 to the nearest ten-thousand.
   a. What is the digit to the right of the ten-thousands place?
   b. Is that digit greater than 5 or less than 5?
   c. Should you leave the ten-thousands digit the same or add 1 to it? Why?
   d. What is 1,374,692 rounded to the nearest ten-thousand?

Round to the given place.

2. 8702; hundreds **8700**
3. 94,655; ten-thousands **90,000**
4. 1,850,817,349; hundred-millions **1,900,000,000**
5. 738; tens **740**
6. 800,000,000,000; trillions **1,000,000,000,000**
7. 3,886,000; hundred-thousands **3,900,000**
8. 2,790,600,073,521; ten-billions **2,790,000,000,000**
9. 22,900; thousands **23,000**
10. Round 84,226,499,391 to the given place.
    a. hundreds b. 10 thousands c. 100 thousands d. 10 billions

Science On August 29, 1989, the planetary explorer *Voyager 2* crossed Pluto's orbit and left the solar system. *Voyager 2* was 2,758,530,928 miles from Earth.

11. Write *Voyager 2*'s distance from Earth in words.
12. Round *Voyager 2*'s distance to the given place. GPS
    a. hundred-thousands b. ten-millions
    c. hundred-millions d. billions
13. **Test Prep** Round ninety-seven thousand, five hundred forty-nine to the nearest thousand. **B**
    Ⓐ 98,500 Ⓑ 98,000 Ⓒ 97,500 Ⓓ 97,500 Ⓔ 97,000

72 *Chapter 2 • Connecting Arithmetic to Algebra*

PRACTICE

Name ______________________ Practice 2-2

Rounding Large Numbers

Round to the given place.

1. 38,721,830, ten-millions **40,000,000**
2. 432,483, ten-thousands **430,000**
3. 1,387,216, tens **1,387,220**
4. 83,172,635,810, hundred-millions **83,200,000,000**
5. 392,621, hundred-thousands **400,000**
6. 471,832,103, millions **472,000,000**
7. 217,384,166,982,364, hundred-billions **217,400,000,000,000**
8. 37,852,408,069,843, ten-thousands **37,852,408,070,000**
9. 3,871,664,397,972, hundred-millions **3,871,700,000,000**
10. 6,378,294,183,275, trillions **6,000,000,000,000**

Major league baseball games were attended by 56,603,451 fans in 1990.

11. Write the number of fans in words. **Fifty-six million, six hundred three thousand, four hundred fifty-one**
12. Round the number of fans to the given place.
    a. hundreds **56,603,500** b. millions **57,000,000**
    c. ten-thousands **56,600,000** d. ten-millions **60,000,000**
    e. thousands **56,603,000** f. hundred-thousands **56,600,000**
13. Thom's kitchen requires 33 feet of wallpaper border. He selects a design that is available in a package containing a 10-foot length. Since 33 rounds to 30, he buys 3 packages. Do you agree with his reasoning? Explain.
    No. He needs *at least* 33 feet, so he should buy 4 packages.

RETEACHING

Name ______________________ Alternative Lesson 2-2

Rounding Large Numbers

Rounding is one way to find a number that's more convenient. Rounding will give you the closest convenient number according to a given place value.

Example

Round 82,439 to the nearest hundred. 8 2 [4] 3 9

There are four steps involved in the rounding process:

Step 1: Find the place value.	The place value is "hundreds."
Step 2: Look at the digit to the right	The digit is 3.
Step 3: If this digit is 5 or greater, add one to the place-value digit. If it's less than 5, leave the place-value digit alone.	3 is less than 5, so it will not change.
Step 4: Change the digits to the right to zeros.	The rounded number is 82,400.

82,439 rounds to 82,400 when rounding to the nearest hundred.

Try It Round 132,874,015 to the nearest hundred-thousands.

a. The hundred-thousands digit is **8**.
b. The digit to the right of the hundred-thousands is **7**.
c. Is that digit 5 or greater? **Yes.**
d. Write the rounded number. Remember to change digits to the right of hundred-thousands to zeros. **132,900,000**

Round each number to the given place.

e. 941 to the tens place **940**
f. 103,555 to the thousands place **104,000**
g. 1,806,090 to the ten-thousands place **1,810,000**
h. 967,063,402 to the hundred-thousands place **967,100,000**
i. 460,027,971 to the millions place **460,000,000**
j. 457,032,333 to the ten-millions place **460,000,000**
k. 384,203,670,159 to the ten-billions place **380,000,000,000**

14. Estimation Arnold's car is about to run out of gas. He estimates that the car can go about 25 miles before this happens. The next gas station is 30 miles away. Should he try to make it to the next station? Explain your answer.

Problem Solving and Reasoning

15. Journal Make a list of everyday situations for which you must use exact numbers. Then make a list of everyday situations when you can use rounded numbers to approximate answers.

16. Critical Thinking While entering 1990 population data into a computer, a census worker mistakenly deleted digits from the populations of two Texas towns.

The worker remembered that both populations rounded to 20,000 to the nearest thousand. What could the two populations be? Explain why.

17. Communicate Claudia must reserve buses to take students to the Science Museum. She thinks that about 263 students will be going. Each bus holds 30 students. How many buses does she need? Why?

Mixed Review

Add. *[Previous course]*

18. 2672 + 2438 + 8616 **13,726**

19. 2107 + 596 + 5632 **8335**

20. 759 + 6675 + 3219 **10,653**

21. 9820 + 423 + 890 **11,133**

Use the data to make a frequency chart and a line plot. *[Lesson 1-4]*

22. 48, 48, 49, 52, 53, 53, 53, 54

23. 101, 94, 96, 103, 98, 100, 100

Find the median, mode, and range. *[Lesson 1-7]*

24. 12, 2, 6, 10, 2, 10, 11

25. 32, 29, 22, 32, 30, 32

26. 44, 48, 31, 57

27. 108, 96, 108, 108, 96, 102, 102

PROBLEM SOLVING 2-2

Exercise Answers

14. No; There is a good chance that Arnold will then have to walk the last 5 miles to the gas station.

15. Possible answers: Use exact numbers when paying for something or when determining clothing sizes. Use rounded numbers when figuring out the approximate price or size of something.

16. The missing digit for Copperas Cove must be 0, and the missing digit for Borger must be 9. Any other digits would not make the populations round to 20,000 to the nearest thousand.

17. 9 buses; 263 must be rounded up otherwise 23 students would not have a bus, and 270 ÷ 30 is 9.

22.

Number	Frequency
48	2
49	1
52	1
53	3
54	1

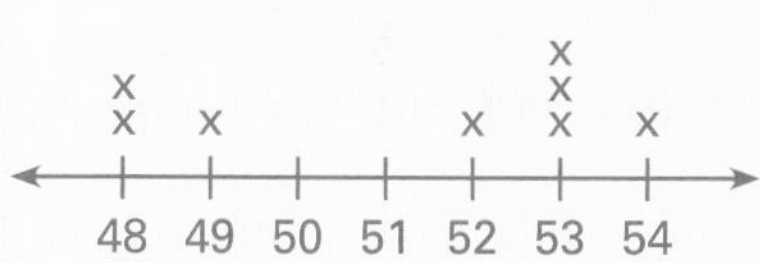

23.

Number	Frequency
94	1
96	1
98	1
100	2
101	1
103	1

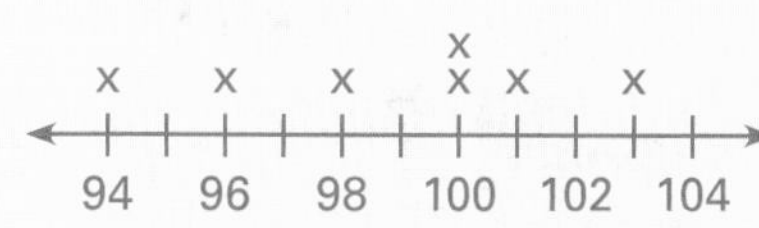

24. Median 10; Modes 2 and 10; Range 10.

25. Median 31; Mode 32; Range 10.

26. Median 46; No mode; Range 26.

27. Median 102; Mode 108; Range 12.

Alternate Assessment

Interview Have students explain the rules for rounding whole numbers.

Quick Quiz

Round 3,145,987,002 to the nearest

1. million. 3,146,000,000
2. hundred-thousand. 3,146,000,000
3. thousand. 3,145,987,000

Available on Daily Transparency 2-2

PROBLEM SOLVING

Name ______________________

Guided Problem Solving 2-2

GPS **PROBLEM 12, STUDENT PAGE 72**

On August 29, 1989, the planetary explorer *Voyager 2* crossed Pluto's orbit and left the solar system. *Voyager 2* was 2,758,530,928 miles from Earth. Round *Voyager 2*'s distance to the given place.

a. hundred-thousands b. ten-millions
c. hundred-millions d. billions

— Understand —

1. How many different place-values are you asked round to? **4**
2. If the digit to the right of the place-value you are rounding to is less than 5, will the place-value digit increase by 1 or remain the same? **Same.**

— Plan —

3. What is the place-value digit and the digit to the right of each place-value?
   a. hundred-thousands **5; 3** b. ten-millions **5; 8**
   c. hundred-millions **7; 5** d. billions **2; 7**

— Solve —

4. Round the distance to the given place value. Remember to write the digits to the right of the place-value digit as zeros.
   a. hundred-thousands **2,758,500,000** b. ten-millions **2,760,000,000**
   c. hundred-millions **2,800,000,000** d. billions **3,000,000,000**

— Look Back —

5. If you rounded all your answers in Question 4 to the nearest billion, would they all be the same? Explain.
   Yes; the digit to the right of 2 billion is greater than 5.

SOLVE ANOTHER PROBLEM

Round 6,832,149,520 to the given place.

a. ten-thousands **6,832,150,000** b. millions **6,832,000,000**
c. hundred-millions **6,800,000,000** d. billions **7,000,000,000**

ENRICHMENT

Name ______________________

Extend Your Thinking 2-2

Decision Making

Horace wants to lose 5 pounds to retain his place on the wrestling team. He knows that for every 3500 calories he cuts from his diet, he will lose 1 pound. Alternately, he could exercise more to burn the additional calories. The tables at the right show the calories in some of Horace's favorite foods and the calories he could burn if he added one hour of exercise.

Favorite Foods	
Quarter-pound Hamburger	450 calories
French Fries	468 calories
Pie Slice	450 calories
Chicken Filet	170 calories
Malt	482 calories

Activities	
Bicycling	600 calories/hour
Calisthenics	425 calories/hour
Swimming	500 calories/hour
Roller skating	700 calories/hour
Jogging	700 calories/hour

1. Horace decides to cut out eating two of his favorite foods twice a week. Which foods should he cut? Explain.
   Possible answer: Malt and pie slice because these high-calorie foods are not nutritionally sound.
2. To the nearest week, how long will it take Horace to lose his 5 pounds if he follows his plan in Question 1? **Possible answer: 10 weeks**
3. Horace decides to exercise three more hours each week instead of watching his diet. Which sport should he add to his schedule? Explain.
   Possible answer: Jogging or roller skating because he will expend more calories per hour.
4. To the nearest week, how long will it take Horace to lose his 5 pounds if he follows his plan in Question 3? **8 weeks.**
5. How many calories will Horace need to cut from his diet each week if he wants to lose 5 pounds in four weeks? **4375 calories.**
6. Describe an alternate plan Horace could follow if he needs to lose 5 pounds in 4 weeks remaining until the wrestling season begins.
   Possible answer: Increase his activities and cut out more junk food than he originally planned.

Lesson Organizer

Objective

- Compare and order large numbers.

NCTM Standards

- 1–4, 6, 7, 11, 13

Review

1. Round 345,029 to the nearest ten-thousand. 350,000
2. Write 345,029 in word form. Three hundred forty-five thousand, twenty-nine
3. Write the answer to 3465 + 20,825 in number-word form. 24 thousand, 290

Available on Daily Transparency 2-3

1 Introduce

Explore

You may wish to use Lesson Enhancement Transparency 6 with **Explore**.

The Point
Students use their knowledge of naming large numbers to order a list of space-probe voyages.

Ongoing Assessment
Students may have difficulty comparing the numbers that are in different forms. Suggest that they put all the numbers in the same form before they compare them.

For Groups That Finish Early
Determine where asteroids at distances of 48 million miles, 245 million miles, and 1,500,000,000 miles would be. Between Mercury and Venus, between Mars and Jupiter, and between Saturn and Uranus.

2-3 Comparing and Ordering Numbers

You'll Learn ...

- to compare and order large numbers

... How It's Used

Stock market traders must compare and order large numbers to determine which companies are the most successful.

▶ Lesson Link You've learned to read, write, and round numbers. Now you will learn how to decide whether one number is greater than another. ◀

Explore Comparing and Ordering

Line Up—That's an Order!

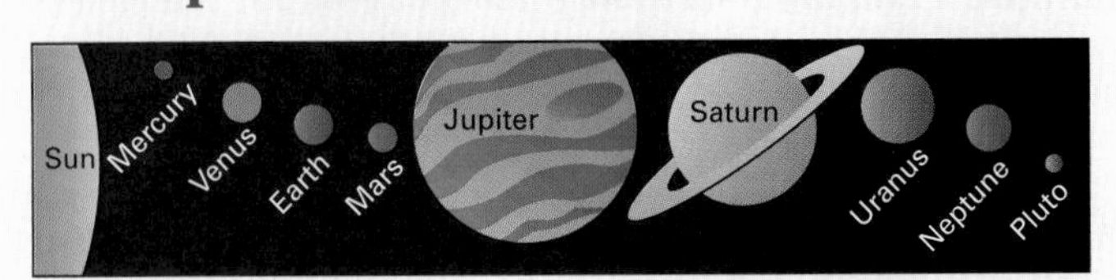

The chart lists eight U.S. space probes sent to the other planets in our solar system and how far the probes were from the sun when they visited the planets or crossed their orbits.

Probe	Distance (mi)
Mariner 2	sixty-seven million
Pioneer 10	500,000,000
Pioneer 10	4,000,000,000
Pioneer 11	3 billion
Mariner 10	forty million
Viking 1	150 million
Voyager 2	1,700,000,000
Voyager 1	one billion

1. Match each probe and its distance with the planet it visited or the planetary orbit it crossed.
2. Explain how you determined which probe matched up with each planet.
3. Suppose a new planet is discovered between the orbits of Neptune and Pluto. Give its possible distance from the sun.

MENTAL MATH

If two whole numbers have different numbers of digits, the number with more digits is greater.

Learn Comparing and Ordering Numbers

To compare two numbers with the same number of digits, start at the left and find the first place-value position that has different digits. The number with the larger digit is the larger number.

236,[4]12
236,[7]83

Since 7 is larger than 4, the second number is larger than the first

MEETING INDIVIDUAL NEEDS

Resources

2-3 Practice
2-3 Problem Solving
2-3 Reteaching
2-3 Enrichment
2-3 Daily Transparency
  Problem of the Day
  Review
  Quick Quiz
Lesson Enhancement Transparency 6

Learning Modalities

Visual For **Explore**, have students write the probe and their distances on index cards so that they can put them in order of distance from the sun more easily.

Social Have students work in groups and discuss situations in which they have to compare or order numbers. Students should also make a list of jobs or careers that would require comparing or ordering numbers.

Challenge

Have students work in cooperative groups of three or four to research and write a report about historical number systems, such as those used by the Egyptians or Mayans. Students should decide which systems used place value. Highlights of each report may be presented to the class.

The symbols > and < are used to compare numbers. The symbol > means "is greater than," and < means "is less than."

Study TIP

You can remember the difference between > and < by recalling that the wider end always faces the bigger amount.

Examples

1 Mount Shasta is 14,162 feet tall. Mount Russell is 14,086 feet tall. Compare the heights of these California mountains.

$\boxed{1}4{,}162$
$\boxed{1}4{,}086$ — The ten-thousands digits are equal. Move to the right.

$1\boxed{4}{,}162$
$1\boxed{4}{,}086$ — The thousands digits are equal. Move to the right.

$14{,}\boxed{1}62$
$14{,}\boxed{0}86$ — In the hundreds place, 1 is greater than 0.

$14{,}162 > 14{,}086$ Mount Shasta is taller than Mount Russell.

2 Order from least to greatest the three craters on the visible side of the moon.

227,000 < 234,000 Compare two at a time.
Schickard < Deslandres

234,000 < 303,000 Use the same symbol in the second comparison.
Deslandres < Bailly

Craters on the Moon

Name	Diameter (m)
Deslandres	234,000
Schickard	227,000
Bailly	303,000

▶ Science Link

Craters are formed when meteors strike the surface of a planet or moon.

The order is Schickard at 227,000 meters, Deslandres at 234,000 meters, and Bailly at 303,000 meters.

Try It

a. Order from least to greatest: 138,417; 146,416; 98,419. **98,419; 138,417; 146,416**

b. The Belkovich crater is 198,000 meters in diameter. The Janssen crater is 190,000 meters in diameter. Compare the two craters. **190,000 < 198,000**

Check Your Understanding

1. Is it easier to compare large numbers when they are written in standard form or in word form? Why?

2. The first digit of a number is 7. Is the number greater than another number whose first digit is 6? Explain.

MATH EVERY DAY

▶ Problem of the Day

A TV network reported that 45,000,000 people (rounded to the nearest million) watched their coverage of a special event. What is the greatest number of viewers that could have watched the newscast? The least number? 45,499,999 viewers; 44,500,000 viewers

Available on Daily Transparency 2-3

An Extension is provided in the transparency package.

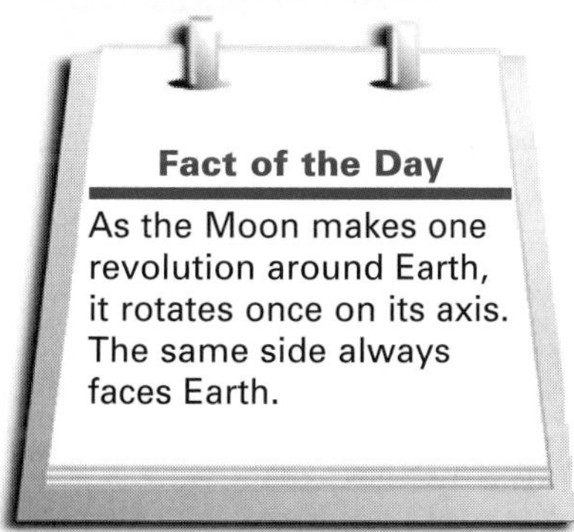

Estimation

Estimate each sum.

1. 189 + 176 400
2. 46 + 59 + 54 + 47 210
3. 423 + 379 800
4. 2593 + 3167 6000

Answers for Explore

1. *Mariner 2*, Venus; *Pioneer 10* (500,000,000), Jupiter; *Pioneer 10* (4,000,000,000), Pluto; *Pioneer 11*, Neptune; *Mariner 10*, Mercury; *Viking 1*, Mars; *Voyager 2*, Uranus; *Voyager 1*, Saturn.
2. Ordered the probe distances from smallest to largest and then matched them to the planets.
3. 3 to 4 billion miles

2 Teach

Learn

Alternate Examples

1. The diameter of Uranus is 31,600 miles. The diameter of Neptune is 30,200 miles. Compare the size of these two planets.

   31,600 > 30,200

   Uranus has a larger diameter than Neptune.

2. Order from least to greatest the distances of the following planets from the Earth.

Planet	Distance from Earth
Mercury	56,983,012 miles
Venus	25,723,000 miles
Mars	48,679,236 miles

   The order is Venus at 25,723,000 miles, Mars at 48,679,236 miles, and Mercury at 56,983,012 miles.

3 Practice and Assess

Check

Be sure students understand that a digit-by-digit comparison is only needed when two numbers have the same number of digits.

Answers for Check Your Understanding

1. Possible answer: Number form is easier. Seeing the digits in the numbers makes it easier to compare them.
2. Not necessarily; It depends what the place values of 7 and 6 are. For example, 72 < 689, but 745 > 63.

2-3 Exercises and Applications

Assignment Guide

- Basic
  1–9, 14–18, 19–20, 25, 28–30, 37, 39
- Average
  1–13 odds, 17–18, 22, 25–26, 28–40 evens
- Enriched
  1–3, 7, 9–12, 17–18, 21–27, 30–40 evens

Exercise Notes

Exercise 18

Error Prevention Students may have difficulty determining the correct order of the three students. Suggest that they draw a picture to help them.

Reteaching

Activity

Materials: Index cards

- Work with a partner. Player 1 writes two numbers on a sheet of paper, lining up the places.
- Using an index card, Player 1 reveals the numbers, one digit at a time from left to right.
- Player 2 decides which number is larger.
- For example, Player 1 writes
  34,129
  34,298
- Player 2 knows the second number is larger as soon as the hundreds place is revealed.

2-3 Exercises and Applications

PRACTICE 2-3

Practice and Apply

Getting Started Compare the numbers, using > or <.

1. 277 [>] 31 **2.** 5768 [>] 924 **3.** 873 [<] 2183 **4.** 327 [>] 91

5. 64 [<] 65 **6.** 158 [<] 185 **7.** 448,119 [<] 448,191

Order each group of numbers from least to greatest.

8. 77; 7,777; 777; 77,777 **77; 777; 7,777; 77,777**

9. 5678; 5768; 5687 **5678; 5687; 5768**

10. 57,000; 56,940; 56,490 **56,490; 56,940; 57,000**

11. 20,200; 22,000; 20,002 **20,002; 20,200; 22,000**

12. 20 million; 500 thousand; 1 billion **500 thousand; 20 million; 1 billion**

13. 10 hundred; 10 million; 1 trillion **10 hundred; 10 million; 1 trillion**

14. 9 hundred; 901; nine **Nine; 9 hundred; 901**

15. 62 thousand; 6 hundred; 29 billion **6 hundred; 62 thousand; 29 billion**

16. Measurement In almost 19 years, *Voyager 1* traveled 11,005,000,000 kilometers, and *Voyager 2* traveled 10,042,000,000 kilometers. Which spacecraft traveled farther? **Voyager 1**

17. Test Prep Choose the smallest number. **D**

Ⓐ 138,528 Ⓑ 13,855 Ⓒ 13,852 Ⓓ 13,555

18. Logic Marisela, Luis, and Raymond are comparing their heights. Luis is 54 inches tall. Marisela is shorter than Luis but 2 inches taller than Raymond. Order the three students from shortest to tallest. **Raymond, Marisela, Luis**

19. Geography The diameter of Earth at the equator is 7926 miles. The diameter from the North Pole to the South Pole is 7898 miles. Which diameter is greater?

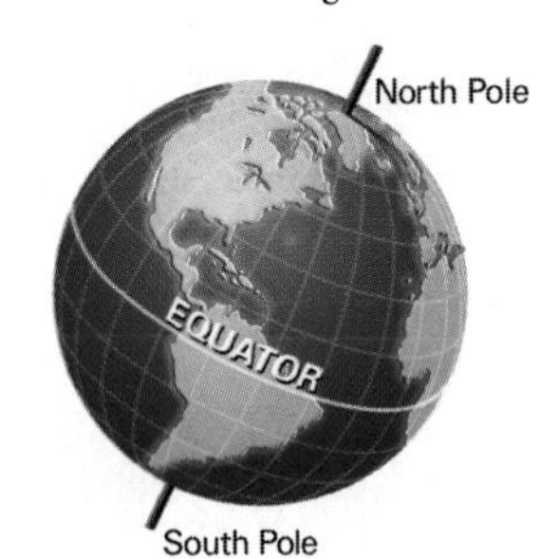

19. The diameter at the equator is greater.

20. Chance In the fall raffle at Oakdale Middle School, 4269 tickets were sold. In the winter raffle, 4629 were sold. In the spring raffle, 4962. Rank the raffles from easiest-to-win to hardest-to-win. **Fall, winter, spring**

21. Geography List the cities in order from largest population to smallest: Rio de Janeiro, Brazil: 12,788,000; Buenos Aires, Argentina: 12,232,000; Calcutta, India: 12,885,000. **Calcutta, Rio de Janeiro, Buenos Aires**

PRACTICE

Name ____________

Practice 2-3

Comparing and Ordering Numbers

Order each group of numbers from least to greatest.

1. 3,000; 20,000; 400; 50 — 50; 400; 3,000; 20,000
2. 38,000; 37,940; 38,010 — 37,940; 38,000; 38,010
3. 6,748; 6,847; 6,487; 6,874 — 6,487; 6,748; 6,847; 6,874
4. 3,333; 33,333; 33; 333 — 33; 333; 3,333; 33,333
5. 78,321; 873,210; 783,210 — 78,321; 783,210; 873,210
6. 1,243; 1,342; 1,324; 1,234 — 1,234; 1,243; 1,324; 1,342
7. 99,909; 99,000; 99,900; 90,000 — 90,000; 99,000; 99,900; 99,909
8. 37,630; 37,628; 37,624; 37,700 — 37,624; 37,628; 37,630; 37,700
9. 82,270; 83,100; 82,200; 82,170 — 82,170; 82,200; 82,270; 83,100
10. 48,380; 48,376; 48,408; 48,480 — 48,376; 48,380; 48,408; 48,480
11. 63,821; 63,900; 63,800; 64,000 — 63,800; 63,821; 63,900; 64,000
12. 10 million; 1 billion; 10 thousand — 10 thousand; 10 million; 1 billion
13. 1,675; 15 hundred; 2 thousand — 15 hundred; 1,675; 2 thousand
14. 19 million; 2 million; 30 thousand — 30 thousand; 2 million; 19 million
15. 200 billion; 5 trillion; 990 million — 990 million; 200 billion; 5 trillion
16. 18 thousand; 18 million; 18,000 — 18,000; 18 thousand; 18 million
17. In 1990, the Broadway show *Cats* grossed $22,941,820 and *Gypsy* grossed $21,941,875. Compare these numbers using < or >.
    22,941,820 > 21,941,875
18. In 1990, 3,379,000 Americans were employed in food stores, 3,665,000 were employed in transportation, and 3,363,000 were employed in finance. Rank these industries from the fewest employees to the most employees.
    Finance, food stores, transportation

RETEACHING

Name ____________

Alternative Lesson 2-3

Comparing and Ordering Numbers

To compare two numbers with the same number of digits, start at the left and find the first place-value position that has different digits. The number with the larger digit is the larger number. The symbols > and < are used to compare numbers.

The symbol > means "is greater than."
The symbol < means "is less than."

Example

Compare 87,812 and 87,349.

The numbers have the same number of digits. Start with the digit at the left.

Step 1:	[8] 7 8 1 2 [8] 7 3 4 9	Compare the ten-thousands digits. They are equal. Move to the right.
Step 2:	8 [7] 8 1 2 8 [7] 3 4 9	Compare the thousands digits. They are equal. Move to the right.
Step 3:	8 7 [8] 1 2 8 7 [3] 4 9	Compare the hundreds digits. 8 is greater than 3.

87,812 is greater than 87,349.
This can also be written as 87,812 > 87,349.

Try It Compare 21,009 and 21,090.

a. Compare the digits, starting at the left. In which place-value positions are the digits the same? ten-thousands, thousands, hundreds

b. For the first two digits that are not the same, which number is larger? 9

c. Which is greater: 21,009 or 21,090? 21,090

d. Compare 6802 and 6820. Which is greater? 6820

Compare the numbers, using > or <.

e. 45 < 54 f. 932 > 923

g. 5676 > 5675 h. 6321 > 6279

i. 11,122 < 11,211 j. 86,321 > 86,279

k. 120,932 > 102,923 l. 707,213 < 778,689

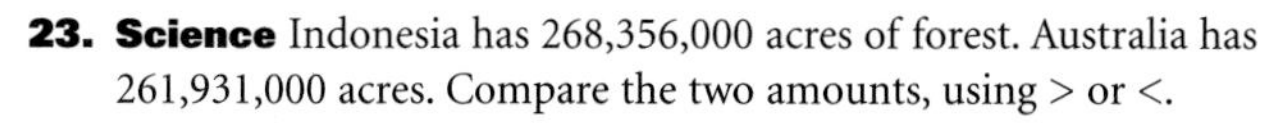

22. Science The two most experienced space women are Shannon Lucid and Elena Kondakova. As of 1996, Lucid had spent 5354 hours in space. As of 1995, Kondakova had spent 2033 hours in space. Compare their hours in space, using > or <.

23. Science Indonesia has 268,356,000 acres of forest. Australia has 261,931,000 acres. Compare the two amounts, using > or <.

Elena Kondakova

Problem Solving and Reasoning

24. Critical Thinking Use the digits 7, 1, 5, 9, and 3 to write the largest and smallest possible 5-digit numbers. Each digit must be used exactly once. Use < or > to compare your answers.

The bar graph shows the five most populated metropolitan areas in the United States, according to the 1990 census. Use the data for Exercises 25–27.

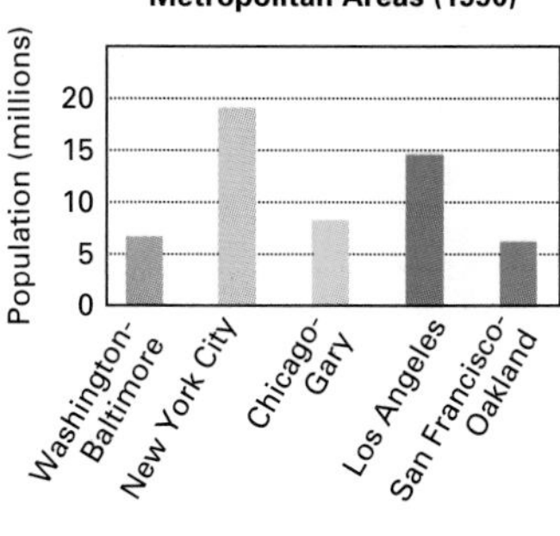

25. Critical Thinking GPS The populations of the five areas are 19,342,013; 6,253,311; 14,531,529; 8,239,820; and 6,727,050. Match each area with its population.

26. Critical Thinking The population of Jakarta, Indonesia, is greater than that of Chicago–Gary. How does Jakarta's population compare with that of San Francisco–Oakland?

27. Communicate Can you tell how Jakarta's population compares with the population of Los Angeles? Why or why not?

Mixed Review

Add. *[Previous course]*

28. 4212 + 2590 + 3856 **10,658**

29. 22,386 + 6,911 **29,297**

30. 356,093 + 734,035 **1,090,128**

31. 160,577 + 64,444 **225,021**

32. 454,232 + 711,804 **1,166,036**

33. 560,380 + 479,120 **1,039,500**

34. 984,909 + 978,099 **1,963,008**

35. 328,040 + 288,045 **616,085**

36. 423,371 + 968,195 **1,391,566**

Find the mean. *[Lesson 1-8]*

37. 40, 34, 50, 39, 61, 34 **43**

38. 72, 92, 83, 47, 101 **79**

39. 123, 98, 112, 131, 121 **117**

40. 204, 342, 267, 412, 383, 439 **341.17 or 341 R1**

PROBLEM SOLVING 2-3

Exercise Notes

Exercise 26

Geography Jakarta is the capital and largest city of Indonesia. It is located on the island of Java. Indonesia is comprised of more than 13,600 islands.

Exercise Answers

22. 5354 > 2033
23. 268,356,000 > 261,931,000
24. Largest number is 97,531; Smallest number is 13,579.
25. Washington–Baltimore 6,727,050; New York–New Jersey 19,342,013; Chicago–Gary 8,239,820; Los Angeles 14,531,529; San Francisco–Oakland 6,253,311.
26. The population of Jakarta is also greater than the population of San Francisco–Oakland.
27. No; Not enough information is given.

Alternate Assessment

Self Assessment Ask students what they found most difficult about comparing whole numbers in this lesson and if they feel that they have mastered comparing two whole numbers with the same number of digits.

Quick Quiz

Compare the numbers using < or >.

1. 283 and 2837 <
2. 34,205 and 34,805 <
3. Order from least to greatest: 345; 3754; 3547; 3745
   345; 3547; 3745; 3754

Available on Daily Transparency 2-3

PROBLEM SOLVING

Name ______________

Guided Problem Solving 2-3

GPS PROBLEM 25, STUDENT PAGE 77

The bar graph shows the five most populated metropolitan areas in the United States, according to the 1990 census.

The populations of the five areas are 19,342,013; 6,253,311; 14,531,529; 8,239,820; and 6,727,050. Match each area with its population.

Most Populated Metropolitan Areas (1990)

Population (millions): 20, 15, 10, 5, 0

Washington-Baltimore, New York-New Jersey, Chicago-Gary, Los Angeles, San Francisco-Oakland

— Understand —

1. Underline what you are asked to do.
2. Circle the information you need.

— Plan —

3. Does Los Angeles or Chicago/Gary have the greater population. Explain. **Los Angeles; The bar is taller.**

— Solve —

4. Use the bar graph. Order the areas from least to greatest population.
   SF-OA WA-BA CH-GA LA NY-NJ
5. Order the populations given from least to greatest.
   6,253,311 6,727,050 8,239,820 14,531,529 19,342,013
6. Match each area with its population.
   SF-OA: 6,253,311; WA-BA: 6,727,050; CH-GA: 8,239,820; LA: 14,531,529; NY-NJ: 19,342,013

— Look Back —

7. How could you solve the problem another way? **Possible answer: List both population sources from greatest to least.**

SOLVE ANOTHER PROBLEM

When graphed, the height of the bar showing the population of Istanbul falls between the bars of Washington/Baltimore and San Francisco/Oakland. Which of the following is an approximation of its population? **c**

a. 6,865,000 b. 5,890,000 c. 6,461,000

ENRICHMENT

Name ______________

Extend Your Thinking 2-3

Critical Thinking

United States Census Data

In 1990, the United States Census populations for all 50 states plus the District of Columbia was 248,709,873. Use the information in the table to answer the questions below. Round your answers to the nearest whole number, if necessary. Your calculator may be a helpful tool!

1990 Population	
California	29,760,021
Florida	12,937,926
Indiana	5,544,159
Maine	1,227,928
Mississippi	5,117,073
New Hampshire	1,109,252
North Dakota	628,800
Rhode Island	1,003,464
Utah	1,722,850
Wisconsin	4,891,769

Source: US Bureau of Census

1. Find the mean (average) population for the 50 states plus the District of Columbia. **4,876,664**
2. Which of the states listed has a population closest to the mean population? **Wisconsin.**
3. What is the mean population for the 10 states in the chart? **6,394,324**
4. How does the mean population of the 10 states compare to the mean population of all 50 states plus the District of Columbia? **Possible answer: It is greater for the ten states.**
5. Between 1980 and 1990, the population of one state increased by about 6,000,000. Which state do you think had the population increase? Why? **Possible answer: California; Since only CA and FL have a population greater than 6,000,000, it is more likely CA increased by $\frac{1}{4}$ than FL doubled.**
6. A company sells its product in each of the 10 states listed in the chart. The company sales manager wants to divide up the states into two groups having approximately the same total populations. Which states could the sales manager group together? **Possible answer: Eastern states–FL, IN, MI, WI, ME, NH, RI (31,831,571 people); Western states–CA, ND, UT (32,111,671 people).**

Lesson Organizer

Objectives

- Use exponents to express numbers.
- Write expressions containing exponents in standard form.

Vocabulary

- Factor, base, exponent, power, squared, cubed

Materials

- Explore: Scientific calculator

NCTM Standards

- 1–5, 7

Review

Find each product.

1. 2 × 2 × 2 × 2 16
2. 3 × 3 × 3 27
3. 3 × 3 × 3 × 3 81
4. 4 × 4 × 4 64

Available on Daily Transparency 2-4

1 Introduce

Explore

You may wish to use Teaching Tool Transparency 23: Scientific Calculator with this lesson.

The Point

Students experiment with the y^x key. They test their ideas by predicting what will happen when specific key sequences are pressed.

Ongoing Assessment

You may have to help students locate the y^x key on their calculators. If students have difficulty organizing their findings, suggest that they use a table to record what keys were pressed and the results.

2-4 Exponents

You'll Learn ...

- to use exponents to express numbers
- to write expressions containing exponents in standard form

... How It's Used

Urban planners use exponents to predict how quickly the population of a city will grow.

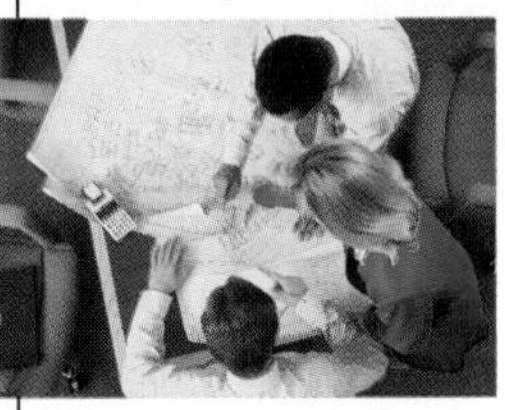

Vocabulary

factor

base

exponent

power

squared

cubed

▶ Lesson Link In this section, you have learned to round and compare large numbers. Now you will learn an easy way to write certain large numbers. ◀

Explore Repeated Multiplication

One, Two, Three, Four ... Press!

Materials: Scientific calculator

1. Use only the numbers 1, 2, 3, and 4. On your calculator, press this sequence:

   1, 2, 3, or 4 y^x 1, 2, 3, or 4 =.

Record the numbers you pressed and the answer given by the calculator.

2. Repeat Step 1 as many times as necessary until you understand how the calculator finds the answer. Explain the calculator's method.
3. Predict each result. Then use your calculator to check your prediction.

   a. 2 y^x 5 = **b.** 6 y^x 2 = **c.** 10 y^x 3 =

4. Find 3 y^x 5 = and 5 y^x 3 = on your calculator. Are the results the same? Why or why not?

Learn Exponents

When you multiply numbers, each number is a **factor** of the result.

Factors

$2 \times 3 \times 5 = 30$

You can represent repeated multiplication of the same number by using exponential notation. The **base** is the number to be multiplied. The **exponent** is the number that tells how many times the base is used as a factor.

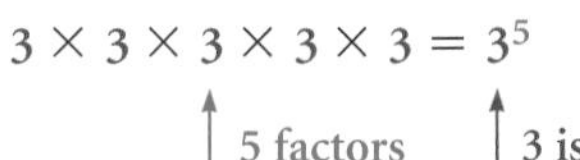

5 is the exponent

$$3 \times 3 \times 3 \times 3 \times 3 = 3^5$$

5 factors 3 is the base

MEETING INDIVIDUAL NEEDS

Resources

- 2-4 Practice
- 2-4 Reteaching
- 2-4 Problem Solving
- 2-4 Enrichment
- 2-4 Daily Transparency
  - Problem of the Day
  - Review
  - Quick Quiz
- Teaching Tool Transparencies 2, 3, 23
- Technology Masters 6, 7
- Chapter 2 Project Master

Learning Modalities

Verbal Students who are discouraged from asking questions at home may be hesitant to ask questions and discuss topics in class. Divide students into small groups to talk about how to write a number with an exponent in standard form and how to write a product in exponential form.

Visual Relate squared numbers to finding the area of a square whose side is the length shown by the base. Relate cubed numbers to finding the volume of a cube whose side is the base.

English Language Development

Discuss the different meanings of the terms *base* and *power*. Then, have students write their own definitions and draw pictures or diagrams to help them remember the meaning. Be sure students understand that *squared* and *cubed* are alternate names for raising a number to the second and third powers.

Numbers involving exponents can be written in three different forms.

Exponential notation: 9^4

Expanded form: $9 \times 9 \times 9 \times 9$

Standard form: 6561

When the base and exponent are small, you can use mental math or pencil and paper to convert numbers to standard form. Otherwise, use the y^x key on your calculator:

$3 \times 3 \times 3 \times 3 \times 3 = 3$ y^x 5 = 243

Examples

1 Write $8 \times 8 \times 8 \times 8 \times 8 \times 8$ using exponents.

$8 \times 8 \times 8 \times 8 \times 8 \times 8 = 8^6$

2 Write 7^4 in expanded form.

$7^4 = 7 \times 7 \times 7 \times 7$

3 Write 5^3 in standard form.

$5^3 = 5 \times 5 \times 5 = 125$

4 When the space probe *Mariner 10* passed the planet Mercury in 1972, the probe was traveling about 19^4 mi/hr. Write 19^4 in standard form.

$19^4 = 19 \times 19 \times 19 \times 19 = 19$ y^x 4 = 130,321

Mariner 10's speed was about 130,321 mi/hr.

Try It

a. Write $12 \times 12 \times 12 \times 12$ using exponents. 12^4

b. Write 5^6 in expanded form. $5 \times 5 \times 5 \times 5 \times 5 \times 5$

c. Use mental math to change 9^2 to standard form. 81

d. Change 11^5 to standard form. 161,051

An exponent is also called a **power**. We read 3^6 as "3 raised to the sixth power," or simply "3 to the sixth power." The second and third powers have special names:

We read 5^2 as "5 to the second power," or 5 **squared**.

We read 8^3 as "8 to the third power," or 8 **cubed**.

Science Link

Mercury takes 88 days to orbit the sun. On her twelfth birthday, a girl born on Earth is over 49 Mercury years old.

The largest number that can be written with two digits is 9^9. It is equal to 387,420,489.

For Groups That Finish Early

Determine the largest number you can use with the y^x key if you first enter a 2.

Follow Up

Have students share their answers concerning how the calculator works. Some students may note that when you use 10 as the first number, the second number tells you how many zeros you need after the 1.

Answers for Explore

1. Possible answer: $4^4 = 256$
2. Possible answer: $4^4 = 4 \times 4 \times 4 \times 4 = 256$
3. a. 32; b. 36; c. 1000
4. $3^5 = 243$; $5^3 = 125$; The results are not the same because $3 \times 3 \times 3 \times 3 \times 3$ does not equal $5 \times 5 \times 5$.

2 Teach

Learn

Review the terms *factor* and *product* with the class. Ask students to compare the numbers written in different forms. Have them identify the factors, the base, the exponent, and the power.

Alternate Examples

1. Write $7 \times 7 \times 7 \times 7 \times 7 \times 7$ using exponents.

   $7 \times 7 \times 7 \times 7 \times 7 \times 7 = 7^6$

2. Write 3^5 in expanded form.

   $3^5 = 3 \times 3 \times 3 \times 3 \times 3$

3. Write 4^5 in standard form.

   $4 \times 4 \times 4 \times 4 \times 4 = 1024$

4. There are 6^3 different combinations that can be tossed with three number cubes. Write 6^3 in standard form.

   $6^3 = 6 \times 6 \times 6 = 216$

   There are 216 different combinations.

MATH EVERY DAY

Problem of the Day

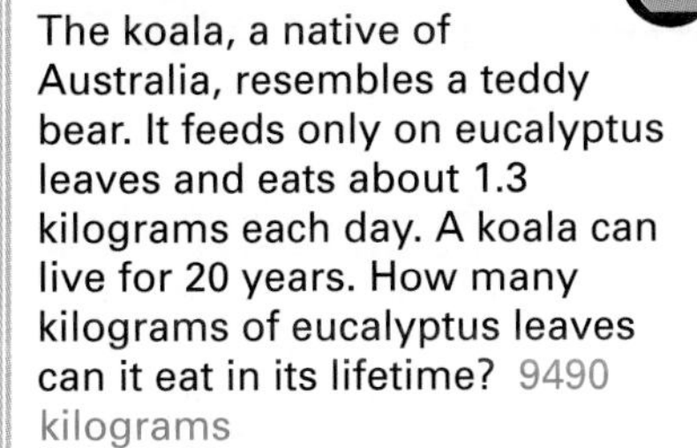

The koala, a native of Australia, resembles a teddy bear. It feeds only on eucalyptus leaves and eats about 1.3 kilograms each day. A koala can live for 20 years. How many kilograms of eucalyptus leaves can it eat in its lifetime? 9490 kilograms

Available on Daily Transparency 2-4

An Extension is provided in the transparency package.

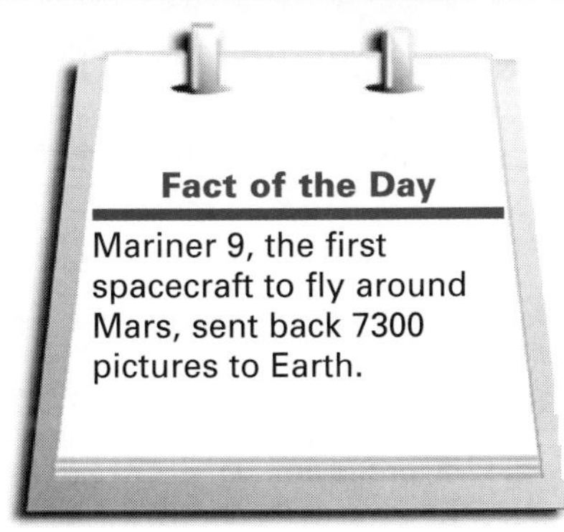

Estimation

Estimate.

1. 93 − 54 40
2. 523 − 325 200
3. 3821 + 7125 11,000

Students are shown two methods of finding the value of 10 raised to a power. One method involves using a calculator, while the other involves using patterns. Students are asked to decide which method they would rather use in a specific situation and why.

Answers for What Do You Think?

1. Answers may vary.
2. The answer would be a 1 followed by twice as many zeros as the value of the exponent.

3 Practice and Assess

Check

Question 2 will help those students who have a tendency to multiply the base and the exponent instead of using the exponent as the number of factors.

Answers for Check Your Understanding

1. Exponents take up less space.
2. No; $3^7 = 2187$ and $7^3 = 343$.
3. The number stays the same.

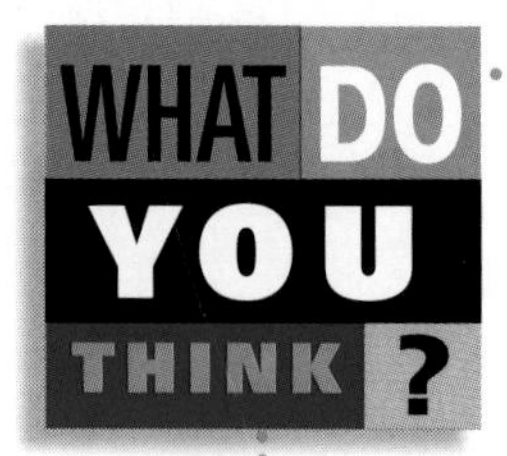

In science class, Tyreka and Ricardo learned that the sun is about 10^8 miles from Earth. They want to evaluate 10^8.

Tyreka thinks ...

I'll use my calculator.

10 y^x 8 = 100,000,000

Ricardo thinks ...

$10^2 = 10 \times 10 = 100$, which is a 1 followed by two zeros.

$10^3 = 10 \times 10 \times 10 = 1{,}000$, which is a 1 followed by three zeros. Each time I multiply by 10, I add one zero to the product. Therefore, 10^8 is a 1 followed by eight zeros, or 100,000,000.

What do you think?

1. Whose method would you use to evaluate 10^{25}? Why?
2. What rule could Ricardo use to evaluate powers of 100?

Keep in mind that 8^3 and 8×3 do not have the same meaning. 8×3 represents repeated addition. It has the same value as $8 + 8 + 8$. 8^3 represents repeated multiplication. It has the same value as $8 \times 8 \times 8$.

$$8 \times 3 = 24, \text{ but } 8^3 = 512.$$

Check Your Understanding

1. What is the advantage of using exponents to write numbers?
2. Is 3^7 the same as 7^3? Explain.
3. What happens to a number when you raise it to the first power?

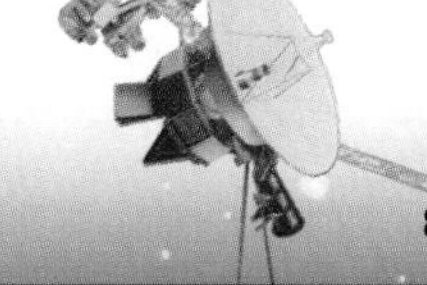

MATH EVERY DAY

Tips from Middle School Teachers

My students enjoy learning how to use a four-function calculator to simplify a number in exponential form by using repeated multiplication. For example, 8^4 can be found using the key sequence: 8 × = = =.

Team Teaching

Work with a science teacher when your class is studying exponents. The science teacher should be able to provide examples where exponents are used. Scientists use exponents to represent numbers that are very large, such as distances of planets, or very small, such as sizes of bacteria. Exponents are also used in describing the process of mitosis, or cell division.

Science Connection

Distances in space can be measured by how far light travels in a certain time. Light travels 186,282.3976 miles in a second. A light year, the distance light travels in a year, is 5,880,000,000,000 miles. The star nearest our Sun is 4.3 light years away.

2-4 Exercises and Applications

Practice and Apply

1. **Getting Started** Answer these questions to write $4 \times 4 \times 4 \times 4 \times 4 \times 4 \times 4$ using an exponent.

a. What number is the factor in the product? 4

b. How many times is the number used as a factor? 7

c. To write $4 \times 4 \times 4 \times 4 \times 4 \times 4 \times 4$ in exponential notation, what number should you use as the base? As the exponent? 4; 7

d. Write $4 \times 4 \times 4 \times 4 \times 4 \times 4 \times 4$ in exponential notation. 4^7

Write using exponents.

2. $5 \times 5 \times 5 \times 5$ 5^4 **3.** $9 \times 9 \times 9 \times 9 \times 9$ 9^5 **4.** $24 \times 24 \times 24$ 24^3 **5.** 79×79 79^2

6. $20 \times 20 \times 20$ 20^3 **7.** $7 \times 7 \times 3 \times 3$ $7^2 \times 3^2$ **8.** $8 \times 8 \times 8 \times 4$ $8^3 \times 4$ **9.** 36 36^1

Write in expanded form.

10. 4^3 **11.** 25^2 **12.** 11^6 **13.** 200^4 **14.** 13^5 **15.** 7^7

16. 10^{10} **17.** 3^4 **18.** 19^6 **19.** 5^9 **20.** 1^{10} **21.** 9^8

Write in standard form.

22. 6^2 36 **23.** 5^3 125 **24.** 10^4 10,000 **25.** 3^5 243 **26.** 13 squared 169

27. 1^{10} 1 **28.** 7^5 16,807 **29.** 2^8 256 **30.** 15^4 50,625 **31.** 9 cubed 729

PRACTICE 2-4

Science **For each number in exponential notation, identify the base and exponent. Use a calculator and write each number in standard form.**

32. In September of 1979, the space probe *Pioneer 11* approached within 114^2 miles of Saturn. The probe was traveling about 4^8 mi/hr. It collected data showing that Saturn's rings are about 11^5 miles wide.

33. Pluto, the planet farthest from the sun, orbits at a speed of about 8^6 miles per day. At this speed, it takes about 3^5 years to orbit the sun.

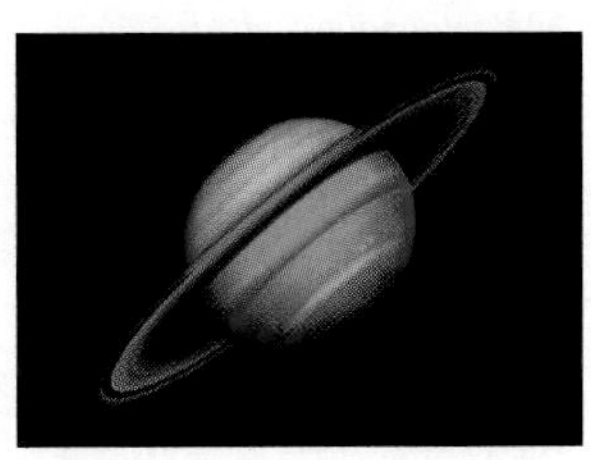

Saturn

Compare, using $<$, $>$, or $=$.

34. 2^3 $\boxed{<}$ 3^2 **35.** 5^4 $\boxed{>}$ 5×4 **36.** 1^{12} $\boxed{<}$ 12^1 **37.** 10^{15} $\boxed{<}$ 10^{16}

2-4 Exercises and Applications

Assignment Guide

- **Basic**
  1–5, 10–15, 22–26, 34–40, 42–52 evens
- **Average**
  1–31 odds, 32–41, 43–53 odds
- **Enriched**
  6–9, 16–21, 27–31, 33–41, 43–53 odds

Exercise Answers

10. $4 \times 4 \times 4$

11. 25×25

12. $11 \times 11 \times 11 \times 11 \times 11 \times 11$

13. $200 \times 200 \times 200 \times 200$

14. $13 \times 13 \times 13 \times 13 \times 13$

15. $7 \times 7 \times 7 \times 7 \times 7 \times 7 \times 7$

16. $10 \times 10 \times 10 \times 10 \times 10 \times 10 \times 10 \times 10 \times 10 \times 10$

17. $3 \times 3 \times 3 \times 3$

18. $19 \times 19 \times 19 \times 19 \times 19 \times 19$

19. $5 \times 5 \times 5 \times 5 \times 5 \times 5 \times 5 \times 5 \times 5$

20. $1 \times 1 \times 1 \times 1 \times 1 \times 1 \times 1 \times 1 \times 1 \times 1$

21. $9 \times 9 \times 9 \times 9 \times 9 \times 9 \times 9 \times 9$

32. 114^2: base 114, exponent 2, 12,996; 4^8: base 4, exponent 8, 65,536; 11^5: base 11, exponent 5, 161,051.

33. 8^6: base 8, exponent 6, 262,144; 3^5: base 3, exponent 5, 243.

PRACTICE

Name ______________________

Practice 2-4

Exponents

Write using exponents.

1. $3 \times 3 \times 3 \times 3$ 3^4
2. 364×364 364^2
3. $2 \times 2 \times 2 \times 2 \times 2 \times 2 \times 2$ 2^7
4. $13 \times 13 \times 13$ 13^3
5. $8 \times 8 \times 8 \times 7 \times 7$ $8^3 \times 7^2$
6. 49 7^2

Write in expanded form.

7. 10^4 $10 \times 10 \times 10 \times 10$
8. 6^5 $6 \times 6 \times 6 \times 6 \times 6$
9. 3^2 3×3
10. 7^3 $7 \times 7 \times 7$
11. 12^4 $12 \times 12 \times 12 \times 12$
12. 5 cubed $5 \times 5 \times 5$

Write in standard form.

13. 5^4 625
14. 2^6 64
15. 11 squared 121
16. 10^7 10,000,000
17. 12^2 144
18. 6 cubed 216

Compare using $<$, $>$, or $=$.

19. $4^2 \; (=) \; 2^4$
20. $4^3 \; (<) \; 3^4$
21. $5^8 \; (<) \; 5^9$
22. $3^8 \; (>) \; 3 \times 8$
23. $2^5 \; (>) \; 5^2$
24. $10^3 \; (>) \; 10 + 10 + 10$
25. $5^3 \; (=) \; 5 \times 5 \times 5$
26. $7^3 \; (<) \; 3^7$
27. $10^4 \; (>) \; 4 \times 10$

For each number in exponential notation, identify the base, exponent, and power. Use a calculator to write each number in standard form.

28. A typical American kid watches about 18^4 television advertisements between birth and high school graduation.

base 18 exponent 4

power 4 standard form 104,976

29. The highest point in Kentucky is Black Mountain. Its height is about 2^{12} feet.

base 2 exponent 12

power 12 standard form 4,096

RETEACHING

Name ______________________

Alternative Lesson 2-4

Exponents

When you multiply numbers, each number is a **factor** of the result. Repeated multiplication can be represented by using exponential notation. The **base** is the number to be multiplied. The **exponent** is the number that tells you how many times the base is used as a factor.

5 is the exponent.

$3 \times 3 \times 3 \times 3 \times 3 = 3^5$

5 factors 3 is the base.

Example 1

Write $4 \times 4 \times 4$ using exponents.

The number to be multiplied is 4, so 4 will be the base.
The base is used as a factor 3 times, so 3 will be the exponent.

$4 \times 4 \times 4 = 4^3$

Try It Write $7 \times 7 \times 7 \times 7 \times 7 \times 7$ using exponents.

a. What is the base? 7
b. What is the exponent? 6
c. Write $7 \times 7 \times 7 \times 7 \times 7 \times 7$ using exponents. 7^6

Write using exponents.

d. $25 \times 25 \times 25$ 25^3
e. $6 \times 6 \times 6 \times 6 \times 6 \times 6 \times 6$ 6^7
f. $10 \times 10 \times 10 \times 10$ 10^4
g. $9 \times 9 \times 9 \times 9 \times 9 \times 9$ 9^6

Example 2

Write 3^4 in expanded and standard forms.

The base is 3: It is the number being multiplied.
The exponent is 4: It is the number of times the base is multiplied.

In expanded form, $3^4 = 3 \times 3 \times 3 \times 3$.
In standard form, $3^4 = 81$.

Try It Write in expanded and standard forms.

	Expanded	Standard
h. 5^3	$5 \times 5 \times 5$	125
i. 4^4	$4 \times 4 \times 4 \times 4$	256
j. 2^5	$2 \times 2 \times 2 \times 2 \times 2$	32

Reteaching

Activity

- Fold a sheet of paper in half and record the number of layers. First fold: 2 layers
- Continue folding the paper in half until it has been folded 5 times. Record the number of layers after each fold. Second fold: 4 layers; Third fold: 8 layers; Fourth fold: 16 layers; Fifth fold: 32 layers.
- How many layers will there be after 6 folds? 7 folds? 64;128
- What do you notice about the number of layers after each additional fold? The number of layers is doubled.

Exercise Notes

■ Exercises 39 and 41

Extension Point out to students that these questions involve finding the root, the inverse operation of finding a power.

■ Exercise 41

Problem-Solving Tip You may wish to use Teaching Tool Transparencies 2 and 3: Guided Problem Solving, pages 1–2.

Project Progress

You may want to have students use Chapter 2 Project Master.

Exercise Answers

39. a. 1 hr, 2^1 cells
   2 hr, 2^2 cells
   3 hr, 2^3 cells
   4 hr, 2^4 cells
   5 hr, 2^5 cells
   6 hr, 2^6 cells
   7 hr, 2^7 cells
   8 hr, 2^8 cells
   9 hr, 2^9 cells
   10 hr, 2^{10} cells
   b. 50 hours, 2^{50} cells

Alternate Assessment

Performance Have students work in groups of three or four. Each group should determine what they learned in class today. Together they should write a letter to an absent student, explaining what they learned. Have the groups share their letters with the class.

▶ Quick Quiz

1. Write 5^6 in expanded form. $5 \times 5 \times 5 \times 5 \times 5 \times 5$
2. Write 3^5 in standard form. 243
3. Identify the base and the exponent in 5^6. 5 is the base; 6 is the exponent.
4. Write $13 \times 13 \times 13$ using exponents. 13^3

Available on Daily Transparency 2-4

PROBLEM SOLVING 2-4

38. **Test Prep** Track A is 3^7 yards long. Track B is three times longer than Track A. How long is Track B? A

Ⓐ 3^8 Ⓑ 3^{21} Ⓒ 9^{21} Ⓓ 6^{14}

Problem Solving and Reasoning

39. Critical Thinking The number of bacteria cells in a biology experiment doubles every hour. After 1 hour there are 2 cells, after 2 hours there are 2×2 (or 4) cells, after 3 hours there are $2 \times 2 \times 2$ (or 8) cells, and so on.

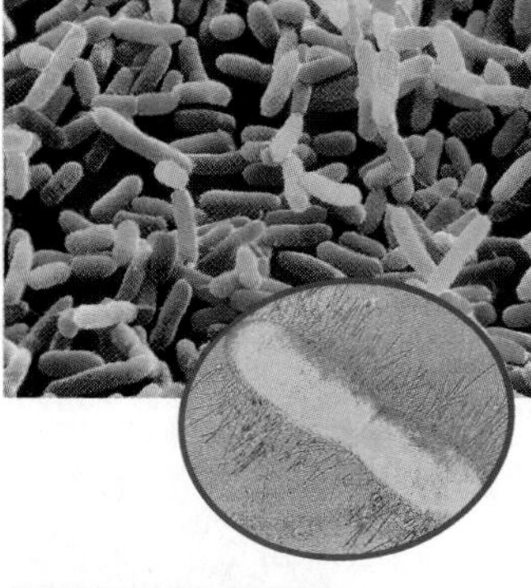
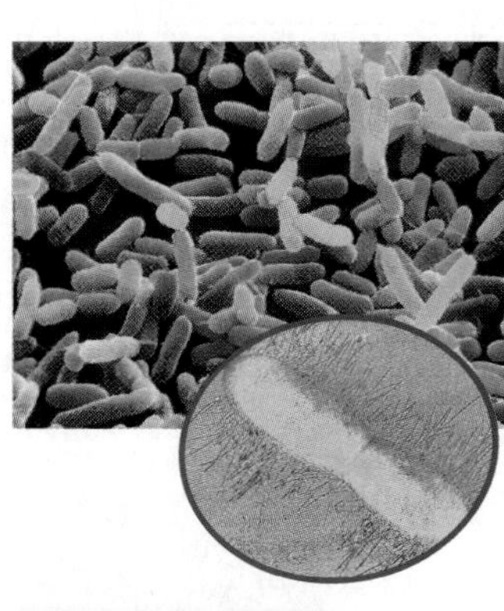

a. Use exponents to write the number of cells after each of the first 10 hours of the experiment.

b. Write an expression in exponential notation for the number of cells after 50 hours.

40. Number Sense Find each number.

GPS **a.** The number that equals 100 when it is squared 10

b. The number that equals 27 when it is cubed 3

41. Choose a Strategy What whole number, when raised to the fourth power, equals 1296? 6

Problem Solving STRATEGIES

- Look for a Pattern
- Make an Organized List
- Make a Table
- Guess and Check
- Work Backward
- Use Logical Reasoning
- Draw a Diagram
- Solve a Simpler Problem

Mixed Review

Multiply. *[Previous course]*

42. $2 \times 2 \times 2 \times 2$ 16 **43.** $3 \times 3 \times 3 \times 3$ 81

44. $4 \times 4 \times 4 \times 4$ 256 **45.** $2 \times 3 \times 2 \times 3$ 36

46. $2 \times 4 \times 2 \times 4$ 64 **47.** $3 \times 4 \times 3 \times 4$ 144

Add. *[Previous course]*

48. \$13,427.00 + \$46,212.00 \$59,639.00 **49.** \$7295.63 + \$1754.89 \$9050.52

50. \$824,788 + \$567,673 \$1,392,461 **51.** \$8,691,288 + \$7,643,841 \$16,335,129

52. \$372,150 + \$517,720 \$889,870 **53.** \$8,542,505 + \$3,276,023 \$11,818,528

Project Progress

Choose six different ways that you could travel. For example, one of them might be by bicycle. For each method, determine how far you could travel in one hour.

Problem Solving
Understand
Plan
Solve
Look Back

PROBLEM SOLVING

Name ____________

Guided Problem Solving 2-4

GPS **PROBLEM 40, STUDENT PAGE 82**

Find each number.

a. Find the number that equals 100 when it is squared.

b. Find the number that equals 27 when it is cubed.

— Understand —

1. Circle the information you need.
2. What does "squared" mean? A factor times itself.
3. What does "cubed" mean? A factor times itself times itself.

— Plan —

4. How can finding the factors of each number help you solve the problem? Possible answer: A factor squared or cubed may equal the number.
5. What are the factors of 100? 1, 2, 4, 5, 10, 20, 25, 50, 100
6. What are the factors of 27? 1, 3, 9, 27

— Solve —

7. Multiply each factor by itself the appropriate number of times. Which factor in Item 5 will equal 100 when squared? 10
8. Multiply each factor by itself the appropriate number of times. Which factor in Item 6 will equal 27 when cubed? 3

— Look Back —

9. Write a number sentence using exponents to show each answer. Possible answer: $100 = 10^2$; $27 = 3^3$.
10. How could you have found the answer using a different strategy? Possible answer: Guess and check using mental math.

SOLVE ANOTHER PROBLEM

Find each number.

a. Find the number which equals 225 when it is squared. 15

b. Find the number which equals 512 when it is cubed. 8

ENRICHMENT

Name ____________

Extend Your Thinking 2-4

Patterns in Numbers

You have learned that repeated multiplication can be represented using exponential notation. You may discover some interesting patterns when working with these numbers.

The table at the right shows powers of 2 from 2^1 to 2^{10} in exponential and standard forms.

Powers of 2	Powers of 3
$2^1 = 2$	$3^1 = 3$
$2^2 = 4$	$3^2 = 9$
$2^3 = 8$	$3^3 = 27$
$2^4 = 16$	$3^4 = 81$
$2^5 = 32$	$3^5 = 243$
$2^6 = 64$	$3^6 = 729$
$2^7 = 128$	$3^7 = 2187$
$2^8 = 256$	$3^8 = 6561$
$2^9 = 512$	$3^9 = 19{,}683$
$2^{10} = 1024$	$3^{10} = 59{,}049$

1. Describe the pattern in the table. Possible answer: Exponent increases by 1; value doubles. Ones digits: 2, 4, 8, 6, 2, 4, 8, 6 . . .
2. Continue the pattern. Write the next three numbers in exponential and standard forms. 2^{11}; 2048 2^{12}; 4096 2^{13}; 8192
3. Complete the chart above to represent the powers of 3 from 3^1 through 3^{10}. What patterns do you see in these numbers? Possible answer: Exponent increases by 1; number in standard form triples. Ones digits form pattern.
4. Are the patterns the same for the powers of 2 and 3? Why or why not? Possible answer: Yes. Exponent increases by 1; number in standard form increases by a factor equal to the base. Ones digits form pattern.
5. What do you think the pattern will be if the base is 8? Explain. Possible answer: Exponent increases by 1; number in standard form increases by a factor of 8. Ones digits form pattern. Patterns are similar to ones in Items 1 and 2.

Section 2A Connect

Our solar system has nine planets. As far as we know, the only planet in our solar system with intelligent life on it is Earth.

Planets are starting to be detected around other stars as well. One distant star known as PSR1257 + 12 is suspected of having planets orbiting it.

Greetings from Planet Earth

Current research indicates that there are two planets orbiting the star PSR1257 + 12. Let's call them Planet 1 and Planet 2.

The table gives the approximate distances of four of our planets from our sun, and of Planets 1 and 2 from PSR1257 + 12.

Distance from Local Star	
Planet	Distance (km)
Earth	148 million
Mars	228,260,860
Mercury	58,000,000
Venus	one hundred five million
Planet 1	52 million
Planet 2	eighty million

1. Suppose Planets 1 and 2 were in our solar system and the distances in the table were the distances from our sun. Make a sketch showing all six planets lined up beside our sun in their correct order. Label each planet with its name and its distance from the sun.
2. Make a list that states how far each planet is from Earth. (Assume that all of the planets are in a straight line.)
3. Make three lists of the distances from the sun from least to greatest. In the first list, round all the distances to the nearest million. In the second list, round to the nearest ten-million. In the third list, round to the nearest hundred-million. If you were writing a report about the planets, which list would you use? Why?
4. The farther from a star a planet is, the longer the planet takes to orbit the star. The orbital times in Earth days of the six planets listed in the table are approximately 5^4, 15^2, 3^4, 7^3, 8^2, and 10^2. Match each planet with the approximate time it takes to orbit its star.

83

Greeting from Planet Earth

The Point

In *Greetings from Planet Earth* on page 65, students discussed the technology and mathematics needed to study the universe. Now they will compare, order, and describe distances within the solar system.

About the Page

- Ask students to explain how they might determine the distance between the planets and the Sun.
- Remind students that it may be easier to compare and order numbers written in exponential notation if they first express the numbers in standard form.

Ongoing Assessment

In Question 1, check that students have correctly ordered the planets and written the numbers in standard form.

Extension

Have students express the approximate orbital times of the six planets on a bar graph. Remind them to label the axes.

Answers for Connect

1. Sketch should show the planets with these distances labeled and in this order from the Sun: Planet 1, 52,000,000; Mercury, 58,000,000; Planet 2, 80,000,000; Venus, 105,000,000; Earth, 148,000,000; Mars, 228,260,860.
2.

Planet	Distance from Earth
Planet 1	96,000,000
Mercury	90,000,000
Planet 2	68,000,000
Venus	43,000,000
Mars	80,260,860

3. To write a report, use the first list. It is the most accurate.

Planet	Distance from Sun
Planet 1	52,000,000
Mercury	58,000,000
Planet 2	80,000,000
Venus	105,000,000
Earth	148,000,000
Mars	228,000,000

Planet	Distance from Sun
Planet 1	50,000,000
Mercury	60,000,000
Planet 2	80,000,000
Venus	110,000,000
Earth	150,000,000
Mars	230,000,000

Planet	Distance from Sun
Planet 1	100,000,000
Mercury	100,000,000
Planet 2	100,000,000
Venus	100,000,000
Earth	200,000,000
Mars	200,000,000

4.

Planet	Orbital Time
Planet 1	8^2
Mercury	3^4
Planet 2	10^2
Venus	15^2
Earth	7^3
Mars	5^4

2A Review

Review Correlation

Item(s)	Lesson(s)
1–6	2-1, 2-2
7	2-1, 2-4
8	2-3
9	2-2
10–16	2-3
17	2-1
18, 19	2-4

Test Prep

Test-Taking Tip

Tell students they can use word association to help them remember some key words and properties in problems. In this problem, students can picture an ice cube, which has 3 dimensions, to help them remember that "cubing" means "3rd power."

Answers for Review

7. a. 864°F
   b. Possible answer: $2^5 \times 3^4$ is bigger. The difference between 3^4 and 3^3 is bigger than the difference between 2^6 and 2^5.
8. 7,310; 16,864; 18,510; 19,340; 20,320; 22,834; 29,028.
9. 7,000; 17,000; 19,000; 19,000; 20,000; 23,000; 29,000.
10. Possible answer: Ordering numbers and putting words in alphabetical order are similar in that both methods follow a certain pattern. They are different because numbers depend on place value but words do not.
17. Juanita is right. 1,000 thousand is 1,000,000 which is the same as 1 million.

Section 2A Review

REVIEW 2A

Write each number in standard form. Then round that number to the place indicated.

1. 4^2; tens **16; 20**
2. 5^3; tens **125; 130**
3. 10^5; hundred-thousands **100,000; 100,000**
4. 8^4; thousands **4096; 4000**
5. 9^2; hundreds **81; 100**
6. 16^5; ten-thousands **1,048,576; 1,050,000**
7. **Science** The Russian space probe *Venera* measured the surface temperature of Venus as $2^5 \times 3^3$ degrees Fahrenheit.
   a. Give the temperature in standard notation.
   b. Without calculating, decide which is greater, $2^6 \times 3^3$ or $2^5 \times 3^4$. Explain how you made your decision.

Venus

The table lists the highest points on the seven continents.

Continent	Elevation (ft)
Africa	19,340
Asia	29,028
Antarctica	16,864
Australia	7,310
Europe	18,510
North America	20,320
South America	22,834

8. Order the elevations from least to greatest.
9. Round the elevations to the nearest thousand.
10. Journal Compare ordering numbers to putting words in alphabetical order.

Compare, using $<$, $>$, or $=$.

11. 9 million $\boxed{=}$ 9,000,000
12. 2^5 $\boxed{>}$ 2×5
13. 50,999 $\boxed{<}$ 51,000
14. 2080 $\boxed{>}$ two thousand eight
15. 3^2 $\boxed{>}$ 2^3
16. 47,350 $\boxed{>}$ 4,735
17. **Communicate** Juanita says that 1000 thousand is the same as 1 million. Seth says that there is no such number as 1000 thousand. Who is right? Explain.

Test Prep

Find the area of a square by squaring the length of a side. Find the volume of a cube by cubing the length of a side.

18. Find the area of a square with a side of 5. **B**
    Ⓐ 10 Ⓑ 25 Ⓒ 32 Ⓓ 50
19. Find the volume of a cube with a side of 6. **C**
    Ⓐ 36 Ⓑ 64 Ⓒ 216 Ⓓ 729

Resources

Practice Masters
Section 2A Review

Assessment Sourcebook
Quiz 2A

TestWorks
Test and Practice Software

PRACTICE

Name ______________________

Practice

Section 2A Review

Write each number in standard form. Then round that number to the place indicated.

1. 3^4; tens
   standard form **81**
   rounded **80**
2. 7^5; thousands
   standard form **16,807**
   rounded **17,000**
3. 5^4; hundreds
   standard form **625**
   rounded **600**

The table lists the 1990 populations of several American cities.

City	Population
Detroit, MI	1,027,974
St. Louis, MO	396,685
Cleveland, OH	505,616
Chattanooga, TN	152,466
Pittsburgh, PA	369,879

4. Order the populations from least to greatest.
   152,466; 369,879; 396,685; 505,616; 1,027,974
5. Round each population to the nearest ten-thousand.
   150,000; 370,000; 400,000; 510,000; 1,030,000

Compare using $<$, $>$, or $=$.

6. 37,990 $\bigcirc\!\!<$ 38,000
7. 4^5 $\bigcirc\!\!>$ 5^4
8. 630,000 $\bigcirc\!\!>$ six thousand, thirty
9. 8,000,000,000 $\bigcirc\!\!<$ 8 trillion
10. 7×3 $\bigcirc\!\!<$ 7^3
11. 6580 $\bigcirc\!\!<$ 64,800
12. The scatterplot shows the number of dogs and cats in several pet stores. *[Lesson 1-3]*
    a. Which point represents the store with the most dogs? **C**
    How many dogs does this store have? **16**
    b. Which two points represent stores with the same number of cats? **D and F**
    How many cats does each of these stores have? **15**

Section 2B

Number Sense and Operation Sense

Visit www.teacher.mathsurf.com for links to lesson plans from teachers and other professionals, NCTM information, and other sites.

LESSON PLANNING GUIDE

Student Edition / Ancillaries*

LESSON		MATERIALS	VOCABULARY	DAILY	OTHER
	Section 2B Opener				
2–5	**Mental Math**		Distributive Property	2-5	
2–6	**Estimating Sums and Differences**			2-6	Lesson Enhancement Trans. 7
2–7	**Estimating Products and Quotients**			2-7	Teaching Tool Trans. 2, 3
2–8	**Order of Operations**		order of operations	2-8	Technology Master 8 Ch. 2 Project Master
2–9	**Numerical Patterns**	hundred chart, colored pencils or markers		2-9	Teaching Tool Trans. 13
	Connect				Interdisc. Team Teaching 2B
	Review				Practice 2B; Quiz 2B; *TestWorks*

* Daily Ancillaries include Practice, Reteaching, Problem Solving, Enrichment, and Daily Transparency. Teaching Tool Transparencies are in *Teacher's Toolkits*. Lesson Enhancement Transparencies are in *Overhead Transparency Package*.

SKILLS TRACE

LESSON	SKILL	FIRST INTRODUCED GR. 4	GR. 5	GR. 6	DEVELOP	PRACTICE/ APPLY	REVIEW
2–5	Computing mentally.	✘			pp. 86–87	pp. 88–89	pp. 106, 108, 131, 306
2–6	Estimating sums and differences.	✘			pp. 90–91	pp. 92–93	pp. 113, 131, 249
2–7	Estimating products and quotients.	✘			pp. 94–95	pp. 96–97	pp. 117, 131, 253
2–8	Using order of operations.			✘ p. 98	pp. 98–99	pp. 100–101	pp. 131, 184, 258
2–9	Identifying number patterns.	✘			pp. 102–104	pp. 105–106	pp. 131, 189, 327

CONNECTED MATHEMATICS

The unit *Prime Time (Factors and Multiples)*, from the **Connected Mathematics** series, can be used with Section 2B.

INTERDISCIPLINARY TEAM TEACHING

Math and Literatuare

(Worksheet pages 9–10: Teacher pages T9–T10)

In this lesson, students use number sense and operation sense in literature.

Name ________________ *Math and Literature*

"The Gold Bug"

Use number sense and operation sense in literature.

American writer Edgar Allan Poe (1809–1849) wrote poetry and short stories, some of which included fascinating mathematical puzzles. For example, in "The Pit and the Pendulum," a frightening story of torture and cruelty, the main character is a prisoner who has been tied to a wood framework below a swinging, razor-sharp pendulum. With each passing of the pendulum over the prisoner's midsection, the blade drops a little lower. The prisoner mentally calculates the amount of each drop and the amount of time he has before the pendulum slices into his skin.

In another of Poe's stories, "The Gold Bug," Poe writes about a man who is trying to find a buried treasure. To find the treasure, the man must figure out a coded message. As he does so, he discovers that he must tie a string to a gold bug (a large, dead, gold-colored beetle) and drop it through the eye of a human skull, which is nailed high on a tree. Where the bug lands is the spot where the treasure is buried.

Finally, as the man gazes at the treasure of gold and jewels, Poe has him do some mental math and estimation to determine the value of his treasure.

Among the contents of the treasure chest are the following items. Use this list to help you answer the questions that follow.

- gold coins
- 110 diamonds
- 18 rubies
- 310 emeralds
- 21 sapphires
- 1 opal
- various gold settings out of which the precious stones had fallen
- approximately 200 solid gold rings and earrings
- 30 solid gold chains
- 5 solid gold containers in which incense is burned
- an immense solid gold punch bowl
- 197 richly jeweled gold watches
- 83 religious gold ornaments

1. The main character estimates the value of three of the watches at $500 each. Use mental math to calculate the total value of the three watches.

Students should mentally perform the following operation: 3 × $500 = $1500.

2. a. The main character estimates the total value of the treasure at $1,500,000. What do you think the treasure would be worth today? ("The Gold Bug" was written in 1843. Assume that since then, the value of gold and jewels has increased 15–20 times.)

Based on the information provided, students should estimate the current value at between $22,500,000 and $30,000,000.

Name ________________ *Math and Literature*

b. The main character also estimates that there are 350 pounds of treasure, not counting the gold watches. Assume that every gold piece is solid gold. Also assume that the weight of the precious gems is five pounds. What would be the total value of the treasure's gold pieces today? (Hint: You can find the current value of gold in a newspaper's business pages or on the Internet. It will be listed as dollars per ounce. Remember, there are 16 ounces in a pound.) Set up and solve an equation that includes all necessary operations.

345 pounds of solid gold × 16 oz/pound × value of gold in $/oz

3. Imagine that you have located a treasure chest full of solid gold coins, silver coins, and copper coins. Each coin weighs one ounce. Complete the following chart to calculate the value of your treasure. The chart has been completed for gold. What is the total value of your treasure?

$181,885

4. Of what value are math skills to a writer?

There will be many situations in which math skills will come in handy when writers are explaining a sequence of events or describing such things as dimensions, distances, shapes, and the like.

5. List and briefly describe any books or short stories you have read, or movies you have seen, in which math played a role.

Students should indicate whether math is integral or incidental to the story.

6. Although "The Gold Bug" was written more than 150 years ago, it is a story that people still enjoy reading. Get a copy of "The Gold Bug" and read it. On a separate sheet of paper explain why you think the story is still interesting to read.

See below.

Type of Coins	Number of Coins	Approximate Current Value of Metal	Equation	Total Value of Coins
gold	456	$390/ounce	456 × $390	$177,840
silver	789	$5/ounce	789 × $5	$3945
copper	1600	$1/pound	(1600÷16) × $1	$100

Answers

6. Answers will vary. Students might say that stories about finding treasures have always been exciting because people living at all times have dreamed of easy riches.

BIBLIOGRAPHY

FOR TEACHERS

The Reader's Digest Illustrated Book of Dogs. Pleasantville, NY: Reader's Digest Association, 1993.

Discovery Box Series: Planets. New York, NY: Scholastic, 1996.

Mount, Ellis and List, Barbara A. *Milestones in Science and Technology.* Phoenix, AZ: Oryx Press, 1994.

Spangler, David. *Math for Real Kids.* Glenview, IL: Good Year Books, 1997.

FOR STUDENTS

Patneaude, David. *The Last Man's Reward.* Bloomington, IL: Library Book Selection Service, 1996.

SECTION 2B

Number Sense and Operation Sense

▶ Consumer Link ▶ www.mathsurf.com/6/ch2/collection

First Class Collectibles

One hundred years ago, a boy received a letter with a 50¢ stamp on it. He threw away the envelope, but saved the letter to give to his grandchildren.

One hundred years ago, a boy received a letter and $500. He threw away the $500, but saved the letter to give to his grandchildren.

As strange as it may sound, the two stories above are the exact same story. If someone in 1898 saved a 50¢ Trans-Mississippi stamp, his or her grandchildren could sell it today for over $500. This may sound like a lot of money, but to someone who collects stamps, it might be worth it.

People collect all sorts of things, from autographs to automobiles. A good collector uses several skills when trying to assemble the best possible collection for the least amount of money. One of the most important skills to have is a good understanding of mathematics.

1. Why are some items in a collection more expensive than others?

2. How does having a good understanding of mathematics help you build a collection for the least amount of money?

85

Section 2B

Theme: Collections

World Wide Web

If your class has access to the World Wide Web, you might want to use the activities found at the Web site address given. The interdisciplinary link relates to topics discussed in this section.

About the Page

This page introduces the theme of the section, collections, and discusses the value of old stamps and letters.

Ask ...

- What kinds of things do people collect?
- How is a value placed on an autograph, a stamp, or a baseball card?
- Are there things we are using today that you think might become collectible?

Extension

The following activity does not require access to the World Wide Web.

Consumer
Interested students can visit their local post office to get information about stamp collecting. A free catalogue of philatelic products can be obtained from: Philatelic Fulfillment Service Center, U.S. Postal Service, PO Box 449997, Kansas City MO 64144-9997.

Answers for Questions

1. Possible answers: An old item in good condition is usually more valuable.
2. Possible answers: Mathematics can help you find or make good deals on buying or selling pieces of a collection.

Connect

On page 107, students will write math problems that apply estimation techniques and the Distributive Property.

Where are we now?

In Section 2A, students learned to round, compare, and order large numbers and to write numbers with exponents.

They learned how to

- read and write large numbers.
- round numbers in real-life situations.
- compare and order large numbers.
- use exponents to express numbers and write expressions containing exponents in standard form.

Where are we going?

In Section 2B, students will

- solve problems mentally.
- estimate sums and differences.
- estimate products and quotients.
- apply the order of operations when solving problems.

Lesson Organizer

Objective

- Simplify problems mentally using patterns, the Distributive Property, compatible numbers, and compensation.

Vocabulary

- Distributive Property

NCTM Standards

- 1–4, 7, 8, 10

2-5 Mental Math

You'll Learn ...

- to simplify problems mentally using patterns, the Distributive Property, compatible numbers, and compensation

... How It's Used

Waiters and waitresses use mental math to verify that the bills they give to their customers are correct.

Vocabulary

Distributive Property

▶ Lesson Link You've learned many ways to deal with one number, including rounding, graphing, and writing with exponents. Now you will learn some methods for operating on two or more numbers mentally. ◀

Explore Mental Math

Stamp of Excellence!

During the annual Carson Stamp Convention, the sponsors ran a contest. Each participant had to simplify the ten math problems below without using paper and pencil or a calculator. The top scorer won a collectible Vietnamese chameleon stamp.

a. 60×100 **b.** 37×16 **c.** $25 + 16 + 75$ **d.** $381 + 99$ **e.** $315 \div 12$

f. 19×4 **g.** $1200 \div 4$ **h.** $4 \times 25 \times 7$ **i.** 21×5 **j.** $498 + 795$

1. Which problems do you think nearly all your classmates could simplify correctly in their heads? Which could almost no one simplify correctly? Explain.
2. Rank the problems in order of difficulty, from easiest to hardest.
3. Explain how you would simplify the three easiest problems in your head.
4. For each of the three problems you chose, write a similar problem that could be simplified mentally using the same method. Trade problems with a partner and simplify each other's problems mentally.

Learn Mental Math

It is often convenient to simplify math problems mentally. Here are several mental math techniques that are especially useful.

Compatible Numbers Compatible numbers are pairs of numbers that can be computed easily. Combine compatible numbers, and then combine what remains.

▶ Review

Find the number(s) that fit all the clues.

- The number has 5 digits.
- The number rounds to 12,000.
- The sum of the first and last digits is 8.
- Every digit is different.
- The product of the second and fourth digits is 12.

12,367 or 12,467

Available on Daily Transparency 2-5

1 Introduce

Explore

The Point
Students explore strategies for doing arithmetic mentally by choosing arithmetic problems that most of their classmates could simplify correctly.

Ongoing Assessment
If students have trouble ordering the problems from easiest to hardest, suggest that they sort the problems into three groups—easy, medium, and hard.

For Groups That Finish Early
Find ways to do the more difficult problems in your heads. Share your ideas with your group.

MEETING INDIVIDUAL NEEDS

Resources

- **2-5** Practice
- **2-5** Reteaching
- **2-5** Problem Solving
- **2-5** Enrichment
- **2-5** Daily Transparency
  - Problem of the Day
  - Review
  - Quick Quiz

Learning Modalities

Visual Have students make a poster with a diagram that illustrates the use of the Distributive Property in finding products.

Social Have students work in groups of three or four simplifying problems while identifying and discussing the mental math strategies that they are using.

English Language Development

Discuss how the names of the mental math strategies are derived from their everyday meanings. Ask students to describe pairs of things that are compatible (things that go together) or situations that involve compensation (trading).

Students may need assistance with spelling and vocabulary. Assess their journals for content rather than language.

Patterns When multiplying numbers that end in zeros, multiply the non-zero parts and annex one zero to your answer for each zero in the problem. When dividing numbers that end in zeros, subtract the number of zeros in the divisor from the number of zeros in the dividend to find the number in the quotient.

Compensation Choose a number close to the number in the problem. Then adjust the answer to compensate for the number you chose.

The Distributive Property Break numbers into smaller numbers. Calculate using the smaller numbers, and then put your answers together.

Remember

The *Commutative Property* states that changing the order of addends or factors does not change the sum or product. For example, $4 \times 7 = 28$, and $7 \times 4 = 28$. **[Previous course]**

Examples

Simplify.

1 20×700

Use patterns:

$2 \times 7 = 14$

1 zero + 2 zeros = 3 zeros

$20 \times 700 = 14{,}000$

2 $5{,}400{,}000 \div 90$

Use patterns:

$54 \div 9 = 6$

5 zeros − 1 zero = 4 zeros

$5{,}400{,}000 \div 90 = 60{,}000$

3 $25 + 18 + 75$

25 and 75 are compatible because they are easy to add.

$25 + 18 + 75 = (25 + 75) + 18$

$= 100 + 18 = 118$

4 58×3

Since 58 is close to 60, you can use compensation:

$58 \times 3 = 60 \times 3$ (minus 2×3)

$= 180 - 6 = 174$

Remember

The *Associative Property* states that changing the grouping of addends or factors does not change the sum or product. For example, $(5 + 3) + 7 = 15$, and $5 + (3 + 7) = 15$. **[Previous course]**

5 A collector offered to sell five World's Fair posters at $32 apiece. Use the Distributive Property to find the total cost.

$32 \times 5 = (30 + 2) \times 5$ Break 32 into 30 + 2.

$= (30 \times 5) + (2 \times 5)$ Multiply each piece by 5.

$= (150) + (10) = 160$ Add the pieces together.

Try It

Simplify.

a. 4000×300 **1,200,000** **b.** $210{,}000 \div 700$ **300** **c.** 61×3 **183** **d.** $285 + 47 + 15$ **347**

e. $50 \times 2 \times 13$ **1300** **f.** $296 + 55$ **351** **g.** 29×6 **174** **h.** 102×7 **714**

MATH EVERY DAY

Problem of the Day

What three pennies can you move in the first group to make it like the group on the right?

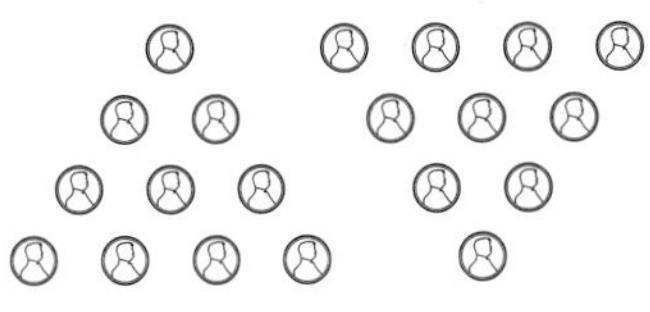

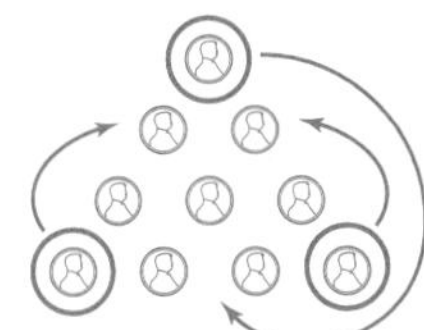

Available on Daily Transparency 2-5

An Extension is provided in the transparency package.

Fact of the Day

The earliest modern comic, "The Yellow Kid," appeared in 1896. The dialog was first printed inside a comic's frame.

Estimation

Estimate each sum.

1. $261 + 232$ 500
2. $638 + 712 + 584$ 1900
3. $29 + 29 + 29 + 29$ 120

Answers for Explore

1. Classmates could solve a, c, d, f, g, h, i, and j because the numbers are easy to add, subtract, multiply, or divide; b and e are harder because there doesn't seem to be any connection between the numbers.
2. Possible answer: a, c, g, d, h, i, j, b, e.
3. Possible answer: a: $6 \times 1 = 6$, so $60 \times 100 = 6000$; c: 3: Add 25 and 75 first to get 100 and then add 16; g: $12 \div 4$ is 3, so $1200 \div 4$ is 300.
4. Possible answer: a: 400×100; c: $50 + 32 + 50$; g: $600 \div 3$.

2 Teach

Learn

Alternate Examples

Simplify.

1. 300×50

   Use patterns: $3 \times 5 = 15$
   2 zeros + 1 zero = 3 zeros
   $300 \times 50 = 15{,}000$

2. $42{,}000 \div 700$

   Use patterns: $42 \div 7 = 6$
   3 zeros − 2 zeros = 1 zero
   $42{,}000 \div 700 = 60$

3. $30 + 58 + 70$

   30 and 70 are compatible because they are easy to add.

   $30 + 58 + 70 = (30 + 70) + 58$
   $= 100 + 58$
   $= 158$

4. 49×4

   Since 49 is close to 50, you can use compensation.

   $49 \times 4 = 50 \times 4$ (minus 1×4)
   $= 200 - 4$
   $= 196$

5. A collector offered to buy 6 Olympic pins at $43 each. Use the Distributive Property to find the total cost.

   $43 \times 6 = (40 + 3) \times 6$
   Break 43 into 40 + 3.

   $(40 \times 6) + (3 \times 6)$
   Multiply each piece by 6.

   $(240) + (18) = 258$
   Add the pieces together.

2-5 Exercises and Applications

Assignment Guide

- Basic
  1–20, 43–48, 51, 52–66 evens
- Average
  10–30, 42–51, 52–66 evens
- Enriched
  20–51, 53–65 odds

3 Practice and Assess

Check

Answers for Check Your Understanding

1. Some compatible numbers for addition are 25 and 75, 50 and 50, 60 and 40, 25 and 25; Some compatible numbers for multiplication are 10, 100, 1000, etc.
2. Possible Answer: So you can solve a problem quickly, or when you don't have access to paper, pencil, or a calculator.

Exercise Answers

1. c. 2,400,000 d. 24,000,000

16. 1119

23. 35,000

25. 7,200,000

26. 1336

30. 180,000

34. 3,600,000

40. 600,000,000

Reteaching

Activity

Materials: Index cards

- Work in groups of three or four. On index cards, write ten problems, using each mental math strategy at least once.
- Exchange problems with another group.
- Have one student draw a card. If the correct answer is given in ten seconds, then he or she keeps the card. If not, then the first player to answer correctly wins the card.
- The player with the most cards at the end wins.

Check Your Understanding

1. Compatible numbers are numbers that are easy to add or multiply together. What are some pairs of compatible numbers for addition? For multiplication?
2. Why is it useful to be able to do arithmetic in your head?

2-5 Exercises and Applications

PRACTICE 2-5

Practice and Apply

1. **Getting Started** Use patterns to simplify each problem.

   a. 60 × 4 240 b. 600 × 40 24,000 c. 6,000 × 400 d. 6,000 × 4,000
   e. 210 ÷ 3 70 f. 2,100 ÷ 30 70 g. 2,100 ÷ 300 7 h. 21,000 ÷ 3,000 7

Simplify.

2. 40 × 20 800
3. 251 + 314 565
4. 96 + 117 213
5. 4 × 11 × 25 1100
6. 24 × 2 48
7. 240 ÷ 6 40
8. 25 + 23 + 75 123
9. 49 × 3 147
10. 198 + 123 321
11. 2,500 ÷ 50 50
12. 68 + 31 99
13. 50 × 2 × 9 900
14. 30 × 600 18,000
15. 31 × 4 124
16. 750 + 119 + 250
17. 99 × 7 693
18. 53 × 3 159
19. 89 × 6 534
20. 819 + 120 939
21. 700 × 5 3500
22. 147 − 99 48
23. 250 × 4 × 35
24. 90 + 57 + 10 157
25. 9,000 × 800
26. 800 + 336 + 200
27. 58 × 5 290
28. 560,000 ÷ 80 7,000
29. 2,645 + 213 2858
30. 5,000 × 18 × 2
31. 461 − 295 166
32. 112 × 4 448
33. 1,800,000 ÷ 9,000 200
34. 12,000 × 300
35. 42 × 8 336
36. 79 + 98 + 3 180
37. 550 − 25 525
38. 22 + 88 110
39. 84 − 34 50
40. 1,200,000 × 500
41. 29 × 6 174
42. Marcie bought a movie poster for $4.45 plus $0.34 sales tax. Find the total cost of the poster. $4.79
43. GPS At the Metropolitan Coin Fair, Robbie sold 99 coins from his collection of 876. How many coins did he have left? 777
44. **Science** The moon is about 240,000 miles from Earth. How long would it take you to fly to the moon at a speed of 40,000 miles per day? 6 days

PRACTICE

Name ______________ **Practice 2-5**

Mental Math

Simplify.

1. 60 × 70 4,200
2. 162 + 37 199
3. 142 + 321 463
4. 2 × 21 × 5 210
5. 3 × 81 243
6. 2,700 ÷ 9 300
7. 162 + 17 + 38 217
8. 38 × 7 266
9. 295 + 85 380
10. 28,000 ÷ 700 40
11. 37 + 42 79
12. 20 × 50 × 37 37,000
13. 100 × 300 30,000
14. 62 × 5 310
15. 875 + 627 + 125 1,627
16. 42 × 9 378
17. 79 × 4 316
18. 164 + 135 299
19. 8 × 1,200 9,600
20. 173 − 98 75
21. 25 × 40 × 17 17,000
22. 38 + 87 + 62 187
23. 70 × 3,000 210,000
24. 600 + 327 + 400 1,327
25. 87 × 4 348
26. 3,800 ÷ 20 190
27. 3,143 + 222 3,365
28. 300 × 160 48,000
29. 20 × 21 × 50 21,000
30. 387 − 295 92
31. 213 × 2 426
32. 63,000 ÷ 700 90
33. 750,000 ÷ 2,500 300
34. 64 + 46 110
35. 12,387 − 4,387 8,000
36. 38,000 ÷ 190 200
37. 52 × 40 2,080
38. 39 × 90 3,510
39. 5 × 37 × 200 37,000
40. 6,700 + 1,200 7,900
41. 8,416 − 8,116 300
42. 83,725 − 300 83,425
43. 389 + 711 1,100
44. 100,000 ÷ 40 2,500
45. 320,000 ÷ 400 800
46. 310 × 40 12,400
47. 56,000 ÷ 800 70
48. 185 + 32 217
49. 90,000 ÷ 300 300
50. 520,000 ÷ 130 4,000
51. 2,587 − 198 2,389
52. 64,107 − 304 63,803
53. 2,200 × 30 66,000
54. 63,000 ÷ 90 700
55. It takes 300 gallons of water to produce one pound of synthetic rubber. How many gallons of water does it take to produce 8 pounds of synthetic rubber? 2,400 gallons
56. A typical box of personal bank checks contains 200 checks which have been assembled in 8 booklets. How many checks are in each booklet? 25 checks

RETEACHING

Name ______________ **Alternative Lesson 2-5**

Mental Math

It is often convenient to simplify math problems mentally. There are several mental math techniques that are especially useful.

Example 1

Use compensation to simplify.

a. 74 × 4

74 is close to 70.

74 × 4 = 70 × 4 (plus 4 × 4)
= 280 + 16 = 296

74 × 4 = 296

b. 98 + 30

98 is close to 100.

98 + 30 = 100 + 30 (minus 2)
= 130 − 2 = 128

98 + 30 = 128

Try It Use compensation to simplify.

a. 22 × 9 198 b. 48 × 5 240
c. 17 + 6 23 d. 33 − 5 28
e. 108 × 8 864 f. 152 + 25 177

Example 2

Use the Distributive Property to simplify 85 × 7.

Break 85 into 80 + 5.
Multiply each piece by 7. Find 80 x 7 and 5 x 7.
Add the pieces together.

85 × 7 = (80 + 5) × 7
= (80 × 7) + (5 × 7)
= (560) + (35)
= 595

85 × 7 = (80 + 5) × 7 = 595

Try It Use the Distributive Property to simplify.

g. 56 × 8 448 h. 4 × 104 416
i. 5 × 45 225 j. 9 × 42 378
k. 7 × 64 448 l. 3 × 55 165

45. Craig earns $5 per hour at his after-school job. One week he worked 21 hours. Find his total earnings for the week. $105

Use the bar graph to answer each question.

46. How many yards did Marcus swim? 300

47. How much farther did he swim in freestyle than butterfly? 50 yards

48. **Test Prep** Simplify 48×6. C

Ⓐ 24 Ⓑ 72

Ⓒ 288 Ⓓ 300

Marcus's Swimming Record

Distance (yd): 0, 25, 50, 75, 100, 125

Butterfly, Freestyle, Backstroke, Breaststroke

Problem Solving and Reasoning

49. Journal Explain the difference between using compatible numbers and compensation. Give examples to illustrate your answer.

50. **Communicate** Which problem is easier to simplify with mental math, $20 \times 19 \times 5$ or $20 \times 19 \times 6$? Explain your reasoning.

51. **Critical Thinking** Janet has $13.64, and she wants to buy a board game for $15.84. How much more money does she need? If the game goes on sale for $2.00 less, will she have enough money? $2.20; No

Mixed Review

Write in standard form. *[Lesson 2-1]*

52. six hundred forty-eight million, two hundred twenty-eight thousand, nine hundred seventy-three 648,228,973

53. three hundred thirty-five million, seven hundred twenty-eight thousand, six hundred forty-two 335,728,642

Write in words. *[Lesson 2-1]*

54. 467,987,382 55. 5,976,321,401 56. 5983 57. 3,093,002

Subtract. *[Previous course]*

58. 412 − 176 236 59. 91,233 − 17,974 73,259 60. 845,213 − 685,787 159,426

61. 6,329,432 − 3,654,987 2,674,445 62. 54,987 − 3,283 51,704 63. 94,040 − 32,804 61,236

64. 4,931,515 − 34,687 4,896,828 65. 7,237,802 − 5,091,465 2,146,337 66. 111,996 − 22,197 89,799

PROBLEM SOLVING 2-5

PROBLEM SOLVING

Name ______ **Guided Problem Solving 2-5**

GPS PROBLEM 43, STUDENT PAGE 88

At the Metropolitan Coin Fair, Robbie sold 99 coins from his collection of 876. How many coins did he have left?

Understand

1. What are you asked to find? Number of coins Robbie has left.

Plan

2. What operation will you use to find the answer? Subtraction.
3. Which method could be used to solve the problem using mental math? a

a. compensation b. compatible numbers c. Distributive Property

4. Why did you choose that method? Possible answer: 99 is close to 100. It is easy to subtract 100 from 876, add 1 to the difference.
5. Which of the following is a good estimate of the answer? b

a. about 900 b. about 800 c. about 700

Solve

6. Write a number sentence to show the total number of coins in Robbie's collection. 876 − 99 = 777
7. How many coins did Robbie have left? 777 coins

Look Back

8. How else could you have used compensation to find the answer? Possible answer: 875 − 100 + 2 = 777.
9. How can you check your answer? Possible answer: Add the answer and 99. Sum should be 876.

SOLVE ANOTHER PROBLEM

Joanna has a collection of 145 toys from fast-food children's meals. She gave 27 toys to her sister. How many does she have now? 118 toys.

ENRICHMENT

Name ______ **Extend Your Thinking 2-5**

Critical Thinking

When you add the numbers in each row, each column, and each diagonal of a magic square, the sum is the same.

8	9	13
15	10	5
7	11	12

Magic sum: 30

1. Use your mental math skills to complete these magic squares. Write the magic sum.

a.

15	31	17
23	21	19
25	11	27

Magic sum: 63

b.

2	9	7
11	6	1
5	3	10

Magic sum: 18

2. Use your math skills to create a magic square using the numbers 1–9.

2	7	6
9	5	1
4	3	8

Magic sum: 15

3. The product of this magic square is the same when you multiply each row, each column, and each diagonal. Complete the magic square.

12	1	18
9	6	4
2	36	3

Magic product: 216

Exercise Notes

Exercise 49

Problem-Solving Tip Encourage students to identify which mental math strategy they are using in simplifying a problem. They may realize that they favor one strategy over another.

Exercises 58–66

Estimation Have students estimate the difference and then use a calculator to actually compute the difference.

Exercise Answers

49. Possible answer: Using compatible numbers means the numbers already add, subtract, multiply, or divide together easily, like 125 + 375. Using compensation means using compatible numbers that are close to the actual numbers, like 99 + 101, and then adjusting the answer.

50. $20 \times 19 \times 5$ is easier because 20 and 5 are compatible numbers.

54. Four hundred sixty-seven million, nine hundred eighty-seven thousand, three hundred eighty-two

55. Five billion, nine hundred seventy-six million, three hundred twenty-one thousand, four hundred one

56. Five thousand, nine hundred eighty-three

57. Three million, ninety-three thousand, two

Alternate Assessment

Your may want to use the *Interactive CD-ROM Journal* with this assessment.

Journal Have students write about their favorite mental math strategy. They should explain why they like to use the strategy, as well as give examples.

Quick Quiz

Do these mentally.

1. 40,000 ÷ 80 500
2. 250 + 565 + 750 1565
3. 267 − 199 68
4. 33×7 231

Available on Daily Transparency 2-5

2-6
Lesson Organizer

Objective

- Estimate sums and differences using front-end estimation and clustering.

NCTM Standards

- 1–4, 6

Review

1. 35 + 78 113
2. 241 + 378 619
3. 902 − 345 557
4. 554 − 398 156
5. Which problems can you do mentally? Answers may vary.

Available on Daily Transparency 2-6

1 Introduce

Explore

You may wish to use Lesson Enhancement Transparency 7 with this lesson.

The Point
Students invent estimation strategies to find a set of four different pennies with a total cost as close as possible to $30 without going over.

Ongoing Assessment
Some students may try to solve the problem using exact numbers. Encourage them to use estimation to select coins.

For Groups That Finish Early
Find other sets of coins with a total cost close to $30.

2-6 Estimating Sums and Differences

You'll Learn ...

- to estimate sums and differences using front-end estimation and clustering

... How It's Used

While working on a project, painters often estimate results to gauge their progress.

Lesson Link You've learned to use mental math to find exact answers. In this lesson, you'll learn to estimate answers to addition and subtraction problems when you don't need exact answers. ◄

Explore Estimating Sums and Differences

A Penny for Your Thoughts

The table gives prices of 1913 Lincoln-head pennies from three mints in five different qualities. Prices are in dollars.

Mint	Good	Very Good	Fine	Very Fine	Extremely Fine
Denver	0.85	1.95	3.79	8.30	16.75
Philadelphia	0.49	0.65	1.19	2.75	9.20
San Francisco	5.15	6.65	7.45	11.19	24.95

1. Without using a calculator, try to find a set of four different pennies with a total cost that is as close to $30 as possible without going over $30. Keep trying until you find a set of four as close to $30 as possible.
2. Estimate how close your total is to $30. Explain how you made your estimates.
3. Find the total cost of your four pennies exactly. Compare your results with those of other students.
4. If you round two prices to estimate their sum, how can you be sure that your estimate does not exceed the actual sum?
5. Without using a calculator, how can you tell that the combined cost of the Denver and the San Francisco pennies in fine condition is greater than $11?

DID YOU KNOW?

The most valuable Lincoln-head penny was minted in 1909 in San Francisco. This penny has the initials VDB, which stand for its designer Victor D. Brenner. Today, a Brenner penny in perfect condition is worth about $750.

MEETING INDIVIDUAL NEEDS

Resources

- **2-6** Practice
- **2-6** Reteaching
- **2-6** Problem Solving
- **2-6** Enrichment
- **2-6** Daily Transparency
  - Problem of the Day
  - Review
  - Quick Quiz
- Lesson Enhancement Transparency 7

Learning Modalities

Verbal Ask students to describe situations in which they would want estimates to be low or high. For example, an engineer estimating how much weight a bridge can carry would want to use a low estimate.

Visual Draw an arrangement of dots such as the one shown and ask students to estimate the number of dots. Ask students whether their estimate is high or low and how they know.

• • • • • •
• • • • • •
• • • •
• • • •

Inclusion

Students may have difficulty learning two methods of estimation at once. Focus on one method at a time. After they have mastered one estimating skill, they might go on to learn another. Helping students acquire at least one functional estimation method will improve their problem-solving abilities.

Learn Estimating Sums and Differences

When you don't need an exact answer to a problem, you can estimate. When using *front-end estimation,* add or subtract using only the first digit of each number. Estimate the sum or difference of the remaining digits and add this to the first estimate. For a more accurate estimate, calculate using the first *two* digits.

Examples

1 Estimate 982 − 539 using one-digit front-end estimation.

$$\begin{array}{r} 982 \\ -\ 539 \\ \hline 400 \\ +\ 40 \\ \hline 440 \end{array}$$

Subtract the first digit in each number.
Add 40 because 82 − 39 is about 40.

2 Estimate using the first two digits: 23,745 + 54,881

$$\begin{array}{r} 23{,}745 \\ +\ 54{,}881 \\ \hline 77{,}000 \\ +\ 1{,}600 \\ \hline 78{,}600 \end{array}$$

Add the first two digits in each number.
Add 1,600 because 745 + 881 is about 1,600.

When adding several numbers that are approximately equal, use *clustering* to estimate the sum. Replace all of the numbers with a single number close to them that is easy to multiply. Then multiply.

Example 3

A scientist measured four strides of a dinosaur. Estimate the combined length of the four strides.

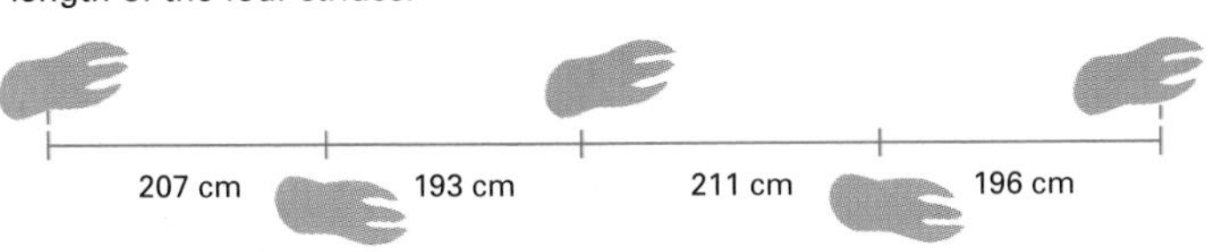

Each distance is approximately 200 cm.

200 + 200 + 200 + 200 = 4 × 200 = 800

The dinosaur walked about 800 cm.

MENTAL MATH

When you add a group of equal numbers, you can use multiplication as a shortcut.

Try It Possible answers are given.

Estimate. **a.** 773 + 848 **1600** **b.** 6707 − 4559 **2000** **c.** 307 + 297 + 299 **900**

MATH EVERY DAY

Problem of the Day

Cara was arranging a window display of books at the mall. She put 1 book in the first row, 4 books in the second row, 7 books in the third row, and so on. How many books did she put in the seventh row? 19 books

Available on Daily Transparency 2-6

An Extension is provided in the transparency package.

Mental Math

Do these mentally.

1. 50 + 20 + 80 + 49 + 50 249
2. 328 − 199 129
3. 60 × 700 42,000
4. 42 × 3 126

Answers for Explore

1. A Philadelphia Extremely Fine, a Denver Very Fine, a San Francisco Very Fine, and a Philadelphia Fine.
2. Almost $30 as $9.20 + $8.30 = $17.50, $1.19 + $11.19 is about $12.50, and $17.50 + $12.50 = $30.
3. $29.88
4. If you round both of the numbers to be smaller than they are, then the estimate cannot be bigger than the actual sum.
5. Since $3 + $7 = 10 and $0.79 + $0.45 is over $1, the sum must be over $11.

2 Teach

Learn

Alternate Examples

1. Estimate 876 − 453 using one-digit front-end estimation.

$$\begin{array}{r} 876 \\ -\ 453 \\ \hline 400 \\ +\ 20 \\ \hline 420 \end{array}$$

Subtract the first digit.
76 − 53 is about 20.

2. Estimate using the first two digits: 43,257 + 52,913

$$\begin{array}{r} 43{,}257 \\ +\ 52{,}913 \\ \hline 95{,}000 \\ +\ 1{,}200 \\ \hline 96{,}200 \end{array}$$

Add the first 2 digits.
257 + 913 is about 1200.

3. Alice needed to know about how many newspapers were distributed to the middle school. Here are the enrollments: Grade 6, 444; Grade 7, 465; Grade 8, 451.

   Each grade has about 450 students.

   450 + 450 + 450 = 3 × 450 = 1350

   About 1350 newspapers were distributed.

2-6 Exercises and Applications

Assignment Guide

- **Basic**
  1–12, 22–23, 27–29, 31–38
- **Average**
  5–17, 22–30, 31–37 odds
- **Enriched**
  9–30, 31–37 odds

3 Practice and Assess

Check

Answers for Check Your Understanding

1. Possible answer: Exact answers are needed when figuring out how much to pay for a group of items or using precise numbers in scientific studies. Estimates are satisfactory when figuring out about how much something will cost.
2. No; They are similar, but front-end estimation usually uses the first digit or two without rounding.

Reteaching

Activity

Roll	Turn 1	Turn 2	Turn 3
1	2,125	3,125	37,683
2	3,243	2,187	39,049
3	2,256	1,024	41,250
4	3,625	5,625	44,034
5	2,729	6,561	45,789
6	1,512	2,048	50,219

Materials: Number cubes

- Work with a partner. Toss a number cube three times. After each toss, record the number from the table that is the score for that turn. For example, if a 3, 6, and 1 are tossed, record 2,256, 2,048, and 37,683 as your scores.
- Estimate the sum of your scores. The player whose sum is closest to 50,000 wins the round.
- If both players' estimates are close to 50,000 you may have to find the actual sum of each score.

Check Your Understanding

1. Describe some real-life addition and subtraction situations that require exact answers. Describe some where estimates are satisfactory.
2. Is front-end estimation the same as rounding and adding? Explain.

2-6 Exercises and Applications

PRACTICE 2-6

Practice and Apply

1. **Getting Started** Simplify using one-digit front-end estimation, and then two-digit front-end estimation.

   a. 216 + 516 ≈740; ≈740 **b.** 3,006 − 1,811 ≈1200; ≈1200 **c.** 85,002 − 12,667 ≈72,000; ≈73,000 **d.** 880 + 110 ≈1000; ≈990

Estimate. Possible answers are given.

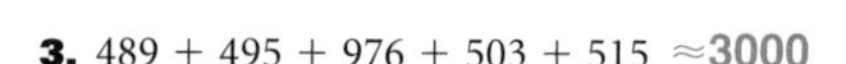

2. 555 + 429 ≈975
3. 489 + 495 + 976 + 503 + 515 ≈3000
4. 7641 − 2578 ≈5100
5. 98 + 107 + 95 + 97 + 103 ≈500
6. 49,245,209 + 53,923,831 + 54,902,756 ≈158,000,000
7. 873 − 549 ≈325
8. 3101 + 3054 + 2916 ≈9000
9. 5,901,877 − 2,635,392 ≈3,300,000
10. 3409 + 7118 ≈10,000
11. 257 + 249 + 241 + 259 ≈1000
12. 48,206 + 81,175 ≈129,000
13. 443,677 + 158,371 + 43 ≈600,000
14. 634,799 + 654 + 863,755 ≈1,500,000
15. 7621 + 8109 + 2117 ≈18,000
16. 14,651 + 23,977 ≈38,500
17. 9 + 11 + 13 + 8 + 7 + 12 + 9 ≈70
18. 21,529 + 40,783 + 377 + 16,403 ≈79,000
19. 8,715,739 + 9,849,129 ≈19,000,000
20. 891 + 677 ≈1600
21. 1577 − 1328 ≈250
22. **Geography** The average depth of the Caribbean Sea is 8685 feet. The average depth of the South China Sea is 5419 feet. About how much deeper is the Caribbean Sea? ≈3300 ft
23. A picture frame measures 36 in. by 18 in. Estimate the distance around the outside of the frame. ≈120 in. GPS

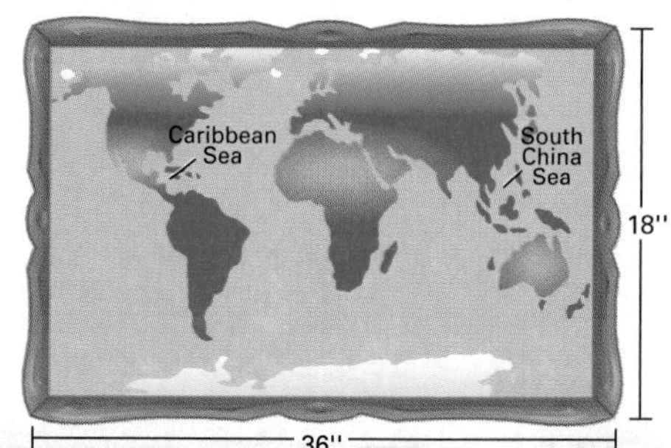

PRACTICE

Name ______________ **Practice 2-6**

Estimating Sums and Differences

Estimate.

1. 38,624 + 83,102 121,700
2. 47,623 − 12,385 35,200
3. 37 + 42 + 43 120
4. 387 + 410 + 405 1,200
5. 824,368 + 217,638 1,042,000
6. 847,167 − 382,208 465,000
7. 6375 − 1890 4,500
8. 7538 + 2317 9,850
9. 163,462 + 3,210 166,700
10. 6138 + 5963 + 6023 + 5874 + 6003 30,000
11. 69 + 73 + 71 + 68 + 70 + 72 + 67 + 72 560
12. 894 + 925 + 888 + 907 + 873 + 895 5400
13. 83,762 + 83,984 + 84,731 + 84,201 336,000
14. 38,124 + 92,064 + 67,312 + 53,720 251,000
15. 1632 + 3129 + 6473 + 3217 14,450
16. 867,530 + 9,874 + 128,382 1,006,000
17. 58,128 + 59,370 + 60,028 + 62,310 240,000
18. 92,163 + 87,920 + 91,325 + 89,012 360,000
19. A world record for dart throwing was set by the Broken Hill Darts Club, who achieved a score of 1,722,249 points in 24 hours. The record score for a women's team is 744,439, achieved by a British team. About how many more points were scored by the Broken Hill Darts Club than by the British team?
    About 980,000 points
20. In 1990, the population of Fresno, CA was 354,202, and the population of New Orleans, LA was 496,938. Estimate the combined population of these two cities.
    About 851,000

RETEACHING

Name ______________ **Alternative Lesson 2-6**

Estimating Sums and Differences

To estimate a sum or difference using *front-end estimation*, add or subtract using only the first digits of each number. Estimate the sum or difference of the remaining digits and add this to the first estimate.

When adding several numbers that are approximately equal, use *clustering* to estimate the sum. Replace all of the numbers with a single number close to them that is easy to multiply. Then multiply.

— Example 1 —

Estimate 640 + 521 using one-digit front-end estimation.

Step 1: Add the first digit in each number: 6 + 5 = 11.

Step 2: Add 60 because 40 + 21 is about 60.

640 + 521 is about 1160.

```
  640
+ 521
 1100
+  60
 1160
```

Try It Estimate 3785 − 1276 using front-end estimation.

a. Which two digits will you subtract first? What is their difference? 3 − 1; 2

b. Estimate the difference of the remaining digits. ≈ 500

c. Estimate 3785 − 1276. ≈ 2500

Estimate using front-end estimation.

d. 2118 + 4632 ≈ 6700

e. 9380 − 5252 ≈ 4100

— Example 2 —

Estimate 310 + 305 + 298 + 296 + 302 using clustering.

Each of the numbers is close to 300. There are 5 numbers.
300 + 300 + 300 + 300 + 300 = 5 × 300 = 1500

So, 310 + 305 + 298 + 296 + 302 is about 1500.

Try It Estimate 189 + 199 + 215 using clustering.

f. What number is close to the three numbers being added? 200

g. How many numbers are being added? 3

h. Estimate 189 + 199 + 215. ≈ 600

Estimate using clustering.

i. 468 + 525 + 491 + 501 ≈ 2000

j. 710 + 745 +699 + 685 + 708 ≈ 3500

24. Literature The letter of the alphabet with the most entries in the *Oxford English Dictionary* is *s*, with 34,556 entries. The next is *c*, with 26,239, and then *p*, with 24,980.

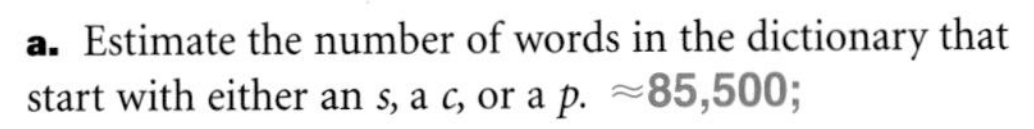

a. Estimate the number of words in the dictionary that start with either an *s*, a *c*, or a *p*. ≈85,500;

b. Estimate the difference between the number of words starting with *c* and the number of words starting with *p*. ≈1000

Use the table for Exercises 25 and 26.

Mint	Number of Coins Made
Denver	15,804,000
Philadelphia	76,532,352
San Francisco	6,101,000

25. Give one-digit and two-digit front-end estimates for the total number of pennies produced. ≈99,000,000; ≈98,400,000

26. Estimate how much more Philadelphia's total was than Denver's. ≈60,500,000

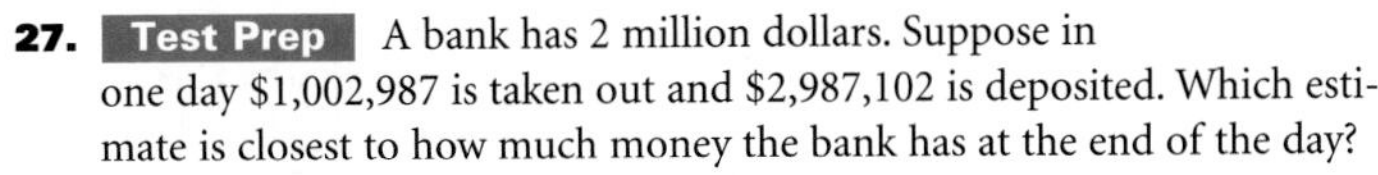

27. **Test Prep** A bank has 2 million dollars. Suppose in one day $1,002,987 is taken out and $2,987,102 is deposited. Which estimate is closest to how much money the bank has at the end of the day?

Ⓐ $1 million Ⓑ $2 million Ⓒ $3 million Ⓓ $4 million

Problem Solving and Reasoning

28. Critical Thinking Erika estimated the sum of 299 + 298 + 297 as 900. Was her estimate high or low? Explain.

29.  Explain how to add a group of numbers using clustering. Give an example to illustrate your answer.

30. Communicate For 86,002 + 17,775, how much more accurate is two-digit front-end estimation than one-digit front-end estimation?

Mixed Review

Round to the given place value. *[Lesson 2-2]*

31. 6,967,243; hundred-thousand 7,000,000

32. 42,352,408; hundred 42,352,400

33. 423,855,211; hundred-million 400,000,000

34. 8,788,212,403; thousand 8,788,212,000

Subtract. *[Previous course]*

35. $823.44 − $127.58 $695.86

36. $212,203 − $83,498 $128,705

37. $62,148.67 − $45,746.23 $16,402.44

38. $753,497.62 − $376,032.07 $377,465.55

PROBLEM SOLVING 2-6

Exercise Notes

Exercises 2–21

Estimation Depending upon the estimation method selected, students may get slightly different estimates than those given. It may be helpful to ask students to explain how they found their answers.

Exercise 24

Extension This is a good problem to use to discuss different estimation methods. Have students share how they solved the problem.

Exercise Answers

27. D

28. Erika's estimate was high. Each of the numbers is less than 300.

29. Replace all of the numbers with a single number close to them that is easy to multiply, and then multiply. For example, 49 + 51 + 53 is about 3 × 50, or 150.

30. Since the two-digit front-end estimate is 103,800 and the one-digit front-end estimate is 104,000, the two-digit front-end estimate is closer to the actual sum of 103,777 by 200.

Alternate Assessment

You may want to use the *Interactive CD-ROM Journal* with this assessment.

Journal Ask students to write a paragraph describing the different methods of estimating and explaining how they decide which method to use.

PROBLEM SOLVING

Name ______________ **Guided Problem Solving 2-6**

GPS PROBLEM 23, STUDENT PAGE 92

A picture frame measures 36 in. by 18 in. Estimate the distance around the outside of the frame.

— Understand —

1. Underline what you are asked to do.
2. What are the dimensions of the frame? 36 in. by 18 in.

— Plan —

3. Draw a picture of the rectangular frame. Label the length of each side. (36 in., 18 in., 18 in., 36 in.)
4. Which numbers will you add to find the total distance around the frame? 36 + 36 + 18 + 18
5. Will you use front end-estimation or clustering to estimate the answer. Why? Possible answer: Front-end, since numbers do not cluster around a convenient number.

— Solve —

6. Write a number sentence showing the numbers you used to estimate your answer. Possible answer: 30 + 30 + 10 + 10 + 30 = 110.
7. Write a sentence to give the estimated distance around the frame. Possible answer: The distance around the outside of the picture frame is about 110 inches.

— Look Back —

8. How could you find your answer in another way? Possible answer: Use mental math to find the exact answer.

SOLVE ANOTHER PROBLEM

A rectangular dog pen measures 96 in. by 84 in. Estimate the distance around the outside of the dog pen. Show the numbers you used to estimate. Possible answer: 100 + 100 + 80 + 80 = 360; 360 in.

ENRICHMENT

Name ______________ **Extend Your Thinking 2-6**

Decision Making

When you shop, you always have choices to make. Use the price list at the right to help you make some catalogue purchases.

For each answer show the items you selected and their prices.

	Price List
T-shirts	$12.99 each
Belt	$13.50 each
Socks	$3.00/pair
Jeans	$34.99/pair
Sweatshirt	$18.99 with team logo $15.99 plain
Shoes	$48.95 pair

1. Suppose you buy three different items. What is the least amount and the greatest amount you could spend? 1 T-shirt, 1 belt, 1 pair of socks: $29.49; 1 pair of shoes, 1 sweatshirt with team logo, 1 pair of jeans: $102.93.
2. Suppose you have $40. Can you buy 2 pairs of socks and 2 sweatshirts? Explain. Yes. Buy 2 plain sweatshirts at $15.99 each and 2 pairs of socks at $3 each.
3. Suppose you have $140. Can you buy one of each item? Explain. No. The total cost is $148.41—more than $140.
4. You have won a shopping spree! You can spend up to $100, but not more than $100. Which items can you buy to spend as close as possible to $100? Why did you choose those items? Possible answer: Shoes, $48.95; jeans, $34.99; T-shirt, $12.99; socks, $3; Total is $99.93.
5. There was a coupon in the newspaper that offered a $15 discount when a purchase totaled $100 or more. You can use the coupon when you go on your shopping spree. How would that change your answer to Question 4? Explain. Possible answer: I could spend about $15 more and buy a belt to complete the outfit for a total cost of $113.43.

Quick Quiz

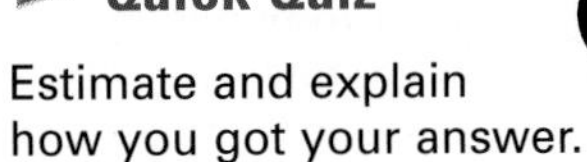

Estimate and explain how you got your answer.

1. 34,728 + 42,519 77,200; Two-digit front-end estimation
2. 934,362 − 438,299 500,000; One-digit front-end estimation
3. 289 + 302 + 311 + 298 + 301 1500; Clustering

Available on Daily Transparency 2-6

2-7 Lesson Organizer

Objective

- Estimate products and quotients using rounding and compatible numbers.

NCTM Standards

- 1–4, 7, 13

Review

Round 32,456,278,199 to the indicated place.

1. Thousands 32,456,278,000
2. Millions 32,456,000,000
3. Ten-thousands 32,456,280,000
4. Hundred-millions 32,500,000,000

Available on Daily Transparency 2-7

1 Introduce

Explore

The Point
Students estimate products and quotients to compare costs for marbles on each day.

Ongoing Assessment
Some students may divide to find the cost for one marble each day and then answer the questions. Others may note, however, that marbles cost less in March than in February because in March you get one more marble for the same price as in February.

For Groups That Finish Early
Terry spent $563 on Peppermint Swirl marbles from February through May. How many marbles did she buy and in which months? 5 for $250 in April; 4 for $164 in May; Either 3 for $149 in February or 4 for $149 in March.

2-7 Estimating Products and Quotients

You'll Learn ...

- to estimate products and quotients using rounding and compatible numbers.

... How It's Used

Chefs use estimation skills to determine about how much of an ingredient should be used in cooking.

▶ Lesson Link In the last lesson, you learned convenient methods for estimating answers to addition and subtraction problems. Now you will learn two methods that work well with multiplication and division problems. ◀

Explore Estimating

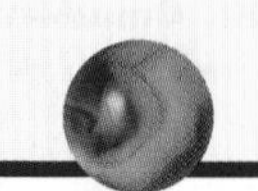

Cat's Eyes and Immies

The Marbelous Marbles shop sells a rare type of marble known as a Peppermint Swirl. The price of this marble changes each month.

Peppermint Swirls	
January	1 for $58
February	3 for $149
March	4 for $149
April	5 for $250
May	2 for $82

Answer the questions without using a calculator.

1. In February, did the price for one marble go up or down? Explain.
2. In March, did the price for one marble go up or down? Explain.
3. In April, did the price for one marble go up or down? Explain.
4. In May, did the price for one marble go up or down? Explain.
5. In which month was the price the highest? Explain.
6. In which month was the price the lowest? Explain.

Remember
To round a number, look at the digit to the right of the place you want to round to. If the digit is 5 or greater, round up. If it is less than 5, leave the digit being rounded the same. [Page 71]

Learn Estimating Products and Quotients

Like sums and differences, products and quotients can be estimated when you don't need exact answers. To estimate a product or quotient using *rounding,* round all numbers so that each contains only one nonzero digit. Then multiply or divide.

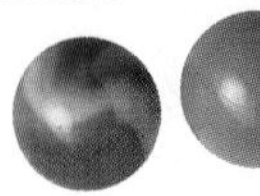

MEETING INDIVIDUAL NEEDS

Resources

- 2-7 Practice
- 2-7 Reteaching
- 2-7 Problem Solving
- 2-7 Enrichment
- 2-7 Daily Transparency
  - Problem of the Day
  - Review
  - Quick Quiz
- Teaching Tool Transparencies 2, 3

Learning Modalities

Verbal Have students write and perform a short skit in which the characters must solve a variety of estimation problems.

Logical Have students investigate which estimation methods give better answers in which situations.

Challenge

Have students look through newspapers for examples of cars, appliances, or any other items that come with one or more options. Have them write problems in which they must either estimate the total cost of the item with several options or compare the cost of the item with different packages of options.

Examples

Estimate, using rounding.

1 429×16

$429 \times 16 \approx 400 \times 20$ Round.

$= 8000$

2 $1170 \div 45$

$1170 \div 45 \approx 1000 \div 50$ Round.

$= 20$

Try It

Estimate, using rounding.

a. 84×279 $\approx$24,000

b. $7912 \div 43$ $\approx$200

Remember

The symbol $\approx$ means "is approximately equal to." **[Previous course]**

To estimate using *compatible numbers*, rewrite the problem using numbers that go together easily. Then multiply or divide.

Examples

3 Estimate 48×12 using compatible numbers.

$48 \times 12 \approx 50 \times 10 = 500$

4 Ted scored 231 points during the 28-game basketball season. Estimate the average number of points he scored each game.

$231 \div 28 \approx 240 \div 30 = 8$

He scored about 8 points per game.

Try It

Estimate, using compatible numbers.

a. 22×31 600

b. $553 \div 79$ 7

Check Your Understanding

1. Would rounding and compatible numbers be good estimation strategies for addition and subtraction problems? Explain.
2. Explain two ways you could estimate $3177 \div 45$.

MATH EVERY DAY

Problem of the Day

On her birthday, Jennifer spent half of her savings at the mall and then donated \$5 to charity. She received \$25 as a birthday gift. Now she has \$128. How much money did Jennifer have before she went to the mall?
\$216

Available on Daily Transparency 2-7

An Extension is provided in the transparency package.

Fact of the Day

By 1995, Michael Jordan had played 684 games, scoring 21,998 points. He averaged a record 32.2 points a game.

Mental Math

Do these mentally.

1. 42×8 336
2. $72{,}000 \div 80$ 900
3. $345 + 298$ 643
4. $72 + 35 + 65$ 172

Answers for Explore

1. Down; Compared to January, the price of one marble is less.
2. Down; In February, 3 marbles cost \$149, in March, 4 marbles cost the same amount.
3. Up; Compared to March, the price of one marble is more.
4. Down; Compared to April, the price of one marble is less.
5. January; The price of one marble is \$58.
6. March; The price of one marble is about \$40.

2 Teach

Learn

Some students may be comfortable rounding each factor to either one or two digits. For example, 429×16 could be rounded to $400 \times 15 = 6000$ or $430 \times 20 = 8600$. Students should note that the first of these estimates is a little low, while the second is quite high.

Alternate Examples

Estimate using rounding.

1. 378×18

   Round to $400 \times 20 = 8000$

2. $2078 \div 39$

   Round to $2000 \div 40 = 50$

3. Estimate 53×18 using compatible numbers.

   $53 \times 18 \approx 50 \times 20 = 1000$

4. Sue scored 327 points during the 29-game basketball season. Estimate the average number of points she scored each game.

   $327 \div 29 \approx 330 \div 30 = 11$
   She averaged about 11 points each game.

3 Practice and Assess

Check

Answers for Check Your Understanding

1. Yes; Because rounding and compatible numbers would make addition and subtraction easy and still give close answers.
2. Estimate by solving $3000 \div 50$ or $3200 \div 40$.

2-7 Exercises and Applications

Assignment Guide

- **Basic** 1–20, 35–41 odds, 44–62 evens
- **Average** 1–25, 34–42, 44–62 evens
- **Enriched** 6–42, 43–61 odds

Exercise Notes

Exercises 2–33

Error Prevention Watch for students who place the incorrect number of zeros in the product or quotient. Review the process of multiplying and dividing multiples of ten.

Exercise 36

Social Studies In the United States, the newspaper with the highest daily circulation is *USA Today* at approximately 1,500,000 copies for its Monday through Thursday editions and almost 2,000,000 copies for its weekend edition. The *New York Times* has a circulation of 1,700,000 for its Sunday paper.

Reteaching

Activity

Materials: Index cards

- Work in groups of three or four. Label half of the index cards with the digits 1 through 9 and shuffle.
- Label the other half with a variety of numbers from 11 through 99 and shuffle. Keep each set separate.
- Draw two cards, one from each set. Estimate the product of the two numbers, while the other players check your work.

2-7 Exercises and Applications

PRACTICE 2-7

Practice and Apply

1. Getting Started Estimate, using rounding.

a. 560×4 2400 **b.** $7800 \div 22$ 400 **c.** 68×472 35,000 **d.** $9433 \div 300$ 30

Estimate, using compatible numbers.

e. $372 \div 56$ 6 **f.** 58×5 300 **g.** $8099 \div 8$ 1000 **h.** 27×4286 120,000

Estimate. Possible answers are given.

2. $183 \div 21$ 9 **3.** 7111×7888 56,000,000 **4.** $327 \div 64$ 5 **5.** 488×53 25,000

6. $4522 \div 92$ 50 **7.** $9 \times 11 \times 17$ 1700 **8.** $11 \times 23 \times 98$ 23,000 **9.** $777 \div 38$ 20

10. 217×308 60,000 **11.** $207 \times 6 \times 15$ 15,000 **12.** $24{,}111 \div 84$ 300 **13.** 54×82 4000

14. $4270 \div 38$ 100 **15.** $2803 \div 24$ 100 **16.** $1895 \div 463$ 4 **17.** 463×719 350,000

18. $5 \times 26 \times 12$ 1250 **19.** $175 \div 28$ 6 **20.** $425 \div 59$ 7 **21.** $51 \times 14 \times 19$ 14,000

22. $358 \div 7$ 50 **23.** $149 \div 4$ 40 **24.** 29×41 1200 **25.** $19 \times 4 \times 7$ 560

26. $248 \times 5 \times 8$ 10,000 **27.** $23{,}714 \div 522$ 50 **28.** 185×29 6000 **29.** $200{,}000 \div 720$ 300

30. $2733 \div 71$ 40 **31.** $103 \div 54$ 2 **32.** $3625 \div 581$ 6 **33.** $5 \times 9 \times 2457$ 100,000

34. Tracy collects old sheet music. In a bin at a flea market, she found 19 songs priced at $4.95 apiece. Estimate the total cost of the music. $100

35. Industry Flight 777 carries 54 passengers, each with 2 suitcases. Each suitcase weighs, on average, 36 pounds. If the airplane was built to carry 5000 pounds of luggage, is the flight over or under its limit? Under

GPS

36. Social Science The *Yomiuri Shimbun* in Japan is the daily newspaper with the highest circulation, at 8,700,000 papers per day. If one day's papers were distributed evenly among Japan's four islands, about how many newspapers would be on each island? 2,200,000

37. Measurement There are 5280 feet in a mile and 12 inches in a foot. Estimate the number of inches in a mile. 60,000

Hokkaido

Honshu

PRACTICE

Name ____________

Practice 2-7

Estimating Products and Quotients

Estimate.

1. 38 × 47 2,000 2. 58 × 72 4,200 3. 867 × 12 9,000
4. 163 ÷ 39 4 5. 894 ÷ 293 3 6. 37,183 ÷ 191 200
7. 79 × 195 16,000 8. 12,375 ÷ 29 400 9. 5417 ÷ 59 90
10. 83,921 ÷ 49 1,700 11. 2414 ÷ 62 40 12. 7398 ÷ 369 20
13. 8700 ÷ 910 10 14. 3972 ÷ 217 20 15. 732 × 47 35,000
16. 55,760 ÷ 692 80 17. 64,900 ÷ 129 500 18. 995 × 24 24,000
19. 934 × 193 200,000 20. 9583 ÷ 163 60 21. 43,972 ÷ 493 90
22. 72,389 ÷ 8888 8 23. 29 × 817 24,000 24. 447 ÷ 153 3
25. 893 ÷ 61 15 26. 95,831 ÷ 398 240 27. 143,698 ÷ 119 1,200
28. 7862 ÷ 101 80 29. 869 ÷ 27 30 30. 621,830 ÷ 7012 90
31. 4982 × 61 300,000 32. 350,123 ÷ 698 500 33. 592 × 29 18,000
34. 738 × 691 490,000 35. 1284 × 691 700,000
36. 94 × 83 × 41 288,000 37. 37 × 61 × 59 144,000
38. 872 × 6100 5,400,000 39. 99 × 41 × 67 280,000
40. 6843 × 592 4,200,000 41. 13 × 61 × 8127 4,800,000
42. 8397 × 1975 16,000,000 43. 367 × 824 × 7 2,240,000
44. 624 × 832 480,000 45. 384 × 718 280,000

46. Akira Matsushima rode a unicycle 3260 miles across the United States in 44 days. Estimate how far he traveled every day.

About 75 miles

47. There are 60 minutes in an hour, 24 hours in a day, and 365 days in a year. Estimate the number of minutes in a year.

About 480,000 minutes

RETEACHING

Name ____________

Alternative Lesson 2-7

Estimating Products and Quotients

Like sums and differences, products and quotients can be estimated when you don't need exact answers. To estimate a product or quotient using *rounding,* round all numbers so that each contains only one nonzero digit. Then multiply or divide.

To estimate using *compatible numbers,* rewrite the problem using numbers that go together easily. Then multiply or divide.

Example 1

Estimate 87 × 104 using rounding.

104	→	Round 104 to 100.	→	100
× 87	→	Round 87 to 90.	→	× 90
				9000

So, 87 × 104 is about 9000.

Try It Estimate 937 × 67 using rounding.

a. Round 937 to the nearest hundred. 900

b. Round 67 to the nearest ten. 70

c. Multiply the two rounded numbers to estimate 937 × 67. 63,000

Estimate, using rounding.

d. 280 × 32 9000 e. 77 × 21 1600 f. 86 × 402 36,000

Example 2

Estimate 154 ÷ 38 using compatible numbers.

Step 1: Decide which numbers go together easily. Think: 154 is about **160**. 38 is about **40**.

Step 2: Substitute the compatible numbers and find the quotient. 160 ÷ 40 = 4

So, 154 ÷ 38 is about 4.

Try It Possible answers: Items g – k

Estimate 472 ÷ 84 using compatible numbers.

g. Which two numbers go together easily? 480 and 80

h. Divide the compatible numbers to estimate 472 ÷ 84. 6

Estimate using compatible numbers.

i. 252 ÷ 61 4 j. 536 ÷ 51 10 k. 790 ÷ 92 9

38. Carlos has been offered $825 for his collection of 19 model train cabooses. He wants to get an average of at least $40 per caboose. Should he accept the offer? Explain how he can use estimation to decide.

39. **Test Prep** Choose the best estimate for 5,985 × 89. C

Ⓐ 4,000,000 Ⓑ 450,000 Ⓒ 540,000 Ⓓ 600,000

Problem Solving and Reasoning

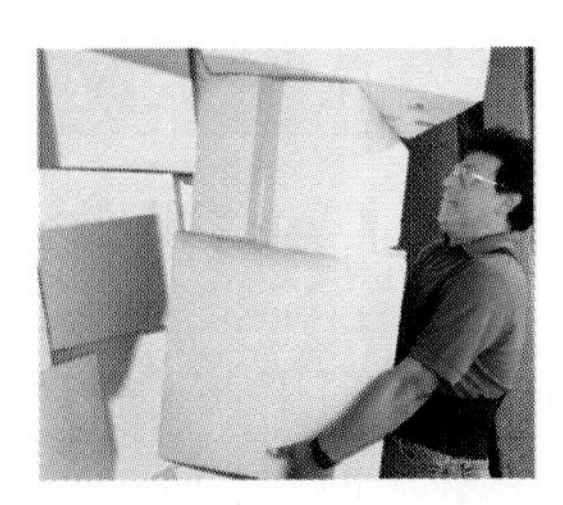

40. Critical Thinking You are stacking 105-lb boxes on a freight elevator. A sign on the elevator says, "Do not exceed 1000 pounds total." What is the maximum number of boxes you can stack on the elevator? Explain your reasoning.

41. Journal List two situations where it is better to have an exact answer than an estimate, and explain why.

42. Choose a Strategy Leslie won some money in a contest. After spending $12 on a CD, almost $34 on new bicycle tires, and about $16 on a pair of pants, she has about $15 left over. Estimate how much money Leslie won. Explain your answer.

Problem Solving STRATEGIES

- Look for a Pattern
- Make an Organized List
- Make a Table
- Guess and Check
- Work Backward
- Use Logical Reasoning
- Draw a Diagram
- Solve a Simpler Problem

Mixed Review

Compare. Use > or <. *[Lesson 2-3]*

43. 2156 [<] 2157 **44.** 324,265,129 [>] 324,264,872 **45.** 19,667 [<] 190,675

46. 3189 [<] 3891 **47.** 267 [<] 627 **48.** 134,256 [<] 134,265

Order the numbers from least to greatest. *[Lesson 2-3]*

49. 1023; 10; 356; 1009; 383
10; 356; 383; 1009; 1023

50. 22,456; 122,802; 21,904; 122,501
21,904; 22,456; 122,501; 122,802

Multiply. *[Previous course]*

51. 20 × 607 12,140 **52.** 50 × 505 25,250 **53.** 60 × 304 18,240 **54.** 70 × 801 56,070

55. 14 × 18 252 **56.** 26 × 21 546 **57.** 60 × 52 3120 **58.** 83 × 57 4731

59. 12 × 12 144 **60.** 21 × 25 525 **61.** 63 × 34 2142 **62.** 99 × 99 9801

PROBLEM SOLVING 2-7

Exercise Notes

Exercise 42

Problem-Solving Tip You may wish to use Teaching Tool Transparencies 2 and 3: Guided Problem Solving, pages 1–2.

Exercise Answers

38. Yes; Estimate $825 ÷ 19 to be about $800 ÷ 20 = $40.

40. 9 because 105 × 10 = 1050 and that's 50 pounds too much.

41. Possible answer: Exact answers are needed when figuring out how much to pay for a group of items because you have to pay the exact amount. Exact answers are needed when using precise numbers in scientific studies because otherwise the results of the study might be wrong.

42. She could have won $75, because $10 + $35 + $15 + $15 is equal to $75.

Alternate Assessment

Interview Ask students to describe a situation in which they would estimate a product or quotient.

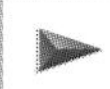

Quick Quiz

Estimate:

1. 719 × 31 21,000
2. 24 × 39 800
3. 5,693 ÷ 68 80
4. 598,888 ÷ 198 3,000

Available on Daily Transparency 2-7

PROBLEM SOLVING

Name ____________ **Guided Problem Solving 2-7**

GPS PROBLEM 35, STUDENT PAGE 96

Flight 777 carries 54 passengers, each with 2 suitcases. Each suitcase weighs, on average, 36 pounds. If the airplane was built to carry 5000 pounds of luggage, is the flight over or under its limit?

— Understand —

1. What are you asked to find? Whether the suitcases weigh over or under the weight limit of 5000 pounds.

— Plan —

2. Why is it acceptable to estimate to find the answer? Possible answer: An exact weight of the suitcases is not necessary.

3. Which method will you use to estimate? b
 a. Front-end estimation b. Rounding c. Compensation

— Solve —

4. Estimate the number of suitcases that are on the plane.
 2 × 50 = 100

5. Estimate the total number of pounds that the suitcases weigh.
 40 × 100 = 4000

6. Compare your estimate to 5000 lb. Is the flight over or under its limit? Under.

— Look Back —

7. How could you have solved the problem another way?
 Possible answer: Estimate by multiplying any combination of passengers, suitcases, and weights or calculate actual answer.

SOLVE ANOTHER PROBLEM

Flight 897 carries 48 passengers, each with 2 suitcases. Each suitcase weighs, on average, 43 pounds. If the airplane was built to carry 4800 pounds of luggage, is the flight over or under its limit?
Under; 50 × 2 × 40 = 4000; 4000 < 4800.

ENRICHMENT

Name ____________ **Extend Your Thinking 2-7**

Patterns in Numbers

A crystal grows in an orderly way due to the pattern of its atoms. Some number patterns grow the same way. See if you can see why the patterns below can be compared to crystals.

1. Examine the pattern. What changes do you see in each successive line in the pattern?
 6 × 6 = 36
 66 × 66 = 4356
 666 × 666 = 443,556
 6666 × 6666 = 44,435,556
 Possible answer: Additional 6 in factor; another 4 and 5 in product. One less 4 and 5 than there are 6s in factor.

2. What will be the next two lines in the number pattern?
 66,666 × 66,666 = 4,444,355,556;
 666,666 × 666,666 = 444,443,555,556

3. What will be the tenth line in the number pattern?
 6,666,666,666 × 6,666,666,666 = 44,444,444,435,555,555,556

4. Examine the pattern. What changes do you see in each successive line in the pattern?
 2 × 2 = 4
 32 × 32 = 1,024
 332 × 332 = 110,224
 3,332 × 3,332 = 11,102,224
 Possible answer: Same number of 1s and 2s in product as there are 3s in factor.

5. What will be the next two lines in the number pattern?
 33,332 × 33,332 = 1,111,022,224;
 333,332 × 333,332 = 111,110,222,224

6. What will be the tenth line in the number pattern?
 3,333,333,332 × 3,333,333,332 = 11,111,111,102,222,222,224

7. How do these patterns grow like crystals?
 Possible answer: Like crystals, the numbers grow in an orderly way.

2-8

Lesson Organizer

Objective

- Use order of operation rules to solve arithmetic problems.

Vocabulary

- Order of operations

NCTM Standards

- 1–6

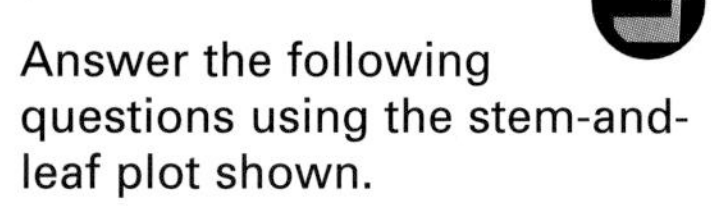

Review

Answer the following questions using the stem-and-leaf plot shown.

Stem	Leaf
1	0 1 1 2 5
2	1 2 3 6 6 7 8
3	0 0 0 1 1
4	8

1. What is the outlier? 48
2. What is the median? 26
3. What is the mode? 30

Available on Daily Transparency 2-8

1 Introduce

Explore  

The Point
Students look at results generated by two different calculators to develop the rules for order of operations.

Ongoing Assessment
Some students may have difficulty figuring out what the HP 9820 calculator did; they can only see the left-to-right computation. Ask them to try doing another operation first instead of starting at the left.

For Groups That Finish Early
Ask students to predict the value each calculator would give for the expression: $3 \times 5 + 16 \div 4$.

2-8 Order of Operations

You'll Learn ...

- to use order of operation rules to solve arithmetic problems

... How It's Used

Cashiers must use the same rules to calculate prices that involve sales tax, discounts, and coupons.

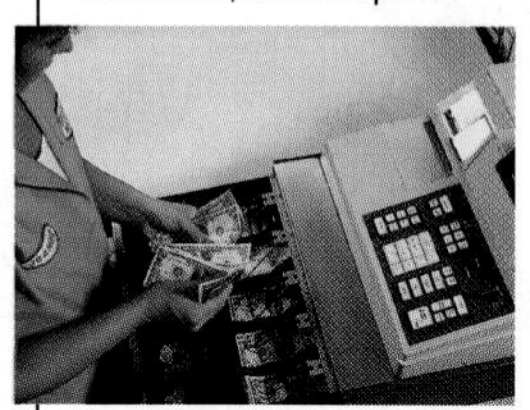

Vocabulary

order of operations

▶ Lesson Link You've learned how to work with arithmetic problems with one operation. Now you'll learn how to simplify problems using several operations. ◀

Explore Order of Operations

The Calculators That Didn't Always Agree

David Hicks collects calculators and has a calculator museum on the World Wide Web. One of his calculators is an early HP-01 calculator watch from the 1970s. Another is the HP 9820, one of the first algebraic calculators. Each calculator processed arithmetic problems in a different way.

1. Sometimes the calculators gave different answers because each one did a different part of the problem first. For each problem, determine which operation each calculator did first.
2. Using your answers, explain which operation the HP-01 calculator watch does first.
3. Using your answers, explain which operation the HP 9820 calculator does first.
4. Predict the values that each calculator gave for each expression:

   a. $50 - 10 \div 2$ **b.** $12 \times 6 - 3$ **c.** $14 + 21 \div 7$ **d.** $20 + 5 \times 3$

Problem	HP-01	HP 9820
$3 + 4 \times 5$	35	23
$2 + 8 \times 6$	60	50
$9 \times 4 - 8$	28	28
$6 + 15 \div 3$	7	11
$20 - 16 \div 4$	1	16
$42 \div 7 + 3$	9	9

▶ Technology Link

To find out if your calculator follows order of operation rules, press 2 [+] 3 [×] 4 [=]. If the answer is 14, the calculator follows the rules.

Learn Order of Operations

The value of an expression that involves several operations depends on the order in which you perform the operations. Suppose you wanted to simplify $9 + 6 \div 3$. You could add first or divide first.

Adding first:	$9 + 6 = 15$
Now divide:	$15 \div 3 = 5$

Dividing first:	$6 \div 3 = 2$
Now add:	$9 + 2 = 11$

MEETING INDIVIDUAL NEEDS

Resources

- **2-8** Practice
- **2-8** Reteaching
- **2-8** Problem Solving
- **2-8** Enrichment
- **2-8** Daily Transparency
  - Problem of the Day
  - Review
  - Quick Quiz
- Technology Master 8
- Chapter 2 Project Master

Learning Modalities

Musical Have students make up a song or rhyme about order of operations.

Logical Have students use a calculator to evaluate an expression that requires using order of operations. Require the students to rewrite the expression after each operation is performed.

English Language Development

You may want to help students remember the order of operations by using the mnemonic:

Please	Parentheses
Excuse	Exponents
My **D**ear	Multiplication and Division from left to right
Aunt **S**ally	Addition and Subtraction from left to right

Mathematicians use parentheses to show which part of the problem should be done first. But some problems don't have parentheses. To make sure everyone gets the same answer for a problem, mathematicians use a set of rules known as the **order of operations**.

ORDER OF OPERATIONS

1. Simplify inside parentheses.
2. Simplify exponents.
3. Multiply and divide from left to right.
4. Add and subtract from left to right.

Examples

Simplify.

1 $7 \times (3 + 2)$

$7 \times (3 + 2) = 7 \times 5$ Simplify inside parentheses first.

$= 35$ Multiply.

2 5×3^2

$5 \times 3^2 = 5 \times 9$ Simplify exponents first.

$= 45$ Multiply.

3 $12 + 5 \times 4$

$12 + 5 \times 4 = 12 + 20$ Multiply first.

$= 32$ Add.

4 $16 \div 2 \times 9$

$16 \div 2 \times 9 = 8 \times 9$ Do left part first.

$= 72$ Do right part.

Try It

Simplify.

a. $28 - 12 \div 4$ 25 **b.** $36 \div 12 \div 3$ 1 **c.** $19 - 4^2$ 3 **d.** $8 \times (10 - 4)$

Check Your Understanding

1. Why do you need the order of operation rules to compute $20 + 5 \times 3$?
2. Give a real-world example of something you could do in several ways that people have agreed to do the same way.

MATH EVERY DAY

Problem of the Day

How many rectangles can you find in this geometric figure?

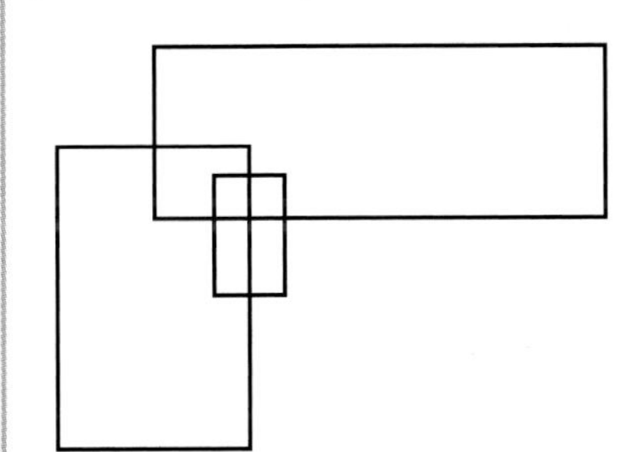

12 rectangles

Available on Daily Transparency 2-8

An Extension is provided in the transparency package.

Fact of the Day

The first electronic computer, built in 1943 in Great Britain, was used to break German codes in World War II.

Estimation

Estimate.

1. $2{,}400{,}456 \div 4\ 3{,}028$ 800
2. $234 \times 402 \div 100$ 800
3. 201×201 40,000

Answers for Explore

1. HP-01; HP 9820:
   Addition; Multiplication
   Addition; Multiplication
   Multiplication; Multiplication
   Addition; Division
   Subtraction; Division
   Division; Division
2. The HP-01 did operations from left to right, in the order they appeared.
3. The HP 9820 did multiplication or division before addition or subtraction.
4. HP-01; HP 9820:
   a. 20; 45
   b. 69; 69
   c. 5; 17
   d. 75; 35

2 Teach

Learn

Alternate Examples

Simplify.

1. $5 \times (4 + 8)$

   $5 \times (4 + 8) = 5 \times 12 = 60$
2. 7×2^3

   $7 \times 2^3 = 7 \times 8$
   $= 56$
3. $15 + 6 \times 7$

   $15 + 6 \times 7 = 15 + 42$
   $= 57$
4. $24 \div 3 \times 5 = 8 \times 5$
   $= 40$

Answers for Try It

d. 48

3 Practice and Assess

Check

Answers for Check Your Understanding

1. Without the rules, one person could get 75 and another could get 35.
2. Possible answer: In the United States people have agreed to drive on the right side of the street. In the United Kingdom and Japan people have agreed to drive on the left side of the street.

2-8 Exercises and Applications

Assignment Guide

- **Basic**
  1–19, 33–43 odds, 44–46, 50–58, 60
- **Average**
  1, 10–19, 21–29 odds, 30–46, 49–59 odds
- **Enriched**
  1, 10–44 evens, 45–49, 50–62 evens

Exercise Notes

Exercises 2–29

Error Prevention If students make errors in the early exercises, have them use parentheses to group the multiplication and division parts of each problem.

Exercise Answers

1. a. Multiplication; b. Addition; c. Division; d. Simplify exponent; e. Subtraction; f. Multiplication; g. Subtraction; h. Subtraction

30. 10,000

36. $2 \times (3 + 6) = 18$

37. $20 \times (15 - 2) = 260$

38. $(4 + 4^2) \div 5 = 4$

39. $2 \times (6^2 - 8) = 56$

40. $6 + (8 \div 2) = 10$ or no parentheses needed

41. $(12 + 10) \div 11 = 2$

42. $(5 \times 4) \div 2 = 10$ or $5 \times (4 \div 2) = 10$ or no parentheses needed

43. $(5 + 4) \div 3 = 3$

44. Possible answers:
a. $16 \div 2 + 1 = 9$
b. $20 \div 2 - 1 = 9$
c. $2^2 \times 2 + 1 = 9$

Reteaching

Activity

Materials: Index cards numbered 1–10, 4 of each number

- Work with a partner. Shuffle the cards. Pick 3 cards. Write as many number sentences with different answers as you can using all three numbers and any of the following: +, −, ×, ÷, ( ).
- Score one point for each number sentence your partner does not have. The first player to get 25 points wins.

2-8 Exercises and Applications

Practice and Apply

1. **Getting Started** State which operation should be performed first.
   a. $36 - (29 \times 102)$ b. $(62 + 45) \times 58$ c. $119 \div 26 - 13$ d. $8^7 - 132$
   e. $(36 - 29) \times 102$ f. $62 + 45 \times 58$ g. $119 \div (26 - 13)$ h. $(8 - 132)^7$

Simplify each expression.

2. $25 - 10 \div 5$ 23
3. $14 + 7 \times 6$ 56
4. $30 \times 6 + 2$ 182
5. $50 \div 5 - 2$ 8
6. $32 \div 8 \div 4$ 1
7. $2 \times 4 \times 6$ 48
8. $15 \div 3 \times 5$ 25
9. $9 \times 6 \div 2$ 27
10. $10 - 8 - 2$ 0
11. $(10 - 8) - 2$ 0
12. $10 - (8 - 2)$ 4
13. $(6^2 + 4) \times 3$ 120
14. $50 \div 5^2$ 2
15. $6^2 - 9$ 27
16. $(4 + 5)^2$ 81
17. $10^2 \times 3$ 300
18. $6^2 - 2 \times 6$ 24
19. $2^3 + 8 \div 4$ 10
20. $7^2 - 4^2 \times 3$ 1
21. $9 - (4 - 1)^2$ 0
22. $4 \times (5 - 3)$ 8
23. $(8 + 7) \div 3$ 5
24. $6 \times (9 - 4)^2$ 150
25. $(7 + 3)^2 \div 5$ 20
26. $32 - 6 + 5 \times 4$ 46
27. $40 + 18 \div 2 - 16$ 33
28. $45 \div 9 - 21 \div 7$ 2
29. $144 \div 9 \div 8 \div 2$ 1

Use mental math to evaluate.

30. $30{,}000 - 5{,}000 \times 4$
31. $6 + 48{,}000{,}000 \div 800{,}000$ 66
32. $60 \times 4 \div 3 + 19$ 99
33. $5{,}000 + 400 \times 8$ 8200
34. $60 + 60 \div 60$ 61
35. $200 - 200 \div 20$ 190

Insert parentheses to make each statement true.

36. $2 \times 3 + 6 = 18$
37. $20 \times 15 - 2 = 260$
38. $4 + 4^2 \div 5 = 4$
39. $2 \times 6^2 - 8 = 56$
40. $6 + 8 \div 2 = 10$
41. $12 + 10 \div 11 = 2$
42. $5 \times 4 \div 2 = 10$
43. $5 + 4 \div 3 = 3$

44. **Number Sense** Find an arithmetic expression equal to 9 that contains the following operations.
    a. Addition and division
    b. Subtraction and division
    c. Addition, multiplication, and an exponent

45. **Test Prep** Danielle bought 3 pairs of earrings on sale. They normally sell for $4.50 each. Which expression describes the final amount of her purchase? B
    Ⓐ $(4.50 \times 3) - 1.00$ Ⓑ $(4.50 - 1.00) \times 3$ Ⓒ $(3 - 1.00) \times 4.50$

PRACTICE 2-8

PRACTICE

Name ____________________ **Practice 2-8**

Order of Operations

Evaluate each expression.

1. $6 \times 3 \div 2$ 9
2. $4 + 3 \times 7$ 25
3. $12 \div 4 + 2$ 5
4. $36 \div (6 + 3)$ 4
5. $8 \times 10 \div 5$ 16
6. $50 \div 10 + 15$ 20
7. $13 - 2 - 4$ 7
8. $25 - (12 - 10)$ 23
9. $(3 + 7^2) \div 4$ 13
10. $(9 - 4)^2$ 25
11. 6×2^3 48
12. $(38 \div 19)^5$ 32
13. $8^2 - 5^2$ 39
14. $(21 - 15)^2 - 20$ 16
15. $600 \div 2 \div 3 \div 5$ 20
16. $125 \div (25 \div 5)$ 25
17. $6 \times 5 - 2^2$ 26
18. $128 \div 16 - 8 \div 2$ 4
19. $80{,}000 - 6 \times 5{,}000$ 50,000
20. $9000 + 7 \times 300$ 11,100
21. $21 + 39{,}000 \div 1{,}300$ 51
22. $700 - 300 \div 10$ 670
23. $20 \times 7 \div 5 + 11$ 39
24. $69{,}000 \div (1700 + 600)$ 30

Insert a pair of parentheses to make each statement true.

25. $3 \times (7 + 4) \times 8 = 264$
26. $18 \div (3 + 3) = 3$
27. $(8 + 16) \div 4 = 6$
28. $500 \div (50 \div 2) \div 5 = 4$
29. $(3 \times 2)^2 - 1 = 35$
30. $48 \div (12 \times 2) = 2$

31. A store has 27 six-packs, 15 twelve-packs, and 34 single cans of soda. Write an expression using the numbers 27, 6, 15, 12, and 34 to show how many cans the store has all together. Do not use parentheses unless they are necessary. Then evaluate your expression to find the number of cans.

    $27 \times 6 + 15 \times 12 + 34 = 376$

32. Find an arithmetic expression equal to 25 that contains the following operations.
    a. addition and multiplication Answers will vary.
    b. subtraction and division Answers will vary.
    c. addition and at least one exponent Answers will vary.
    d. division and an exponent Answers will vary.

RETEACHING

Name ____________________ **Alternative Lesson 2-8**

Order of Operations

To make sure everyone gets the same answer for any given problem, mathematicians use a set of rules known as the **order of operations.**

The rules for order of operations are:
1. Simplify inside parentheses.
2. Simplify exponents.
3. Multiply and divide from left to right.
4. Add and subtract from left to right.

Example 1

Simplify $5 \times (2 + 4)$.

Follow the order of operations.

$5 \times (2 + 4)$ Simplify inside parentheses first.
$= 5 \times 6 = 30$ Multiply.

$5 \times (2 + 4)$ simplified is 30.

Example 2

Simplify $8 \div 2^2$

$8 \div 2^2$ Simplify exponents first.
$= 8 \div 4 = 2$ Divide.

$8 \div 2^2$ simplified is 2.

Try It Simplify $6 + 4^2 - 12$. $6 + 4^2 - 12$

a. There are no parentheses. So simplify exponents. $6 +$ 16 $- 12$
b. There are no numbers to multiply or divide. So add and subtract from left to right. Add the first two numbers. 22 $- 12$
c. Subtract. 10

Simplify.

d. $(35 - 15) \div 4$ 5
e. $8 \times 2 + 4$ 20
f. $17 - 5 \times 2$ 7
g. $4 \times 6 \div 3$ 8
h. $5 \times (5 + 6)$ 55
i. $4^2 + 2 \div 2$ 17
j. $10 \div 5 \times 2$ 4
k. $5^2 - (3 \times 6)$ 7
l. $3 \times 2^3 \div 6$ 4
m. $8 + 5 - 6$ 7

46. **Test Prep** The dance committee needs 3 balloons at each of 15 tables. They also need 50 balloons for each of the four walls of the room. For other decorations, they need 35 balloons, and the committee will order 10 extra balloons. Which is the correct order of operations? B

Ⓐ $3 + 15 + 50 + 4 + 35 + 10$　Ⓑ $3 \times 15 + 50 \times 4 + 35 + 10$

Ⓒ $3 \times 15 + 50 \times 4 + 35 \times 10$　Ⓓ $3 + 50 \times 15 + 4 + 35 \times 10$

47. Joy bought four snow globes at $7.00 each. She used a $2.00 coupon. After the coupon, the tax came to $1.96. Joy's father paid half of the final cost. Write an expression that describes the situation and equals the total money Joy paid.

Problem Solving and Reasoning

48. **Critical Thinking** A painter said that a wall measured "twenty plus ten squared" square feet. Explain two possible meanings of the comment. Using the order of operations, what is the correct mathematical meaning of what the painter said?

49. **Critical Thinking** You order a large pizza, three large drinks, and a bag of apples. You split the cost evenly with three friends. What order of operations would you use to find out how much each person should pay?

Mixed Review

Simplify. *[Lesson 2-4]*

50. 30^2 900　51. 10^5 100,000　52. 3^3 27　53. 4^6 4096　54. 27^3 19,683　55. 14^4 38,416

Express in exponential notation and simplify. *[Lesson 2-4]*

56. $8 \times 8 \times 8 \times 8$ $8^4 = 4096$　57. $2 \times 2 \times 2 \times 2 \times 2 \times 2 \times 2$ $2^7 = 128$　58. $4 \times 4 \times 4 \times 4$ $4^4 = 256$

Multiply. *[Previous course]*

59. 127×489 62,103　60. $856 \times 45,625$ 39,055,000　61. $28,598 \times 67,204$ 1,921,899,992　62. $123,087 \times 765,294$ 94,197,742,578

Project Progress

Once you know how far you can travel in an hour for each of your six methods, estimate how far you could travel in 24 hours. Save your estimates. Then calculate the exact amount you could travel in 24 hours.

Problem Solving
Understand
Plan
Solve
Look Back

PROBLEM SOLVING 2-8

Exercise Notes

Exercises 59–62

Error Prevention Students should recognize that they need to use calculators in order to get accurate answers to these problems.

Project Progress

You may want to have students use Chapter 2 Project Master.

Exercise Answers

47. $(4 \times 7.00 - 2.00 + 1.96) \div 2$

48. The painter could mean $20 + 10^2$ or $(20 + 10)^2$; The correct mathematical meaning is $20 + 10^2$.

49. Multiplication (to find price of three drinks), addition (to find total cost), division (to find cost for each person).

Alternate Assessment

Self Assessment Have students write about their understanding of order of operations. Ask them to identify what they have learned and what they still need to work on. Have them write examples of problems they can do easily and ones that are hard for them.

Quick Quiz

Evaluate each expression.

1. $3 + 5 \times 6$ 33
2. $4 - 6 \div 3$ 2
3. $12 \div 4 + 6 \times 7$ 45
4. $52 + 3 \times 6$ 70
5. $(6 - 2) \times 8 + 1$ 33

Available on Daily Transparency 2-8

PROBLEM SOLVING

Name ____________

Guided Problem Solving 2-8

GPS PROBLEM 44, STUDENT PAGE 100

Find an arithmetic expression equal to 9 that contains the following operations.

a. Addition and division
b. Subtraction and division
c. Addition, multiplication, and an exponent

Understand

1. What number must each expression equal? 9
2. How many expressions will you write? 3 expressions.

Plan

3. How many operations will you perform in each expression?
   a. Part a 2　b. Part b 2　c. Part c 3
4. Which operation will you perform first in each expression?
   a. Part a Division.　b. Part b Division.　c. Part c Exponents.

Solve Possible answers:

5. To write expression a, choose two numbers and perform the first operation. Show the numbers you choose. $9 \div 3 = 3$
6. What number would you need to use with the second operation so that the value of the expression is 9? Write the expression. If you cannot find a number, change the numbers you used in Item 5. $6 + 9 \div 3$
7. Repeat the steps in Items 5 and 6 to write expression b. $10 - 9 \div 9$
8. To write expression c, repeat the step in Item 5. Choose a number and perform the second operation. Then repeat the steps in Item 7. $1 + 2 \times 2^2$

Look Back

9. Find another solution for each problem.
   Possible answers: $4 + 25 \div 5$; $15 - 12 \div 2$; $0 + 1 \times 3^2$.

SOLVE ANOTHER PROBLEM

Write an arithmetic expression equal to 12 which contains subtraction, an exponent, and division.
Possible answer: $14 - 2^2 \div 2$.

ENRICHMENT

Name ____________

Extend Your Thinking 2-8

Visual Thinking

Analyze the shapes on the grid to find the pattern. Then complete the missing section in the center.

2-9 Lesson Organizer

Objective

- Identify and continue numerical patterns based on addition and subtraction.

Materials

- Explore: Hundred charts, colored pencils or markers

NCTM Standards

- 1–4, 8

Review

Write each of the following numbers in standard form.

1. 7^2 49
2. 2^4 16

Write each of the following in exponential notation.

3. $5 \times 5 \times 5 \times 5$ 5^4
4. $18 \times 18 \times 18 \times 18 \times 18 \times 18 \times 18$ 18^7

Available on Daily Transparency 2-9

1 Introduce

Explore

You may wish to use Teaching Tool Transparency 13: Hundred Chart with **Explore**.

The Point
Students use a hundred chart to create and interpret visual models of numerical patterns.

Ongoing Assessment
Ask students to identify patterns that involve lists of numbers that are increasing.

Answers for Explore

1.

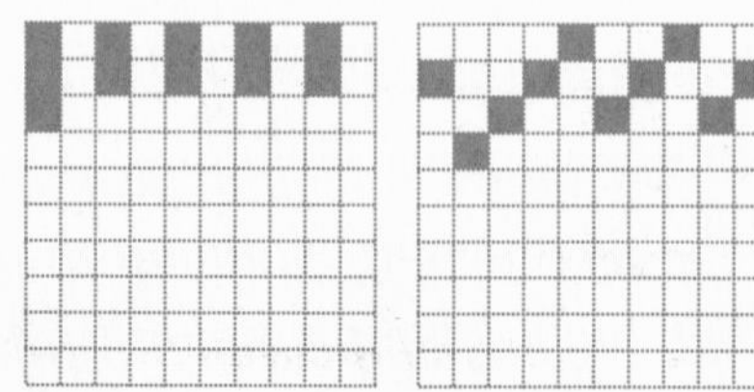

2-9 Numerical Patterns

You'll Learn ...

- to identify and continue numerical patterns based on addition and subtraction

... How It's Used

Lifeguards use numerical patterns when determining the times for high tides and low tides.

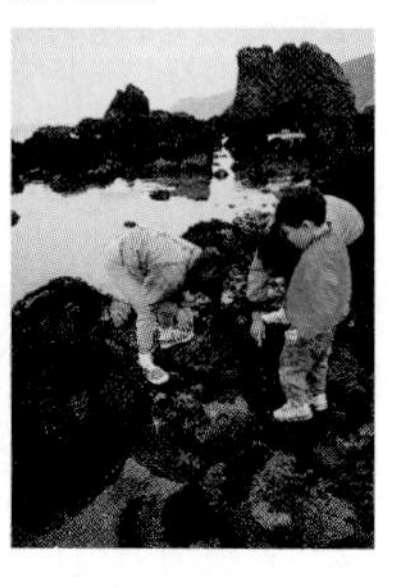

▶ Lesson Link You have seen how number sense can help you solve arithmetic problems. Now you'll learn how to use number sense to identify and extend numerical patterns. ◀

Explore Numerical Patterns

Gridlock!

Materials: Hundred charts, Colored pencils or markers

1. For each list of numbers, color in all the list's numbers in a different hundred chart.

   List A: 1, 3, 5, 7, 9, 11, 13, 15, 17, 19, 21

   List B: 5, 8, 11, 14, 17, 20, 23, 26, 29, 32

   List C: 97, 86, 75, 64, 53

   List D: 100, 99, 98, 97, 96, 95, 94, 93, 92, 91

2. For each hundred chart, if you continued to color numbers in the same pattern, would the number 44 be colored? Explain.
3. Make a pattern of your own like the ones shown. Color in a hundred chart, and then write a list of all the numbers less than 50 in your pattern.
4. Trade lists with a partner. Ask the partner to determine if a certain number greater than 50 will be in your pattern.

DID YOU KNOW?

Fractals are complex mathematical pictures based on simple patterns that are repeated over and over.

Learn Numerical Patterns

A numerical pattern is a list of numbers that occur in some predictable way. Numerical patterns can be used to describe real-world things, such as population growth and the decay of materials. They can also be used to generate art such as fractals, which are complex math pictures created by repeating a simple math pattern.

MEETING INDIVIDUAL NEEDS

Resources

- **2-9** Practice
- **2-9** Reteaching
- **2-9** Problem Solving
- **2-9** Enrichment
- **2-9** Daily Transparency
  - Problem of the Day
  - Review
  - Quick Quiz
- Teaching Tool Transparency 13

Learning Modalities

Kinesthetic Use some type of manipulative, such as blocks, to show number patterns.

Individual Encourage students to monitor what they are thinking as they look for a pattern. Ask if they guess and check when they are looking for patterns and if their first guess is always correct.

Inclusion

Many students have difficulty perceiving patterns when only one learning modality is used (numbers only, pictures or cubes only, words only). Translating from one modality to another can be very helpful for students. You may want to group students with different modality preferences together to help improve comprehension.

Many patterns use addition and subtraction. To find the pattern, write the number that you need to add or subtract to find the next number in the pattern.

Examples

For each pattern, find the next three numbers.

1 8, 15, 22, 29, 36, ...

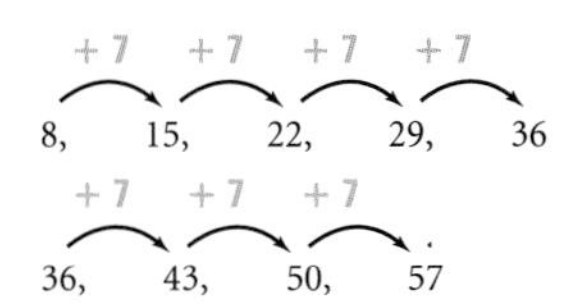

Write the number you must add to each number to get the next number.

Use the pattern to calculate the next three numbers.

2 50, 49, 47, 44, 40, ...

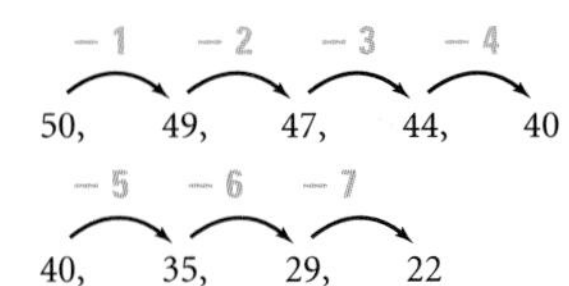

Write the number you must subtract to get the next number.

Use the pattern to calculate the next three numbers.

3 14, 24, 22, 32, 30, ...

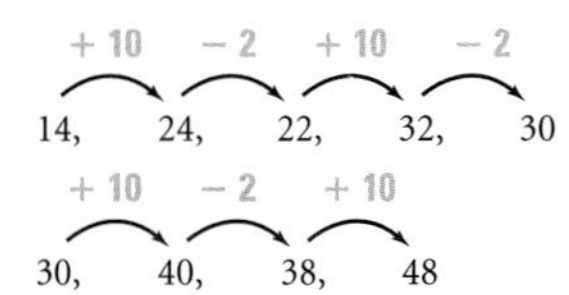

Write the number you must add or subtract to get the next number.

Use the pattern to calculate the next three numbers.

4 Ayana bought a stamp for $3. The dealer told her that next year it would be worth $6, the year after that $12, and the year after that $24. If the stamp continues to increase in value this way, what will it be worth in 6 years?

3, 6, 12, 24, ...? — Write the pattern.

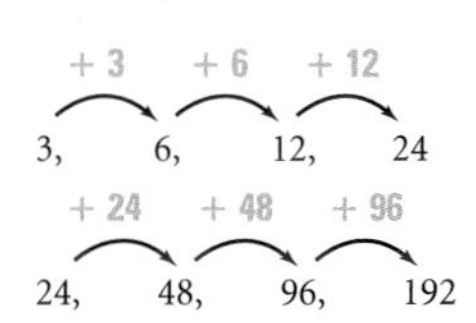

Write the number you must add to get the next number.

Use the pattern to calculate the value 6 years from now.

The stamp will be worth $192 dollars.

▶ Language Link

Stamp collectors are sometimes known as *philatelists* (fill-lah-tuhl-ists).

Try It

For each pattern, find the next number.

a. 10, 12, 15, 19, 24, ... **b.** 30, 26, 22, 18, 14, ...

MATH EVERY DAY

▶ Problem of the Day

486,486 is a *tantonym*, a six-digit number that contains a pattern of repeating digits. Write any three-digit number. Repeat these digits again so you have a tantonym. Divide this number by 13, then by 11, then by 7. Describe what happens. The original 3-digit number appears.

Available on Daily Transparency 2-9

An Extension is provided in the transparency package.

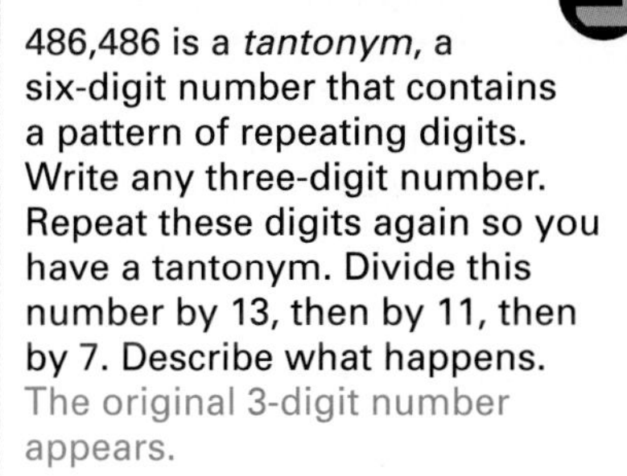

Fact of the Day

Many people enjoy collecting postage stamps. The first gummed stamps issued in the United States went on sale in 1847.

Mental Math

Do these mentally.

1. $3 \times 32 + 1$ 97
2. $400 \div 40 - 5$ 5
3. $30 + 129 + 22$ 181
4. $2001 - 198$ 1803

Answers for Explore

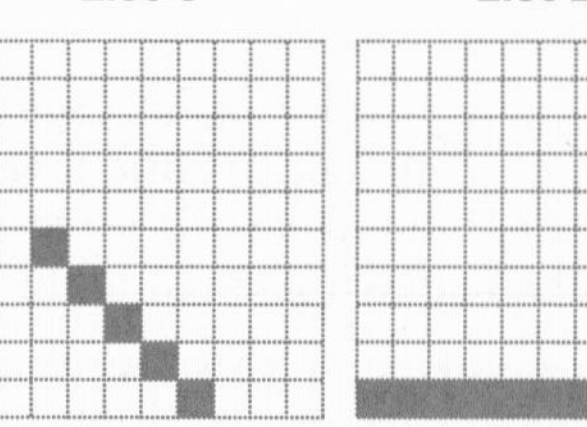

2. List A: No, 44 is not an odd number; List B: Yes, the pattern adds 3 to the previous number; List C: No, the pattern subtracts 11 from the previous number; List D: Yes, every number is included.

3–4. Answers may vary.

2 Teach

Learn

Alternate Examples

For each example, find the next three numbers.

1. 5, 11, 17, 23, 29, ...

   +6 +6 +6 +6
   5, 11, 17, 23, 29

   +6 +6 +6
   29, 35, 41, 47

2. 60, 58, 54, 48, 40, ...

   −2 −4 −6 −8
   60, 58, 54, 48, 40

   −10 −12 −14
   40, 30, 18, 4

3. 1, 6, 3, 8, 5, ...

   +5 −3 +5 −3
   1, 6, 3, 8, 5

   +5 −3 +5
   5, 10, 7, 12

4. Jose has a baseball card that is worth $4 now. The dealer says it will be worth $8 next year, $16 the year after that, and $32 the year after that. If the card continues to increase in value this way, what will it be worth five years from now?

   +4 +8 +16
   4, 8, 16, 32

   +32 +64
   32, 64, 128

   The card will be worth $128.

Answers for Try It

a. 30 b. 10

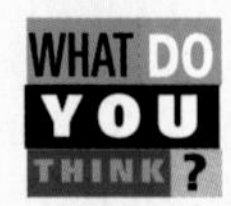

Students see two different ways of looking at a number pattern. One involves adding, while the other involves multiplying and adding.

Answers for What Do You Think?

1. Possible answer: Susana's method, because she doesn't have to keep track of what she needs to add or multiply every time to get the new number.
2. Add 2^2 to the 1st number, 2^3 to the 2nd number, 2^4 to the 3rd number, 2^5 to the 4th, and so on.

3 Practice and Assess

Check

Students should note that by finding the differences between terms, we can use arithmetic to help us extend and describe patterns.

Answers for Check Your Understanding

1. Arithmetic helps you understand how to get from one number to the next in a pattern.
2. No. Possible answers: Some go up and down; Some go up or down by varying amounts.

Skye and Susana are doing an experiment on the growth of mold. The table shows the data they collected. They want to know how long it will take for the mold to weigh at least 1000 grams.

Day	Weight (g)
1	3
2	7
3	15
4	31
5	63

Skye thinks . . .

The pattern is to add twice as much as the number you added before. I'll continue the pattern until I reach 1000 or more.

+ 4, + 8, + 16, + 32, + 64, + 128, + 256, + 512

3, 7, 15, 31, 63, 127, 255, 511, 1023

It will weigh more than one thousand grams on Day 9.

Susana thinks . . .

The pattern is that each number is one more than twice the previous number. I'll continue the pattern until I reach 1000 or more.

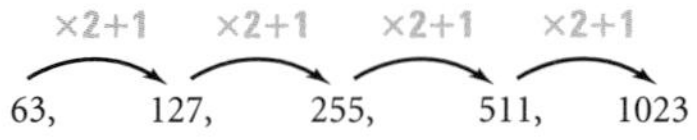

63, 127, 255, 511, 1023

It will weigh more than 1000 grams on Day 9.

What do you think?

1. If you had to continue the pattern without using a calculator, which method would you prefer? Explain.
2. Can you describe the pattern in a way that is different from both Skye's and Susana's methods? Explain.

Check Your Understanding

1. How can you use arithmetic to understand a numerical pattern?
2. Does every numerical pattern go up or down by the same number?

MEETING MIDDLE SCHOOL CLASSROOM NEEDS

Tips from Middle School Teachers

I use the hundred chart that the students generate in **Explore** as a bulletin board display and challenge students to find as many of the patterns as they can. Sometimes this is very competitive, but at other times, the students work together to find patterns. I usually give two prizes: one for the person or team who finds the most patterns and one for the person whose pattern is found least often.

Team Teaching

Ask other team members for examples of number patterns that students can use for analysis. Good examples might be plant or animal growth, population, or costs.

Consumer

Sometimes the stamps most valued by collectors are those containing a printing error. In 1989 an American buyer paid $1.1 million for a "Curtiss Jenny" plate block of four 24-cent stamps from 1918 with an inverted image of an airplane.

2-9 Exercises and Applications

Practice and Apply

1. a. Add b. Add c. Subtract d. Subtract e. Subtract f. Subtract g. Subtract h. Add

1. **Getting Started** Determine if you add or subtract to get the next number.

a. 5, 10, 15, 20, … **b.** 4, 8, 12, 16, … **c.** 13, 10, 7, 4, … **d.** 22, 21, 20, …
e. 33, 28, 23, 18,… **f.** 64, 57, 50, 43, … **g.** 18, 12, 6, 0, … **h.** 28, 32, 36, …

Write the number you must add or subtract to get the next number.

2. 17, 21, 25, 29, 33, … Add 4
3. 15, 18, 21, 24, 27, … Add 3
4. 7, 7, 7, 7, 7, … Add or subtract 0
5. 22, 35, 48, 61, 74, … Add 13
6. 38, 31, 24, 17, 10, … Subtract 7
7. 9, 8, 7, 6, 5, …
8. 1234, 1244, 1254, 1264, 1274, … Add 10
9. 45, 56, 67, 78, 89, … Add 11
10. 66, 72, 78, 84, 90, … Add 6
11. 7826, 7797, 7768, 7739, 7710, … Subtract 29
12. 299, 267, 235, 203, 171, … Subtract 32
13. 42, 34, 26, 18, 10, … Subtract 8
14. 999, 1002, 1005, 1008, 1011, … Add 3
15. 29, 44, 59, 74, 89, … Add 15
16. 101, 91, 81, 71, 61, … Subtract 10
17. 2158, 2216, 2274, 2332, 2390, … Add 58

Find the next three numbers in the pattern.

18. 142, 143, 145, 148, 152, … 157, 163, 170
19. 299, 293, 288, 282, 277, … 271, 266, 260
20. 480, 492, 486, 498, 492, 504, … 498, 510, 504
21. 106, 100, 94, 88, 82, … 76, 70, 64
22. 89, 79, 70, 62, 55, … 49, 44, 40
23. 965, 968, 974, 983, 995, … 1010, 1028, 1049
24. 62, 59, 64, 61, 66, … 63, 68, 65
25. 6, 8, 7, 9, 8, … 10, 9, 11
26. 43, 44, 46, 49, 53, … 58, 64, 71
27. 0, 5, 20, 45, 80, … 125, 180, 245
28. 22, 24, 28, 34, 42, … 52, 64, 78
29. 1111, 1115, 1119, 1123, 1127, … 1131, 1135, 1139
30. 15, 21, 27, 33, 39, … 45, 51, 57
31. 441, 394, 410, 363, 379, … 332, 348, 301

32. Tanya bought a collector's baseball card for $34. She was told that it would be worth $11 more each year. How much will the card be worth in 10 years? $144

33. Tanya sold a baseball card for $38. Its value increased $4 each of the four years she owned it. How much did she originally pay for the card? $22

PRACTICE 2-9

2-9 Exercises and Applications

Assignment Guide

- **Basic** 1–17, 25–30, 32–35, 38–56 evens
- **Average** 1–31 odds, 32–36, 38–48, 49–55 odds
- **Enriched** 3–17 odds, 18–48, 50–56 evens

Exercise Notes

Exercises 1–17

Extension You may want to ask students to write the next three numbers in the pattern for each of these exercises.

Exercise 32

Problem-Solving Tip Some students may think of the solution to this problem as 10 × 11 + 34 rather than generating all of the numbers in the list. Students should be encouraged to look at different ways of solving the problem, deciding for themselves which way they prefer.

PRACTICE

Name ______________

Practice 2-9

Numerical Patterns

Write the number you must add or subtract to get the next number.

1. 3, 10, 17, 24, 31, ... Add 7
2. 88, 87, 86, 85, 84, ... Subtract 1
3. 91, 86, 81, 76, 71, ... Subtract 5
4. 5, 8, 11, 14, 17, ... Add 3
5. 47, 43, 39, 35, 31, ... Subtract 4
6. 21, 30, 39, 48, 57, ... Add 9
7. 225, 240, 255, 270, ... Add 15
8. 144, 132, 120, 108, ... Subtract 12
9. 681, 660, 639, 618, ... Subtract 21
10. 318, 355, 392, 429, ... Add 37

Find the next three numbers in the pattern.

11. 6, 14, 22, 30, 38, 46, 54, 62, ...
12. 100, 92, 84, 76, 68, 60, 52, 44, ...
13. 20, 30, 35, 45, 50, 60, 65, 75, ...
14. 123, 110, 97, 84, 71, 58, 45, 32, ...
15. 217, 302, 387, 472, 557, 642, 727, ...
16. 5, 11, 23, 47, 95, 191, 383, 767, ...
17. 1, 2, 4, 8, 16, 32, 64, 128, ...
18. 294, 276, 258, 240, 222, 204, 186, ...
19. 20, 24, 30, 38, 48, 60, 74, 90, ...
20. 1, 4, 9, 16, 25, 36, 49, 64, ...
21. 21, 26, 24, 29, 27, 32, 30, 35, ...

22. In 1996, it cost 32¢ to mail a 1-oz letter, 55¢ to mail a 2-oz letter, 78¢ to mail a 3-oz letter, and $1.01 to mail a 4-oz letter. If the pattern continues, how much did it cost to send a 7-oz letter? $1.70

23. **Science** Kris is conducting a science experiment with bacteria. She begins with 15 organisms. If the number of organisms triples every day, how many organisms will she have after 4 days? 1215

RETEACHING

Name ______________

Alternative Lesson 2-9

Numerical Patterns

A **numerical pattern** is a list of numbers that occur in some predictable way. Many patterns use addition and subtraction. To find the pattern, write the number that you need to add or subtract to find the next number in the pattern.

— Example 1 —

Find the next three numbers in this pattern: 25, 30, 35, 40,...

Step 1: Determine the pattern: 25 30 35 40 (+5 +5 +5)

Since each number in the pattern is 5 more than the number before, the pattern is add 5.

Step 2: Use the pattern to calculate the next three numbers.
40 + 5 = **45** 45 + 5 = **50** 50 + 5 = **55**

The next three numbers in the pattern are 45, 50, and 55.

Try It Find the next three numbers in this pattern: 92, 90, 88, 86, ...

a. Pattern: −2
b. Next three numbers: 84, 82, 80

Find the next three numbers in the pattern.

c. 15, 30, 45, 60, ... 75, 90, 105
d. 24, 21, 18, 15, ... 12, 9, 6

— Example 2 —

Find the next three numbers in this pattern: 1, 7, 2, 8, 3, 9, 4,...

Step 1: Determine the pattern: 1 7 2 8 3 9 4 (+6 −5 +6 −5 +6 −5)

The pattern is add 6, subtract 5.

Step 2: Use the pattern to calculate the next three numbers.
4 + 6 = **10** 10 − 5 = **5** 5 + 6 = **11**

The next three numbers in the pattern are 10, 5, and 11.

Try It Find the next three numbers in this pattern: 10, 20, 15, 25, 20, 30, ...

e. Pattern: +10, −5
f. Next three numbers: 25, 35, 30

Find the next three numbers in the pattern.

g. 5, 4, 9, 8, 13, 12, ... 17, 16, 21
h. 6, 4, 8, 6, 10, 8, ... 12, 10, 14
i. 20, 22, 25, 27, 30, ... 32, 35, 37
j. 60, 50, 45, 35, 30, ... 20, 15, 5

Reteaching

Activity

Materials: Cubes

- In each of the following, the total number of cubes used makes a pattern. Find the next two numbers in each pattern. Describe each pattern in words.

1. 7, 9; Add 2.

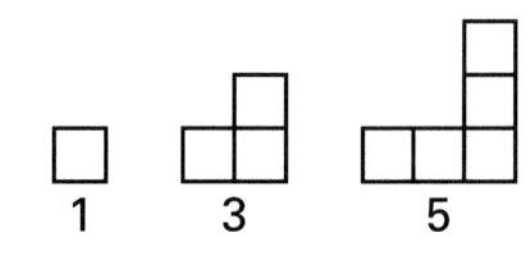

2. 14, 17; Add 3.

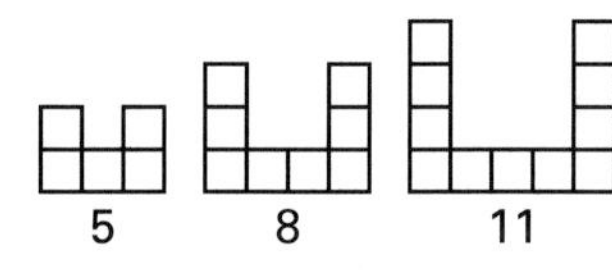

3. 20, 24; Add 4.

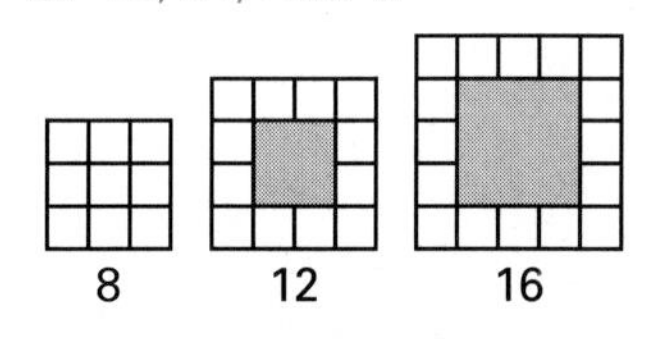

Exercise Notes

■ **Exercises 49–56**

Error Prevention Students should select an appropriate method for doing these problems, using calculators when there are many digits.

Exercise Answers

37. 2, 8, 32, 128, 512, 2048

38. After 9 more steps in the first set of numbers and after 8 more steps in the second set of numbers, both sets will have the number 378.

39. Possible answer: Look at about 5 numbers to know what the pattern looks like.

40. Add the previous 2 numbers together to get the next number. Next numbers: 34, 55, 89.

Alternate Assessment

Portfolio Have students select examples of their work in this section that illustrate their understanding of estimation, mental math, order of operations, and/or number patterns.

► Quick Quiz

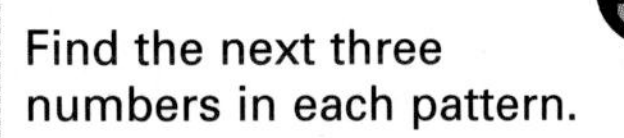

Find the next three numbers in each pattern.

1. 77, 72, 67, 62, 57, ... 52, 47, 42
2. 10, 17, 24, 31, 38, ... 45, 52, 59
3. 5, 6, 8, 11, 15, ... 20, 26, 33
4. 20, 22, 21, 23, 22, ... 24, 23, 25
5. 5, 10, 20, 40, 80, ... 160, 320, 640

Available on Daily Transparency 2-9

34. Science Jeff is conducting a science experiment with a three-rabbit population. Every month, the rabbit population doubles. How many rabbits will he have after 5 months? 96

35. Social Science In 1965, there were 500 students entering Atherton Middle School. In 1975, there were 450. In 1985, there were 525. In 1995, there were 475. If this pattern continues, how many students will there be in 2005? 550

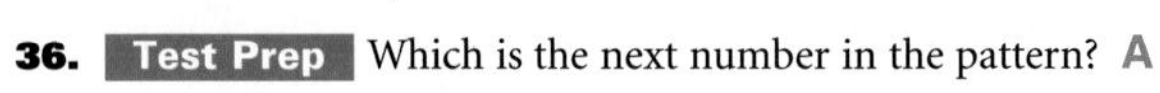

36. **Test Prep** Which is the next number in the pattern? A

224, 230, 222, 228, 220, 226, ...

Ⓐ 218 Ⓑ 220 Ⓒ 232 Ⓓ 234

Problem Solving and Reasoning

37. Critical Thinking Create a six-number pattern that starts at 2, ends at 2048, and uses multiplication to get the next number.

38. Communicate After how many more steps will these patterns have a matching number in them? Explain.

234, 246, 258, 270, ... and 235, 248, 261, 274, ...

39. Journal How many numbers in a pattern do you need to see to figure out the pattern?

40. Critical Thinking The following pattern is called the *Fibonacci series*, named after the thirteenth-century mathematician who developed it. Describe the pattern and find the next three numbers.

1, 1, 2, 3, 5, 8, 13, 21, ...

PROBLEM SOLVING 2-9

Mixed Review

Simplify mentally. *[Lesson 2-5]*

41. $64 + 102$ 166 **42.** $150 + 157$ 307 **43.** $1762 - 101$ 1661 **44.** $22,839 - 10,838$ 12,001

45. 41×5 205 **46.** $236 + 504 + 44$ 784 **47.** $36,000 \div 6,000$ 6 **48.** $49,000 \div 700$ 70

Multiply. *[Previous course]*

49. $\$2.34 \times 52$ \$121.68 **50.** $\$6.35 \times 365$ \$2317.75 **51.** $\$245.75 \times 754$ \$185,295.50 **52.** $261 \times \$982.20$ \$256,354.20

53. $\$1.70 \times 14$ \$23.80 **54.** $\$4.87 \times 21$ \$102.27 **55.** $\$66.06 \times 22$ \$1453.32 **56.** $11 \times \$34.57$ \$380.27

PROBLEM SOLVING

Name ______________

Guided Problem Solving 2-9

GPS PROBLEM 34, STUDENT PAGE 106

Jeff is conducting a science experiment with a (three-rabbit population.) (Every month, the rabbit population doubles.) How many rabbits will he have (after 5 months?)

— Understand —

1. Circle the information you need.
2. What does it mean for the population to "double?" Two times larger.
3. Will the rabbit population get larger or smaller? Larger.

— Plan —

4. Will you use addition or multiplication to solve the problem? Either.
5. What is the numerical pattern? Double the preceding number.
6. Which would be a reasonable answer for the number of rabbits Jeff will have in 5 months? b

   a. about 20 b. about 200 c. about 2000

— Solve —

7. How many rabbits will Jeff have after 1 month? 6 rabbits.
8. Continue the pattern for months 1, 2, 3, 4, and 5.

   3, 6 (after: 1 mo), 12 (2 mo), 24 (3 mo), 48 (4 mo), 96 (5 mo)

9. Write a sentence to give the final answer. Possible answer: Jeff will have 96 rabbits after 5 months.

— Look Back —

10. What other strategies could you have used to find the answer? Possible answer: Make a Table.

SOLVE ANOTHER PROBLEM

Marie is conducting a science experiment with a four-mouse population. Every 2 months, the mouse population doubles. How many mice will she have after 8 months? 64 mice.

ENRICHMENT

Name ______________

Extend Your Thinking 2-9

Patterns in Numbers

Number patterns are like secret codes. Once you understand what the pattern is, you have the ability to extend the pattern. Create some number patterns and then share them with others in your class. See if you can "unlock the codes" of your classmates' number patterns.

1. The number pattern, "1, 4, 13, 16, 25..." is a two-addition pattern. The pattern is "+3, +9, +3, +9..." Create another pattern that is a two-addition pattern. Show at least ten numbers in your pattern.
   Possible answer: Pattern: +0, +2; 1, 1, 3, 3, 5, 5, 7, 7, 9, 9.
2. What is the number pattern in this sequence, "50, 60, 55, 65, 60, 70...?" Create another sequence of numbers using the same operations. Show at least ten numbers in your pattern.
   Possible answer: Pattern: +10, –5; 10, 20, 15, 25, 20, 30, 25, 35, 30, 40.
3. You can also use multiplication and division to create patterns. Create a pattern in which all numbers will be even numbers. Use at least three operations. Show at least ten numbers in your pattern.
   Possible answer: Pattern: ×2, +4, ÷2; 2, 4, 8, 4, 8, 12, 6, 12, 16, 8.
4. Create a pattern in which all numbers will be odd numbers. Use at least three operations. Show at least ten numbers in your pattern.
   Possible answer: Pattern: ×1, –2, +4; 5, 5, 3, 7, 7, 5, 9, 9, 7, 11.
5. A pattern needs to contain sufficient numbers to establish the pattern. Find at least three ways that these numbers could start a pattern: 2, 4... Then find the next five numbers in each pattern.
   Possible answer: Pattern: +2, –1; 2, 4, 3, 5, 4, 6, 5;
   Pattern: ×2, +3; 2, 4, 7, 14, 17, 34, 37;
   Pattern: +2, x2; 2, 4, 8, 10, 20, 22, 44.

Section 2B Connect

In this section, you've learned about simplifying problems mentally, using estimation techniques, the order of operations, and numerical patterns. Now you will apply what you have learned by creating a test that requires the use of these techniques.

First Class Collectibles

Write a test consisting of nine word problems. Each problem should involve one or more of the prices of the collectibles shown on this page. You can use the same collectible in more than one problem.

Three of your problems should ask for mental math solutions.

Three of your problems should ask for estimated solutions.

Three of your problems should ask for the next number in a numerical pattern.

Your problems should require test-takers to use some (though not necessarily all) of these methods: patterns, the Distributive Property, compatible numbers, compensation, front-end estimation, clustering, and rounding. Be sure to give the answers to all of your problems.

Here's a sample problem: Estimate how many short penguins you can buy for $100. Answer: About 5.

First Class Collectibles

The Point

In *First Class Collectibles* on page 85, students discussed the value of old stamps and letters. Now they will incorporate estimation techniques and the Distributive Property in problems they write about collectibles.

About the Page

- Tell students that they have the opportunity to be the teacher or author and to write the test for this section.
- Remind students to keep the objectives of these lessons in mind as they write problems. Review the **You'll Learn ...** statements at the beginning of each lesson.
- Tell students to make the problems interesting and challenging, but not too hard or too easy.
- Ask students to write answers to their problems.

Ongoing Assessment

Check that students are writing clear and appropriate questions, using the required objectives.

Extension

- Divide students into small groups. Have one student administer the test he or she wrote to the other students in the group. Each student administering a test should collect and grade that test.
- Ask the students taking the test to evaluate the test they took for clarity and to determine if the test problems tested mental math, estimating solutions, and numerical patterns.
- Each student in the group should have an opportunity to give his or her test to the other students.

Answers for Connect

Answers may vary.

2B Review

Review Correlation

Item(s)	Lesson(s)
1–5	2-5
6–18	2-6, 2-7
19–23	2-8
24–26	2-6

Test Prep

Test-Taking Tip

Tell students that more than one form of estimation can be used in judging unreasonable answers. In Exercise 25, students can use front-end estimation to eliminate Answers A and C. Clustering can then be used to eliminate Answer D.

Answers for Review

24. Possible answer: In 1980 the stamp was worth almost 100 million times its original value.

Section 2B Review

REVIEW 2B

Simplify, using mental math.

1. 300×200 60,000 **2.** $4 \times 3 \times 25$ 300 **3.** $604 + 275$ 879 **4.** 19×5 95 **5.** $240{,}000 \div 60$ 4000

Estimate.

6. $3479 + 4625$ 8000 **7.** $503 \times 22 \times 3$ 30,000 **8.** $488 \div 7$ 70 **9.** $831 - 546$ 300

10. $8281 + 3444$ 11,000 **11.** $24{,}700 - 8{,}300$ 17,000 **12.** $49 \times 2 \times 16$ 1600 **13.** $2409 \div 81$ 30

14. $23 + 26 + 27 + 20$ 100 **15.** 98×230 23,000 **16.** 19×42 800 **17.** $413 + 405 + 399 + 385$ 1600

18. Antique postcards cost $5 each. Estimate how many you could buy for $550. 110

In Exercises 19–23, match the problem and the solution. Each solution is used exactly once.

19. $(6 - 3) \times (5 + 1 \times 4)$ C — A. 0

20. $5^2 + 7$ B — B. 32

21. $5 + 3 \times 5 + 3 \times 5$ D — C. 27

22. $(100 \div 50 - 2) \times 3$ A — D. 35

23. $8^2 - 2^2 + 4^2$ E — E. 76

24. Communicate An 1856 British Guiana stamp originally sold for 1¢. In 1980, a stamp collector bought it for $935,000. Using any method you can think of, compare the 1856 value of the stamp with the 1980 value.

Test Prep

On a multiple-choice test, you can use estimation to eliminate unreasonable answers.

25. Find the sum: 2,487 + 2,546 + 2,490 + 2,531 B

Ⓐ 1,054 Ⓑ 10,054 Ⓒ 20,540 Ⓓ 6,054

26. Find the difference: 20,050 − 5,100 − 9,995 C

Ⓐ 13,955 Ⓑ 495 Ⓒ 4,955 Ⓓ 35,145

Resources

Practice Masters
Section 2B Review

Assessment Sourcebook
Quiz 2B

TestWorks
Test and Practice Software

PRACTICE

Name ______________________ Practice

Section 2B Review

Simplify using mental math.

1. 8 × 7 × 25 1,400 2. 127 + 311 438 3. 60,000 ÷ 300 200
4. 40 × 5,000 200,000 5. 97 + 387 484 6. 450,000 ÷ 150 3,000

Estimate.

7. 3,827 + 1,789 5,600 8. 364 × 738 280,000 9. 58 + 62 + 57 + 61 240
10. 5,394 − 1,286 4,100 11. 3,842 + 9,169 13,000 12. 71,835 ÷ 5981 12

In Exercises 13–16, match the problem and the operation needed to solve it. Each operation is used exactly once.

Sherry's class has 35 students. Carrie's class has 28 students.

13. Sherry's class is split into five equal groups. How many students are in each group? D
14. How much larger is Sherry's class than Carrie's? B
15. Everyone in Sherry's class shook hands with everyone in Carrie's class. How many handshakes took place? C
16. Sherry's class and Carrie's class went on a field trip together. How many students went on the trip? A

(A) addition
(B) subtraction
(C) multiplication
(D) division

Use the Channel Capacity of U.S. Televisions graph to answer each question. *[Lesson 1-1]*

Channel Capacity of U.S. Televisions, 1993
37-48 channels 25%
49 or more channels 45%
12-36 channels 30%

17. What percent of U.S. televisions had 49 or more channels? 45%

18. Which category included exactly 25% of the televisions? 37–48 channels

19. Cedina needs to give a 1293-kilobyte computer file to her friend. Since the capacity of her floppy disk, 1440 kilobytes, rounds to 1000 kilobytes, she is worried that the file might not fit on the disk. Should she be concerned? Explain.
No. 1,293 is less than 1,440.

Introduction to Algebra

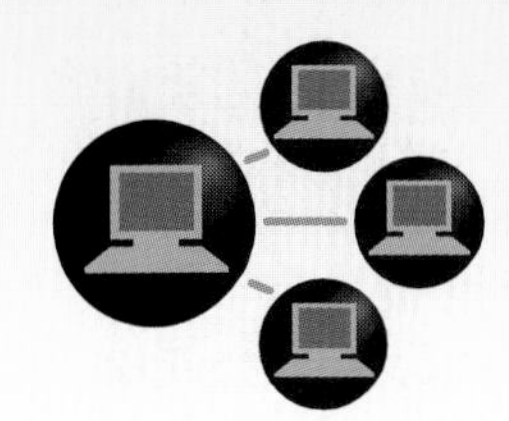

Visit **www.teacher.mathsurf.com** for links to lesson plans from teachers and other professionals, NCTM information, and other sites.

LESSON PLANNING GUIDE

Student Edition			Ancillaries*	
LESSON	MATERIALS	VOCABULARY	DAILY	OTHER
Section 2C Opener				
2-10 Variables and Expressions		variable, constant, expression	2-10	Technology Master 9
2-11 Writing Expressions		sum, difference, product, quotient	2-11	
2-12 Using Equations		equation	2-12	*Interactive CD-ROM Lesson*
2-13 Solving Equations			2-13	Technology Master 10 Ch. 2 Project Master *WW Math*—Middle School
Technology	spreadsheet software			*Interactive CD-ROM Spreadsheet/Grapher Tool*
Connect				Interdisc. Team Teaching 2C
Review				Practice 2C; Quiz 2C; *TestWorks*
Extend Key Ideas				
Chapter 2 Summary and Review				
Chapter 2 Assessment				Ch. 2 Tests Forms A–F *TestWorks*; Ch. 2 Letter Home
Cumulative Review, Chapters 1–2				Cumulative Review Ch. 1–2

* Daily Ancillaries include Practice, Reteaching, Problem Solving, Enrichment, and Daily Transparency. Teaching Tool Transparencies are in *Teacher's Toolkits*. Lesson Enhancement Transparencies are in *Overhead Transparency Package*.

SKILLS TRACE

LESSON	SKILL	FIRST INTRODUCED GR. 4	GR. 5	GR. 6	DEVELOP	PRACTICE/APPLY	REVIEW
2-10	**Evaluating expressions.**			✘ p. 110	pp. 110–111	pp. 112–113	pp. 121, 131, 141, 312, 332
2-11	**Translating words to expressions.**			✘ p. 114	pp. 114–115	pp. 116–117	pp. 131, 146
2-12	**Testing values in equations.**			✘ p. 118	pp. 118–119	pp. 120–121	pp. 131, 152, 338
2-13	**Solving equations.**			✘ p. 122	pp. 122–123	pp. 124–125	pp. 131, 156, 345

INTERDISCIPLINARY TEAM TEACHING

Math and Science/Technology

(Worksheet pages 11–12: Teacher pages T11–T12)

In this lesson, students use introductory algebra to explore SCUBA diving.

Name ______________________ ***Math and Science/Technology***

Gearing Up to Dive Down

Use introductory algebra to explore SCUBA diving.

Oceanography is the study of the world's oceans. The scientists who specialize in this work are called oceanographers. Oceanographers explore many things in the oceans. For example, they trace the paths and temperatures of huge rivers in the ocean, which are called currents. They study waves and the salts that are dissolved in ocean water. They study how the oceans formed and how their bottoms are still changing, and they study the millions of different living things—animals, plants, and even tiny microorganisms—that live and interact in the ocean.

Some oceanographers explore the oceans from ships on the surface. Others go down thousands of feet in small submarines. Those who study the first few hundred feet of the ocean use a special device that frees them to swim with the fishes. That device was invented by two scientists in 1943, one of whom is Frenchman Jacques Cousteau, the most famous oceanographer in the world. His partner was another Frenchman, Emile Gagnon. The device they invented was SCUBA, which stands for self-contained underwater breathing apparatus.

Cousteau and Gagnon's invention consists of one, two, or three cylinders, or tanks, which divers carry on their backs. The cylinders contain a supply of compressed air which divers breathe through a special mouthpiece called a regulator. The regulator keeps the air flowing smoothly and comfortably as the diver moves from one depth to another. It does this by delivering the air at the same pressure as the surrounding water. The pressure of the water is caused by its weight. The deeper the water, the greater the pressure. For a diver to breathe under water, the pressure of the air coming out of the mouthpiece must equal the pressure of the water. So you can appreciate the importance of a regulator.

Before undersea explorers can make a dive, they must consider the amount of air in their tanks, the depth of their dive, and how active they will be. All of these factors determine how long a diver can stay under the water.

Scuba divers carry a limited supply of compressed air in one or more tanks strapped to their backs. Before entering the water, scuba divers must calculate how long their air supply will last so they do not run out of air while deep underwater.

Name ______________________ ***Math and Science/Technology***

1. Divers know how much air is in their tanks before they put them on. They also know that if they are very active in the water, they will use up more air than if they are less active. The following two expressions describe this situation.

First expression

Amount of air = 2 full tanks

Depth = 50 feet

Activity = swimming

Time till air runs out = 60 minutes

Second expression

Amount of air = 2 full tanks

Depth = 50 feet

Activity = floating

Time till air runs out = 90 minutes

What is the variable in the expressions?

activity

2. a. Using scuba gear, some divers reach a depth of 400 feet or more. However, the farther down divers go, the greater the water pressure that is exerted on them. The water pressure, in turn, affects the rate at which air is used by the diver. The greater the depth, the faster the air will be used up. What is the variable in these expressions?

depth or water pressure

b. A diver dives to an unknown number of feet. (Let d represent the unknown number of feet.) Then, she doubles her depth. Then she triples her depth, and finally, she quadruples her depth. Write expressions to represent each stage of the diver's plunge.

$d, 2d, 3d, 4d$

3. Write an equation for each situation:

a. A diver dives 49 feet, then f feet, and then 68 feet. He descends a total of 150 feet.

$49 + f + 68 = 150$

b. A diver dives 247 feet and then comes back up t feet to 112 feet.

$247 - t = 112$

4. Why is it important that divers be able to calculate mathematical equations before they begin their dives?

See below.

5. Why was Cousteau and Gagnon's invention of scuba equipment a breakthrough in undersea exploration technology?

See below.

6. At sea level, the gases we breathe—mainly nitrogen and oxygen—are either harmless or beneficial to us. But deep in the water, these gases can be deadly. Do some research to find out the conditions under which nitrogen and oxygen can be dangerous to a diver's health. Describe how those dangers can be avoided.

See below.

7. Do some research on new developments in diving technology Create a display of your findings by mounting and labeling drawings or photographs.

Answers

4. Students' responses may vary. There are variables that must be considered, such as physical activity and depth or water pressure, so divers will know how long their air will last while they are under the water.

5. It allowed divers to move about freely under the water. Before the invention of scuba equipment, divers' movements were limited by air hoses and life lines.

6. Dangers: "rapture of the deep" (nitrogen narcosis), bends, oxygen poisoning. Avoidance: breathing different gas mixtures, slow ascent.

BIBLIOGRAPHY

FOR TEACHERS

Mount, Ellis and List, Barbara A. *Milestones in Science and Technology*. Phoenix, AZ: Oryx Press, 1994.

Discovery Box Series: Planets. New York, NY: Scholastic, 1996.

The Reader's Digest Illustrated Book of Dogs. Pleasantville, NY: Reader's Digest Association, 1993.

Spangler, David. *Math for Real Kids*. Glenview, IL: Good Year Books, 1997.

FOR STUDENTS

The Times Atlas and Encyclopedia of the Sea. New York, NY: Harper & Row, 1990.

SECTION

2C Introduction to Algebra

▶ Science Link ▶ www.mathsurf.com/6/ch2/oceans

JOURNEY TO THE BOTTOM OF THE SEA

Oceanographers use many tools to study the ocean, such as scuba equipment, diving spheres, remote controlled robots, and mathematics. What do we know about life under the sea?

500 ft Most familiar fish and mammals live near the surface. Pressure about 220 lb/in².

1,000 ft Sharks, whales, octopus, and squid venture this depth. Pressure about 440 lb/in².

2,300 ft Lower limit for light. All creatures below this point live in total darkness. Pressure about 1,000 lb/in².

3,200 ft Some fish here have large eyes for seeing in the dark. Others make their own light. Pressure about 1,400 lb/in².

6,400 ft Fish here are gelatin-like. Many are blind. Pressure about 2,800 lb/in².

10,000 ft Water temperature only a few degrees above freezing. Little food, a few simple organisms. Pressure about 4,400 lb/in².

35,840 ft Deepest point in ocean. Temperature below freezing. Pressure about 15,800 lb/in².

1 Compare the pressures at 500 ft and 1,000 ft; at 3,200 ft and 6,400 ft; at 1,000 ft and 10,000 ft. What patterns do you see? Do you think it's possible to predict the pressure at any depth? Explain.

2 Why do darkness, coldness, and pressure increase as you descend farther into the ocean?

Where are we now?

In Section 2B, students used number sense to solve arithmetic problems.

They learned how to

- solve problems mentally.
- estimate sums and differences.
- estimate products and quotients.
- apply the order of operations when solving problems.

Where are we going?

In Section 2C, students will

- identify and extend number patterns.
- write expressions using variables.
- translate words into mathematical expressions.
- write and solve equations.

Section 2C

Theme: Oceans

World Wide Web

If your class has access to the World Wide Web, you might want to use the information found at the Web site addresses given. The interdisciplinary link relates to topics discussed in this section.

About the Page

This page introduces the theme of the section, oceans, and discusses the study and exploration of the ocean.

Ask ...

- Did you ever go swimming in the ocean and see any fish or other animal life?
- Have you visited an aquarium to see the plant and animal life that lives in the sea?
- Why does pressure increase as you go deeper into the water?

Extension

The following activity does not require access to the World Wide Web.

Science

Have students investigate careers related to the study of the ocean and report their findings to the class.

Answers for Questions

1. If the depth is twice as deep, pressure is twice as much; if depth is ten times as deep, pressure is ten times as much. Using this pattern, it would be possible to predict the pressure at any depth.
2. Darkness and coldness increase because the sun's rays cannot travel down that far. Pressure increases the farther down you go because there is more water above you.

Connect

On page 127, students will determine the cost of renting equipment for deep-sea research.

2-10 Lesson Organizer

Objectives

- Understand the difference between a variable and a constant.
- Evaluate expressions.

Vocabulary

- Variable, constant, expression

NCTM Standards

- 1–4, 9

▶ Review

Evaluate each expression.

1. $4 + 3 \times 10$ 34
2. $25 - 6 \div 3$ 23
3. $6^2 + 14 - 7 \times 2$ 36
4. $(7 - 3)^2 + 1$ 17

Available on Daily Transparency 2-10

1 Introduce

Explore

The Point
Students examine a situation involving selling price, cost, and profit to note patterns and see the need for variables.

Ongoing Assessment
Some students may compute profit by subtracting the processing cost from the value of the gold without noticing that they can simply multiply the number of building-size volumes by 150.

For Groups That Finish Early
Describe the patterns you found in the chart.

Follow Up
Ask students to share their responses to Step 2. Be sure to probe for alternative ways of finding the number in the third column.

2-10 Variables and Expressions

You'll Learn ...

- the difference between a variable and a constant
- to evaluate expressions

... How It's Used

Accountants use variables to represent how much money a certain investment will return over time.

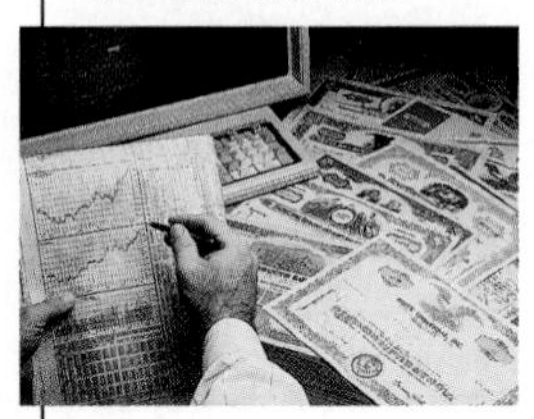

Vocabulary

variable

constant

expression

▶ **Lesson Link** You've learned to work with arithmetic expressions like 3×25, where both numbers are known. In this lesson, you'll learn how to work with expressions with one unknown number. ◀

Explore Operations and Patterns

Mining Your Own Business

The ocean is a treasure trove of dissolved materials. For example, a volume of sea water the size of a 30-story building contains about $400 worth of dissolved gold. Suppose you have invented a way to recover the gold from a building-size volume of water for $250.

1. Complete the table to show how much money you can make processing gold from ocean water.

Number of Building-Size Volumes	Value of Gold	Processing Cost	Profit
1	$400	$250	$150
2			
3			
4			
5			
10			
20			
50			
100			

2. How did you find each value in the second column? The third column? The fourth column?
3. Find the values in each column for 1 million building-size volumes of water.

MEETING INDIVIDUAL NEEDS

Resources

2-10 Practice
2-10 Reteaching
2-10 Problem Solving
2-10 Enrichment
2-10 Daily Transparency
  Problem of the Day
  Review
  Quick Quiz
Technology Master 9

Learning Modalities

Verbal Nonsense words can be used to represent a variable. This helps students understand that they can call the variable anything they want.

Visual Use visual examples of situations that involve expressions such as finding number of hands in a class by doubling the number of people in the class.

Challenge

Have students write and evaluate expressions with two operations, such as $2x + 3$. This combines the work with variables with the work done previously with order of operations.

Learn Variables and Expressions

A **variable** is a quantity that can change or vary. Water temperature is a variable because it changes from hour to hour. Mathematicians use letters to represent variables.

A quantity that does not change is a **constant**. The freezing temperature of water at sea level is a constant. It is always 32 degrees Fahrenheit.

An **expression** is a mathematical phrase involving constants, variables, and operation symbols. There are different ways to represent different operations.

Addition	Subtraction	Multiplication	Division
$8 + x$	$8 - x$	$8x$	$\frac{8}{x}$

If you know the values of the variable, you can evaluate the expression by replacing the variable with each value. This is known as substituting a value for the variable.

DID YOU KNOW?

x is the letter that mathematicians use most often for a variable, but you can use any letter to represent a variable.

Examples

Evaluate the expression for $x = 1$, 2, and 3.

1 $x + 5$

x	$x + 5$
1	$1 + 5 = 6$
2	$2 + 5 = 7$
3	$3 + 5 = 8$

2 $11 - x$

x	$11 - x$
1	$11 - 1 = 10$
2	$11 - 2 = 9$
3	$11 - 3 = 8$

3 $4x$

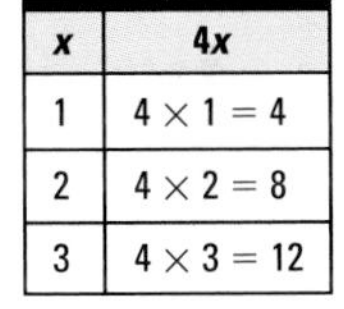

x	$4x$
1	$4 \times 1 = 4$
2	$4 \times 2 = 8$
3	$4 \times 3 = 12$

4 $\frac{12}{x}$

x	$\frac{12}{x}$
1	$12 \div 1 = 12$
2	$12 \div 2 = 6$
3	$12 \div 3 = 4$

Technology Link

Calculator buttons use variables to represent the number in the display. For example, the x^2 button will square the number in the display.

Try It

Evaluate the expression for $x = 3$, 4, and 5.

a. $7x$ 21, 28, 35 **b.** $15 - x$ 12, 11, 10 **c.** $\frac{60}{x}$ 20, 15, 12 **d.** $x + 23$ 26, 27, 28

MATH EVERY DAY

Problem of the Day

The perimeter of a rectangular room is 78 feet. One side measures 21 feet. What do the other sides measure? 18 ft, 18 ft, 21 ft

Available on Daily Transparency 2-10

An Extension is provided in the transparency package.

Fact of the Day

The deepest place in the ocean, the Marianas trench, is more than 6,000 feet deeper than Mount Everest is high.

Estimation

Estimate.

1. 52,023,445 ÷ 51,212 1000
2. 711 × 3,013 2,100,000
3. 41,923 ÷ 867 50

Answers for Explore

1. See page C2.
2. Multiplied 400 by the Number of Building-Size Volumes; multiplied 250 by the Number of Building-Size Volumes; subtracted the Processing Cost from the Value of the Gold or multiplied 150 times the Number of Building-Size Volumes.
3. Number of Volumes 1,000,000

   Value of Gold 400,000,000

   Processing Cost 250,000,000

   Profit 150,000,000

2 Teach

Learn

Alternate Examples

Evaluate each expression for $x = 1$, 2, and 3.

1.

x	$7 + x$
1	8
2	9
3	10

2.

x	$15 - x$
1	14
2	13
3	12

3.

x	$8x$
1	8
2	16
3	24

4.

x	$\frac{18}{x}$
1	18
2	9
3	6

2-10 Exercises and Applications

Assignment Guide

- **Basic**
  1–39 odds, 40–42, 45–53 odds
- **Average**
  1, 15–43, 45–54
- **Enriched**
  1, 15–44, 45–53 odds

3 Practice and Assess

Check

Answers for Check Your Understanding

1. Using a variable allows you to write and evaluate expressions.
2. $4m$; $100m$

Exercise Notes

Exercises 3–14

Error Prevention Point out that only the variable is replaced by a number; the signs between variables are operation signs that do not change.

Reteaching

Activity

Materials: Envelopes, unit squares made from construction paper

- Use an envelope marked with the letter x to represent the variable and unit squares for the number.
- Evaluate each expression for $x = 3$, 6, and 10 by putting 3, 6, and then 10 squares in the envelope.

1. $x + 2$ 5, 8, 12
2. $x + 6$ 9, 12, 16
3. $x + 5$ 8, 11, 15

- To evaluate an expression such as $2x$ for $x = 3$, 6, and 10, mark 2 envelopes with x and put 3, 6, and then 10 squares in each envelope.
- Evaluate each expression for $x = 3$, 6, and 10.

4. $4x$ 12, 24, 40
5. $7x$ 21, 42, 70
6. $5x$ 15, 30, 50

Check Your Understanding

1. What is the advantage of using a variable to represent a number?
2. How many quarters are there in m dollars? How many pennies?

2-10 Exercises and Applications

PRACTICE 2-10

Practice and Apply

1. **Getting Started** State whether the quantity should be represented by a variable or a constant.
   a. Number of days in January
   b. Price of a calculator
   c. Number of students in a school
   d. Number of inches in a foot
   e. Number of people in a state
   f. Number of giraffes in a herd

   a. Constant b. Variable c. Variable
   d. Constant e. Variable f. Variable

2. Complete the table.

x	$x + 1$	$2x$	$18 \div x$	$x - 1$
1	$1 + 1 = 2$	$2 \times 1 = 2$	$18 \div 1 = 18$	$1 - 1 = 0$
2	$2 + 1 = 3$	$2 \times 2 = 4$	$18 \div 2 = 9$	$2 - 1 = 1$
3	$3 + 1 = 4$	$2 \times 3 = 6$	$18 \div 3 = 6$	$3 - 1 = 2$

Evaluate each expression for $x = 2$, 3, and 4.

3. $x + 7$ 9, 10, 11
4. $12 - x$ 10, 9, 8
5. $6x$ 12, 18, 24
6. $\frac{24}{x}$ 12, 8, 6
7. $12 + x$ 14, 15, 16
8. $6x$ 12, 18, 24
9. $8x$ 16, 24, 32
10. $x - 1$ 1, 2, 3
11. $15 + x$ 17, 18, 19
12. $11x$ 22, 33, 44
13. $\frac{36}{x}$ 18, 12, 9
14. $\frac{x}{1}$ 2, 3, 4

Evaluate each expression for $x = 3$, 5, and 9.

15. $20 - x$ 17, 15, 11
16. $9x$ 27, 45, 81
17. $\frac{45}{x}$ 15, 9, 5
18. $36x$ 108, 180, 324
19. $x + 3$ 6, 8, 12
20. $x + 12$ 15, 17, 21
21. x 3, 5, 9
22. $\frac{135}{x}$ 45, 27, 15
23. $x + x$ 6, 10, 18
24. $1x$ 3, 5, 9
25. x^2 9, 25, 81
26. x^3 27, 125, 729

Evaluate each expression for $x = 2$, 4, and 7.

27. $\frac{56}{x}$ 28, 14, 8
28. $x - 2$ 0, 2, 5
29. $3x$ 6, 12, 21
30. $\frac{28}{x}$ 14, 7, 4
31. $5x$ 10, 20, 35
32. $8x$ 16, 32, 56
33. $4x$ 8, 16, 28
34. $16 - x$ 14, 12, 9
35. $27 + x$ 29, 31, 34
36. $39 + x$ 41, 43, 46
37. $x + 12$ 14, 16, 19
38. $\frac{x}{1}$ 2, 4, 7

PRACTICE

Name ______________________

Practice 2-10

Variables and Expressions

1. Complete the table by evaluating each expression for $x = 2$, 3, and 4.

x	$x + 5$	$17 - x$	$9x$	$\frac{144}{x}$	$x \times 7$	x^2	$5x$
2	7	15	18	72	14	4	10
3	8	14	27	48	21	9	15
4	9	13	36	36	28	16	20

2. Complete the table by evaluating each expression for $x = 3$, 5, and 9.

x	$16 + x$	$x - 3$	$12 \times x$	$90 \div x$	$20x$	$100 - x$	$x \div x$
3	19	0	36	30	60	97	1
5	21	2	60	18	100	95	1
9	25	6	108	10	180	91	1

3. Complete the table by evaluating each expression for $x = 2$, 4, and 7.

x	$x + 43$	$30 - x$	$x \times x$	$x \times 10$	$2x$	$\frac{112}{x}$	x^3
2	45	28	4	20	4	56	8
4	47	26	16	40	8	28	64
7	50	23	49	70	14	16	343

Complete the table.

4. Americans as a whole consume 90 acres of pizza every day.

Number of days	Number of acres of pizza
1	90
2	180
3	270
4	360
d	$90d$

5. Tennis balls are sold in packages of three balls.

Number of balls	Number of packages
30	10
72	24
378	126
999	333
t	$t/3$

RETEACHING

Name ______________________

Alternative Lesson 2-10

Variables and Expressions

A **variable** is a quantity that can change or vary. Mathematicians use letters to represent variables.

A quantity that does not change is a **constant.**

An **expression** is a mathematical phrase involving constants, variables, and operation symbols. There are different ways to represent different operations. Four examples are shown below.

Addition:	$x + 6$	x is the variable.	6 is the constant.
Subtraction:	$91 - x$	x is the variable.	91 is the constant.
Multiplication:	$3x$ or $3 \times x$	x is the variable.	3 is the constant.
Division:	$12 \div x$ or $\frac{12}{x}$	x is the variable.	12 is the constant.

If you know the values of the variable, you can *evaluate* the expression by replacing the variable with each value. This is known as *substituting a value for the variable.*

Example

Evaluate $2x$ for $x = 4$, 6, and 8.

$2x$ means "2 times x." To evaluate the expression, you need to substitute a value for x.

When $x = 4$, substitute 4 for x: You can make a table to evaluate the expression for multiple values of x.

x	$2x$
4	$2 \times 4 = 8$
6	$2 \times 6 = 12$
8	$2 \times 8 = 16$

So $2x = 8$ when $x = 4$, $2x = 12$ when $x = 6$, and $2x = 16$ when $x = 8$.

Try It Evaluate $x + 12$ for $x = 2$, 5, and 10.

a. Substitute 2 for x. Solve: $2 + 12 =$ 14
b. Substitute 5 for x. Solve: $5 + 12 =$ 17
c. Substitute 10 for x. Solve: $10 + 12 =$ 22

Evaluate each expression for $x = 2$, 5, and 10.

d. $6x$ 12 30 60
e. $x - 1$ 1 4 9
f. $50 \div x$ 25 10 5
g. $27 + x$ 29 32 37
h. $16 - x$ 14 11 6
i. $\frac{100}{x}$ 50 20 10

Complete each table.

39. History In 1776, there were 13 stars on every United States flag.

Number of Flags	Number of Stars
1	
2	
3	
4	
w	

40. Science An average blue whale eats 9000 pounds of food each day. GPS

Amount of Food (lb)	Number of Days
63,000	
81,000	
126,000	
f	

41. Test Prep Choose the expression that would generate the given data. A

Ⓐ $b + 6$ Ⓑ $4b$

Ⓒ $2b$ Ⓓ $b - 8$

b	Data
2	8
4	10
6	12

Problem Solving and Reasoning

42. Journal Explain the meaning of $7x$ and explain how to evaluate $7x$ for $x = 3$ and $x = 4$.

43. Critical Thinking Match the situation to the correct expression.

a. Fingers on t hands (including thumbs) **i.** $t - 5$

b. Price of a \$$t$ CD with a \$5 coupon **ii.** $5t$

c. Price of a \$$t$ sweater with \$5 tax **iii.** $t + 5$

44. Communicate Which of the following expressions will always have the same solution, no matter what you choose for x? Explain.
$x + 3$, $5 - x$, $0x$

Mixed Review

Estimate. *[Lesson 2-6]*

45. 1567 + 5408 7000 **46.** 21,805 + 79,502 102,000 **47.** 45,405 − 9,826 35,000

48. 4305 − 1875 2000 **49.** 3615 + 2778 6400 **50.** 31,618 − 17,611 14,000

Choose the numbers that can be divided by the first number with no remainder. *[Previous course]*

51. 8 (28, 64, 8, 739, 384, 502) 64, 8, 384 **52.** 4 (26, 552, 450, 482, 116, 74) 552, 116

53. 6 (17, 24, 30, 51, 67, 74) 24, 30 **54.** 9 (21, 37, 45, 55, 82, 93) 45

PROBLEM SOLVING 2-10

Exercise Answers

39. Number of stars: 13, 26, 39, 52, $13w$

40. Number of days: 7, 9, 14, $f \div 9000$

42. $7x$ is the same as $7 \times x$. Value of $7x$ for $x = 3$ is $7 \times 3 = 21$ and for $x = 4$ is $7 \times 4 = 28$.

43. a. ii

b. i

c. iii

44. Zero times x will always result in 0 because any number multiplied by 0 is always 0.

Alternate Assessment

Performance Have students work in small groups to write explanations of how they calculated the entries in each column of the table in **Explore**.

Quick Quiz

Evaluate each expression for the given value of the variable.

1. $\frac{80}{a}$, $a = 2$ 40
2. $30 - b$, $b = 4$ 26
3. $7c$, $c = 8$ 56
4. $d + 13$, $d = 5$ 18

Available on Daily Transparency 2-10

PROBLEM SOLVING

Name ______________ **Guided Problem Solving 2-10**

GPS PROBLEM 40, STUDENT PAGE 113

Complete the table. An average blue whale eats 9000 pounds of food each day.

Amount of Food (lb)	Number of Days
63,000	7
81,000	9
126,000	14
f	$f \div 9000$

— Understand —

1. How many pounds of food does an average blue whale eat each day? 9000 pounds
2. What do you need to find to complete the table? Number of days it takes a blue whale to eat a specified amount of food.
3. What does f represent in the table? An amount of food.

— Plan —

4. What operation will you use to complete the table? Division.
5. How can you use patterns to find your answer? Possible answer: Divide the non-zero number; then subtract zeros to find the quotient.

— Solve —

6. Write the expression you used to find the number of days it takes to eat 63,000 lb of food. $63{,}000 \div 9000$
7. Write the expression you would use to find the number of days it would take to eat f pounds of food. $f \div 9000$
8. Complete the table above.

— Look Back —

9. How can you be sure that the expression you wrote for f days is correct? Evaluate the expression for a value of f.

SOLVE ANOTHER PROBLEM

Complete the table. A wild elephant eats 500 pounds of food each day.

Amount of Food (lb)	Number of Days
4,000	8
10,500	21
x	$x \div 500$

ENRICHMENT

Name ______________ **Extend Your Thinking 2-10**

Patterns in Numbers

When evaluating an expression with two operations, follow the order of operations–multiply or divide, then add or subtract.

1. Evaluate each expression for $x = 5$: $x + 1$, $2x + 1$, $3x + 1$, ... 6, 11, 16
2. Describe the pattern in Question 1. Possible answer: The pattern increases by the value of x, so it is "Add x."
3. Write an expression to show the tenth term in the pattern. $10x + 1$
4. Evaluate each expression for $x = 5$: $\frac{1}{x}$, $\frac{1}{2x}$, $\frac{1}{3x}$, ... Evaluate the term beneath the bar, and write as a fraction. $\frac{1}{5}$, $\frac{1}{10}$, $\frac{1}{15}$
5. Describe the pattern in Question 4. Possible answer: The pattern is "Add x to the denominator."
6. Use an expression to show the twentieth term in the pattern. $\frac{1}{20x}$
7. Evaluate each expression for $x = 5$: $x - 1$, $2x - 2$, $3x - 3$, ... 4, 8, 12
8. Describe the pattern in Question 7. Possible answer: The pattern is "Add $x - 1$."
9. Write an expression to show the fifteenth term in the pattern. $15x - 15$
10. Evaluate the expressions for the patterns in Questions 1, 4, and 7 using other values for x. Do the patterns you found always work? Explain. Possible answer: No. Zero cannot be used to evaluate the expressions in Question 4 because division by zero is undefined.

2-11 Lesson Organizer

Objective
- Translate phrases and situations into mathematical expressions.

Vocabulary
- Sum, difference, product, quotient

NCTM Standards
- 1–4, 9, 12

Review

Give words that suggest each operation.

Possible answers are given.

1. Add Plus, more than, increased by.
2. Subtract Minus, less, less than, take away.
3. Multiply Times, product of.
4. Divide Divide by, divide into, quotient of.

Available on Daily Transparency 2-11

1 Introduce

Explore

The Point
Students create word problems to match each of the four arithmetic operations.

Ongoing Assessment
There may be a great deal of variance in the quality of the problems written by students; encourage students to elaborate upon the situations in order to improve their problems.

For Groups That Finish Early
Exchange your problems with another group and check that you agree that the problems match the solutions.

Answers for Explore
1. Possible answers: Mary had 15 CDs. Bob gave her 13 more. How many CDs did she have in total?

2-11 Writing Expressions

You'll Learn ...
- to translate phrases and situations into mathematical expressions

... How It's Used
Expressions allow veterinarians to compare the growth rates of animals.

Vocabulary
sum
difference
product
quotient

Lesson Link You've learned how to evaluate expressions. Now you will learn how to translate word problems into the language of constants, variables, and expressions.

Explore Writing Expressions

Mister Ree Stories

Late last night Mister Ree wrote a test consisting of four word problems. Unfortunately, he was so tired when he finished that he mistakenly tossed the problems into his waste basket. This morning, all he can find are his solutions:

$15 + 13 = 28$ $140 - 60 = 80$ $12 \times 5 = 60$ $48 \div 4 = 12$

1. For each solution, write a word problem that has that solution. You may not use the words *add, subtract, multiply,* or *divide,* or any forms of these words. Instead, think of a situation that leads naturally to the use of each operation.
2. Share your problems with the class. Help your teacher compile a list of situations in which you can use each arithmetic operation.

Remember
The numbers that you multiply together to get a product are called *factors* of the product.
[Page 78]

Learn Writing Expressions

Some words in English can be translated into specific mathematical operations.

Word	Definition	Numerical Expression	Variable Expression
Sum	The result of adding numbers	$3 + 5$	$6 + x$
Difference	The result of subtracting numbers	$8 - 24$	$y - 10$
Product	The result of multiplying numbers	2×9	$5b$
Quotient	The result of dividing numbers	$20 \div 5$	$\frac{a}{2}$

MEETING INDIVIDUAL NEEDS

Resources
- 2-11 Practice
- 2-11 Reteaching
- 2-11 Problem Solving
- 2-11 Enrichment
- 2-11 Daily Transparency
  - Problem of the Day
  - Review
  - Quick Quiz

Learning Modalities

Verbal When students are translating English phrases into algebraic expressions, have them work in pairs, read the phrase aloud, discuss the meaning of the phrase, and then write the appropriate expression.

Musical Have different students make up songs that illustrate the ways in which different operations can be expressed using words.

English Language Development

Have students create an expression file. Laminate cards so students can write on them with grease pencils. On one side of a card, have students write word expressions such as 3 *times a number.* On the other side of the card, have them write the mathematical expression $3n$.

Have students add new vocabulary to their reference book.

To translate situations that don't use these words, you need to choose an operation that is appropriate for the situation. It may be easier to choose an operation if you first replace the variable with a number.

Examples

Write as an expression.

1 What is the product of 20 and k?

Product means multiplication.

$20k$

2 What is the difference of g and 6?

Difference means subtraction.

$g - 6$

3 Mae bought b bananas and ate 3. How many does she have?

If Mae bought 10 bananas and ate 3, she'd have 7 bananas, because $10 - 3 = 7$. The operation to use is subtraction.

$b - 3$

4 Tanisha had a 200-page book about the *Titanic*. She read p pages each day. How many days did it take to read the book?

If Tanisha read 10 pages each day, it would take 20 days, because $200 \div 10 = 20$. The operation to use is division.

$\frac{200}{p}$

Try It

Write as an expression.

a. What is the sum of c and 8? $c + 8$ **b.** What is the quotient of n and 9? $\frac{n}{9}$

c. Rafael raked r bags of leaves. Nicole raked 5 bags. How many bags of leaves were raked altogether? $r + 5$

d. Jake ran x laps every day for 7 days. How many laps did he run? $7x$

History Link

The HMS *Titanic* had 1522 passengers and crew members on board when it sank. Only 705 survived.

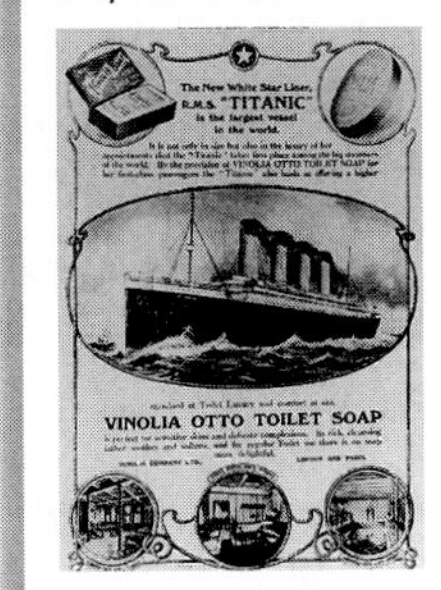

Check Your Understanding

1. Other than *sum, difference, product,* and *quotient,* what words suggest addition? Subtraction? Multiplication? Division?

2. Give a situation suggested by each expression: $10 - n$; $\frac{y}{24}$; $50p$.

MATH EVERY DAY

Problem of the Day

A giant pumpkin weighs 309 pounds more than a pumpkin of average size. Write an expression that represents how much the giant pumpkin weighs. $x + 309$ when x represents the weight of a pumpkin of average size.

Available on Daily Transparency 2-11

An Extension is provided in the transparency package.

Fact of the Day

Many English words come from other languages. "Quotient" comes from the Latin word *quotiens*, which means how many times.

Mental Math

Do these mentally.

1. $300 + 450 + 700$ 1450
2. $54{,}000 \div 90$ 600
3. 3×199 597
4. 7×31 217

Answers for Explore

There are 140 students in the 6th grade. 60 students ride the bus to school. How many 6th-graders do not ride the bus?

Ruth bought 12 tickets at $5 each. How much did she spend in all?

48 chairs were put into 4 equal rows. How many chairs were in each row?

2. Answers may vary.

2 Teach

Learn

Alternate Examples

Write as an expression.

1. What is the product of 7 and y?

   "Product" means multiplication. $7 \times y$

2. What is the difference of 9 and m?

   "Difference" means subtraction. $9 - m$

3. Angela needs $\$d$ to buy a kite. She has $6. How much more money does she need?

   If Angela has $6 and needs $\$d$, she needs $d - 6$ more dollars. The operation to use is subtraction. $d - 6$

4. David has a bag of 1500 jelly beans. He eats 100 jelly beans each day. How many days will the bag of jelly beans last?

   If David eats 100 jelly beans each day, the bag will last $1500 \div 100 = j$ days. The operation to use is division. $\frac{1500}{j}$

3 Practice and Assess

Check

Answers for Check Your Understanding

1. Add, increase, decrease, more, less, per day, per week, shared equally
2. Possible answers: Chi had 10 apples. She gave n to Mark. How many apples does she have now?; A class of 24 students shared y ounces of juice. How many ounces did each student get?; What is the cost of 50 items at a price of p for each item?

2-11 Exercises and Applications

Assignment Guide

- Basic
  1–18, 24–27, 29, 31–45 odds
- Average
  1–4, 8–27, 29, 30–44 evens
- Enriched
  1–4, 11–29, 31–45 odds

Exercise Notes

Exercises 2–3

Error Prevention Students are most likely to have difficulty with getting the terms in the correct order in subtraction and division. Have them list all of the ways $x - 5$ could be read. (x minus 5, 5 less than x, x less 5, x take away 5, etc.) and $x \div 5$ (x divided by 5, the quotient of x and 5, 5 into x, etc.).

Exercise 22

Health An apple has 80 calories, a banana has 100 calories, a cup of whole strawberries has 55 calories, and a 4×8 inch wedge of watermelon has 110 calories. Have students use this information to write problems similar to Exercise 22.

Reteaching

Activity

- Work with a partner.
- Take turns with your partner saying expressions such as "What is the product of t and 12." Have your partner write the correct expression.
- Exchange roles with your partner. Each person should say at least five expressions.
- Check that you and your partner agree that each expression is written correctly.

2-11 Exercises and Applications

Practice and Apply

Getting Started Match the description to the expression.

1. A number plus 5 A
2. 5 take away a number C
3. 5 into x groups F
4. A number 5 times D

A. $x + 5$ **B.** $x - 5$ **C.** $5 - x$ **D.** $5x$ **E.** $\frac{5}{x}$ **F.** $\frac{x}{5}$

Write the phrase as an expression.

5. q times 10 $10q$
6. Half of h $h \div 2$
7. d times 6 $6d$
8. j and 2 more $j + 2$
9. s minus 3 $s - 3$
10. 52 smaller than d $d - 52$
11. v multiplied by 20 $20v$
12. z doubled $2z$
13. y decreased by 3 $y - 3$
14. w divided by 3 $\frac{w}{3}$
15. 5 less than n $n - 5$
16. r to the third power r^3

Write an expression to answer each question.

17. What is the difference of n and 4? $n - 4$
18. What is 8 more than x? $x + 8$
19. If x students are organized into equal teams of 8, how many teams are there? $\frac{x}{8}$
20. There are 12 groups with p penguins in each group. How many penguins are there? $12p$

Write the problem as an expression.

21. **Fine Arts** The German composer Ludwig van Beethoven wrote s more symphonies than his countryman Johannes Brahms. Brahms wrote four symphonies. How many did Beethoven write? $4 + s$
22. **Health** An orange has 62 calories. It has c fewer calories than a nectarine. How many calories does a nectarine have? $62 + c$
23. **Science** The temperature at the North Pole was 146 degrees Fahrenheit cooler than the temperature in Quito, Ecuador. The temperature in Quito was t degrees. What was the temperature at the North Pole? $t - 146$ degrees

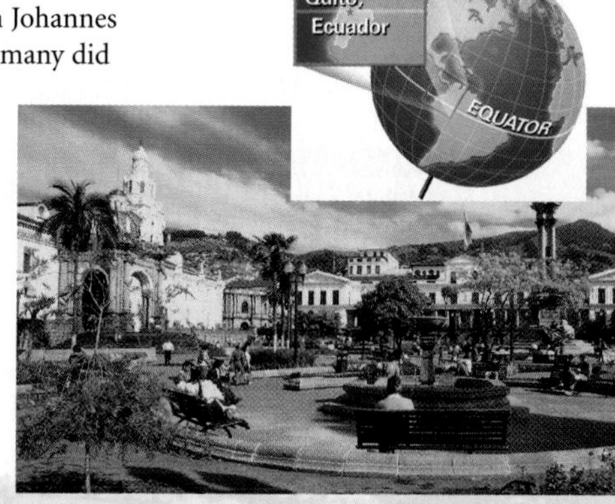

PRACTICE 2-11

PRACTICE

Name ______________

Practice 2-11

Writing Expressions

Write the phrase as an expression.

1. 12 more than x $x + 12$
2. x less than 36 $36 - x$
3. one-third of a $\frac{a}{3}$
4. 17 times s $17 \times s$
5. b multiplied by 5 $b \times 5$
6. y to the fourth power y^4
7. 64 plus k $64 + k$
8. u tripled $3u$
9. p cubed p^3
10. 18 minus x $18 - x$
11. 4 less than k $k - 4$
12. z increased by 12 $z + 12$

Write an expression to answer each question.

13. What is the product of 82 and g? $82g$
14. What is the difference between n and 7? $n - 7$
15. What is the quotient of 32 and x? $32 \div x$
16. What is the sum of h and 7? $h + 7$
17. What is 31 less than c? $c - 31$
18. What is the fifth power of t? t^5
19. What is one-eighth of r? $\frac{r}{8}$
20. Carolyn made t batches of 12 cookies. How many cookies did she make? $12t$
21. A jar holds n ounces of jam. How many jars are needed for 200 ounces of jam? $\frac{200}{n}$

Write the problem as an expression.

22. **History** Thomas Jefferson was born in 1801. George Washington was born y years earlier. In what year was George Washington born? $1801 - y$
23. **Science** A spider has 8 legs. How many legs do s spiders have? $8s$

RETEACHING

Name ______________

Alternative Lesson 2-11

Writing Expressions

Some words in English can be translated into specific mathematical operations.

Word	Definition	Numerical Expression	Variable Expression
sum	The result of **adding** numbers	$7 + 2$	$8 + x$
difference	The result of **subtracting** numbers	$12 - 3$	$28 - y$
product	The result of **multiplying** numbers	4×16	$8c$

To translate situations that don't use these words, you need to choose an operation that is appropriate for the situation. It may be easier to choose an operation if you first replace the variable with a number.

Example

Write an expression to answer: What is the quotient of 99 divided by x?

Step 1: What operation is being done? A quotient is the answer when dividing, so use division to write the expression.

Step 2: Use the appropriate sign to write the expression: $99 \div x$ or $\frac{99}{x}$

The expressions $99 \div x$ and $\frac{99}{x}$ shows the quotient of 99 divided by x.

Try It Write an expression to answer: What is 12 minus r?

a. What operation is being done? Subtraction.
b. Write the expression. $12 - r$

Write an expression to answer each question.

c. What is 32 times as big as y? $32y$
d. What is 24 more than n? $n + 24$
e. What is 11 less than b? $b - 11$
f. What is d divided by 5? $d \div 5$ or $\frac{d}{5}$
g. What is g plus 10? $g + 10$
h. Brian has p pencils and bought 4 more. How many does he have? $p + 4$
i. Tammy plants 6 rows of t tomato plants each. How many tomato plants did she plant? $6t$

24. Literature Author Jules Verne's fictional submarine, the *Nautilus*, traveled 20,000 leagues under the sea. Let m leagues equal 1 mile. How many miles did the *Nautilus* travel? $\frac{20,000}{m}$

25. Geography Lake Michigan covers about 22,278 square miles. Lake Iliamna in Alaska covers only m miles. How much larger is Lake Michigan? $22,278 - m$ square miles

26. Test Prep Thirty-six people at a picnic equally shared a watermelon weighing p pounds. Choose the expression to use to find the weight of each share. B

Ⓐ $\frac{36}{p}$ Ⓑ $\frac{p}{36}$

Ⓒ $p \times 36$ Ⓓ $36p$

Carmen Lomas Garza, "Sandia/Watermelon" 1986. Gouache painting. Collection of Dudley D.Brooks & Tomas Ybarra-Frausto, New York, NY.

Problem Solving and Reasoning

27. Journal Choose an operation (addition, subtraction, multiplication, or division) and describe three situations that require that operation.

28. Communicate For each expression, write a situation that the expression might describe.

$n - 60$; $60n$; $\frac{60}{n}$; $n + 60$

29. Critical Thinking Write an expression for the distance around each square.

a.  x, x

b. 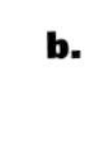 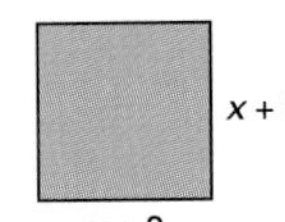 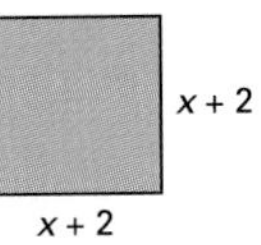 $x + 2$, $x + 2$

c. 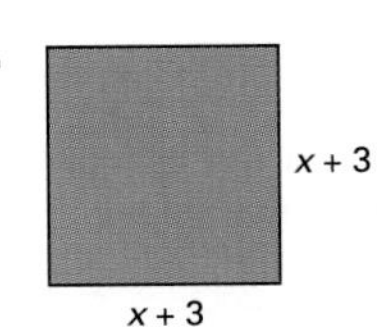 $x + 3$, $x + 3$

Mixed Review

Estimate. *[Lesson 2-7]*

30. 103×64 ≈6400 **31.** 63,880,204 ÷ 80,129 ≈800 **32.** 8212×779 ≈6,400,000 **33.** 495×508 ≈250,000

34. 52,305 ÷ 4,967 ≈10 **35.** 112,635 ÷ 52,175 ≈2 **36.** 633×490 ≈300,000 **37.** 123 ÷ 41 ≈3

Divide. *[Previous course]*

38. 154 ÷ 7 22 **39.** 1464 ÷ 12 122 **40.** 627 ÷ 33 19 **41.** 20,097 ÷ 63 319

42. 210 ÷ 5 42 **43.** 624 ÷ 8 78 **44.** 2470 ÷ 10 247 **45.** 56,316 ÷ 13 4332

PROBLEM SOLVING 2-11

Exercise Notes

Exercise 26

Test Prep Students may have considerable difficulty deciding which number is the divisor. Have them substitute a constant such as 2 or 4 for the variable in each problem in order to decide.

Exercise 29

Problem-Solving Tip Students do not need to simplify their expressions for this problem. Some may write $4(x + 3)$ for c, for example, while others may write $x + 3 + x + 3 + x + 3 + x + 3$. Only rarely will a student write $4x + 12$.

Exercise Answers

27. Answers may vary.

28. Answers may vary.

29. a. $x + x + x + x$, or $4x$

b. $x + 2 + x + 2 + x + 2 + x + 2$, or $4x + 8$

c. $x + 3 + x + 3 + x + 3 + x + 3$, or $4x + 12$

Alternate Assessment

Portfolio Students should select some of the problems they have written in this lesson to include in their portfolio, explaining why they have selected them and what they learned from doing the problems.

Quick Quiz

Write each phrase as an expression.

1. 10 more than a $a + 10$
2. The product of 7 and y $7y$
3. 15 divided by c $\frac{15}{c}$
4. d less than 45 $45 - d$

Available on Daily Transparency 2-11

PROBLEM SOLVING

Name ____________ **Guided Problem Solving 2-11**

GPS PROBLEM 29, STUDENT PAGE 117

Write an expression for the distance around each square.

a. (x, x) b. ($x + 2$, $x + 2$) c. ($x + 3$, $x + 3$)

— Understand —

1. What is the length of each side of the square shown in
   a. square a? x b. square b? $x + 2$ c. square c? $x + 3$
2. How do you find the distance around a square? Possible answers: Add sides' lengths.
3. How many expressions will you write? 3 expressions.

— Plan —

4. Write an expression showing the distance around a square when each side of the square is 10 cm? 10 + 10 + 10 + 10

— Solve —

5. Write an expression for distance around square a by substituting the length of the side for 10 in the expression you wrote in Item 4. $4x$
6. Repeat the steps in Item 5 to write an expression for the distance around square b. $4(x + 2) = 4x + 8$
7. Repeat the steps in Item 5 to write an expression for the distance around square c. $4(x + 3) = 4x + 12$

— Look Back —

8. You solved a simpler problem to find the answer. What other strategy could you have used? Make a Table.

SOLVE ANOTHER PROBLEM

Write an expression for the distance around each equilateral triangle?

a. (y) $3y$ b. ($y + 2$) $3y + 6$ c. ($y + 4$) $3y + 12$

ENRICHMENT

Name ____________ **Extend Your Thinking 2-11**

Visual Thinking

A two-dimensional shape that can be folded to make a three-dimensional shape is called a net. These nets make a cube when folded. For each net below, circle the letter of the cube that could **not** be made by the net.

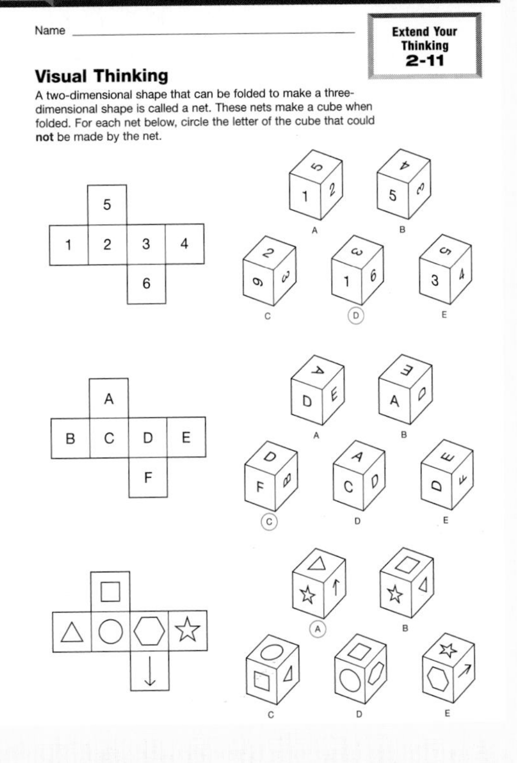

INTERACTIVE LESSON

2-12 Lesson Organizer

Objectives

- Understand what an equation is.
- Determine if an equation is true or false.

Vocabulary

- Equation

NCTM Standards

- 1–4, 9

Review

Evaluate each expression.

1. $8 - 2 \times 3$ 2
2. $(4 + 5) \div 3$ 3
3. $2^3 + 1$ 9
4. $3 \times 4 - 15 \div 3$ 7

Available on Daily Transparency 2-12

1 Introduce

Explore

The Point
Students work backward to determine how many of each type of fish were in the tank before changes were made.

Ongoing Assessment
Some students may have difficulty isolating the relevant information for each question. Point out that Steps 1–4 each use information from one of the bullets.

For Groups That Finish Early
Pairs of students may switch problems with each other and discuss the solutions. They may also write their problems on the board or on a transparency for class discussion.

2-12 Using Equations

You'll Learn ...

- what an equation is
- to determine if an equation is true or false

... How It's Used

Meteorologists use equations to convert temperatures between the Fahrenheit and Celsius measuring systems.

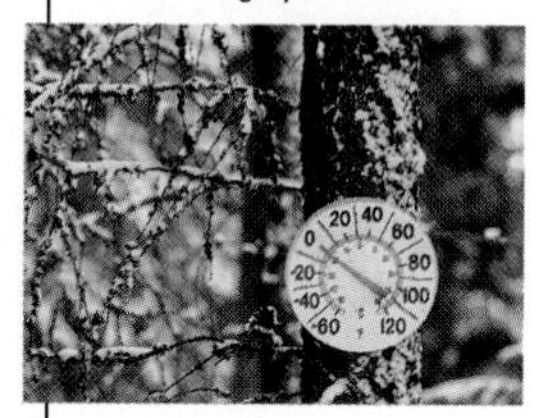

Vocabulary

equation

Science Link

Fish that live a mile below sea level have unusual traits that help them survive. These can include flat, uncrushable bodies and glow-in-the-dark skin.

Lesson Link In the last lesson, you learned how to write expressions where the final answer was unknown. Now, you'll learn how to write expressions where the answer is known. ◄

Explore Using Equations

Tanks for the Anemones!

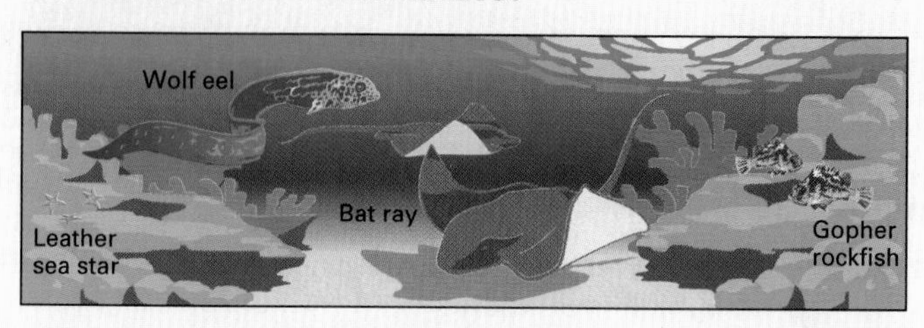

On Monday afternoon, four staff members at the Bay City Aquarium made these changes in the central aquarium.

- Leon tripled the number of leather starfish. Now there are 30.
- Val removed 4 bat rays. Now there are 7.
- Rico added 5 gopher rockfish. Now there are 13.
- Wendy took out half of the wolf eels. Now there are 10.

The list gives the number of each type of fish on Monday morning, before any changes were made.

Monday Morning
8
10
55
20
13
11
7

1. Which is the number of leather starfish? How can you tell?
2. Which is the number of bat rays? How can you tell?
3. Which is the number of gopher rockfish? How can you tell?
4. Which is the number of wolf eels? How can you tell?
5. Choose a type of fish and write your own question like one of these. Switch questions with a partner and discuss the answers.

MEETING INDIVIDUAL NEEDS

Resources

- 2-12 Practice
- 2-12 Reteaching
- 2-12 Problem Solving
- 2-12 Enrichment
- 2-12 Daily Transparency
  - Problem of the Day
  - Review
  - Quick Quiz

Interactive CD-ROM Lesson

Learning Modalities

Logical Have students work with a partner to think of problems that could be solved by writing an equation. Students should share some of their situations with the class, and the rest of the class should determine the equation being described.

Visual Have students use squares of construction paper to represent the different fish in **Explore.** Use a different color for each type of fish.

Inclusion

Materials: Balance scale, paper clips

Students may benefit from using a balance scale to illustrate solving simple equations. Write the equation $x + 9 = 21$ on the chalkboard. Model the equation by placing 9 clips on one side of the scale and 21 on the other. Have students balance the scale, thus determining the value of x. Continue the activity with similar problems.

Learn Using Equations

An **equation** is a mathematical sentence that uses an equal sign, =, to show that two expressions are equal. An equation can be either true or false.

$5 + 7 = 12$ is true. $16 - 6 = 12$ is false.

$30 \div 5 = 6$ is true. $3 \times 5 = 35$ is false.

An equation with a variable can also be true or false, depending on the value of the variable.

If $x = 5$, $x + 6 = 11$ is true. If $x = 12$, $x + 6 = 11$ is false.

Examples

Is the equation true for the given value of the variable?

1 $5y = 40$, $y = 8$

$5 \times 8 \stackrel{?}{=} 40$ Substitute 8 for *y*.

$40 = 40$ Multiply.

The equation is true.

2 $r + 20 = 35$, $r = 10$

$10 + 20 \stackrel{?}{=} 35$ Substitute 10 for *r*.

$30 \neq 35$ Add.

Since 10 + 20 does not equal 35, the equation is false.

Try It

Is the equation true for the given value of the variable?

a. $\frac{30}{z} = 3$, $z = 6$ No **b.** $h - 12 = 24$, $h = 12$ No **c.** $5 + d = 5$, $d = 0$ Yes

Like expressions, equations can be used to model real-world situations. For example, the recommended depth for recreational diving is 130 feet. If you dive *d* feet and you have 50 more feet before you reach the limit, you could model this as $d + 50 = 130$.

Science Link

The deepest point on Earth is in the Mariana Trench in the Pacific Ocean. It is more than 10 kilometers below sea level. The highest point, Mount Everest, is less than 9 kilometers above sea level.

Check Your Understanding

1. What are the differences between an equation and an expression?
2. Does every equation have a variable? Explain.

MATH EVERY DAY

Problem of the Day

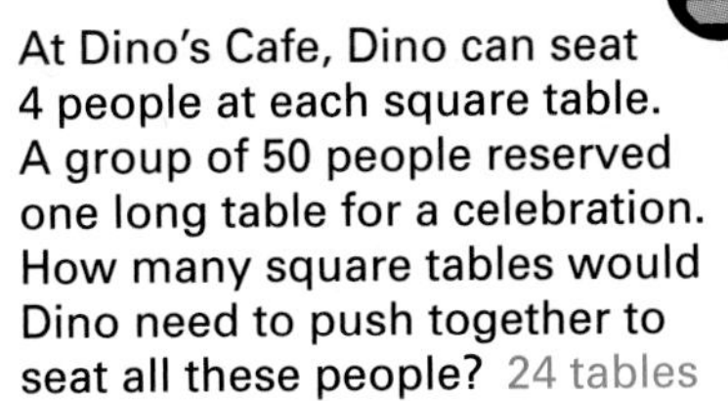

At Dino's Cafe, Dino can seat 4 people at each square table. A group of 50 people reserved one long table for a celebration. How many square tables would Dino need to push together to seat all these people? 24 tables

Available on Daily Transparency 2-12

An Extension is provided in the transparency package.

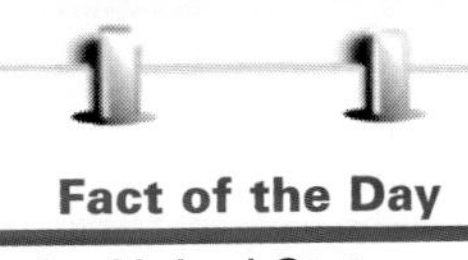

Fact of the Day

In the United States there are 55 species of fish, 12 species of snails, 50 species of clams, and 10 species of crustaceans on the endangered list.

Estimation

Estimate.

1. $35{,}670 \div 5800$ 6
2. $44{,}500 + 155{,}200$ 200,000
3. $302 \times 19{,}734$ 6,000,000

Answers for Explore

1. 10; "Tripled" means he multiplied the number of starfish by 3 to get 30.
2. 11; "Removed 4" means she subtracted 4 bat rays from 11, leaving 7.
3. 8; He had to add 5 rockfish to 8 to get 13 of them.
4. 20; "Took out half" means she divided 20 by 2 to get 10 wolf eels.
5. Answers may vary.

2 Teach

Learn

Ask students for an example of a false equation. Be sure that they include examples like $3 + 4 = 5$.

Alternate Examples

1. Is $3a = 36$ true for $a = 12$?

   $3 \times 12 \stackrel{?}{=} 36$

   Substitute 12 for *a*. Multiply.

   $36 = 36$

   The equation is true.

2. Is $45 - m = 10$ true for $m = 20$?

   $45 - 20 \stackrel{?}{=} 10$

   Substitute 20 for *m*. Subtract.

   $25 \neq 10$

   Since $25 \neq 10$, the equation is false.

3 Practice and Assess

Check

It may be helpful to have students generate their own examples of equations and expressions before answering these questions.

Answers for Check Your Understanding

1. Possible answers: An expression does not contain an equal sign; An equation does contain an equal sign.
2. No; $2 \times 5 = 10$ is an equation.

2-12 Exercises and Applications

Assignment Guide

- **Basic**
  1–10, 20–22, 26–30, 34–58 evens
- **Average**
  1, 11–19, 22–28 evens, 29, 32–58 evens
- **Enriched**
  3–23 odds, 24–32, 33–47 odds, 49–58

Exercise Notes

Exercises 2–19

Remind students that $5k$ is the same as $5 \times k$ and $24 \div x$ is the same as $\frac{24}{x}$.

Exercises 20–27

Error Prevention Students may give an answer different from that given in the answer key. If the equation is equivalent to the one in the key, then it should be considered acceptable. Students need to understand that there is often more than one way to write an equation.

Reteaching

Activity

Materials: Number cubes

- Write an equation with a variable, such as $4 + x = 10$.
- Toss the number cubes and state whether the sum of the numbers tossed makes the equation true or false.
- For example, if the equation is $4 + x = 10$ and a sum of 7 is tossed, then the equation is false.
- Repeat this until you have written ten equations.

2-12 Exercises and Applications

Practice and Apply

1. Getting Started State if the equation is true or false.

a. $3 + 10 \stackrel{?}{=} 13$ T **b.** $16 - 12 \stackrel{?}{=} 6$ F **c.** $12 + 5 \stackrel{?}{=} 18$ F **d.** $16 - 12 \stackrel{?}{=} 4$ T **e.** $63 + 3 \stackrel{?}{=} 69$ F
f. $20 \times 6 \stackrel{?}{=} 130$ F **g.** $15 \div 3 \stackrel{?}{=} 5$ T **h.** $27 \div 9 \stackrel{?}{=} 4$ F **i.** $6 \times 16 \stackrel{?}{=} 96$ T **j.** $3 \times 7 \stackrel{?}{=} 21$ T

Is the equation true for the given value of the variable?

2. $8 + r = 17, r = 9$ Yes **3.** $16 - x = 7, x = 12$ No **4.** $w - 23 = 2, w = 19$ No
5. $5h = 25, h = 5$ Yes **6.** $s + 45 = 52, s = 7$ Yes **7.** $10y = 30, y = 3$ Yes
8. $\frac{15}{q} = 5, q = 5$ No **9.** $22y = 24, y = 2$ No **10.** $\frac{w}{12} = 2, w = 24$ Yes
11. $12 \times t = 48, t = 4$ Yes **12.** $v - 13 = 16, v = 29$ Yes **13.** $9 \times 3l = 28, l = 3$ No
14. $\frac{14}{u} = 25, u = 7$ No **15.** $45m = 3, m = 1$ No **16.** $\frac{0}{n} = 0, n = 30$ Yes
17. $\frac{e}{3} = 7, e = 21$ Yes **18.** $\frac{42}{p} = 24, p = 2$ No **19.** $1k = 2, k = 2$ Yes

Write an equation for each situation.

20. Mary had f oranges and gave 1 to Byron. She had 3 oranges left. $f - 1 = 3$

21. Jarrod bought 12 snacks and shared them equally among p people. Each person got 3 snacks. $\frac{12}{p} = 3$

22. Nigel has 2 green shirts, b blue shirts, and 3 white shirts. He has a total of 8 shirts. $2 + b + 3 = 8$

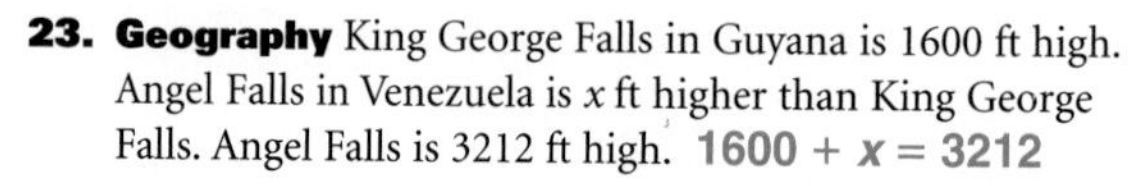

23. Geography King George Falls in Guyana is 1600 ft high. Angel Falls in Venezuela is x ft higher than King George Falls. Angel Falls is 3212 ft high. $1600 + x = 3212$

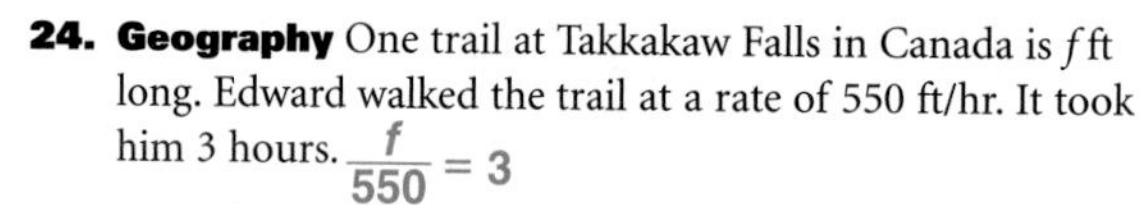

24. Geography One trail at Takkakaw Falls in Canada is f ft long. Edward walked the trail at a rate of 550 ft/hr. It took him 3 hours. $\frac{f}{550} = 3$

25. Mona bought \$84 worth of computer supplies and paid d dollars in sales tax. The total came to \$88. $84 + d = 88$

26. Sheena bought r rolls of film at \$4 per roll and paid \$60. $4r = 60$

Angel Falls, Venezuela

PRACTICE

Name ____________

Practice 2-12

Using Equations

Is the equation true for the given value of the variable?

1. $x + 5 = 17, x = 22$ False
2. $3 - y = 1, y = 2$ True
3. $4x = 24, x = 6$ True
4. $g - 7 = 11, g = 18$ True
5. $s \div 7 = 3, s = 21$ True
6. $u + 12 = 31, u = 20$ False
7. $h - 13 = 21, h = 34$ True
8. $64 \div n = 16, n = 8$ False
9. $20 \times t = 300, t = 160$ False
10. $18 - c = 10, c = 8$ True
11. $m + 40 = 92, m = 50$ False
12. $x \div 5 = 15, x = 75$ True
13. $3k = 27, k = 9$ True
14. $z - 9 = 61, z = 52$ False
15. $12 + v = 21, v = 7$ False
16. $5w = 20, w = 4$ True
17. $n - 6 = 24, n = 18$ False
18. $k \div 8 = 9, k = 56$ False
19. $m + 12 = 61, m = 49$ True
20. $j + 17 = 86, j = 79$ False

Write an equation for each situation.

21. Jim had 18 CDs. He bought x more. Then he had 21 CDs. $18 + x = 21$
22. Rolando baked 4 loaves of bread, each weighing w oz. The total weight was 80 oz. $4w = 80$
23. Veronica had m marbles. She gave 5 to Marco. She had 12 marbles left. $m - 5 = 12$
24. The lunch period at Eisenhower School is normally 35 minutes. On Thursday, students were given an extra t minutes, so they had 55 minutes for lunch. $35 + t = 55$
25. Stella dealt an entire deck of 52 cards to make h hands. Each hand had 13 cards. $52 \div h = 13$
26. **Careers** The average executive burns an average of 105 calories per hour at work. This is c calories more than the average secretary, who burns 88 calories per hour. $105 = 88 + c$
27. **Social Studies** Each of the 50 United States has s U.S. Senators. There are 100 U.S. Senators all together. $50s = 100$

RETEACHING

Name ____________

Alternative Lesson 2-12

Using Equations

An **equation** is a mathematical sentence that uses an equal sign, =, to show that two expressions are equal. An equation can be either true or false. For example, $13 + 12 = 25$ is true because both sides have the same value and $85 - 21 = 82$ is false because both sides of the equation do **not** have the same value.

An equation with a variable can also be true or false, depending on the value of the variable.

Example

Is the equation true for the given value of the variable?

a. $4y = 24, y = 6$
$4 \times 6 \stackrel{?}{=} 24$ Substitute 6 for y.
$24 = 24$ Multiply.

Since both sides of the equation have the same value, the equation is true.

b. $8 + a = 10, a = 3$
$8 + a \stackrel{?}{=} 10$ Substitute 3 for a.
$11 \neq 10$ Add.

Since both sides of the equation do **not** have the same value, the equation is false.

Try It

Is the equation true for the given value of the variable: $28 \div x = 7, x = 4$?

a. What value will you substitute for x? 4

b. Rewrite the equation, substituting for x. $28 \div 4 = 7$

c. Is the equation you wrote in Item b true or false? True.

Is the equation true for the given value of the variable?

d. $k + 65 = 100, x = 25$ No. **e.** $9y = 72, y = 8$ Yes.
f. $56 - j = 40, j = 20$ No. **g.** $\frac{r}{3} = 5, r = 15$ Yes.
h. $2w = 60, w = 30$ Yes. **i.** $p - 6 = 6, p = 22$ No.
j. $7 \times b = 49, b = 7$ Yes. **k.** $m \div 4 = 2, m = 10$ No.
l. $40 + q = 60, q = 25$ No. **m.** $16 - h = 7, h = 9$ Yes.

27. Super Sports is selling a Grand Slam baseball bat for \$75. The same bat is on sale at Scoreboard for b. You can save \$26 dollars if you buy the bat at Scoreboard. $75 - b = 26$

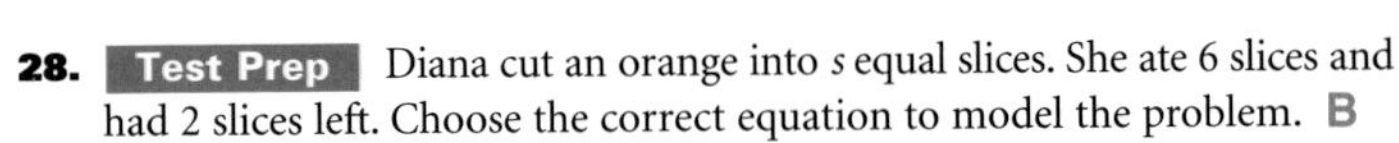

28. **Test Prep** Diana cut an orange into s equal slices. She ate 6 slices and had 2 slices left. Choose the correct equation to model the problem. B

Ⓐ $s + 6 = 2$ Ⓑ $s - 6 = 2$ Ⓒ $6s = 2$ Ⓓ $6 - s = 2$

Problem Solving and Reasoning

29. Choose a Strategy Franz and Jenna built a rectangular treehouse. The north and south walls were each f feet long. The east and west walls were $f + 2$ feet long. The total distance around the treehouse was 24 feet. Was the north wall 6 feet long? Explain. GPS

Problem Solving STRATEGIES
- Look for a Pattern
- Make an Organized List
- Make a Table
- Guess and Check
- Work Backward
- Use Logical Reasoning
- Draw a Diagram
- Solve a Simpler Problem

30. Critical Thinking For an addition equation like $2 + x = 5$, how many values will make the equation true? Explain.

31. Journal Explain why an equation is either true or false, but an expression is neither true nor false. Give examples in your answer.

32. Communicate Juan states that $x \times 0 = 4$ will always be false, no matter what value is put in for the variable. Do you agree? Explain.

Mixed Review

Write each multiplication equation as a division equation using the same numbers. *[Previous course]*

33. $5 \times 111 = 555$ — $555 \div 111 = 5$
34. $40 \times 30 = 1200$ — $1200 \div 30 = 40$
35. $32 \times 48 = 1536$ — $1536 \div 48 = 32$
36. $77 \times 8 = 616$ — $616 \div 8 = 77$
37. $42 \times 13 = 546$ — $546 \div 13 = 42$
38. $31 \times 31 = 961$ — $961 \div 31 = 31$
39. $23 \times 86 = 1978$ — $1978 \div 86 = 23$
40. $18 \times 98 = 1764$ — $1764 \div 98 = 18$

Write each division equation as a multiplication equation using the same numbers. *[Previous course]*

41. $64 \div 8 = 8$ — $8 \times 8 = 64$
42. $2100 \div 700 = 3$ — $3 \times 700 = 2100$
43. $32 \div 4 = 8$ — $4 \times 8 = 32$
44. $99 \div 9 = 11$ — $9 \times 11 = 99$
45. $3528 \div 56 = 63$ — $63 \times 56 = 3528$
46. $4402 \div 71 = 62$ — $62 \times 71 = 4402$
47. $1044 \div 12 = 87$ — $87 \times 12 = 1044$
48. $2025 \div 45 = 45$ — $45 \times 45 = 2025$

Evaluate the expression for x = 1, 2, and 3. *[Lesson 2-10]*

49. $12 + x$ 13; 14; 15 **50.** $3x$ 3; 6; 9 **51.** $\frac{36}{x}$ 36; 18; 12 **52.** $x - 1$ 0; 1; 2 **53.** $6x$ 6; 12; 18

54. $7x$ 7; 14; 21 **55.** $\frac{30}{x}$ 30; 15; 10 **56.** $8 - x$ 7; 6; 5 **57.** $x + 7$ 8; 9; 10 **58.** $5x$ 5; 10; 15

PROBLEM SOLVING 2-12

Exercise Notes

Exercise 29

Problem-Solving Tip Students are not expected to know how to add polynomials here. Instead they can work backward and substitute 6 for f and compare sides to realize that the perimeter cannot be as small as 24 feet.

Exercise Answers

29. No; It is 5 feet long.

30. Only $x = 3$ will make the equation true.

31. Possible answer: An equation is true or false for a given value of the variable because the equal sign is making a claim that the two sides of the equation are equal. An expression does not have an equal sign, so is not making any claim.

32. Yes; 4 divided by any number is never zero.

Alternate Assessment

You may want to use the *Interactive CD-ROM Journal* with this assessment.

Journal Have students describe the difference between an equation and an expression. Their description should include examples of each.

Quick Quiz

1. Is the equation $7 \times 8 = 55$ true or false?
 False. $7 \times 8 = 56$.
2. Is $8 - x = 5$ true for $x = 3$? Explain your answer.
 Yes. $8 - 3 = 5$.
3. Write an equation for the following situation: Sharon made d cookies for the bake sale at school. She put 3 cookies in a bag. She has 50 bags in all. How many cookies did Sharon make?
 $d \div 3 = 50$ or $3 \times 50 = d$

Available on Daily Transparency 2-12

PROBLEM SOLVING

Name ______________________

Guided Problem Solving 2-12

GPS PROBLEM 29, STUDENT PAGE 121

Franz and Jenna built a rectangular treehouse. The north and south walls were each f feet long. The east and west walls were $f + 2$ feet long. The total distance around the treehouse was 24 feet. Was the north wall 6 feet long? Explain.

Understand

1. How do you find the distance around a rectangular figure? Add the lengths of the four sides.
2. What is the distance around the treehouse? 24 feet.
3. What are the dimensions of the treehouse? f feet by $(f + 2)$ feet

Plan

4. Write an equation showing the distance around the treehouse. Possible answer: $4f + 4 = 24$

Solve

5. Substitute 6 for f in your equation. If the north wall is 6 feet long, what is the distance around the treehouse? 28 feet.
6. Could the treehouse have a north wall that is 6 feet long? Explain. No. If north wall is 6 ft, then adjoining walls must be 8 ft. So distance around is 28 ft. $28 \neq 24$.

Look Back

7. What is another strategy you could use to solve the problem? Draw a diagram; label the lengths of the sides and add.

SOLVE ANOTHER PROBLEM

The Hot Shot Club placed a colored border around the outside of the hallway bulletin board. They used 32 feet of crepe paper. The width of the bulletin board was w feet. The length was $w + 4$ feet. Was the width of the bulletin board 6 feet long? Explain.

Yes. Since the distance around is $4w + 8$, substitute 6 for w. $w = 32$, which is the distance given.

ENRICHMENT

Name ______________________

Extend Your Thinking 2-12

Decision Making

Suppose you were offered these opportunities. Which choice would you make? Explain why you would make each choice. Show an equation, number pattern, or other mathematical explanation to support your decision.

1. Which would you rather receive? Why?
 a. One penny the first day, two pennies the second, four pennies the third, eight pennies the fourth, and so on for one month.
 b. One dollar each day for one month.
 Possible answer: Option a, which has a much greater balance; Option a, 0.01 + 0.02 + 0.04 + ... = 10,737,418.23; Option b, \$1 + \$1 + \$1 + ... = 30.
2. Suppose you were paying money to a friend. Would that change your answer to Question 1? Why or why not?
 Possible answer: Yes. Option b would be better because less money would be paid out.
3. Suppose you win a sweepstakes that pays money for thirty days. You have a choice of two options, **a** or **b**. The first day you are given 1 dollar. Which options would you choose? Why?
 a. The amount you receive is doubled every two days.
 b. The amount you receive is tripled every four days.
 Possible answer: Option a, which has the greater balance; Option a pattern: 1, 1, 2, 2, 4, 4, ... Winnings equal \$65,534. Option b pattern: 1, 1, 1, 1, 3, 3, 3, 3, 9, 9, 9, 9, ... Winnings equal \$8746.
4. Write a problem like the others on this page. Trade papers with a classmate and try to solve each other's problems.
 Check students' work.

2-13 Lesson Organizer

Objective

- Find the value of the variable that makes an equation true.

NCTM Standards

- 1–4, 9

▶ Review

Find the next three numbers in each pattern.

1. 4, 7, 10, 13, 16, ...
   19, 22, 25
2. 2400, 1200, 600, ...
   300, 150, 75
3. 975, 964, 953, 942, ...
   931, 920, 909

Available on Daily Transparency 2-13

1 Introduce

Explore

The Point
Students evaluate expressions and then reverse the process. They develop their own methods for solving the equations and explain these methods.

Ongoing Assessment
Ask students to share how they found the values in the first column in Step 2. Ask students to look for alternative ways to do the problems. Stress that there is no one "right" way to do these problems.

Answers for Explore

1. a. 0; 2; 3; 7
   b. 24; 12; 8; 6
2. a. 3; 7; 12; 24
   b. 3; 7; 14; 21
3. Explanations may involve using subtraction to find the value for x and using division to find the value for x.

2-13 Solving Equations

You'll Learn ...

- to find the value of the variable that makes an equation true

... How It's Used

Skateboard designers use equations to determine how much weight a skateboard can hold.

▶ Lesson Link You have learned how to find out if a given value for a variable will make an equation true. Now you will learn how to find the value that will make an equation true. ◀

Explore Solving Equations

Turning the Tables

1. Copy the tables, and evaluate the expressions with the given values.

x	$x - 3$
3	
5	
6	
10	

x	$\frac{24}{x}$
1	
2	
3	
4	

2. Copy the tables, and find the values for the variable that will provide the given values for the expressions.

x	$x + 7$
	10
	14
	19
	31

x	$2x$
	6
	14
	28
	42

3. Explain how you found the values in the first column.

Learn Solving Equations

Most real-world situations that involve equations with variables do not provide you with a value to check in the equation. Sometimes you need to find the exact value that will make an equation true. This is known as solving the equation.

MEETING INDIVIDUAL NEEDS

Resources

2-13 Practice
2-13 Reteaching
2-13 Problem Solving
2-13 Enrichment
2-13 Daily Transparency
 Problem of the Day
 Review
 Quick Quiz

Technology Master 10

Chapter 2 Project Master

Wide World of Mathematics Middle School: The Census

Learning Modalities

Visual Some students think that the variable has to be on the left side of an equation. Include examples with the variable on the right, such as $14 = x - 3$.

Logical Challenge students to develop strategies for solving more complex equations, such as $2x + 1 = 7$.

Kinesthetic Use algebra tiles or a balance scale to model and solve equations.

Inclusion

Be creative in testing students. Most students need extra time to do their best. Watch to see that students do not get stuck on a single question they cannot answer.

It is also important to provide enough space for answering questions. This will help to avoid spatial confusion.

Number sense can help you solve equations. Think of equations as questions where the variable is read as "What number?" For example, $z + 5 = 7$ can be read as "What number plus 5 equals 7?" Use mental math to answer the question.

Examples

Solve each equation.

1 $w + 13 = 20$

$w + 13 = 20$	Read as "What number plus 13 equals 20?"
$\mathbf{7} + 13 = 20$	Use mental math.
$20 = 20$ ✓	Check to see that the equation is true.

w is equal to 7.

2 $x - 10 = 14$

$x - 10 = 14$	Read as "What number minus 10 equals 14?"
$\mathbf{24} - 10 = 14$	Use mental math.
$14 = 14$ ✓	Check to see that the equation is true.

x is equal to 24.

3 $9y = 180$

$9y = 180$	Read as "What number times 9 equals 180?"
$9 \times \mathbf{20} = 180$	Use mental math.

y is equal to 20.

4 Karen divided her diving time into 25-minute periods. There were 4 periods all together. How many minutes did she spend diving?

$\frac{z}{25} = 4$	Write an equation.
$\frac{z}{25} = 4$	Read as "What number divided by 25 equals 4?"
$\frac{\mathbf{100}}{25} = 4$	Use mental math.

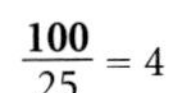

She spent 100 minutes diving.

DID YOU KNOW?

There are currents underneath the surface of the ocean, just like in a river. Divers need to swim in order to stay in place.

Try It

Solve. **a.** $a + 7 = 22$ $a = 15$ **b.** $b - 12 = 51$ $b = 63$ **c.** $5c = 110$ $c = 22$ **d.** $\frac{d}{4} = 12$ $d = 48$

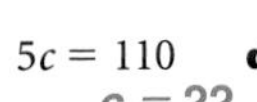

Check Your Understanding

1. Can x have any value in $x + 5$? Can x have any value in $x + 5 = 7$? Explain.
2. How can you use mental math to help solve an equation?

2 Teach

Learn

Alternate Examples

Solve each equation.

1. $6 + k = 28$. Read as "6 plus what number equals 28?"

   $6 + \mathbf{22} = 28$

   $28 = 28\surd$

   k is equal to 22.

2. $y - 15 = 50$ Read as "What number minus 15 equals 50?"

   $\mathbf{65} - 15 = 50\surd$

   $50 = 50$

   y is equal to 65.

3. $7d = 42$. Read as "7 times what number equals 42?"

   $7 \times \mathbf{6} = 42$

   $42 = 42\ \surd$

   d is equal to 6.

4. $\frac{x}{8} = 11$. Read as "What number divided by 8 equals 11?"

   $\frac{\mathbf{88}}{8} = 11$

   $11 = 11\ \surd$

   x is equal to 88.

3 Practice and Assess

Check

The questions in this section continue to develop students' understanding of the difference between expressions and equations.

Answers for Check Your Understanding

1. Yes; Any value can be substituted in $x + 5$ or in $x + 5 = 7$. However, for $x + 5 = 7$, some values of x will result in a true equation, some in a false equation.
2. Possible answer: You can substitute a value for the variable and then use mental math to see if the result is a true equation.

MATH EVERY DAY

Problem of the Day

Suppose you were standing on the other side of this stained glass window. Draw the way it would appear to you.

Answer:

Available on Daily Transparency 2-13

An Extension is provided in the transparency package.

Fact of the Day

The average depth of the Pacific Ocean is 12,921 feet and the average depth of the Atlantic Ocean is 11,730 feet.

Mental Math

Do these mentally.

1. $45 + 55 + 179$ 279
2. 900×400 360,000
3. 29×6 174
4. 32×7 224

2-13 Exercises and Applications

Assignment Guide

- **Basic**
  1–5, 11–20, 19–37 odds, 38, 42, 44–49
- **Average**
  2–20 evens, 21–37 odds, 38–48 evens
- **Enriched**
  1–10, 18–43, 45–49 odds

Exercise Notes

Exercises 1–10

Students may take two very different approaches to these problems. Some students will solve the problems and then decide whether the answer is greater or less than 6. Others will substitute 6 in for the variable and see whether the left side of the equation is too big or too small.

Reteaching

Activity

Materials: Balance scale, paper clips

- Use paper clips to model the equation $x + 12 = 20$
- Put 12 paperclips on the left and 20 on the right. How many clips do you need to add on the left to balance the scale?
  $8 + 12 = 20$ So $x = 8$.

Try these:

1. $s + 4 = 11$ $s = 7$
2. $12 - p = 7$ $p = 5$
3. $3w = 18$ Think: "I need to put 3 equal groups of clips on the left to balance 18." $w = 6$
4. $5y = 35$ $y = 7$
5. $4t = 16$ $t = 4$
6. $8x = 40$ $t = 5$

PRACTICE 2-13

2-13 Exercises and Applications

Practice and Apply

Getting Started Use mental math to determine if the value of the variable must be greater than 6 or less than 6.

1. $r + 5 = 10$ Less
2. $q - 3 = 6$ Greater
3. $12 - w = 8$ Less
4. $3r = 6$ Less
5. $6 \times t = 24$ Less
6. $\frac{28}{i} = 7$ Less
7. $p - 16 = 32$ Greater
8. $12 + d = 29$ Greater
9. $\frac{f}{7} = 14$ Greater
10. $g \times 10 = 80$ Greater

Find the given value of *x* that makes the equation true.

11. $x + 7 = 9$ $x = 1, 2, 3,$ or 4 2
12. $x - 5 = 4$ $x = 7, 8, 9,$ or 10 9
13. $2x = 16$ $x = 2, 4, 6,$ or 8 8
14. $x - 3 = 2$ $x = 5, 6, 7,$ or 8 5
15. $3 + 5 = x$ $x = 2, 5, 8,$ or 15 8
16. $\frac{x}{2} = 6$ $x = 2, 4, 6,$ or 12 12
17. $\frac{x}{5} = 2$ $x = 5, 10, 15,$ or 20 10
18. $\frac{18}{x} = 3$ $x = 6, 12, 15,$ or 18 6

Find the values for the variable that will provide the given values for the expressions.

19.

n	$n - 12$
22	10
26	14
31	19
43	31

20.

n	$\frac{n}{12}$
12	10
28	14
56	19
84	31

Solve the equation.

21. $5j = 30$ $j = 6$
22. $12 + l = 18$ $i = 6$
23. $9k = 54$ $k = 6$
24. $z + 3 = 37$ $z = 34$
25. $19 - v = 13$ $v = 6$
26. $8b = 64$ $b = 8$
27. $\frac{72}{n} = 9$ $n = 8$
28. $\frac{m}{4} = 21$ $m = 84$
29. $z - 38 = 42$ $z = 80$
30. $d + 4 = 37$ $d = 33$
31. $\frac{100}{g} = 20$ $g = 5$
32. $5p = 150$ $p = 30$
33. $21 + k = 30$ $k = 9$
34. $w - 30 = 80$ $w = 110$
35. $\frac{r}{2} = 84$ $r = 168$
36. $37 - x = 15$ $x = 22$
37. **Test Prep** Choose the correct value for x if $12x = 120$. B

    Ⓐ 0 Ⓑ 10 Ⓒ 100 Ⓓ 1000

PRACTICE

Name ____________

Practice 2-13

Solving Equations

Find the given value of x that makes the equation true.

1. $\frac{x}{7} = 4$; $x = 28, 35, 42,$ or 49
   $x = 28$
2. $x - 6 = 13$; $x = 18, 19, 20,$ or 21
   $x = 19$
3. $5x = 45$; $x = 6, 7, 8,$ or 9
   $x = 9$
4. $x + 8 = 17$; $x = 8, 9, 10,$ or 11
   $x = 9$

Find the values for the variable that will provide the given values for the expressions.

5.

u	$u + 16$
2	18
15	31
48	64
84	100

6.

k	$6k$
4	24
7	42
10	60
15	90

Solve the equation.

7. $x + 7 = 30$ $x = 23$
8. $m - 10 = 7$ $m = 17$
9. $\frac{s}{8} = 13$ $s = 104$
10. $11t = 88$ $t = 8$
11. $d - 12 = 69$ $d = 81$
12. $21 + g = 42$ $g = 21$
13. $7u = 35$ $u = 5$
14. $n \div 7 = 8$ $n = 56$
15. $b - 7 = 24$ $b = 31$

Write an equation for each situation and then solve the equation.

16. The top three best-selling albums of all time are Michael Jackson's *Thriller* (24 million copies), Fleetwood Mac's *Rumours* (17 million copies), and Boston's *Boston* (b million copies). The three albums sold a combined total of 56 million copies. How many million copies of *Boston* were sold?
    $24 + 17 + b = 56$; 15 million copies
17. The main audience section of the Mel Mello Center for the Arts has 9 rows of c chairs. There are 126 chairs all together. How many chairs are in each row?
    $9c = 126$; 14 chairs

RETEACHING

Name ____________

Alternative Lesson 2-13

Solving Equations

Sometimes you need to find the exact value that will make an equation true. This is known as *solving the equation.*

Think of equations as questions where the variable is read as "what number?" For example, $a + 3 = 10$ can be read as "What number plus 3 equals 10?" Use mental math to answer the question.

Example

Solve $y - 8 = 7$.

Step 1: Read as: "What number minus 8 equals 7?" $y - 8 = 7$
Step 2: Use mental math. $15 - 8 = 7$
Step 3: Check to see that the equation is true. $7 = 7$

In the equation $y - 8 = 7$, y is equal to 15.

Try It

Solve $a + 5 = 12$.

a. What number plus 5 equals 12? 7 so $a =$ 7
b. Show that the equation is true. $12 = 12$

Solve $3x = 18$.

c. What number times 3 equals 18? 6 so $x =$ 6
d. Show that the equation is true. $18 = 18$

Solve $m \div 3 = 20$.

e. What number divided by $3 = 20$? 60 so $m =$ 60
f. Show that the equation is true. $20 = 20$

Solve each equation.

g. $y + 15 = 50$ $y =$ 35
h. $b - 4 = 8$ $b =$ 12
i. $\frac{w}{2} = 6$ $w =$ 12
j. $3 \times c = 27$ $c =$ 9
k. $28 - p = 19$ $p =$ 9
l. $t + 8 = 26$ $t =$ 18
m. $11s = 110$ $s =$ 10
n. $81 \div k = 9$ $k =$ 9
o. $17 + r = 40$ $r =$ 23
p. $h \div 3 = 12$ $h =$ 36

Write an equation for each situation and then solve it.

38. Geography The top three gold-producing countries produce 1171 tonnes (metric tons) of gold. South Africa produces 584 tonnes. Australia produces 256 tonnes. The United States produces u tonnes. How much does the United States produce?

GPS

39. The French submarine *Nautile* can dive to 20,000 ft. Diving at x ft/hr, it takes 20 hours to reach the maximum depth. How fast must the *Nautile* dive to reach that depth?

40. Geography The largest desert in the world is the Sahara Desert, which covers 3,500,000 square miles. The second largest desert, the Australian Desert, is d square miles, 2,030,000 less than the Sahara. How big is the Australian Desert?

Practice and Problem Solving

41. Critical Thinking If the average depth of the Arctic Ocean is tripled, the result is 114 meters more than 3000 meters. The equation $3x - 114 = 3000$ models this situation. Find the average depth of the Arctic Ocean. 1038 m

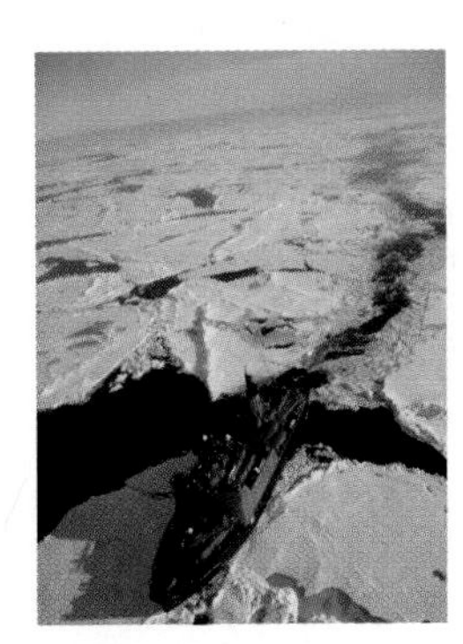

42. Communicate Jamie wanted to use her calculator to find the value of x that makes $56x + 716 = 5140$. Describe how to do it.

43. Critical Thinking Suppose $a + b = 10$. If the value of a increases by 2, how must the value of b change so that the equation is still true? It must decrease by 2.

PROBLEM SOLVING 2-13

Mixed Review

Write each addition equation as a subtraction equation with the same numbers. *[Previous course]*

44. $22 + 8 = 30$ $30 - 22 = 8$

45. $49 + 151 = 200$ $200 - 151 = 49$

46. $25 + 34{,}567{,}890 = 34{,}567{,}915$ $34{,}567{,}915 - 34{,}567{,}890 = 25$

Write each subtraction equation as an addition equation with the same numbers. *[Previous course]*

47. $53 - 10 = 43$ $43 + 10 = 53$

48. $163 - 57 = 106$ $106 + 57 = 163$

49. $180{,}000 - 21{,}000 = 159{,}000$ $159{,}000 + 21{,}000 = 180{,}000$

Project Progress

For each of your six methods, refer to your calculations of how far you could travel in 24 hours. Evaluate whether or not your calculations are reasonable. For an unreasonable answer, how could you adjust it to be more reasonable?

Problem Solving
Understand
Plan
Solve
Look Back

Exercise Notes

Exercises 44–46

Students may have alternative responses that are correct. Be sure all correct responses are validated.

Project Progress

You may want to have students use Chapter 2 Project Master.

Exercise Answers

38. $584 + 256 + u = 1171$; The U.S. produces 331 tonnes.

39. $20x = 20{,}000$; It must dive at 1000 ft/hr.

40. $3{,}500{,}000 - 2{,}030{,}000 = d$; The Australian Desert is 1,470,000 mi^2.

42. Possible answer: She could try different values of x until she got a true equation.

Alternate Assessment

Performance Ask students to create a visual overview, such as a word map, of what they have learned about equations.

Quick Quiz

Solve each equation.

1. $8 + a = 19$ $a = 11$
2. $b - 11 = 9$ $b = 20$
3. $\frac{c}{7} = 4$ $c = 28$
4. $9d = 54$ $d = 6$

Available on Daily Transparency 2-13

PROBLEM SOLVING

Name ______________

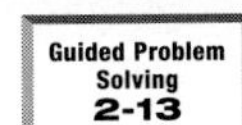
Guided Problem Solving 2-13

GPS PROBLEM 37, STUDENT PAGE 125

Write an equation for the situation and then solve it.

The top three gold-producing countries produce 1171 tonnes (metric tons) of gold. South Africa produces 584 tonnes. Australia produces 256 tonnes. The United States produces u tonnes. How much does the United States produce?

— Understand —

1. Circle the number of tonnes produced by each country.
2. How many tonnes are produced by the three countries? 1171 tonnes.

— Plan —

3. What operation would you use to find the total number of tonnes produced by the three countries? Addition.
4. Write an expression showing the number of tonnes produced by the three countries. $584 + 256 + u$

— Solve —

5. Write an equation showing the gold production for the three countries. Use your answer to Item 4 as one side of the equation. $584 + 256 + u = 1171$
6. How much gold did South Africa and Australia produce in all? 840 tonnes.
7. Substitute the total tonnes produced by South Africa and Australia for the two values in your equation. Rewrite the equation. $840 + u = 1171$
8. Solve the equation. How much does the United States produce? 331 tonnes.

— Look Back —

9. How can you check you answer to be sure it is correct? Possible answer: Add answer to tonnes produced by South Africa and Australia to see if the sum is 1171.

SOLVE ANOTHER PROBLEM

Write and solve an equation: One year, Ghana produced 26 tonnes of gold, Mexico produced 9 tonnes, and China produced g tonnes. Together they produced 155 tonnes. How much did China produce?
$26 + 9 + g = 155$; 120 tonnes.

ENRICHMENT

Name ______________

Extend Your Thinking 2-13

Critical Thinking

When an equation has two variables, you can find different values for the variables and still have a true equation.

1. Complete the table for $f - 2 = g$. Choose any values for f and g that make the equation true.

f	g
2	0
6	4
10	8

2. Analyze the table. What happens to the value of g when the value of f increases by four? The value of g increases by 4.
3. Suppose the equation was rewritten as $f - g = 2$. What do you think will happen to the value of g when the value of f increases by four so that the equation is still true? Explain your reasoning. Possible answer: g increases by 4; difference will always be 2.
4. Suppose the equation was rewritten as $g + 2 = f$. What do you think will happen to the value of g when the value of f increases by four so that the equation is still true? Explain your reasoning. Possible answer: g increases by 4; difference must be 2.
5. How are the equations in Questions 2, 3, and 4 alike? How are they different? Possible answer: Same variables and constants; same relationships between variables; different operations.
6. Suppose that $j \div k = 2$. If the value of j is halved, what will happen to the value of k for the equation to still be true? k is halved.
7. What other equations can you write using the same variables and numbers as in Question 6? What do you think will happen to the value of k when the value of j is halved so that each of your new equations is still true? Explain your reasoning. Possible answer: $j \div 2 = k$, $2k = j$; Since the equations are related, values of the variables will have the same changes.

Technology

Using a Spreadsheet • Using Guess and Check

The Point
Students see how spreadsheets can be used to solve systems of equations.

Materials
Spreadsheet software

Resources

Interactive CD-ROM Spreadsheet/Grapher Tool

About the Page
If students are not familiar with spreadsheets:

- Discuss how to enter and use formulas.
- Mention that on some spreadsheets a formula is preceded by "+" instead of "=".
- Point out how to substitute values for variables and where the result will appear.

Ask ...
- What happens when 50 and 25 are entered for x and y? The computer calculates $x - y$ and xy and then enters 25 in cell B4, and 1250 in cell B5.
- In Step 4, explain why you would not enter $x = 15$ and $y = 10$. $15 - 10$ is not equal to 25.

Answers for Try It
a. $x = 30$ and $y = 6$

b. $x = 24$ and $y = 1$

On Your Own
For the third question, you may want to discuss when it may not be faster to use a spreadsheet.

Answers for On Your Own
- So that the × for multiplication is not confused with the letter x or the variable x.
- If the difference of x and y is 25, you need to change both x and y so that the difference stays correct.
- Answers may vary.

TECHNOLOGY

Using a Spreadsheet — Using Guess and Check

Problem: What values for x and y will make these two equations true at the same time: $x - y = 25$ and $xy = 150$?

You can use your spreadsheet to set up two formulas that will help you use the "guess and check" method to find the values.

	A	B	C
1	x		
2	y		
3			
4	x – y		
5	xy		
6			
7			

1 Enter the information into the spreadsheet as shown.

	A	B	C
1	x	50	
2	y	25	
3			
4	x – y	25	
5	xy	1250	
6			
7			

2 In cell B4, enter the formula =B1–B2. **In cell B5, enter the formula** =B1*B2.

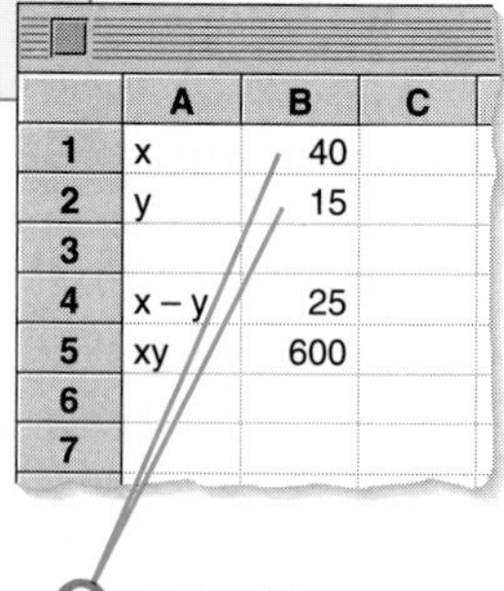

	A	B	C
1	x	40	
2	y	15	
3			
4	x – y	25	
5	xy	600	
6			
7			

3 Enter values into cell B1 for x and cell B2 for y so that the answer for $x - y$ is 25.

4 Change your values for x and y until $x - y = 25$ and xy is 150. If the answer for xy is too high, choose smaller values for x and y. If the answer for xy is too low, choose bigger values for x and y.

	A	B	C
1	x	30	
2	y	5	
3			
4	x – y	25	
5	xy	150	
6			
7			

Solution: The answer is $x = 30$ and $y = 5$.

TRY IT

a. Find a solution for $x + y = 36$ and $\frac{x}{y} = 5$.

b. Find a solution for $xy = 24$ and $\frac{x}{y} = 24$.

ON YOUR OWN

- Why do you think the multiplication formula uses an "*" and not an "x" for multiplication?
- When going from a bad guess to a better guess, why is it important to change the values for both x and y?
- Is it faster to find a solution for x and y with a spreadsheet or without a spreadsheet? Explain.

Meeting NCTM Standards

Curriculum Standards

STANDARDS

	Standard		pages
1	**Problem Solving**	Skills and Strategies	136, 152, 156, 172, 180, 194, 198
		Applications	140–141, 145–146, 151–152, 155–156, 157, 162–163, 167–168, 171–172, 173, 179–180, 183–184, 188–189, 193–194, 197–198, 199
		Exploration	138, 142, 148, 153, 160, 163, 164, 169, 176, 181, 185, 190, 195
2	**Communication**	Oral	137, 144, 150, 161, *163*, 166, 170, 175, 178, 182, 184, 187, 192, 196
		Written	141, 146, *152*, 156, 163, 168, 172, 180, 184, 189, 194, 198
		Cooperative Learning	*138, 142, 148, 153, 160, 164, 166, 169, 176, 181, 185, 190, 195*
3	**Reasoning**	Critical Thinking	141, 146, 152, 156, 163, 168, 172, 180, 184, 189, 194
4	**Connections**	Mathematical	See Standards 5–7, 9, 10, 12, 13 below.
		Interdisciplinary	Social Studies 134, *178*; Literature 135, 148; Geography *159*, *175*; Science 135, *137*, 139, 140, 143, *144*, 145, 149, *150*, 151, 153, 155, 198; History 140, *175*, 177, 178, 180, *183*, 191, 194, 196, *198*; Health 141, 163, 184, 188, *192*, 193; Sports 134, 141, *187*; Career 172; Consumer *159*, *192*; Social Science 156
		Technology	138, 147, 153, 154, *155*, 158, 159, 167, 182, 186
		Cultural	134, 159, 160, 161, 165, *166*, 167
5	**Number and Number Relationships**		138–146, 162
6	**Number Systems and Number Theory**		148–156, 171
7	**Computation and Estimation**		*139*, 145, *149*, *154*, 160–168, *170*, 176–194
9	**Algebra**		169–172, 195–198
10	**Statistics**		151, 186
12	**Geometry**		169, 171, 174
13	**Measurement**		142, 145, 146, 158, *167*, 174, 184, 189

Italic type indicates Teacher Edition reference.

Teaching Standards

Focus on Pacing

Mathematical thinking takes place in an environment that allows adequate time for students to puzzle and think. Teachers should

- provide the time necessary to explore sound mathematics and grapple with significant ideas and problems.
- allow students to be stuck.

Assessment Standards

Focus on Coherence

Performance The Coherence Standard requires that assessment activities be matched to the skill or concept which is to be assessed. Performance assessment activities can be created which offer students an opportunity to demonstrate their knowledge individually or as part of a group. In Chapter 3, the teacher is asked to assess

- the student's ability to estimate with decimals.
- a group's conclusions about rounding decimals as an indicator of its members' abilities.

TECHNOLOGY

For the Teacher

- **Teacher Resource Planner CD-ROM**
  Use the teacher planning CD-ROM to view resources available for Chapter 3. You can prepare custom lesson plans or use the default lesson plans provided.

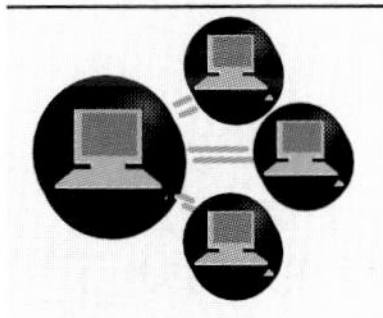

- **World Wide Web**
  Visit **www.teacher.mathsurf.com** for links to lesson plans from teachers and other professionals, NCTM information, and other sites.

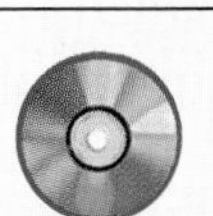

- **TestWorks**
  TestWorks provides ready-made tests and can create custom tests and practice worksheets.

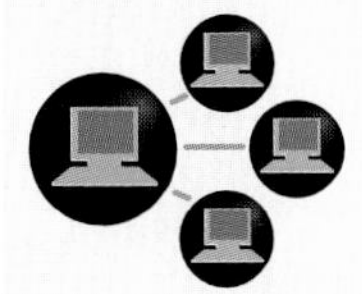

For the Parent

- **World Wide Web**
  Parents can use the Web site at **www.parent.mathsurf.com.**

For the Student

- **Interactive CD-ROM**
  Lesson 3-9 has an *Interactive CD-ROM Lesson*. The *Interactive CD-ROM Journal* and *Interactive CD-ROM Spreadsheet/Grapher Tool* are also used in Chapter 3.

- **Wide World of Mathematics**
  Lesson 3-3 Middle School: In 0.01 Second
  Lesson 3-4 Middle School: Hubble Telescope

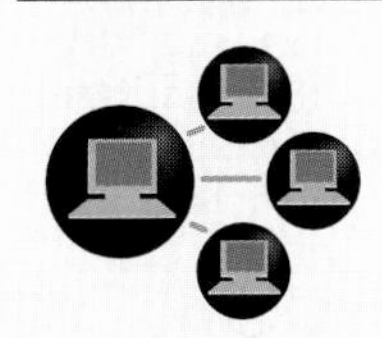

- **World Wide Web**
  Use with Chapter and Section Openers; Students can go online to the Scott Foresman-Addison Wesley Web site at **www.mathsurf.com/6/ch3** to collect information about chapter themes.

STANDARDIZED - TEST CORRELATION

SECTION 3A

LESSON	OBJECTIVE	ITBS Form M	CTBS 4th Ed.	CAT 5th Ed.	SAT 9th Ed.	MAT 7th Ed.	Your Form
3-1	• Write numbers in decimal notation. • Represent decimal numbers using a grid model.	✘	✘	✘ ✘	✘	 ✘	
3-2	• Round decimal numbers. • Measure length with a metric ruler.		 ✘			 ✘	
3-3	• Compare and order decimals.	✘		✘	✘	✘	
3-4	• Represent numbers in scientific notation.						

SECTION 3B

LESSON	OBJECTIVE	ITBS Form M	CTBS 4th Ed.	CAT 5th Ed.	SAT 9th Ed.	MAT 7th Ed.	Your Form
3-5	• Estimate sums, differences, products, and quotients with decimals.				✘	✘	
3-6	• Add and subtract with decimals.	✘	✘	✘	✘	✘	
3-7	• Solve equations that involve adding and subtracting decimals.			✘	✘	✘	

SECTION 3C

LESSON	OBJECTIVE	ITBS Form M	CTBS 4th Ed.	CAT 5th Ed.	SAT 9th Ed.	MAT 7th Ed.	Your Form
3-8	• Multiply a whole number by a decimal.	✘	✘	✘	✘	✘	
3-9	• Multiply a decimal times a decimal.	✘		✘	✘	✘	
3-10	• Divide a decimal number by a whole number.	✘	✘	✘	✘	✘	
3-11	• Divide decimal numbers by decimal numbers.			✘		✘	
3-12	• Solve decimal equations with multiplication and division. • Solve equations using inverse operations.			✘		✘ ✘	

Key: ITBS - Iowa Test of Basic Skills; CTBS - Comprehensive Test of Basic Skills; CAT - California Achievement Test; SAT - Stanford Achievement Test; MAT - Metropolitan Achievement Test

ASSESSMENT PROGRAM

Traditional Assessment

QUICK QUIZZES	SECTION REVIEW	CHAPTER REVIEW	CHAPTER ASSESSMENT FREE RESPONSE	CHAPTER ASSESSMENT MULTIPLE CHOICE	CUMULATIVE REVIEW
TE: pp. 141, 146, 152, 156, 163, 168, 172, 180, 184, 189, 194, 198	SE: pp. 158, 174, 200 *Quiz 3A, 3B, 3C	SE: pp. 202–203	SE: p. 204 *Ch. 3 Tests Forms A, B, E	*Ch. 3 Tests Forms C, E	SE: p. 205 *Ch. 3 Test Form F; Quarterly Test Ch. 1–3

Alternate Assessment

INTERVIEW	JOURNAL	ONGOING	PERFORMANCE	PORTFOLIO	PROJECT	SELF
TE: p. 184	SE: pp. 141, 146, 156, 163, 168, 184, 189, 194, 198 TE: pp. 136, 141, 152, 156, 180, 194, 198	TE: pp. 138, 142, 148, 153, 160, 164, 169, 176, 181, 185, 190, 195	SE: pp. 204, 205 TE: pp. 146, 163 *Ch. 3 Tests Forms D, E	TE: pp. 168, 189	SE: pp. 152, 163, 189 TE: p. 135	TE: p. 172

*Tests and quizzes are in *Assessment Sourcebook*. Test Form E is a mixed response test.
Forms for Alternate Assessment are also available in *Assessment Sourcebook*.

TestWorks: Test and Practice Software

MIDDLE SCHOOL PACING CHART

REGULAR PACING

Day	5 classes per week
1	Chapter 3 Opener; Problem Solving Focus
2	Section **3A** Opener; Lesson **3-1**
3	Lesson **3-2**; Technology
4	Lesson **3-3**
5	Lesson **3-4**
6	**3A** Connect; **3A** Review
7	Section **3B** Opener; Lesson **3-5**
8	Lesson **3-6**
9	Lesson **3-7**
10	**3B** Connect; **3B** Review
11	Section **3C** Opener; Lesson **3-8**
12	Lesson **3-9**
13	Lesson **3-10**
14	Lesson **3-11**
15	Lesson **3-12**
16	**3C** Connect; **3C** Review; Extend Key Ideas
17	Chapter 3 Summary and Review
18	Chapter 3 Assessment Cumulative Review, Chapters 1–3

BLOCK SCHEDULING OPTIONS

Block Scheduling for
Complete Course

Chapter 3 may be presented in

- twelve 90-minute blocks
- fifteen 75-minute blocks

Each block consists of a combination of

- Chapter and Section Openers
- Explores
- Lesson Development
- Problem Solving Focus
- Technology
- Extend Key Ideas
- Connect
- Review
- Assessment

For details, see *Block Scheduling Handbook.*

Block Scheduling for
Interdisciplinary Course

Each block integrates math with another subject area.

In Chapter 3, interdisciplinary topics include

- Spiders
- Currency
- Oregon Trail

Themes for Interdisciplinary Team Teaching 3A, 3B, and 3C are

- Spiders
- Food for Thought
- Prescription Decoders

For details, see *Block Scheduling Handbook.*

Block Scheduling for
Lab-Based Course

In each block, 30–40 minutes is devoted to lab activities including

- Explores in the Student Edition
- Connect pages in the Student Edition
- Technology options in the Student Edition
- Reteaching Activities in the Teacher Edition

For details, see *Block Scheduling Handbook.*

Block Scheduling for
Course with *Connected Mathematics*

In each block, investigations from **Connected Mathematics** replace or enhance the lessons in Chapter 3.

Connected Mathematics topics for Chapter 3 can be found in

- *Bits and Pieces II*

For details, see *Block Scheduling Handbook.*

INTERDISCIPLINARY BULLETIN BOARD

Set Up

Prepare a bulletin board with sections for various track-and-field events.

Procedure

- Have small groups of students research world track-and-field records expressed as decimals for events such as the high jump, long jump, pole vault, discus throw, hammer throw, and javelin throw.
- Groups should find out the men's and women's world record for an event, if both exist, and the date(s) a record was set.
- They should draw the event on the bulletin board with appropriate information listed with it.

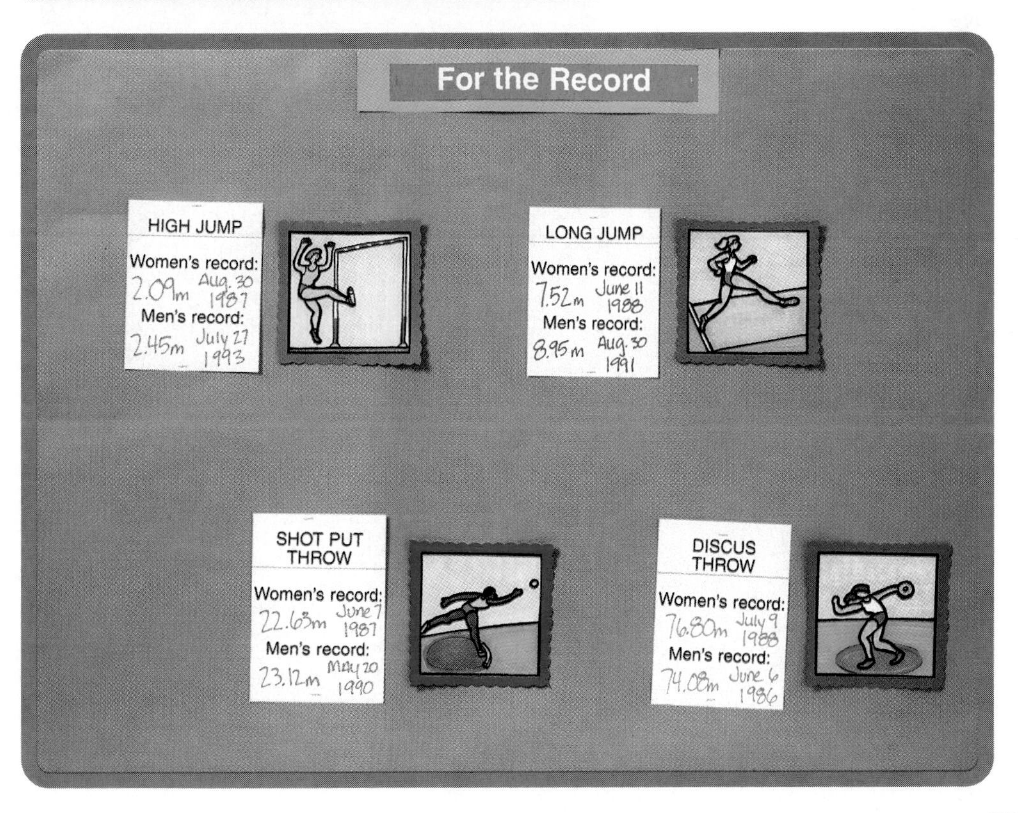

Chapter 3

The information on these pages shows how decimals are used in real-life situations.

World Wide Web

If your class has access to the World Wide Web, you might want to use the information found at the Web site addresses given.

Extensions

The following activities do not require access to the World Wide Web.

Entertainment
Have students investigate Olympic records in the 100-meter dash since 1988 to find out if Carl Lewis's Olympic record still stands. In 1992, Linford Christie won in 9.96 sec and in 1996, Donovan Baily won in 9.84 sec., breaking Lewis's record.

People of the World
Ask students to find an example of the use of commas instead of decimal points in a foreign newspaper or magazine to share with the class.

Social Studies
Use these questions for discussion: Why is zero so important? How do we use it?

Science
Have students investigate major earthquakes that have occurred around the world.

Arts & Literature
Ask students to explain why O. Henry's statement creates a problem. Ask them to give some penny amounts that would be possible. It is impossible to have $1.87 in change with exactly 60 pennies. The number of pennies would have to have either a 2 or a 7 in the ones place.

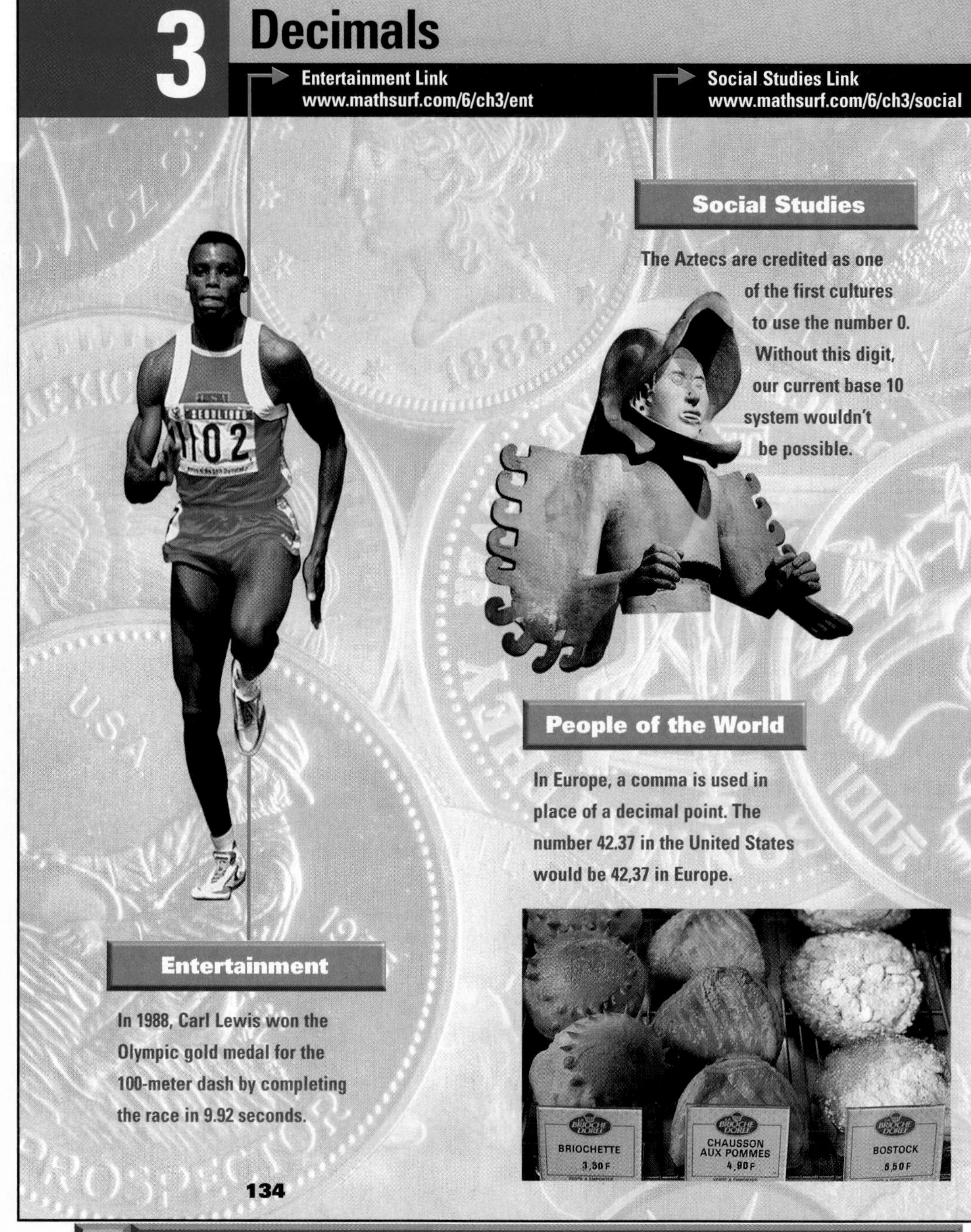

3 Decimals

Entertainment Link
www.mathsurf.com/6/ch3/ent

Social Studies Link
www.mathsurf.com/6/ch3/social

Social Studies

The Aztecs are credited as one of the first cultures to use the number 0. Without this digit, our current base 10 system wouldn't be possible.

People of the World

In Europe, a comma is used in place of a decimal point. The number 42.37 in the United States would be 42,37 in Europe.

Entertainment

In 1988, Carl Lewis won the Olympic gold medal for the 100-meter dash by completing the race in 9.92 seconds.

134

TEACHER TALK

Meet Alma Ramirez

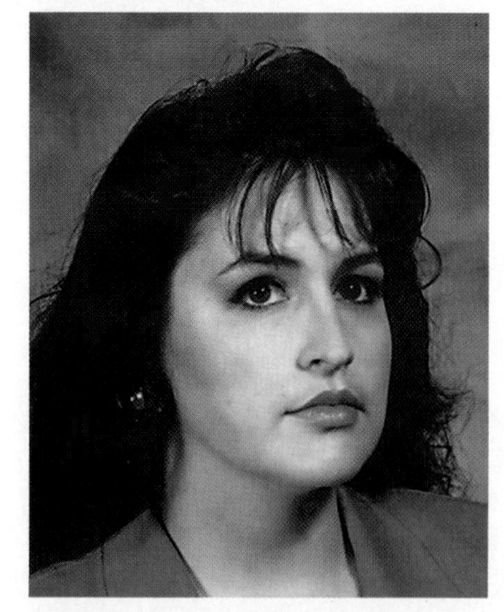

Oakland Charter Academy
Oakland, California

When introducing decimals, I find it useful to cut cord, string, and ribbon into one-meter strips and tape them around the room. I have students estimate where the 0.5 meter mark should be, the 0.25 meter mark, the 0.05 meter mark, and so on. I have students label these points. These points become constant reference points as students move from ordering and comparing decimals to adding and subtracting decimals.

The strips allow students to develop an intuitive sense of the relative magnitude of decimals. For example, they can readily see that 0.05 is less than 0.5 and that 0.5 is the same as 0.50 because both 0.5 and 0.50 equal $\frac{1}{2}$. Relating decimals to metric measurements provides students with a real-world application of decimals.

Science Link
www.mathsurf.com/6/ch3/science

Arts & Literature

In *The Gift of the Magi,* O. Henry stated "One dollar and eighty-seven cents. That was all. And sixty cents of it was in pennies." He never explained how this was possible.

Science

The Richter scale uses decimals to measure earthquake intensity. A 1.3 earthquake is recorded but not felt. A 6.1 earthquake destroys buildings. Earthquakes above 7.9 cause total destruction.

KEY MATH IDEAS

Decimal numbers can be used to describe numbers that are in between whole numbers.

Decimal place values, such as tenths and hundredths, describe amounts that are smaller than 1.

Decimal numbers can be rounded to the nearest place value in the same way that whole numbers can.

Decimal numbers can be added and subtracted like whole numbers when the decimal points of the numbers are lined up.

You can multiply and divide decimal numbers as if they were whole numbers, but you need to pay special attention to where the decimal point is placed in the answer.

CHAPTER PROJECT

Problem Solving
Understand
Plan
Solve
Look Back

In this project, you will investigate your own personal budget by analyzing how much money you spend over a certain period of time. Begin by estimating how much you spend per week on food, travel, and entertainment.

135

PROJECT ASSESSMENT

You may choose to use this project as a Performance Assessment for the chapter.

Performance Assessment Key

Level 4 Full Accomplishment

Level 3 Substantial Accomplishment

Level 2 Partial Accomplishment

Level 1 Little Accomplishment

Suggested Scoring Rubric

Level	Criteria
4	•Demonstrates good organizational and estimation skills in documenting information. •Clearly displays information in a bar graph.
3	•Adequately organizes and estimates documented information. •Displays data in an appropriate graph.
2	•Attempts to organize and estimate documented information. •Attempts to display data in a graph.
1	•Information is not well organized and estimates are not reasonable. •Has difficulty choosing appropriate graph on which to display data.

Chapter Project

Students collect data on their own spending habits and analyze how they spend their money over a period of time. Based on the data they collect, they can make a personal budget.

Resources
Chapter 3 Project Master

Introduce the Project

- Discuss the kinds of things students spend their money on every week. Help students list these items in categories such as food, clothing, and entertainment.
- Help students create a form on which they can list their expenses to help them record expenditures in an orderly way.
- Discuss how to estimate how much they spend each week on each category in their list.

Project Progress

Section A, page 152 Students keep a record of everything they spend money on.

Section B, page 163 Students arrange their expenditures in categories, and find the total of each category. This may be a good time to reevaluate spending habits.

Section C, page 189 Students display collected data on a bar graph to summarize their spending habits.

Community Project

A community project for Chapter 3 is available in *Home and Community Connections.*

Cooperative Learning

You may want to use Teaching Tool Transparency 1: Cooperative Learning Checklist with **Explore** and other group activities in this chapter.

Problem Solving Focus

Reading the Problem

The Point
Students focus on understanding the information in the problem without actually solving the problem.

Resources
Teaching Tool Transparency 18: Problem-Solving Guidelines

 *Interactive CD-ROM Journal*

About the Page

Using the Problem-Solving Process
Talk about suggestions for reading a problem:

- Read the problem two or three times before beginning.
- Determine what the problem is about.
- Determine what the problem is asking.

Answers for Problems

1. a. Cats and homes in America
   b. How many homes are there in America?
   c. 57 million
   d. 186 homes
   e. Possible answer: Question: Are there more homes with cats or without? Answer: Without.
2. a. Registered dogs in the American Kennel Club.
   b. Was the combined number of Dalmations, Dachshunds, and Pomeranians greater than or less than the number of Labrador Retrievers?
   c. 42,621
   d. Dachshunds
   e. Possible answer: Question: How many more Labrador Retrievers were there than Dalmations? Answer: 83,772

Journal

Ask students to write a paragraph explaining the importance of reading a problem carefully before trying to solve it.

Problem Solving
Understand
Plan
Solve
Look Back

Reading the Problem

When you are trying to understand a problem and you are stuck, it sometimes helps to answer simpler questions about the problem. Thinking about the information that has been given can sometimes help you decide upon a new strategy for solving the problem.

Problem Solving Focus

Read each problem, and answer the questions about the problem.

DEL MONTE KENNEL CLUB, INC.

1 According to the American Veterinary Medical Association, 31 out of every 100 households in America have pet cats. The average number of cats per household is 2. If there are an estimated 57,000,000 pet cats in America, how many homes are there in America?

a. What is the problem about?

b. What is the problem asking for?

c. About how many pet cats are there in America?

d. If an average neighborhood had 600 homes in it, how many of those homes would have cats?

e. Write and answer a question of your own.

2 One year the American Kennel Club had 126,393 registered Labrador Retrievers. There were also 42,621 Dalmatians, 46,129 Dachshunds, and 39,947 Pomeranians. Was the combined number of Dalmatians, Dachshunds, and Pomeranians bigger or smaller than the number of Labrador Retrievers?

a. What is the problem about?

b. What is the problem asking for?

c. How many Dalmatians were registered?

d. Were there more Dachshunds or more Pomeranians?

e. Write and answer a question of your own.

Additional Problem

In 1991 the U.S. Government spent $1,651,000 to save the Puerto Rican parrot, $1,629,000 to save a species of culthroat trout, and $1,524,000 on the black-footed ferret. The same year they spent $4,624,000 on the Florida panther. Did the government spend as much on saving the panther as on the other three species combined?

1. What is the problem about? The amount of money spent to save four endangered species.
2. What is the problem asking for? A comparison of the amount spent on three species to the amount spent on the panther.
3. How would you solve this problem? Add the numbers $1,651,000, $1,629,000, and $1,524,000 and compare the sum to $4,624,000.

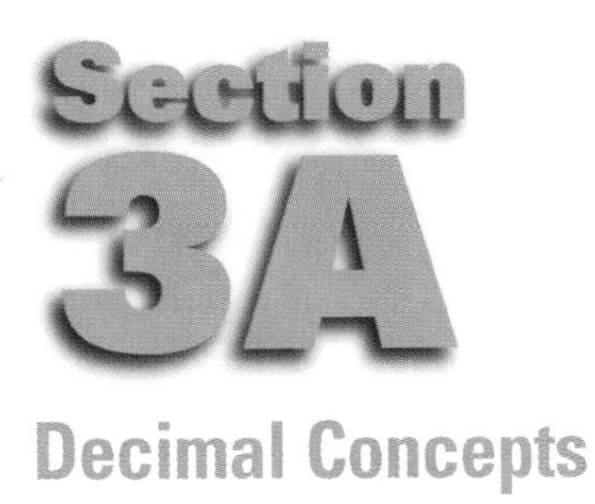

Decimal Concepts

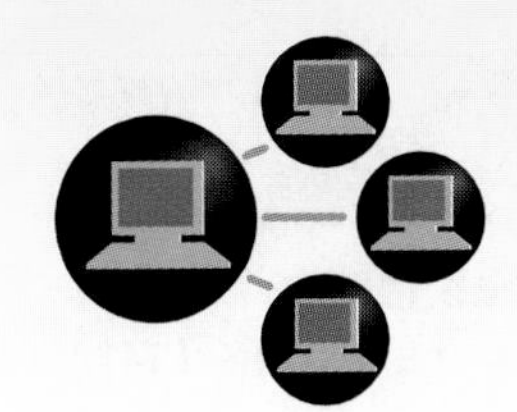

Visit www.teacher.mathsurf.com for links to lesson plans from teachers and other professionals, NCTM information, and other sites.

LESSON PLANNING GUIDE

Student Edition / Ancillaries

LESSON		MATERIALS	VOCABULARY	DAILY	OTHER
	Chapter 3 Opener				Ch. 3 Project Master Ch. 3 Community Project Teaching Tool Trans. 1
	Problem Solving Focus				Teaching Tool Trans. 18 *Interactive CD-ROM Journal*
	Section 3A Opener				
3-1	**Decimal Notation**	calculator		3-1	Teaching Tool Trans. 4, 11, 12 Lesson Enhancement Trans. 8
3-2	**Rounding Decimals**	meter stick, masking tape, cotton balls, spreadsheet software		3-2	Teaching Tool Trans. 16 Technology Master 11
	Technology				*Interactive CD-ROM Spreadsheet/Grapher Tool*
3-3	**Comparing and Ordering Decimals**			3-3	Teaching Tool Trans. 5 Lesson Enhancement Trans. 9 Technology Master 12 Ch. 3 Project Master *WW Math*—Middle School
3-4	**Scientific Notation**	scientific calculator	scientific notation	3-4	Teaching Tool Trans. 23 Technology Master 13 *WW Math*—Middle School
	Connect				Interdisc. Team Teaching 3A
	Review				Practice 3A; Quiz 3A; *TestWorks*

SKILLS TRACE

LESSON	SKILL	FIRST INTRODUCED GR. 4	GR. 5	GR. 6	DEVELOP	PRACTICE/ APPLY	REVIEW
3-1	**Identifying decimal place values.**	✘			pp. 138–139	pp. 140–141	pp. 158, 202, 219
3-2	**Rounding decimals.**	✘			pp. 142–144	pp. 145–146	pp. 168, 202, 292
3-3	**Comparing and ordering decimals.**	✘			pp. 148–150	pp. 151–152	pp. 172, 202, 224
3-4	**Using scientific notation.**			✘ p. 153	pp. 153–154	pp. 155–156	pp. 180, 200, 202, 214, 354

CONNECTED MATHEMATICS

Investigation 6 in the unit *Bits and Pieces II (Using Rational Numbers)*, from the **Connected Mathematics** series, can be used with Section 3A.

INTERDISCIPLINARY TEAM TEACHING

Math and Science/Technology

(Worksheet pages 13–14: Teacher pages T13–T14)

In this lesson, students apply decimal concepts to very small objects.

Name ______________________ ***Math and Science/Technology***

STRONG THINGS IN SMALL PACKAGES

Apply decimal concepts to very small objects.

Spiders generally have a bad reputation. Because most kinds of spiders are poisonous, many people are afraid of them. This is understandable, but unfortunate. Spiders also do a lot of good. The Panamese wheel spider, for example, eats an average of 1.63 insects a day, or almost 600 insects a year. Multiply that figure by the millions of wheel spiders that live in and around Panama, and you can appreciate how important these spiders are in maintaining the balance of nature.

A spider must, of course, catch its prey before it can eat it. Spiders do this in various ways. The spiders you are most familiar with trap their victims, or prey, in the sticky threads of a web.

A spider's web is made of spider silk, which the spider makes in its body. Spiders use organs called spinnerets to spin silk. Spinnerets are located on the rear of the spider's abdomen. Spiders have from two to six spinnerets. Liquid silk, which is made in silk glands inside the spider's abdomen, is fed into the spinnerets. Some kinds of liquid silk harden outside the spider's body. Other kinds produce sticky threads. Both kinds can trap insects. Even large insects can be caught in a spider's web. That's because the strands of the web are very strong. Even though a strand can be as narrow as 0.00002 mm in diameter, ounce for ounce, it is stronger than steel. Spider silk is so strong that it has been called the strongest natural fiber known to humans.

There are many things besides spider webs that are small but very strong. Think about a strand of human hair, for example. If you pull it, it usually does not break. Instead, it comes out at the root. Butterfly wings are paper thin, but they are strong enough to carry the butterfly's weight from flower to flower.

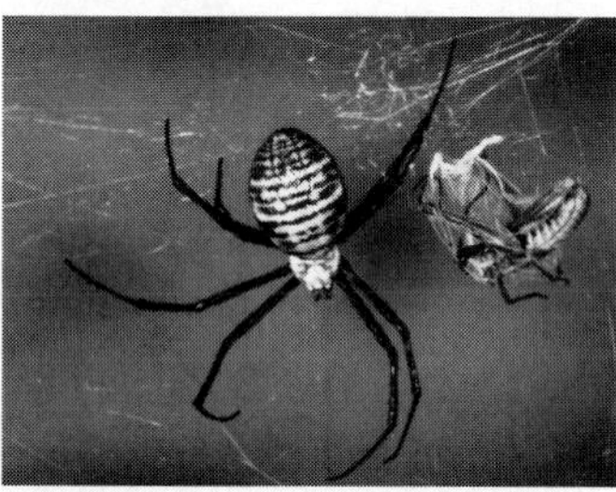

Spiders can leisurely dine on insects, which are snared in incredibly strong spider's silk.

Name ______________________ ***Math and Science/Technology***

The following table contains some of nature's very small things.

Object	Approximate Size in Millimeters
world's smallest spider	0.5
black widow spider	12.5
spider silk (diameter)	0.00002
world's smallest moth (wingspan)	1.975
butterfly's wing (thickness)	0.038
dog flea	2.5
dog tick	5.0
carpenter ant	12.5
diameter of average human hair	0.078

1. Which objects in the table measure less than one millimeter?

   world's smallest spider, diameter of spider silk, thickness of butterfly wing, diameter of average human hair

2. Using number words, write the measurement of the diameter of a spider's silk.

   two hundred-thousandths of a millimeter

3. To appreciate how thin spiders' silk is, determine how many strands of spider silk lying side by side it would take to equal one millimeter.

   50,000

4. Why is it important that scientists be able to work with very small values?

   Scientists need to be able to measure the weight, size, quantity, or other characteristics of things in nature that are very small. These include cells, molecules, and atoms.

5. What does the information given in this lesson tell you about size and strength?

   Students' responses will vary. Students may say that things do not have to be large to be strong or that small things can be very strong.

6. Although spiders' silk does not have much value at this time, the silk used to make all sorts of silk fabrics is quite valuable. Do some research to find out from where this silk comes, what its characteristics are, and how it is used in the fabric industry. Write a report of your findings.

BIBLIOGRAPHY

FOR TEACHERS

Burril, Gail and John C. *Data Analysis and Statistics Across the Curriculum*. Reston, VA: NCTM, 1992.

Cassutt, Michael. *Who's Who in Space*. New York, NY: Macmillan, 1993.

Shaw, Jean. *From the File Treasury*. Reston, VA: NCTM, 1991.

Spangler, David. *Math for Real Kids*. Glenview, IL: Good Year Books, 1997.

FOR STUDENTS

Arnold, Caroline. *The Olympic Summer Games*. New York, NY: Watts, 1991.

Booth, Basil. *Earthquakes and Volcanoes*. New York, NY: New Discovery Books, 1992.

Dineen, Jacqueline. *The Aztecs*. New York, NY: New Discovery Books, 1992.

Hanna, Jack. *Jungle Jack Hanna's Pocketful of Bugs*. New York, NY: Scholastic/Cartwheel Books, 1996.

SECTION 3A

Decimal Concepts

▶ Science Link ▶ www.mathsurf.com/6/ch3/spiders

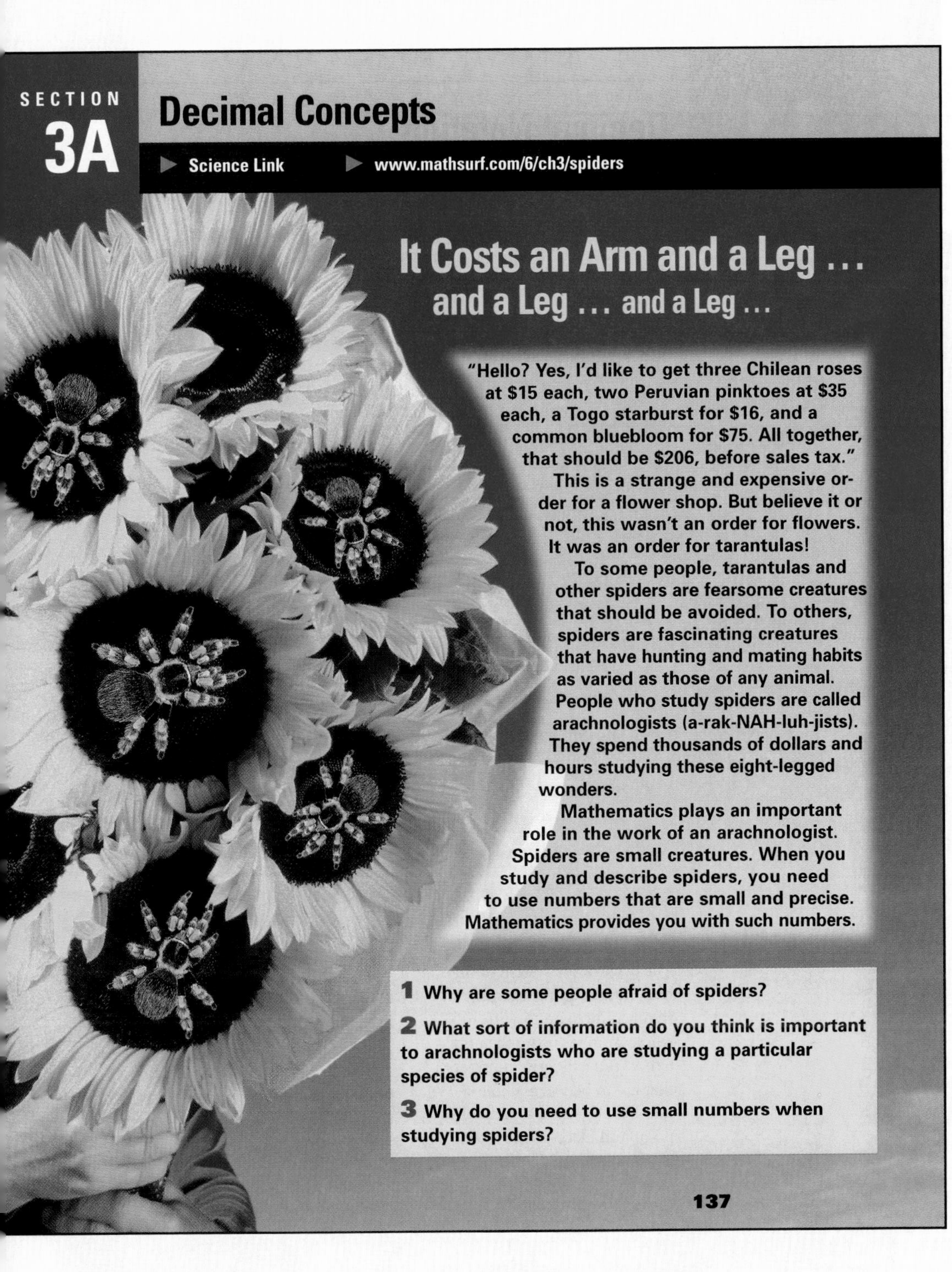

It Costs an Arm and a Leg … and a Leg … and a Leg …

"Hello? Yes, I'd like to get three Chilean roses at $15 each, two Peruvian pinktoes at $35 each, a Togo starburst for $16, and a common bluebloom for $75. All together, that should be $206, before sales tax."

This is a strange and expensive order for a flower shop. But believe it or not, this wasn't an order for flowers. It was an order for tarantulas!

To some people, tarantulas and other spiders are fearsome creatures that should be avoided. To others, spiders are fascinating creatures that have hunting and mating habits as varied as those of any animal. People who study spiders are called arachnologists (a-rak-NAH-luh-jists). They spend thousands of dollars and hours studying these eight-legged wonders.

Mathematics plays an important role in the work of an arachnologist. Spiders are small creatures. When you study and describe spiders, you need to use numbers that are small and precise. Mathematics provides you with such numbers.

1 Why are some people afraid of spiders?

2 What sort of information do you think is important to arachnologists who are studying a particular species of spider?

3 Why do you need to use small numbers when studying spiders?

137

Where are we now?

In Grade 5, students

- worked with tenths, hundredths, and thousandths.
- explored equivalent decimals.
- located decimals on a number line.
- explored comparing and ordering decimals.

Where are we going?

In Section 3A, students will

- name and write numbers in decimal notation.
- round decimals.
- measure with a metric ruler.
- compare and order decimals.
- write numbers in scientific notation.

Theme: Spiders

World Wide Web

If your class has access to the World Wide Web, you might want to use the information found at the Web site address given. The interdisciplinary link relates to topics discussed in this section.

About the Page

This page introduces the theme of the section, spiders, and discusses the need for small and precise numbers when describing small creatures.

Ask …

- Why do you think spiders spin webs? Webs are used to catch insects for food.
- What are tarantulas? Large spiders native to Southwestern United States and South and Central America.

Extension

The following activity does not require access to the World Wide Web.

Science

People think spiders are insects, but scientists classify spiders as *arachnids* which differ from insects in many ways. Have students list ways in which spiders and insects differ. Possible answers: Spiders have 8 legs, no wings or antenna; Insects have 6 legs, wings and antenna.

Answers for Questions

1. Possible answer: They think spiders will bite.
2. Possible answer: The spider's eating habits, mating habits, web building, and whether or not it is poisonous.
3. Possible answer: Small numbers are needed to make accurate measurements.

Connect

On page 157, students will use decimals to compare and contrast the length of spiders.

3-1 Lesson Organizer

Objectives

- Write numbers in decimal notation.
- Represent decimal numbers using a grid model.

Materials

- Explore: Calculator

NCTM Standards

- 1–6

Review

State the value of 6 in each of these numbers.

1. 3462 tens
2. 611 hundreds
3. Write 15,705 in word form. fifteen thousand, seven hundred five

Available on Daily Transparency 3-1

1 Introduce

Explore

You may wish to use Teaching Tool Transparency 4: Place-Value Charts and Lesson Enhancement Transparency 8 with **Explore**.

The Point
Students complete the place-value chart to discover the connection between place values less than one and decimal notation.

Ongoing Assessment
Make sure students recognize the relationship between the place values of each column.

Answers for Explore

1. Row 2: $\frac{100}{1}$; $\frac{10}{1}$; $\frac{1}{1}$; $\frac{1}{10}$; $\frac{1}{100}$;
   Row 3: 100.; 10.; 1.; 0.1; 0.01
2. Row 1: 1 ÷ 1000; Row 2: $\frac{1}{1000}$; Row 3: 0.001
3. They represent parts of a whole.
4. Similar: Use same numbers; Different: Numbers on left are larger values than numbers on right.

3-1 Decimal Notation

You'll Learn ...

- how to write numbers in decimal notation
- how to represent decimal numbers using a grid model

... How It's Used

Seismologists use decimal numbers to describe the amount of energy released in an earthquake. Measurements are taken off of seismographs and translated into amount of energy.

▶ Lesson Link In Chapter 2, you learned to name and write whole numbers. Now you'll see how to name and write numbers that are not whole numbers, especially numbers between 0 and 1. ◄

Explore Decimal Notation

What's the Name of That Place?

Materials: Calculator

	Hundreds	Tens	Ones		
Arithmetic Form	100 ÷ 1	10 ÷ 1	1 ÷ 1	1 ÷ 10	1 ÷ 100
Fraction Form	$\frac{100}{1}$				
Calculator Form					

1. Use a calculator and your knowledge of patterns to complete the table.
2. Add one more column to the right of the table, and fill in the column so that it continues the pattern.
3. The names of the three columns to the right are "Tenths," "Hundredths," and "Thousandths." Explain the reasons for these names.
4. How are the columns to the right of the "Ones" similar to the columns to the left of the "Ones"? How are they different?

Learn Decimal Notation

The place-value system of ones, tens, hundreds, thousands, and so on, allows you to write any whole number using the digits 0 to 9. You can write numbers that are in between whole numbers by using a decimal point and place values that are smaller than ones.

Thousands, Hundreds, Tens, Ones, Tenths, Hundredths, Thousandths

1 . 3 7

1    $0.3 = \frac{3}{10}$ $0.07 = \frac{7}{100}$

MEETING INDIVIDUAL NEEDS

Resources

- 3-1 Practice
- 3-1 Reteaching
- 3-1 Problem Solving
- 3-1 Enrichment
- 3-1 Daily Transparency
  - Problem of the Day
  - Review
  - Quick Quiz
- Teaching Tool Transparencies 4, 11, 12
- Lesson Enhancement Transparency 8

Learning Modalities

Visual Have students make a large place-value chart for the bulletin board. Have them extend the chart to include both very large and very small place values.

Kinesthetic Have students use place-value blocks to represent various decimals.

English Language Development

Watch for students who do not hear the difference between "tens" and "tenths" or between "hundreds" and "hundredths" when the words are spoken. Point out that the words sound almost the same but have different though related meanings.

Ask students to provide examples of decimal notation from their native countries. Elicit their prior knowledge about decimals, pointing out that in most countries, all measurements are based on a decimal system.

Examples

1 What decimal number does the grid represent?

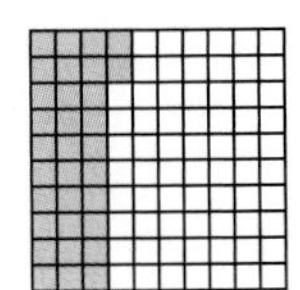

The grid represents 0.32

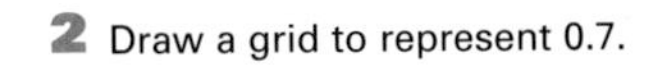

2 Draw a grid to represent 0.7.

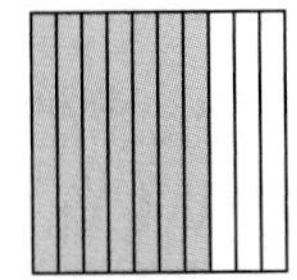

3 Write one and twenty-one thousandths in decimal form.

one and twenty-one thousandths = 1.021

4 A desert tarantula measures 6.94 cm in length. Write this in word form.

6.94 = six and ninety-four hundredths.

▶ Science Link

Desert tarantulas seldom bite people. Their venom is usually no more dangerous than a bee sting.

Try It

What decimal numbers does each grid represent?

a. 0.81

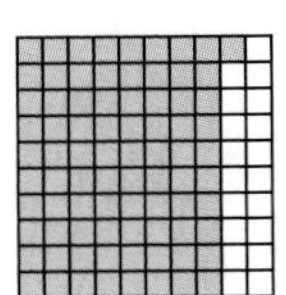

b. 0.4

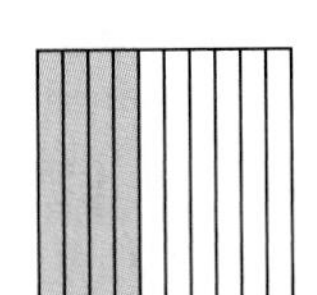

Represent in grid form. **c.** 0.2 **d.** 0.13

Write in word form. **e.** 3.051 **f.** 0.171 **g.** 0.47 **h.** 8.1

Write in number form. **i.** nine hundredths 0.09

j. two and one hundred one thousandths 2.101

Study TIP

All the place values smaller than one have names that end in *ths.*

Check Your Understanding

1. How many tenths are in a whole? How many hundredths? How many thousandths?
2. How many hundredths are in a tenth?
3. Why is the United States money system referred to as a decimal system?

MATH EVERY DAY

▶ Problem of the Day

Claude has 3 wigs, 4 sets of eyeglasses, and 2 sets of mustaches. How many different disguises can he make using these items? 24 disguises

Available on Daily Transparency 3-1

An Extension is provided in the transparency package.

Estimation

Estimate.

1. 123,432 + 505,339 600,000
2. 7,819,119 + 6,999,999 15,000,000
3. 789 + 912 1700
4. 34,566 + 57,987 90,000

2 Teach

Learn

You may wish to use Teaching Tool Transparencies 11: 10 × 10 Grids and 12: Tenths Grids with this lesson.

Alternate Examples

1. What decimal number does the grid represent?

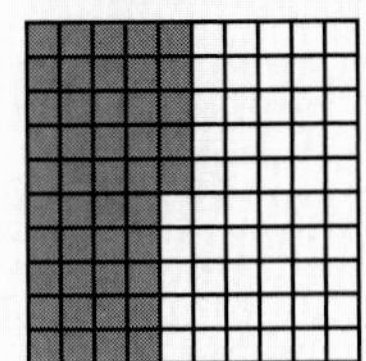

The grid represents 0.45.

2. Draw a grid to represent 0.6.

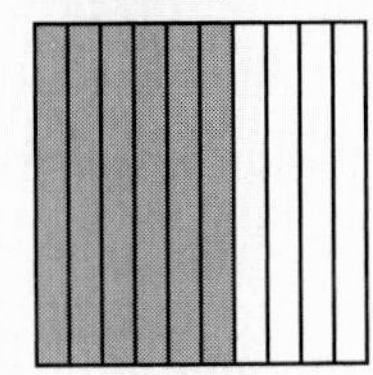

3. Write two and six thousandths in number form.
   Two and six thousandths = 2.006.
4. A winning long jump measured 8.95 m. Write this in word form.
   8.95 = eight and ninety-five hundredths.

Answers for Try It

c.

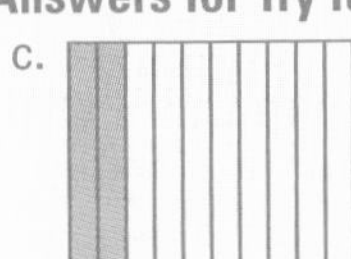

d.

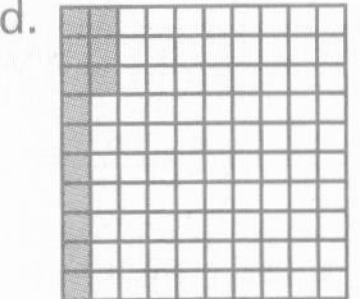

e. three and fifty-one thousandths

f. one hundred seventy-one thousandths

g. forty-seven hundredths

h. eight and one tenth

3 Practice and Assess

Check

Answers for Check Your Understanding

1. 10 tenths; 100 hundredths; 1000 thousandths
2. 10 hundredths
3. Possible answer: Because it uses place values based on 100 cents to the dollar.

3-1 Exercises and Applications

Assignment Guide

- **Basic**
  1–22, 29–31, 35–37, 42–45
- **Average**
  1–22, 29–31, 35–49 odds
- **Enriched**
  1–29 odds, 30–34, 36–48 evens

Exercise Answers

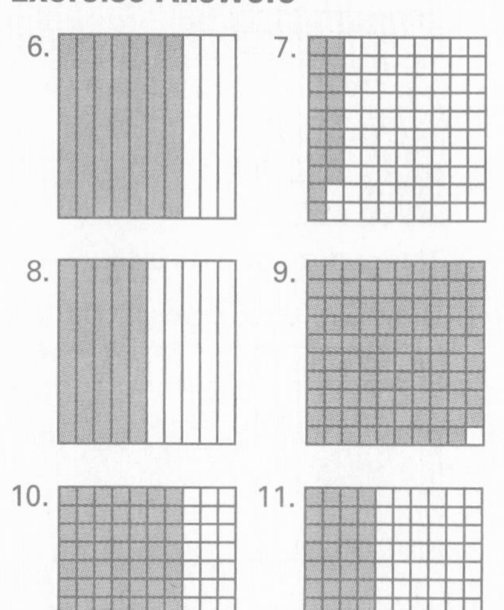

3-1 Exercises and Applications

Practice and Apply

1. **Getting Started** Write each fraction as a decimal.

   a. $\frac{6}{10}$ 0.6 **b.** $\frac{43}{100}$ 0.43 **c.** $\frac{312}{1000}$ 0.312 **d.** $\frac{9}{10}$ 0.9 **e.** $\frac{97}{1000}$ 0.097 **f.** $\frac{8}{100}$ 0.08

What decimal number does each grid or set of grids represent?

2. 0.80

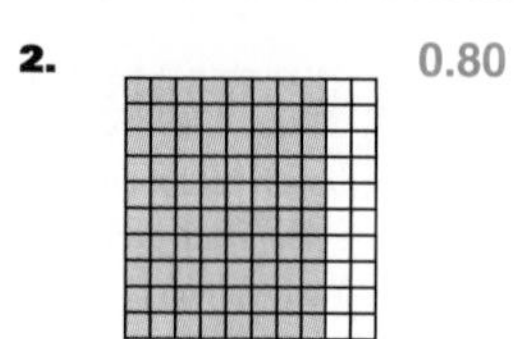

3. 0.78

4. 0.37

5. 2.45

Draw a grid to represent each decimal.

6. 0.7 **7.** 0.18 **8.** 0.5 **9.** 0.99 **10.** 0.67 **11.** 0.37

For Exercises 12–17, write the number as a decimal.

12. fifty-one hundredths 0.51

13. one and sixty-seven thousandths 1.067

14. three and forty-two hundredths 3.42

15. eight hundredths 0.08

16. one hundred sixty-seven thousandths 0.167

17. two tenths 0.2

18. History The ancient Greeks discovered that a person's height from the floor to the waist is about sixty-two hundredths of the total height. Write this number as a decimal. 0.62

19. Science The average body length of a dust mite is fifteen thousandths of an inch. Write this number as a decimal. 0.015

20. Science The earth revolves around the sun once every three hundred sixty-five and twenty-four hundredths of a day. Write this number as a decimal. 365.24

PRACTICE 3-1

PRACTICE

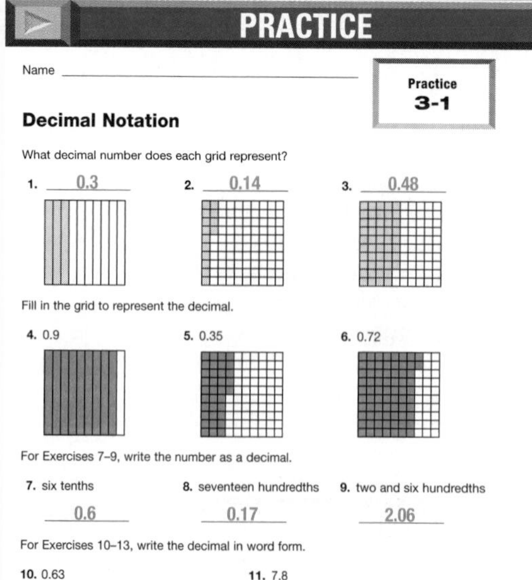

Name ______________________ Practice 3-1

Decimal Notation

What decimal number does each grid represent?

1. 0.3   2. 0.14   3. 0.48

Fill in the grid to represent the decimal.

4. 0.9   5. 0.35   6. 0.72

For Exercises 7–9, write the number as a decimal.

7. six tenths 0.6   8. seventeen hundredths 0.17   9. two and six hundredths 2.06

For Exercises 10–13, write the decimal in word form.

10. 0.63 sixty-three hundredths   11. 7.8 seven and eight tenths

12. 0.012 twelve thousandths   13. 0.09 nine hundredths

14. The average American eats three and thirty-six hundredths pounds of peanut butter each year. Write this number as a decimal. 3.36

15. A 150-pound person contains 97.5 pounds of oxygen and 0.165 pounds of sodium. Write both decimal numbers in word form.
Ninety-seven and five tenths; one hundred sixty-five thousandths

RETEACHING

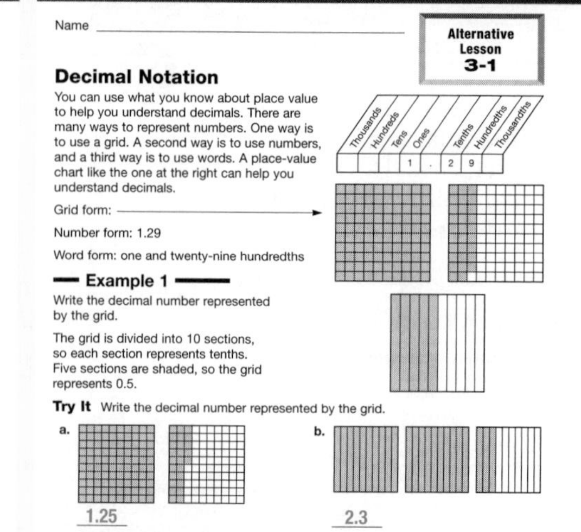

Name ______________________ Alternative Lesson 3-1

Decimal Notation

You can use what you know about place value to help you understand decimals. There are many ways to represent numbers. One way is to use a grid. A second way is to use numbers, and a third way is to use words. A place-value chart like the one at the right can help you understand decimals.

Grid form:

Number form: 1.29

Word form: one and twenty-nine hundredths

Example 1

Write the decimal number represented by the grid.

The grid is divided into 10 sections, so each section represents tenths. Five sections are shaded, so the grid represents 0.5.

Try It Write the decimal number represented by the grid.

a. 1.25   b. 2.3

Example 2

Write four and three hundred eleven thousandths as a decimal.

You know that the decimal point is read as "and", so the decimal is 4.311.

Try It Write each number as a decimal.

c. twelve hundredths 0.12   d. eight tenths 0.8

e. three and four hundred ninety-seven thousandths 3.497

f. five and twenty-six hundredths 5.26

g. six and forty-three hundredths 6.43

h. two and eight hundred seventy-four thousandths 2.874

Reteaching

Activity

Materials: Tenths grids, 10 × 10 grids

- Use tenths grids and 10 × 10 grids to represent 0.8 and 0.08.
- Place the 10 × 10 grid on top of the tenths grid to see what fractional part of the whole each represents. Which is larger? 0.8
- Use the grids to show two ways to represent 0.20. 20 squares on the 10 × 10 grid or 2 strips on the tenths grid.

Write the decimal in word form.

21. 0.67 **22.** 0.075 **23.** 8.611 **24.** 5.09 **25.** 12.006 **26.** 0.4

27. Sports In 1988 Florence Griffith-Joyner broke the women's world record in the 100-meter dash with a time of 10.48 seconds. Write her time in word form. Ten and forty-eight hundredths

28. Health Eighteen baked snack crackers contain 0.5 grams of saturated fat and 1.5 grams of unsaturated fat. Write both decimal numbers in word form. Five tenths; one and five tenths

29. Test Prep Choose the decimal form for two and twenty-nine hundredths. B

Ⓐ 229.00 Ⓑ 2.29

Ⓒ 2.029 Ⓓ 0.229

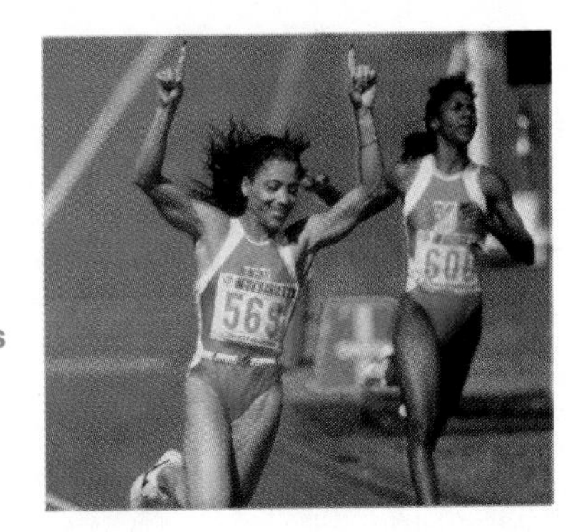

Problem Solving and Reasoning

30. Communicate Draw a grid that represents 0.4. Then draw a grid that represents 0.40. Explain the similarities and differences between the two grids.

32. Journal Why does a place-value chart not have a column for "oneths"?

31. Critical Thinking GPS Jarvis made a four-digit number with 0, 3, 6, and 8. The number was smaller than 5 but bigger than 1. What could his number be? Explain.

33. Critical Thinking How many numbers are there between 1.01 and 1.10? Explain.

Mixed Review

For each data set, make a frequency chart and a line plot. *[Lesson 1-4]*

34. 3, 4, 7, 9, 10, 4, 6, 3, 10, 3, 6, 5, 12, 3, 5, 8, 7

35. 20, 50, 70, 80, 40, 100, 30, 60, 70, 70, 70, 80, 30, 20, 50, 10, 50

Evaluate each expression for the given values of the variable. *[Lesson 2-10]*

36. $g + 13$; $g = 2, 3, 4$ 15; 16; 17 **37.** $d - 10$; $d = 21, 18, 15$ 11; 8; 5 **38.** $3k$; $k = 4, 6, 10$ 12; 18; 30

39. $\frac{r}{2}$; $r = 2, 16, 22$ 1; 8; 11 **40.** $5p$; $p = 2, 6, 7$ 10; 30; 35 **41.** $20 - b$; $b = 3, 5, 19$ 17; 15; 1

Simplify. *[Previous course]*

42. 286 + 312 598 **43.** 618 − 202 416 **44.** 200 × 317 63,400 **45.** 606 ÷ 202 3

46. 792 + 488 1280 **47.** 931 − 575 356 **48.** 497 × 101 50,197 **49.** 956 ÷ 478 2

PROBLEM SOLVING 3-1

PROBLEM SOLVING

Name ______ **Guided Problem Solving 3-1**

GPS PROBLEM 31, STUDENT PAGE 141

Jarvis made a four-digit number with 0, 3, 6, and 8. The number was smaller than 5 but bigger than 1. What could his number be? Explain.

— Understand —

1. How many digits will there be in Jarvis's number? 4 digits.
2. Underline the clue that helps you find the first digit.

— Plan —

3. Is Jarvis's number a whole number or a decimal? Explain. Decimal, because it must have three digits to the right of the decimal point.

— Solve —

4. Write the first digit of one number made from 0, 3, 6, and 8 in the first box at the right. Explain how you know. 3 . ☐☐☐ It is the only digit that is between 1 and 5.
5. Write the remaining digits in as many ways as you can. 3.068, 3.086, 3.608, 3.680, 3.806, 3.860
6. Look at each way you listed the digits in Item 5. Does the order of the remaining three digits make any difference in whether the number is less than 5 or greater than 1? Explain. No, all of the decimals are between 1 and 5.

— Look Back —

7. What strategy can you use to make sure that you have listed all the possible numbers that meet the criteria? Possible answer: Make an Organized List.

SOLVE ANOTHER PROBLEM

Agatha made a five-digit number with 0, 3, 5, 8, and 9. The number is bigger than 39 and smaller than 53. The thousandths digit is 3 times the tenths digit. What number did Agatha make? 50.389

ENRICHMENT

Name ______ **Extend Your Thinking 3-1**

Visual Thinking

The shading of each figure represents a decimal. Circle the figure that represents the greater decimal

1. 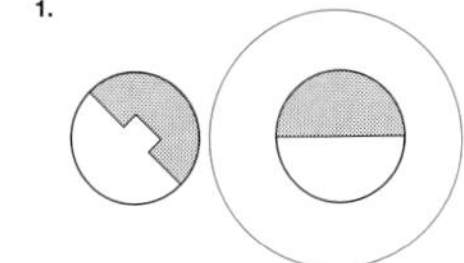
2. 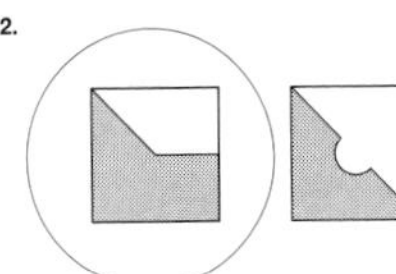
3. 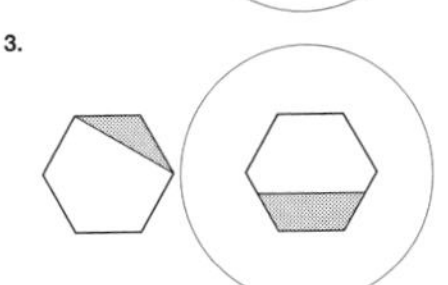
4. 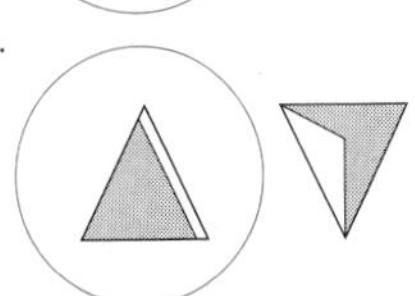

Shade each figure to approximate the decimal. Possible answers:

5. 0.5 6. 0.33 7. 0.95 8. 0.05

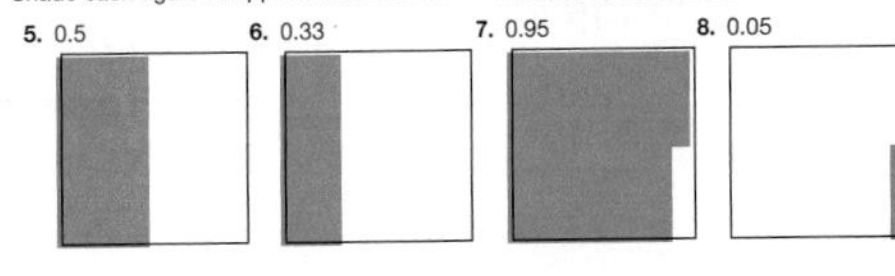

9. 0.24 10. 0.65 11. 0.78 12. 0.52

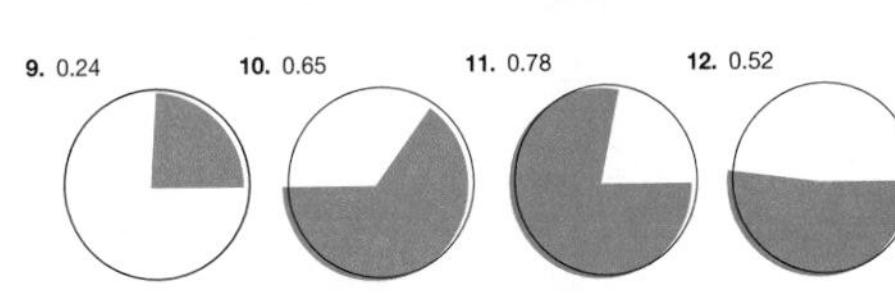

Exercise Answers

21. Sixty-seven hundredths
22. Seventy-five thousandths
23. Eight and six hundred eleven thousandths
24. Five and nine hundredths
25. Twelve and six thousandths
26. Four tenths
30. 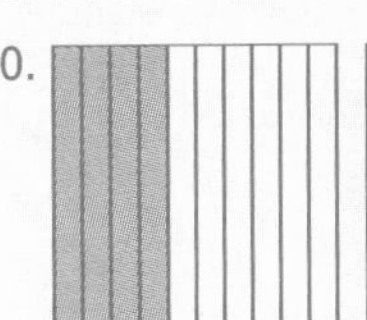 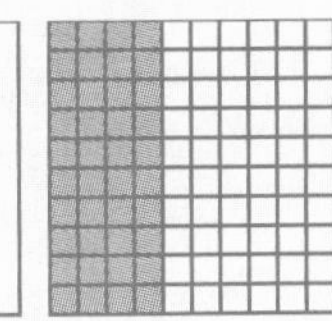

Similar: Colored area is the same size; Different: 0.40 is made up of squares.

31. 3.608 is less than 5 and greater than 1; Any number with 3 in the ones place and with no higher place value would work.
32. The "oneths" column is the same as the ones column.
33. An infinite amount; Decimals can go on forever.

34–35. See page C2.

Alternate Assessment

You may want to use the *Interactive CD-ROM Journal* with this assessment.

Journal Have students write a paragraph explaining why 0.0001 and 0.001 represent different numbers, yet 0.1 and 0.10 represent the same number.

► Quick Quiz

1. What number does the grid represent?

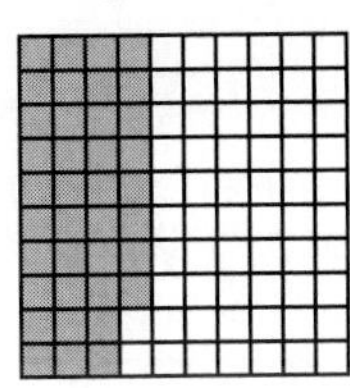

0.38

2. Write six and thirty-one thousandths in number form. 6.031
3. Write 625.40 in word form. six hundred twenty-five and forty hundredths

Available on Daily Transparency 3-1

3-2

Lesson Organizer

Objectives

- Round decimal numbers.
- Measure length with a metric ruler.

Materials

- Explore: Meter stick, masking tape, cotton balls

NCTM Standards

- 1–5, 7, 13

Review

Round 46,037 to the place indicated.

1. tens 46,040
2. hundreds 46,000
3. thousands 46,000

Would you estimate the length of each item in meters or centimeters?

4. pencil centimeters
5. height of door meters

Available on Daily Transparency 3-2

1 Introduce

Explore

You may wish to use Teaching Tool Transparency 16: Rulers with this lesson.

The Point
Students play a game to connect the process of rounding to the idea of closest number.

Ongoing Assessment
Students may need assistance in seeing the area on the ruler that produces numbers closer to 0.5 than to either 0 or 1.

3-2 Rounding Decimals

You'll Learn ...

- how to round decimal numbers
- how to measure length with a metric ruler

... How It's Used

Architects round decimal measurements when drawing blueprints.

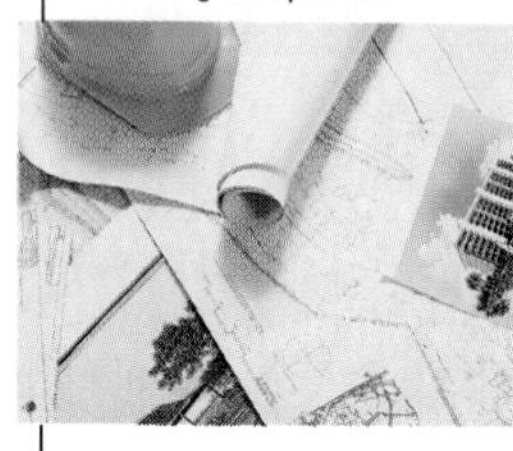

Lesson Link In the last chapter, you rounded whole numbers in order to estimate answers. You can round decimals for the same purpose.

Rounding decimals is often useful when you are measuring lengths. Three units often used to measure length are the meter, the centimeter, and the millimeter. The meter (m) is about the distance from the floor to a doorknob. A centimeter (cm) is $\frac{1}{100}$ of a meter. A millimeter (mm) is $\frac{1}{1000}$ of a meter.

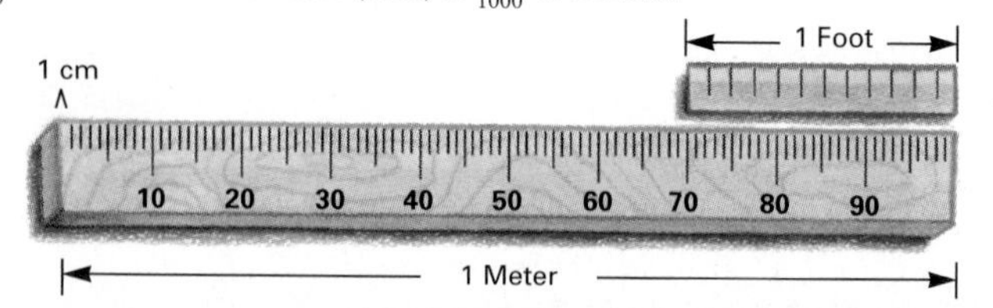

Explore Rounding Decimals

(DES: Did You Know?)

It's a Toss Up!

Materials: Meterstick, Masking tape, Cotton balls

Play the following game in groups of 2 to 4.

1. Put a length of tape 1 meter long on the floor. Mark one end 0 and the other end 1.
2. Stand at the 0 end of the tape. Estimate whether a cotton ball that you toss will land closer to 0 or to 1. Toss the ball. Give yourself a point if your estimate was right. Everyone should take four turns, making an estimate each time.
3. Using the meterstick, draw nine lines on the tape to divide it into ten equal sections. Label each new line with a decimal number (0.1, 0.2, 0.3, up to 0.9). Take four turns again, this time estimating to the nearest tenth. Score one point for each correct estimate.

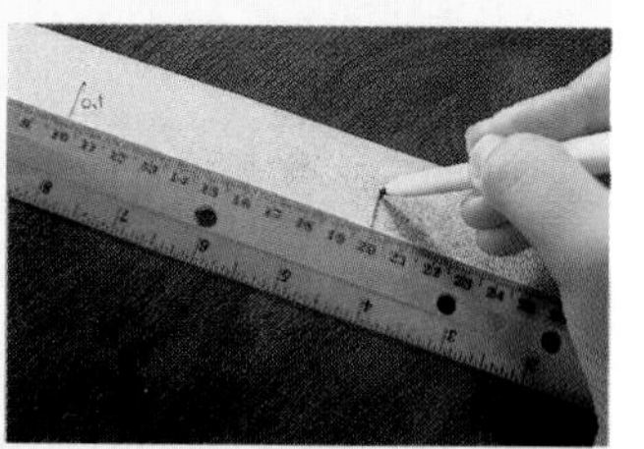

4. In which round did you score the most points? Why?
5. Which would be easier, a game where you had to hit 0.5, or one where you had to hit a number closer to 0.5 than to either 0 or 1? Why?

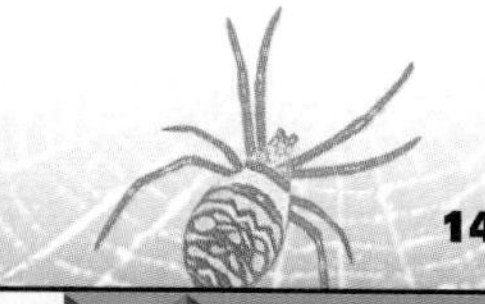

MEETING INDIVIDUAL NEEDS

Resources

- **3-2** Practice
- **3-2** Reteaching
- **3-2** Problem Solving
- **3-2** Enrichment
- **3-2** Daily Transparency
  - Problem of the Day
  - Review
  - Quick Quiz
- Teaching Tool Transparency 16
- Technology Master 11

Learning Modalities

Logical Have students write a list of steps to follow in rounding a decimal to a given place value. If they know about flowcharting, have them make a flowchart.

Visual Have students make a bulletin board display of several different objects that are not the same length but which have the same length when rounded to the nearest centimeter.

Kinesthetic Before you begin **Explore,** you may wish to identify how a meter stick can be divided into ten 10 dm sections, 100 cm sections, and 1000 mm sections. Have students measure the length of their math book in decimeters, centimeters, and millimeters to familiarize them with using a meter stick.

English Language Development

Some students will be confused by the use of the word *rounding*. They might think it is related to circles. Stress that a rounded number is less precise than the original number.

Learn Rounding Decimals

Recall that you can *round* numbers when you want to estimate an answer, or when you don't need as precise a measurement as the one you are given.

To round a number, look at the digit to the right of the place you want to round to. If the digit is 5 or greater, round up. If it is less than 5, round down.

Remember

Rounding is a method of finding an estimate that's the *closest* to a given place value.

[Page 70]

Examples

1 A scale on a microscope slide allows a biologist to estimate lengths to the nearest hundredth of a centimeter. A spider egg measures 0.1347 cm in length. Find the biologist's estimate of the egg's length.

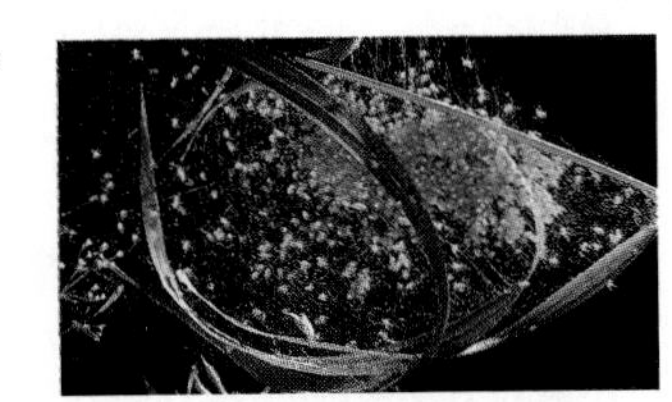

0.1[3]47 — Find the place value.
↑ hundredths

0.1[3]47 — Look at the digit to the right. If it is 5 or greater, add 1 to the place-value digit. If it's less than 5, leave the place-value digit alone.

0.13 — Drop the digits to the right of the place value.

The length is approximately 0.13 cm.

2 A baseball player's batting average is rounded to the nearest thousandth. In 1924, Rogers Hornsby of the St. Louis Cardinals achieved the highest batting average in modern baseball history: .4235074. What was his average rounded to the nearest thousandth?

↓ This is the thousandths place.

0.42[3]5074

↑ The digit to the right is 5 or greater. Add 1 to the thousandths place.

Hornsby's batting average was 0.424.

Science Link

Spiders are not insects, although they also are invertebrates, or animals without spines. They belong to a separate class of arthropods called Arachnida.

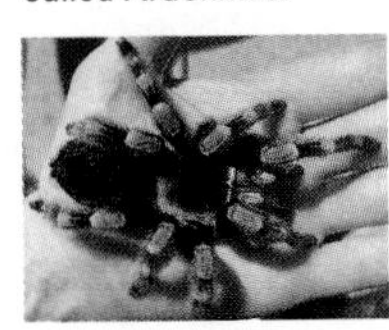

Try It

Round to the given place.

a. 0.846, tenths 0.8 **b.** 7.045, hundredths 7.05 **c.** 3.461825, thousandths 3.462

d. A spitting spider can squirt a sticky substance on a prey that is up to 1.905 cm away. What is this distance rounded to the nearest tenth? 1.9

MATH EVERY DAY

Problem of the Day

Iranian craftsmen, known for their artistry, make Persian rugs in their homes or in small shops. Suppose one section of a 2-section Persian rug is 25 inches long. The other section of the rug is as long as the first section plus half the rug's entire length. How long is the rug?

Let x = length of entire rug

$25 + 25 + \frac{1}{2}x = x$

100 inches, or 8 ft 4 inches long

Available on Daily Transparency 3-2

An Extension is provided in the transparency package.

Fact of the Day

Spiders are found almost anywhere they can find food. Spiders live in swamps, deserts, woods, and even under water and near the top of Mount Everest.

Mental Math

Find each sum mentally.

1. $\frac{1}{2} + \frac{1}{2}$ 1
2. $\frac{2}{3} + \frac{1}{3}$ 1
3. $\frac{3}{4} + \frac{1}{4}$ 1
4. $\frac{3}{5} + \frac{2}{5}$ 1

For Groups That Finish Early

Which would be easier, a game where you had to hit a number closer to 0.5 than to either 0 or 1, or one where you had to hit a number closer to 0.8 than to 1. The second game would be easier because the area for success is greater than that for the first game.

Follow Up

Have students share the results of their experiments orally.

Answers for Explore

1–3. Anwers may vary.

4. Possible answer: First round; It is easier to guess correctly.

5. Possible answer: Second game; There is a larger area to hit.

2 Teach

Learn

Alternate Examples

1. The green walkingstick insect measures 8.74 cm in length. Round this length to the nearest tenth of a centimeter.

   8.74

   8.[7]**4**

   8.7

   The length is approximately 8.7 cm.

2. A sprinter's average time over ten trials in the Olympic 100-meter dash is 10.196 seconds Round the time to the nearest hundredth.

   10.1[9]**6**

   The sprinter's time is approximately 10.20 seconds.

Alternate Examples

3. What is the length of this piece of chalk to the nearest centimeter and the nearest tenth of a centimeter?

cm 1 2 3 4 5 6 7 8 9 10

The edge of the chalk is between the 6 mark and 7 mark. To the nearest centimeter, the chalk is 6 cm long.

The edge of the chalk is between the 6.3 mark and the 6.4 mark, but closer to the 6.4 mark. To the nearest tenth of a centimeter, the chalk is 6.4 cm long.

3 Practice and Assess

Check

Be sure students understand the connection between rounding and measuring to the nearest unit of measure. Point out that when the digit to the right of the place value is 5 or greater, this is comparable to a measurement mark being halfway or more between two markings on a measuring instrument.

Answers for Check your Understanding

1. Possible answer: If the object measures to less than halfway to the next centimeter measure, then round down. If the object measures to halfway or more to the next centimeter, round up.
2. Possible answer: The rounding process is the same, but when rounding to thousands the decision is based on the number in the hundreds place and when rounding to thousandths the decision is based on the number in the ten-thousandths place.

You can use a metric ruler to measure the length of an object in centimeters. Most objects do not equal an exact number of centimeters, so centimeter measurements are usually rounded to the nearest centimeter, or the nearest tenth of a centimeter.

Example 3

What is the length of the pencil to the nearest centimeter and the nearest tenth of a centimeter?

On a metric ruler, the numbered divisions represent centimeters. The tip of the pencil is between the 10 mark and the 11 mark, and it is closer to the 11 mark. To the nearest centimeter, the pencil is 11 cm long.

Problem Solving TIP

When measuring with a ruler, make sure one edge of the object being measured lines up with the 0-mark on the ruler.

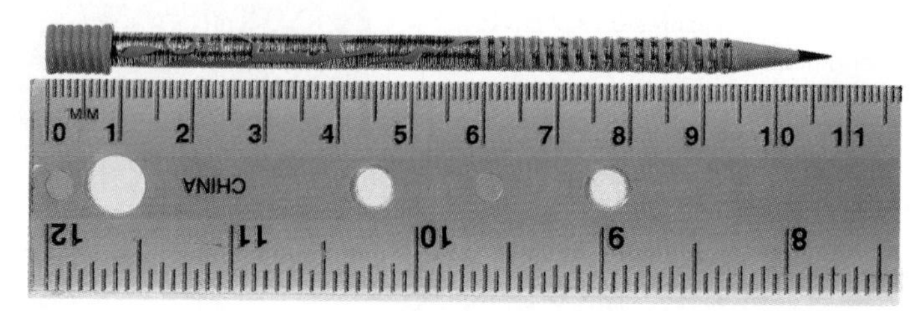

On a metric ruler, each centimeter is divided into ten sections. Each section is one tenth of a centimeter. The tip of the pencil is between the 10.7 mark and the 10.8 mark, but closer to the 10.8 mark. To the nearest tenth of a centimeter, the pencil is 10.8 cm long.

Try It

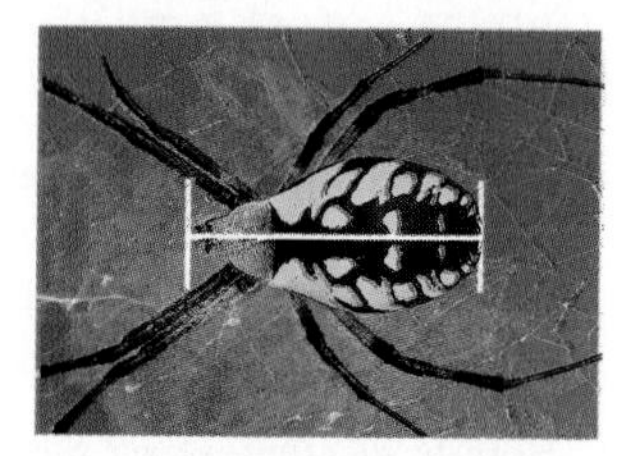

a. Estimate the length of the spider's body to the nearest centimeter and the nearest tenth of a centimeter. 3 cm; 2.5 cm

b. Estimate the length of the "Check Your Understanding" bar to the nearest centimeter and the nearest tenth of a centimeter. 13 cm; 13.1 cm

Check Your Understanding

1. How is measuring to the nearest centimeter on a metric ruler like rounding?

2. How is rounding to thousands similar to rounding to thousandths? How is it different?

MEETING MIDDLE CLASSROOM NEEDS

Tips from Middle School Teachers

I have students look for various numbers in newspaper or magazine articles and then have them discuss whether they think the numbers are rounded or precise. Then I have students prepare a display of the articles and headlines using precise numbers and another display showing uses of rounded numbers. I ask students to describe any patterns they notice regarding when and how precise and rounded numbers are used.

Team Teaching

Work with a physical education teacher or a baseball or softball coach to discuss how batting averages are computed. It may be helpful if students can work with actual data from some recent games.

Science Connection

After a spider catches its prey, it injects digestive enzymes into the prey's body. These enzymes turn the prey's tissues to liquid. The spider feeds by sucking out the liquid.

3-2 Exercises and Applications

Practice and Apply

1. **Getting Started** Round to the nearest whole number.

   a. 0.78 1 b. 2.65 3 c. 3.34 3 d. 0.11 0 e. 1.49 1 f. 2.22 2

Round to the underlined place value.

2. 10.674 10.67
3. 5.81 5.8
4. 56.098 56.10
5. 0.4715 0.472
6. 11.99 12
7. 4.345 4.3
8. 904.846 904.8
9. 0.1002 0.100
10. 0.2802 0.280
11. 33.456 33.5
12. 8.928 8.93
13. 16.1287 16.13
14. 4.002 4.0
15. 7.3006 7.30
16. 26.903 26.90
17. 88.3 88
18. 4.67 4.7
19. 7.342 7.3
20. 52.09 52.1
21. 8.203 8.2
22. 7.3921 7.392
23. 0.7893 0.7893
24. 3.0191 3.019
25. 56.82 60

26. **Science** The largest sea spider ever found was 75 cm long from leg to leg. The smallest sea spider measures only 0.1 cm. Round the length of the smallest sea spider to the nearest centimeter. 0 cm

27. **Estimation** Jonathan has discovered a trail of ants on his porch. Each ant is about 0.93 cm long, and he guesses there are almost 1000 of them. Estimate how long the ant trail is. 1000 cm

28. **Test Prep** Round 182.9807 to the nearest hundredth. Choose the correct answer. A

   Ⓐ 182.98 Ⓑ 182.981 Ⓒ 183 Ⓓ 200

Measurement Estimate each object's height to the nearest centimeter and tenth of a centimeter.

29. 2 cm; 2.2 cm 30. 3 cm; 2.8 cm 31. 5 cm; 5.4 cm

HMS

6 Jamar Bayless

GRADE SIGNATURE

32. 33.

4 cm; 3.6 cm 3 cm; 2.5 cm

PRACTICE 3-2

PRACTICE

Name ______ Practice 3-2

Rounding Decimals

Round to the underlined place value.

1. 42.4 42
2. 7.7961 7.8
3. 96.08 96.1
4. 13.2093 13.209
5. 1.88 1.9
6. 3.292 3.3
7. 27.27 27
8. 191.8 192
9. 796.84 796.8
10. 8.465 8
11. 59.305 59.3
12. 8.094 8.09

Estimate each object's length to the nearest centimeter and tenth of a centimeter.

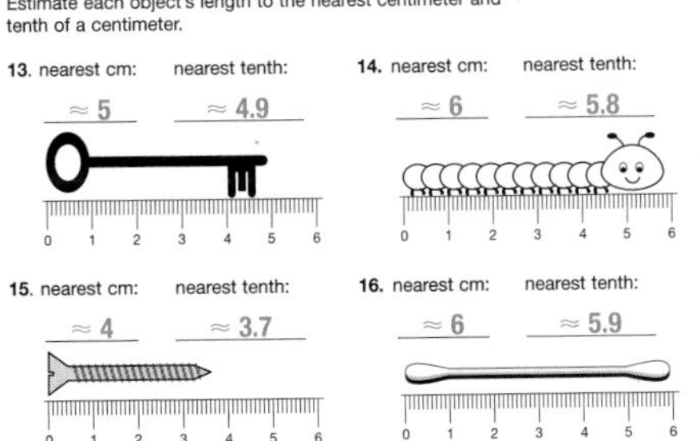

13. nearest cm: ≈ 5 nearest tenth: ≈ 4.9
14. nearest cm: ≈ 6 nearest tenth: ≈ 5.8
15. nearest cm: ≈ 4 nearest tenth: ≈ 3.7
16. nearest cm: ≈ 6 nearest tenth: ≈ 5.9

17. **Measurement** One liter is equal to 1.0567 quarts. Round this value to the nearest hundredth of a quart. 1.06 quarts

18. Colleen's house is made of bricks measuring about 20.955 cm long, and she guesses that each row in one wall is about 60 bricks long. Estimate the length of the wall.

Possible answer: About 1260 cm or 12.6 m

RETEACHING

Name ______ Alternative Lesson 3-2

Rounding Decimals

You can *round* numbers to estimate answers. To round a number, look at the digit to the right of the place you want to round to. If the digit is 5 or greater, round up. If it is less than 5, round down.

Example 1

Round 34.0592 to the nearest hundredth.

Step 1: Find the place value. — The 5 is in the hundredths place.

Step 2: Look at the digit to the right — The digit is 9.

Step 3: If this digit is 5 or greater, round up. If it's less than 5, round down. — 9 is greater than 5, so round up.

Step 4: Drop the digits to the right. — The rounded number is 34.06.

34.0592 rounds to 34.06 when rounding to the nearest hundredth.

Try It Round 0.241 to the nearest tenth.

a. The tenths digit is 2. Underline it.

b. The digit to the right of the tenths digit is 4.

c. Is that digit 5 or greater? No.

d. Write the rounded number. Drop any digits to the right of tenths. 0.2

Round to the given place.

e. 4.652, tenths 4.7 f. 19.304, hundredths 19.30

Example 2

What is the length of the eraser to the nearest centimeter and the nearest tenth of a centimeter?

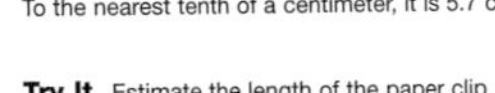

The end of the eraser is between the 5.5 mark and the 6 mark. Use 5.7 as an estimate.

To the nearest centimeter, the eraser is 6.0 cm. To the nearest tenth of a centimeter, it is 5.7 cm.

Try It Estimate the length of the paper clip to the

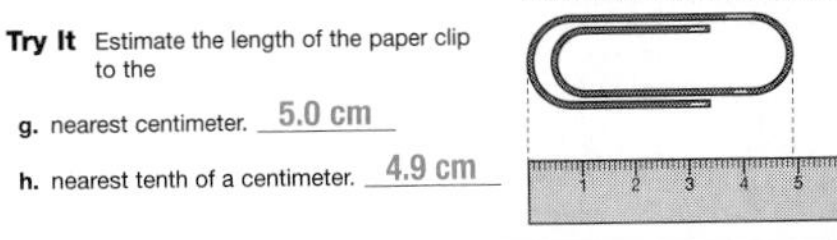

g. nearest centimeter. 5.0 cm

h. nearest tenth of a centimeter. 4.9 cm

3-2 Exercises and Applications

Assignment Guide

- Basic
  1–20, 26–40 evens, 41, 43
- Average
  1–20, 26, 28, 29–39 odds, 40–44
- Enriched
  3–27 odds, 28–44 evens

Exercise Notes

Exercise 9

Error Prevention Some students may write 0.1 instead of 0.100. Remind them that even though both numbers are equal, the second indicates the number was rounded to thousandths while the first would indicate the number was rounded to tenths.

Reteaching

Activity

Materials: Meter stick

- Work in groups of three or four.
- Locate the mark for 23 cm on a meterstick. Is the mark closer to 20 cm or 30 cm? 20 cm
- Locate 23.7 cm on a meter stick. Is it closer to 23 cm or 24 cm? 24 cm
- Use a meter stick to round the following measurements to the nearest centimeter.

1. 37.6 cm 38 cm
2. 40.1 cm 40 cm
3. 53.2 cm 53 cm
4. 10.9 cm 11 cm
5. 52.7 cm 53 cm
6. 26.4 cm 26 cm

Exercise Answers

36. Possible answer: 1.462
37. To the right of the 9 is a 5, so the 9 becomes a 10 and 4.9 rounds to 5.0.
38. No; 5.9999999 rounded to the ten millionths place is 5.9999999.
39. Measuring instruments cannot be completely accurate; Measuring instruments aren't all the same.
40. Possible answers: Wendell could have rounded 3.4682 to tenths; Terry could have rounded to thousandths.

41–42. See page C2.

Alternate Assessment

Performance Finishing times for the medal winners in the Men's 400-meter at the 1996 Summer Olympic Games are given. Have students work in groups and discuss whether the medal results would have been any different if the times had been rounded to the nearest tenth of a second.
Gold Medal: Michael Johnson, USA, 43.49 sec.
Silver: Medal: Roger Black, Britain, 44.41 sec.
Bronze Medal: Davis Kamoga, Uganda, 44.53 sec. Results would have been the same: 43.5, 44.4, 44.5.

Quick Quiz

Round the scores for the following 1996 Women's Summer Olympic Individual Gymnastic Events to the nearest hundredth and nearest tenth.

1. Balance Beam: Shannon Miller, USA, 9.862; Lilia Podkopayeva, Ukraine, 9.825; Gina Gogean, Romania, 9.787 9.86, 9.9; 9.83, 9.8; 9.79, 9.8
2. Floor Exercises: Lilia Podkopayeva, Ukraine, 9.887; Simona Amanar, Romania, 9.850; Dominique Dawes, USA, 9.837 9.89 9.9; 9.85, 9.9; 9.84, 9.8

Available on Daily Transparency 3-2

Measurement Estimate each object's length to the nearest centimeter and millimeter.

34. 5 cm; 49 mm

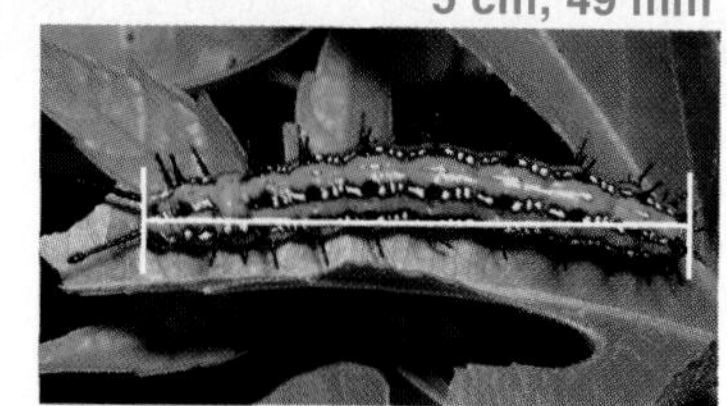

35. 6 cm; 55 mm

Problem Solving and Reasoning

36. Critical Thinking Form a decimal out of the digits 1, 2, 4, 6, and 8, so that the decimal will round up if rounded to the nearest tenth but stay the same if rounded to the nearest hundredth. You do not need to use all five digits.

37. Communicate Explain why 4.95 rounded to the nearest tenth is 5.0.

38. Communicate Carlos says that the number 5.9999999 will round up to the same answer, no matter what place you round to. Is he right? Explain.

39. Journal Why is a measurement always an estimate?

40. Critical Thinking Wendell and Terry both rounded the number 3.4682. Wendell says that he rounded the number up. Terry says that he rounded the number down. To what place value might the number have been rounded by Wendell? By Terry? Explain.

GPS

Mixed Review

For each set of data, draw a bar graph. *[Lesson 1-5]*

41. Number of Juice Cans Sold

Apple	28
Grape	24
Orange	37
Cranberry	21

42. Number of Telephones in House

None	1
One	4
Two	12
Three or more	6

For each situation, write an expression. [Lesson 2-11]

43. Elaine ate 12 crackers, and then she ate k more. How many crackers did Elaine eat? $12 + k$

44. Carlos worked for five days. He earned w dollars each day. How many dollars did Carlos earn? $5w$

PROBLEM SOLVING 3-2

PROBLEM SOLVING

Name ____________ Guided Problem Solving 3-2

GPS PROBLEM 40, STUDENT PAGE 146

Wendell and Terry both rounded the number 3.4682. Wendell says that he rounded the number up. Terry says that he rounded the number down. To what place value might the number have been rounded by Wendell? By Terry? Explain.

— Understand —

1. Underline the information that you need.

— Plan —

2. When is a number rounded up? When the digit to the right of the place value to be rounded is 5 or greater.

— Solve —

3. Would you round each number up or down when rounding to the
   a. ones place? Down.
   b. tenths place? Up.
   c. hundredths place? Up.
   d. thousandths place? Down.
4. Wendell rounded up. List all the place values that the number might have been rounded to by Wendell. Explain. Tenths or hundredths (3.5 or 3.47); 6 and 8 are greater than 5.
5. Terry rounded down. List all the place values that the number might have been rounded to by Terry. Explain. Ones or thousandths (3 or 3.468); 4 and 2 are less than 5.

— Look Back —

6. Why didn't you check ten-thousandths as a place value? Possible answer: There is no digit to its right.

SOLVE ANOTHER PROBLEM

Casey and Jenna both rounded the number 42.185. Casey rounded the number up. Jenna rounded the number down. To what place value might the number have been rounded by Casey? By Jenna? Explain.
Casey: tenths or hundredths (42.2 or 42.19); 8 and 5 are equal to or greater than 5. Jenna: tens or ones (40 or 42); 2 and 1 are less than 5.

ENRICHMENT

Name ____________ Extend Your Thinking 3-2

Patterns in Algebra

You can find the relationship between two variables by using a table to find the pattern.

1. The numbers in the table below form a pattern. Each value for x has a related value for y. When $x = 1$, then $y = 5$, and when $x = 2$, then $y = 6$. The rule for finding y shows how these variables are related. The rule $y = x + 4$ means that whatever value x has, the value of y is 4 more. Use the rule to complete the table.

x	1	2	3	10	20	100
y	5	6	7	14	24	104

Use the rule to complete each table.

2. The rule is $y = x - 3$.

x	5	6	7	10	20
y	2	3	4	7	17

3. The rule is $y = 2x$.

x	0	1	2	4	7	10
y	0	2	4	8	14	20

Study each table. Find the rule and complete each table.

4.

x	5	10	12	20	50
y	0	5	7	15	45

rule: $y = x - 5$

5.

x	0	2	5	20	50
y	1	3	6	21	51

rule: $y = x + 1$

6.

x	2	5	10	25	100
y	6	15	30	75	300

rule: $y = 3x$

7.

x	0	3	6	10	15
y	3	6	9	13	18

rule: $y = x + 3$

TECHNOLOGY

Using a Spreadsheet • Formatting Decimal Data

Problem: Given the data below, what's the average number of customers per day rounded to the nearest whole number?

You can use spreadsheets to analyze large amounts of data, and you can also use them to make the data look the way you want it to look.

1 **Enter the information about the number of customers served at a hotdog stand into the spreadsheet as shown:**

	A	B	C	D	E	F	G
1		Mon	Tue	Wed	Thu	Fri	
2	8:00 – 10:00	23	36	67	90	35	
3	10:00 – 12:00	25	4	78	21	47	
4	12:00 – 2:00	79	67	89	87	14	
5	2:00 – 4:00	2	43	55	43	56	
6	4:00 – 6:00	15	56	90	53	23	
7	6:00 – 8:00	45	32	66	14	23	
8							
9	Average						
10							

2 **In cell B8, enter the formula** = average(B2:B7). **This will calculate the Monday average.**

	A	B	C	D	E	F	G
1		Mon	Tue	Wed	Thu	Fri	
2	8:00 – 10:00	23	36	67	90	35	
3	10:00 – 12:00	25	4	78	21	47	
4	12:00 – 2:00	79	67	89	87	14	
5	2:00 – 4:00	2	43	55	43	56	
6	4:00 – 6:00	15	56	90	53	23	
7	6:00 – 8:00	45	32	66	14	23	
8							
9	Average	32	40	74	51	33	
10							

3 **Copy the formula across the row to column F.**

4 **Use the format command to format the averages to show no places after the decimal.**

Solution: The averages, rounded to the nearest whole number, are 32, 40, 74, 51, and 33.

TRY IT

a. If the data was about ounces of ketchup used, you might want to see the data to the nearest tenth. Format the averages to show tenths.

b. If the data was about money collected, you might want to see the data to the nearest hundredth. Format the averages to show hundredths.

ON YOUR OWN

▶ Name a situation where it might make sense to round a number to the nearest thousandth.

▶ If a number in a spreadsheet is 700, can you tell how many places it's been rounded to?

▶ What other ways can you format numbers in a spreadsheet?

147

Technology

Using a Spreadsheet • Formatting Decimal Data

The Point

Students explore how different types of formatting are appropriate for spreadsheets with different types of data.

Materials

Spreadsheet software

Resources

Interactive CD-ROM Spreadsheet/Grapher Tool

About the Page

- The given formula "= average (B2:B7)" may have to be adapted to your particular software.
- The "copy" feature is very efficient for repeating the same formula into other cells. Note that the spreadsheet automatically adjusts the formula to match the corresponding cells in the original formula.

Ask ...

- What formula needs to be entered in order to calculate the average? Answers may vary depending on the software.
- How do you format the spreadsheet to show different numbers of decimal places? Answers may vary depending on the software.

Answers for Try It

a. 31.5, 39.7, 74.2, 51.3, 33.0

b. $31.50, $39.67, $74.17, $51.33, $33.00

On Your Own

For the second question, you might have students list several examples to support their answers.

Answers for On Your Own

- Possible answer: An experiment with very precise measurements.
- No; For example, the original number could have been 749, 688, 700.34, or 700.04.
- Possible answer: Numbers can be bold or underlined, or made to look like money or percents.

3-3 Lesson Organizer

Objective

- Compare and order decimals.

NCTM Standards

- 1–4, 6, 7

Review

Write each number as a fraction and as a decimal.

1. Twenty-seven hundredths $\frac{27}{100}$; 0.27
2. Three tenths $\frac{3}{10}$; 0.3
3. Forty-eight thousandths $\frac{48}{1000}$; 0.048
4. Two and one hundred six thousandths $2\frac{106}{1000}$; 2.106

Available on Daily Transparency 3-3

1 Introduce

Explore

The Point
Students compare decimal numbers to develop an intuitive idea that a number with more digits isn't necessarily a larger number.

Ongoing Assessment
As students attempt to use their knowledge of place value, be alert to those who might be misled by the number of decimal places to the right of the decimal point.

For Groups That Finish Early
Explain how your group decided to order the labels as they did.

3-3 Comparing and Ordering Decimals

You'll Learn ...

- how to compare and order decimals

... How It's Used

Sports officials must compare race times in decimals to determine who won a race.

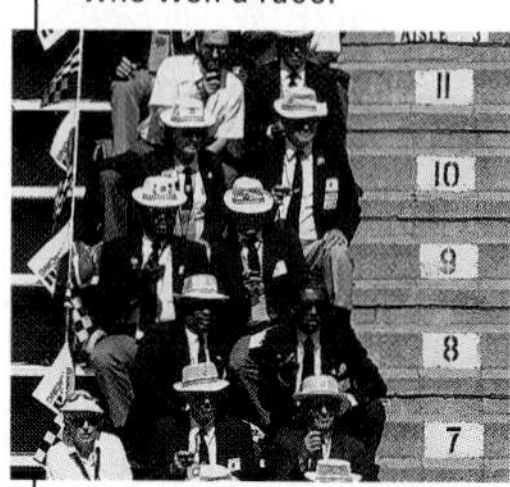

Lesson Link You know how to compare and order large numbers. You can use similar methods to compare and order decimal numbers. ◄

Explore Comparing and Ordering Decimals

Doing It by the Book

Libraries use the Dewey decimal system to arrange nonfiction books. Books are arranged in order of their Dewey decimal numbers. These books are arranged in the correct order, but the labels have fallen off.

THE MYSTERY OF DREAMS
THE UNITED NATIONS
THOSE AMAZING LEECHES
SPIDERS AND THEIR KIN
KILLER BEES
VAN GOGH
BASEBALL'S GREATEST GAMES
THE OLYMPIC GAMES
GOODE'S WORLD ATLAS

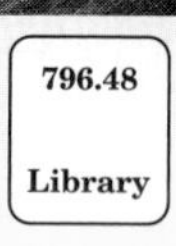

1. Match each label to the correct book.
2. Explain how you decided which label matched each book.
3. If a new book was added between *The United Nations* and *The Mystery of Dreams,* what could its Dewey decimal number be?

Literature Link

The Dewey decimal system breaks all subjects down into ten categories: reference, psychology, religion, social sciences, language, pure science, applied science, the arts, literature, and history.

Learn Comparing and Ordering Decimals

When you *annex* zeros to the right of a decimal number, you do not change the value of the number.

$4.37 = 4.370 = 4.3700 = 4.37000$

Decimals are easy to compare when they have the same number of digits after the decimal point. Annexing zeros can help you do this.

MEETING INDIVIDUAL NEEDS

Resources

- **3-3** Practice
- **3-3** Reteaching
- **3-3** Problem Solving
- **3-3** Enrichment
- **3-3** Daily Transparency
  - Problem of the Day
  - Review
  - Quick Quiz
- Teaching Tool Transparency 5
- Lesson Enhancement Transparency 9
- Technology Master 12
- Chapter 3 Project Master

Wide World of Mathematics Middle School: In 0.01 Second

Learning Modalities

Visual Students may find it easier to understand that annexing zeros doesn't change the value of the number if they represent equivalent numbers such as $\frac{3}{10}$ and $\frac{30}{100}$ on a 10×10 grid.

Social Have students work in groups of three or four to discuss the method they used to answer Step 2 of **Explore**.

English Language Development

Some students may be confused by the use of the word *ordering.* They may relate it to ordering from a catalog or ordering at a restaurant. Point out that ordering numbers means to list them from least to greatest or from greatest to least. Also point out that three or more numbers are *ordered,* but two numbers are *compared.*

Students may not understand the idiom "Doing It by the Book." Ask other students to explain its meaning.

Examples

1 Compare 0.5 and 0.07.

0.50 ☐ 0.07 Annex zeros.

0.5 > 0.07

2 Compare 32.207 and 32.3.

32.207 ☐ 32.**300** Annex zeros.

32.207 < 32.3

Try It

Use > and < to compare the pairs of decimals.

a. 2.8 [>] 2.45 **b.** 0.67 [>] 0.067 **c.** 12.71 [>] 12.2 **d.** 5 [<] 5.2

When you have to order several decimal numbers, using a number line may be faster than annexing zeros.

On a number line, the farther to the right a number is, the greater it is. The farther to the left a number is, the smaller it is.

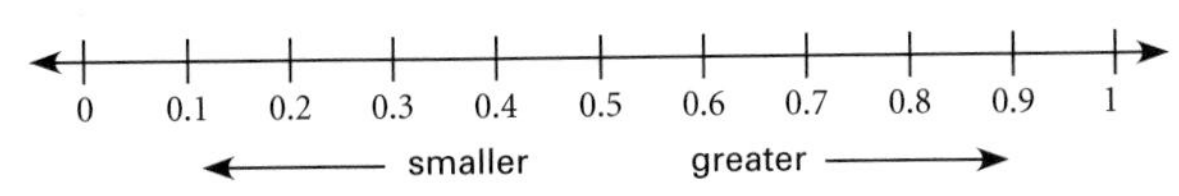

Example 3

Every spider leg is made of seven segments. Kim measured the lengths of the segments in a golden huntsman spider leg. Order the lengths from least to greatest.

Segment Length (cm)		
0.9	0.881	0.804
0.892	0.87	
0.85	0.876	

On a number line, the interval from 0 to 1 can be divided into tenths, hundredths, and (if needed) thousandths. Then, each decimal value can be located.

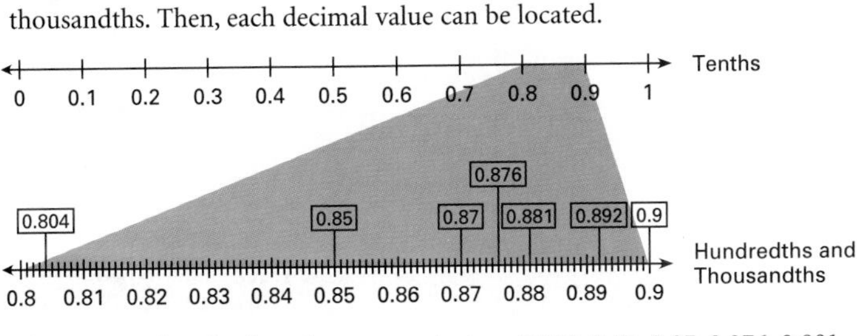

The segment lengths from least to greatest are 0.804, 0.85, 0.87, 0.876, 0.881, 0.892, and 0.9.

Try It

Order from least to greatest: 1.74, 1.08, 1.009, 1.725, 1.6
1.009, 1.08, 1.6, 1.725, 1.74

▶ Science Link

Unlike most spiders, the golden huntsman does not spin an organized web. Instead, it walks in slow search of its prey.

MATH EVERY DAY

▶ Problem of the Day

Mavis devised several treasure hunt clues. To begin the hunt, Mavis told each person to look in their math book between facing pages whose product was 86,730. Between what pages will each person find the first clue?
294 and 295

Available on Daily Transparency 3-3

An Extension is provided in the transparency package.

Fact of the Day

The strongest earthquake in the United States, measuring 8.4 on the Richter Scale, occurred near Prince William Sound, Alaska, in 1964.

Estimation

Do these mentally.

1. 8 + 8 + 8 + 8 + 8 + 8 + 8 56
2. 9 + 9 + 9 + 9 + 9 + 9 + 9 + 9 72
3. 12 + 12 + 12 + 12 + 12 60
4. 25 + 25 + 25 + 25 + 25 + 25 150

Answers for Explore

1. *The Mystery of Dreams:* 154.6; *The United Nations:* 341.23; *Those Amazing Leeches*: 595.1; *Spiders and Their Kin:* 595.4; *Killer Bees:* 595.79; *Van Gogh*: 759.9492; *Baseball's Greatest Games:* 796.357; *The Olympic Games:* 796.48; *Goode's World Atlas:* 912.
2. Possible answer: Order the Dewey decimal numbers from least to greatest.
3. Any number between 154.6 and 341.23.

2 Teach

Learn

You may wish to use Teaching Tool Transparency 5: Number Lines or Lesson Enhancement Transparency 9 with **Example 3.**

Alternate Examples

1. Compare 0.3 and 0.06.

   Annex zeros.

   0.3**0** ☐ 0.06

   0.3 > 0.06

2. Compare 25.309 and 25.6.

   Annex zeros.

   25.309 ☐ 25.6**00**

   25.309 < 25.6

3. In science class Hector measured the following lengths: 0.35, 0.339, 0.368, 0.348, 0.36, 0.364, and 0.4. Order the lengths from least to greatest.

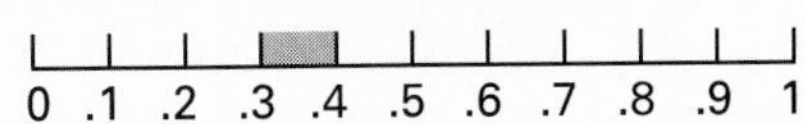

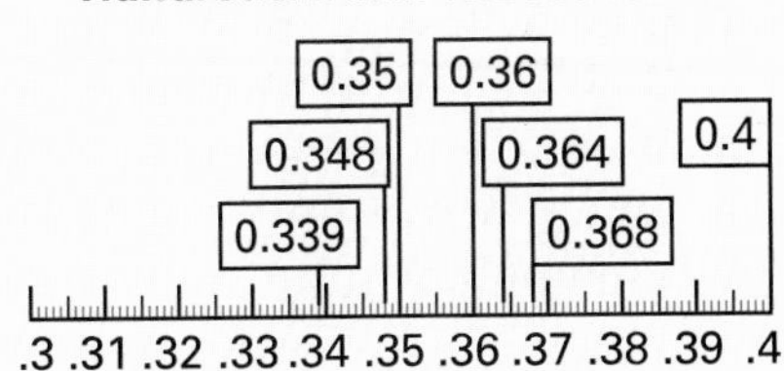

On a number line, the interval from 0 to 1 can be divided into tenths, hundredths, and thousandths. Then, each decimal value can be located.

The lengths from least to greatest are 0.339, 0.348, 0.35, 0.36, 0.364, 0.368, and 0.4.

Students use two different methods to solve a problem. One method uses the annexing of zeros to compare and order the numbers. The other method uses a number line to order the numbers. Students can decide which of the two correct methods is easier for them.

Answers for What Do You Think?

1. Answers may vary.
2. No; On a number line the millionths would be hard to draw.

3 Practice and Assess

Check

Be sure students remember that as they move from left to right in a decimal numeral, each place has $\frac{1}{10}$ the value of previous place. When comparing decimals such as 0.4 and 0.35, the 4 and the 3 each represents tenths so 0.4 is larger than 0.35.

Answers for Check Your Understanding

1. 0.35 only has 3 in the tenths place.
2. Possible answers: 1.522, 1.523
3. The number on the left; It represents the greatest place value.

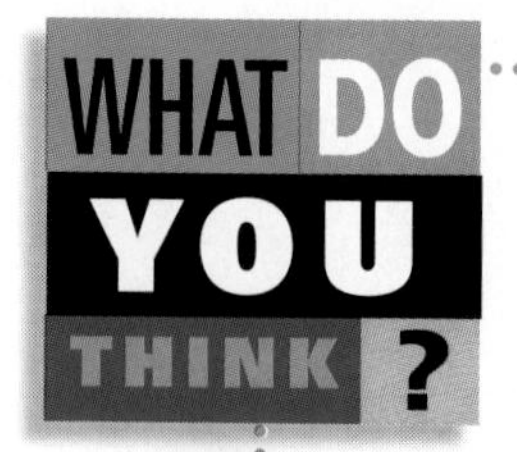

Maritess and Aaron want to rank these earthquakes in order of their measure on the Richter scale.

Earthquakes Around the World		
1755	Lisbon, Portugal	8.75
1906	San Francisco, USA	8.3
1950	Assam, India	8.7
1977	Indonesia	8
1985	Mexico City	8.1

Maritess thinks ...

I'll annex zeros and compare the numbers. 8.75 = 8.75
8.3 = 8.30
8.7 = 8.70
8 = 8.00
8.1 = 8.10

The order is 8, 8.1, 8.3, 8.7, 8.75.

Aaron thinks ...

I'll locate the measurements on a number line.

8 8.1 8.2 8.3 8.4 8.5 8.6 8.7 8.8 8.9 9

The order is 8, 8.1, 8.3, 8.7, 8.75.

What do you think?

1. Which method would you prefer to use? Why?
2. Would both methods work equally well if the measurements went to millionths? Explain.

Check Your Understanding

1. If 35 is greater than 4, why is 0.4 greater than 0.35?
2. Name two numbers between 1.52 and 1.53.
3. You are given two decimal numbers, and you need to decide which one is bigger. Which part of the number should you look at first? Why?

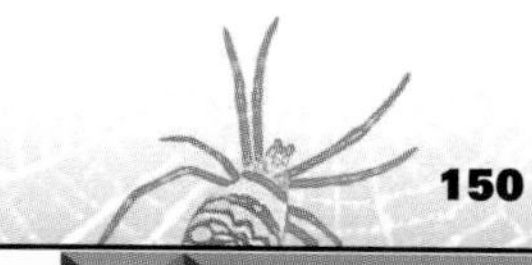

MEETING MIDDLE SCHOOL CLASSROOM NEEDS

Tips from Middle School Teachers

I like to have students visit a grocery store and make a list of the weights and prices of several comparable items such as boxes of cereal or cans of soup. Then I have them order these weights from least to greatest and see whether the prices also are in the same order.

Team Teaching

Work with a school librarian to discuss the Dewey Decimal System for coding library books.

Science Connection

A trap-door spider doesn't make a web. The spider hides inside a burrow it has lined with silk. It lures its prey into the burrow and then closes the trap door. The prey can't climb out up the smooth, silk-lined walls of the burrow.

3-3 Exercises and Applications

Practice and Apply

1. **Getting Started** Annex zeros to the numbers so that they have the same number of digits after the decimal point.

   a. 0.276 and 0.28 — 0.280 **b.** 1.45 and 1.3492 — 1.4500 **c.** 1.67 and 1.679 — 1.670 **d.** 0.3 and 0.4783 — 0.3000

Use $>$, $<$, or $=$ to compare each pair of numbers.

2. 0.193 $>$ 0.187 **3.** 7.32 $=$ 7.320 **4.** 52.1 $<$ 52.16 **5.** 2.1 $>$ 1.94

6. 5.07 $<$ 5.16 **7.** 8.600 $=$ 8.6 **8.** 21.7 $>$ 21.07 **9.** 3.04 $<$ 3.1

10. 66.77 $<$ 67.77 **11.** 34.21 $<$ 35.19 **12.** 98.23 $<$ 98.3 **13.** 6.9 $<$ 6.96

14. 4.6 $=$ 4.60 **15.** 5.03 $<$ 5.30 **16.** 30.1 $<$ 30.11 **17.** 0.02 $<$ 0.20

Science Use the graph for Exercises 18–20. The lengths of the spiders, in no particular order, are 0.872, 0.989, 0.83, 0.746, and 0.675 inches.

18. How long is the golden-silk spider? 0.989 in.

19. How long is the turret spider? 0.675 in.

20. How long is the wolf spider? 0.83 in.

Length of Five Spiders

Length (in.)

Wolf, Turret, Web-weaving, Orb Weaver, Golden-silk

Spider

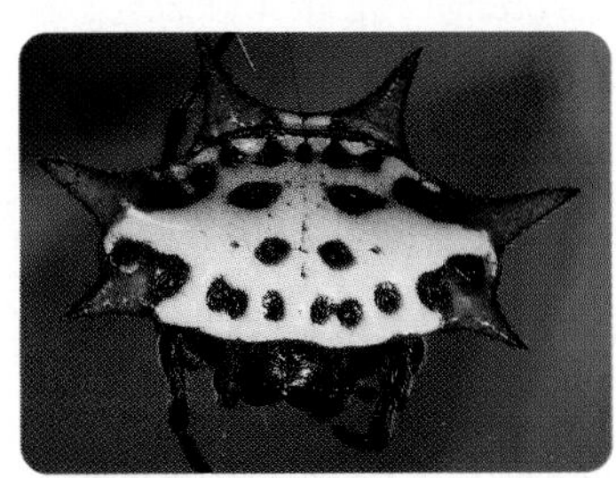

Web-Weaving Spider

Marbled Orb Weaver

Order from least to greatest.

21. 27.948, 27.939, 27.946 — 27.939, 27.946, 27.948

22. 0.53, 0.534, 0.538 — 0.53, 0.534, 0.538

23. 1.23, 2.64, 1.5 — 1.23, 1.5, 2.64

24. 11.066, 11.0666, 11.66 — 11.066, 11.0666, 11.66

25. 2.96, 2.84, 3.02 — 2.84, 2.96, 3.02

26. 0.1147, 0.217, 0.1146 — 0.1146, 0.1147, 0.217

27. 31.7, 31.07, 3.107, 30.17, 310.7 — 3.107, 30.17, 31.07, 31.7, 310.7

28. 2.12, 2.22, 1.22, 1.21, 2.21, 1.11 — 1.11, 1.21, 1.22, 2.12, 2.21, 2.22

PRACTICE 3-3

3-3 Exercises and Applications

Assignment Guide

- **Basic** 1–25, 29, 30, 31–39 odds
- **Average** 2–30, 32–38 evens
- **Enriched** 10–35, 37–39 odds

Exercise Notes

Exercises 18–20

Extension Ask students to find the lengths of the web-weaving and the orb weaver spider. 0.872 in.; 0.746 in.

Exercises 22–24, 26–27

Error Prevention Some students treat decimals as if they are whole numbers and simply compare digits. Remind them to annex zeros after the decimal points so that the numbers have the same number of digits after the decimal point.

PRACTICE

Name ______________________

Practice 3-3

Comparing and Ordering Decimals

For Exercises 1–15, compare using $>$, $<$, or $=$.

1. 0.387 $>$ 0.378 **2.** 4.8 $<$ 4.83 **3.** 12.75 $>$ 12.749

4. 8.32 $>$ 8.23 **5.** 23.65 $>$ 22.66 **6.** 7.382 $<$ 7.823

7. 32.8 $=$ 32.80 **8.** 61.23 $<$ 63.21 **9.** 89.6 $>$ 89.06

10. 5.36 $<$ 6.35 **11.** 2.75 $=$ 2.750 **12.** 11.53 $>$ 11.503

13. 38.97 $<$ 39.87 **14.** 64.381 $>$ 64.38 **15.** 12.46 $<$ 12.48

Use the graph for Exercises 16–18.

Monthly Rainfall in London United Kingdom

Average monthly rainfall (in.): 0, 0.5, 1.0, 1.5, 2.0, 2.5

January, April, July, October

16. Which month has the most rainfall? October

17. Which month has the least rainfall? April

18. Which months have the same amount of rainfall? January and July

Order from least to greatest.

19. 21.600, 21.006, 21.060 — 21.006, 21.060, 21.600

20. 38.88, 38.888, 38.8 — 38.8, 38.88, 38.888

21. 8.23, 8.132, 8.123, 8.213 — 8.123, 8.132, 8.213, 8.23

22. 6.578, 5.687, 5.678, 5.876 — 5.678, 5.687, 5.876, 6.578

23. In 1994, a Greek drachma was worth \$0.0041220, an Italian lira was worth \$0.0006207, a Mexican peso was worth \$0.0002963, and a South Korean won was worth \$0.0012447. Order these currencies from the least value to the greatest value. Peso, lira, won, drachma

24. Science An egg laid by a vervain hummingbird weighs 0.0132 oz, and one laid by a Costa hummingbird weighs 0.017 oz. Which egg is smaller? Vervain hummingbird

RETEACHING

Name ______________________

Alternative Lesson 3-3

Comparing and Ordering Decimals

To compare two decimals, write the decimals so that the decimals have the same number of digits after the decimal point. Remember: writing or *annexing* zeros to the right of a decimal does not change its value.

Example 1

Use $>$ or $<$ to compare 0.08 and 0.6.

Step 1: Annex a zero to 0.6 so that both decimals have the same number of digits after the decimal point. 0.08

Step 2: Compare place values starting with the digit at the left. The ones digits are the same. Compare the tenths digits. 0.60

Since 0 is less than 6, $0.08 < 0.6$.

Try It Use $>$ or $<$ to compare 3.409 and 3.48.

a. How many digits are after the decimal point in 3.409? 3 digits

b. Rewrite 3.48 with the same number of digits after the decimal point. 3.480

c. Compare, starting with the ones digits. 3.409 $<$ 3.48

Use $>$ or $<$ to compare each pair of numbers.

d. 2.33 $>$ 2.033 **e.** 41.039 $<$ 41.05 **f.** 0.479 $>$ 0.45

Example 2

Order from least to greatest: 0.72, 0.227, 1.07.

Write the numbers so that each has the same number of decimal places.

$0.72 = 0.720$
$0.227 = 0.227$
$1.07 = 1.070$

Then compare the numbers starting with the digits on the left.

$1 > 0$
$7 > 2$

The numbers from least to greatest are 0.227, 0.72, 1.07.

Try It Order from least to greatest.

g. 3.04, 0.304, 0.34 — 0.304, 0.34, 3.04

h. 0.205, 0.6, 0.46 — 0.205, 0.46, 0.6

i. 0.98, 0.908, 0.098 — 0.098, 0.908, 0.98

j. 23.04, 32.40, 32.04 — 23.04, 32.04, 32.40

k. 11.011, 10.101, 10.011 — 10.011, 10.101, 11.011

Reteaching

Activity

Materials: 10 × 10 Grids

- Work in groups of three or four. Use 10 × 10 grids to represent the following decimals: 0.30, 0.06, 0.27.
- Put them in order from most shaded to least shaded and read the names of the numbers in order. 0.30, 0.27, 0.06
- Repeat the process for each group of decimals.

1. 0.46, 0.40, 0.61 — 0.61, 0.46, 0.40
2. 0.72, 0.65, 0.67 — 0.72, 0.67, 0.65
3. 0.09, 0.90, 0.95 — 0.95, 0.90, 0.09
4. 0.11, 0.08, 0.81 — 0.81, 0.11, 0.08

Project Progress

You may want to have students use Chapter 3 Project Master.

Exercise Answers

32. Possible answer: Slower time: 25.685 seconds; Faster time: 25.694 seconds. 25.685 will round up to 25.69 and 25.694 will round down to 25.69.
33. Possible answer: 8.743; Annex a zero to 8.75. Then pick a number between 8.739 and 8.750.
34. If Joel annexed zeros, he would see that 7.49 is less than 7.60.
35.

Stem	Leaf
3	0 2 2 6
4	2 4 7 8 9
5	0 1 1 2
6	0 1 1 3 8

36.

Stem	Leaf
0	3 4 4 6 6 7 7 7 8 9
1	0 0 0 1 1 1 1 2 3 3 3 6 9

Alternate Assessment

You may want to use the *Interactive CD-ROM Journal* with this assessment.

Journal Have students tell if 0.45 or 0.54 is larger. Ask them to explain their reasoning using a variety of methods, including pictures, grid models, number lines, and place-value charts.

Quick Quiz

In 1–4, which pairs are the same?

1. 0.07, 0.7 not the same
2. 0.43, 0.34 not the same
3. 0.8, 0.80 same
4. 0.13, 0.31 not the same
5. The finishing times for the fastest women swimmers in the 100 m Butterfly Stroke at the 1996 Summer Olympics are: Liu Limin, China, 59.14 sec.; Angel Martino, USA, 59.23 sec.; Amy van Dyken, USA, 59.13 sec. Who won the gold, silver, and bronze medals? Gold: Van Dyken; Silver: Limin; Bronze: Martino

Available on Daily Transparency 3-3

---

29. **Test Prep** Choose the group of numbers where the value of each decimal number is the same. A

Ⓐ 0.5, 0.50, 0.500 Ⓑ 0.50, 0.05, 0.5 Ⓒ 0.005, 0.050, 0.0500

30. GPS The chart shows the finishing times for a swimming race. Who came in first, second, and third? First Raul, second Josh, third Gabe

Swimmer	Time (sec)
Gabe	32.01
Raul	31.84
Josh	31.92

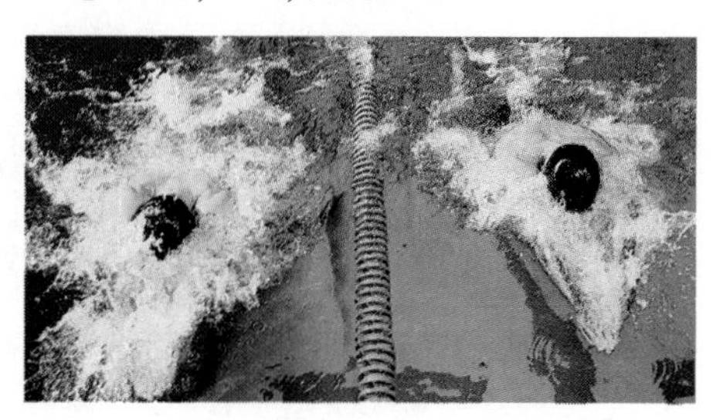

31. The track coach measured the running strides of her distance runners. Sue's stride was 1.34 m, Angela's was 1.41 m, and Temeca's was 1.4 m. The coach chose the two runners with the longest strides to run the 800-meter race. Whom did she choose? Angela and Temeca

Problem Solving and Reasoning

32. Critical Thinking Letti's time in the 50 m freestyle was clocked to the thousandths place but rounded to 25.69 seconds. Give a possible slower time that would round to 25.69. Give a possible faster time that would round to 25.69. Explain.

33. Communicate Write a number that has a thousandths place and is between 8.75 and 8.739. Explain how you chose the number.

34. Communicate Joel says 7.49 is greater than 7.6 because 49 is greater than 6. Explain why Joel's statement is incorrect.

Mixed Review

For the given data, make a stem-and-leaf diagram. *[Lesson 1-6]*

35. 51, 42, 68, 32, 60, 61, 36, 49, 30, 47, 48, 61, 32, 44, 50, 52, 63, 51

36. 7, 9, 10, 13, 12, 11, 6, 4, 7, 3, 6, 10, 13, 16, 13, 11, 10, 7, 11, 8, 4, 11, 19

State whether each equation is true for the given value. *[Lesson 2-12]*

37. $4x = 28; x = 7$ True **38.** $25 - y = 20; y = 15$ False **39.** $12 + p = 20; p = 16$ False

PROBLEM SOLVING 3-3

Project Progress

Start to keep a record of all of the things that you spend money on. For each item, note when you spent the money, what you paid for, and how much it cost.

Problem Solving
Understand
Plan
Solve
Look Back

PROBLEM SOLVING

Name ____________

Guided Problem Solving 3-3

GPS PROBLEM 30, STUDENT PAGE 152

The chart shows the finishing times for a swimming race. Who came in first, second, and third?

Swimmer	Time (sec)
Gabe	32.01
Raul	31.84
Josh	31.92

— Understand —

1. How long did it take Raul to finish the race? 31.84 sec
2. Is the fastest time less than or greater than the slowest time? Explain. Less, because the winner takes less time to finish the race.

— Plan —

3. To list the times in order, which digits will you compare first? Tens Second? Ones Third? Tenths Fourth? Hundredths

— Solve —

4. Write the times in order from least to greatest. 31.84, 31.92, 32.01
5. Write the times in order from fastest to slowest. 31.84, 31.92, 32.01
6. Who came in first? Raul Second? Josh Third? Gabe

— Look Back —

7. Did you need to compare all the place values to order the times? Explain. No, order was found after comparing the tenths digits.

SOLVE ANOTHER PROBLEM

The chart shows the finishing times for a relay race. Who came in first, second, and third? Raylene, Kenisha, Lynn

Runner	Time (sec)
Lynn	28.10
Kenisha	28.01
Raylene	21.08

ENRICHMENT

Name ____________

Extend Your Thinking 3-3

Critical Thinking

Use all ten digits only once to make the number described in each problem. Notice that each number has 3 decimal places. Do not use 0 in either the millions or the thousandths places.

? ? ? ? ? ? ? . ? ? ?

1. The greatest number. 9, 876,543.201
2. The least number. 1,023,456.789
3. When rounded to the nearest tenth, the greatest number that rounds to 5 tenths. 9, 876,432.501
4. When rounded to the nearest tenth, the least number that rounds to 5 tenths. 1,023,567.489
5. When rounded to the nearest whole number, the least odd number 1,023,456.789
6. When rounded to the nearest whole number, the greatest odd number. 9,876,543.201
7. When rounded to the nearest whole number, the greatest even number. 9,876,542.301
8. When rounded to the nearest whole number, the least even number. 1,023,457.689
9. The greatest number less than 5 million. 4,987,653.201
10. The least number greater than 8 million. 8,012,345.679
11. The number closest to 2 million 6 hundred thousand. 2,598,764.301
12. A number with a 3 in the millions place whose sum of the first four digits equals the sum of the last four digits. Now write another number that does not use the same three digits in the decimal places. Possible answers: 3,476,501.928; 3,824,659.701

Scientific Notation

3-4

Lesson Link You've seen that numbers can be extremely large or small. Now you'll see how to use exponents, which you studied in the last chapter, to make writing large numbers easier. ◂

Recall that an *exponent* tells you how many times a number, the *base*, has been used as a factor.

$8 \times 8 \times 8 \times 8 \times 8 = 8^5$
Base: 8 **Exponent:** 5
Read: "8 to the 5th *power*."

You'll Learn ...

- how to represent numbers in scientific notation

... How It's Used

Biologists use scientific notation to track the number of cells in a culture.

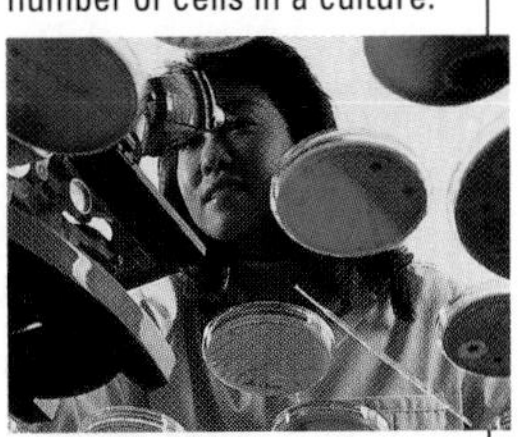

Vocabulary

scientific notation

Explore Scientific Notation

Lots of Naughts

Materials: Scientific calculator

1. Copy the table below. Continue the table for even exponents of 10 from 2 to 16. Use y^x to find how the calculator displays numbers given in exponent form. Example: To find 10^2, use 10 y^x 2 =.

Exponent Form	Number of Factors of 10	Calculator Display	Number of Zeros in Standard Form
10^2	2	100	2
10^4	4	10000	4

2. How does the number of zeros compare with the exponent?
3. Why doesn't the calculator display 1,000,000,000,000 for 10^{12}?
4. How would a calculator display 100,000,000,000,000,000,000?

Science Link

Arachnophobia (a-rak-nuh-FOH-bee-uh) is the fear of spiders.

Learn Scientific Notation

Spiders first appeared on Earth 350,000,000 years ago. Numbers like 350,000,000 can be hard to work with because they have so many zeros. Scientists use **scientific notation** as an easier way to write these numbers. A number in scientific notation is written as the product of a decimal and a power of 10.

3-4 Lesson Organizer

Objective

- Represent numbers in scientific notation.

Vocabulary

- Scientific notation

Materials

- Explore: Scientific calculator

NCTM Standards

- 1–4, 6

Review

Complete the following:

1. 476 × ______ = 4,760,000 10,000
2. ______ × 3.25 = 325 100

Write using exponents:

3. $6 \times 6 \times 6$ 6^3
4. $a \times a \times a \times a \times a$ a^5

Available on Daily Transparency 3-4

1 Introduce

Explore

You may wish to use Teaching Tool Transparency 23: Scientific Calculator

The Point
Students explore scientific notation by studying patterns generated with a calculator's exponent key.

Ongoing Assessment
Students may need assistance in using their calculator and in interpreting the display. Different calculators will express scientific notation in a variety of ways.

For Groups That Finish Early
Multiply 2.3 by powers of ten from 2 to 5, and record the answers. Describe any patterns you notice.

Answers for Explore on next page.

MEETING INDIVIDUAL NEEDS

Resources

- **3-4** Practice
- **3-4** Reteaching
- **3-4** Problem Solving
- **3-4** Enrichment
- **3-4** Daily Transparency
  - Problem of the Day
  - Review
  - Quick Quiz
- Teaching Tool Transparency 23
- Technology Master 13

Wide World of Mathematics Middle School: Hubble Telescope

Learning Modalities

Social Have students work in pairs to allow students with a better understanding of scientific notation to help students who still are having trouble with the concept.

Kinesthetic Have students use scientific calculators to change various numbers to scientific notation. If students have different models of scientific calculators, have them share how scientific notation is displayed on their particular model of scientific calculator.

Challenge

Have students make a map of our solar system showing various distances in both standard form and scientific notation.

Answers for Explore

1. Row 1: 10^6; 6; 1000000; 6
   Row 2: 10^8; 8; 100000000; 8
   Row 3: 10^{10}; 10; 10,000,000,000; 10
   Row 4: 10^{12}; 12; 1,000,000,000,000; 12
   Row 5: 10^{14}; 14; 100,000,000,000,000; 14
   Row 6: 10^{16}; 16; 10,000,000,000,000,000; 16
2. They are the same.
3. The number is too large for the calculator screen.
4. Possible answer: 10^{20} or 1^{20}

2 Teach

Learn

Alternate Examples

1. Write 4.217×10^6 in standard form.

   The exponent is 6. The decimal in the decimal number must be moved 6 places to the right. $4.217 \times 10^6 = 4{,}217{,}000$

2. Write 53,000,000 in scientific notation.

   $53{,}000{,}000 = 5.3 \times ?$

   The first factor must be a number with one digit to the left of the decimal. For 53,000,000, the first factor is 5.3

   The second factor is a power of 10. The exponent equals the number of places the decimal point moves to the left. For 53,000,000, it moves 7 places. The power of 10 is 10^7. $53{,}000{,}000 = 5.3 \times 10^7$.

To convert a number from scientific notation to standard form, move the decimal point to the right the same number of places as the power.

Scientific notation	Standard form
$3.5 \times 10^8 = 350{,}000{,}000$ ←	3.5 with decimal point moved 8 places to the right.

To convert a number from standard form to scientific notation, write the number as the product of two factors.

- The first factor is a decimal number with one digit before the decimal.
- The second factor is a power of 10 in exponent form.

Standard form	Scientific notation
26,800 =	2.68×10^4
↑ number with one digit before the decimal	↑ power of 10 in exponent form

HINT

Many calculators have an "EE" button that lets you put numbers into scientific notation. Enter the first factor, then press EE, then the exponent. For example, 3.2×10^5 would be

Examples

1 Write 5.133×10^7 in standard form.

The exponent is 7. The decimal in the decimal number must be moved 7 places to the right.

$5.133 \times 10^7 = 51{,}330{,}000$

2 Write 437,000,000 in scientific notation.

$437{,}000{,}000 = 4.37 \times ?$ Write decimal factor.

The first factor must be a number with one digit to the left of the decimal. For 437,000,000, the first factor is 4.37.

The second factor is a power of 10. The exponent equals the number of places the decimal point moves to the left. For 437,000,000, it moves 8 places. The power of 10 is 10^8.

$437{,}000{,}000 = 4.37 \times 10^8$

Try It

Write in standard form. **a.** 3×10^4 30,000 **b.** 9.062×10^{10} 90,620,000,000

Write in scientific notation. **c.** 52,000 5.2×10^4 **d.** 1,740,000,000 1.74×10^9

Most calculators show scientific notation with an E (for exponent) instead of a power of 10. For example, 7.55 E 14 has the same meaning as 7.55×10^{14}, or 755,000,000,000,000.

MATH EVERY DAY

Problem of the Day

Norm increases his study time by 1 minute each night. At the end of 6 nights, he has studied a total of 315 minutes. How many minutes did he study the first night? 50 minutes

Available on Daily Transparency 3-4

An Extension is provided in the transparency package.

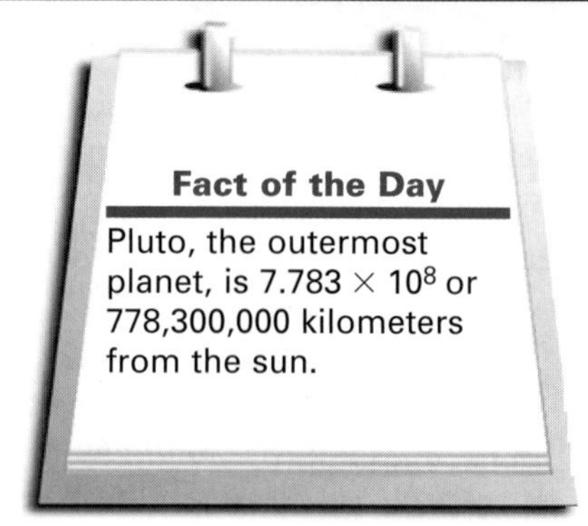

Estimation

Estimate.

1. $\frac{1}{2}$ of 49 25
2. $\frac{1}{3}$ of 16 5
3. $\frac{1}{4}$ of 78 20
4. $\frac{1}{5}$ of 99 20

3 Practice and Assess

Check

Answers for Check Your Understanding

1. Yes; $10 \times 10 \times 10 = 1000$
2. Advantages: Shorter, easier to use with big numbers; Disadvantage: It is more difficult to understand the value of the number.

Check Your Understanding

1. Is 10^3 equal to 1000? Explain.
2. What advantages does scientific notation have over standard notation? What disadvantages does it have?

3-4 Exercises and Applications

Practice and Apply

1. **Getting Started** Write the missing exponent.

   a. $47,000 = 4.7 \times 10^?$ 4 **b.** $800,000 = 8 \times 10^?$ 5 **c.** $5380 = 5.38 \times 10^?$ 3

Write each number in standard form.

2. 8.3×10^3 8300
3. 7.5×10^4 75,000
4. 6.7×10^6 6,700,000
5. 2×10^5 200,000
6. 6.89×10^4 68,900
7. 8.89×10^6 8,890,000
8. 2.3×10^2 230
9. 2.459×10^{12} 2,459,000,000,000
10. 1.02×10^2
11. 4.456×10^{11}
12. 2.405×10^{14}
13. 6.9×10^9
14. 7×10^{12}
15. 3.7×10^5
16. 2.33×10^4
17. 5.7×10^7
18. **Science** The adult human body contains 5×10^{13} cells. Write this number in standard form. 50,000,000,000,000
19. **Science** Scientists believe there may be 5×10^4 to 1×10^5 kinds of spiders. Write both numbers in standard form. 50,000; 100,000
20. **Science** Large female spiders can lay more than 2×10^3 eggs at one time. Write this number in standard form. 2000

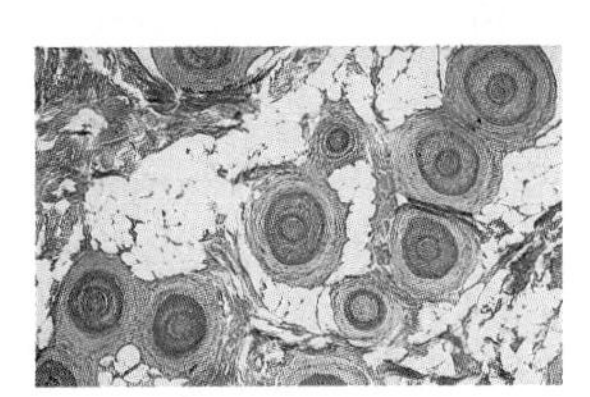

Write each number in scientific notation.

21. 5,000 5×10^3
22. 3,200 3.2×10^3
23. 160,000 1.6×10^5
24. 4,700,000 4.7×10^6
25. 7,900,000,000 7.9×10^9
26. 99,000,000,000 9.9×10^{10}
27. 51 million 5.1×10^7
28. 3 billion 3×10^9
29. 6 trillion 6×10^{12}
30. 47,000 4.7×10^4
31. 500 5×10^2
32. 32,000,000 3.2×10^7
33. **Science** In some species, newborn spiders travel to other areas by making parachutes out of their silk thread. Sailors more than 12,000,000 feet out at sea have seen these "flying" spiders. Write the number in scientific notation. 1.2×10^7

PRACTICE 3-4

3-4 Exercises and Applications

Assignment Guide

- **Basic** 1–12, 18–28, 35–37, 40–46 evens
- **Average** 1–18, 20–29, 35–40, 41–45 odds
- **Enriched** 1–35 odds, 37–46

Exercise Notes

Exercises 22–26

Error Prevention Students may assume that the power of 10 for scientific notation matches the number of zeros in the numeral. Stress that the power of ten matches the number of places that the decimal point will move.

Exercise Answers

10. 102
11. 445,600,000,000
12. 240,500,000,000,000
13. 6,900,000,000
14. 7,000,000,000,000
15. 370,000
16. 23,300
17. 57,000,000

Reteaching

Activity

Materials: Calculator

- Multiply 7.3 by 10, then press [=] to get 73 as the result.
- Continue to multiply by 10 by pressing the [=] sign 10 times and record the results. The first three rows follow:

  7.3 [×] 10 [=] 73

  $7.3 \times 10^1 = 73$

  7.3 [×] 10 [×] 10 [=] 730

  $7.3 \times 10^2 = 730$

  7.3 [×] 10 [×] 10 [×] 10 [=] 7300

  $7.3 \times 10^3 = 7300$

- Discuss the patterns that you see when you multiply by powers of 10. You must annex zeros and the decimal point moves to the right the same number of places as the power of 10.

PRACTICE

Name ________________ **Practice 3-4**

Scientific Notation

For exercises 1–13, write the number in standard form.

1. 2.87×10^2 287
2. 3.982×10^4 39,820
3. 5.843×10^5 584,300
4. 8.95×10^3 8,950
5. 5.47×10^6 5,470,000
6. 4.638×10^4 46,380
7. 7.140×10^3 7,140
8. 1.457×10^5 145,700
9. 8.292×10^7 82,920,000
10. 1.419×10^9 1,419,000,000
11. 9.47×10^5 947,000
12. 4.5185×10^{11} 451,850,000,000
13. 6.09577×10^{13} 60,957,700,000,000
14. **Geography** The area of Saudi Arabia is about 7.57×10^5 square miles. Write this number in standard form. 757,000

For exercises 15–29, write the number in scientific notation.

15. 38,700 3.87×10^4
16. 16 billion 1.6×10^{10}
17. 8 million 8×10^6
18. 6,540 6.54×10^3
19. 60,000 6×10^4
20. 43,950 4.395×10^4
21. 85 trillion 8.5×10^{13}
22. 682,300 6.823×10^5
23. 2,137,000 2.137×10^6
24. 238,000,000 2.38×10^8
25. 560,000,000 5.6×10^8
26. 341,700,000 3.417×10^8
27. 4,382,000,000,000 4.382×10^{12}
28. 5,863,000,000,000 5.863×10^{12}
29. 493,000,000,000 4.93×10^{11}
30. **Astronomy** The sun is about 149,597,900 km away from Earth. Write this number in scientific notation. 1.495979×10^8

RETEACHING

Name ________________ **Alternative Lesson 3-4**

Scientific Notation

Scientific notation is an easier way to write very large and very small numbers. A number in scientific notation is written as the product of a number between 1 and 10 and a power of 10. You write the power of 10 using exponents, with 10 as the base and the number of times 10 is a factor as the exponent.

Example 1

Write 4.2×10^7 in standard form.

The power of 10 tells you how many places to move the decimal point. Move the decimal point to the right 7 places. $4.2 \times 10^7 = 42,000,000$ (7 places)

So, $4.2 \times 10^7 = 42,000,000$.

Try It Write 6.12×10^9 in standard form.

a. How many places to the *right* will the decimal point move? 9 places.

b. $6.12 \times 10^9 =$ 6,120,000,000

Write each number in standard form.

c. 5.6×10^7 56,000,000 d. 1.82×10^6 1,820,000

Example 2

Write 7,089,000 in scientific notation.

Write 7,089,000 as a product of two numbers. The first factor is the decimal number with one digit before the decimal. To write this number, move the decimal point to the left 6 places. 7,089,000 (6 places)

The second factor is a power of 10. The exponent is the number of places the decimal point was moved. 10^6

So, $7,089,000 = 7.089 \times 10^6$

Try It Write 908,000 in scientific notation.

e. How many places to the *left* will the decimal point move? 5 places.

f. What is the first factor? 9.08 g. What is the second factor? 10^5

h. $908,000 =$ 9.08×10^5

Write each number in scientific notation.

i. 423,000,000 4.23×10^8 j. 50,600,000 5.06×10^7

k. 120,000, 1.2×10^5 l. 90,060,000,000 9.006×10^{10}

Exercise Notes

■ Exercise 34

Social Science In 1995, the worldwide life expectancy at birth for males was 61 years and for females was 64 years.

Exercise Answers

37. The first factor must be a number greater than or equal to 1 and less than 10.
38. Since there is one non-zero digit to the immediate right of the 4, it's one less than the exponent.

Alternate Assessment

You may want to use the *Interactive CD-ROM Journal* with this assessment.

Journal Ask students to make an entry in their journals explaining why the decimal point moves when converting numbers from standard form to scientific notation, and vice versa.

Quick Quiz

Write in standard form.

1. 6.8×10^4 68,000
2. 2.073×10^9 2,073,000,000

Write in scientific notation.

3. 450,000 4.5×10^5
4. 603,800,000 6.038×10^8

Available on Daily Transparency 3-4

---

34. Social Science According to the *World Almanac,* there were 5.7 billion people on Earth in 1995. Write this number in scientific notation. 5.7×10^9

35. Test Prep Choose the correct scientific notation for 58,000,000. D

Ⓐ 5.8×10^5 Ⓑ 58×10^5 Ⓒ 5.8×10^6 Ⓓ 5.8×10^7

36. Science Complete the table.

Planet	km from Sun in Scientific Notation	km from Sun in Standard Form	km from Sun in Number-Word Form
Mercury	5.8×10^7	58,000,000	58 million
Venus	1.1×10^8	110,000,000	110 million
Earth	1.5×10^8	150,000,000	150 million
Mars	2.3×10^8	230,000,000	230 million

Problem Solving and Reasoning

37. Communicate Explain why the correct scientific notation for 361,000 is 3.61×10^5, not 361×10^3.

38. Journal How is the number of zeros at the end of 45,000,000,000 related to the exponent in 4.5×10^{10}?

39. Critical Thinking What would be the standard form of 3.65×10^0? Explain. 3.65; $10^0 = 1$

40. Choose a Strategy In 1993, the U.S. Post Office released a large number of stamps picturing Elvis Presley. In scientific notation, the exponent is 8. The decimal factor has three digits, all of them odd. It's greater than 5.13, less than 5.19, and all the digits are different. How many Elvis Presley stamps were issued in 1993? 5.17×10^8

Problem Solving STRATEGIES

- Look for a Pattern
- Make an Organized List
- Make a Table
- Guess and Check
- Work Backward
- Use Logical Reasoning
- Draw a Diagram
- Solve a Simpler Problem

Elvis Presley
Graceland Mansion
3764 Elvis Presley Blvd.
Memphis, TN 38116

Mixed Review

Find the median and the mode for the given data. *[Lesson 1-7]*

41. Number of minutes spent brushing teeth: 5, 7, 5, 3, 12, 8, 6, 8, 10, 11, 7 median: 7; modes: 5, 7, 8

42. Number of left-handed students in each class: 3, 0, 2, 1, 1, 0, 2, 2, 0, 2 median: 1.5; mode: 2

Solve. *[Lesson 2-13]*

43. $5h = 50$ 10 **44.** $m - 13 = 20$ 33 **45.** $20 + k = 32$ 12 **46.** $\frac{36}{b} = 6$ 6

PROBLEM SOLVING 3-4

156 *Chapter 3 • Decimals*

PROBLEM SOLVING

Name ______

Guided Problem Solving 3-4

GPS PROBLEM 40, STUDENT PAGE 156

In 1993, the U.S. Post Office released a large number of stamps picturing Elvis Presley. In scientific notation, the exponent is 8. The decimal factor has three digits, all of them odd. It's greater than 5.13, less than 5.19, and all the digits are different. How many Elvis Presley stamps were issued in 1993?

— Understand —

1. What are you asked to find? How many Elvis stamps were issued in 1993.
2. How will the number of stamps be written? b
   a. Standard notation b. Scientific notation

— Plan —

3. Write the power of ten for the number of stamps. 10^8
4. The digits in the decimal factor are odd. Which digits could be in the decimal factor? 1, 3, 5, 7, 9
5. The decimal factor is between 5.13 and 5.19. Which digit is
   a. in the ones place? 5 b. in the tenths place? 1
   c. Since no digit can be repeated in the answer, which digit can be used in the hundredths place? 7

— Solve —

6. Combine the information you found in Items 4 and 5 to write a sentence stating how many Elvis stamps were issued in 1993. There were 5.17×10^8 Elvis stamps issued in 1993.

— Look Back —

7. Which strategy did you use to find your answer? Use Logical Reasoning.

SOLVE ANOTHER PROBLEM

A number in scientific notation uses only digits that are multiples of 3, except for the base of 10 in the power of ten. Each digit is used once and the number is the largest number possible. What is the number? 6.3×10^9

ENRICHMENT

Name ______

Extend Your Thinking 3-4

Decision Making

When you make a purchase, often you have a choice to give the clerk exact change or to receive change.

1. A cashier has only one-dollar bills, quarters, and dimes. List all the ways you could receive \$2.50 in change.

\$1.00	\$0.25	\$0.10	\$1.00	\$0.25	\$0.10	\$1.00	\$0.25	\$0.10
2	2	0	1	2	10	0	8	5
2	0	5	1	0	15	0	4	15
1	6	0	0	10	0	0	0	25
1	4	5	0	2	20			

2. Which of the combinations from Question 1 will provide you with the fewest coins? Which will provide you with the greatest number of coins? 2 one-dollar bills and 2 quarters; 25 dimes.
3. If you had a choice, why might you want as many coins as possible returned as part of your change? Possible answer: You need change for vending machines, bus fare, or video games.
4. If you had a choice, why might you pay for a purchase with exact change? Possible answer: You don't want to carry coins in your pocket.
5. If you were to get change for a ten-dollar bill today, what would be the best combination of bills and coins for you? Explain. Possible answer: One five-dollar bill, four one-dollar bills, and four quarters to have change to buy juice from the vending machine and pay back a friend.

Section 3A Connect

In this section, you've seen how to use decimals to write numbers between whole numbers, as well as numbers in scientific notation. Now you will use this knowledge to plan a spider exhibit.

It Costs an Arm and a Leg ... and a Leg ... and a Leg ...

The local zoo is planning a new exhibit on spiders. The curator of the zoo wants you to help plan the exhibit for orb weavers. Most orb weavers spin spiraling orb webs on support lines that stretch out from the center. The table lists information on six types of orb weavers found in North America.

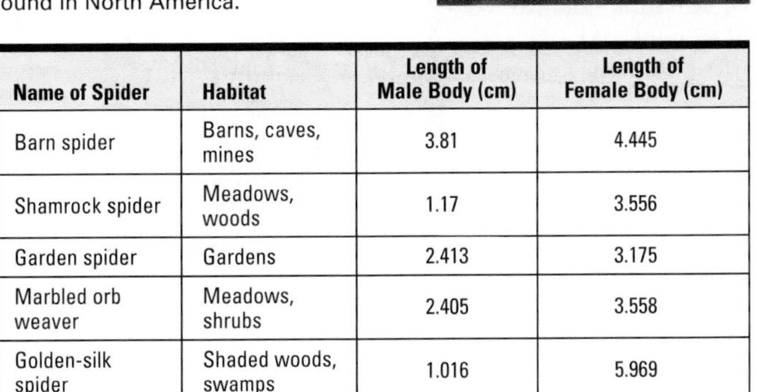

Name of Spider	Habitat	Length of Male Body (cm)	Length of Female Body (cm)
Barn spider	Barns, caves, mines	3.81	4.445
Shamrock spider	Meadows, woods	1.17	3.556
Garden spider	Gardens	2.413	3.175
Marbled orb weaver	Meadows, shrubs	2.405	3.558
Golden-silk spider	Shaded woods, swamps	1.016	5.969
Silver argiope	Fields, gardens	1.143	3.56

1. Order the spiders by (a) length of male and (b) length of female.

2. Choose one spider. If males were placed end-to-end, about how many would fit along a meterstick? How many females would fit along a meterstick? Explain how you made your estimate.

3. The curator expects 4.5×10^4 people to visit the exhibit during the first year. The staff arachnologist expects 2.3×10^5 people. Who is expecting more people? Explain.

It Costs an Arm and a Leg ... and a Leg ... and a Leg ...

The Point

In *It Costs an Arm and a Leg ... and a Leg ... and a Leg ...* on page 137, students learned about spiders. Now they will compare and order the lengths of spiders.

About the Page

- Remind students that the decimal point separates the whole number from the decimal part of the number which represents values between 0 and 1.
- Remind students to compare the place value of each digit in the decimal number when they are ordering the spiders by length.
- Check that students know how many centimeters equal one meter.

Ongoing Assessment

Check that students have ordered the numbers correctly in Question 1.

Extension

Ask students to check the accuracy of their estimates in Question 2. Have pairs of students

- select one spider on the list.
- round its length to the nearest tenth.
- carefully measure and cut a piece of paper the length of their spider.
- use that paper as the unit of measure on a meter stick to determine how many spiders of that variety will fit on the meter stick.

Have each pair of students report their results to the class.

Answers for Connect

1. a. From shortest to longest: Golden-silk, silver argiope, shamrock, marbled orb weaver, garden, barn.
   b. From shortest to longest: Garden, shamrock, marbled orb weaver, silver argiope, barn, golden-silk.
2. Possible answers: Barn spider: 25 males, 25 females; Used rounding.
3. Arachnologist; $4.5 \times 10^4 = 45{,}000$; $2.3 \times 10^5 = 230{,}000$.

3A Review

Review Correlation

Item(s)	Lesson(s)
1–4	3-1
5–12	3-2
13–26	3-4
27	3-2

Test Prep

Test-Taking Tip

Tell students to read the entire multiple-choice question carefully before answering. This question gives information that is very helpful in selecting the correct answer.

Answers for Review

13. a. KB: 1000; MB: 1,000,000; GB: 1,000,000,000

b. 2.4×10^9

Section 3A Review

Write each as a decimal.

1. $\frac{7}{10}$ 0.7 **2.** $\frac{49}{100}$ 0.49 **3.** twenty-six and five-tenths 26.5 **4.** sixty-three hundredths 0.63

Measurement **Measure each length to the nearest centimeter.**

5. 2 cm

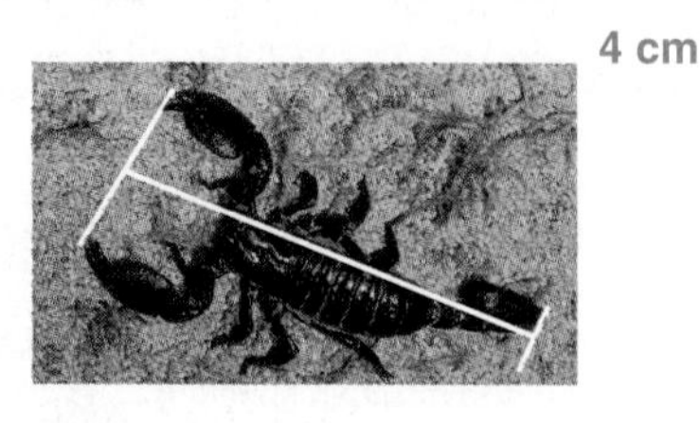

6. 4 cm

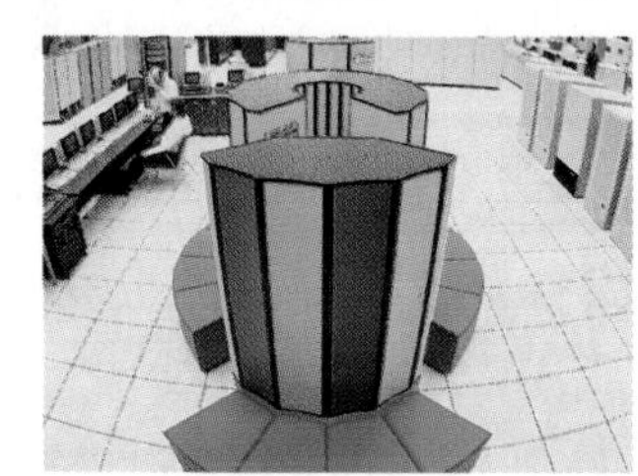

Round to the underlined place value.

7. 0.14 0.1 **8.** 0.351 0.35 **9.** 2.417 2.42 **10.** 0.0813 0.081 **11.** 6.968 7.0 **12.** 1.9827 1.983

13. Technology Computer memory is measured in bytes. The three usual measures are kilobytes (KB: 10^3 bytes), megabytes (MB: 10^6 bytes), and gigabytes (GB: 10^9 bytes).

a. Write each measure of bytes in standard form.

b. A Cray Computer has 2.4 gigabytes of memory. Write the number in scientific notation.

Write each number in standard form.

14. 7×10^3 7000 **15.** 1.2×10^8 120,000,000 **16.** 2.92×10^5 292,000 **17.** 5.6×10^5 560,000 **18.** 1×10^{11} 100,000,000,000

Write each number in scientific notation.

19. 45 billion 4.5×10^{10} **20.** 480,000 4.8×10^5 **21.** 6,780,000 6.78×10^6 **22.** 63 trillion 6.3×10^{13}

23. 60,000,000 6×10^7 **24.** 320,000 3.2×10^5 **25.** 56,900 5.69×10^4 **26.** 41 thousand 4.1×10^4

REVIEW 3A

Test Prep

Remember that in scientific notation, a number with a large exponent is bigger than a number with a small exponent.

27. Which of the following statements is true? A

Ⓐ $3.4 \times 10^5 > 4.7 \times 10^3$ Ⓑ $3.4 \times 10^5 = 4.7 \times 10^3$ Ⓒ $3.4 \times 10^5 < 4.7 \times 10^3$

Resources

Practice Masters
Section 3A Review

Assessment Sourcebook
Quiz 3A

TestWorks
Test and Practice Software

PRACTICE

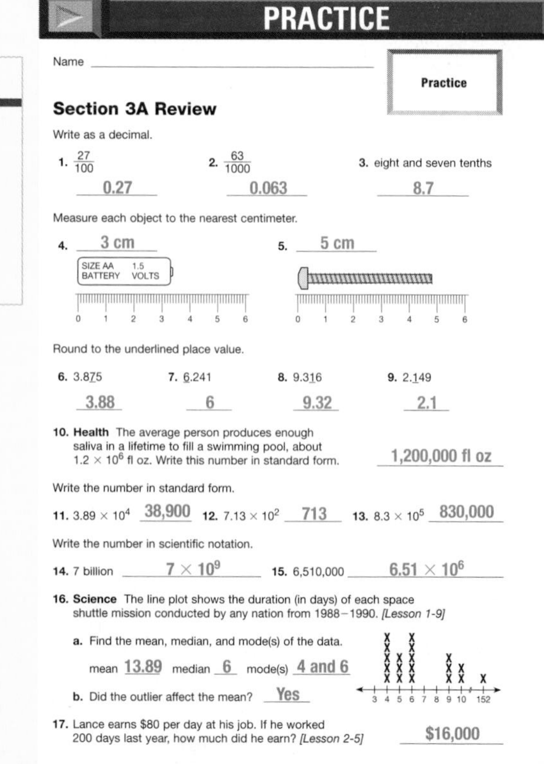

Name ______ Practice

Section 3A Review

Write as a decimal.

1. $\frac{27}{100}$ 0.27 2. $\frac{63}{1000}$ 0.063 3. eight and seven tenths 8.7

Measure each object to the nearest centimeter.

4. 3 cm 5. 5 cm

Round to the underlined place value.

6. 3.875 3.88 7. 6.241 6 8. 9.316 9.32 9. 2.149 2.1

10. **Health** The average person produces enough saliva in a lifetime to fill a swimming pool, about 1.2×10^6 fl oz. Write this number in standard form. 1,200,000 fl oz

Write the number in standard form.

11. 3.89×10^4 38,900 12. 7.13×10^2 713 13. 8.3×10^5 830,000

Write the number in scientific notation.

14. 7 billion 7×10^9 15. 6,510,000 6.51×10^6

16. **Science** The line plot shows the duration (in days) of each space shuttle mission conducted by any nation from 1988–1990. *[Lesson 1-9]*

a. Find the mean, median, and mode(s) of the data.

mean 13.89 median 6 mode(s) 4 and 6

b. Did the outlier affect the mean? Yes

17. Lance earns $80 per day at his job. If he worked 200 days last year, how much did he earn? *[Lesson 2-5]* $16,000

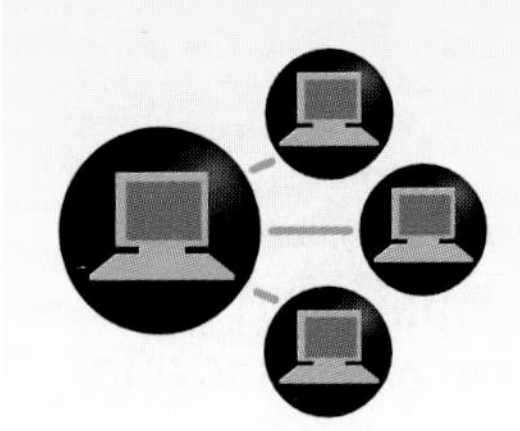

Visit www.teacher.mathsurf.com for links to lesson plans from teachers and other professionals, NCTM information, and other sites.

Section 3B
Adding and Subtracting with Decimals

LESSON PLANNING GUIDE

Student Edition / Ancillaries*

LESSON		MATERIALS	VOCABULARY	DAILY	OTHER
	Section 3B Opener				
3-5	**Estimating with Decimals**			3-5	Ch. 3 Project Master
3-6	**Adding and Subtracting Decimal Numbers**	10 x 10 grids, colored pencils		3-6	Teaching Tool Trans. 11
3-7	**Solving Decimal Equations: Addition and Subtraction**			3-7	Teaching Tool Trans. 2, 3 Technology Master 14
	Connect				Interdisc. Team Teaching 3B
	Review				Practice 3B; Quiz 3B; *TestWorks*

* Daily Ancillaries include Practice, Reteaching, Problem Solving, Enrichment, and Daily Transparency. Teaching Tool Transparencies are in *Teacher's Toolkits*. Lesson Enhancement Transparencies are in *Overhead Transparency Package*.

SKILLS TRACE

LESSON	SKILL	FIRST INTRODUCED GR. 4	GR. 5	GR. 6	DEVELOP	PRACTICE/ APPLY	REVIEW
3-5	**Estimating with decimals.**	✘			pp. 160–161	pp. 162–163	pp. 174, 184, 203, 232
3-6	**Adding and subtracting decimals.**	✘			pp. 164–166	pp. 167–168	pp. 174, 189, 203, 236
3-7	**Solving decimal equations using addition and subtraction.**			✘ p. 169	pp. 169–170	pp. 171–172	pp. 174, 194, 203, 258

CONNECTED MATHEMATICS

Investigation 6 in the unit *Bits and Pieces II (Using Rational Numbers)*, from the **Connected Mathematics** series, can be used with Section 3B.

INTERDISCIPLINARY TEAM TEACHING

Math and Social Studies

(Worksheet pages 15–16: Teacher pages T15–T16)

In this lesson, students add and subtract decimals to compare past and present food prices.

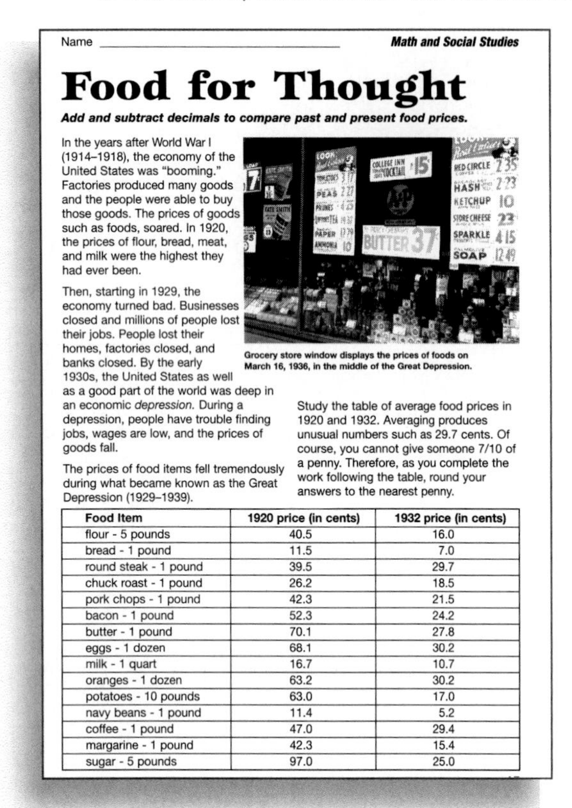

Name ______________________ *Math and Social Studies*

Food for Thought

Add and subtract decimals to compare past and present food prices.

In the years after World War I (1914–1918), the economy of the United States was "booming." Factories produced many goods and the people were able to buy those goods. The prices of goods such as foods, soared. In 1920, the prices of flour, bread, meat, and milk were the highest they had ever been.

Then, starting in 1929, the economy turned bad. Businesses closed and millions of people lost their jobs. People lost their homes, factories closed, and banks closed. By the early 1930s, the United States as well as a good part of the world was deep in an economic *depression.* During a depression, people have trouble finding jobs, wages are low, and the prices of goods fall.

The prices of food items fell tremendously during what became known as the Great Depression (1929–1939).

Grocery store window displays the prices of foods on March 16, 1936, in the middle of the Great Depression.

Study the table of average food prices in 1920 and 1932. Averaging produces unusual numbers such as 29.7 cents. Of course, you cannot give someone 7/10 of a penny. Therefore, as you complete the work following the table, round your answers to the nearest penny.

Food Item	1920 price (in cents)	1932 price (in cents)
flour - 5 pounds	40.5	16.0
bread - 1 pound	11.5	7.0
round steak - 1 pound	39.5	29.7
chuck roast - 1 pound	26.2	18.5
pork chops - 1 pound	42.3	21.5
bacon - 1 pound	52.3	24.2
butter - 1 pound	70.1	27.8
eggs - 1 dozen	68.1	30.2
milk - 1 quart	16.7	10.7
oranges - 1 dozen	63.2	30.2
potatoes - 10 pounds	63.0	17.0
navy beans - 1 pound	11.4	5.2
coffee - 1 pound	47.0	29.4
margarine - 1 pound	42.3	15.4
sugar - 5 pounds	97.0	25.0

Name ______________________ *Math and Social Studies*

1. In 1920, you go shopping for a week's groceries. On a separate sheet of paper, make a grocery list with the price of each item written next to it.
   a. Without adding up the costs, estimate the total.
   Answers will vary.
   b. Add the cost of the items, and round your answer to the nearest penny.
   Answers will vary.
   c. By how much is the actual cost over or under your estimate?
   Answers will vary.
2. In 1932, you go shopping for a week's groceries. On a separate sheet of paper, make a list of the same items you bought in 1920. Write the price of each item next to each item. Add the cost of the items, and round your answer to the nearest penny. How much more (or less) did you spend in 1932?
   Students' answers will vary but the amount spent will be less than in 1920.
3. Call or visit a local grocery store to find the current prices of the items listed in the table. Then, write the same grocery list that you wrote for questions 1 and 2, but list today's prices next to the items. What is your total grocery bill? How much larger (or smaller) is it than in 1920? Than in 1932?
   See below.
4. It is 1920, and you are throwing a dinner party to celebrate your company's successful year. For the party, you need the following:
   8 pounds of pork chops
   2 pounds of navy beans
   10 pounds of potatoes
   2 pounds of margarine
   3 dozen oranges
   1 quart of milk
   2 pounds of coffee
   2 pounds of bread
   What is the amount of your total bill in dollars after rounding to the nearest penny?
   See below.
5. Comparing food prices in 1920 and 1932 gives you some information about life in these times. However, to get a fuller picture you need to know how much of a person's or family's income went to purchase groceries. Do research to find out what an average person or family earned in 1920 and 1932.
   a. What proportion of a person's or family's income was used to buy items you listed for question 1. (Hint: to find the answer, divide the cost of the groceries by the weekly income. Round to the hundredths place.)
   See below.
   b. Were people better off financially in 1920 than in 1932? Explain.
   See below.

Answers

3. Totals will vary but will be greater than for 1920 or 1932. Check that students have provided the following: a complete list of items in the table with current prices; a grocery list to match the list written for questions 1 and 2; a total for the current grocery list; and the difference between the current total and the 1920 and 1932 totals.
4. 42.3 + 42.3 + 42.3 + 42.3 + 42.3 + 42.3 + 42.3 + 42.3 + 11.4 + 11.4 + 63.0 + 42.3 + 42.3 + 63.2 + 63.2 + 63.2 + 16.7 + 47.0 + 47.0 + 11.5 + 11.5 = 832.1 ÷ 100 = \$8.32
5. a. The answer will be two decimals that can be compared.
   b. Better off in 1920 since a smaller proportion of their income went to buy groceries.

BIBLIOGRAPHY

FOR TEACHERS

Burril, Gail and John C. *Data Analysis and Statistics Across the Curriculum.* Reston, VA: NCTM, 1992.

Cassutt, Michael. *Who's Who in Space.* New York, NY: Macmillan, 1993.

Shaw, Jean. *From the File Treasury.* Reston, VA: NCTM, 1991.

Spangler, David. *Math for Real Kids.* Glenview, IL: Good Year Books, 1997.

FOR STUDENTS

The World Almanac and Book of Facts. Mahwah, NJ: Funk & Wagnalls, 1996.

Section 3B

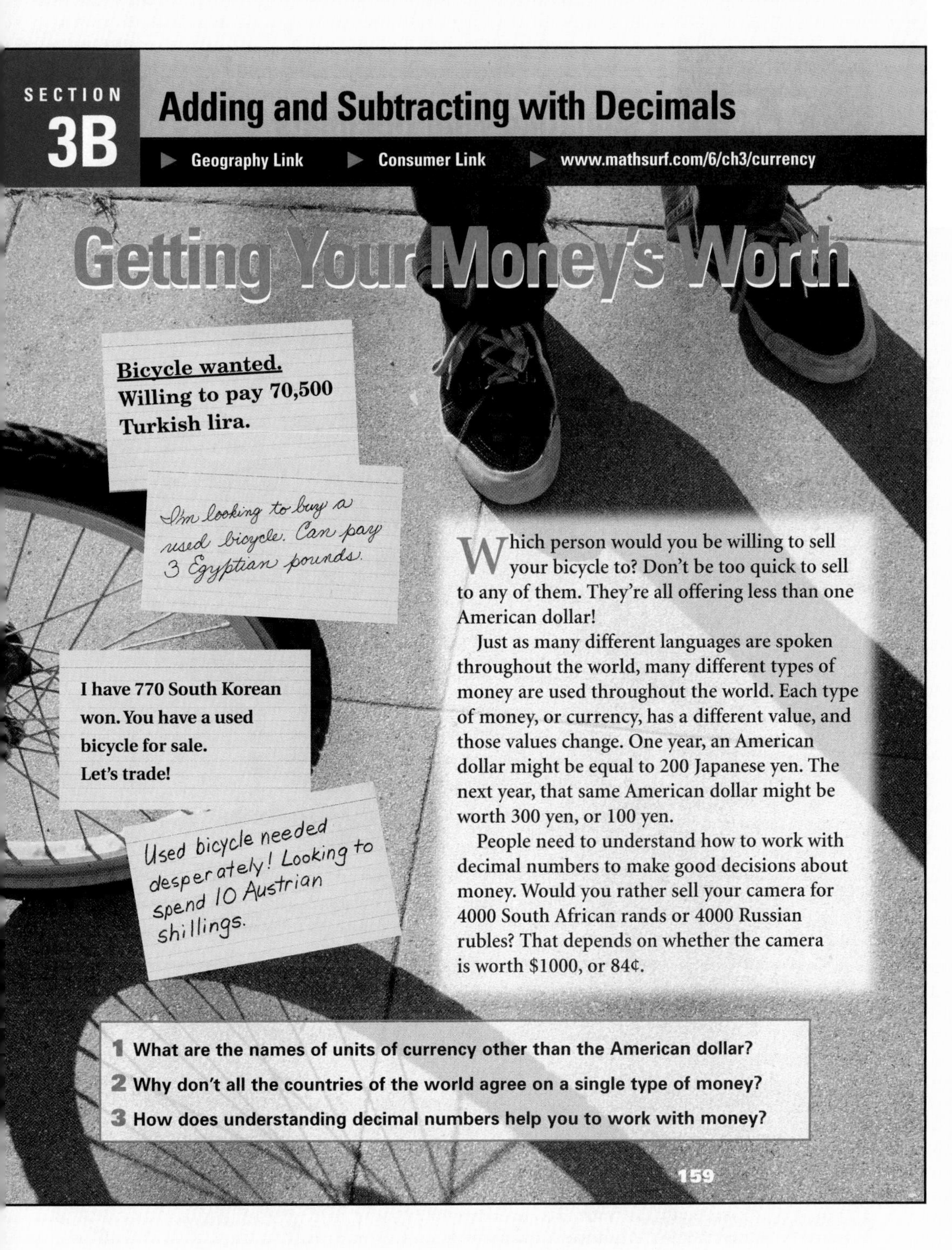

SECTION 3B

Adding and Subtracting with Decimals

▶ Geography Link ▶ Consumer Link ▶ www.mathsurf.com/6/ch3/currency

Getting Your Money's Worth

Which person would you be willing to sell your bicycle to? Don't be too quick to sell to any of them. They're all offering less than one American dollar!

Just as many different languages are spoken throughout the world, many different types of money are used throughout the world. Each type of money, or currency, has a different value, and those values change. One year, an American dollar might be equal to 200 Japanese yen. The next year, that same American dollar might be worth 300 yen, or 100 yen.

People need to understand how to work with decimal numbers to make good decisions about money. Would you rather sell your camera for 4000 South African rands or 4000 Russian rubles? That depends on whether the camera is worth $1000, or 84¢.

1 What are the names of units of currency other than the American dollar?

2 Why don't all the countries of the world agree on a single type of money?

3 How does understanding decimal numbers help you to work with money?

159

Theme: Currency

World Wide Web

If your class has access to the World Wide Web, you might want to use the information found at the Web site address given. These interdisciplinary links relate to topics discussed in this section.

About the Page

This page introduces the theme of the section, currency, and discusses the varying value of foreign currency when compared to the American dollar.

Ask ...

- Why is it important to know the currency of other countries?
- How can you find the value of an item in American dollars when you are spending the currency of another country?

Extensions

The following activities do not require access to the World Wide Web.

Geography

Newspapers print exchange rate tables. Have students choose a country and follow the value of that currency for a week or two. Have students report their findings.

Consumer

Each country has its own currency. Have students select a country and describe its money. Have them present their findings on a poster.

Answers for Questions

1. Possible answer: Australian dollar, Italian lira, South African rands.
2. Possible answer: They have not been able to agree on how much it would be worth.
3. Possible answer: Money is often in decimal form.

Connect

On page 173, students will use information given on an exchange rate table to convert money from the units of one country to those of another.

Where are we now?

In Section 3A, students learned to

- name and write numbers between 0 and 1.
- round decimals.
- measure with a metric ruler.
- compare and order decimals.
- write numbers in scientific notation.

Where are we going?

In Section 3B, students will

- estimate sums, differences, products, and quotients with decimals.
- add and subtract decimals.
- solve addition and subtraction equations involving decimals.

Lesson Organizer

Objective

- Estimate sums, differences, products, and quotients with decimals.

NCTM Standards

- 1–5, 7

Review 

Round to the nearest tenth.

1. 34.572 34.6
2. 0.139 0.1
3. 5.97 6.0

Round to the nearest whole number.

4. 142.6408 143
5. 0.49 0

Available on Daily Transparency 3-5

1 Introduce

Explore  

The Point
Students use menu prices and intuitive rounding techniques to determine if certain combinations of foods can be purchased for the dollar amount given.

Ongoing Assessment
Check to see if students are applying the rounding techniques learned earlier in a consistent manner.

For Groups That Finish Early
Have students review their estimates and give a rationale for their decision.

Answers for Explore

1. A. Yes
   B. No
   C. No
   D. No
2. Answers may vary.

3-5 Estimating with Decimals

You'll Learn ...

- how to estimate sums, differences, products, and quotients with decimals

... How It's Used

Fabric designers use estimates when purchasing supplies.

▶ Lesson Link In the last chapter, you used several ways to estimate sums, differences, products, and quotients with whole numbers. Now you'll use some of those same methods to estimate with decimals. ◀

Explore Estimating with Decimals

Miso, Dal, and Apple Pie

Here's the menu for International Night at North Side Middle School:

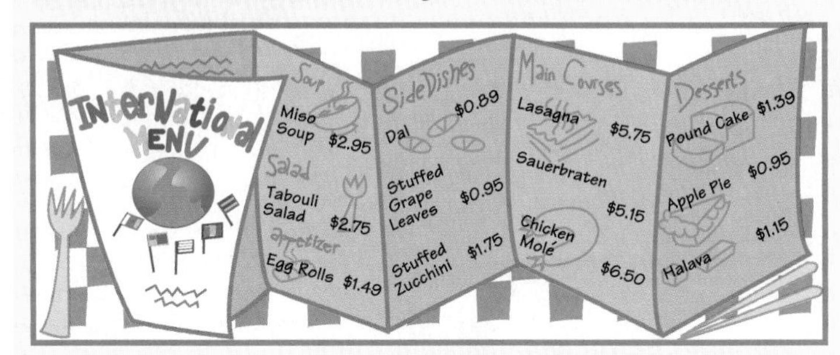

1. Decide whether you can buy each meal for the given price. You may not use paper and pencil or a calculator. Instead, estimate the sum. There are no tips or sales tax.
   A. Miso soup, dal, lasagna, apple pie: $11
   B. Tabouli salad, stuffed zucchini, sauerbraten: $7
   C. Egg rolls, chicken molé, halava: $8
   D. Tabouli salad, stuffed grape leaves, lasagna, pound cake: $10
2. For each meal, state whether you are "certain," "somewhat certain," or "not certain" that you made the correct decision.

Learn Estimating with Decimals

You can use *rounding* to estimate sums and differences with decimals. Most of the time, people round decimal values to the closest whole number. To be more accurate, they round to the closest tenth.

MEETING INDIVIDUAL NEEDS

Resources

- **3-5** Practice
- **3-5** Reteaching
- **3-5** Problem Solving
- **3-5** Enrichment
- **3-5** Daily Transparency
  - Problem of the Day
  - Review
  - Quick Quiz
- Chapter 3 Project Master

Learning Modalities

Verbal Have students explain how they determine compatible numbers when estimating products and quotients of decimals.

Individual In their journals, have students list some cases in their experience where they might need to estimate with decimals. To get students started, ask if any of them have ever had to figure the amount of tip on a restaurant bill.

English Language Development

In discussing compatible numbers, you may want to point out that the word *compatible* can be used to describe people who get along well together. Likewise, compatible numbers work well together because they involve known multiplication or division facts.

Example 1

While vacationing in Australia, Tanya saw a poster for $4.50 and a shirt for $14.95 that she wanted to buy. She had $20. Was it enough?

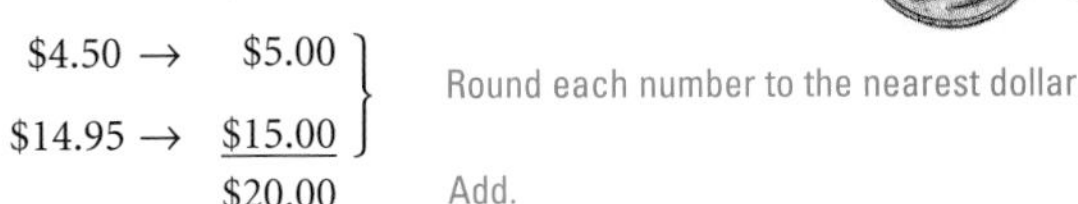

$4.50 → $5.00
$14.95 → $15.00 } Round each number to the nearest dollar.
$20.00 Add.

The cost was about $20. Since Tanya rounded up, the actual sum is less than the estimate. Tanya had enough to buy the poster and the shirt.

You can also use rounding to estimate a decimal product or quotient. Rounded numbers may not be easier to use than the original numbers.

$36.95 \div 7.39 = ?$
↓ ↓
$37 \div 7 = ?$

For that reason, *compatible numbers* often work better for estimating decimal products and quotients.

DID YOU KNOW?

Many countries use a unit of currency called the *dollar*. This includes Australia, Canada, Jamaica, New Zealand, Singapore, Taiwan, Tonga, and the United States.

Remember

Compatible numbers are numbers that go together easily, such as 75 + 25 or 4 × 100. **[Page 86]**

Examples

2 Estimate 9.88 × 23.15.

9.88 → 10
23.15 → 23 } Choose numbers compatible for multiplying.

$10 \times 23 = 230$

3 Estimate $158.75 ÷ $28.95.

158.75 → 150
28.95 → 30 } Choose numbers compatible for dividing.

$150 ÷ $30 = 5

Try It

Estimate each sum, difference, product, or quotient.

a. $14.63 + $19.26 $34 **b.** 58.37 – 22.84 35 **c.** 67.52 × 9.18 630 **d.** 47.13 ÷ 6.4 8

Check Your Understanding

1. How can you decide whether a decimal estimate is high or low?
2. Some problems involving decimals require an exact answer. For others, an estimate is good enough. Give an example of each.

MATH EVERY DAY

Problem of the Day

Carly drew a triangle using three points on the circle as vertices. How many triangles in all can she draw that will have their vertices on the points of the circle?

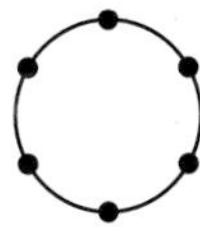

20 triangles; If the six points are labeled A–F, these triangles can be formed: *ABC, ABD, ABE, ABF, ACD, ACE, ACF, ADE, ADF, AEF, BCD, BCE, BCF, BDE, BDF, BEF, CDE, CDF, CEF, DEF.*

Available on Daily Transparency 3-5

An Extension is provided in the transparency package.

Fact of the Day

In 1995, there were 5,845,268,648 one-dollar bills and 2,334,235,253 one-hundred-dollar bills in circulation.

Mental Math

Find each sum mentally.

1. 80 + 80 + 80 + 80 320
2. 70 + 70 + 70 + 70 + 70 + 70 420
3. 900 + 900 + 900 + 900 3600
4. 150 + 150 + 150 + 150 600

2 Teach

Learn

Alternate Examples

1. At a baseball game, Juan decided to buy a shirt for $12.95 and a cap for $5.75. Was $20 enough to purchase them?

   Round each number to the nearest dollar.

   $12.95 → 13.00
   $5.75 → 6.00
   19.00

   The total cost was about $19. Since Juan rounded up, he had enough to buy the shirt and cap.

2. Estimate 88.2 × 1.8.

   Choose numbers compatible for multiplying.

   88.2 → 90
   1.8 → 2

   $90 \times 2 = 180$

3. Estimate $402.13 ÷ $83.02.

   Choose numbers compatible for dividing.

   402.13 → 400
   83.02 → 80

   $400 ÷ $80 = $5

3 Practice and Assess

Check

Answers for Check Your Understanding

1. Keep track of whether you round the numbers up or down.
2. Possible answer: Exact numbers are needed when paying for groceries. Estimated numbers are acceptable when deciding if you have enough money to pay for purchases.

3-5 Exercises and Applications

Assignment Guide

- **Basic**
  1–35 odds, 36, 42–51
- **Average**
  6–36, 38–42, 45–51 odds
- **Enriched**
  8–38 evens, 40–43,
  44–50 evens

Exercise Notes

Exercise 36

Test Prep If students selected D, they rounded the first number to 700 and the second to 25. Point out that rounding to the nearest hundred is not necessary because 675 and 25 are numbers that can be added mentally, and 700 is very close to the actual sum.

3-5 Exercises and Applications

Practice and Apply

1. **Getting Started** Choose the better estimate.

a. 5.417×8.53; 40 or 50 **50** **b.** $124.93 \div 5.17$; 20 or 25 **25**

c. $39.76 - 30.02$; 10 or 15 **10** **d.** $0.53 + 3.6029$; 5 or 7 **5**

Estimate each sum, difference, product, or quotient.

2. $\$31.27 + \$18.52$ **$50** **3.** $\$5.93 - \$3.68$ **$2** **4.** $\$4.98 \times 9$ **$45** **5.** $39.43 \div 8$ **5**

6. $10.581 - 1.203$ **10** **7.** $6.53 + 2.48$ **9** **8.** $15.391 - 8.67$ **6** **9.** 62.3×4.9 **300**

10. 27.32×4.09 **120** **11.** $\$7.84 \times 28$ **$240** **12.** $30.49 \div 4.7$ **6** **13.** $31.23 \div 5.1$ **6**

14. $35.617 + 0.816$ **37** **15.** $89.632 - 47.32$ **43** **16.** 14.32×2.26 **30** **17.** $36.26 + 36.7$ **73**

18. $\$8.47 - \$1.26$ **$7** **19.** 1.628×82.09 **164** **20.** $23.42 + 89.67$ **113** **21.** 27.83×62.9 **1800**

22. $65.298 + 14.83$ **80** **23.** $\$102.36 \div 48.2$ **$2** **24.** $63.501 - 3.999$ **60** **25.** $37.32 \div 5.99$ **6**

26. $0.756 + 63.5$ **65** **27.** 93.278×86.059 **8100** **28.** $12.89 - 10.432$ **3** **29.** 45.01×16.3 **900**

30. $67.8425 + 13.67$ **82** **31.** $321.8 \div 28.45$ **11** **32.** $\$19.59 - \$5.95$ **$14** **33.** $54.69 \div 11.9$ **5**

Number Sense **Use the picture for Exercises 34 and 35.**

34. About how many CDs could you buy with $40? With only $20? **2; 1**

35. One week the music store sold 35 copies of the more expensive CD. Estimate how much money the store collected from those sales. **About $700**

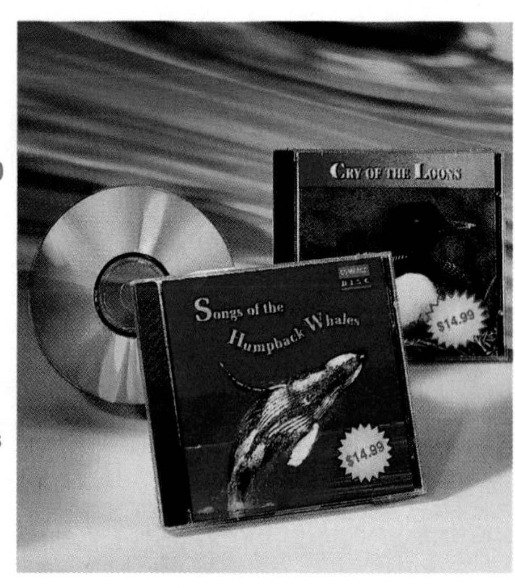

36. **Test Prep** Choose the best estimate of $675.324 + 24.9645$. **C**

Ⓐ 675 Ⓑ 699

Ⓒ 700 Ⓓ 725

37. A recipe required 18.5 ounces of pineapple. Raphael had three and a half 5.4-ounce cans. Did he have enough pineapple for the recipe? **Yes**

38. Karima had $50. She looked at a coat for $34.99 and a pair of shoes for $17.45. Did she have enough money for both items? **No**

PRACTICE 3-5

PRACTICE

Name ______________________ **Practice 3-5**

Estimating with Decimals

Estimate each sum, difference, product, or quotient.

1. $3.68 + 1.75$ ≈ 6	**2.** 38.73×7.9 ≈ 312	**3.** $12.837 - 2.14$ ≈ 11	**4.** $63.917 \div 7.6$ ≈ 8
5. $13.6875 + 7.94$ ≈ 22	**6.** $18.374 - 8.47$ ≈ 10	**7.** 31.27×5.837 ≈ 186	**8.** $75.59 \div 4.23$ ≈ 19
9. $81.238 + 61.59$ ≈ 143	**10.** $163.94 - 39.4$ ≈ 125	**11.** $\$8.47 \times 7.31$ ≈ $56	**12.** $15.83 \div 3.57$ ≈ 4
13. $8.743 + 9.14$ ≈ 18	**14.** $28.6 - 13.14$ ≈ 16	**15.** 8.138×7.2 ≈ 56	**16.** $39.61 \div 4.83$ ≈ 8
17. $3.941 + 14.83$ ≈ 19	**18.** $68.1 - 15.23$ ≈ 53	**19.** 3.6×5.12 ≈ 20	**20.** $96.3 \div 6.41$ ≈ 16
21. $1.09 + 3.06$ ≈ 4	**22.** $\$53.82 - \$16.24$ ≈ $38	**23.** 18.39×1.94 ≈ 36	**24.** $56.43 \div 13.8$ ≈ 4
25. $8.3 + 12.741$ ≈ 21	**26.** $38.89 - 15.63$ ≈ 23	**27.** 21.4×5.2 ≈ 105	**28.** $196.4 \div 6.9$ ≈ 28
29. $37.14 + 9.3$ ≈ 46	**30.** $103.45 - 23.2$ ≈ 80	**31.** 9.74×39.1 ≈ 390	**32.** $35.74 \div 5.63$ ≈ 6

33. You go to a garage sale where all books are priced at $0.35.

a. About how many books could you buy for $10.00? **About 30**

b. Miguel bought 18 books. About how much did he pay? **About $6.00**

34. Tonja has 3 dogs which are all about the same size. If the dogs weigh a total of 83.4 lb, estimate the weight of each dog. **About 28 lb**

35. Fred wants to buy a $15.95 CD and a $9.35 book. He has $24.00. Does he have enough money for the two items? **No**

RETEACHING

Name ______________________ **Alternative Lesson 3-5**

Estimating with Decimals

Two ways to estimate with decimals are *rounding* and *compatible numbers*. Compatible numbers often work better for estimating products and quotients.

Example 1

Use rounding to estimate the sum: $12.89 + $14.29.

Round each number to the nearest dollar by looking at the first number to the right of the decimal point. $12.89 → $13.00; + 14.29 → + 14.00

Add. $27.00

The estimated sum is $27.00.

Try It Use rounding to estimate the difference: $124.772 - 49.55$.

a. Round to the nearest whole number. 124.777 **125** 49.55 **50**

b. Subtract to estimate the difference. **75**

Use rounding to estimate each sum or difference.

c. $\$23.78 + \$79.82$ **$104** **d.** $72.089 + 11.78$ **84**

e. $\$54.88 - \$23.40$ **$32** **f.** $188.36 - 59.99$ **128**

Example 2

Use compatible numbers to estimate $239.15 \div 33.7$.

Look for numbers that are close to those being divided but are easy to divide mentally. $239.15 \div 33.7$ ↓ ↓

Divide. $240 \div 30 = 8$

The estimated quotient is 8.

Try It Use compatible numbers to estimate 88.23×91.009. **Possible answers:**

g. Which two numbers are easier to multiply? **90 and 90**

h. Multiply the compatible numbers to estimate 88.23×91.009. **8100**

Use compatible numbers to estimate each product or quotient.

i. 48.23×5.45 **250** **j.** 74.87×8.75 **630**

k. $65.04 \div 7.83$ **8** **l.** $129.49 \div 11.24$ **10**

m. 37.8×8.9 **360** **n.** $519.9 \div 90.6$ **6**

Reteaching

Activity

Materials: Index cards

- Work in pairs. Use at least 12 index cards. On each card, write an amount in dollars and cents.
- Pick two cards at a time.
- Estimate the sum of the two amounts. Then estimate the difference of the two amounts.
- Replace the cards, reshuffle, and take turns so that each partner has several turns.

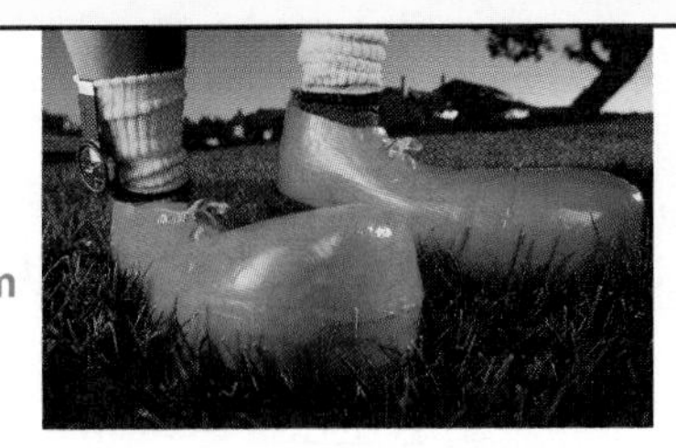

39. Health Carlos's dad uses a pedometer to determine how far he walks. He walked 16.4 km in 5 days. Estimate about how far he went each day. About 3 km

Problem Solving and Reasoning

40. Critical Thinking Joe used estimation to solve these problems. For each problem, explain how Joe might have arrived at his estimate.

a. $0.78 + 0.39 \approx 1.2$ $0.8 + 0.4$

b. $0.45 \times 0.6 \approx 0.24$ 0.4×0.6

c. $\$21.16 - \$12.41 \approx \$10$ $\$20 - \$10$

41. Communicate Bev estimated $71.69 \div 8.51$ to be about 9. Write a note to Bev to explain why 9 is not a good estimate. What is a better estimate? $72 \div 9 = 8$

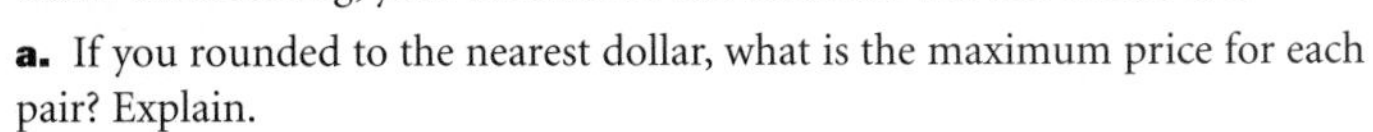

42. Critical Thinking You bought four pairs of pants at the same price. Based on rounding, your estimate of the total cost was $40 before tax.

a. If you rounded to the nearest dollar, what is the maximum price for each pair? Explain.

b. If you rounded to the nearest dollar, what is the minimum price? Explain.

43. Journal Describe a situation involving money where it makes more sense to round up than down. Describe a situation involving money where it makes more sense to round down.

Mixed Review

Find the mean of each set of data. *[Lesson 1-8]*

44. 135, 136, 132, 137, 130, 131, 135 ≈133.714 **45.** 72, 68, 55, 62, 70, 69, 57, 72 65.625

Write each fraction as a decimal. *[Lesson 3-1]*

46. $\frac{78}{100}$ 0.78 **47.** $\frac{32}{100}$ 0.32 **48.** $\frac{3}{10}$ 0.3 **49.** $\frac{789}{1000}$ 0.789 **50.** $\frac{560}{1000}$ 0.560 **51.** $\frac{5}{100}$ 0.05

Project Progress

Take your expenses and group them into categories. For example, you might have a category for "food." Total the amount of money spent in each category.

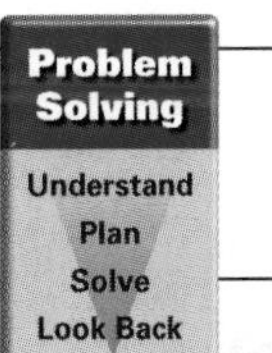

PROBLEM SOLVING 3-5

Exercise Notes

Exercise 39

Extension The answer is between 3 and 4 km. If 16.4 is rounded to 15, the estimate will be 3 km. If 16.4 is rounded to 20, the estimate will be 4 km. Have students tell whether the exact answer will be closer to 3 or 4 and explain their reasoning.

Project Progress

You may want to have students use Chapter 3 Project Master.

Exercise Answers

42. Possible answers: a. $10.49, $10.50 would round to $11 per pair, or $44; b. $9.50, $9.49 would round to $9 per pair, or $36.

43. Possible answers: Round up: To bring enough money to pay for dinner; Round down: To figure out the least amount something might cost.

Alternate Assessment

Performance Present the following problem to students. Mary says that 72×0.45 will give an answer close to 35. Ask students to explain if they agree or disagree with Mary's conclusion. Then ask students to give several examples to illustrate their thinking.

Quick Quiz

Estimate each sum, difference, product, or quotient.

1. $48.23 + $11.67 $60
2. $31.39 − $19.95 $10
3. 47.8×8.4 400
4. $62.9 \div 7.1$ 9

Available on Daily Transparency 3-5

PROBLEM SOLVING

Name ______

Guided Problem Solving 3-5

GPS PROBLEM 42, STUDENT PAGE 163

You bought four pairs of pants at the same price. Based on rounding, your estimate of the total cost was $40 before tax.

a. If you rounded to the nearest dollar, what is the maximum price for each pair? Explain.

b. If you rounded to the nearest dollar, what is the minimum price? Explain.

Understand

1. Underline the information you need.
2. To estimate, you will round to the nearest dollar.

Plan

3. Each pair of pants costs the same amount. What is the estimated cost of each pair of pants? $10
4. To find the maximum price, will you look for a number that rounds up or rounds down to 10? Explain. Rounds down. It is greater than a number rounded up to 10.

Solve

5. What is the maximum price for each pair of pants? $10.49
6. What is the minimum price for each pair of pants? $9.50

Look Back

7. Write number sentences to check your answers. 10.49 + 10.49 + 10.49 + 10.49 = 41.96 ≈ 40; 9.50 + 9.50 + 9.50 + 9.50 = 38 ≈ 40

SOLVE ANOTHER PROBLEM

You bought three CDs at the same price. Based on rounding, your estimate of the total cost was $36 before tax. If you rounded to the nearest dollar, what is the maximum price for each CD? What is the minimum price? Explain your answers.

Maximum price: $12.49; Minimum price: $11.50; Costs should round to $12 since 36 ÷ 3 = 12.

ENRICHMENT

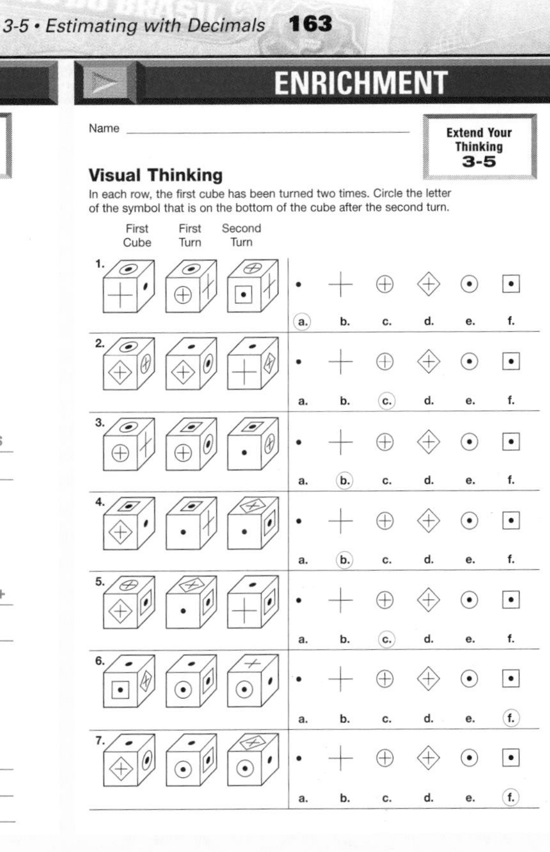

Name ______

Extend Your Thinking 3-5

Visual Thinking

In each row, the first cube has been turned two times. Circle the letter of the symbol that is on the bottom of the cube after the second turn.

First Cube | First Turn | Second Turn

1. a. b. c. d. e. f. (answer: a)
2. a. b. c. d. e. f. (answer: c)
3. a. b. c. d. e. f. (answer: b)
4. a. b. c. d. e. f. (answer: b)
5. a. b. c. d. e. f. (answer: c)
6. a. b. c. d. e. f. (answer: f)
7. a. b. c. d. e. f. (answer: f)

3-6 Lesson Organizer

Objective

- Add and subtract with decimals.

Materials

- Explore: 10 x 10 Grids, colored pencils

NCTM Standards

- 1–4, 7, 13

Review

Add.

1. 235 + 45 + 9 289
2. 8900 + 138 + 89 + 6 9133
3. 58,000 + 9000 + 50 + 8 67,058
4. 60,000 − 499 59,501
5. 100,000 − 5884 94,116
6. Jesse added 2222 and 222 and got 4442. What mistake did he probably make? He wrote 222 under 2222, but placed it in the wrong position so he did not add corresponding place values.

Available on Daily Transparency 3-6

1 Introduce

Explore

You may wish to use Teaching Tool Transparency 11: 10 × 10 Grids with **Explore**.

The Point
Students use models to explore how adding and subtracting decimals is similar to adding and subtracting whole numbers.

Ongoing Assessment
Some students might try to color both the tenths and the hundredths for the first number before going to the second number. This makes the coloring process harder to understand.

For Groups That Finish Early
Have students make up other examples they could model on the grid.

3-6 Adding and Subtracting Decimal Numbers

You'll Learn ...

- how to add and subtract with decimals

... How It's Used

Pilots have to add decimal amounts to determine how far they've flown.

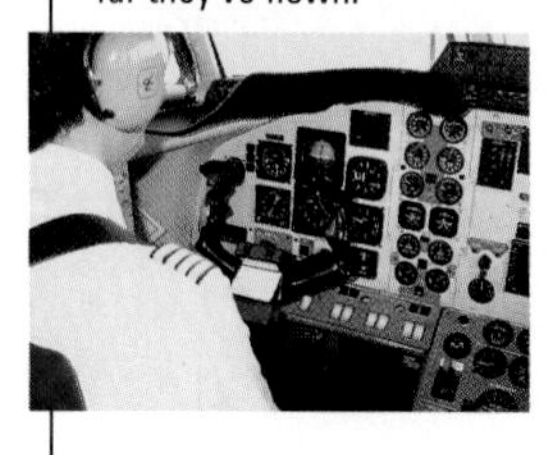

Lesson Link In the last lesson, you estimated the solutions to problems involving decimals. Now you will find sums and differences exactly. ◄

Explore Adding and Subtracting Decimal Numbers

Square Dance

Materials: Hundreds grids, Colored pencils

Adding Decimals

- Color the tenths for the first number.
- Color the tenths for the second number.
- Color the hundredths for the first number.
- Color the hundredths for the second number.
- Describe the number modeled in the grid.

$$\begin{array}{r} 0.14 \\ +\,0.67 \\ \hline 0.81 \end{array}$$

1. Model these problems.

   a. 0.35 + 0.42 **b.** 0.63 + 0.20 **c.** 0.16 + 0.77 **d.** 0.85 + 0.07

Subtracting Decimals

- Color the first number.
- Cross out the second number from the first number.
- Describe the amount left over in the grid.

$$\begin{array}{r} 0.75 \\ -\,0.36 \\ \hline 0.39 \end{array}$$

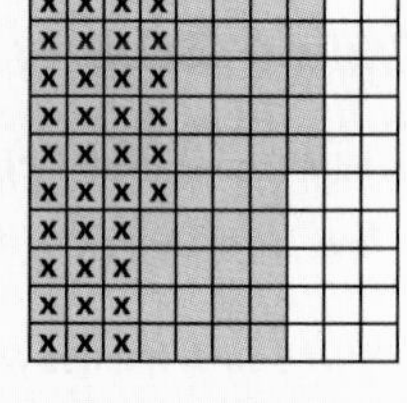

2. Model these problems.

   a. 0.68 − 0.27 **b.** 0.93 − 0.40

   c. 0.52 − 0.19 **d.** 0.88 − 0.49

3. In the problem 0.07 + 0.03 = 0.10, the numbers being added both have hundredths. When you add them together, why are there no hundredths in the answer?

4. In the problem 0.52 − 0.08 = 0.44, how can you take eight hundredths away from the first number when the first number only has a "2" in the hundredths place?

MEETING INDIVIDUAL NEEDS

Resources

3-6 Practice
3-6 Reteaching
3-6 Problem Solving
3-6 Enrichment
3-6 Daily Transparency
 Problem of the Day
 Review
 Quick Quiz
Teaching Tool Transparency 11

Learning Modalities

Visual Have students make models similar to the ones in **Explore** to show addition and subtraction of decimals. Have them display the models on a bulletin board.

Kinesthetic Have students use manipulative materials such as place-value blocks to represent addition and subtraction of decimals.

Inclusion

When writing exercises, have students turn their papers sideways so that the lines can be used to separate columns. Then have them circle the operation sign to check that they are doing the right step.

Learn Adding and Subtracting Decimal Numbers

When you add, you must make sure you're adding tenths to tenths, hundredths to hundredths, and so on. To do this, line up the decimal points. Then add as if you were adding whole numbers.

Example 1

Add 1.7 and 2.49.

Estimate: 2 + 2 = 4.

Line up the decimal points.

↓

$$\begin{array}{r} 1.7 \\ +\ 2.49 \\ \hline 4.19 \end{array}$$

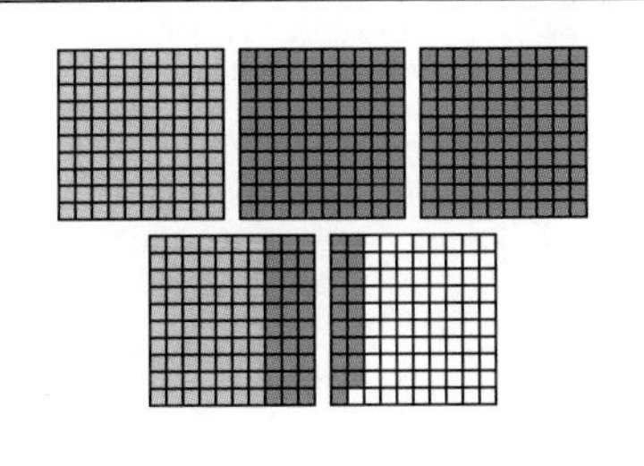

Use the same plan when subtracting decimals. Line up the decimal points, and then subtract as if you were subtracting whole numbers. Annex zeros if the second number has more digits after the decimal than the first.

Example 2

The United Kingdom uses a decimal currency based on the *pound* (£). Paul has £1.8. Edmund has only £1.38. How many more pounds does Paul have?

Subtract to find the difference.

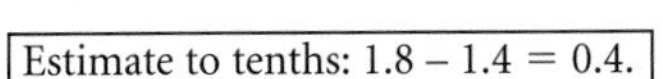

Estimate to tenths: 1.8 – 1.4 = 0.4.

Line up the decimal points.

↓

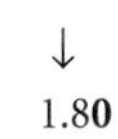

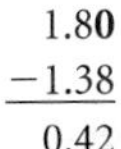

$$\begin{array}{r} 1.80 \\ -1.38 \\ \hline 0.42 \end{array}$$

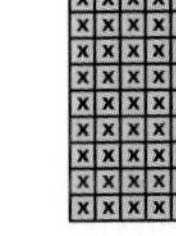

Annex zeros.

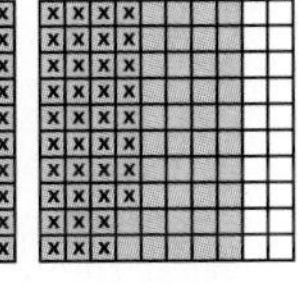

Paul has £0.42 more than Edmund.

Remember

Annexing zeros to the right of a decimal number does not change the value of the number.
[Page 148]

Try It

Find the sum or difference.

a. 4.631 + 3.986 8.617 **b.** 8.592 – 4.635 3.957 **c.** 5.6 + 1.973 7.573 **d.** 7.3 – 4.45 2.85

MATH EVERY DAY

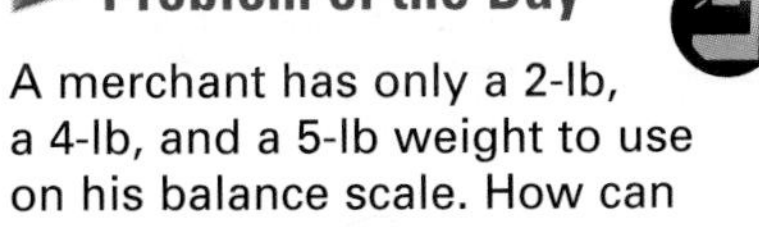

Problem of the Day

A merchant has only a 2-lb, a 4-lb, and a 5-lb weight to use on his balance scale. How can he measure 3 lb of pecans to sell to his customer?
Possible answer: Use the 2-lb weight on one side of the scale and the 5-lb weight on the other side. Then add pecans to the 2-lb side until the scale balances.

Available on Daily Transparency 3-6

An Extension is provided in the transparency package.

Fact of the Day

In 1970, one U.S. dollar equaled 2.3959 United Kingdom pounds. In 1996, one U.S. dollar was equal to 0.6051 of a U.K. pound.

Estimation

Estimate.

1. 213 ÷ 71 3
2. 415 ÷ 59 7
3. 538 ÷ 59 9
4. 245 ÷ 48 5

Answers for Explore

1. a. b.

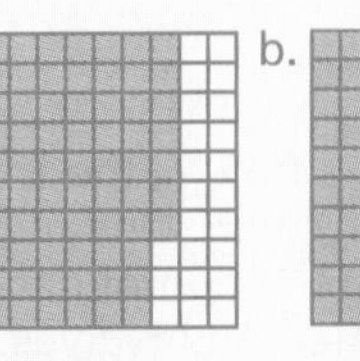

c. d.

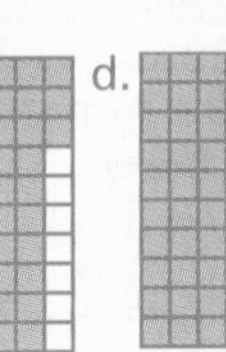

2. a. b.

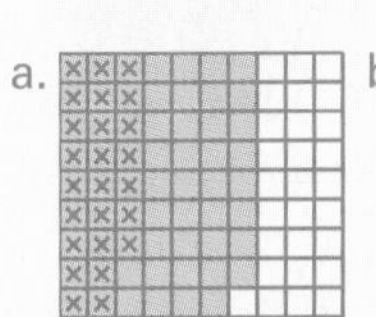

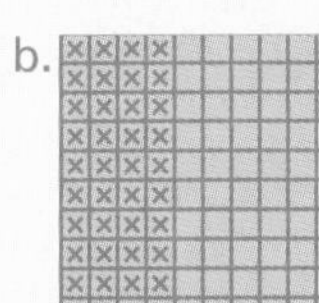

c. d.

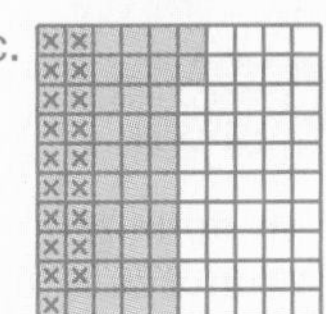

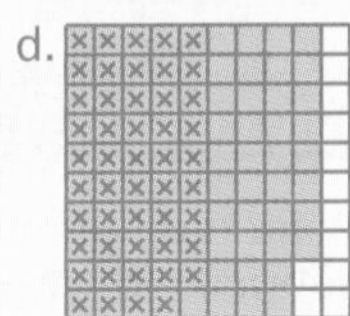

3. There are 10 hundredths, which is the same as 1 tenth.
4. You can borrow one tenth from the five tenths and convert the tenth into ten hundredths.

2 Teach

Learn

Alternate Examples

1. Add 3.8 and 6.87.

   Estimate: 4 + 7 = 11

$$\begin{array}{r} 3.8 \\ +\ 6.87 \\ \hline 10.67 \end{array}$$

2. In a science experiment one plant grew 6.4 cm and another grew 4.32 cm. How much more did the first plant grow?

   Subtract to find the difference.

   Estimate to tenths: 6.4 – 4.3 = 2.1

$$\begin{array}{r} 6.40 \\ -\ 4.32 \\ \hline 2.08 \end{array}$$

   The first plant grew 2.08 cm more than the second.

Students see two methods of solving a problem. One method involves subtraction of decimals. The other method involves estimation. Students can decide which of the two methods is easier for them.

Answers for What Do You Think?

1. Answers will vary.
2. She rounded up only a small amount in each case.

3 Practice and Assess

Check

Point out that when adding or subtracting whole numbers, digits with the same place value are added or subtracted. Explain that a decimal point is usually not inserted after the last digit, but that it could be.

Remind students that when they add and subtract with money, the decimal point must be vertically aligned.

Answers for Check Your Understanding

1. Possible answer: Each number must be added or subtracted from its same place value.
2. After adding, subtract one of the numbers from the answer and you should get the other number. After subtracting, add the second number to the answer and you should get the first number.

You may want to check your answer to a decimal subtraction problem. You can do this by adding the second number in the subtraction problem to the answer. The sum should be the first number in the problem.

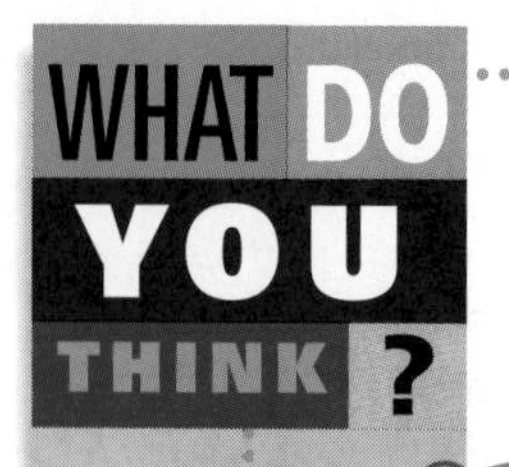

The Sports Center in Vancouver, Canada, sells Crown croquet sets for $34.70. The Athletic Club sells them for $49.85. A Sports Center ad claims that they beat the Athletic Club's price by $25. Van and Lauren want to know if the claim is correct.

Van thinks ...

I'll subtract.

$$\begin{array}{r} 49.85 \\ -\ 34.70 \\ \hline 15.15 \end{array}$$

The claim is wrong.

Lauren thinks ...

I'll estimate by rounding 49.85 to 50 and 34.70 to 35.

50 − 35 = 15. My estimate is close to the actual difference.

The claim is wrong.

What do you think?

1. Which method would you use to verify the claim? Why?
2. How did Lauren know that her estimate was close to the actual difference?

Check Your Understanding

1. Why is it important to line up the decimal points when adding or subtracting decimal numbers?
2. How can you check to see if you have added or subtracted two decimal numbers accurately?

MEETING MIDDLE SCHOOL CLASSROOM NEEDS

Tips from Middle School Teachers

Students have a more intuitive feel for money situations than for abstract decimals. When possible, I try to relate decimal situations to money.

Cooperative Learning

Have students form groups to research other types of currencies such as the peso, the franc, and the rupee.

Cultural Connection

Some students may have used a currency other than U.S. currency. Have these students bring examples of foreign coins and currencies to class and discuss the similarities and differences of these currencies.

3-6 Exercises and Applications

Practice and Apply

1. **Getting Started** Choose the equation that the grid models.

a.

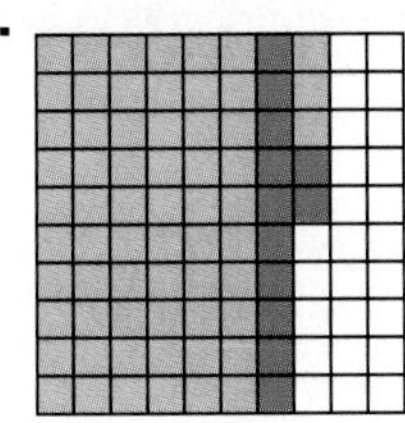

i **i.** 0.63 + 0.12 = 0.75

ii. 0.63 + 0.21 = 0.51

b.

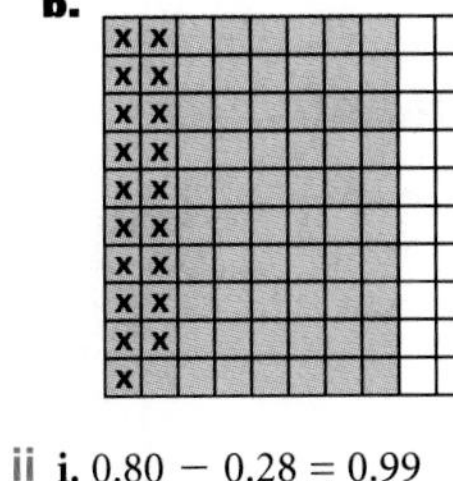

ii **i.** 0.80 − 0.28 = 0.99

ii. 0.80 − 0.19 = 0.61

c.

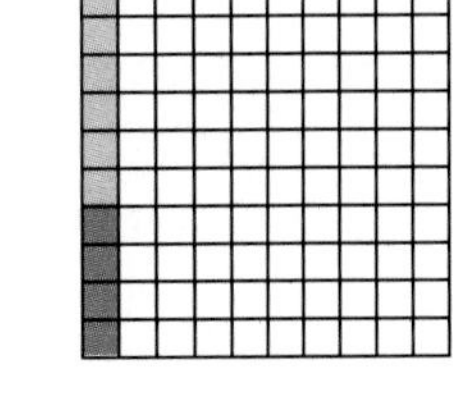

i **i.** 0.06 + 0.04 = 0.10

ii. 0.06 + 0.04 = 1.00

Simplify.

2. 3.56 + 8.75 12.31 **3.** 94.716 − 47.81 46.906 **4.** 34.982 − 8.52 26.462 **5.** 8.2 + 0.2 8.4

6. 7.5 − 0.492 7.008 **7.** $25 − $13.75 $11.25 **8.** 23.05 + 67.06 90.11 **9.** 12.904 + 13 25.904

10. 3.06 + 4.902 7.962 **11.** 78.234 − 12.0056 66.2284 **12.** 14 − 7.95 6.05 **13.** 0.001 + 0.06 0.061

14. 3.2 − 1.2 2 **15.** $38 − $27.99 $10.01 **16.** 74.008 + 1.021 75.029 **17.** 11.6 + 2.78 14.38

18. 54.81 + 54.81 109.62 **19.** 506 − 63.8178 442.1822 **20.** 60.49 − 44.72 15.77 **21.** 34.8 + 6.89 41.69

22. 700.01 − 34.906 665.104 **23.** 93.952 − 89.005 4.947 **24.** 7960 + 3245 11,205 **25.** 10.678 + 5 15.678

26. $4.26 + $32.07 + $0.52 $36.85 **27.** 6.3 + 7.23 + 29.1 42.63 **28.** 50 + 2.852 + 13.6 66.452

29. $72.61 + $1.45 + $2.51 $76.57 **30.** 4.5 + 2.78 + 30.01 37.29 **31.** 7.8 + 80 + 16.87 104.67

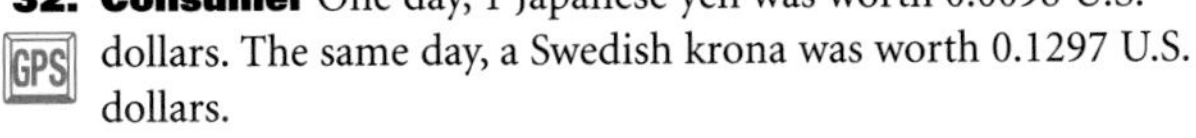

32. Consumer One day, 1 Japanese yen was worth 0.0098 U.S. dollars. The same day, a Swedish krona was worth 0.1297 U.S. dollars.

GPS

a. How much more was the krona worth than the yen? $0.1199

b. On the same day, 1 Thai baht was worth 0.0398 U.S. dollars. How much U.S. money equals one baht plus one yen? $0.0496

33. **Test Prep** Sam has 0.25 cup of milk, 0.333 cup of water, and 0.01 cup of vanilla. When he mixes the ingredients, how much liquid does he have? D

Ⓐ 0.359 cup Ⓑ 1.143 cups

Ⓒ 0.55 cup Ⓓ 0.593 cup

PRACTICE 3-6

PRACTICE

Name ____________

Practice 3-6

Adding and Subtracting Decimal Numbers

Simplify.

1. 2.84 + 1.9 4.74
2. 3.824 − 1.73 2.094
3. 9.876 + 1.349 11.225
4. 8.67 − 4.21 4.46
5. $3.87 + $12.43 $16.30
6. 21.874 − 3.69 18.184
7. 5.3 + 8.49 13.79
8. 24.3 − 7.631 16.669
9. 5.87 + 9.321 15.191
10. 8.743 − 2.38 6.363
11. 5.61 + 21.379 26.989
12. 5.3 − 2.1483 3.1517
13. 9.6413 − 2.14 7.5013
14. 8.365 + 9.3 17.665
15. 12.67 − 10 2.67
16. 43 + 5.374 48.374
17. 39.74 − 5.678 34.062
18. 21.473 + 8.2 29.673
19. 193.8 − 21.73 172.07
20. $84.67 + $91.49 $176.16
21. 36.04 + 9.87 45.91
22. 56.583 − 39.42 17.163
23. $48.43 − $27.62 $20.81
24. 394.2 + 7.165 401.365
25. 2.375 + 6.841 + 9.3894 18.6054
26. 8.23 + 12.7 + 6.74 + 9.32 36.99
27. 7.124 + 8.1 + 9.32 + 7 31.544
28. 9.45 + 6.38 + 7.42 + 21.63 44.88
29. Three lizards weighing 1.57 oz, 1.438 oz, and 1.6412 oz are in a cage. What is their combined weight? 4.6492 oz
30. **Science** Jupiter rotates once every 9.925 hr, and Saturn rotates once every 10.673 hr. Saturn's rotation is how much longer than Jupiter's rotation? 0.748 hr

RETEACHING

Name ____________

Alternative Lesson 3-6

Adding and Subtracting Decimal Numbers

When you add or subtract decimals, first line up the decimal points, and annex zeros if necessary. Then add or subtract as if you were adding or subtracting whole numbers.

Example 1

Add 1.4 and 1.63. Use models if you like.

Line up the decimal points. Annex zeros so that both numbers have the same number of digits to the right of the decimal point.

1.40
+ 1.63

Add, beginning with the hundredths.

3.03

The sum of 1.4 and 1.63 is 3.03.

Try It Add. Use models if you like.

a. 0.59 + 0.6 = 1.19

b. 1.2 + 0.23 = 1.43

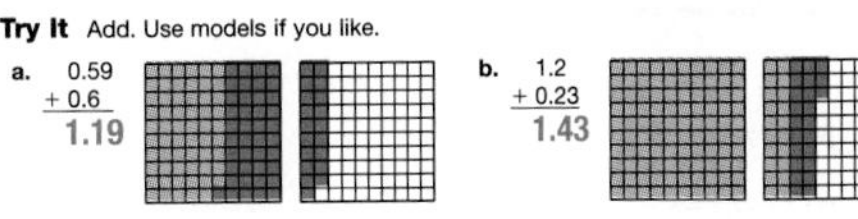

c. 2.026 + 0.42 2.446

d. 0.713 + 6.8 7.513

Example 2

Subtract 1.7 − 0.34. Use models if you like.

Line up the decimal points. Annex zeros so that both numbers have the same number of digits to the right of the decimal point.

1.70
− 0.34

Subtract, beginning with the hundredths.

1.36

The difference between 1.7 and 0.34 is 1.36.

Try It Subtract. Use models if you like.

e. 1.06 − 0.8 = 0.26

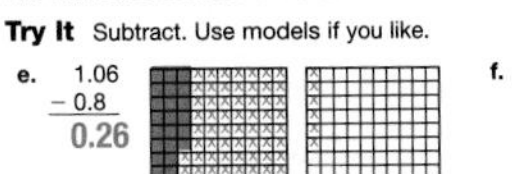

f. 1.9 − 1.49 = 0.41

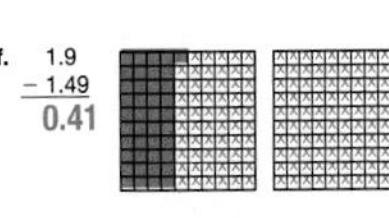

g. 72 − 13.409 58.591

h. 32.4 − 0.481 31.919

3-6 Exercises and Applications

Assignment Guide

- **Basic** 1–31 odds, 32–33, 38–39, 42–47
- **Average** 2–32 evens, 33–35, 37–47 odds
- **Enriched** 5–31 odds, 32–37, 38–46 evens

Exercise Notes

Exercises 6–7, 11–12, 15, 19, 22

Error Prevention Watch for students who simply "bring down" the extra bottom numbers from the subtrahend. Remind them to annex zeros in the top number so that both numbers have the same number of decimal places.

This error is usually less common when a dollar sign is added before the decimal number. You may wish to use Exercises 7 and 15 as examples before assigning the exercises.

Reteaching

Activity

Materials: Meter stick or centimeter ruler

- Work in groups of three. Measure at least five different objects in your classroom to the nearest tenth of a centimeter.
- Use the results from step 1 to find the total length of all the objects you measured.
- Find the difference between the largest and smallest measurements.

Exercise Notes

■ Exercise 34

Extension Some students may have model trains. If possible, have them bring examples to class. Use the trains to illustrate the various gauges.

■ Exercises 38–41

Extension Have students make stem and leaf diagrams of the data.

Exercise Answers

35. Possible answers: a. The first three; b. 13.34 min; c. 1.66 min; d. 4
36. Possible answers: 1.5432 and 0.6789
37. Similar: Addition and subtraction rules are the same; Different: Decimal numbers have a decimal point.
38. With outlier: mean 55, median 46.5, modes 45 and 50; Without outlier: mean 46.429, median 46, modes 45 and 50.
39. With outlier: mean 26.5, median 20.5, modes 19 and 20. Without outlier: mean 20.571, median 20, modes 19 and 20.
40. With outlier: mean 11.667, median 11, modes 10 and 11; Without outlier: mean 10.875, median 11, modes 10 and 11.
41. With outlier: mean 34.333, median 38, mode 35; Without outlier: mean 38.375, median 38.5, mode 35.

Alternate Assessment

Portfolio Have students pick out several exercises from their homework that they think best exemplify the concepts of this lesson.

▶ Quick Quiz

Simplify.

1. 4.07 + 8.45 12.52
2. 2.34 + 7.984 10.324
3. \$20 − \$1.95 \$18.05
4. 0.529 − 0.32 0.209
5. 409 − 76.456 332.544

Available on Daily Transparency 3-6

34. Model trains come in various sizes. G-gauge track is 5.3975 cm wide. O-gauge track is 3.175 cm wide. N-gauge track is 0.79375 cm wide.

a. How much wider is G-gauge track than O-gauge track? 2.2225 cm

b. How much wider is O-gauge track than N-gauge track? 2.38125 cm

Problem Solving and Reasoning

35. Critical Thinking You and your friend won a radio contest and get to be DJs for part of a day. You must put together a 15-minute segment of consecutive songs chosen from the list. No more than 2 minutes can be left at the end of the set.

a. Which songs would you pick?

b. How much time would the songs use?

c. How much time do you have left at the end of your segment?

d. What is the maximum number of songs that you could choose to fill 15 minutes?

SONGS	TIME
Born in the USA (Bruce Springsteen)	4.65 min
On Bended Knee (Boyz II Men)	5.48 min
Old Time Rock and Roll (Bob Seger)	3.21 min
I Only Want To Be With You (Hootie and the Blowfish)	3.76 min
Are You Ready For This? (B2 Unlimited)	3.77 min
YMCA (Village People)	3.48 min

36. Critical Thinking Use each of the digits 0–9 exactly once. Make two decimal numbers whose sum is close to 2 and whose difference is close to 1.

37.  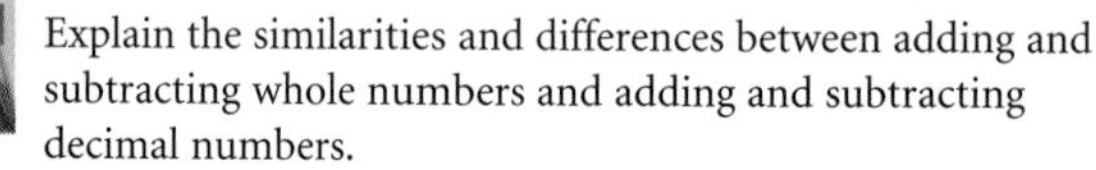 Explain the similarities and differences between adding and subtracting whole numbers and adding and subtracting decimal numbers.

Mixed Review

Find the mean, median, and modes with and without the outlier. *[Lesson 1-9]*

38. 45, 46, 47, 42, 45, 50, 50, 115

39. 23, 68, 19, 22, 19, 20, 21, 20

40. 10, 10, 10, 12, 12, 11, 11, 11, 18

41. 42, 38, 39, 40, 41, 37, 2, 35, 35

Round to the given place value. *[Lesson 3-2]*

42. 0.273, hundredths 0.27

43. 5.998, thousandths 5.998

44. 62.73, tenths 62.7

45. 34.5, ones 35

46. 2.006, hundredths 2.01

47. 0.156, tenths 0.2

PROBLEM SOLVING 3-6

168 *Chapter 3 • Decimals*

PROBLEM SOLVING

Name ______________________ **Guided Problem Solving 3-6**

GPS PROBLEM 32, STUDENT PAGE 167

One day, 1 Japanese yen was worth 0.0098 U.S. dollars. The same day, a Swedish krona was worth 0.1297 U.S. dollars.

a. How much more was the krona worth than the yen that day?

b. On the same day, 1 Thai baht was worth 0.0398 U.S. dollars. How much U.S. money equals one baht plus one yen?

— Understand —

1. How many U.S. dollars was one Japanese yen worth? 0.0098
2. How many U.S. dollars was one Swedish krona worth? 0.1297
3. How many U.S. dollars was one Thai baht worth? 0.0398

— Plan —

4. Which operation will you use to find how much more one currency is than another? Subtraction.
5. Which operation will you use to find how much two currencies are worth together? Addition.

— Solve —

6. How much more was the krona worth than the yen? Compare in U.S. dollars. \$0.1199
7. How many U.S. dollars equal one baht plus one yen? \$0.0496

— Look Back —

8. Would a grid model help you find the answer? Explain. Possible answer: Yes, it would be easier to count in a 100 × 100 grid.

SOLVE ANOTHER PROBLEM

One day, 1 Canadian dollar was worth 0.7319 U.S. dollars. The same day, a German mark was worth 0.6430 U.S. dollars.

a. How much more was the Canadian dollar worth than the German mark that day? \$0.0889

b. On the same day, 1 Pakistani rupee was worth 0.0252 U.S. dollars. How much U.S. money equals one mark plus one rupee? \$0.6682

ENRICHMENT

Name ______________________ **Extend Your Thinking 3-6**

Visual Thinking

The two figures on the left share a common property. Circle the figure on the right that shares the same property.

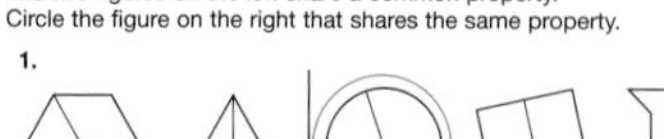

1. 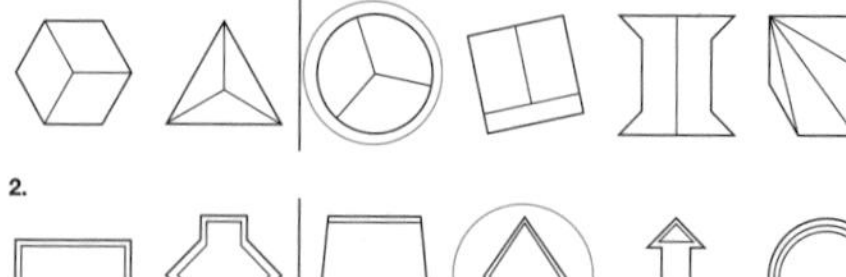

2. 

3. 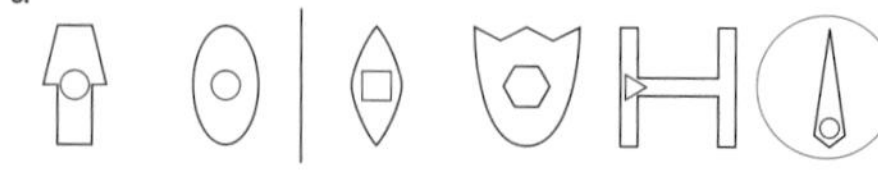

4. 

5. 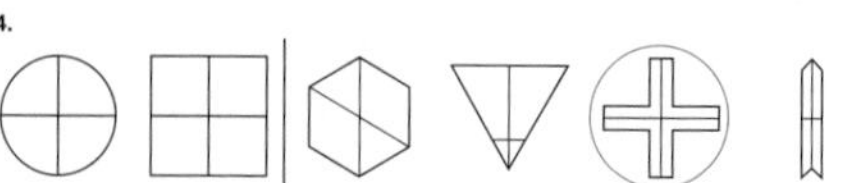

6. 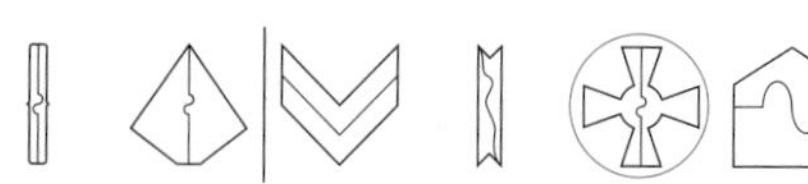

Solving Decimal Equations: Addition and Subtraction

3-7

▶ Lesson Link You've used mental math to solve equations involving whole numbers. Now you'll use the same method to solve addition and subtraction equations involving decimals. ◀

You'll Learn ...

■ to solve equations that involve adding and subtracting decimals

... How It's Used

Store managers use decimal equations to determine how much to subtract from the price of an item on sale.

Explore Missing Lengths

Where in the World ...?

These diagrams show the measurements of two sides of a triangle. The total distance around the triangle is also given.

Distance = 19.8

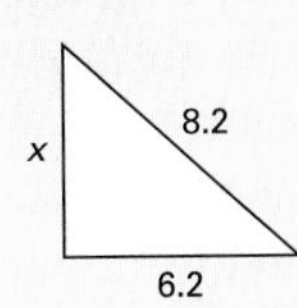

Distance = 16.2

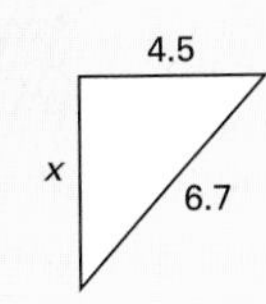

Distance = 19.3

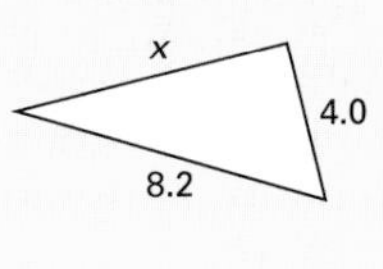

Distance = 14.7

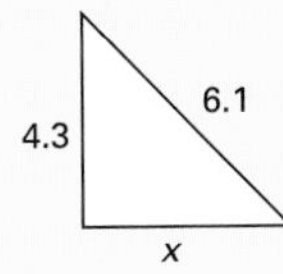

Distance = 23.3

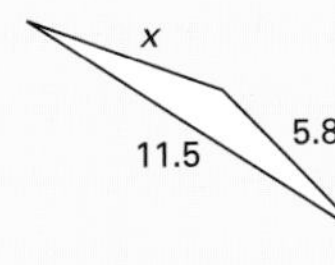

Distance = 27.6

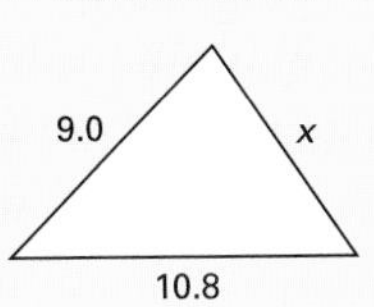

Value of *x* 5.0 4.3 6.0 5.4 7.1 7.8

1. Match each diagram to the correct value of *x*.
2. Choose one diagram and write an equation using addition that describes the diagram.
3. Choose a different diagram and write an equation using subtraction that describes the diagram.
4. Can each diagram be described with both an addition equation and a subtraction equation? Explain.

MEETING INDIVIDUAL NEEDS

Resources

3-7 Practice
3-7 Reteaching
3-7 Problem Solving
3-7 Enrichment
3-7 Daily Transparency
  Problem of the Day
  Review
  Quick Quiz
Teaching Tool Transparencies 2, 3
Technology Master 14

Learning Modalities

Kinesthetic Have students use calculators as an aid for solving and checking equations in this lesson.

Social Have students work together in pairs to solve the equations in this lesson. Encourage them to translate from symbols to words as they solve the equations.

Challenge

Have students solve the following problem:

Together a pencil and a notebook cost $1. The notebook costs $0.90 more than the pencil. How much does each cost? Notebook, $0.95; Pencil, $0.05

3-7 Lesson Organizer

Objective

- Solve equations that involve adding and subtracting decimals.

NCTM Standards

- 1–4, 6, 7, 9, 12

▶ Review

Solve.

1. $x + 10 = 38$ $x = 28$
2. $a - 7 = 17$ $a = 24$
3. $y + 215 = 325$ $y = 110$
4. $w + 50 = 900$ $w = 850$

Available on Daily Transparency 3-7

1 Introduce

Explore

The Point

Students practice decimal addition and subtraction by finding the missing side of a triangle when the perimeter is known.

Ongoing Assessment

Watch for students who add all the given measurements when they write an addition equation. For example, for the first triangle they might write $x = 6.2 + 8.2 + 19.8$. Explain that the total distance, 19.8, is the sum of the three sides.

For Groups That Finish Early

Write another equation that could be used to find the perimeter of each triangle.

Answers for Explore

1. a. 5.4; b.5.0; c. 7.1; d. 4.3; e. 6.0; f. 7.8
2. Possible answer: D: $4.3 + 6.1 + x = 14.7$
3. Possible answer: C: $19.3 - x = 12.2$
4. Yes; Addition and subtraction are the opposites of each other.

2 Teach

Learn

Some students may need some extra help in translating equations into words. Remind them that a variable can be read as "What number."

Alternate Examples

1. Solve $x + 3.8 = 8.9$

   5.1 + 3.8 = 8.9

   8.9 = 8.9 √

   The value of x is 5.1

2. A gas tank holds 15 gallons. When Sarah filled the tank, only 13.4 gallons were needed. How much gas was in the tank before she filled it?

   Let g = the gas in the tank before it was filled.

   $g + 13.4 = 15.$

   1.6 + 13.4 = 15

   15 = 15 √

   There were 1.6 gallons in the tank.

3 Practice and Assess

Check

Answers for Check Your Understanding

1. Yes, the equations are equivalent.
2. Possible answer: After 2.5 gallons of gas were used, 15.3 gallons were left. How much gas was there at the beginning?

Learn Solving Addition and Subtraction Equations

Recall that you can solve addition and subtraction equations with whole numbers using mental math. You can also solve equations with decimals in the same way.

Examples

1 Solve $x + 2.3 = 3.4$.

$x + 2.3 = 3.4$	Read as "What number plus 2.3 equals 3.4?"
$\mathbf{1.1} + 2.3 = 3.4$	Use mental math.
$3.4 = 3.4$ ✓	Check to see that the equation is true.

The value of x is 1.1.

2 Jean planned to hike the Mount Wolf trail. The first day, she hiked 8 miles. The second day, she reached the end of the trail, where a sign stated the trail was 10.6 miles long. How far did she hike the second day?

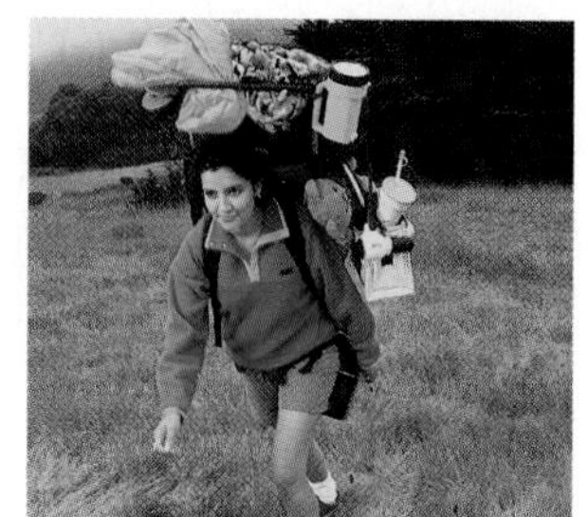

Let x = the distance Jean hiked the second day.

Problem Solving TIP

You can also solve the problem by using subtraction to work backwards. What is 10.6 − 8?

$8 + x = 10.6$	Read as "What number plus 8 equals 10.6?"
$8 + \mathbf{2.6} = 10.6$	Use mental math.
$10.6 = 10.6$ ✓	Check to see that the equation is true.

Jean hiked 2.6 miles the second day.

Try It

Solve each equation.

a. $x + 9.4 = 19.5$ $x = 10.1$

b. $n - 0.5 = 10.1$ $n = 10.6$

c. $j + 7.1 = 12.2$ $j = 5.1$

d. $p - 2.0 = 0.2$ $p = 2.2$

Check Your Understanding

1. Would you solve $4.3 + x = 7.7$ the same way you'd solve $x + 4.3 = 7.7$? Explain.
2. Give a real-world problem modeled by $n - 2.5 = 15.3$.

MATH EVERY DAY

Problem of the Day

Cindy can join these links into one long chain by opening and closing 4 links. How can she join the chains using only 3 links?

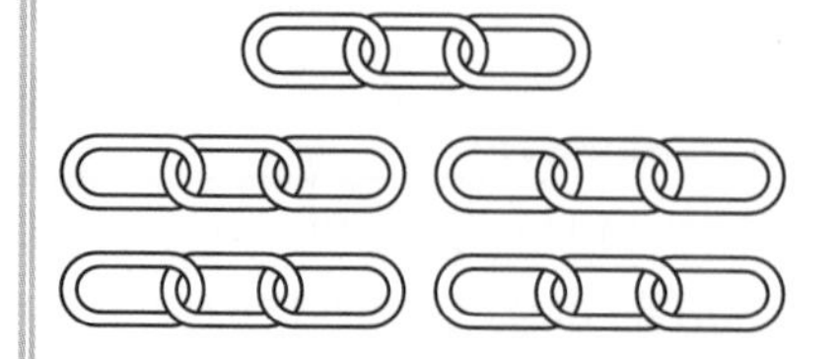

Cindy can open all the links on one small chain and use them to join the other small chains.

Available on Daily Transparency 3-7

An Extension is provided in the transparency package.

Fact of the Day

Hikers can follow the Appalachian Trail through 14 states from Maine to Georgia, across more than 165,000 acres.

Estimation

Is each sum less than or greater than 100?

1. 46 + 52 + 75 >
2. 35 + 31 + 29 <
3. 41 + 9 + 45 <
4. 27 + 27 + 27 <

3-7 Exercises and Applications

Practice and Apply

1. **Getting Started** State if each equation is true or false for $h = 1.4$.

a. $h - 1.3 = 0.1$ T **b.** $h + 2.4 = 4.0$ F **c.** $0.6 + h = 2.0$ T **d.** $5.8 - h = 3.4$ F

Solve.

2. $11.6 - b = 8.3$ $b = 3.3$ **3.** $0.12 + d = 0.52$ $d = 0.4$ **4.** $\$75.40 + n = \$100$ $n = \$24.60$

5. $x + 5.7 = 13.8$ $x = 8.1$ **6.** $y - 10.1 = 60$ $y = 70.1$ **7.** $u + \$12.60 = \$14.97$ $u = \$2.37$

8. $25.001 - n = 24$ $n = 1.001$ **9.** $w + 7.4 = 35.6$ $w = 28.2$ **10.** $p - 4.01 = 15.08$ $p = 19.09$

11. $1.12 + a = 2.34$ $a = 1.22$ **12.** $0.06 - v = 0.02$ $v = 0.04$ **13.** $c + 14.99 = 15.01$ $c = 0.02$

14. $e + 4.35 = 10.5$ $e = 6.15$ **15.** $\$16.75 + f = \$20$ $f = \$3.25$ **16.** $g + 8.7 = 10.1$ $g = 1.4$

17. $i - 42.7 = 45$ $i = 87.7$ **18.** $j + 0.088 = 0.099$ $j = 0.011$ **19.** $m - 0.035 = 0.053$ $m = 0.088$

20. $r + 32.45 = 62.78$ $r = 30.33$ **21.** $3.43 - w = 1.11$ $w = 2.32$ **22.** $k + \$66.45 = \$76.90$ $k = \$10.45$

23. $100.7 - z = 40.7$ $z = 60$ **24.** $l - 682 = 0.251$ $l = 682.251$ **25.** $t + 1.33 = 2$ $t = 0.67$

Geometry Given the distance around the shape, find the length of the unknown side.

26. Total distance: 25.5 m $y = 9.7$

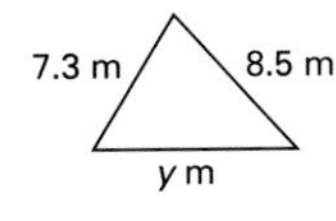

27. Total distance: 40 cm $g = 12.1$

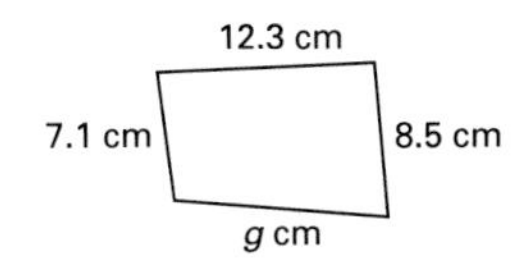

28. **Operation Sense** Jorge won a cash prize in a contest. He donated half of the money to his Boy Scout troop. Then he spent \$19.49 on a computer game and put the rest, \$30.51, into his savings account. How much money did he win? \$100

GPS

29. **Test Prep** Choose the correct value for x:
$x + 2.91 = 4.01$. A

Ⓐ 1.1 Ⓑ 2.9

Ⓒ 2.11 Ⓓ 6.92

PRACTICE 3-7

3-7 Exercises and Applications

Assignment Guide

- **Basic**
  1–27 odds, 28–29, 33, 36–42 evens
- **Average**
  7–27 odds, 28–31, 33–41 odds
- **Enriched**
  11–27 odds, 28–35, 36–42 evens

Exercise Notes

Exercises 4, 7, 15, 22

Extension Have students make up real-world problems that could be modeled by these equations.

Exercise 29

Test Prep If students selected D, they added 2.91 and 4.01 instead of subtracting 2.91 from 4.01. Stress the importance of checking the reasonableness of an answer.

Reteaching

Activity

Materials: Catalogs, newspapers

- Work in groups of three. Use catalog or newspaper advertisements to find items you would like to buy.
- Make a list of the items and their prices. Do not show your list to the other people in you group.
- Have two people in your group tell the price of one item on their list.
- Have the third person find the total price of an item on his or her list and the two other items, without telling the price of his or her item.
- Work together to write an equation that models how to find the cost of the third item. Solve the equation.
- Check that the solution is the price of the third person's item.
- Repeat the activity using different prices and taking turns being the person who doesn't tell the price of the item selected.

PRACTICE

Name ______________________ **Practice 3-7**

Solving Decimal Equations: Addition and Subtraction

Solve.

1. $h + 3.6 = 8.6$ $h =$ 5
2. $b - 7 = 12.3$ $b =$ 19.3
3. $9 + t = 12.4$ $t =$ 3.4
4. $10 - a = 3.4$ $a =$ 6.6
5. $r + 2.2 = 5.7$ $r =$ 3.5
6. $n - 6.2 = 11.4$ $n =$ 17.6
7. $8 + j = 15.34$ $j =$ 7.34
8. $14.3 - g = 6.3$ $g =$ 8
9. $m + 7.3 = 9.1$ $m =$ 1.8
10. $d - 10.3 = 1.8$ $d =$ 12.1
11. $6.3 + f = 10.5$ $f =$ 4.2
12. $3.9 - c = 3.1$ $c =$ 0.8
13. $q + \$18.3 = \$20$ $q =$ \$1.7
14. $k - 5.1 = 2.9$ $k =$ 8
15. $3.89 + x = 5.2$ $x =$ 1.31
16. $18.4 - u = 9.6$ $u =$ 8.8
17. $e + 2.7 = 10$ $e =$ 7.3
18. $r - 7.5 = 3.1$ $r =$ 10.6
19. $5.62 + p = 5.99$ $p =$ 0.37
20. $8.3 - y = 2.7$ $y =$ 5.6

Geometry Given the distance around the shape, find the length of the unknown side.

21. Total distance: 31.9 cm $w =$ 12.4 cm

10.8 cm, w, 8.7 cm

22. Total distance: 62.5 m $v =$ 21.9 m

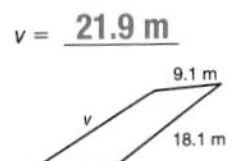

23. Yesterday Stephanie spent \$38.72 on new shoes and \$23.19 on computer software. When she was finished, she had \$31.18. How much money did she have before she went shopping? \$93.09

24. The owner of a used music store bought a compact disc for \$4.70 and sold it for \$9.45. Write and solve an equation to find the profit.
\$4.70 + p = \$9.45; p = \$4.75

RETEACHING

Name ______________________ **Alternative Lesson 3-7**

Solving Decimal Equations: Addition and Subtraction

You can solve addition and subtraction equations involving decimals by using mental math. You can also work backward to solve for the variable.

— Example —

Solve $x + 5.3 = 6.6$.

Step 1: Think: What number plus 5.3 equals 6.6? $x + 5.3 = 6.6$

Step 2: Use mental math. $\mathbf{1.3} + 5.3 = 6.6$

Step 3: Check to see that the equation is true. $6.6 = 6.6$ ✓

You could also work backward to solve for x.

When you work backward, you start with the answer. To get to the beginning, you can subtract the known addend. This will give you the same answer. $6.6 - 5.3 = 1.3$

In the equation $x + 5.3 = 6.6$, x is equal to 1.3.

Try It Solve $a - 5.2 = 3.1$.

a. What number minus 5.2 equals 3.1? 8.3 so $a =$ 8.3

b. Show that the equation is true. $8.3 - 5.2 = 3.1$

Solve $0.5 + b = 2.3$.

c. What number plus 0.5 equals 2.3? 1.8 so $b =$ 1.8

d. Show that the equation is true. $0.5 + 1.8 = 2.3$

Solve $8.6 - c = 4.3$.

e. What number subtracted from 8.6 equals 4.3? 4.3 so $c =$ 4.3

f. Show that the equation is true. $8.6 - 4.3 = 4.3$

Solve.

g. $d + 1.8 = 2.9$ $d = 1.1$

h. $2.9 + e = 3.5$ $e = 0.6$

i. $\$1.95 + f = \$2.15$ $f = \$0.20$

j. $g + \$0.75 = \$1.00$ $g = \$0.25$

k. $h - 2.4 = 2.1$ $h = 4.5$

l. $0.35 - j = 0.25$ $j = 0.1$

m. $k - 0.12 = 0.24$ $k = 0.36$

n. $0.45 - y = 0.44$ $y = 0.01$

Exercise Notes

■ Exercise 35

Problem-Solving Tip You may wish to use Teaching Tool Transparencies 2 and 3: Guided Problem Solving, pages 1–2.

Exercise Answers

30. $\$66.75 - \$46.25 = p$; $p = \$20.50$

31. $\$26.49 + \$18.50 = s$; $s = \$44.99$

33. a. 6

b. $x + 12.8 = 18.8$
$x + 16 = 22$
$x + 19.2 = 25.2$

c. Possible answer:
$x + 1.1 = 9.1$
$x + 1.2 = 9.2$
$x + 1.3 = 9.3$

39. Five hundred sixty billion, three hundred twenty-six million, seven hundred thousand

40. Four million, nine hundred eighty-three thousand, two hundred twenty-eight

41. Two trillion, eight hundred ninety-two billion, three hundred sixty-two thousand, four hundred twenty-one

42. Seven hundred sixty-three thousand, two hundred eighteen

Alternate Assessment

Self Assessment Have students make a list of any equations they solved incorrectly in this lesson. Then have them write a sentence or two explaining their error, followed by the correct solution.

▶ Quick Quiz

Solve.

1. $m + 3.1 = 7.5$ 4.4
2. $y - 5.9 = 10$ 15.9
3. $2.25 + x = 5.55$ 3.3
4. $50.9 - x = 30.9$ 20

Available on Daily Transparency 3-7

Career When a store buys something at one price and then sells it at a higher price, the difference in prices is called the ***profit***. For Exercises 30 and 31, write and solve an equation for the situation.

30. A store owner obtained a jacket for \$46.25 and sold it for \$66.75. What was the profit?

31. A pair of tennis shoes cost the store owner \$26.49. She wants to make a profit of \$18.50. What should the selling price be?

Problem Solving and Reasoning

32. Critical Thinking In West Lafayette, the fine for a speeding ticket in dollars is $\$32.62 + x$, where x is the miles per hour over the speed limit.

a. What is the fine for going 38.6 mi/hr in a 25 mi/hr school zone? \$46.22

b. Ed was fined \$50.50 for speeding in this school zone. How fast was he traveling? 42.88 mi/hr

33. Communicate Study the pattern:

$x + 3.2 = 9.2$

$x + 6.4 = 12.4$

$x + 9.6 = 15.6$

a. What is the value of x?

b. What are the next three equations in this pattern?

c. Invent your own pattern using addition of decimals and $x = 8$.

34. Critical Thinking Maurice has 30 m of fence to make a rectangular dog run. The width can only be 3.75 m because of the shape of his yard. What is the maximum length of the dog run? 11.25 m

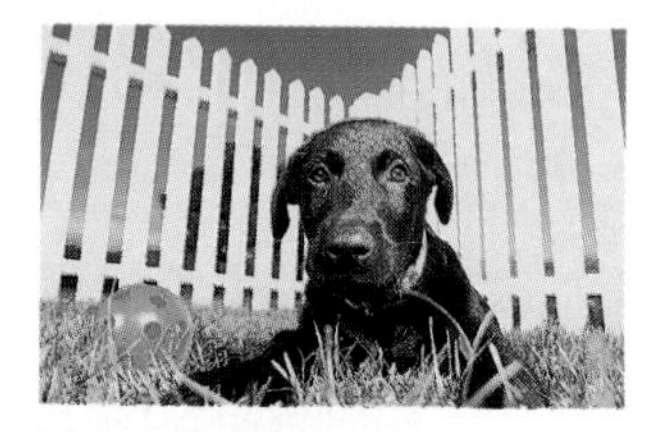

35. Choose a Strategy Brandi, Molly, and Leah have a total of \$4.25. Brandi has a dollar more than Molly. Brandi has twice as much as Leah. How much money does each girl have? Brandi: \$2.10; Molly: \$1.10; Leah: \$1.05

Problem Solving STRATEGIES
- Look for a Pattern
- Make an Organized List
- Make a Table
- Guess and Check
- Work Backward
- Use Logical Reasoning
- Draw a Diagram
- Solve a Simpler Problem

PROBLEM SOLVING 3-7

Mixed Review

Order from least to greatest. *[Lesson 3-3]*

36. 4.663, 4.664, 4.65 — 4.65, 4.663, 4.664
37. 0.123, 0.672, 1.784 — 0.123, 0.672, 1.784
38. 32.5, 32.67, 32.495 — 32.495, 32.5, 32.67

Write each number in word form. *[Lesson 2-1]*

39. 560,326,700,000 **40.** 4,983,228 **41.** 2,892,000,362,421 **42.** 763,218

PROBLEM SOLVING

Name ______________________ **Guided Problem Solving 3-7**

GPS **PROBLEM 28, STUDENT PAGE 171**

Jorge won a cash prize in a contest. He donated half of the money to his Boy Scout troop. Then he spent \$19.49 on a computer game and put the rest, \$30.51 into his savings account. How much money did he win?

— Understand —

1. What are you asked to find? How much money Jorge won.
2. What was the first thing Jorge did with his winnings? Gave half to his Boy Scout troop.
3. What were the second and third things Jorge did with his winnings? Spent \$19.49 on computer game and saved \$30.51.

— Plan —

4. Which strategy will you use to find the answer? a
   a. Work Backward b. Look for a Pattern c. Make a Table
5. Jorge donated half of his winnings to the Boy Scouts. What fraction did he spend on other things? Half.
6. What is the first operation you will use? Addition.

— Solve —

7. How much money did Jorge have before he bought the game? \$50
8. How much did Jorge win in the contest? \$100

— Look Back —

9. What other strategies could you use to find the answer? Possible answer: Guess and Check; Solve a Simpler Problem.

SOLVE ANOTHER PROBLEM

Hector received some cash for his birthday. He spent \$14.30 on a CD and donated \$25.00 to a charity. He put half of what was left into his savings account. He has \$17.85 left. How much money did he receive on his birthday? \$75

ENRICHMENT

Name ______________________ **Extend Your Thinking 3-7**

Critical Thinking

Use your number sense to complete each puzzle.

1. Solve each equation. Then write your answers in the circles so that the differences between any two circles in a row are the same.

Possible answer:

a. $g + 1.8 = 4.2$ $g = 2.4$
b. $h - 0.5 = 9.7$ $h = 10.2$
c. $5.9 + k = 6.8$ $k = 0.9$
d. $m + 1.819 = 6.519$ $m = 4.7$
e. $15.1 - r = 8.9$ $r = 6.2$
f. $s - 2.5 = 0.4$ $s = 2.9$
g. $10.2 - t = 3.5$ $t = 6.7$
h. $8.1 + w = 14.5$ $w = 6.4$

2. Solve each equation. Then write your answers in the circles so that the sums of any two circles in a row are the same.

Possible answer:

a. $x + 4.3 = 6.5$ $x = 2.2$
b. $y - 1.4 = 1.9$ $y = 3.3$
c. $12.1 - a = 8$ $a = 4.1$
d. $5.6 - z = 2.8$ $z = 2.8$
e. $b + 12.5 = 13.4$ $b = 0.9$
f. $c - 2.9 = 1.7$ $c = 4.6$
g. $7.8 + d = 9.5$ $d = 1.7$
h. $e + 10.6 = 11.0$ $e = 0.4$

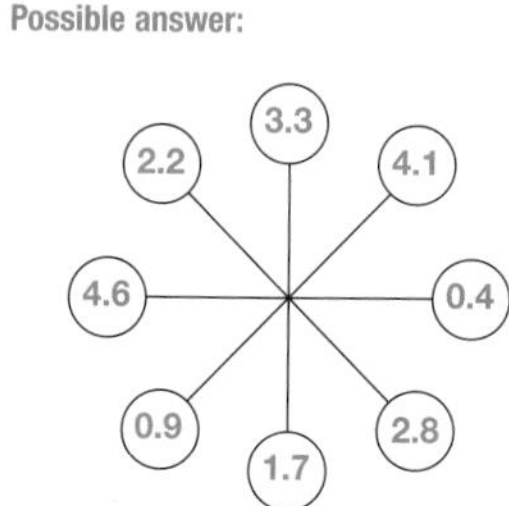

Section 3B Connect

In this section, you've seen that many countries use different types of money. In order to convert one kind of money to another, you need to know the *exchange rate*. You'll have a chance to use exchange rates—and your knowledge of decimals—to plan a trip to five nations.

Getting Your Money's Worth

Country	Basic Unit	Value of One Unit in U.S. Dollars ($)	Number of Units One U.S. Dollar Will Buy
Belgium	Franc	0.03258	30.693
Chile	Peso	0.00243	410.80
China	Yuan	0.12038	8.3071
Colombia	Peso	0.00096	1046.50
India	Rupee	0.02802	35.695
Indonesia	Rupiah	0.00043	2340.70
Ireland	Punt	1.62054	0.61708
Nigeria	Naira	0.01264	79.10
Pakistan	Rupee	0.02807	35.6189
Switzerland	Franc	0.82816	1.2075

1. List five countries from the table that you would like to visit.
2. You plan to spend $200 U.S. in each country. Estimate the amount of each country's money you will get in exchange for your $200 U.S.
3. After your trip, you have 3 units of each country's money left to exchange for U.S. dollars. For each country, state how much the 3 units are worth in U.S. dollars. Round to the nearest cent.
4. How much of the $1000 you started with did you spend?

173

Getting Your Money's Worth

The Point

In *Getting Your Money's Worth* on page 159, students were introduced to the different types of money used throughout the world. Now they will use a foreign exchange rate table to compare foreign currency to the U.S. dollar.

About the Page

- Discuss columns 3 and 4 so that students understand what each represents and how the table is used to compare foreign currency to the U.S. dollar.
- Suggest that students round the number of units one U.S. dollar will buy to the nearest whole number before they estimate.
- Tell students that banks and currency exchanges charge a fee to exchange currency. In these problems, the fees are not included.

Ongoing Assessment

Check that students have estimated the amount of money correctly in Question 2 and determined the correct amount of money in Question 3.

Extension

Have students solve the following problem. On a visit to Belgium you see a gift you would like to purchase for your mother. The price is 350 francs. Use the information on the table to estimate its cost in U. S. dollars. About $11

Answers for Connect:

1. Possible answer: China, Chile, Nigeria, India, Belgium.
2. Possible answer: China 1600 renmimbi; Chile 82000 pesos; Nigeria 16000 naira; India 7000 rupees; Belgium 6000 francs.
3. Possible answer: China $0.36; Chile $0.01; Nigeria $0.04; India $0.08; Belgium $0.10.
4. Possible answer: $997.40

3B Review

Review Correlation

Item(s)	Lesson(s)
1–3	3-5
4–10	3-1
11–16	3-6
17–19	3-7
20	3-6

Test Prep

Test-Taking Tip

Tell students that a good night's rest the night before a test helps them to concentrate and do their best work. In this problem, the numbers differ by the placement of a decimal point, a difference that can be easily missed by a tired student.

Section 3B Review

Measurement Estimate the height to the nearest tenth of a centimeter.

1. 2.7 cm

2. 2.9 cm

3. 3.3 cm

Write each number in decimal form.

4. thirty-five hundredths 0.35 **5.** two and five tenths 2.5 **6.** sixty-four thousandths 0.064

7. 0.88

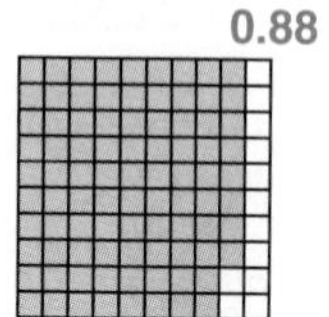

8. 0.64

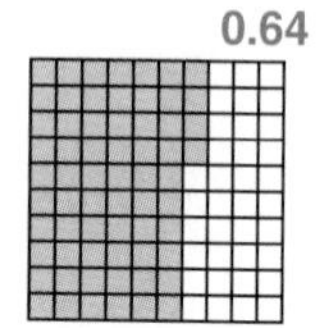

9. 0.03

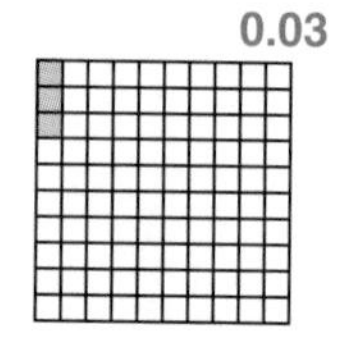

10. 0.9

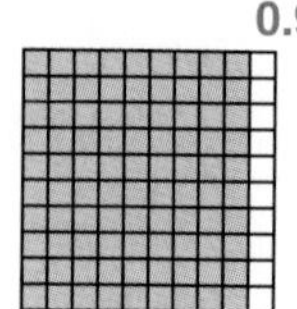

Simplify.

11. $4.5 + 23.9$ 28.4 **12.** $8.65 - 4.2$ 4.45 **13.** $3.05 + 2.111$ 5.161 **14.** $6.01 - 2.222$ 3.788

Geometry Find the distance around the shape.

15. 13.776 cm

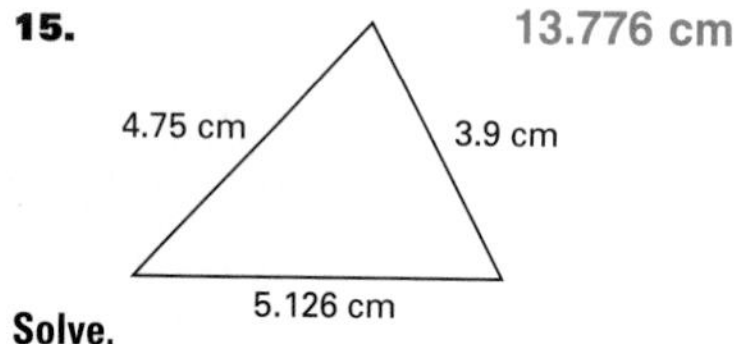

16. 55.6 cm

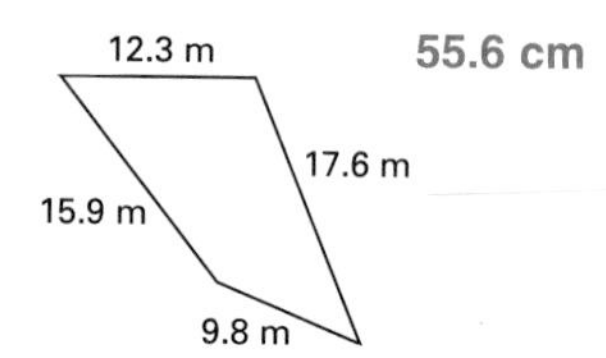

Solve.

17. $x - 7.2 = 16.85$ $x = 24.05$ **18.** $y + 12.52 = 19.37$ $y = 6.85$ **19.** $9.8 + n = 27.3$ $n = 17.5$

REVIEW 3B

Test Prep

Estimation can help to confirm that you've done the problem correctly as well as help eliminate unreasonable answers.

20. Choose the correct answer for $9.56 + 5.77$. C

Ⓐ 0.1533 Ⓑ 1.533 Ⓒ 15.33 Ⓓ 153.3

Resources

Practice Masters
Section 3B Review

Assessment Sourcebook
Quiz 3B

TestWorks
Test and Practice Software

PRACTICE

Name ______________________ Practice

Section 3B Review

Estimate the length to the nearest tenth of a centimeter.

1. 4.2 2. 0.7

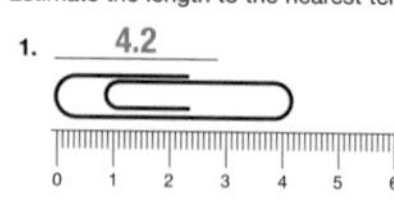

Write each number in decimal form.

3. eight and thirty-two hundredths 8.32
4. sixty-five thousandths 0.065

Simplify.

5. $8.73 - 5.2$ 3.53 6. $12.3 + 6.84$ 19.14 7. $21.37 - 6.41$ 14.96

Find the distance around the shape.

8. 65.11 cm 9. 82.64 cm 10. 30.34 m

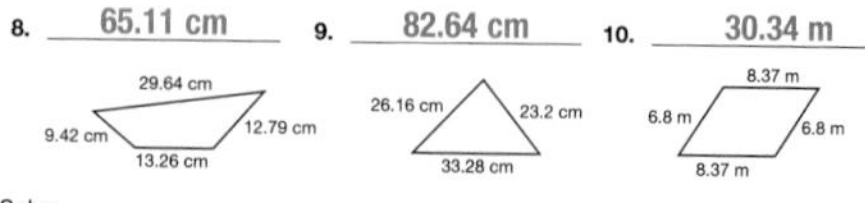

Solve.

11. $c + 3.4 = 7.5$ $c =$ 4.1 12. $13.2 - p = 9.7$ $p =$ 3.5 13. $15 + h = 24.3$ $h =$ 9.3

14. Rick has $100 in his wallet. He wants to buy a clock for $34, a comforter for $44, and a pair of jeans for $24. Since he has estimated the sum as $30 + $40 + $20 = $90, he is confident that he has enough money for his purchases. Do you agree? Explain. *[Lesson 2-2]*

No. He rounded down. The actual sum is $102.

15. Jennifer bought some stock for $24 per share. For the next 6 months, the stock increased in value each month by $3 per share. How much was each share worth 6 months after she bought it? *[Lesson 2-9]* $42

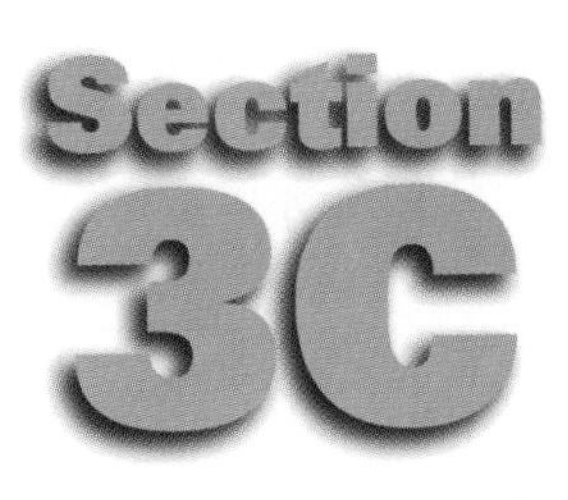

Multiplying and Dividing with Decimals

Visit **www.teacher.mathsurf.com** for links to lesson plans from teachers and other professionals, NCTM information, and other sites.

LESSON PLANNING GUIDE

Student Edition / Ancillaries*

LESSON		MATERIALS	VOCABULARY	DAILY	OTHER
	Section 3C Opener				
3-8	**Multiplying a Whole Number by a Decimal**	10 x 10 grids, colored pencils		3-8	Teaching Tool Trans. 11 Lesson Enhancement Trans. 10
3-9	**Multiplying a Decimal by a Decimal**	10 x 10 grids, colored pencils		3-9	Teaching Tool Trans. 11 *Interactive CD-ROM Lesson*
3-10	**Dividing by a Whole Number**	tenths grids	dividend, divisor, quotient	3-10	Teaching Tool Trans. 12 Ch. 3 Project Master
3-11	**Dividing by a Decimal**	tenths grids		3-11	Teaching Tool Trans. 12
3-12	**Solving Decimal Equations: Multiplication and Division**			3-12	Teaching Tool Trans. 2, 3 Technology Master 15
	Connect				Lesson Enhancement Trans. 11 Interdisc. Team Teaching 3C
	Review				Practice 3C; Quiz 3C; *TestWorks*
	Extend Key Ideas				
	Chapter 3 Summary and Review				
	Chapter 3 Assessment				Ch. 3 Tests Forms A–F *TestWorks*; Ch. 3 Letter Home
	Cumulative Review, Chapters 1–3				Cumulative Review Ch. 1–3 Quarterly Test Ch. 1–3

* Daily Ancillaries include Practice, Reteaching, Problem Solving, Enrichment, and Daily Transparency. Teaching Tool Transparencies are in *Teacher's Toolkits*. Lesson Enhancement Transparencies are in *Overhead Transparency Package*.

SKILLS TRACE

LESSON	SKILL	FIRST INTRODUCED GR. 4	GR. 5	GR. 6	DEVELOP	PRACTICE/ APPLY	REVIEW
3-8	**Multiplying whole numbers by decimals.**		✘		pp. 176–178	pp. 179–180	pp. 198, 200, 203, 439
3-9	**Multiplying two decimals.**		✘		pp. 181–182	pp. 183–184	pp. 200, 203, 274, 447
3-10	**Dividing decimals by whole numbers.**		✘		pp. 185–187	pp. 188–189	pp. 200, 203, 452
3-11	**Dividing decimals by decimals.**			✘ p. 190	pp. 190–192	pp. 193–194	pp. 200, 203, 284, 452
3-12	**Solving decimal equations using multiplication and division.**			✘ p. 195	pp. 195–196	pp. 197–198	pp. 200, 203, 292

CONNECTED MATHEMATICS

Investigation 6 in the unit *Bits and Pieces II (Using Rational Numbers)*, from the **Connected Mathematics** series, can be used with Section 3C.

INTERDISCIPLINARY TEAM TEACHING

Math and Science/Technology

(Worksheet pages 17–18: Teacher pages T17–T18)

In this lesson, students use decimals to prepare prescriptions.

Name ______________ *Math and Science/Technology*

Prescription Decoders

Use decimals to prepare prescriptions.

Pharmacists do a lot more than just read doctors' prescriptions and count out pills. Look at the following example of a pharmacist's duties to discover how decimals play an important part in a pharmacist's job.

A prescription written by a doctor states that a young child should receive 0.33 of a teaspoon of a certain medicine four times each day for ten days. The pharmacist must use her math skills to correctly prepare the prescription.

First, the pharmacist remembers that there are five milliliters in a teaspoon. She multiplies 5 × 0.33 to find out how many milliliters are in 0.33 of a teaspoon. The answer is 1.65 milliliters. Since the child needs the medicine four times each day, the pharmacist multiplies 4 × 1.65. The answer is 6.6 milliliters. Finally, the pharmacist multiplies 10 × 6.6 since the child needs the medicine for ten days. The answer is 66 milliliters. The pharmacist then fills a bottle with 66 milliliters of the liquid medicine.

Pharmacists are members of the medical profession. They work with doctors to determine how much of a medicine will help a patient most. Several details must be considered, such as the age of the patient, the patient's weight, and other medicines the patient may be taking.

In the United States, people interested in becoming pharmacists go to a pharmacy college for five years. They take many courses, including mathematics. One of the things pharmacists must be good at is converting from one measurement to another, because different doctors write prescriptions in different ways. The following table contains examples of the kinds of conversions pharmacists make every day. Use the table to help you solve some of the problems that follow.

Common Conversions Used by Pharmacists	
20 drops	1 milliliter (mL)
1 teaspoon (tsp)	5 mL
1 tablespoon (tbs)	15 mL
1 fluid ounce (oz)	30 mL

1. a. A child has an earache. His doctor has prescribed a liquid antibiotic and instructed that the antibiotic be used for 7 days even though the infection may seem to go away after only a few days. The prescription states that each dose should equal 6.25 mL. The pharmacist fills a bottle with 150 mL of the antibiotic. How many doses are in the bottle?

150 mL ÷ 6.25 mL/dose =
24 doses

b. If the child's mother gives the child 3 doses a day for 7 days, how many milliliters of the antibiotic will the child get?

6.25 mL/dose × 3 doses/day
× 7 days = 131.25 mL

Name ______________ *Math and Science/Technology*

c. Why do you think the doctor said that the antibiotic should be taken for 7 days even if the infection seemed to go away?

See below.

2. A patient has an eye infection, and her doctor prescribes eye drops for 7 days. The patient will use a total of 8 drops per day. How many milliliters of medicine will the patient need altogether?

(8 drops/day × 7 days) ÷
20 drops/mL = 2.8 mL

3. a. A teenager has acne. Her dermatologist writes a prescription for three small jars of skin cream. Before the pharmacist can dispense each jar of cream, however, he must prepare it by mixing 3 mL of ethyl alcohol with a powdered medicine used to treat acne. Then he mixes the solution with a type of gel and places the mixture in a jar. If it takes 23.3 g of powder to make one jar of cream, how many grams will the pharmacist use to make three jars?

3 × 23.3 g = 69.9 g

b. How many milliliters of ethyl alcohol will the pharmacist use to make the three jars?

3 mL × 3 jars = 9 mL

4. How is a knowledge of decimals helpful to a pharmacist?

See below.

5. a. A pharmacist reads on a medicine's label that a patient with a throat infection must take 1.5 tsp of an antibiotic per day for each 2.5 kg of body weight. The pharmacist is preparing the medicine for a child who weighs 15 kg. How many teaspoons will the child need per day?

(15 kg ÷ 2.5 kg) ×
1.5 tsp/day = 9 tsp per day

b. The child must take the medicine for 7 days. How many milliliters will the pharmacist put into the medicine bottle?

(9 tsp/day × 5 mL/tsp) ×
7 days = 315 mL

6. A young girl had a mild allergic reaction to penicillin, so her doctor prescribes 0.75 oz of another medicine that will stop the reaction. How many milliliters of medicine should the pharmacist give the girl?

0.75 oz × 30 mL/oz =
22.5 mL

7. The labels on drug, vitamin, cosmetic, and food containers often show the percentages of ingredients in a container. Since "percent" means per hundred, a percent can easily be converted into a decimal. For example, 75% = 0.75. Read product labels that include percents. Convert to decimals and make pie charts to compare amounts of each ingredient. Which ingredient is present in the greatest amount?

See below.

Answers

1. c. Some of the germs might still be alive and cause the earache to come back.

4. Students' answers will vary. Students may suggest that pharmacists have to convert from one type of measurement to another, they have to mix medicines, and they have to divide medicines. Often these jobs include decimals.

7. Answers will vary. The most common ingredient often is a carrier or filler such as water, alcohol, or starch.

BIBLIOGRAPHY

FOR TEACHERS

Burril, Gail and John C. *Data Analysis and Statistics Across the Curriculum.* Reston, VA: NCTM, 1992.

Cassutt, Michael. *Who's Who in Space.* New York, NY: Macmillan, 1993.

Shaw, Jean. *From the File Treasury.* Reston, VA: NCTM, 1991.

Spangler, David. *Math for Real Kids.* Glenview, IL: Good Year Books, 1997.

FOR STUDENTS

Rubel, David. *The United States in the 19th Century.* New York, NY: Scholastic Timelines, 1996.

Section 3C

SECTION 3C

Multiplying and Dividing with Decimals

▶ History Link ▶ Geography Link ▶ www.mathsurf.com/6/ch3/OR_Trail

Trials and Trails

Imagine that your family is driving from Missouri to Oregon.

"Dad, how long until we get to Oregon?"

"About two months."

"Can we ride inside the car today?"

"Don't be silly. If we do that, where will we put our stuff?"

"We're out of food."

"If we walk quickly, we should be at the next store tomorrow. Ask Mom for a vinegar drink."

"We left Mom in Nebraska when she got sick."

Does this sound like an odd conversation?

If you replace the word car with wagon, it could be an ordinary conversation for pioneers on the Oregon Trail.

In the 1800s, more than a quarter of a million people traveled this dangerous trail to the western United States. They faced disease and harsh weather while walking this 2000-mile trail with nothing more than a wagon and a team of oxen. Fortunately, those early pioneers had one advanced tool at their disposal: mathematics.

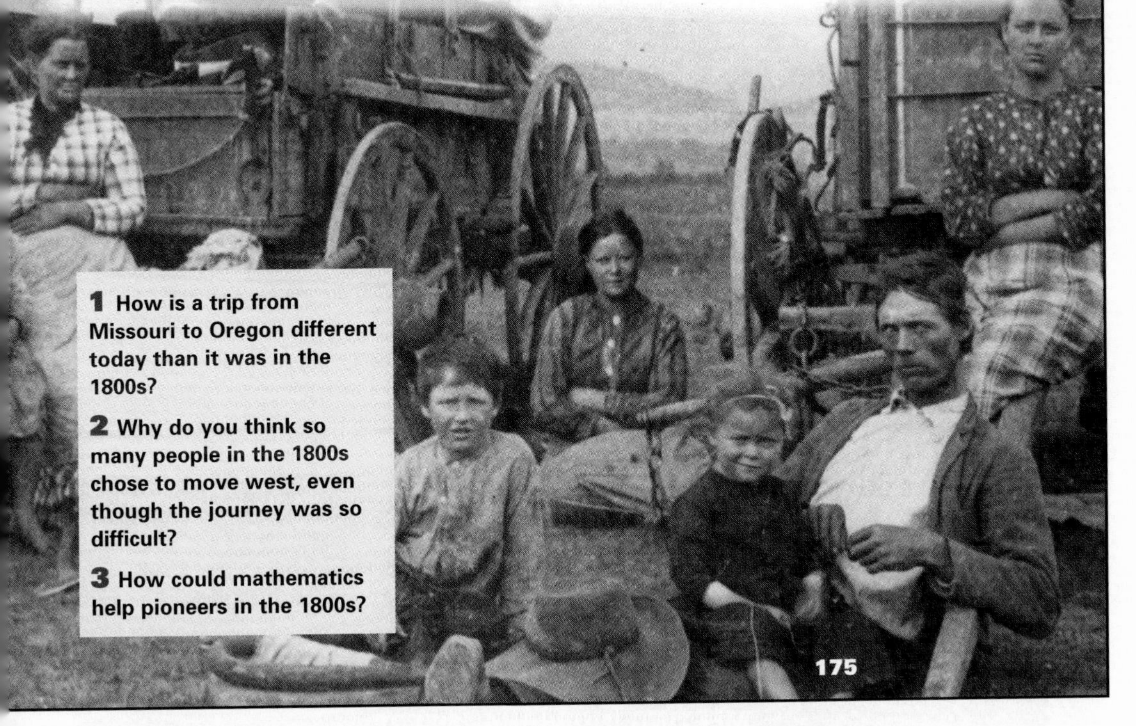

1 How is a trip from Missouri to Oregon different today than it was in the 1800s?

2 Why do you think so many people in the 1800s chose to move west, even though the journey was so difficult?

3 How could mathematics help pioneers in the 1800s?

175

Where are we now?

In Section 3B, students learned how to

- estimate sums, differences, products, and quotients with decimals.
- add and subtract decimals.
- solve addition and subtraction equations involving decimals.

Where are we going?

In Section 3C, students will

- multiply and divide using decimals.
- use mental math to solve multiplication and division equations with decimals.
- solve decimal equations with multiplication and division.

Theme: The Oregon Trail

World Wide Web

If your class has access to the World Wide Web, you might want to use the information found at the Web site address given. The interdisciplinary links relate to topics discussed in this section.

About the Page

This page introduces the theme of the section, the Oregon Trail, and discusses the problems faced by the pioneers traveling the trail.

Ask ...

- Do you think you could have survived the trip over the Oregon Trail?
- What kind of food do you think they had?

Extensions

The following activities do not require access to the World Wide Web.

History
Travel on the Oregon Trail was a test of strength and endurance. Have students research the problems faced by these pioneers and report their findings to the class.

Geography
The Oregon Trail was the longest of the great overland routes used in the westward expansion of the United States. Have students determine the route and the states through which it passed. Ask students to draw the Oregon Trail on a map.

Answers for Questions

1. Possible answer: We have paved roads and cars.
2. Possible answer: There was unclaimed land and the promise of money.
3. Possible answer: Mathematics was used to figure distances and food rationing.

Connect

On page 199, students will compute time and mileage as they plan a backpacking trip.

3-8 Lesson Organizer

Objective

- Multiply a whole number by a decimal.

Materials

- Explore: 10 x 10 Grids, colored pencils

NCTM Standards

- 1–4, 7

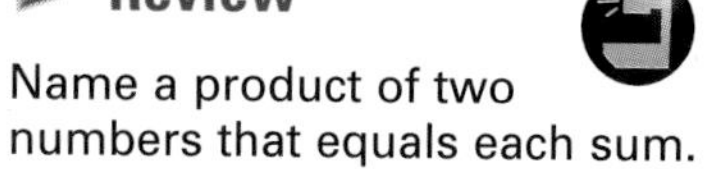

Review

Name a product of two numbers that equals each sum.

1. 2 + 2 + 2 + 2 4 × 2
2. 7 + 7 + 7 3 × 7
3. 6 + 6 + 6 + 6 + 6 5 × 6
4. 5 + 5 + 5 + 5 + 5 + 5 6 × 5

Available on Daily Transparency 3-8

1 Introduce

Explore

You may wish to use Teaching Tool Transparency 11: 10 × 10 Grids with **Explore**.

The Point
Students model multiplication of whole numbers by decimals to see how decimal multiplication is like whole number multiplication.

Ongoing Assessment
Check that students understand that they first color the tenths as many times as the whole number, and then the hundredths as many times as the whole number.

For Groups That Finish Early
Find other pairs of factors that have the same product as Step1a.
Possible answers: 5 × 0.12, 6 × 0.10, 3 × 0.20, 4 × 0.15

Answers for Explore
1. a. b.

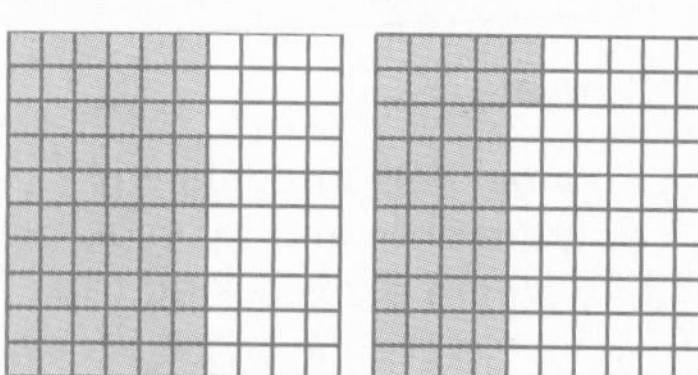

3-8 Multiplying a Whole Number by a Decimal

You'll Learn ...
- how to multiply a whole number by a decimal

... How It's Used
Civil engineers multiply with decimals to find how much weight a bridge can support.

▶ Lesson Link You know how to multiply whole numbers, and you know how to add decimals. Now you'll multiply a whole number by a decimal. ◀

Explore Multiplying a Whole Number by a Decimal

You Too Can Be a Model Student!

Materials: Hundreds squares, Colored pencils

Multiplying a Whole Number by a Decimal

- Color the tenths for the decimal number. Do this as many times as the whole number.
- Color the hundredths for the decimal number. Do this as many times as the whole number.
- Describe the number modeled in the grid.

$$\begin{array}{r} 0.41 \\ \times\ 3 \\ \hline \end{array}$$

1. Model these problems.
   a. 2 × 0.30 **b.** 3 × 0.14 **c.** 4 × 0.44 **d.** 6 × 0.27
   e. 7 × 0.09 **f.** 5 × 0.20 **g.** 9 × 0.22 **h.** 0 × 0.68
2. When you multiply a whole number by a decimal less than one with tenths and no hundredths, does your answer have tenths? Hundredths? Why?
3. When you multiply a whole number by a decimal less than one with hundredths and no tenths, does your answer have tenths? Hundredths? Why?
4. When you multiply a decimal and a whole number, is your answer larger than the whole number or smaller than the whole number?

Learn Multiplying a Whole Number by a Decimal

Recall that multiplication is repeated addition. Multiplying a whole number by a decimal is the same as repeatedly adding the decimal to itself the same number of times as the whole number.

MEETING INDIVIDUAL NEEDS

Resources

- 3-8 Practice
- 3-8 Reteaching
- 3-8 Problem Solving
- 3-8 Enrichment
- 3-8 Daily Transparency
  - Problem of the Day
  - Review
  - Quick Quiz
- Teaching Tool Transparency 11
- Lesson Enhancement Transparency 10

Learning Modalities

Visual Have students make other models similar to the ones in **Explore** to show multiplication of whole numbers by decimals. You may wish to have students color in each set of tenths or hundredths in a different color or with a different pattern. Have them display the models on a bulletin board.

Kinesthetic Have students use play money, including coins as well as paper money. Then have them work together to model multiplication of amounts in dollars and cents by whole numbers.

Inclusion

Some students may have difficulty transferring their knowledge of whole numbers to their work with decimals. Continue to point out the similarities as you work through the exercises.

Example 1

Multiply 2.5 × 3.

One way to find the product is to add 2.5 three times:

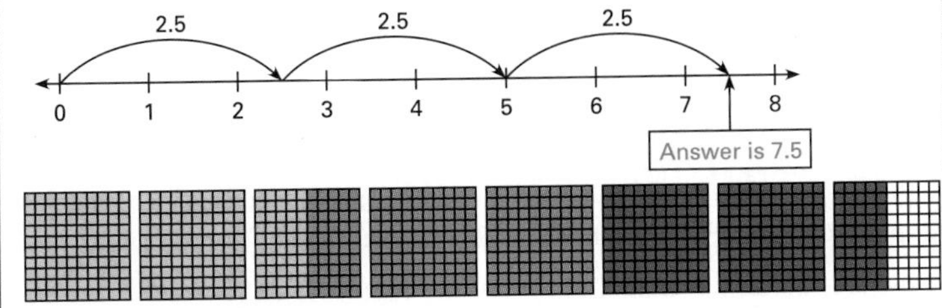

$2.5 \times 3 = 7.5$

> **MENTAL MATH**
> You can also use the Distributive Property. Add the whole numbers three times: $2 + 2 + 2 = 6$. Add the decimal parts three times: $0.5 + 0.5 + 0.5 = 1.5$. Add 6 and 1.5 to get 7.5.

You can use arithmetic to multiply a whole number by a decimal. Multiply as though you were multiplying two whole numbers. Then count the number of digits after the decimal in the decimal factor. Place the decimal in the answer so that the answer has the same number of digits after the decimal.

$$\begin{array}{r} 43 \\ \times\, 0.27 \\ \hline 301 \\ 86 \\ \hline 11.61 \end{array}$$

Example 2

On the Oregon Trail, each family member over 10 years of age was given 1.5 cups of beans per day. When the Conyers family traveled the trail in 1852, all seven members were over 10. How many cups of beans did the family eat each day?

$$\begin{array}{r} 1.5 \\ \times\, 7 \\ \hline 105 \end{array}$$

Multiply as for whole numbers.

There is one digit after the decimal in the decimal factor, 1.5.

The product should have one digit after the decimal → 10.5.

The family ate 10.5 cups of beans per day.

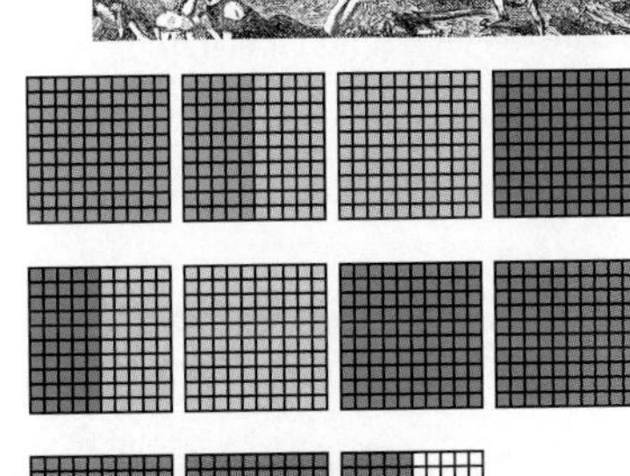

> **History Link**
> People were always searching for faster ways to travel west. During the California gold rush of 1849, some people took ships across the Gulf of Mexico to the Isthmus of Panama. They crossed the land to the Pacific Ocean and took another ship up to California.

Answers for Explore

c.

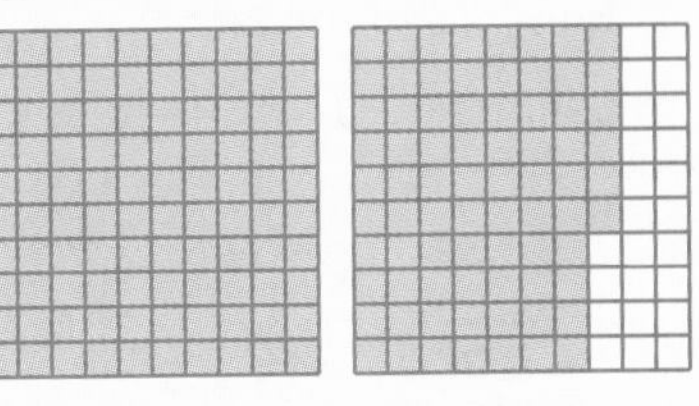

d.

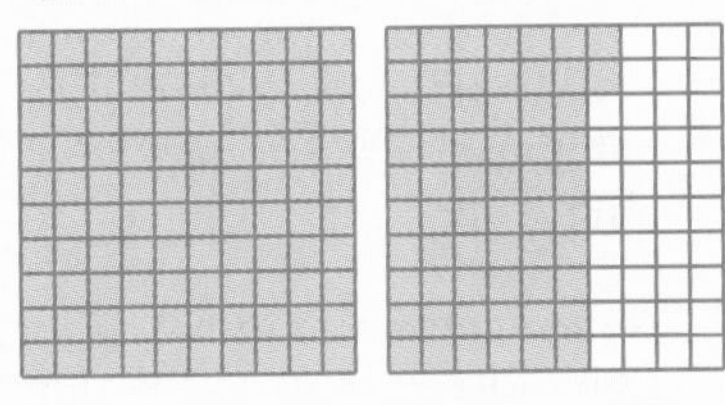

e. f.

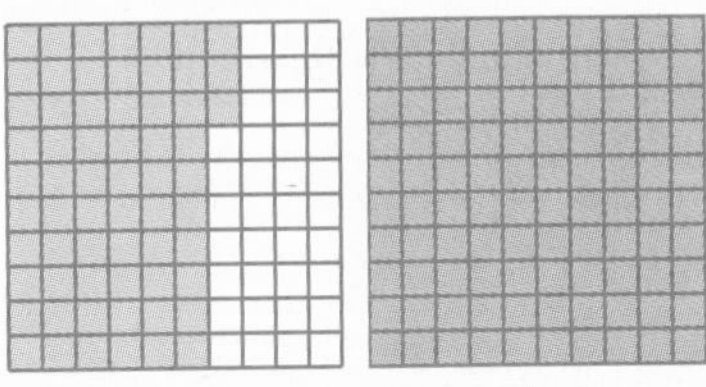

g.

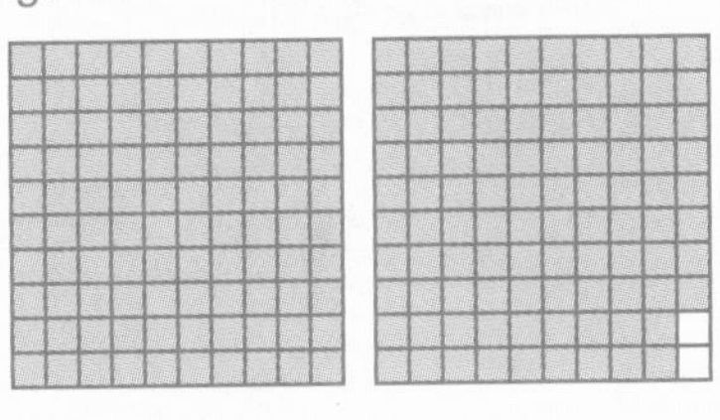

h.

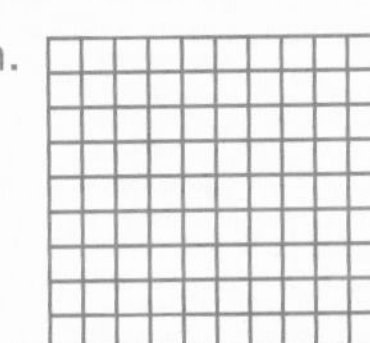

2. It might have tenths; It will not have hundredths.
3. It might have both.
4. Smaller

MATH EVERY DAY

Problem of the Day

Chim has 10 coins, but none of them are half-dollar coins. He can pay the exact price for any purchase from \$0.01 to \$0.99. What coins does Chim have? 3 quarters, 2 dimes, 1 nickel, 4 pennies

Available on Daily Transparency 3-8

An Extension is provided in the transparency package.

Fact of the Day

Lewis and Clark left St. Louis, Missouri, for Oregon with 32 men in the spring of 1804. They did not arrive in Oregon until the spring of 1805.

Mental Math

Do these mentally.

1. $1 \times 8 \times 1 \times 2$ 16
2. $2 \times 5 \times 25 \times 4$ 1000
3. $2 \times 50 \times 6 \times 8$ 4800
4. $4 \times 50 \times 25 \times 2$ 10,000

2 Teach

Learn

You may wish to use Lesson Enhancement Transparency 10 with **Example 1**.

Alternate Examples

1. Multiply 3.2×3.
   Add 3.2 three times:
   $3.2 + 3.2 + 3.2 = 9.6$
   $3.2 \times 3 = 9.6$.
2. Each day a dog is walked 1.2 miles. How many miles is the dog walked in 7 days?

   $$\begin{array}{r} 1.2 \\ \times\, 7 \\ \hline 8.4 \end{array}$$

   The dog is walked 8.4 miles in 7 days.

Alternate Examples

3. Multiply 7.82×39.

   Estimate: $7.82 \times 39 \approx 8 \times 40 = 320$

$$\begin{array}{r} 7.82 \\ \times \quad 39 \\ \hline 7038 \\ 2346\ \\ \hline 304.98 \end{array}$$

4. Find the cost of 1000 photocopies costing \$0.08 apiece.

   $0.08 \times 1000 = ?$

   Annex zeros and move decimal point three places to the right

   0.**080** = 80

   The cost is \$80.

3 Practice and Assess

Check

Answers for Check Your Understanding

1. $5 \times 0.03 = 0.15$ and $5 \times 0.003 = 0.015$. So $5 \times 0.03 > 5 \times 0.003$.
2. 1

Example 3

Multiply 4.71×23.

Estimate: $4.71 \times 23 \approx 5 \times 25 = 125$

$$\begin{array}{r} 4.71 \\ \times\ 23 \\ \hline 1413 \\ 942\ \\ \hline 10833 \end{array}$$

Since there are two digits after the decimal in the decimal factor 4.<u>71</u>, the product is 108.<u>33</u>. The estimate of 125 confirms that this is reasonable.

Remember

If you annex zeros to the end of a decimal, you do not change its value. [Page 148]

Use these shortcuts to multiply a number by 10, 100, or 1000:

- To multiply by 10, move the decimal point one place to the right.
- To multiply by 100, move the decimal point two places to the right.
- To multiply by 1000, move the decimal point three places to the right.

  You may need to annex zeros to the number if there aren't enough places to move the decimal to the right.

Example 4

History Link

Mailing letters in the 1800s by Pony Express was expensive. It cost \$10 to mail a 1-ounce letter. For the same price, you could buy 100 pounds of bacon.

Pony Express riders carried mail in a leather saddle bag called a *mochila*. A rider normally carried about 1000 letters, each weighing 0.6 oz. Find the weight of the mail in a mochila.

$0.6 \times 1000 = ?$

↓ Annex zeros so you can move the decimal point.

$0.600 = 600$

↑ Move decimal point three places to the right.

The weight was about 600 oz.

Try It

Multiply. **a.** 1.2×4 4.8 **b.** 0.6×7 4.2 **c.** 9.813×12 117.756 **d.** 0.62×100 62

Check Your Understanding

1. Which is greater, 5×0.03 or 5×0.003? Explain.
2. A number has three places after the decimal. If you multiply the number by 100, how many decimal places will the product have?

MEETING MIDDLE SCHOOL CLASSROOM NEEDS

Tips from Middle School Teachers

I like to use catalogs of various types. They can be used in a variety of situations involving operations with decimals. Catalogs of specific interest to students are sports, music, clothing, and holiday catalogs. Ask students to bring to class any catalogs they might receive in the mail.

Team Teaching

Work with a science teacher. Discuss why decimals are so useful when using the metric system.

Social Studies Connection

On April 3, 1860, the Pony Express began fast overland mail service between Missouri and California, nearly 2,000 miles. Riders changed horses every 7 to 20 miles. Delivery took 8 to 10 days. The service ended when the telegraph line to California was completed in October 1861.

3-8 Exercises and Applications

Practice and Apply

1. **Getting Started** Choose the equation that the grid models.

a.

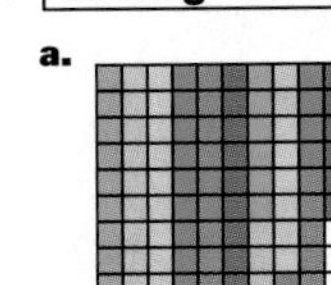

b.

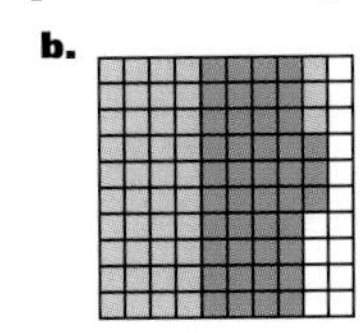

c.

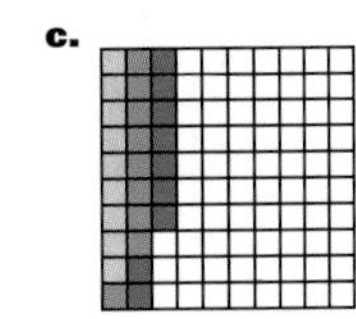

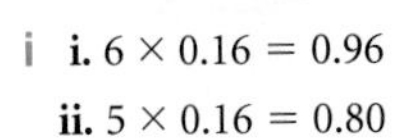

a. i **i.** $6 \times 0.16 = 0.96$ **ii.** $5 \times 0.16 = 0.80$

b. ii **i.** $2 \times 0.19 = 0.38$ **ii.** $2 \times 0.43 = 0.86$

c. i **i.** $3 \times 0.09 = 0.27$ **ii.** $6 \times 0.03 = 0.18$

Insert a decimal in each answer to make the equation true.

2. $76.89 \times 23 = 176847$ 1768.47 **3.** $4 \times 8.53 = 3412$ 34.12 **4.** $5.6 \times 72 = 4032$ 403.2

5. $3.004 \times 8 = 24032$ 24.032 **6.** $9 \times 3.33 = 2997$ 29.97 **7.** $14 \times 62.345 = 87283$ 872.83

Multiply.

8. 10×3.578 35.78 **9.** 100×3.578 357.8 **10.** 1000×3.578 3578 **11.** 8.7×6 52.2

12. 13.9×7 97.3 **13.** 143×6.1 872.3 **14.** 448×0.2 89.6 **15.** $\$86.15 \times 7$ $603.05

16. $\$6.85 \times 19$ $130.15 **17.** 415×0.031 12.865 **18.** 5.283×46 243.018 **19.** 8.07×10 80.7

20. 100×74.4 7440 **21.** 3.85×1000 3850 **22.** 10×0.059 0.59 **23.** $\$25.39 \times 100$ $2539

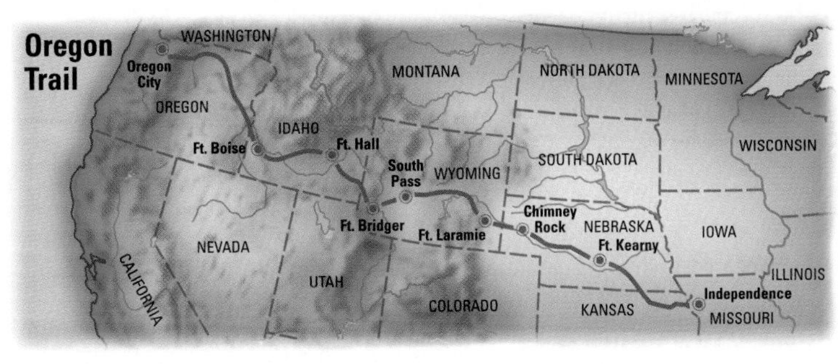

24. In 1843, in Independence, Missouri, Teresa bought 6 chocolate bars for her family. Each bar was 0.8 oz. How many ounces did she buy? 4.8

25. In 1847, at St. Joseph, Missouri, Reuben sold bushels of dried apples for $1.50 a bushel. How much would 4 bushels cost? $6

3-8 Exercises and Applications

Assignment Guide

- Basic
  1–24, 27, 30–42 evens
- Average
  2–28, 31–41 odds
- Enriched
  8–32, 34–42 evens

Exercise Notes

Exercises 2–7

Error Prevention Watch for students who count decimal places before the decimal point to determine where to place the decimal point. For example, in Exercise 2, they would write 17.6847 instead of 1768.47. Remind them to count decimal places after the decimal point.

Exercise 24

Extension Have students find the weights of several common candy bars and then find the weight in ounces for 6 such bars.

PRACTICE

Name ____________________

Practice 3-8

Multiplying a Whole Number by a Decimal

Insert a decimal point in the answer to make the equation true.

1. $12 \times 8.76 = 105.12$ 2. $4.67 \times 7 = 32.69$ 3. $3.375 \times 8 = 27.000$

4. $7 \times 2.831 = 19.817$ 5. $9.26 \times 15 = 138.90$ 6. $2.36 \times 21 = 49.56$

7. $10 \times 4.63 = 46.30$ 8. $17 \times 9.37 = 159.29$ 9. $5.63 \times 8 = 45.04$

10. $7.41 \times 16 = 118.56$ 11. $1.01 \times 7 = 7.07$ 12. $3.94 \times 4 = 15.76$

Multiply.

13. 2.76×10 27.6 14. 2.76×100 276 15. 2.76×1000 2,760 16. 8.137×20 162.74

17. 61×4.731 288.591 18. 15.167×15 227.505 19. 6×26.34 158.04 20. 18.5×3 55.5

21. 10×18.438 184.38 22. $\$3.94 \times 5$ $19.70 23. 31.2×1000 31,200 24. 4×16.81 67.24

25. 2×18.3876 36.7752 26. 13×5.61 72.93 27. 6.25×12 75 28. 4.39×10 43.9

29. 4.161×5 20.805 30. $8 \times \$11.72$ $93.76 31. 14×31.347 438.858 32. 17.4×9 156.6

33. 17×3.17 53.89 34. 5.631×11 61.941 35. 1000×9.34 9,340 36. 8×3.812 30.496

37. A can contains 0.17 kg of tomato paste. How much tomato paste would be in 8 cans? 1.36 kg

38. In a typical day, Cheryl works for 8 hours at the rate of $7.61 per hour. She also buys lunch for $5.43. How much does she have at the end of the day? $55.45

RETEACHING

Name ____________________

Alternative Lesson 3-8

Multiplying a Whole Number by a Decimal

When you multiply a whole number by a decimal, multiply as though you were multiplying two whole numbers. Then count the number of digits after the decimal in the factors. Write the answer with the same number of decimal places after the decimal point.

Example

Multiply 0.45×3.

One way to find a product is to use repeated addition.

A second way to find the product is to multiply as though you were multiplying two whole numbers.

Count the number of digits after the decimal point in each factor. There are two digits after the decimal point in 0.45. There are no digits after the decimal point in 3.

Multiply.

Place the decimal point. Since the two factors have a total of two digits after the decimal point, the product will also have two digits after the decimal point.

0.45 ← 2 decimal places
× 3 ← 0 decimal places
1.35 ← 2 decimal places

So, $0.45 \times 3 = 01.35$.

Try It Multiply 12.79×5.

a. The decimal factor is 12.79.

b. How many decimal places will be in the answer? 2 decimal places.

c. What is the product? 63.95

Multiply.

d. 32.4×6 194.4 e. 5.6×4 22.4

f. 324×0.28 90.72 g. 25.98×12 311.76

h. 1.65×10 16.5 i. 1.11×34 37.74

j. 25×5.7 142.5 k. 8.111×9 72.999

l. 18×1.41 25.38 m. 6×3.422 20.532

n. 1.02×6 6.12 o. 9×20.4 183.6

Reteaching

Activity

Materials: Newspapers

- Work in pairs. Use newspaper advertisements. Make a list of costs of several items that you would need to buy if you were purchasing refreshments for a class party.
- Then decide the quantity of each item you would need to buy and determine the total cost for that item. For example, 3 cans of lemonade at $1.49 each would cost $3 \times 1.49 = \$4.47$.
- Find the total cost for the party.

Exercise Answers

29. Yes, he only needs $16.20.
31. $231 \times 6 = 1386$, $23.1 \times 6 = 138.6$, $2.31 \times 6 = 13.86$; As the decimal moves in the first factor, it moves in the answer.
32. Possible answer: Add $2.75 + 2.75 + 2.75 + 2.75 + 2.75 + 2.75 and explain that multiplication is the same as repeated addition.
35. 5540
36. 79,200,000
37. 14,200
38. 13,970,000,000
39. 928,000
40. 7,000,000,000,000
41. 1,932,000
42. 254,000,000

Alternate Assessment

You may want to use the *Interactive CD-ROM Journal* with this assessment.

Journal Have students describe a situation that would require multiplying a decimal by a whole number and then show how they would carry out the computation.

Quick Quiz

Multiply.

1. 10×5.67 56.7
2. 1000×5.67 5670
3. 5.18×5 25.9
4. 3.124×14 43.736

Available on Daily Transparency 3-8

26. History Salt was a valuable possession to the travelers of the Oregon Trail. It improved the taste of the food and took little space to store. According to the graph, how much salt did the Olsen family use on July 4? 0.07 lb

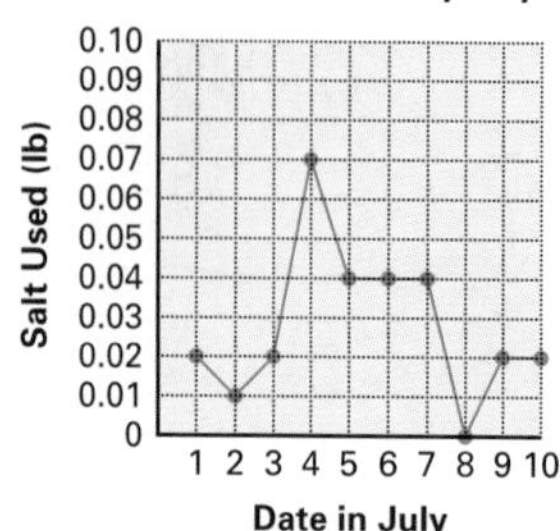

27. **Test Prep** Choose the correct answer for 5.69×29. C

Ⓐ 1.6501 Ⓑ 16.501

Ⓒ 165.01 Ⓓ 16,501

28. History A wagon train on the Oregon Trail averaged 17.3 miles per day across the plains. How far did it get in a week? 121.1 miles

Problem Solving and Reasoning

29. Critical Thinking Jamie wants to buy 5.4 feet of wood for a bookshelf. The wood costs $3 a foot, and Jamie has $17.50. Does he have enough for all the wood he wants? Explain.

31. Communicate Compare the products of 231×6, 23.1×6, and 2.31×6. Explain where the decimal is in each answer.

32. Communicate You meet someone along the trail who never learned how to multiply. He wants to buy 6 wagon wheels from you at $2.75 each. How would you explain to him that $6 \times \$2.75 = \$16.50$?

30. Choose a Strategy GPS Andrea drinks 54.3 ounces of milk every week. She also drinks a 6-ounce can of orange juice and 8 glasses of water every day. If she drinks 544.3 ounces of liquid in a week and every glass of water is the same size, how big is each glass of water? 8 oz

Problem Solving STRATEGIES

- Look for a Pattern
- Make an Organized List
- Make a Table
- Guess and Check
- Work Backward
- Use Logical Reasoning
- Draw a Diagram
- Solve a Simpler Problem

PROBLEM SOLVING 3-8

Mixed Review

Order each group of numbers from least to greatest. *[Lesson 2-3]*

33. 34,890,000; 34,891,000; 34,790,001
34,790,001; 34,890,000; 34,891,000

34. 784,983; 784,982; 785,984
784,982; 784,983; 784,984

Write each number in standard form. *[Lesson 3-4]*

35. 5.54×10^3 **36.** 7.92×10^7 **37.** 1.42×10^4 **38.** 1.397×10^{10}

39. 9.28×10^5 **40.** 7×10^{12} **41.** 1.932×10^6 **42.** 2.54×10^8

PROBLEM SOLVING

Name ______________

Guided Problem Solving 3-8

GPS PROBLEM 30, STUDENT PAGE 180

Andrea drinks 54.3 ounces of milk every week. She also drinks a 6-ounce can of orange juice and 8 glasses of water every day. If she drinks 544.3 ounces of liquid in a week and every glass of water is the same size, how big is each glass of water?

— Understand —

1. What are you asked to find? How many ounces in one glass.
2. Circle the data given in ounces per week.
3. Underline the data given in ounces per day.

— Plan —

4. How will you find how much Andrea drinks in one week when you are given the amount she drinks each day? Multiply by 7.
5. How many glasses of water does she drink each day? 8 glasses
6. How many glasses of water does she drink each week? 56 glasses
7. How many ounces of orange juice does she drink each week? 42 oz

— Solve —

8. How many ounces of milk and juice does she drink each week? 96.3 oz
9. Subtract to find how many ounces of water she drinks each week. 448 oz
10. Divide by 56 to find how many ounces each glass of water holds. 8 oz

— Look Back —

11. How can you work backward to check your answer? Multiply 8 oz by 7; multiply 56 by 8; add: 448 + 42 + 54.3 = 544.3; 544.3 oz

SOLVE ANOTHER PROBLEM

Kelsey earns $65.30 every week working at a grocery store and $5 every day walking a neighbor's dog. She also watches her brother for 2 hours every day. If she earns $128.30 each week, how much does she earn each hour she watches her brother? $2

ENRICHMENT

Name ______________

Extend Your Thinking 3-8

Patterns in Numbers

In an arithmetic sequence the change between each term, or number, is the same. In the arithmetic sequence below 0.6 is added to each term to get the next term.

0.4, 1.0, 1.6, 2.2, 2.8, 3.4,...

To find the tenth term in an addition sequence, add the first term and nine times the change between adjacent terms in the sequence. So for the sequence above, you would make the following calculation:

0.4 + 9(0.6) = 0.4 + 5.4 = 5.8

The tenth term in the sequence is 5.8.

You can write this as the formula $x = a + (n - 1)d$, where x is the term you want to find, a is the first term, n is the position of the term you want to find, and d is the change between terms. It can be used to find any term in an addition sequence.

Find the change, the tenth term, and the fiftieth term in each arithmetic sequence.

	Change	Tenth term	Fiftieth term
1. 1.2, 1.7, 2.2,...	+ 0.5	5.7	25.7
2. 0.2, 0.6, 1.0,...	+ 0.4	3.8	19.8
3. 1.3, 1.8, 2.3,...	+ 0.5	5.8	25.8
4. 4.8, 6.2, 7.6,...	+ 1.4	17.4	73.4
5. 10.1, 19.2, 28.3,...	+ 9.1	92	456
6. 0.05, 0.14, 0.23,...	+ 0.09	0.86	4.46
7. 1.06, 1.28, 1.5,...	+ 0.22	3.04	11.84
8. 15, 16.6, 18.2,...	+ 1.6	29.4	93.4
9. 8.8, 15.1, 21.4,...	+ 6.3	65.5	317.5
10. 6.1, 8.3, 10.5,...	+ 2.2	25.9	113.9
11. 9.4, 10.1, 10.8,...	+ 0.7	15.7	43.7
12. 26.53, 29.70, 32.87,...	+ 3.17	55.06	181.86

Multiplying a Decimal by a Decimal

3-9

▶ Lesson Link You know how to multiply a whole number by a decimal. Now you'll multiply a decimal by a decimal, using the same method for placing a decimal point in a product. ◀

You'll Learn ...

■ how to multiply a decimal times a decimal

... How It's Used

Firefighters multiply decimals to determine how much water a hose can spray at a given pressure for a given amount of time.

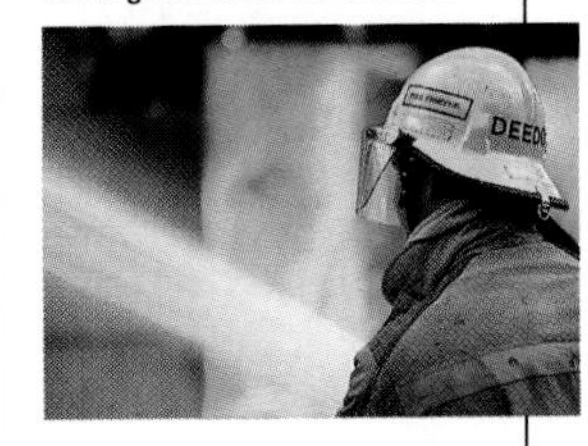

Explore Multiplying a Decimal by a Decimal

Hunting for Hundredths

Materials: Hundreds squares, Colored pencils

Multiplying a Decimal by a Decimal

- Color the first number vertically.
- Color the second number horizontally.
- Describe the section in the grid where the two numbers overlap.

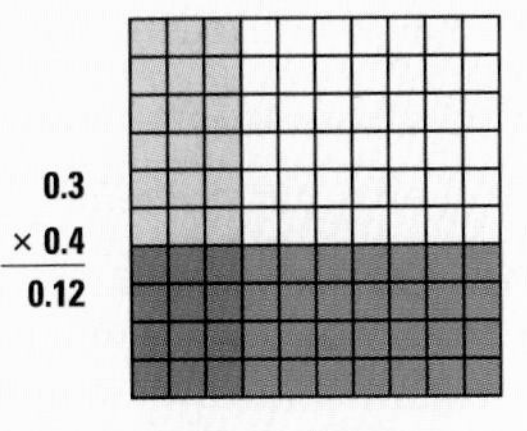

1. Model these problems.

a. 0.3 × 0.2 **b.** 0.6 × 0.6 **c.** 0.8 × 0.3 **d.** 0.4 × 0.7

e. 0.9 × 0.5 **f.** 0.5 × 0.2 **g.** 0.7 × 0.1 **h.** 0.6 × 0.0

2. If you multiply two decimals that only go to tenths, does your answer only go to tenths? Explain.

3. When you multiply two decimal numbers between zero and one, is your answer bigger than both, smaller than both, or bigger than one but smaller than the other?

Learn Multiplying a Decimal by a Decimal

Multiplying a decimal by a decimal is similar to multiplying a decimal by a whole number. Multiply the two numbers as if they were whole numbers. The product of a decimal multiplication problem should have the same number of decimal places as the sum of the number of decimal places in both factors.

$$\begin{array}{r} 4.3 \\ \times\ 2.7 \\ \hline 301 \\ 86\ \ \\ \hline 11.61 \end{array}$$

INTERACTIVE LESSON

3-9 Lesson Organizer

Objective

- Multiply a decimal times a decimal.

Materials

- Explore: 10 x 10 Grids, colored pencils

NCTM Standards

- 1–6, 13

▶ Review

Round to the nearest whole number to estimate each product.

1. 3.9 × 5.1 20
2. 7.88 × 8.01 64
3. 0.89 × 9.91 10
4. 5.78 × 3.1 18

Available on Daily Transparency 3-9

1 Introduce

Explore

You may wish to use Teaching Tool Transparency 11: 10 × 10 Grids with **Explore**.

The Point

Students use a model for multiplying decimals by decimals to understand the placement of the decimal point in the product.

Ongoing Assessment

For Step 1h, watch for students who think that the model shows that the answer is 0.6 rather than 0.

For Groups That Finish Early

How would the model differ from those in **Explore** if you were multiplying a decimal greater than 1 by a decimal less than 1?

Answers for Explore on next page.

MEETING INDIVIDUAL NEEDS

Resources

3-9 Practice
3-9 Reteaching
3-9 Problem Solving
3-9 Enrichment
3-9 Daily Transparency
Problem of the Day
Review
Quick Quiz
Teaching Tool Transparency 11

Interactive CD-ROM Lesson

Learning Modalities

Visual Encourage students to be creative when shading the decimal models in **Explore**. For example, they might color the first number using a wave pattern and the second number using a fish pattern. The overlap would then show fish in waves. Have students display their diagrams on a bulletin board.

Social Have students complete **Explore** in pairs with one person shading the first number vertically and the other person shading the second number horizontally.

English Language Development

Be sure students understand what is meant by annexing zeros. Point out that buildings sometimes have annexes, that is, adjoining portions that were added after the original portion was built.

Answers for Explore

1. a. b.

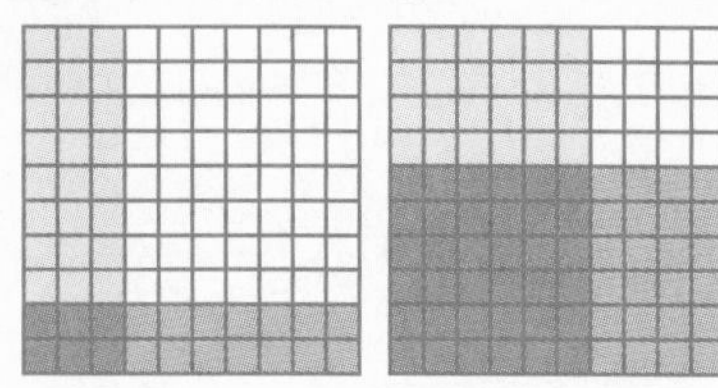

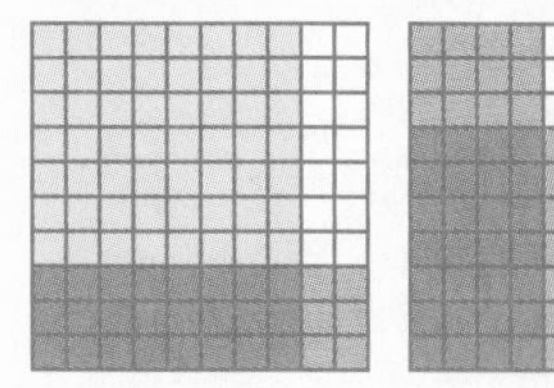

c. d.

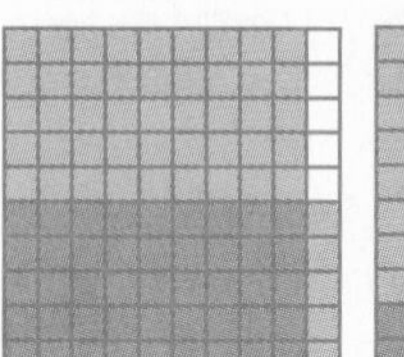

e. f.

g. h.

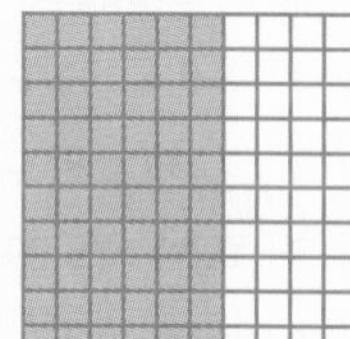

2. No, it could have hundredths; $0.5 \times 0.5 = 0.25$
3. Smaller than both.

2 Teach

Learn

Alternate Examples

1. Multiply: 6.7×4.2

   Estimate: $7 \times 4 = 28$

$$\begin{array}{r} 6.7 \\ \times\ 4.2 \\ \hline 134 \\ 268 \\ \hline 28.14 \end{array}$$

2. Multiply: 0.082×6.1

   Estimate: $0.08 \times 6 = 0.48$

$$\begin{array}{r} 0.082 \\ \times\ 6.1 \\ \hline 82 \\ 492 \\ \hline 0.5002 \end{array}$$

3. Multiply 38×0.1

   $38 \times 0.1 = 3.8$

4. Multiply 9×0.001

   $9 \times 0.001 = 0.009$

Study TIP

During a test or quiz, estimating the answer can help you determine if the answer is reasonable.

Examples

1 Multiply: 4.8×2.3

Estimate: $5 \times 2 = 10$

4.8	1 decimal place
× 2.3	1 decimal place
144	
96	
11.04	2 decimal places

2 Multiply: 0.064×3.7

Estimate: $0.06 \times 4 = 0.24$

0.064	3 decimal places
× 3.7	1 decimal place
448	
192	
0.2368	4 decimal places

Use these shortcuts to multiply a number by 0.1, 0.01, or 0.001:

- To multiply by 0.1, move the decimal point one place to the left.
- To multiply by 0.01, move the decimal point two places to the left.
- To multiply by 0.001, move the decimal point three places to the left.

You may have to annex zeros in order to move the decimal point.

annexed zeros

$5.47 \times 0.001 = 0.00547$

Examples

3 Multiply: 21×0.1

$21 \times 0.1 = 2.1$

4 Multiply: 6×0.001

$6 \times 0.001 = 0.006$

HINT

If you press the [.] button on a calculator before pressing any number keys, the calculator will automaticly put a 0 in front of the decimal point. To enter 0.1, you only need to press [.] 1.

Try It

Multiply.

a. 0.4×23.6 9.44 b. 52.4×2.8 146.72 c. 0.009×4.1 0.0369

d. 5677×0.01 56.77 e. 210×0.001 0.21 f. 6×0.1 0.6

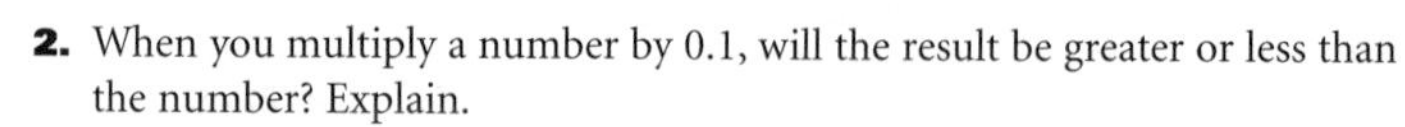

Check Your Understanding

1. Which is greater, 6.2×0.4 or 6.2×0.04? Explain.
2. When you multiply a number by 0.1, will the result be greater or less than the number? Explain.
3. How is multiplying a decimal by a decimal similar to multiplying two whole numbers?

MATH EVERY DAY

Problem of the Day

Suppose you have five marbles. Four of them weigh the same. One is heavier. How can you find the heavier marble by using a balance scale no more than two times?

Put two marbles on each side. If they balance, the marble left over is heavier. If they do not balance, put one marble from the heavier pair on each side of the balance scale to find which marble is heavier.

Available on Daily Transparency 3-9
An Extension is provided in the transparency package.

Fact of the Day

A large bucket of buttered popcorn at a movie theater has as much as 145 grams of fat, almost as much fat as eight hamburgers.

Mental Math

Do these mentally.

1. 9×20 180
2. 30×80 2,400
3. 40×700 28,000
4. 900×900 810,000

3-9 Exercises and Applications

Practice and Apply

1. **Getting Started** Choose the equation that the grid models.

a. 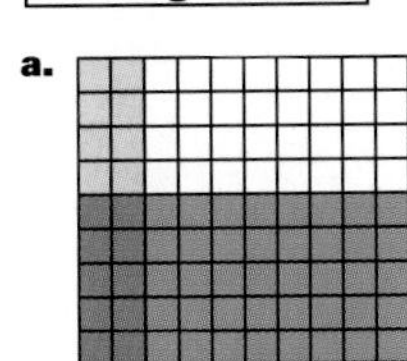

b. 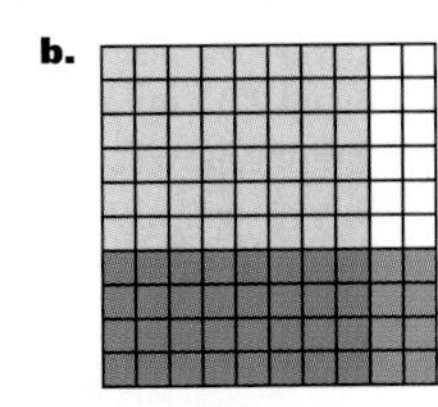

c. 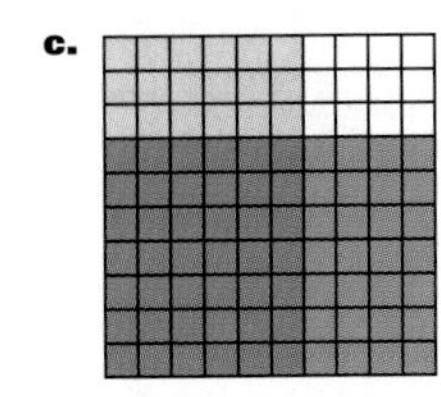

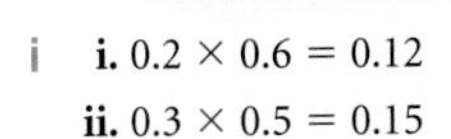

a.	b.	c.
i **i.** $0.2 \times 0.6 = 0.12$	i **i.** $0.8 \times 0.4 = 0.32$	ii **i.** $0.6 \times 0.7 = 4.2$
ii. $0.3 \times 0.5 = 0.15$	**ii.** $0.8 \times 0.4 = 0.032$	**ii.** $0.6 \times 0.7 = 0.42$

Insert a decimal in each answer to make the equation true.

2. $0.57 \times 0.102 = 05814$ 0.05814
3. $4.17 \times 0.23 = 09591$ 0.9591
4. $1.9 \times 13.2 = 2508$ 25.08
5. $1.567 \times 5.23 = 819541$ 8.19541
6. $4.09 \times 1.2 = 4908$ 4.908
7. $65.1 \times 65.1 = 423801$ 4238.01

Multiply.

8. 0.1×75.4 7.54
9. 0.01×6.8 0.068
10. 0.001×265.3 0.2653
11. 0.65×0.01 0.0065
12. 97.8×0.1 9.78
13. 4.25×0.001 0.00425
14. 4.2×6.3 26.46
15. 5.8×6.7 38.86
16. 9.7×0.6 5.82
17. 5.4×4.3 23.22
18. 0.29×0.4 0.116
19. 1.3×0.42 0.546
20. 2.07×0.03 0.0621
21. 6.24×8.7 54.288
22. 0.08×6.5 0.52
23. 9.37×0.08 0.7496
24. 10.2×0.4 4.08
25. 0.31×2.5 0.775
26. 0.4×0.18 0.072
27. 0.92×4.6 4.232

Estimate first. Then solve.

28. In 1863, at Fort Kearny, Nebraska, gingham cloth sold for $0.25 a yard. Mrs. Parks bought 16.5 yards to make clothes for her family. How much did she spend on cloth? $4; $4.13

29. In 1863, emigrants could buy rice for $0.11 per pound in Chimney Rock, Nebraska. The Wilson's barrel could hold 19.25 pounds. How much did it cost to fill the barrel? $2; $2.12

GPS

PRACTICE 3-9

PRACTICE

Name ______________

Practice 3-9

Multiplying a Decimal by a Decimal

Insert a decimal point in the answer to make the equation true.

1. $3.7 \times 19.8 = 7\ 3.2\ 6$
2. $5.7 \times 19.9 = 1\ 1\ 3.4\ 3$
3. $2.9 \times 13.82 = 4\ 0.0\ 7\ 8$
4. $10.2 \times 9.49 = 9\ 6.7\ 9\ 8$
5. $12.14 \times 8 = 9\ 7.1\ 2$
6. $16.6 \times 7.1 = 1\ 1\ 7.8\ 6$
7. $3.0 \times 5.18 = 1\ 5.5\ 4$
8. $10.9 \times 10.611 = 1\ 1\ 5.6\ 5\ 9\ 9$

Multiply.

9. 9.031×0.5 4.5155
10. 0.01×9.1 0.091
11. 50.9×0.9 45.81
12. 0.6×0.07 0.042
13. 0.2×0.278 0.0556
14. 9.2×0.25 2.3
15. 5.6×4.8 26.88
16. 0.02×0.3 0.006
17. 0.6×0.005 0.003
18. 55.5×0.07 3.885
19. 0.3×38.8 11.64
20. 0.5×2.1 1.05
21. 0.01×7.3 0.073
22. 52.62×0.8 42.096
23. 0.42×0.2 0.084
24. 7.07×4.9 34.643

25. A health food store sells granola for $1.80 per pound. How much would 1.3 pounds of granola cost? $2.34

26. **Health** Raw broccoli has 0.78 mg of iron per cup. How much iron is in 2.3 cups of broccoli? 1.794 mg

Compare using <, >, or =.

27. $6.14 \times 0.25 < 61.4 \times 2.5$
28. $0.03 \times 12.4 = 0.3 \times 1.24$
29. $5.2 \times 62.9 > 0.52 \times 6.29$
30. $4.7 \times 8.17 < 4.7 \times 81.7$
31. $7.0 \times 1.72 = 0.07 \times 172.0$
32. $8.54 \times 27.0 = 85.4 \times 2.7$

33. **Consumer** If gasoline costs $1.539 per gallon, how much would you pay for 12.64 gallons? (Round your answer to the nearest cent.) $19.45

RETEACHING

Name ______________

Alternative Lesson 3-9

Multiplying a Decimal by a Decimal

Multiply a decimal by a decimal as if the two numbers were whole numbers. Then count the number of digits to the right of the decimal point in each decimal factor. Finally, write the product. The product should have the same number of digits to the right of the decimal as there are in both factors. In some cases, you must annex zeros in order to have the correct number of digits to the right of the decimal point.

Example

Multiply: 0.31×0.18.

Count the number of digits after the decimal point in each factor. There are two digits after the decimal point in 0.31. There are two digits after the decimal point in 0.18.

$$\begin{array}{rl} 0.31 & \leftarrow \text{2 decimal places} \\ \times\ 0.18 & \leftarrow \text{2 decimal places} \\ \hline 248 & \\ 31 & \\ \hline 0.0558 & \leftarrow \text{4 decimal places} \end{array}$$

Multiply.

Place the decimal point. The two factors have a total of four digits after the decimal point, so the product will also have four digits after the decimal point. Since there are only 3 digits in the product, you will need to **annex** one zero. Notice that another zero is placed before the decimal point.

So, $0.31 \times 0.18 = 0.0558$.

Try It Multiply: 2.08×0.4.

a. How many decimal places are in 2.08? 2 places.
b. How many decimal places are in 0.4? 1 place.
c. How many decimal places will be in the product? 3 places.
d. What is the product? 0.832

Multiply.

e. 0.28×3.2 0.896
f. 0.183×2.4 0.4392
g. 15.21×0.45 6.8445
h. 5.07×0.73 3.7011
i. 8.4×0.01 0.084
j. 1.4×0.001 0.0014
k. 0.94×0.001 0.00094
l. $0.001 \times .0.001$ 0.000001
m. 300×0.002 0.6
n. 0.005×200 1

Assignment Guide

- **Basic**
  2–26 evens, 29, 35, 37, 40–54 evens
- **Average**
  1–37 odds, 38, 41–55 odds
- **Enriched**
  8–26 evens, 29–39, 40–54 evens

3 Practice and Assess

Check

Answers for Check Your Understanding

1. $6.2 \times 0.4 = 2.48$ and $6.2 \times 0.04 = 0.248$
2. Less than; The decimal of the number moves to the left.
3. Multiplication rules are the same.

Exercise Notes

Exercises 9, 13, 20, 26

Error Prevention Watch for students who annex zeros at the end of the nonzero digits instead of between the decimal point and the nonzero digits. Stress the importance of estimation in determining if answers are reasonable.

Exercises 28–29

History Fort Kearney and Chimney Rock were settlements on the Oregon Trail, which followed the route of the Platte River. The Platte River cuts through the entire state of Nebraska in an east-west direction.

Reteaching

Activity

Materials: 10×10 Grids

- Work with a partner. Use 10×10 grids to model 2.4×0.3.
- Use the same method as in **Explore.** This time, however, you will have to use three 10×10 grids.

Exercise Notes

■ Exercise 34

Health Many food items give the grams of fat per serving, but the serving size does not always represent the typical amount eaten by some people.

■ Exercise 35

Test Prep If students selected D, they placed the decimal point as if they were adding the decimals. Remind them that estimation will help them place the decimal point correctly.

Exercise Answers

37. $0.4 \times 0.2 = 0.08$; The product should have the same number of decimal places as the sum of the number of decimal places in both factors.

38. Multiplying by 1000 makes the number 1000 times larger; Multiplying by 0.001 makes the number 1000 times smaller.

39. Possible answer: A bag of flour costs $0.49. How much do 3.5 bags cost?

Alternate Assessment

Interview Have students identify the errors in the following problems and arrive at a correct response for each.

1. $0.3 \times 0.7 = 2.1$
2. $5.25 \times 0.002 = 52.50$

Quick Quiz

Multiply.

1. 18.8×0.01 0.188
2. 0.001×9.1 0.0091
3. 7.8×3.1 24.18
4. 0.47×6.5 3.055

Available on Daily Transparency 3-9

Compare, using <, >, or =.

30. 79.1×0.1 [>] 79.1×0.01 **31.** 0.001×12.5 [<] 0.01×12.5

32. 2.4×0.134 [>] 0.24×0.134 **33.** 15.2×0.38 [=] 1.52×3.8

34. Health Ava read on the wrapper that a candy bar had 12.5 g of fat. One gram of fat gives you 9.4 calories. How many calories from fat are in the candy bar? 117.5

35. Test Prep The Lyau's new car averaged 27.3 miles per gallon on a recent trip. If the gas tank holds 16.5 gallons, how far can they go on a tank of gas? C

Ⓐ 4.5 miles Ⓑ 45.04 miles Ⓒ 450.45 miles Ⓓ 4504.5 miles

36. Measurement Joel decided that his wrapping string should be 42.6 times longer than the piece shown here. How long should his string be? 289.68 cm

Problem Solving and Reasoning

37. Critical Thinking Explain why $0.4 \times 0.2 \neq 0.8$.

38. Communicate Explain why multiplying numbers by 1000 moves the decimal to the right, and multiplying by 0.001 moves the decimal to the left.

39. 

Imagine you are on the Oregon Trail in 1845. Write a problem that you might encounter on the trail that you can solve by multiplying two decimals.

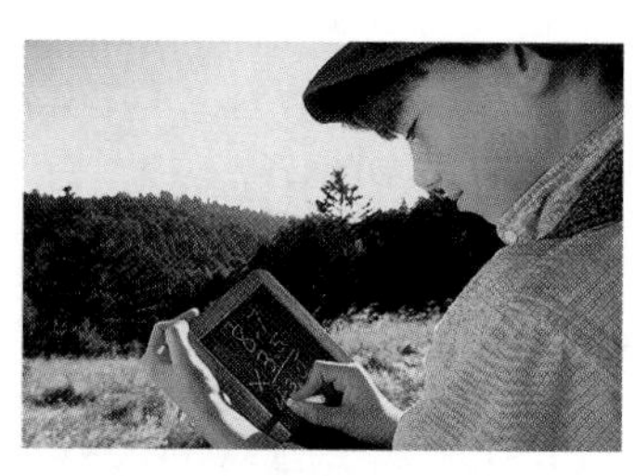

Mixed Review

Simplify each expression, using the correct order of operations. *[Lesson 2-8]*

40. $50 - 10 \div 2$ 45 **41.** $72 \div 9 - 1$ 7 **42.** $6 \times 5 \times 3$ 90 **43.** $4^2 \times 2 - 3$ 29

44. $3 \times (8 - 6)$ 6 **45.** $4 \div 2 - 0^6$ 2 **46.** $50 \div 10 \times 4$ 20 **47.** $(3 \times 4)^2 - 1$ 143

Estimate each sum, difference, product, or quotient. *[Lesson 3-5]*

48. $65.79 + 12.56$ 79 **49.** $7.67 - 5.33$ 3 **50.** 7.87×10.06 80 **51.** $12.29 \div 4.47$ 3

52. $72.593 + 3.485$ 76 **53.** $21.09 - 11.06$ 10 **54.** $55.88 \div 10.48$ 6 **55.** 9.5×3.667 40

PROBLEM SOLVING 3-9

PROBLEM SOLVING

Name ______

Guided Problem Solving 3-9

GPS PROBLEM 29, STUDENT PAGE 183

Estimate first. Then solve.

In 1863, emigrants could buy rice for $0.11 per pound in Chimney Rock, Nebraska. The Wilson's barrel could hold 19.25 pounds. How much did it cost to fill the barrel?

— Understand —

1. Circle the information you need.

— Plan —

2. Which operation will you use to find the cost to fill the barrel? Multiplication.
3. Estimate your answer by rounding.
   a. Round $0.11 to the nearest tenth. 0.1
   b. Round $19.25 to the nearest ten. 20

— Solve —

4. Use your rounded numbers to estimate the cost. $2.00
5. Find the actual cost to fill the barrel. Round your answer to the nearest cent. $2.12

— Look Back —

6. How can you tell if your answer is reasonable?
   Possible answer: It is close to the estimate in Item 4.
7. Why did you have to round your answer to Item 5?
   Possible answer: There is no monetary amount for $2.1175, so it had to be rounded to the nearest cent.

SOLVE ANOTHER PROBLEM

Estimate first. Then solve.

In 1996, brown rice cost $1.09 per pound. How much would it cost the Wilsons to fill their 19.25-pound barrel with rice in 1996?

$20; $20.98

ENRICHMENT

Name ______

Extend Your Thinking 3-9

Decision Making

Suppose you need to buy fabric to make costumes for the school play. The budget is $16 for each costume. You need 12 costumes made from brown fabric. Each brown costume needs 3.25 yards of fabric. You need 8 costumes made from red fabric. Each red costume needs 3.5 yards of fabric.

You have gotten prices from two stores.

Store A: Brown fabric is $4.25 per yard. Red fabric is $4.75 per yard. On any purchase over $40, you will receive a $10 coupon for your next purchase. This store is 5 miles from school.

Store B: Both fabrics are $4.50 per yard. This store is walking distance from school.

1. What is the maximum budget for the fabric? $320.00
2. Complete the following tables to find the cost at each store.

Store A	Yards per costume	Cost per yard	Cost per costume	Number of costumes	Total cost
Red	3.5	$4.75	$16.625	8	$133.00
Brown	3.25	$4.25	$13.8125	12	$165.75
Both					$298.75

Store B	Yards per costume	Cost per yard	Cost per costume	Number of costumes	Total cost
Red	3.5	$4.50	$15.75	8	$126.00
Brown	3.25	$4.50	$14.625	12	$175.50
Both					$301.50

3. At which store would you buy the fabric for the costumes? Explain.
   Possible answer: Store B because the difference in cost is minimal and the store is close to the school. The coupon is meaningless unless additional fabric will be needed in the near future.

Dividing by a Whole Number

3-10

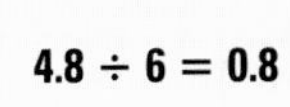 In the first lesson in this section, you worked with multiplication problems with decimal answers. Now you will learn to do division problems with decimal answers. ◀

You'll Learn ...

■ how to divide a decimal number by a whole number

... How It's Used

Dieticians divide decimal numbers to determine the amount of protein a person should eat per day.

Vocabulary

dividend

divisor

quotient

Explore Dividing by a Whole Number

Strip Mining

Materials: Tenths strips

Dividing by a Whole Number

- Color the first number.
- Break the first number down into equal groups. The number of groups should equal the second number.
- Describe one group in the grid.

4.8 ÷ 6 = 0.8

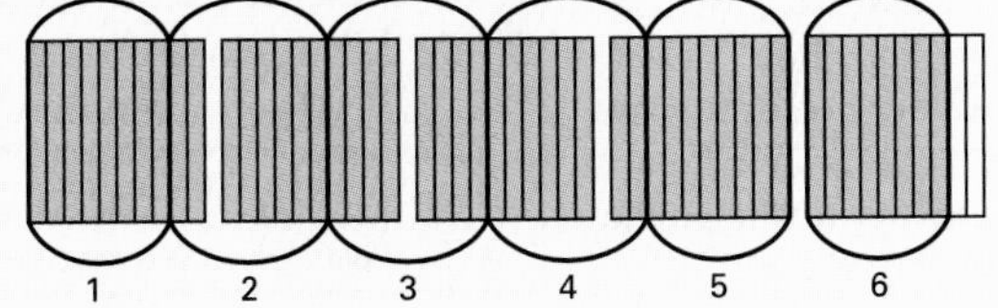

1. Model these problems.

   a. 2.0 ÷ 5 b. 2.1 ÷ 3 c. 2.4 ÷ 4 d. 3.5 ÷ 7

2. Does 2.4 ÷ 3 have the same answer as 3 ÷ 2.4? Explain.

3. How is dividing a decimal by a whole number similar to dividing a whole number by a whole number?

Learn Dividing by a Whole Number

When you divide one number by another, the number being divided is the **dividend**. The number you divide by is the **divisor**. The answer is the **quotient**.

When you divide by a whole number, you break the dividend into groups of equal size.

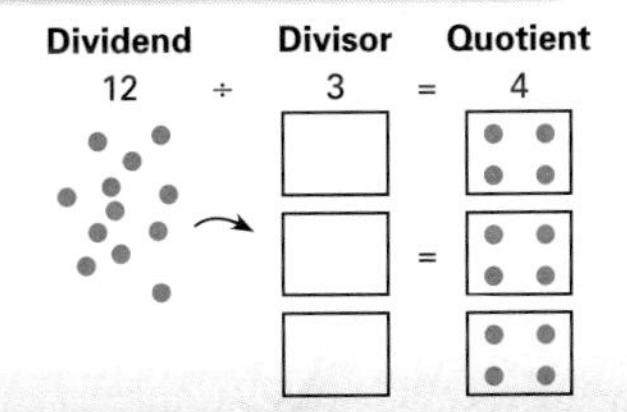

MEETING INDIVIDUAL NEEDS

Resources

3-10 Practice
3-10 Reteaching
3-10 Problem Solving
3-10 Enrichment
3-10 Daily Transparency
- Problem of the Day
- Review
- Quick Quiz

Teaching Tool Transparency 12

Chapter 3 Project Master

Learning Modalities

Visual Have students use 10 × 10 grids instead of tenths grids to model division.

Kinesthetic Have students use play money, including coins as well as paper money. Have them work together to divide various amounts of money into equal amounts. Point out that some amounts cannot be split into equal amounts.

English Language Development

Students often confuse the words *dividend* and *divisor.* Stress that the divisor is the number they are dividing by. Point out that the divisor might appear first as in $4\overline{)20.6}$, second, as in 20.6 ÷ 4, or in the denominator in fractional form, as in $\frac{20.6}{4}$. Have students read division problems aloud and explain that the divisor is the number that follows the phrase *divided by.* Display division problems with each term clearly identified.

3-10 Lesson Organizer

Objective
- Divide a decimal number by a whole number.

Vocabulary
- Dividend, divisor, quotient

Materials
- Explore: Tenths grids

NCTM Standards
- 1–4, 7, 13

Review 

Estimate.

1. 36.7 ÷ 4 9
2. 148.9 ÷ 3 50
3. 478.9 ÷ 62 8
4. 415.8 ÷ 69 6

Available on Daily Transparency 3-10

1 Introduce

Explore  

You may wish to use Teaching Transparency 12: Tenths Grids with **Explore**.

The Point

Students use models to explore the meaning of dividing a decimal by a whole number.

Ongoing Assessment

Watch for students who answer yes for Step 2. Ask a similar question using whole numbers. Is 8 ÷ 2 the same as 2 ÷ 8?

For Groups That Finish Early

How can you check the answer to a division problem? Multiply the answer by the number you're dividing by. The result should equal the original number.

Answers for Explore on next page.

Answers for Explore

1. a. 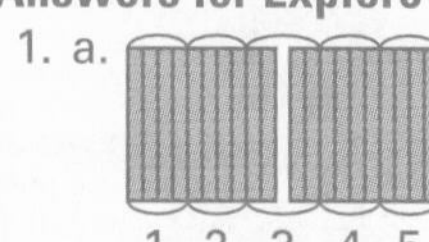

b. 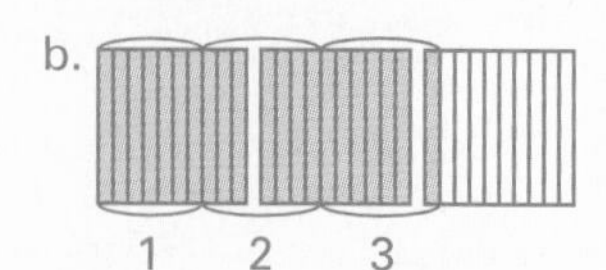

c. 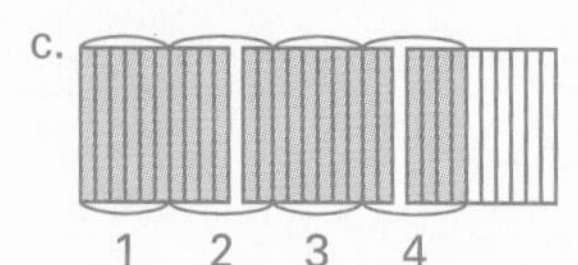

d. 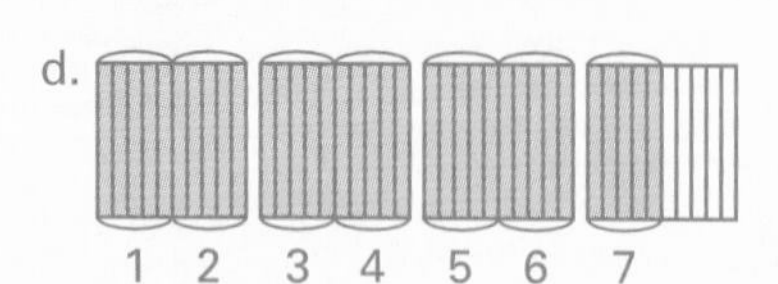

2. No; $2.4 \div 3 = 0.8$ and $3 \div 2.4 = 1.25$
3. Division rules are the same.

2 Teach

Learn

Alternate Examples

1. Divide: $161.28 \div 42$.

   Estimate: $160 \div 40 = 4$

   $$\begin{array}{r} 3.84 \\ 42\overline{)161.28} \\ -126 \\ \hline 35\,2 \\ -33\,6 \\ \hline 1\,68 \\ -1\,68 \\ \hline 0 \end{array}$$

2. Divide: $729.6 \div 8$.

   Estimate: $720 \div 8 = 90$

   $$\begin{array}{r} 91.2 \\ 8\overline{)729.6} \\ -72 \\ \hline 09 \\ -8 \\ \hline 1\,6 \\ -1\,6 \\ \hline 0 \end{array}$$

3. In four games of miniature golf, Jamie scored 91, 98, 101, and 86. Find her mean score for the four games.

   Total scores $= 91 + 98 + 101 + 86 = 376$

   Mean $= 376 \div 4 = 94$
   The mean score is 94.

Sometimes a decimal quotient is so long that the calculator cannot show the entire number. In that case, the calculator may round the quotient to a shorter number.

When you have a decimal dividend, divide as if you were dividing whole numbers. Then place a decimal point in the quotient directly above the decimal point in the dividend.

$$\begin{array}{r} 2.53 \\ 27\overline{)68.31} \\ 54 \\ \hline 14\,3 \\ 13\,5 \\ \hline 81 \\ 81 \\ \hline \end{array}$$

Examples

1 Divide: $153.92 \div 32$

Estimate: $150 \div 30 = 5$

$$\begin{array}{r} 4.81 \\ 32\overline{)153.92} \\ 128 \\ \hline 25\,9 \\ 25\,6 \\ \hline 32 \\ 32 \\ \hline \end{array}$$

2 Divide: $427.8 \div 6$

Estimate: $420 \div 6 = 70$

$$\begin{array}{r} 71.3 \\ 6\overline{)427.8} \\ 42 \\ \hline 07 \\ 6 \\ \hline 1\,8 \\ 1\,8 \\ \hline \end{array}$$

Remember

The mean is the result of dividing the sum of a set of numbers by the number of numbers in the set. [Page 45]

3 In May 1860, Nevada rider "Pony Bob" Haslam used four horses to make the longest run in Pony Express history. Find the mean distance run by each horse.

Horse	From	To	Distance (mi)
1	Friday's	Buckland's	60
2	Buckland's	Carson Sink	35
3	Carson Sink	Cold Springs	37
4	Cold Springs	Smith's Creek	30

Total distance $= 60 + 35 + 37 + 30 = 162$.
Add distances and divide by 4 to find the mean.

Mean $= 162 \div 4$

Estimate: $160 \div 4 = 40$

$$\begin{array}{r} 40.5 \\ 4\overline{)162.0} \\ 16 \\ \hline 02\,0 \\ 2\,0 \\ \hline \end{array}$$ ← Annex a zero.

The mean distance run by each horse was 40.5 miles.

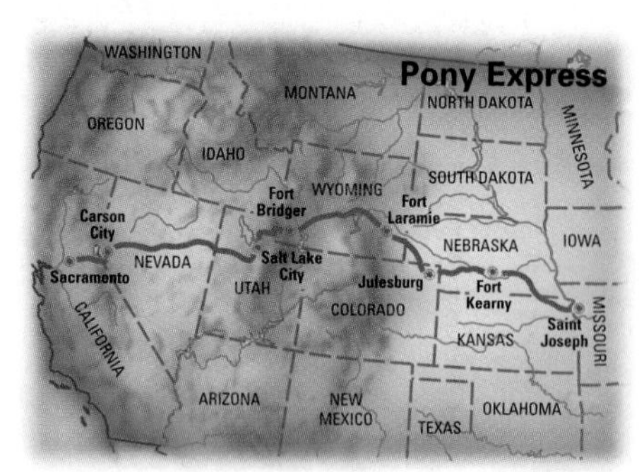

MATH EVERY DAY

Problem of the Day

Copy the first figure. Show how you can cut it into two pieces to make it exactly fit the second figure.

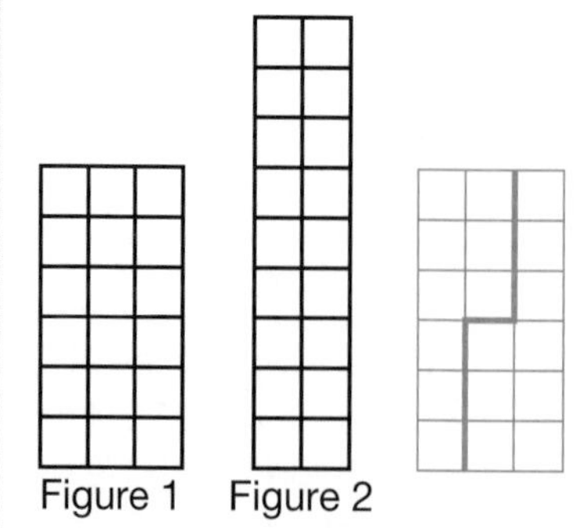

Available on Daily Transparency 3-10

An Extension is provided in the transparency package.

Fact of the Day

There were 190 relay stations along the Pony Express route. It took about 2 minutes to change horses at each station.

Mental Math

Do these mentally.

1. 100×100 10,000
2. 10×1000 10,000
3. $10{,}000 \div 1000$ 10
4. $100{,}000 \div 100$ 1000

Use these shortcuts to divide a number by 10, 100, or 1000:

- To divide by 10, move the decimal point one place to the left.
- To divide by 100, move the decimal point two places to the left.
- To divide by 1000, move the decimal point three places to the left.

Recall that multiplying by powers of 10 that are less than 1, such as 0.1, 0.01, and 0.001, also moves the decimal place to the left.

Example 4

The table gives the estimated world population at two times 100 years apart. What is the average increase in population per year?

World Population (estimated)	
Year (A.D.)	Population
1900	1,600,000,000
2000	6,261,000,000

$$\begin{array}{r} 6{,}261{,}000{,}000 \\ -\ 1{,}600{,}000{,}000 \\ \hline 4{,}661{,}000{,}000 \end{array}$$

The total increase in 100 years is about 4,661,000,000.

To find the average increase per year, divide by 100:

4,661,000,000 ÷ 100 = 46610000.00

The average annual population increase is about 46,610,000.

Try It

Divide.

a. 154.4 ÷ 8 19.3 **b.** 20.47 ÷ 23 0.89 **c.** 8.029 ÷ 74 0.1085

d. 26.2 ÷ 100 0.262 **e.** 3.012 ÷ 1000 0.003012 **f.** 45 ÷ 10 4.5

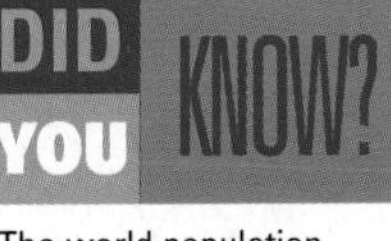

The world population is currently increasing faster than 1 person per second. In the time it takes to read this, more than 25 babies will have been born worldwide.

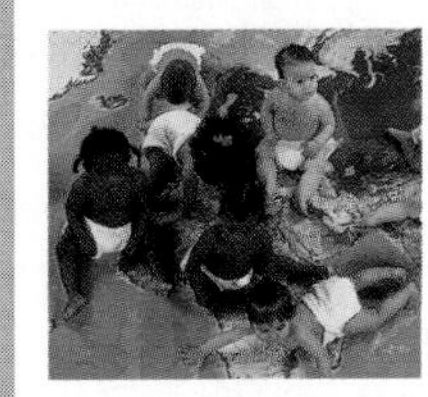

Check Your Understanding

1. If you divide a number with three places after the decimal by a whole number, how many decimal places are in the answer? Explain.
2. Dividing by 10 is the same as multiplying by 0.1. Explain. Can you think of other pairs of powers of 10 where dividing by one of them is the same as multiplying by the other?
3. How can you use multiplication to check a quotient?

Alternate Examples

4. In 100 years the population of a city increased from 8,000 to 152,000. Assuming the population increased at a steady rate, by about how about much did it increase each year?

$$\begin{array}{r} 152{,}000 \\ -\ 8{,}000 \\ \hline 144{,}000 \end{array}$$

The total increase in 100 years was about 144,000.

Divide 144,000 by 100.

144,000 ÷ 100 = 1,440.

The mean annual population increase was about 1,440.

3 Practice and Assess

Check

Answers for Check Your Understanding

1. It depends on the numbers, but the answer will have at least 3 decimal places.
2. Dividing by 10 makes the number 10 times smaller; Multiplying by 0.1 also makes the number 10 times smaller; Dividing by 100 is the same as multiplying by 0.01.
3. The quotient multiplied by the divisor equals the dividend.

MEETING MIDDLE SCHOOL CLASSROOM NEEDS

Tips from Middle School Teachers

I like to have students bring empty food cartons or cans that show weights involving decimals. Then I have them discuss why they might need to divide some of these decimal amounts by whole numbers.

Team Teaching

Work with a social studies teacher to discuss changes in populations for various cities or countries. Try to find population changes during the last 100 years and then find the mean increase per year.

Sports Connection

In sports such as diving, skating, and gymnastics, competitors are rated by scores that are decimals. In gymnastics, 10 is the highest possible score. Most contestants seldom score perfect 10s.

3-10 Exercises and Applications

Assignment Guide

- Basic
  1–7, 9–29 odds, 32–46 evens
- Average
  2–34 evens, 37–49 odds
- Enriched
  2–50 evens

Exercise Notes

Exercises 2–7

Error Prevention Check that students are able to answer these exercises correctly before moving on to Exercises 8–27.

Exercise 29

Health In pioneer times people were not aware of the ill effects of diets high in saturated fats. Lard is made from animal fat and is much higher in saturated fat per gram than many vegetable oils.

Reteaching

Activity

Materials: Newspapers, tenths grids

- Work in small groups. Find newspaper grocery advertisements that are selling items in quantity such as 3 cans of peaches selling for $2.19.
- Each person in the group should pick several such advertisements.
- Write division problems to find the cost of one item, such as 2.19 ÷ 3. Use tenths grids to model each problem.

3-10 Exercise and Applications

Practice and Apply

1. **Getting Started** Choose the equation that the grid models.

a.

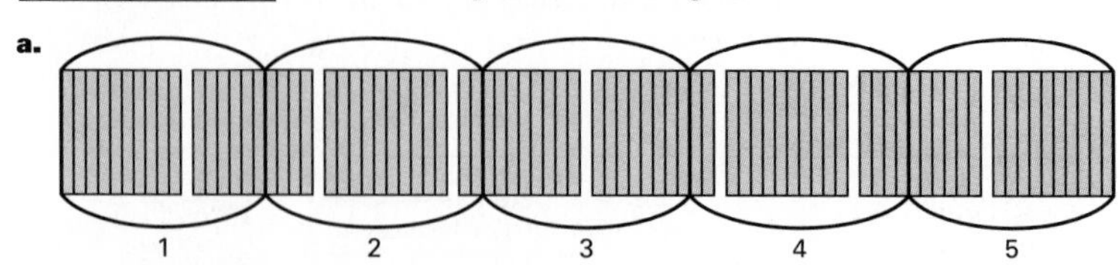

i. 8 ÷ 5 = 1.6 ii. 8 ÷ 5 = 16

b.

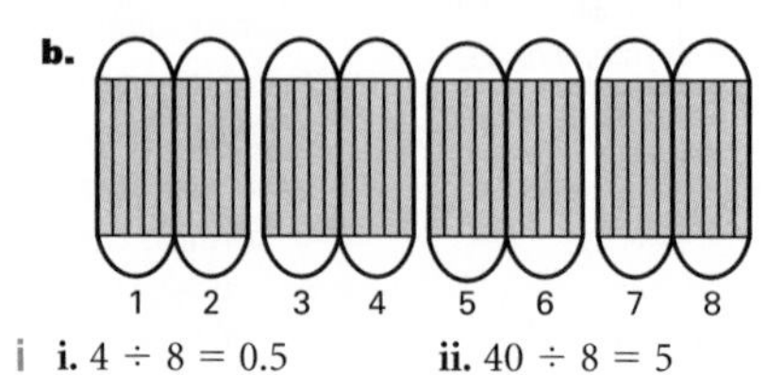

i. 4 ÷ 8 = 0.5 ii. 40 ÷ 8 = 5

c.

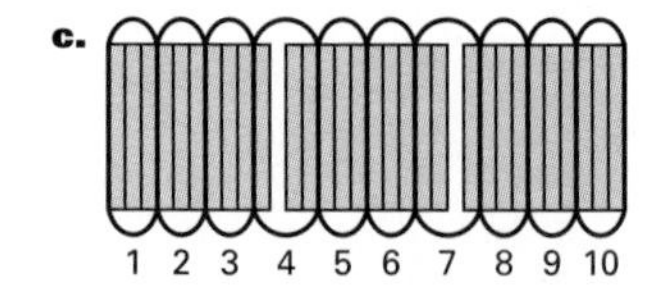

i. 3 ÷ 10 = 0.3 ii. 30 ÷ 10 = 3

Insert a decimal in each answer to make the equation true.

2. 24.36 ÷ 6 = 406 4.06 **3.** 287.63 ÷ 49 = 587 5.87 **4.** 0.475 ÷ 5 = 095 0.095

5. 99.4 ÷ 100 = 994 0.994 **6.** 4.96 ÷ 10 = 0496 0.496 **7.** 25.8 ÷ 1000 = 0258 0.0258

Divide.

8. 27.24 ÷ 6 4.54 **9.** 13.932 ÷ 9 1.548 **10.** 987.6 ÷ 12 82.3 **11.** 133.414 ÷ 41 3.254

12. 49.92 ÷ 16 3.12 **13.** 0.104 ÷ 8 0.013 **14.** 341.6 ÷ 56 6.1 **15.** 2.856 ÷ 34 0.084

16. 15.25 ÷ 61 0.25 **17.** 9.92 ÷ 8 1.24 **18.** 615.34 ÷ 10 61.534 **19.** 945.25 ÷ 19 49.75

20. 40.24 ÷ 8 5.03 **21.** 382.092 ÷ 17 22.476 **22.** 0.126 ÷ 7 0.018 **23.** 56.88 ÷ 3 18.96

24. 3.534 ÷ 6 0.589 **25.** 2.035 ÷ 5 0.407 **26.** 37.5 ÷ 3 12.5 **27.** 4.69 ÷ 7 0.67

28. Along the Oregon Trail, the trader's post in Fort Laramie, Wyoming, sold a 16-pound box of beef jerky for $5.92. What was the cost per pound? $0.37

29. **Health** The emigrants used lard for their cooking oil. Fifteen grams of lard have 141 calories. How many calories are in 1 gram? 9.4

PRACTICE 3-10

PRACTICE

Name ______________________

Practice 3-10

Dividing by a Whole Number

Insert a decimal point in the answer to make the equation true.

1. 37.164 ÷ 76 = 0.4 8 9 **2.** 110.24 ÷ 32 = 3.4 4 5 **3.** 41.34 ÷ 6 = 6.8 9

4. 320.662 ÷ 67 = 4.7 8 6 **5.** 143.68 ÷ 20 = 7.1 8 4 **6.** 15.9 ÷ 3 = 5.3

7. 6.3 ÷ 7 = 0.9 **8.** 17.505 ÷ 3 = 5.8 3 5 **9.** 6.532 ÷ 4 = 1.6 3 3

Divide.

10. 33.628 ÷ 14 2.402 **11.** 111.618 ÷ 39 2.862 **12.** 22.8 ÷ 19 1.2 **13.** 257.24 ÷ 59 4.36

14. 162.5 ÷ 65 2.5 **15.** 27.23 ÷ 7 3.89 **16.** 16.668 ÷ 3 5.556 **17.** 23.94 ÷ 63 0.38

18. 190.4 ÷ 28 6.8 **19.** 23.58 ÷ 20 1.179 **20.** 20.305 ÷ 5 4.061 **21.** 0.931 ÷ 19 0.049

22. 90.034 ÷ 59 1.526 **23.** 385.92 ÷ 48 8.04 **24.** 179.8 ÷ 58 3.1 **25.** 5.337 ÷ 3 1.779

26. 36.11 ÷ 23 1.57 **27.** 244.29 ÷ 51 4.79 **28.** 150.92 ÷ 49 3.08 **29.** 15.98 ÷ 47 0.34

30. 503.7 ÷ 69 7.3 **31.** 12.6 ÷ 42 0.3 **32.** 4.14 ÷ 9 0.46 **33.** 113.26 ÷ 14 8.09

34. 465.272 ÷ 76 6.122 **35.** 469.7 ÷ 61 7.7 **36.** 8.6 ÷ 86 0.1 **37.** 13.425 ÷ 15 0.895

38. Keith paid $24.57 for 9 blank videotapes. How much did each tape cost? $2.73

39. In 1988, a team of 32 divers set a record by pedaling a tricycle 116.66 miles underwater. Find the mean distance pedaled by each diver. 3.645625

RETEACHING

Name ______________________

Alternative Lesson 3-10

Dividing by a Whole Number

When you divide a decimal by a whole number, divide the decimal as if you were dividing whole numbers. Then place the decimal point in the quotient directly above the decimal point in the dividend. Sometimes you may need to annex zeros in the dividend so that you can divide until the remainder is zero.

0.24 ← quotient
5)1.2
divisor dividend

Example

Divide: 435 ÷ 50.

Divide 50 into 435. Write the quotient above the 5.

Find 8 × 50 = 400. Subtract from 435.

Write a 0 after the decimal point in 435.

Divide 350 by 50. Write the quotient above the 0.

Write the decimal point in the quotient above the decimal point in the dividend.

So, 435 ÷ 50 = 8.7

```
   8.7
50)435.0
   400
    35 0
    35 0
```

Try It Divide 83.2 ÷ 4.

a. Divide as if you were dividing whole numbers. Show your work. 20.8 (4)83.2)

b. Will you need to annex zeros in the dividend? No.

c. Write the quotient. Place the decimal point above the decimal point in the quotient.

Divide. Write your answer above the dividend.

d. 3)22.65 7.55 **e.** 5)376.15 75.23 **f.** 7)91.14 13.02 **g.** 12)2.172 0.181

h. 6)42.9 7.15 **i.** 4)1.04 0.26 **j.** 8)50.2 6.275 **k.** 25)114.9 4.596

30. Maria spent $13.50 buying her class 30 ice cream bars. How much did each bar cost? **$0.45**

31. Measurement The distance between Fort Boise, Idaho, and Oregon City is 413 mi. On the emigrant's map, the distance was 3 in. How many miles does an inch on the map represent? **137.667 mi**

32. Test Prep Choose the correct solution to 24.501 ÷ 3. **C**

Ⓐ 0.0816 Ⓑ 0.816 Ⓒ 8.167 Ⓓ 81.67

Problem Solving and Reasoning

33. 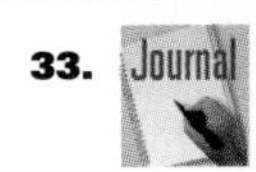 Explain why dividing a number by 100 is the same as multiplying by 0.01.

34. Critical Thinking In a gymnastic competition, Dominique scored 9.5, 9.6, 9.5, 9.4, 9.7, and 9.6. Kim scored 9.5, 9.4, 9.6, 9.7, 9.7, and 9.5. Who had the higher average score? Explain.

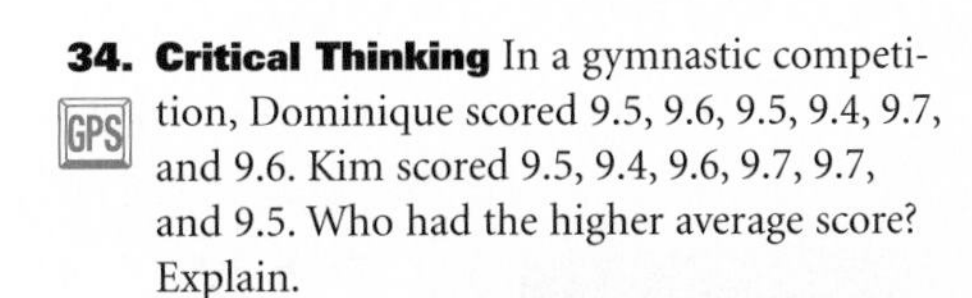

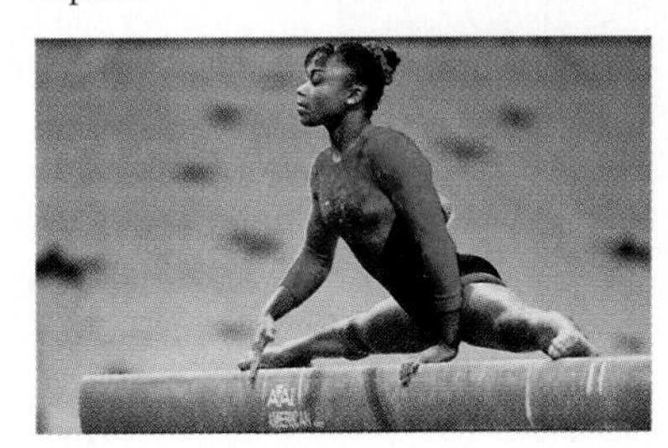

35. Critical Thinking In a whole-number division problem, both divisor and dividend are whole numbers. What kind of whole-number division problems have whole-number answers, and what kind of whole-number problems have decimal answers?

36. Communicate Suppose you are on the Oregon Trail in 1848. Invent a problem you would solve by dividing a decimal by a whole number.

Mixed Review

Find the next three numbers in each pattern. *[Lesson 2-9]*

37. 55, 60, 61, 66, 67, 72, … **73, 78, 79**

38. 2, 4, 8, 16, 32, … **64, 128, 256**

39. 38, 37, 35, 32, 28, … **23, 17, 10**

40. 31, 39, 30, 38, 29, 37, … **28, 36, 27**

41. 45, 42, 39, 36, … **33, 30, 27**

42. 79, 82, 86, 91, 97, … **104, 112, 121**

Simplify. *[Lesson 3-6]*

43. 49.02 + 3.05 **52.07**

44. 56.75 − 46.25 **10.5**

45. 0.267 − 0.26 **0.007**

46. 19.31 + 21.4 **40.71**

47. 6.98 − 3.45 **3.53**

48. $23.40 − $16.22 **$7.18**

49. 5.847 + 1.152 **6.999**

50. 14.23 + 6.28 **20.51**

Project Progress

Draw a bar graph of the data you have collected about your expenses. Decide how to scale your bar graph to best show your data. Label each bar clearly, and make sure the height matches the dollar amount it represents.

Problem Solving: Understand, Plan, Solve, Look Back

PROBLEM SOLVING 3-10

Exercise Notes

Exercise 32

Test Prep Remind students that an estimate may be all they need to find the correct answer. The answer must be C because it is the only choice that is about 8.

Project Progress

You may want to have students use Chapter 3 Project Master.

Exercise Answers

33. For both operations, the answer is the given number with its decimal point moved two places to the left.

34. Kim; Dominique's average: 9.55, Kim's average: 9.57

35. Possible answer: Whole-number answers occur when the dividend can be divided into n equal-size groups, where n is the divisor; Decimal number answers occur when the groups cannot be divided into n equal-sized groups.

36. Possible answer: The cook has 10.5 cups of rice. How many cups does each of six people receive?

Alternate Assessment

Portfolio Have students select one or more examples of their work that demonstrate the concept of dividing a decimal number by a whole number.

Quick Quiz

Divide.

1. 7.8 ÷ 6 **1.3**
2. 57.6 ÷ 18 **3.2**
3. 18.8 ÷ 100 **0.188**
4. 2.045 ÷ 5 **0.409**

Available on Daily Transparency 3-10

PROBLEM SOLVING

Name ____________

Guided Problem Solving 3-10

GPS PROBLEM 34, STUDENT PAGE 189

In a gymnastic competition, Dominique scored 9.5, 9.6, 9.5, 9.4, 9.7, and 9.6. Kim scored 9.5, 9.4, 9.6, 9.7, 9.7, and 9.5. Who had the higher average score? Explain.

— Understand —

1. Circle Dominique's scores.
2. Underline Kim's scores.
3. How many scores did each girl receive? **6 scores.**

— Plan —

4. How do you find the average score? **Add each person's scores and divide the sum by the number of scores.**

— Solve —

5. How many points did each girl score in all?
   a. Dominique **57.3 points** b. Kim **57.4 points**
6. What was each girl's average score?
   a. Dominique **9.55** b. Kim **About 9.57**
7. Who had the higher average score? Explain. **Kim, since 9.57 > 9.55.**

— Look Back —

8. How could you find who had the higher average without doing all the calculations? **Possible answer: Compare total points. In 6 events, Kim scored more points, so she would have a higher average.**

SOLVE ANOTHER PROBLEM

In an ice skating competition, Alex scored 7.2, 7.5, 7.1, 6.9, and 7.7. Mario scored 7.1, 7.5, 7.8, 7.0, and 6.9. Who had the higher average score? Explain.

Alex, because 7.28 > 7.26.

ENRICHMENT

Name ____________

Extend Your Thinking 3-10

Critical Thinking

Where Cassie lives it rains almost every day in the summer. She recorded the daily rainfall for one week and started the graph below to display her data.

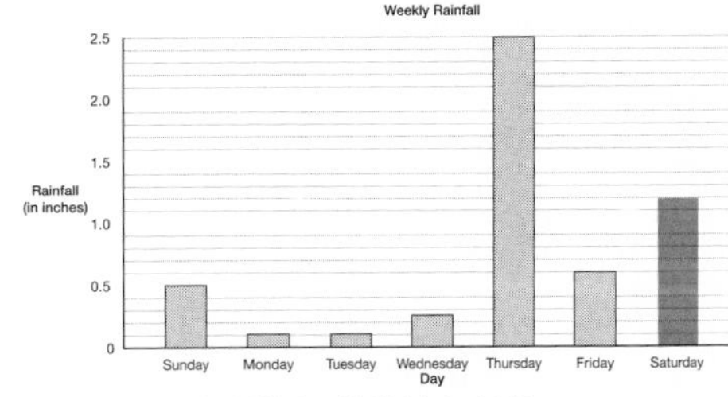

1. On Saturday, it rained 1.2 inches. Add that day's rainfall to Cassie's graph.
2. How much more did it rain on the day with the most rainfall than on the day with the least rainfall? **2.4 in.**
3. The sum of the rainfall on two days equals the amount of rain that fell on Friday. Which two days were these? **Sunday and Monday; Sunday and Tuesday.**
4. The amount of rain that fell on Saturday is twice the amount of rain that fell on another day. Which day was this? **Friday.**
5. The sum of the rainfall on some days equals the amount of rain that fell on Thursday. Which days were these? **Sunday, Monday, Tuesday, Friday, and Saturday.**
6. What was the total weekly rainfall? **5.25 in.**
7. What is the mean daily rainfall? **0.75 in.**
8. What is the median rainfall? **0.5 in.**
9. What is the mode of the rainfall data? **0.1 in.**

3-11

Lesson Organizer

Objective

- Divide decimal numbers by decimal numbers.

Materials

- Explore: Tenths grids

NCTM Standards

- 1–4, 7

Review

Divide.

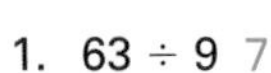
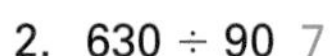

1. 63 ÷ 9 7
2. 630 ÷ 90 7
3. 6300 ÷ 900 7
4. 63000 ÷ 9000 7
5. What do you notice about the dividends and divisors in Exercises 1–4? Each succeeding dividend and divisor is 10 times as large as the preceding.

Available as Daily Transparency 3-11

1 Introduce

Explore

The Point
Students use models to explore the meaning of dividing a decimal by a decimal.

Ongoing Assessment
Watch for students who draw the wrong conclusion when answering Step 2.

For Groups That Finish Early
Write at least two other problems similar to those in **Explore** and predict the answers.
Possible answers: 6.3 ÷ 0.7 = 9 or 3.6 ÷ 0.6 = 6

3-11 Dividing by a Decimal

You'll Learn ...

- how to divide decimal numbers by decimal numbers

... How It's Used

Pharmacists divide by decimals to determine how to best fill prescriptions for medicine.

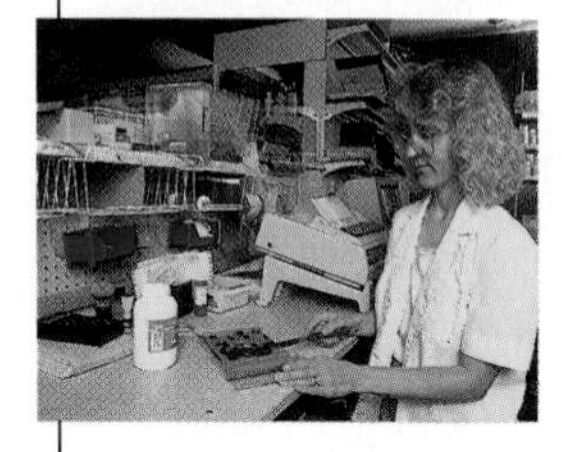

Lesson Link In the last section, you divided by a whole number when the dividend is a decimal. Now you'll build on that skill by dividing by a decimal. ◄

Explore Dividing by a Decimal

Divided We Stand

Materials: Tenths grid

Dividing by a Decimal

- Color the first number.
- Break the first number down into groups. Each group should be as large as the second number.
- Describe the number of groups in the grid.

1 2 3 4

2.8 ÷ 0.7 = 4

1. Model these problems.
   a. 3.0 ÷ 0.3 b. 4.5 ÷ 0.9 c. 4.2 ÷ 0.7 d. 3.6 ÷ 0.6
   e. 2.4 ÷ 0.8 f. 2.5 ÷ 0.5 g. 2.6 ÷ 0.1 h. 1.2 ÷ 0.1
2. When you divide a number by a decimal less than 1, is your answer smaller or larger than the number you started with?
3. In the problem 3.0 ÷ 0.6 = 5.0, which number represents the number of groups? Which number represents the size of the groups?

Learn Dividing by a Decimal

Dividing by a decimal is like dividing by a whole number. When you divide by a decimal, you break the dividend into groups of equal size.

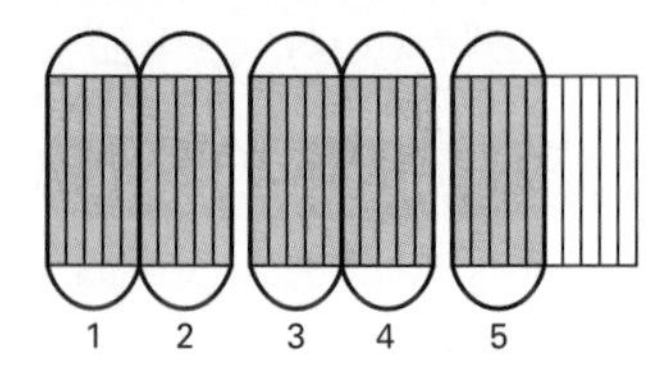

The model illustrates the quotient of 2.5 ÷ 0.5. There are 5 equal-size groups of 0.5 in 2.5. Therefore, 2.5 ÷ 0.5 = 5.

MEETING INDIVIDUAL NEEDS

Resources

3-11 Practice
3-11 Reteaching
3-11 Problem Solving
3-11 Enrichment
3-11 Daily Transparency
 Problem of the Day
 Review
 Quick Quiz
Teaching Tool Transparency 12

Learning Modalities

Visual Have students create a poster showing how to compute the unit price of an item for which the total price and total weight are known.

Social Have students work in small groups to model each problem in **Explore**. Have students take turns doing each part of process.

Challenge

Have students gather information from car dealers on the predicted average miles per gallon for various new cars. Then have students explain how they would determine whether these predicted mileages are reasonable. Also, have them give reasons why actual mileages might vary from predicted mileages.

A problem with a decimal divisor can be difficult to solve. But, you can change the problem to one without a decimal divisor. Notice that when you multiply the dividend and the divisor by the same number, the quotient stays the same.

	Dividend	÷	Divisor	=	Quotient
	6	÷	2	=	3
Multiply dividend and divisor by 10	60	÷	20	=	3
Multiply dividend and divisor by 100	600	÷	200	=	3
Multiply dividend and divisor by 1000	6000	÷	2000	=	3

When you have a decimal divisor, multiply both divisor and dividend by a power of 10 that will make the divisor a whole number.

$2.618 \div 0.34 = 261.8 \div 34.$

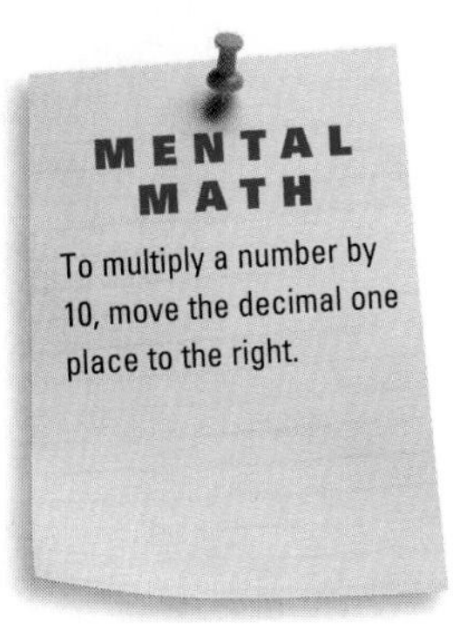

History Link

Pioneers who couldn't complete the Oregon Trail before winter would often die from the harsh weather and lack of food.

Examples

1 Find the quotient: 5.76 ÷ 1.6

$5.76 \div 1.6 = 57.6 \div 16.$ Multiply dividend and divisor by 10 to make the divisor a whole number.

```
    3.6
16)57.6
   48
    96
    96
```

Divide.

The quotient is 3.6.

2 The Caldwells traveled the Oregon Trail in 1870. They traveled 2212 miles in 126.4 days. Find the mean daily distance.

Mean distance $= 22120. \div 1264.$ Multiply dividend and divisor by 10 to make the divisor a whole number.

```
        17.5
1264)22120.0
     1264
      9480
      8848
       6320
       6320
```

Divide.

The mean daily distance was 17.5 miles.

Answers for Explore

1. See page C2.
2. The answer is larger.
3. 5.0 groups; 0.6 in each group

2 Teach

Learn

Alternate Examples

1. Find the quotient: 7.65 ÷ 1.7.

   Multiply dividend and divisor by 10 to make the divisor a whole number: 76.5 ÷ 17.

```
    4.5
17)76.5
  - 68
     85
   - 85
      0
```

   The quotient is 4.5.

2. A ship traveled 3111 miles in 127.5 hours. Find the mean hourly distance.

   Mean distance = 3111 ÷ 127.5.

   3111 ÷ 127.5 = 31110. ÷ 1275.

```
         24.4
1275)31110.0
    - 2550
       5610
     - 5100
        5100
      - 5100
           0
```

   The mean hourly distance was 24.4 miles.

MATH EVERY DAY

Problem of the Day

Each day, Irene rides her bicycle 2.5 kilometers farther than Yoki, and Kaneko rides her bicycle 0.7 more kilometers than Irene. Altogether they ride 15 kilometers each day. How far does each student ride her bicycle in 5 days?
Irene, 28 kilometers;
Yoki, 15.5 kilometers;
Kaneko, 31.5 kilometers

Available on Daily Transparency 3-11

An Extension is provided in the transparency package.

Fact of the Day

The transcontinental railroad was finished in 1869. In 1868, 425 miles of track were laid. A record 10 miles were laid in one day.

Estimation

Estimate.

1. 4.5 × 4.5 25
2. 7.8 × 9.1 72
3. 12.1 × 4.3 48
4. 105.7 × 8.8 900

Students see two methods of solving a problem. One method involves dividing to find the cost per ounce for a packaged mix. The other method involves multiplying the cost per ounce by the number of ounces needed.

Answers for What Do You Think?

1. Answers may vary.
2. Peter: Multiplying $0.22 by 32.5 should result in $7.15; Sonia: Dividing $7.80 by either number should result in the other number.

3 Practice and Assess

Check

You may need to remind students that they can multiply both dividend and divisor by the same nonzero number without affecting the answer.

Answers for Check Your Understanding

1. Possible answers: $200 \div 25$; $2.0 \div 0.25$
2. Possible answer: The larger the size of each group (divisor), the fewer groups you will have (quotient). The smaller the size of each group, the more groups you will have.

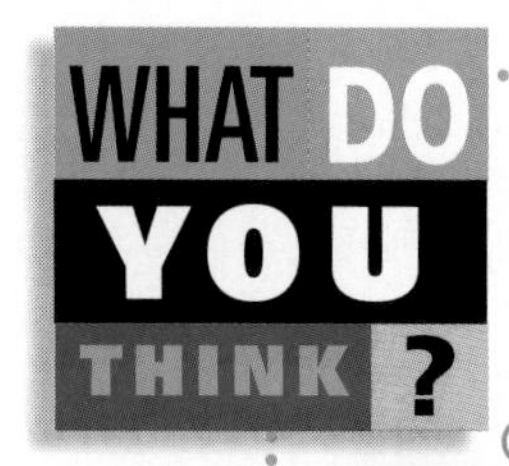

Peter and Sonia wanted to buy 30 ounces of trail mix for a 3-day hike. Trail mix sells for $0.26 per ounce, or 32.5-ounce packages for $7.15. Which is the better buy?

Peter thinks . . .

I'll divide the cost of the package by the weight to determine the price per ounce.

$7.15 \div 32.5 = 71.5 \div 325$

$$\begin{array}{r} .22 \\ 325\overline{)71.50} \\ \underline{650} \\ 650 \\ \underline{650} \end{array}$$

The package sells for $0.22 an ounce. This is a lower price per ounce. The package is a better buy.

Sonia thinks . . .

I'll find the cost of 30 ounces at the price per ounce.

$$\begin{array}{rl} 0.26 & \\ \underline{\times\ 30} & \text{2 decimal places} \\ 0 & \\ \underline{+\ 780} & \\ 7.80 & \text{2 decimal places} \end{array}$$

30 ounces would cost $7.80, which is more than the package. The package is the better buy.

What do you think?

1. Which method would be easier to do with mental math? Paper and pencil? A calculator?
2. How could Peter check to see that his arithmetic was correct? How could Sonia check to see that her arithmetic was correct?

Check Your Understanding

1. Write two decimal division problems with the same quotient as $20 \div 2.5$.
2. Why is the answer to a division problem smaller than the dividend when you divide by a whole number, but bigger when you divide by a decimal between 0 and 1?

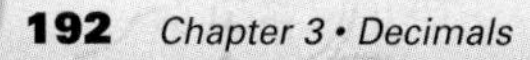

MEETING MIDDLE SCHOOL CLASSROOM NEEDS

Tips from Middle School Teachers

I find that some students understand why we multiply dividend and divisor by the same number when I write division problems in fraction form. Students are used to changing fractions by multiplying or dividing numerator and denominator by the same number.

Consumer Connection

Students are often confronted with a decision like the one discussed in **What Do You Think?** Point out the importance of being able to decide which of two or more products is the best buy. Ask students to consider what other factors they should think about when deciding which product is the best buy. Explain that lowest cost is only one factor in determining which product is the best buy.

Health Connection

A generic drug is the same chemical as the brand-name version. The generic drug can cost 30% to 80% less than the name brand. About one-half of the drugs sold today can be bought in generic form.

3-11 Exercises and Applications

Practice and Apply

1. **Getting Started** Choose the equation that the grid models.

a.

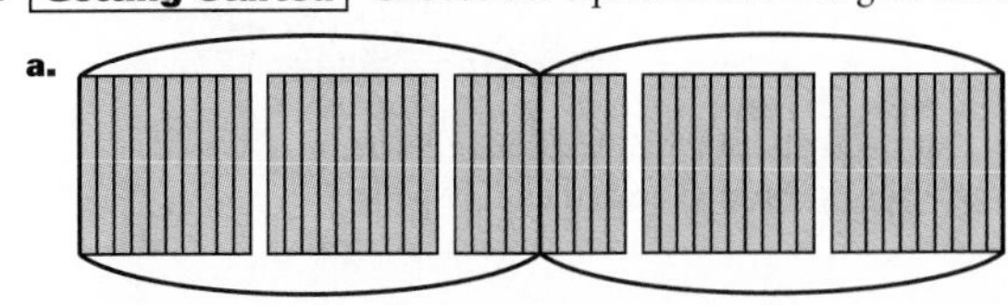

ii i. 50 ÷ 25 = 2

ii. 5 ÷ 2.5 = 2

b.

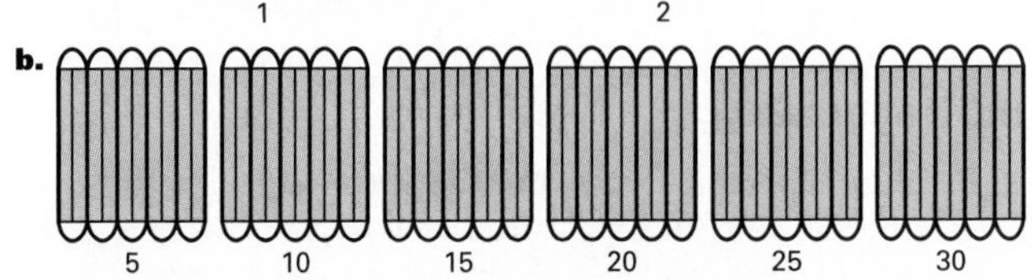

ii i. 60 ÷ 20 = 30

ii. 6 ÷ 0.2 = 30

c.

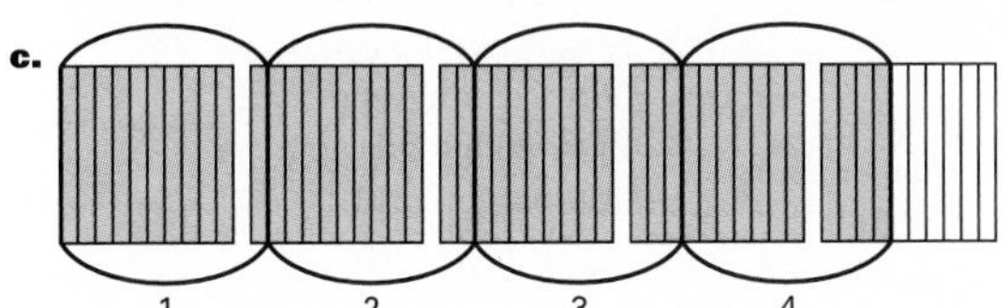

i i. 4.4 ÷ 1.1 = 4

ii. 44 ÷ 11 = 33

Insert a decimal in each answer to make the equation true. Annex zeros if necessary.

2. 10.58 ÷ 2.3 = 46 4.6 **3.** 2.24 ÷ 0.8 = 28 2.8 **4.** 6.12 ÷ 1.8 = 34 3.4

5. 0.0036 ÷ 0.009 = 4 0.4 **6.** 98.6 ÷ 2.9 = 34 34.0 **7.** 45.505 ÷ 9.5 = 479 4.79

Divide.

8. 0.685 ÷ 2.74 0.25 **9.** 9.483 ÷ 8.7 1.09 **10.** 0.8449 ÷ 0.71 1.19 **11.** 2.4 ÷ 0.3 8

12. 0.104 ÷ 0.08 1.3 **13.** 0.427 ÷ 6.1 0.07 **14.** 0.804 ÷ 0.4 2.01 **15.** 5.49 ÷ 0.9 6.1

16. 422.1 ÷ 60.3 7 **17.** 69.09 ÷ 7 9.87 **18.** 126.28 ÷ 8.2 15.4 **19.** 13.3666 ÷ 6.89 1.94

20. 0.3321 ÷ 4.1 0.081 **21.** 50.4 ÷ 1.2 42 **22.** 6.89 ÷ 1.3 5.3 **23.** 2.59 ÷ 0.7 3.7

24. 6.684 ÷ 0.06 111.4 **25.** 3.48 ÷ 5.8 0.6 **26.** 87.4 ÷ 0.38 230 **27.** 2.5 ÷ 0.005 500

28. **Health** A pharmacist has 808.4 g of a generic medicine. She must fill capsules with 37.6 g of the medicine per capsule. How many capsules can she fill? 21

PRACTICE 3-11

Fort Kearney

3-11 Exercises and Applications

Assignment Guide

- Basic
  1, 2–28 evens, 31–33, 38–54 evens
- Average
  3–33 odds, 34, 37–53 odds
- Enriched
  8–30 evens, 31–36, 38–54 evens

Exercise Notes

- **Exercises 9 and 13**

Error Prevention Watch for students who give the answer for Exercise 9 as 1.9 instead of 1.09 and the answer for Exercise 13 as 0.7 instead of 0.07. Remind them that zeros must be inserted as placeholders in each quotient.

PRACTICE

Name ______________________

Practice 3-11

Dividing by a Decimal

Insert a decimal point in the answer to make the equation true.

1. 7.4096 ÷ 1.1 = 6•7 3 6 **2.** 22.3443 ÷ 5.49 = 4•0 7 **3.** 3.1515 ÷ 1.5 = 2•1 0 1

4. 4.8225 ÷ 2.5 = 1•9 2 9 **5.** 17.22 ÷ 4.1 = 4•2 0 **6.** 12.576 ÷ 2.4 = 5•2 4

Divide.

7. 11.5213 ÷ 0.7	**8.** 5.18 ÷ 0.7	**9.** 8.7 ÷ 4.35	**10.** 37.014 ÷ 5.97
16.459	7.4	2	6.2
11. 0.3798 ÷ 0.18	**12.** 0.65232 ÷ 13.59	**13.** 100.859 ÷ 8.65	**14.** 0.51272 ÷ 0.754
2.11	0.048	11.66	0.68
15. 1.8136 ÷ 0.2	**16.** 46.2 ÷ 16.5	**17.** 3.915 ÷ 13.05	**18.** 1.44 ÷ 1.6
9.068	2.8	0.3	0.9
19. 20.013 ÷ 2.1	**20.** 0.65355 ÷ 0.15	**21.** 1.265 ÷ 0.23	**22.** 19.76 ÷ 2.6
9.53	4.357	5.5	7.6
23. 2.2242 ÷ 0.33	**24.** 46.02 ÷ 3.9	**25.** 1.512 ÷ 0.672	**26.** 0.061 ÷ 0.1
6.74	11.8	2.25	0.61
27. 3.86 ÷ 3.86	**28.** 7.896 ÷ 3.29	**29.** 9.8072 ÷ 5.33	**30.** 3.0768 ÷ 0.8
1	2.4	1.84	3.846
31. 0.908 ÷ 4.54	**32.** 0.056 ÷ 1.4	**33.** 9.57 ÷ 2.9	**34.** 0.414 ÷ 4.6
0.2	0.04	3.3	0.09
35. 92.7 ÷ 12.36	**36.** 1.9312 ÷ 1.136	**37.** 18.65 ÷ 2.5	**38.** 132.16 ÷ 11.2
7.5	1.7	7.46	11.8

39. **Science** Jupiter revolves around the Sun once every 11.86 years. How many times does it revolve in 40.324 years? 3.4

40. **Health** 4.7 oz of pistachio nuts contain 1.786 mg of zinc. How much zinc is in 1 oz of pistachios? 0.38 mg

RETEACHING

Name ______________________

Alternative Lesson 3-11

Dividing by a Decimal

When you divide by a decimal, you need to rewrite the problem so that you are dividing by a whole number. You can do this by multiplying the divisor by a power of 10 that will make the divisor a whole number and multiplying the dividend by the same factor. Remember that you can multiply a decimal by 10, 100, or 1000 by moving the decimal point to the right 1, 2, or 3 places.

2.0 ← quotient
1.2)24.0
divisor dividend

Example

Find the quotient: 7.84 ÷ 1.4.

Multiply the divisor and the dividend by 10 to make the divisor a whole number. Move the decimal point 1 place to the right in each number. 1.4)7.84 → 14.)78.4

Divide as you would with whole numbers.

```
   5.6
14.)78.4
    70
     8 4
     8 4
```

Remember to write the decimal point in the quotient above the moved decimal point in the dividend.

So, 7.84 ÷ 1.4 = 5.6.

Try It Divide: 5.65 ÷ 4.52.

```
    1.25
4.52)5.65
```

a. Divide as if you were dividing whole numbers. Show your work.

b. How many decimal places are in the divisor? 2 places.

c. Move the decimal point in the divisor and dividend. Will you need to annex zeros in the dividend? Yes.

d. Write the quotient. Place the decimal point above the moved decimal point in the quotient.

Divide. Write your answer above the dividend.

e. 0.04)0.38 9.5 f. 0.25)4.05 16.2 g. 0.85)7.055 8.3 h. 3.7)0.296 0.08

i. 5.6 ÷ 0.4 14 j. 0.72 ÷ 0.9 0.8

k. 2.25 ÷ 0.5 4.5 l. 0.636 ÷ 0.6 1.06

m. 2.52 ÷ 0.7 3.6 n. 0.027 ÷ 0.03 0.9

Reteaching

Activity

Materials: Newspapers

- Work in groups of three. Cut out advertisements from newspapers that contain the cost of items as well as the weight of the items.
- Check that both the cost and weight are decimal numbers.
- Divide the cost of the item by its weight to determine the cost per ounce.
- For example, tortilla chips were advertised at $1.99 for 14.25 ounces. The cost per ounce is found by dividing 1.99 by 14.25.
- Make a chart giving the unit price for at least six items.

Exercise Notes

■ Exercise 30

Consumer Point out that odometers measure to the nearest tenth of a mile and gasoline pumps measure to the nearest tenth of a gallon.

Exercise Answers

34. Dividing by a number greater than 1 will give you an answer smaller than the dividend. Dividing by a number less than 1 will give you an answer greater than the dividend.
35. Moves the decimal to the right; $5 \div 0.1 = 50$; $5 \div 0.01 = 500$, $5 \div 0.001 = 5000$
36. 0.0625, 0.03125, 0.015625; Divide by 2
37. $15 \times 15 \times 15$
38. $8 \times 8 \times 8 \times 2 \times 2 \times 2 \times 2$
39. $7 \times 7 \times 7 \times 8 \times 8$
40. 29×29
41. $34 \times 34 \times 34 \times 34 \times 34 \times 34 \times 34 \times 34 \times 34$
42. $6 \times 6 \times 6 \times 6 \times 6 \times 6 \times 6 \times 6 \times 6 \times 6 \times 6$
43. $1 \times 1 \times 1 \times 1 \times 1$
44. $2 \times 2 \times 2 \times 2 \times 2$
45. $3 \times 3 \times 3 \times 3 \times 3 \times 3$
46. $4 \times 4 \times 4 \times 4 \times 4 \times 4 \times 4 \times 4 \times 6 \times 6 \times 6 \times 6 \times 6 \times 6 \times 6$
47. $10 \times 10 \times 10 \times 10 \times 10 \times 10 \times 10 \times 10 \times 10$
48. $12 \times 12 \times 12 \times 12 \times 12$

Alternate Assessment

You may want to use the *Interactive CD-ROM Journal* with this assessment.

Journal Have students write a paragraph explaining how they know what number to multiply the dividend and divisor by when the divisor is a decimal.

► Quick Quiz

Divide.

1. $2.436 \div 5.8$ 0.42
2. $1.224 \div 0.6$ 2.04
3. $3.5 \div 0.005$ 700
4. $3528 \div 9.8$ 360

Available on Daily Transparency 3-11

29. History In the early 1850s, "Wind Wagon Thomas" invented a wind wagon that was half sailboat and half wagon. The wind wagon would have taken 133.5 days to travel 1968.4 miles. About how fast did the wind wagon travel? **14.74 mi per day**

30. The Figueroas traveled 501.5 miles on 15.4 gallons of gas. How many miles per gallon did they get, to the nearest tenth? **32.6**

31. Test Prep The Smith's wagon train was about 98.98 feet long. Each wagon was about 9.8 feet long. If the wagons traveled end to end, how many wagons were in the train? **A**

Ⓐ 10 Ⓑ 10.1 Ⓒ 11 Ⓓ 100

Problem Solving and Reasoning

32. Critical Thinking In Fort Hall, Idaho, emigrants could buy 10 pounds of candles for \$2.50 or 100 pounds of sugar for \$12.50. Which item costs less per pound? **Sugar**

34.  Explain what numbers you can divide by to get a quotient smaller than the dividend and what numbers you can divide by to get a quotient larger than the dividend.

33. Choose a Strategy GPS Manuel was counting the lights on parade floats. Each float was 36.4 feet long, and they ran bumper to bumper for 5314.4 feet. If there were 150 lights on each float, how many lights did he count? **21,900**

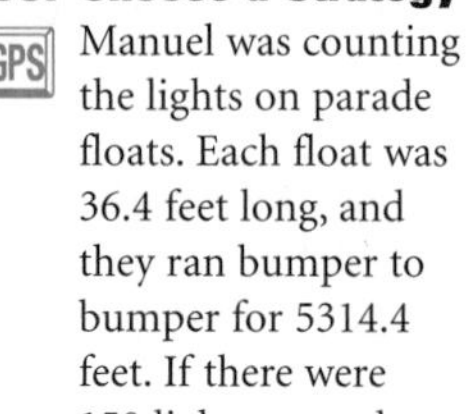

35. Communicate Remember that multiplying by 0.1, 0.01, and 0.001 moves the decimal to the left. Explain what dividing by 0.1, 0.01, and 0.001 does. Show an example of each.

36. Critical Thinking Find the next three numbers in the pattern, and explain what the pattern is:
32, 16, 8, 4, 2, 1, 0.5, 0.25, 0.125, …

Mixed Review

Write each number in expanded form. *[Lesson 2-4]*

37. 15^3 **38.** $8^3 \times 2^4$ **39.** $7^3 \times 8^2$ **40.** 29^2 **41.** 34^9 **42.** 6^{11}

43. 1^5 **44.** 2^5 **45.** 3^6 **46.** $4^8 \times 6^7$ **47.** 10^9 **48.** 12^5

Solve. *[Lesson 3-7]*

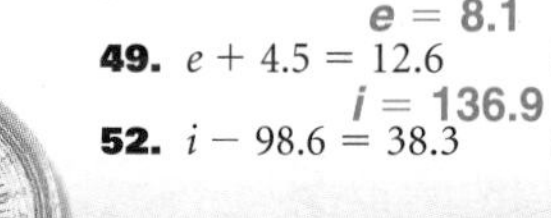

49. $e + 4.5 = 12.6$ $e = 8.1$ **50.** $\$20 + f = \$22.55$ $f = \$2.55$ **51.** $3.9 = g + 2.7$ $g = 1.2$

52. $i - 98.6 = 38.3$ $i = 136.9$ **53.** $j + 0.5 = 1.8$ $j = 1.3$ **54.** $m - 0.056 = 0.077$ $m = 0.133$

PROBLEM SOLVING 3-11

194 *Chapter 3 • Decimals*

PROBLEM SOLVING

Name ____________ **Guided Problem Solving 3-11**

GPS PROBLEM 33, STUDENT PAGE 194

Manuel was counting the lights on parade floats. Each float was 36.4 feet long, and they ran bumper to bumper for 5314.4 feet. If there were 150 lights on each float, how many lights did he count?

— Understand —

1. What are you asked to find? How many lights Manuel counted.
2. Underline the information you need.

— Plan —

3. How can you find how many floats were in the parade? Divide the total length by the length of a float.
4. Given the number of floats, how can you find the number of lights? Multiply the number of floats by the number of lights on each float.

— Solve —

5. Write equations showing the number of floats and lights on floats in the parade.
   a. Floats $5314.4 \div 36.4 = 146$ b. Lights $146 \times 150 = 21{,}900$
6. How many lights did Manuel count? 21,900 lights.

— Look Back —

7. How could you use the strategy, Solve a Simpler Problem, to find the number of lights? Possible answer: Use one-digit whole numbers to discover the steps needed to find the answer.

SOLVE ANOTHER PROBLEM

Cybill was counting the lights on her neighbor's fence. Each section of the fence was 6.2 feet long, and the fence was 210.8 feet long. If there were 25 lights on each section, how many lights did she count?
850 lights.

ENRICHMENT

Name ____________ **Extend Your Thinking 3-11**

Patterns in Numbers

You can find patterns in these division problems.

1. Find each quotient.

a. $80 \div 40 =$ 2	a. $60{,}000 \div 12{,}000 =$ 5
b. $80 \div 20 =$ 4	b. $6{,}000 \div 1{,}200 =$ 5
c. $80 \div 10 =$ 8	c. $600 \div 120 =$ 5
d. $80 \div 5 =$ 16	d. $60 \div 12 =$ 5
e. $80 \div 2.5 =$ 32	e. $6 \div 1.2 =$ 5
f. $80 \div 1.25 =$ 64	f. $0.6 \div 0.12 =$ 5

2. What pattern do you see in the first column? Possible answer: Dividends stay the same, divisors are divided by 2, quotients are multiplied by 2.
3. What pattern do you see in the second column? Possible answer: Dividends are divided by 10, divisors divided by ten, quotients stay the same.
4. Use what you know about the patterns above to find each quotient.

a. $72 \div 36 =$ 2	a. $400 \div 200 =$ 2
b. $72 \div 18 =$ 4	b. $40 \div 20 =$ 2
c. $72 \div 9 =$ 8	c. $4 \div 2 =$ 2
d. $72 \div 4.5 =$ 16	d. $0.4 \div 0.2 =$ 2
e. $72 \div 2.25 =$ 32	e. $0.04 \div 0.02 =$ 2

5. In Question 4, when did you stop calculating and start using what you know about patterns? Why did you stop at that place? Possible answer: Part b, since the patterns are similar to those in Question 1.

Solving Decimal Equations: Multiplication and Division

3-12

▶ Lesson Link In the last section, you used mental math to solve addition and subtraction equations involving decimals. Now you'll use mental math again to solve multiplication and division equations involving decimals. ◀

You'll Learn ...

- how to solve decimal equations with multiplication and division
- how to solve equations using inverse operations when mental math isn't convenient

... How It's Used

Sailors use decimal equations to determine how fast to travel to reach a given port on a given day.

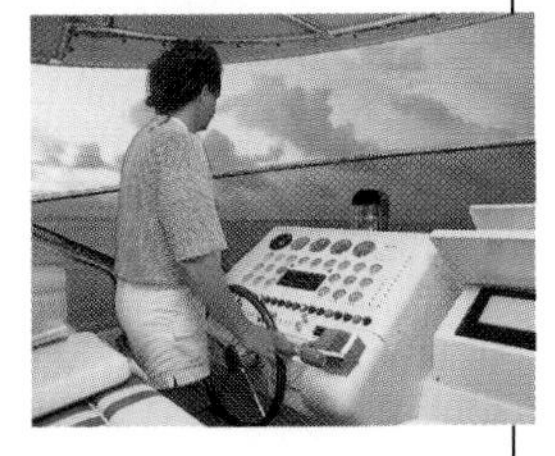

Explore — Multiplication and Division Equations

"Sorry, Shopping Carts Haven't Been Invented Yet!"

The table lists prices of items that pioneers could buy in 1850 in Independence, Missouri, before setting out on the Oregon Trail. The people named actually traveled the Oregon Trail.

- Sarah York said, "I bought 3 of the same item for $9. The price for each item was *v*."
- Henderson Luelling said, "I bought 2 of the same item for $3.40. The price for each item was *w*."
- Narcissa Whitman said, "I paid $0.75 for *x* pounds of rice."
- Peter Burnett said, "I bought 100 of the same item for $15. The price for each item was *y*."
- Randolph Marcy said, "I paid $18 for *z* yards of cloth."

ITEM	COST ($)
Beans	1.50/bushel
Blanket	1.70
Bucket	0.30
Cloth	0.25/yard
Corn Meal	0.17/lb
Flour	3.00/sack
Lard	0.10/lb
Rice	0.15/lb
Salt	0.02/lb
Tent	15.00
Tools	4.50/set

1. Write an equation that represents each pioneer's statement.

2. For each pioneer, list the item purchased, the individual price, and how many items were purchased.

3. Make up a problem involving a pioneer on the Oregon Trail and a price given in the table. Have another student solve your problem.

MEETING INDIVIDUAL NEEDS

Resources

3-12 Practice
3-12 Reteaching
3-12 Problem Solving
3-12 Enrichment
3-12 Daily Transparency
Problem of the Day
Review
Quick Quiz
Teaching Tool Transparencies 2, 3
Technology Master 15

Learning Modalities

Logical Use a flowchart to show the steps involved in solving multiplication or division equations with decimals.

Kinesthetic Use play money, including coins, to represent various situations in which multiplication and division equations with decimals might occur.

Inclusion

Model many simple equations before asking students to write and solve equations. Remind students to add new vocabulary to their reference book.

3-12 Lesson Organizer

Objectives

- Solve decimal equations with multiplication and division.
- Solve equations using inverse operations when mental math isn't convenient.

NCTM Standards

- 1–4, 9

▶ Review

Do these mentally.

1. $8m = 72$ $m = 9$
2. $6x = 24$ $x = 4$
3. $3m = 45$ $m = 15$
4. $\frac{y}{10} = 20$ $y = 200$

Available on Daily Transparency 3-12

1 Introduce

Explore

The Point
Students write and solve multiplication and division equations involving decimals.

Ongoing Assessment
Watch for students who set up equations incorrectly. For example, some might write $\$0.75x = 0.15$ as the equation for Narcissa.

For Groups That Finish Early
What equation would describe the following: "I bought *x* buckets for $1.20." $0.30x = 1.20$ Use the table to write other similar sentences and have other members in your group write an equation that would describe each sentence.

Answers for Explore on next page.

Answers for Explore

1. Sarah: $3v = \$9$; Henderson: $2w = \$3.40$; Narcissa: $\$0.75 \div x = \$0.15$; Peter: $100y = \$15$; Randolph: $\$18 \div z = \$0.25$
2. Sarah: Flour, $3, 3 sacks; Henderson: Blankets, $1.70, 2 blankets; Narcissa: Rice, $0.15, 5 lb; Peter: Rice, $0.15, 100 lb; Randolph: Cloth, $0.25, 72 yards
3. Possible answer: Narcissa Whitman said, "I bought 4 of the same item for $0.68. The price for each item was *j*."

2 Teach

Learn

Alternate Examples

1. Solve: $\frac{x}{6} = 0.7$

   Think of the numbers as whole numbers. Read as "What number divided by 6 equals 7?" Use mental math.

   $\frac{42}{6} = 7$.

   Since there is one digit after the decimal in 0.7, there should be one digit after the decimal in 4.2. So $x = 4.2$.

2. After a year Maria sold a book for 0.6 times what she paid for it. If she sold the book for $9.60, what did she originally pay for it?

   Let p = the original price of the book.

   $0.6p = 9.60$.

   Think of the numbers as whole numbers.

   $6p = 960$. Use mental math. $6 \times \mathbf{160} = 960$.

   There are two decimal places in 9.60 and only one in 0.6. There should be one decimal place in 16.0

   The original price of the book was $16.00.

3 Practice and Assess

Check

Answers for Check Your Understanding

1. Number sense helps you place the decimal point correctly.
2. Possible answer: I bought 0.5 lb of nuts for $3.50. What was the price per pound?

Learn — Solving Multiplication and Division Equations

You can solve multiplication and division equations with decimals using mental math and number sense. Use mental math to determine the digits in the answer. Then, use number sense to determine where the decimal should be placed.

Examples

1 Solve: $\frac{x}{3} = 0.5$

$\frac{x}{3} = 0.5 \rightarrow \frac{x}{3} = 5$ — Think of the numbers as whole numbers. Read as "What number divided by 3 equals 5?"

$\frac{\mathbf{15}}{3} = 5$ — Use mental math.

$\frac{1.5}{3} = 0.5$ — Since there is one digit after the decimal in 0.5, there should be one digit after the decimal in 1.5.

x is equal to 1.5.

2 At Fort Laramie, many emigrants sold their furniture for 0.2 times what they paid for it, just to lighten their wagons. If a family sold a dresser for $3.80, what did they pay for it originally?

Let p = the original price of the dresser.

$0.2p = 3.80 \rightarrow 2p = 380$ — Think of the numbers as whole numbers. Read as "What number times 2 equals 380?"

$2 \times \mathbf{190} = 380$ — Use mental math.

$0.2 \times \mathbf{19.0} = 3.80$ — There are two decimal places in 3.80 and only one in 0.2. There should be one decimal place in 19.0.

The original price of the dresser was $19.00.

Try It

Solve each equation.

a. $3j = 2.1$ $j = 0.7$ **b.** $0.4w = 2.4$ $w = 6$ **c.** $\frac{t}{5} = 1.1$ $t = 5.5$ **d.** $\frac{f}{0.7} = 0.7$ $f = 0.49$

History Link

Traveling the Oregon Trail was expensive. Few poor people made the journey because they could not afford the supplies.

"Pilgrims on the Plains", sketched by Theo. R. Davis

Check — Your Understanding

1. How does number sense help you to solve decimal equations?
2. Give a real-world problem modeled by $0.5x = 3.5$.

MATH EVERY DAY

Problem of the Day

Sound travels at a speed of about 1 mile in 5 seconds. If you see a streak of lightning and count off 22 seconds before you hear a clap of thunder, how far away was the lightning? Write an equation that represents this information. Solve the problem.

If x represents the distance from the lightning, then: $5x = 22$ or $x = 22 \div 5$; 4.4 miles

Available on Daily Transparency 3-12

An Extension is provided in the transparency package.

Fact of the Day

In 1848, the population of San Francisco was about 800. By 1850, it had grown to more than 30,000.

Mental Math

Find each product mentally.

1. $0 \times 10 \times 20$ 0
2. $4 \times 25 \times 16$ 1600
3. $7 \times 11 \times 100$ 7700
4. $4 \times 23 \times 25$ 2300

3-12 Exercises and Applications

Practice and Apply

1. **Getting Started** Which of the given values of x will make the equation true?

   a. $0.024x = 24$; 0.001 or 1000 **1000**

   b. $\frac{450}{x} = 4.5$; 100 or 1000 **100**

   c. $8.5 \div x = 85$; 0.1 or 10 **0.1**

   d. $78.34x = 7.834$; 1 or 0.1 **0.1**

Solve.

2. $0.5d = 0.045$ $d = 0.09$
3. $\frac{e}{3} = 0.21$ $e = 0.63$
4. $\frac{t}{9} = 0.07$ $t = 0.63$
5. $0.7r = 35$ $r = 50$
6. $0.9g = 72$ $g = 80$
7. $1.6w = 0.032$ $w = 0.02$
8. $\frac{p}{0.02} = 4.4$ $p = 0.088$
9. $\frac{s}{1.07} = 107$ $s = 114.49$
10. $9b = 8.1$ $b = 0.9$
11. $\frac{u}{1.5} = 30$ $u = 45$
12. $0.09k = 0.063$ $k = 0.7$
13. $\frac{q}{5} = 2.5$ $q = 12.5$
14. $\frac{p}{0.3} = 11$ $p = 3.3$
15. $0.6h = 3.6$ $h = 6$
16. $0.4m = 0.004$ $m = 0.01$
17. $0.8n = 0.056$ $n = 0.07$
18. $\frac{s}{0.07} = 0.4$ $s = 0.028$
19. $\frac{v}{6} = 1.8$ $v = 10.8$
20. $1.2z = 0.144$ $z = 0.12$
21. $8k = 0.64$ $k = 0.08$
22. $1.1a = 0.066$ $a = 0.06$
23. $\frac{j}{0.7} = 0.2$ $j = 0.14$
24. $\frac{f}{10} = 1.13$ $f = 11.3$
25. $\frac{u}{0.4} = 0.05$ $u = 0.02$

For Exercises 26–31, set up an equation and solve.

26. Along the Oregon Trail, the Spikle family left Fort Boise with 36 kilograms (kg) of flour. They divided it into bags of 0.6 kg. How many bags did they have? $0.6x = 36$; 60

27. The Carlson family spent several days hiking through the Rocky Mountains. Every day, they hiked 8.3 miles. At the end of the vacation, they had hiked a total of 83 miles. How many days did they hike? $8.3d = 83$; 10 days

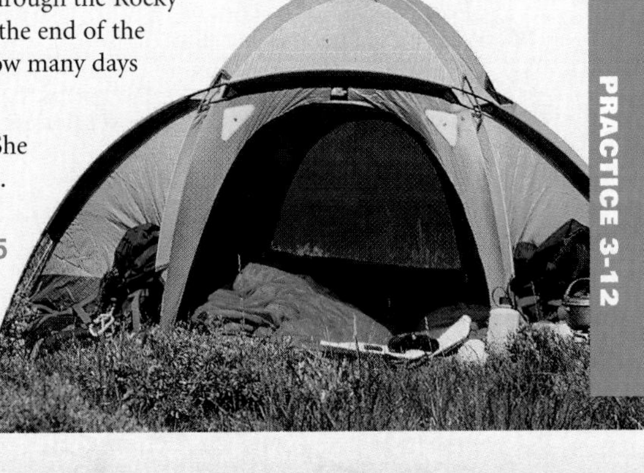

28. Helen put several stamps on a large envelope. She placed 6 stamps of equal value on the envelope. The stamps together were worth \$0.90. How much was each stamp worth? $\frac{0.9}{6} = s$; \$0.15

29. A chemist conducting an experiment took a package of salt and split the contents into nine even groups. Each group weighed 0.08 kilograms. How much salt was in the original package? $\frac{t}{9} = 0.08$; 0.72 kg.

PRACTICE 3-12

Assignment Guide

- **Basic**
  1–25 odds, 26, 31–34, 36–44 evens
- **Average**
  3–31 odds, 32–38, 39–43 odds
- **Enriched**
  6–24 evens, 27–35, 36–44 evens

Exercise Notes

Exercises 2–25

Error Prevention Watch for students who give answers with the correct digits but incorrectly place the decimal point. Remind them that they should always check their answers when they solve an equation.

PRACTICE

Name ______________________

Practice 3-12

Solving Decimal Equations: Multiplication and Division

Solve.

1. $4n = 1.72$ $n =$ 0.43	2. $\frac{d}{2.5} = 1.263$ $d =$ 3.1575	3. $0.9g = 9.99$ $g =$ 11.1	4. $1.9v = 9.025$ $v =$ 4.75
5. $\frac{r}{0.8} = 11.279$ $r =$ 9.0232	6. $\frac{n}{0.5} = 1.537$ $n =$ 0.7685	7. $1.2k = 7.968$ $k =$ 6.64	8. $\frac{s}{0.85} = 2.4$ $s =$ 2.04
9. $8.3y = 28.967$ $y =$ 3.49	10. $\frac{a}{5.5} = 6.25$ $a =$ 34.375	11. $5.9c = 8.555$ $c =$ 1.45	12. $\frac{x}{8.1} = 6.31$ $x =$ 51.111
13. $8.5t = 77.18$ $t =$ 9.08	14. $\frac{b}{3.5} = 6.5$ $b =$ 22.75	15. $1.1s = 0.726$ $s =$ 0.66	16. $\frac{w}{13} = 0.12$ $w =$ 1.56
17. $0.1t = 1.1$ $t =$ 11	18. $\frac{m}{6.7} = 1.57$ $m =$ 10.519	19. $3.59p = 4.308$ $p =$ 1.2	20. $\frac{k}{4.67} = 10.8$ $k =$ 50.436
21. $0.15n = 1.3575$ $n =$ 9.05	22. $\frac{d}{0.243} = 0.1$ $d =$ 0.0243	23. $0.65p = 0.5395$ $p =$ 0.83	24. $\frac{m}{3.902} = 5$ $m =$ 19.51
25. $\frac{r}{0.35} = 2.76$ $r =$ 0.966	26. $\frac{c}{4.1} = 5.48$ $c =$ 22.468	27. $\frac{u}{6.9} = 10.3$ $u =$ 71.07	28. $8.77m = 6.139$ $m =$ 0.7
29. $2.94q = 7.35$ $q =$ 2.5	30. $5.6t = 58.8$ $t =$ 10.5	31. $0.8d = 9.816$ $d =$ 12.27	32. $13.41w = 17.433$ $w =$ 1.3

For Exercises 33 and 34, set up an equation and solve.

33. Yesterday Helen used one-seventh of the vegetable oil in her kitchen. If she used 2.43 oz, how much did she have originally? $\frac{x}{7} = 2.43$; $x = 17.01$ oz

34. **Consumer** In 1994, the Louisiana sales tax on an item was 0.04 times the price of the item. If Tom paid \$1.09 in sales tax when he bought a shirt, what was the price of the shirt? $0.04x = 1.09$; $x = \$27.25$

RETEACHING

Name ______________________

Alternative Lesson 3-12

Solving Decimal Equations: Multiplication and Division

You can solve multiplication and division equations using mental math and number sense. Use mental math to determine the digits in the answer and number sense to decide where to place the decimal point.

Example

Solve $4x = 3.6$.

Step 1: Think of the numbers as whole numbers. $4x = 3.6 \rightarrow 4x = 36$

Step 2: Think: What number times 4 equals 36? $4x = 36$

Step 3: Use mental math. $4 \times \mathbf{9} = 36$

Step 4: Determine where to place the decimal point. There is one decimal point in the product, 3.6, so there should be one decimal point in one of the factors. Since there is not a decimal point in the known factor, 4, there will be one decimal point in the value of x. Write 9 as 0.9.

Step 5: Check to see that the equation is true. $4 \times 0.9 = 3.6$

In the equation $4x = 3.6$, x is equal to 0.9.

Try It Solve $a \div 6 = 0.04$.

a. Rewrite the equation using whole numbers. $a \div 6 = 4$

b. What number divided by 6 equals 4? 24

c. The divisor, 6, is a whole number and there are two digits after the decimal point in the quotient, 0.04. How many digits are after the decimal point in the dividend, a? 2 digits.

d. $a =$ 0.24

e. Show that the equation is true. $0.24 \div 6 = 0.04$

Solve each equation.

f. $2r = 1.4$	$r =$ 0.7	g. $s \div 4 = 2.2$	$s =$ 8.8
h. $\frac{b}{5} = 0.5$	$b =$ 2.5	i. $0.7c = 0.49$	$c =$ 0.7
j. $1.5d = 0.45$	$d =$ 0.3	k. $n \div 3 = 1.2$	$n =$ 3.6
l. $0.09c = 0.108$	$c =$ 1.2	i. $\frac{g}{2} = 3.4$	$b =$ 6.8

Reteaching

Activity

Materials: Counters

- Work with counters such as buttons or beans to model solving whole-number equations like $4x = 28$.
- Discuss how you could use these same equations to solve similar decimal equations like $0.4x = 28$.

Exercise Notes

■ Exercise 32

Test Prep If students selected B, they divided 77.5 by 3.1 to get 25. However, the given equation requires that 3.1 be divided by 77.5 to solve for *x*.

■ Exercise 33

History The Santa Fe Trail was a trade route that extended from western Missouri to Santa Fe, New Mexico. It opened in 1821 and was in use until the Santa Fe Railroad opened in 1880.

Problem-Solving Tip You may wish to use Teaching Tool Transparencies 2 and 3: Guided Problem Solving, pages 1–2.

Exercise Answers

34. Possible answer: $0.6x = 7.2$

35. The x could have any value in $0.3x$; for $0.3x = 2.1$, only one value will make the equation true.

Alternate Assessment

You may want to use the *Interactive CD-ROM Journal* with this assessment.

Journal Have students write one or more paragraphs describing how solving equations in this lesson is similar to or different from solving equations in previous lessons.

Quick Quiz

Solve.

1. $0.3m = 0.015$ $m = 0.05$
2. $\frac{y}{4} = 0.16$ $y = 0.64$
3. $\frac{x}{10} = 0.9$ $x = 9$
4. $0.4t = 36$ $t = 90$

Available on Daily Transparency 3-12

---

30. Science In a 2-week science experiment, a corn plant grew four times as much as a bean plant. If the corn plant grew 6.0 cm, how much did the bean plant grow? $4b = 6.0$ cm; 1.5 cm

31. GPS A wagon weighs 165.3 kg. Carrying riders, the wagon weighs 465 kg. What is the weight of the riders? $465 - x = 165.3$; 299.7 kg

32. Test Prep The mass of Object A is 25 grams. The mass of Object B is 77.5 grams. Choose the correct equation, where x is the mass of Object A. A

Ⓐ $3.1x = 77.5$ Ⓑ $77.5x = 3.1$

Ⓒ $\frac{3.1}{x} = 77.5$ Ⓓ Not here

Problem Solving and Reasoning

33. Choose a Strategy Traders used the Santa Fe Trail to take manufactured goods from Kansas City to Santa Fe and return with gold, silver, furs, and wool. The wagons averaged 6.5 miles per hour over the 800-mile trail. They could travel 7 hours per day. How many days would it take the traders to make a round trip from Kansas City? 36

34. Communicate Write an equation involving decimal multiplication or division where the answer is 12.

35. Journal Explain the difference between the expression $0.3x$ and $0.3x = 2.1$.

Problem Solving

STRATEGIES

- Look for a Pattern
- Make an Organized List
- Make a Table
- Guess and Check
- Work Backward
- Use Logical Reasoning
- Draw a Diagram
- Solve a Simpler Problem

Mixed Review

Use the Calories in a Meal graph to answer each question. *[Lesson 1-1]*

36. What is the total number of calories for this meal? 823

37. Which part of the meal has the most calories? Greek pasta salad

38. How many combined calories are in the shake and the dessert? 385

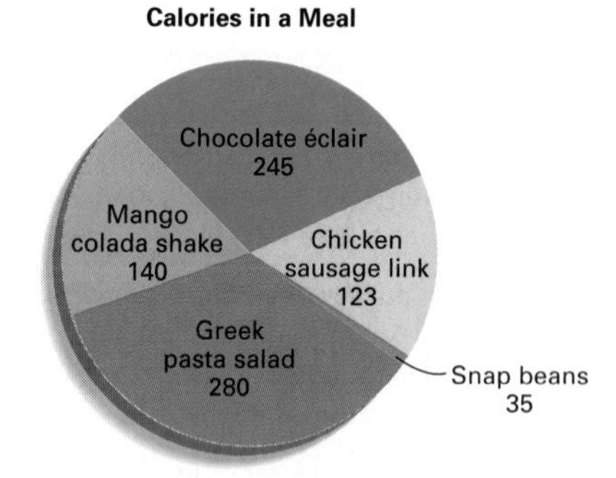

Multiply. *[Lesson 3-8]*

39. 1.45×6 8.7 **40.** 4.07×3 12.21 **41.** 5×4.36 21.8

42. 83×1.2 99.6 **43.** 51×1.06 54.06 **44.** 3.8×5 19

PROBLEM SOLVING 3-12

PROBLEM SOLVING

Name ____________ Guided Problem Solving 3-12

GPS PROBLEM 31, STUDENT PAGE 198

A wagon weighs 165.3 kg. Carrying riders, the wagon weighs 465 kg. What is the weight of the riders?

— Understand —

1. How much does the empty wagon weigh? 165.3 kg
2. How much does the wagon with riders weigh? 465 kg

— Plan —

3. Which operation will you use to find the weight of the riders? Subtraction.
4. Which number sentence would be a good estimate for the weight of the riders? a

a. $500 - 200 = 300$ b. $500 \times 200 = 1000$ c. $500 + 200 = 700$

— Solve —

5. How much more does the wagon carrying riders weigh than the empty wagon? 299.7 kg
6. Write a sentence that gives the weight of the riders. Possible answer: The weight of the riders is 299.7 kg.

— Look Back —

7. Compare the weight you found in Item 5 to your estimate in Item 4. How can you use these two answers to see if your answer is correct? Possible answer: The estimate is 300, and the weight is 299.7. Both amounts are about the same, so the answer is correct.

8. Show another way to check your answer. $299.7 + 165.3 = 465$

SOLVE ANOTHER PROBLEM

A dog weighs 84.8 kg. Carrying a backpack filled with some cans of food, the dog weighs about 100 kg. What is the weight of the cans of food? 15.2 kg

ENRICHMENT

Name ____________ Extend Your Thinking 3-12

Decision Making

Many food products are packaged in a variety of sizes. The list below gives the sizes and costs of fruit juice drinks at one store.

$1.92 single-serving multi-pack (serves 6) $1.12 one quart (serves 4)
$2.16 two quarts (serves 8) $3.52 one gallon (serves 16)

1. Choose two different sizes and give an advantage for buying each. Possible answer: Single servings are convenient to take in lunches; Gallons are better for a large group.

2. What is the cost per serving for each of the fruit juice packages? Which is the most economical? Single: $0.32; Quart: $0.28; Two quarts: $0.27; Gallon: $0.22; Gallon is most economical.

3. Suppose you need to have 22 servings of the juice drink. Which size or sizes of containers would you buy? Explain. Possible answer: One gallon and two quarts is least expensive choice, although there would be 2 servings left over.

4. Choose your favorite breakfast cereal. Go to the grocery store and record the number of ounces, the cost, and the number of servings for each size available. Then compute the cost per serving. Check students' answers.

Size (in ounces)	Cost	Number of servings	Cost per serving

5. Which size is most economical? Check students' answers.

6. Which size box of cereal would you prefer to buy? Explain. Check students' answers.

Section 3C Connect

In this section, you've learned about the historic Oregon Trail. In recent years, new trails have been built for the enjoyment of hikers and backpackers. One of the best known is the John Muir Trail, a 209.8-mile path through California's Sierra Nevada Mountains.

Trials and Trails

You and some friends are planning a 3-day backpacking trip on the John Muir Trail. You want to hike one of the two trail sections shown in these "profiles."

Dollar Lake to Lake Marjorie

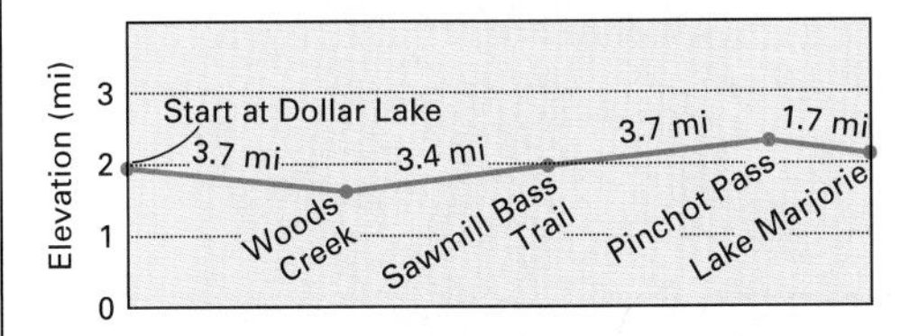

Lower Trinity Lake to Lyell Pass

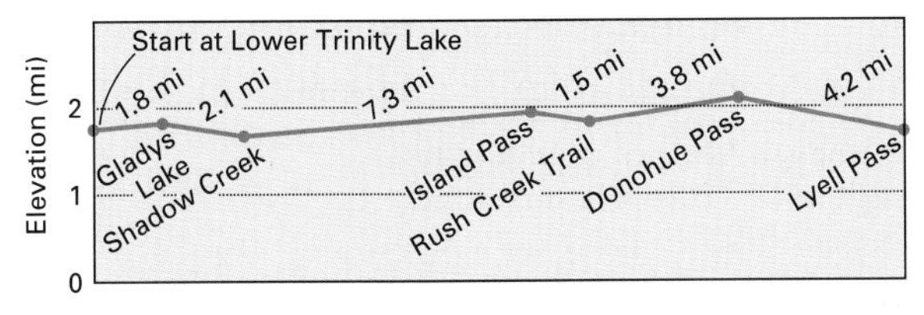

1. Find the length of each trail. Then calculate how long it will take you to hike each trail if you average 2.4 mi/hr.
2. Hiking uphill and downhill takes extra time. Each vertical mile uphill adds 2.5 hr onto the time you calculated in Question 1. Each vertical mile downhill adds 1.5 hr onto the time you calculated in Question 1. Use the vertical scale to estimate the up and down mileage of each trail section. Revise the total trail time you calculated in Question 1.
3. You plan to rest, on average, 0.25 hr for every hour of hiking time. Revise your total trail time again, this time adding rest time.
4. Which trail sections would you choose for a 3-day hike? Explain.

Trials and Trails

The Point

In *Trials and Trails* on page 175, students were introduced to the Oregon Trail. Now they will apply their decimal multiplication and division skills by calculating the time involved when hiking on a trail.

Resources

Lesson Enhancement Transparency 11

About the Page

- Discuss the trail profiles to be sure students understand what is shown.
- Clarify the term *vertical mile.* To help students understand why time is added for traveling vertical miles, ask why hiking uphill or downhill would take more time than hiking on flat ground.
- Ask students how many minutes they are resting each hour. 15 minutes
- Be sure students have answered Question 1 correctly before they continue their work.

Ongoing Assessment

Have students explain how they have calculated the hiking time for each trail.

Extension

Suppose you wanted to hike the entire John Muir Trail. Use the trail times you found in Question 3 to estimate how many hours it would take.

Answers for Connect

1. Section 1: 12.5 mi, 5.2 hrs;
   Section 2: 20.7 mi, 8.6 hrs.
2. Section 1: Up 0.7 mi, down 0.7 mi;
   About 5.2 + 2.8 = 8.0 hrs;
   Section 2: Up 0.7 mi, down 0.8 mi;
   About 8.6 + 3.0 = 11.6 hrs
3. Section 1: 8.0 + 2.00 = 10 hrs;
   Section 2: 11.6 + 2.90 hrs = 14.5 hrs
4. Shadow Creek to Island Pass because it will take a long time going uphill and stopping for rests.

3C Review

Review Correlation

Item(s)	Lesson(s)
1–8	3-4
9	3-8
10	3-11
11	3-8
12	3-9
13–20	3-6
21–22	3-11
23	3-9
24	3-11
25	3-10
26–30	3-12
31	3-2
32–33	3-12
34	3-8
35	3-10
36–37	3-6

Test Prep

Test-Taking Tip

Tell students to check for choices that can be immediately eliminated. In Exercise 36–37, answers C and D are obviously wrong because the whole number part of each choice is too large. Students are really left with a choice of only two answers, not four.

Section 3C Review

Write the number in standard form.

1. 5.6×10^6 5,600,000
2. 3.78×10^3 3780
3. 4×10^8 400,000,000
4. 7.3×10^{11} 730,000,000,000
5. 1.22×10^5 122,000
6. 1.6×10^{12} 1,600,000,000,000
7. 1.6×10^{10} 16,000,000,000
8. 3.94×10^7 39,400,000

Simplify.

9. 4.7×5 23.5
10. $2.4 \div 0.4$ 6
11. 625×0.4 250
12. 3.04×0.3 0.912
13. $12.6 + 8$ 20.6
14. $45.89 + 6.7$ 52.59
15. $80.05 - 20.03$ 60.02
16. $0.06 - 0.057$ 0.003
17. $6.73 - 4.69$ 2.04
18. $31.06 - 29$ 2.06
19. $167.55 + 143.2$ 310.75
20. $16.79 + 4.01$ 20.8
21. $259.2 \div 72$ 3.6
22. $3.68 \div 0.08$ 46
23. 6.65×0.42 2.793
24. $0.264 \div 0.24$ 1.1

25. Students at Washington Middle School formed a hiking club. On Saturdays, they hiked 9.1 km, 8.3 km, 12.4 km, 9.6 km, and 14.5 km. What was the average length of a hike for the club? 10.78 km

Solve.

26. $1.2t = 3.6$ $t = 3$
27. $\frac{u}{6} = 23.7$ $u = 142.2$
28. $0.02b = 0.4$ $b = 20$
29. $0.11n = 5.5$ $n = 50$
30. $\frac{w}{5.7} = 14.8$ $w = 84.36$
31. $s - 7.91 = 16.4$ $s = 24.31$
32. $\frac{t}{0.08} = 18.9$ $t = 1.512$
33. $0.01v = 8.3$ $v = 830$

34. The Mississippi River is 2340 miles long and 3.2 times longer than the Platte/South Platte River. How long is the Platte/South Platte River, to the nearest tenth of a mile? 731.3 miles

35. A store has Oregon Trail trading cards marked at seven for $2.50. How much does one card cost? $0.36

REVIEW 3C

Test Prep

Determining the number of decimal places in the answer can help eliminate wrong answers.

36. Subtract: $72.967 - 12.973$ B
    Ⓐ 58.994 Ⓑ 59.994 Ⓒ 589.94 Ⓓ 599.94

37. Add: $32.409 + 3.864$ B
    Ⓐ 35.273 Ⓑ 36.273 Ⓒ 70.049 Ⓓ 71.049

Resources

Practice Masters
Section 3C Review

Assessment Sourcebook
Quiz 3C

TestWorks
Test and Practice Software

PRACTICE

Name ______________________

Practice

Section 3C Review

Simplify.

1. 3×0.63 1.89
2. 0.016×0.02 0.00032
3. $205.65 \div 15$ 13.71
4. 26×0.009 0.234
5. $16.936 \div 73$ 0.232
6. 36×0.11 3.96
7. 0.05×4.9 0.245
8. $245.49 \div 30$ 8.183
9. 7×0.05 0.35
10. 0.07×0.845 0.05915
11. $140.6 \div 37$ 3.8
12. $27.216 \div 17.01$ 1.6

Write the number in standard form.

13. 3.84×10^3 3,840
14. 1.789×10^5 178,900
15. 6.4432×10^6 6,443,200
16. 6.387×10^9 6,387,000,000
17. 8.3764×10^4 83,764
18. 4.3857×10^{10} 43,857,000,000

Solve.

19. $4.63a = 12.964$ $a =$ 2.8
20. $\frac{d}{6.21} = 8.9$ $d =$ 55.269
21. $5w = 15.05$ $w =$ 3.01
22. $\frac{k}{0.81} = 7.39$ $k =$ 5.9859
23. $1.4f = 0.0882$ $f =$ 0.063
24. $0.9w = 0.5634$ $w =$ 0.626
25. $10.6g = 1.166$ $g =$ 0.11
26. $\frac{t}{4.61} = 6.7$ $t =$ 30.887

27. Five bunches of broccoli weigh 0.94 lb, 1.27 lb, 0.83 lb, 1.07 lb, and 0.98 lb. What is the average of these weights? 1.018 lb

28. **Science** A goat typically lives 4 times as long as a rat. A rat's lifetime lasts t years. Write an expression to show how long a goat lives. $4t$

29. In 1974, the federal minimum wage was $2.00 per hour. Use mental math to determine how much a worker earning minimum wage would be paid for working 38 hours. *[Lesson 2-5]* $76.00

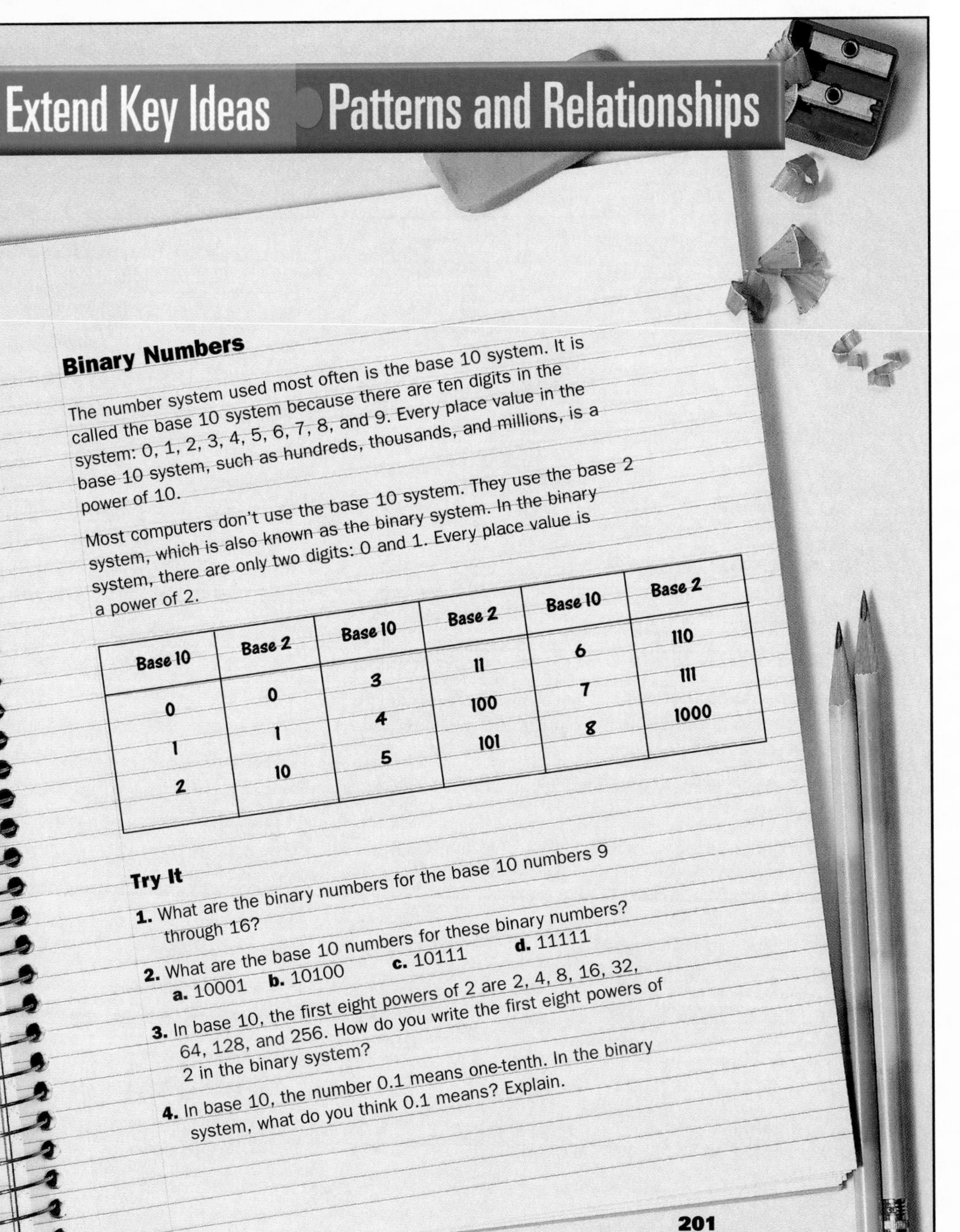

Extend Key Ideas Patterns and Relationships

Binary Numbers

The number system used most often is the base 10 system. It is called the base 10 system because there are ten digits in the system: 0, 1, 2, 3, 4, 5, 6, 7, 8, and 9. Every place value in the base 10 system, such as hundreds, thousands, and millions, is a power of 10.

Most computers don't use the base 10 system. They use the base 2 system, which is also known as the binary system. In the binary system, there are only two digits: 0 and 1. Every place value is a power of 2.

Base 10	Base 2	Base 10	Base 2	Base 10	Base 2
0	0	3	11	6	110
1	1	4	100	7	111
2	10	5	101	8	1000

Try It

1. What are the binary numbers for the base 10 numbers 9 through 16?
2. What are the base 10 numbers for these binary numbers?
   a. 10001 **b.** 10100 **c.** 10111 **d.** 11111
3. In base 10, the first eight powers of 2 are 2, 4, 8, 16, 32, 64, 128, and 256. How do you write the first eight powers of 2 in the binary system?
4. In base 10, the number 0.1 means one-tenth. In the binary system, what do you think 0.1 means? Explain.

201

Binary Numbers

The Point

Students are introduced to binary numbers and convert numbers between base 10 and base 2.

About the Page

- Students might benefit from seeing place-value charts in both base 10 and in base 2. Point out the similarities in the structure of the charts.
- To convert a binary number to a base-10 number, multiply the binary place value by the digit in that column and add the products.
- Computers use the binary system because the two digits can be represented by "on" and "off" switches.

Ask ...

- What are the place values of the columns in a binary number?
  From right to left: 1, 2, 4, 8, 16, 32, and so on.
- What is the binary number 1101 as a number in base 10?
  1(8) + 1(4) + 0(2) + 1(1) = 13

Extension

Have students try these addition problems in base 2. Suggest that they convert to base 10 to check their answers.

1. 11001 + 1100
   100101, 25 + 12 = 37
2. 101101 + 101101
   1011010, 45 + 45 = 90

Answers for Try It

1. 1001, 1010, 1011, 1100, 1101, 1110, 1111, 10000.
2. a. 17, b. 20, c. 23, d. 31
3. 10, 100, 1000, 10000, 100000, 1000000, 10000000, 100000000.
4. In base 10, 0.1 is $\frac{1}{10}$, so in base 2, 0.1 is $\frac{1}{2}$.

Chapter 3 Summary and Review

Review Correlation

Item(s)	Lesson(s)
1	3-1
2	3-2
3	3-3
4	3-4
5–6	3-5
7	3-6
8	3-3, 3-6
9	3-6
10	3-7
11–13	3-5
14	3-11
15	3-9
16	3-8
17	3-10
18	3-12

For additional review, see page 664.

Answers for Review

1. a. 0.25
   b. 0.7
2. a. 5.6
   b. 0.8
3. a. >
   b. <
4. a. 71,600
   b. 395,000
5. ≈ 700; 729.36
6. ≈ 270; 262.277
7. 65.92
8. 4.4 < 4.876
9. 6.4 mm
10. a. $t = 4.6$
    b. $k = 13.5$
11. ≈ 100; 128.8
12. ≈ 12; 13.25
13. ≈ 1; 0.893
14. ≈ 2; 2.2
15. 0.04533
16. 751
17. 0.367
18. 3.1

Chapter 3 Summary and Review

Graphic Organizer

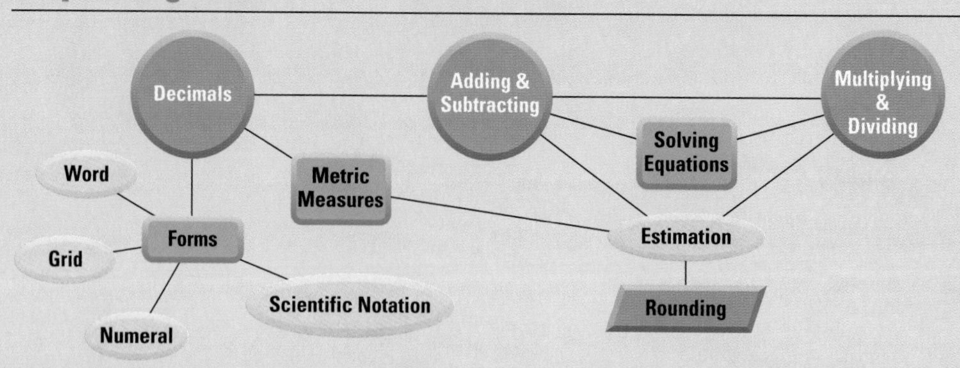

Section 3A Decimal Concepts

Summary

- Decimals can be represented in word, number, or grid form.
- Place values for decimal numbers mirror place values for whole numbers. Use place value to write, order, and compare numbers that are between two whole numbers.
- Annexing zeros or using a number line can help you order and compare decimals.
- Scientific notation is a way to write large numbers in a shorter form. A number in scientific notation has two factors: a number between 1 and 10, and a power of 10.

Review

1. Show each number in decimal form.

a. 25 hundredths

b.

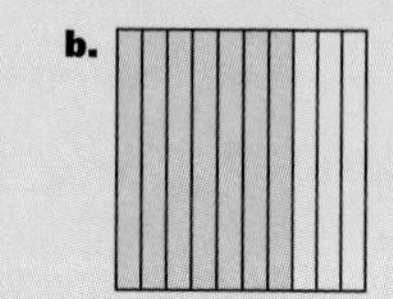

2. Round to the nearest tenth:

a. 5.63 **b.** 0.77

3. Compare using > or <:

a. 2.31 ☐ 2.13 **b.** 0.08 ☐ 0.6

4. Write in standard form:

a. 7.16×10^4 **b.** 3.95×10^5

Resources

Practice Masters
Cumulative Review Chapters 1–3

Assessment Sourcebook
Quarterly Test Chapters 1–3

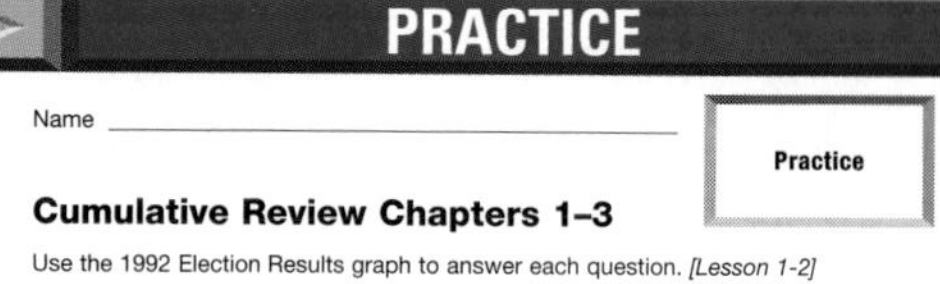

PRACTICE

Name ______________ Practice

Cumulative Review Chapters 1–3

Use the 1992 Election Results graph to answer each question. *[Lesson 1-2]*

1. Who had the most votes? Bill Clinton
2. About how many people voted for Ross Perot? About 19.7 million
3. Estimate the total number of votes shown in the data. About 104 million

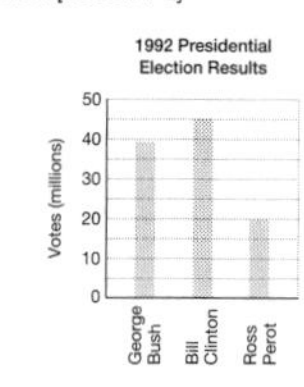

Round to the given place. *[Lesson 2-2]*

4. 27,341, thousands 27,000
5. 3,137,621, hundred-thousands 3,100,000

For Exercises 6–11, compare using <, >, or =. *[Lesson 3-3]*

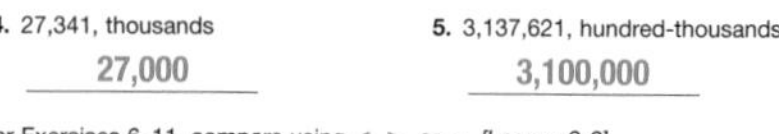

6. 3.9 (>) 3.87 7. 7.03 (<) 7.30 8. 9.26 (<) 9.62
9. 3.4 (<) 4.3 10. 8.64 (=) 8.640 11. 12.75 (>) 12.7499

Estimate each sum, difference, product, or quotient. *[Lesson 3-5]*

12. 12.63 + 4.07 ≈ 17 13. 3.96 − 1.24 ≈ 3 14. \$9.14 × 7.2 ≈ \$63 15. 26.64 ÷ 8.73 ≈ 3

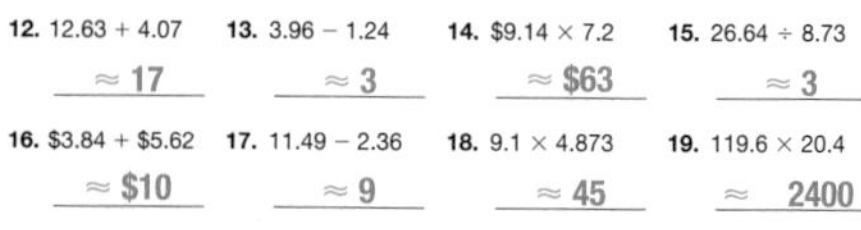

16. \$3.84 + \$5.62 ≈ \$10 17. 11.49 − 2.36 ≈ 9 18. 9.1 × 4.873 ≈ 45 19. 119.6 × 20.4 ≈ 2400

Solve using inverse operations. *[Lesson 3-12]*

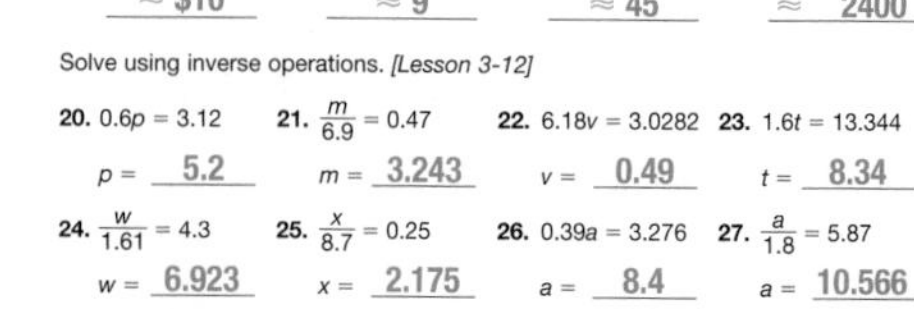

20. $0.6p = 3.12$ $p =$ 5.2
21. $\frac{m}{6.9} = 0.47$ $m =$ 3.243
22. $6.18v = 3.0282$ $v =$ 0.49
23. $1.6t = 13.344$ $t =$ 8.34
24. $\frac{w}{1.61} = 4.3$ $w =$ 6.923
25. $\frac{x}{8.7} = 0.25$ $x =$ 2.175
26. $0.39a = 3.276$ $a =$ 8.4
27. $\frac{a}{1.8} = 5.87$ $a =$ 10.566

Chapter 3 Summary and Review

Section 3B Adding and Subtracting with Decimals

Summary

- Use rounding and mental math to estimate decimal sums, differences, products, and quotients.
- Before adding or subtracting decimals, line up the decimal points in the numbers. This will ensure that the place values in the first number are in line with the same place values in the second number.

Review

5. Estimate and then add 493.76 + 235.6.

6. Estimate and then subtract 336.8 − 74.523.

7. Add 2.76 + 33.9 + 29.26.

8. Compare (7.2 − 2.8) to 4.876.

9. A quarter measures 24.3 mm across. A dime measures 17.9 mm across. How many more millimeters across is the quarter?

10. Solve.

a. $t + 3.2 = 7.8$

b. $k - 7 = 6.5$

Section 3C Multiplying and Dividing with Decimals

Summary

- To multiply with decimals, multiply as if the numbers were whole numbers. The number of digits after the decimal point in the answer should be the same as the total number of digits after any decimal points in the factors.
- To divide with decimals, multiply the divisor and dividend by the power of 10 that makes the divisor a whole number. Then divide, and place a decimal point in the quotient directly above the decimal point in the dividend.
- When multiplying by 10, 100, or 1000, or dividing by 0.1, 0.01, 0.001, move the decimal point the appropriate number of places to the right.
- When dividing by 10, 100, or 1000, or multiplying by 0.1, 0.01, 0.001, move the decimal point the appropriate number of places to the left.

Review

11. Estimate and then multiply 2.3 × 56.

12. Estimate and then divide 53 ÷ 4.

13. Estimate and then multiply 0.47 × 1.9.

14. Estimate and then divide 11.22 ÷ 5.1.

15. Multiply 45.33 × 0.001.

16. Multiply 7.51 × 100.

17. Divide 367 ÷ 1000.

18. Solve $9m = 27.9$.

Chapter 3 Assessment

Assessment Correlation

Item(s)	Lesson(s)
1–2	3-1
3	3-3
4	3-2
5–6	3-4
7–10	3-5
11	3-6
12	3-9
13–14	3-11
15	3-7
16–17	3-12
18	3-6
19	3-9

Answers for Assessment

1. Ten thousandths
2. 300.36
3. 3.05, 3.33, 3.43, 3.76
4. Possible answers: 2.008 and 2.0082.
5. 10.3×10^4
6. 30,800,000,000,000 km
7. ≈ $12; $11.56
8. ≈ 8, 8.0177
9. ≈ 40; 44
10. ≈ 3; 2.604
11. 373.148 K
12. 0.00345
13. 87
14. 28
15. 2.7
16. 1,000,000
17. 3
18. 10.02
19. 4

Answer for Performance Task

60 books; A sketch may show books are stacked 10 deep in six stacks of books with three lengths of 20.7 cm along the 65.3 cm side of the carton and two book widths along the 55 cm side of the carton.

Chapter 3 Assessment

1. What place value is to the left of the hundred-thousandths place?
2. Write three hundred, thirty-six hundredths in number form.
3. One way nails are sized is by their gauge, or thickness. Order these nails from least to greatest according to their gauge in millimeters: 3.76, 3.05, 3.43, 3.33.
4. Name two numbers between 2.007 and 2.009.
5. There are an estimated 103,000 species of bees and wasps. Write this number in scientific notation.
6. A parsec is a unit of distance used in astronomy that is equal to 3.08×10^{13} km. Write this distance in standard notation.

Estimate and then simplify.

7. $17.32 − $5.76
8. $4.9967 + 3.021$
9. $382.8 \div 8.7$
10. 2.8×0.93
11. One kind of scale measures temperature in units called kelvins. The boiling point of gold is at 1074 K, and the boiling point of water is 700.852 K lower. Find the boiling point of water.

Multiply or divide.

12. 3.45×0.001
13. $0.87 \div 0.01$
14. $7 \div 0.25$

Solve.

15. $m + 4.2 = 6.9$
16. $\frac{x}{100} = 10{,}000$
17. $12.3a = 36.9$

Write an equation for each exercise and solve it.

18. What is the difference in size between a wheel 52.52 mm across and one 42.5 mm across?

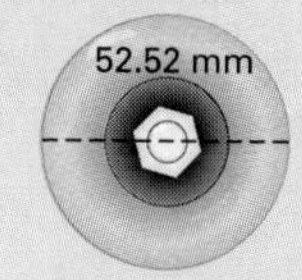

19. A sonora blue butterfly measures 2.1 cm long. A waved sphinx moth measures 8.4 cm long. How many times longer is the moth than the butterfly?

Performance Task

A textbook measures 20.7 cm wide, 26.1 cm long, and 2.8 cm high. What is the greatest number of books a shipping department can pack into a carton 55 cm wide, 65.3 cm long, and 30 cm high? You may draw sketches to help you decide how to pack the books.

Resources

Assessment Sourcebook
Chapter 3 Tests
- Forms A and B (free response)
- Form C (multiple choice)
- Form D (performance assessment)
- Form E (mixed response)
- Form F (cumulative chapter test)

TestWorks
Test and Practice Software

Home and Community Connections
Letter Home for Chapter 3 in English and Spanish

Cumulative Review Chapters 1–3

Test Prep

Performance Assessment

Choose one problem.

Kangaroo Patterns

In the grid, the numbers in every row form decimal patterns. To "hop" from one number to the next, you must always add or subtract the same number. The numbers in every column also form decimal patterns. Find the patterns and fill in the missing values.

Photo Possibilities

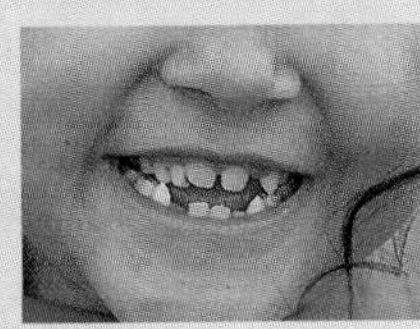

Choose two of the photos. Write a short word problem for each. One problem must use decimals. Each problem must be related to the subject of the photo. Write equations for each problem and solve them.

Worldly Costs

A fast-food chain sells hamburgers in several countries. The price in U.S. dollars of a large hamburger is listed below.

Switzerland	$4.80	Israel	$3.00
Sweden	$3.87	Denmark	$4.40
Germany	$3.22	France	$3.41
Argentina	$3.00	Belgium	$3.50

Construct a graph of the data to help someone visually compare the prices. Then write a paragraph explaining why the type of graph you chose is the best type for comparing the data.

An Exponential Challenge

Write each of the numbers and expressions shown as a single number in standard form. If you add the numbers in each row, which row will have the largest sum?

Team	Round 1	Round 2	Round 3
A	23×10^2	$6^2 - 3 + 5^3$	0.547×10^4
B	$15^3 + 5^2$	0.03×10^5	$3^3 - 4^2 + 24^1$
C	$7^6 \div$ 7 cubed	7 squared	0.007×10^6

Cumulative Review Test Prep

About Performance Assessment

The Performance Assessment options ...

- provide teachers with an alternate means of assessing students.
- address different learning modalities.
- allow students to choose one problem.

Teachers may encourage students to choose the most challenging problem.

Learning Modalities

Kangaroo Patterns
Social Students discover patterns of numbers placed in a grid to fill in missing numbers in the grid.

Photo Possibilities
Verbal Students write and then solve a word problem based on a photograph.

Worldly Costs
Visual Students graph prices of a hamburger in different countries and discuss which graph best shows the comparison of prices.

An Exponential Challenge
Individual Students use critical thinking to write numbers in standard form and to compare numbers.

Answers for Assessment

• Kangaroo Patterns

Missing values in Row 2: 10.45, 10.05, 9.65; Row 3: 18.05, 17.25, 16.85; Row 4: 24.85 and 24.05

• An Exponential Challenge

Row A: 2300, 158, 5470 Sum: 7928; Row B: 3400, 3000, 35 Sum: 6435; Row C: 343, 49, 7000; Sum, 7392. The first row has the largest sum.

Photo Possibilities

4
- Writes two clear and reasonable word problems, one using decimals.
- Is able to write correct equations and solve them.

3
- Writes two word problems, one using decimals.
- Is able to write equations and show their solutions.

2
- Writes at least one clear word problem using decimals.
- Attempts to write and solve an equation for the word problem.

1
- Is unable to write a clear word problem.
- Is unable to write or solve an equation for the word problem.

Performance Assessment Key

See key on page 135.

Suggested Scoring Rubric

Worldly Costs

4
- Accurately draws and labels bar graph.
- Clearly explains why bar graph is the best choice.

3
- Draws and labels bar graph.
- Provides explanation of why bar graph is the best choice.

2
- Attempts to record data in a graph so that prices can be compared visually.
- Unable to explain choice of graph.

1
- Fails to show data in a graph.
- Shows little understanding of how to choose a graph.

Chapter 4

Measurement

▶ OVERVIEW

Section 4A

Units of Measurement: Students learn to find perimeter, convert units within the metric system, and use the customary system of measurement for length, weight, and capacity.

4-1 Perimeter

4-2 Converting in the Metric System

4-3 Using Conversion Factors

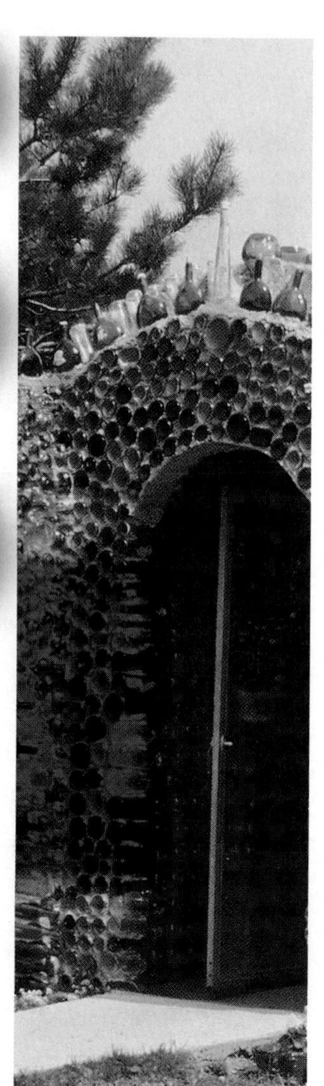

Section 4B

Area of Polygons: Students learn to find the area of squares, rectangles, parallelograms, and triangles.

4-4 Area of Squares and Rectangles

4-5 Area of Parallelograms

4-6 Area of Triangles

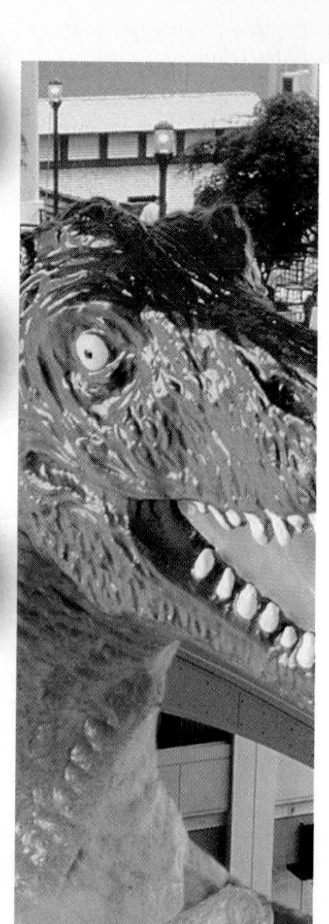

Section 4C

Circles: Students use π to calculate the circumference and the area of circles. Then they learn to find the area of irregular shapes.

4-7 Discovering Pi

4-8 Area of Circles

4-9 Area of Irregular Figures

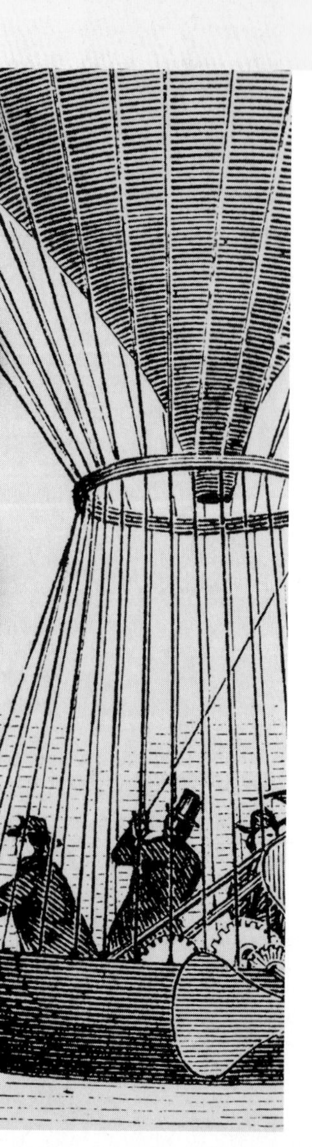

Meeting NCTM Standards

Curriculum Standards

Standard			pages
1	Problem Solving	Skills and Strategies	208, 230, 236, 258
		Applications	213–214, 218–219, 223–224, 225, 231–232, 235–236, 240–241, 243, 248–249, 252–253, 257–258, 259
		Exploration	210, 215, 220, 228, 233, 237, 246, 250, 254
2	Communication	Oral	209, 213, 218, 222, 227, 230, 234, *236*, 239, 245, *249*, 251, *253*, 257
		Written	214, 219, 224, 232, 236, 241, 249, 253, 258
		Cooperative Learning	*210*, *215*, *220*, *222*, *228*, *233*, 237, *246*, *250*, 254, *256*
3	Reasoning	Critical Thinking	214, 219, 224, 232, 236, 241, 249, 253, 258
4	Connections	Mathematical	See Standards 5, 7, 8, 12, 13 below.
		Interdisciplinary	Science 206, 209, 211, 216, *217*, 221, *239*, 245, 247, 253; History 216, 222, 223, 238, 244, 252; Health *212*; Career 218; Fine Arts 231; Geography 235, 258; Language 246, 255; Social Studies 206, *256*; Consumer *227*; Sports 207, *230*; Literature 206; Industry 209, *227*, 245
		Technology	215, 220, 242, 246
		Cultural	207
5	Number and Number Relationships		223, 229, 248, 251, 260, 261
7	Computation and Estimation		*211*, 218, *221*, *234*, *251*, *255*
8	Patterns and Functions		236
12	Geometry		210–214, 225, 228–259
13	Measurement		210–259

Italic type indicates Teacher Edition reference.

Teaching Standards

Focus on Tools for Discourse

Teachers must value and encourage the use of a variety of tools rather than place excessive emphasis on conventional mathematical symbols. Teachers should

- sometimes allow students to select the tools they find most useful.
- sometimes specify tools to help students develop a repertoire of useful tools.

Assessment Standards

Focus on Openness

Self Assessment In an open assessment, students and teachers communicate and build a common understanding of the performance criteria by which the students are to be judged. Self-assessment activities provide opportunities for students to measure their own progress against those criteria. In Chapter 4, students are asked to assess their understanding of

- the metric system.
- area of quadrilaterals.

TECHNOLOGY

For the Teacher

- **Teacher Resource Planner CD-ROM**
  Use the teacher planning CD-ROM to view resources available for Chapter 4. You can prepare custom lesson plans or use the default lesson plans provided.

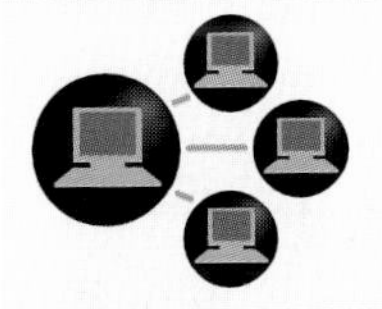

- **World Wide Web**
  Visit **www.teacher.mathsurf.com** for links to lesson plans from teachers and other professionals, NCTM information, and other sites.

- **TestWorks**
  TestWorks provides ready-made tests and can create custom tests and practice worksheets.

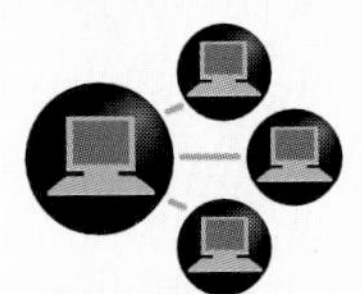

For the Parent

- **World Wide Web**
  Parents can use the Web site at **www.parent.mathsurf.com.**

For the Student

- **Interactive CD-ROM**
  Lesson 4-6 has an *Interactive CD-ROM Lesson*. The *Interactive CD-ROM Journal* and *Interactive CD-ROM Spreadsheet/Grapher Tool* are also used in Chapter 4.

- **Wide World of Mathematics**
  Lesson 4-1 Middle School: Student Engineers
  Lesson 4-4 Middle School: Huge Mall Opens

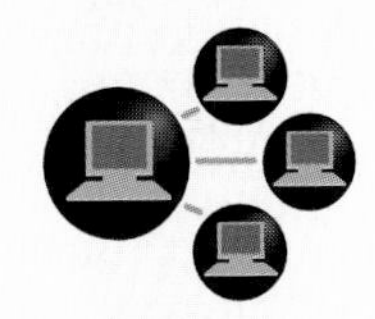

- **World Wide Web**
  Use with Chapter and Section Openers; Students can go online to the Scott Foresman-Addison Wesley Web site at **www.mathsurf.com/6/ch4** to collect information about chapter themes.

- **Jasper Woodbury Videodisc**
  Lesson 4-3: Journey to Cedar Creek

STANDARDIZED - TEST CORRELATION

SECTION 4A

LESSON	OBJECTIVE	ITBS Form M	CTBS 4th Ed.	CAT 5th Ed.	SAT 9th Ed.	MAT 7th Ed.	Your Form
4-1	• Find the perimeter of a geometric figure.		✘	✘	✘	✘	
4-2	• Measure using the metric system and convert units within the metric system.				✘	✘	
4-3	• Convert units within the customary system of measurement.			✘	✘	✘	

SECTION 4B

LESSON	OBJECTIVE	ITBS Form M	CTBS 4th Ed.	CAT 5th Ed.	SAT 9th Ed.	MAT 7th Ed.	Your Form
4-4	• Find the area of squares and rectangles.		✘	✘	✘	✘	
4-5	• Find the area of parallelograms.				✘		
4-6	• Find the area of a triangle.				✘		

SECTION 4C

LESSON	OBJECTIVE	ITBS Form M	CTBS 4th Ed.	CAT 5th Ed.	SAT 9th Ed.	MAT 7th Ed.	Your Form
4-7	• Find the circumference of a circle.		✘				
4-8	• Find the area of circles.		✘		✘		
4-9	• Find the area of irregular figures.			✘	✘		

Key: ITBS - Iowa Test of Basic Skills; CTBS - Comprehensive Test of Basic Skills; CAT - California Achievement Test; SAT - Stanford Achievement Test; MAT - Metropolitan Achievement Test

ASSESSMENT PROGRAM

Traditional Assessment

QUICK QUIZZES	SECTION REVIEW	CHAPTER REVIEW	CHAPTER ASSESSMENT FREE RESPONSE	CHAPTER ASSESSMENT MULTIPLE CHOICE	CUMULATIVE REVIEW
TE: pp. 214, 219, 224, 232, 236, 241, 249, 253, 258	SE: pp. 226, 244, 260 *Quiz 4A, 4B, 4C	SE: pp. 262–263	SE: p. 264 *Ch. 4 Tests Forms A, B, E	*Ch. 4 Tests Forms C, E	SE: p. 265 *Ch. 4 Test Form F

Alternate Assessment

INTERVIEW	JOURNAL	ONGOING	PERFORMANCE	PORTFOLIO	PROJECT	SELF
TE: pp. 236, 249, 253	SE: pp. 214, 219, 236, 241, 253, 258 TE: pp. 208, 214	TE: pp. 210, 215, 220, 228, 233, 237, 246, 250, 254	SE: p. 264 TE: pp. 224, 232 *Ch. 4 Tests Forms D, E	TE: p. 258	SE: pp. 214, 241, 249 TE: p. 207	TE: pp. 219, 241

*Tests and quizzes are in *Assessment Sourcebook*. Test Form E is a mixed response test. Forms for Alternate Assessment are also available in *Assessment Sourcebook*.

TestWorks: Test and Practice Software

MIDDLE SCHOOL PACING CHART

REGULAR PACING

Day	5 classes per week
1	Chapter 4 Opener; Problem Solving Focus
2	Section **4A** Opener; Lesson **4-1**
3	Lesson **4-2**
4	Lesson **4-3**
5	**4A** Connect; **4A** Review
6	Section **4B** Opener; Lesson **4-4**
7	Lesson **4-5**
8	Lesson **4-6**; Technology
9	**4B** Connect; **4B** Review
10	Section **4C** Opener; Lesson **4-7**
11	Lesson **4-8**
12	Lesson **4-9**
13	**4C** Connect; **4C** Review; Extend Key Ideas
14	Chapter 4 Summary and Review
15	Chapter 4 Assessment Cumulative Review, Chapters 1–4

BLOCK SCHEDULING OPTIONS

Block Scheduling for Complete Course

Chapter 4 may be presented in

- nine 90-minute blocks
- twelve 75-minute blocks

Each block consists of a combination of

- Chapter and Section Openers
- Explores
- Lesson Development
- Problem Solving Focus
- Technology
- Extend Key Ideas
- Connect
- Review
- Assessment

For details, see *Block Scheduling Handbook*.

Block Scheduling for Interdisciplinary Course

Each block integrates math with another subject area.

In Chapter 4, interdisciplinary topics include

- Garbage
- Malls
- Inventions

Themes for Interdisciplinary Team Teaching 4A, 4B, and 4C are

- Measurements for Space Travel
- Area and the World's First Mall
- Houses with Circular Bases

For details, see *Block Scheduling Handbook*.

Block Scheduling for Lab-Based Course

In each block, 30–40 minutes is devoted to lab activities including

- Explores in the Student Edition
- Connect pages in the Student Edition
- Technology options in the Student Edition
- Reteaching Activities in the Teacher Edition

For details, see *Block Scheduling Handbook*.

Block Scheduling for Course with *Connected Mathematics*

In each block, investigations from **Connected Mathematics** replace or enhance the lessons in Chapter 4.

Connected Mathematics topics for Chapter 4 can be found in

- *Covering and Surrounding*
- *Bits and Pieces I*

For details, see *Block Scheduling Handbook*.

INTERDISCIPLINARY BULLETIN BOARD

Set Up

Prepare a bulletin board with sections for various structures made by pre-Columbian cultures.

Procedure

- Have small groups of students research structures made by pre-Columbian cultures. They should find the length of the base and the height measurements of a structure.
- Students should draw the structure on the bulletin board with a scale of 1 cm or 0.5 cm = 1 m.
- Students should name each structure and give its actual base and height measurements. Possible structures and their measurements include: Great Temple Mound (Spiro, OK), 24 m height, 55 m base; Pyramid of the Sun (Mexico), 66 m height, 214 m base; Iroquoian long house (NE, N. AM), 6 m height, 18 m base; and Effigy mound (IL, IA, WI, MN), 2 m height; 100 m base.

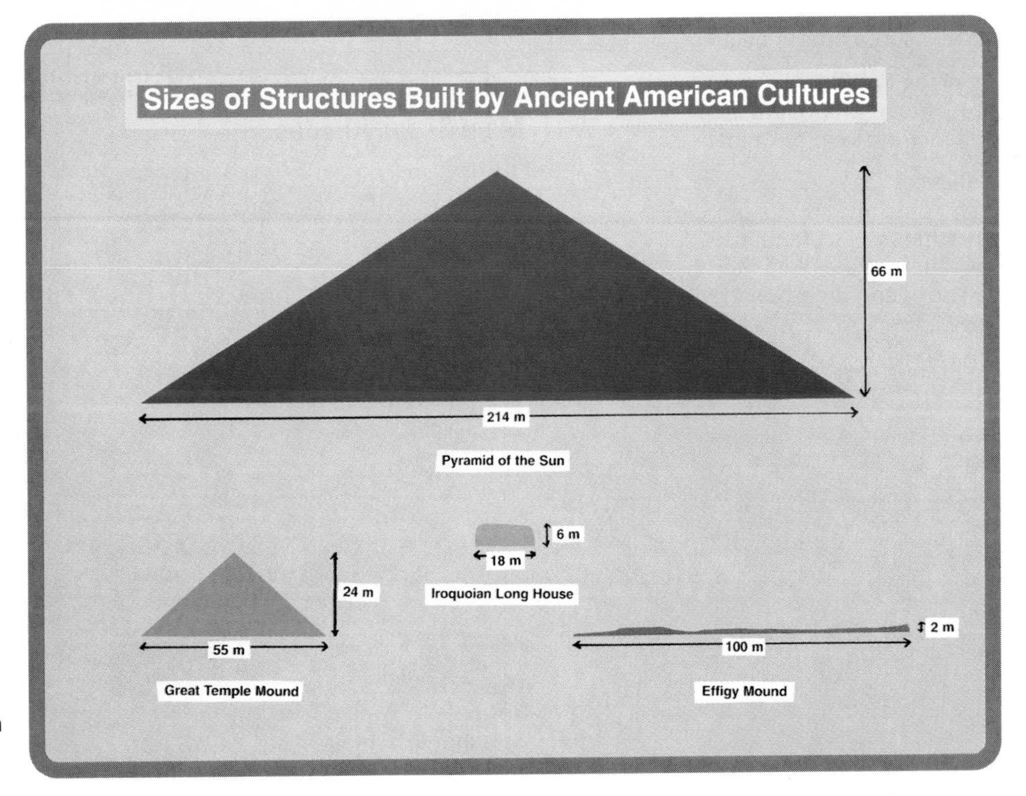

Chapter 4

The information on these pages shows how measurement is used in real-life situations.

World Wide Web

If your class has access to the World Wide Web, you might want to use the information found at the Web site addresses given.

Extensions

The following activities do not require access to the World Wide Web.

Social Studies
Ask students to describe other measurement and calculating tools they know about. Talk about how each tool can be used to help with computations.

Arts & Literature
Ask students whether Jules Verne's statement would be correct at 41°F or at 23°F. Talk about why he might have given two temperatures that are not equal. It could be correct at 23°F, which is below the freezing point of water. He may have done the conversion incorrectly.

Science
Have students prepare a poster or notebook showing items that are about a meter, a gram, or a liter in size. Talk about why standardization of measurements is needed.

People of the World
Ask students to find out facts about the Great Wall of China.

Entertainment
Have students investigate the measurements of a standard football field, baseball diamond, tennis court, and ping-pong table.
Football: $120 \times 53\frac{1}{3}$ yd;
Baseball: 90 ft on a side;
Tennis: 120×60 ft;
Ping-pong: 9×5 ft.

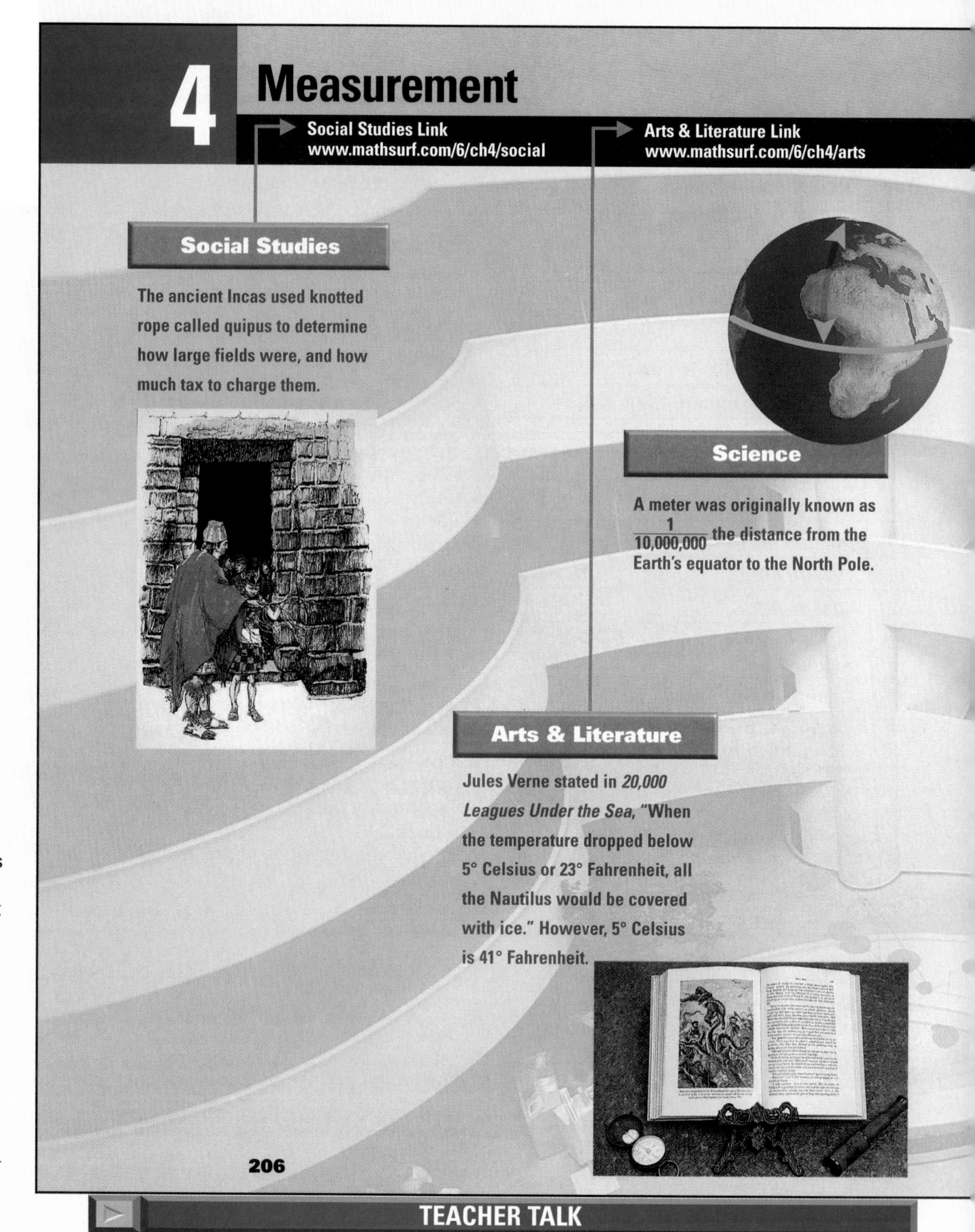

TEACHER TALK

Meet Susan Rhodes

Springfield Public Schools
Springfield, Illinois

I think it is essential that students have hands-on experiences to develop a true understanding of the concepts of perimeter, area, and volume. I have my students build miniature gift boxes about the size of single-serving cereal boxes, 7 cm × 10 cm × 4 cm. Students use centimeter grid paper to measure the correct sizes of the sides of the box and then cut the sides out of tag board. To incorporate the concept of perimeter, I have them trim the boxes with ribbon or heavy yarn.

As a challenge, I ask students to design as many different gift boxes as they can that will hold a certain number of cubic centimeters. Students are often surprised that boxes that look different have the same volume.

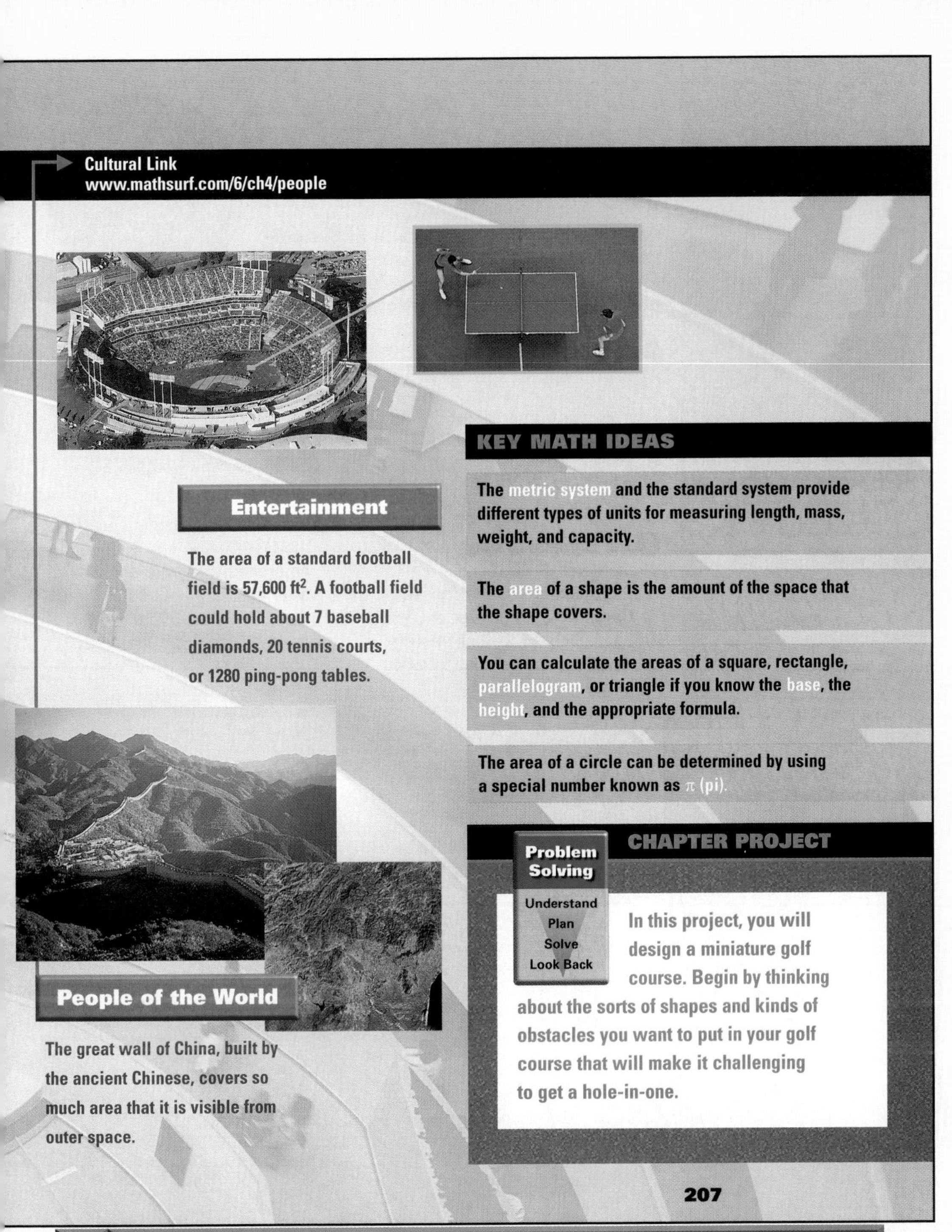

Entertainment

The area of a standard football field is 57,600 ft^2. A football field could hold about 7 baseball diamonds, 20 tennis courts, or 1280 ping-pong tables.

People of the World

The great wall of China, built by the ancient Chinese, covers so much area that it is visible from outer space.

KEY MATH IDEAS

The metric system and the standard system provide different types of units for measuring length, mass, weight, and capacity.

The area of a shape is the amount of the space that the shape covers.

You can calculate the areas of a square, rectangle, parallelogram, or triangle if you know the base, the height, and the appropriate formula.

The area of a circle can be determined by using a special number known as π (pi).

CHAPTER PROJECT

Problem Solving

Understand
Plan
Solve
Look Back

In this project, you will design a miniature golf course. Begin by thinking about the sorts of shapes and kinds of obstacles you want to put in your golf course that will make it challenging to get a hole-in-one.

207

PROJECT ASSESSMENT

You may choose to use this project as a performance assessment for the chapter.

Performance Assessment Key

Level 4 Full Accomplishment

Level 3 Substantial Accomplishment

Level 2 Partial Accomplishment

Level 1 Little Accomplishment

Suggested Scoring Rubric

Level	Criteria
4	• Design of golf course includes all required shapes as well as other interesting shapes and challenging obstacles. • Measurements are realistic and all calculations are accurate.
3	• Design of golf course includes all required shapes and some obstacles. • Measurements are reasonable and most calculations are accurate.
2	• Design of golf course includes most required shapes and few obstacles. • Measurements are unrealistic and calculations are incomplete.
1	• Design of golf course includes some required shapes and no obstacles. • Measurements and calculations are incorrect.

Chapter Project

Students use what they know about measurement to design a miniature golf course.

Resources

Chapter 4 Project Master

Introduce the Project

- Describe miniature golf courses and show pictures of such courses, if possible. Be sure students understand what is involved in the game and how it is played.
- Ask students to describe some of the kinds of things that they would like to see in a miniature golf course.
- Discuss where students could go to find information about miniature golf courses.

Project Progress

Section A, page 214 Students make a rough sketch, with reasonable dimensions and interesting shapes, of the first four holes of their miniature golf course.

Section B, page 241 Students check that some of the holes on their golf course use rectangular and triangular shapes.

Section C, page 249 Students complete the design of their miniature golf course by including a circle or part of a circle in the final golf hole. Then they calculate the perimeter of the final golf hole.

Community Project

A community project for Chapter 4 is available in *Home and Community Connections.*

Cooperative Learning

You may want to use Teaching Tool Transparency 1: Cooperative Learning Checklist with **Explore** and other group activities in this chapter.

Problem Solving Focus

Finding Unnecessary Information

The Point

Students focus on determining whether a problem has unnecessary information and, if so, which information is not needed.

Resources

Teaching Tool Transparency 18: Problem-Solving Guidelines

 *Interactive CD-ROM Journal*

About the Page

Using the Problem-Solving Process

In order to solve a problem, students must be able to weed out the extraneous information and focus on the information needed to solve the problem. Discuss these suggestions for evaluating the given information:

- Read the problem two or three times before beginning.
- Decide what kind of information is needed to solve the problem.
- Analyze all the information given and eliminate unnecessary information.

Ask ...

- How would you organize the information given in a problem to determine what is necessary and what is not?
- How do you know if you have unnecessary information?

Answers for Problems

1. All numerical information is necessary. Answer: 2 days
2. The diameters in kilometers are unnecessary. Answer: 20 miles
3. All numerical information is necessary. Answer: 30 days
4. The dates are not necessary. Answer: 82 orbits

Journal

Ask students to write a problem that has more information than needed. Have them give some suggestions for determining which information is not needed.

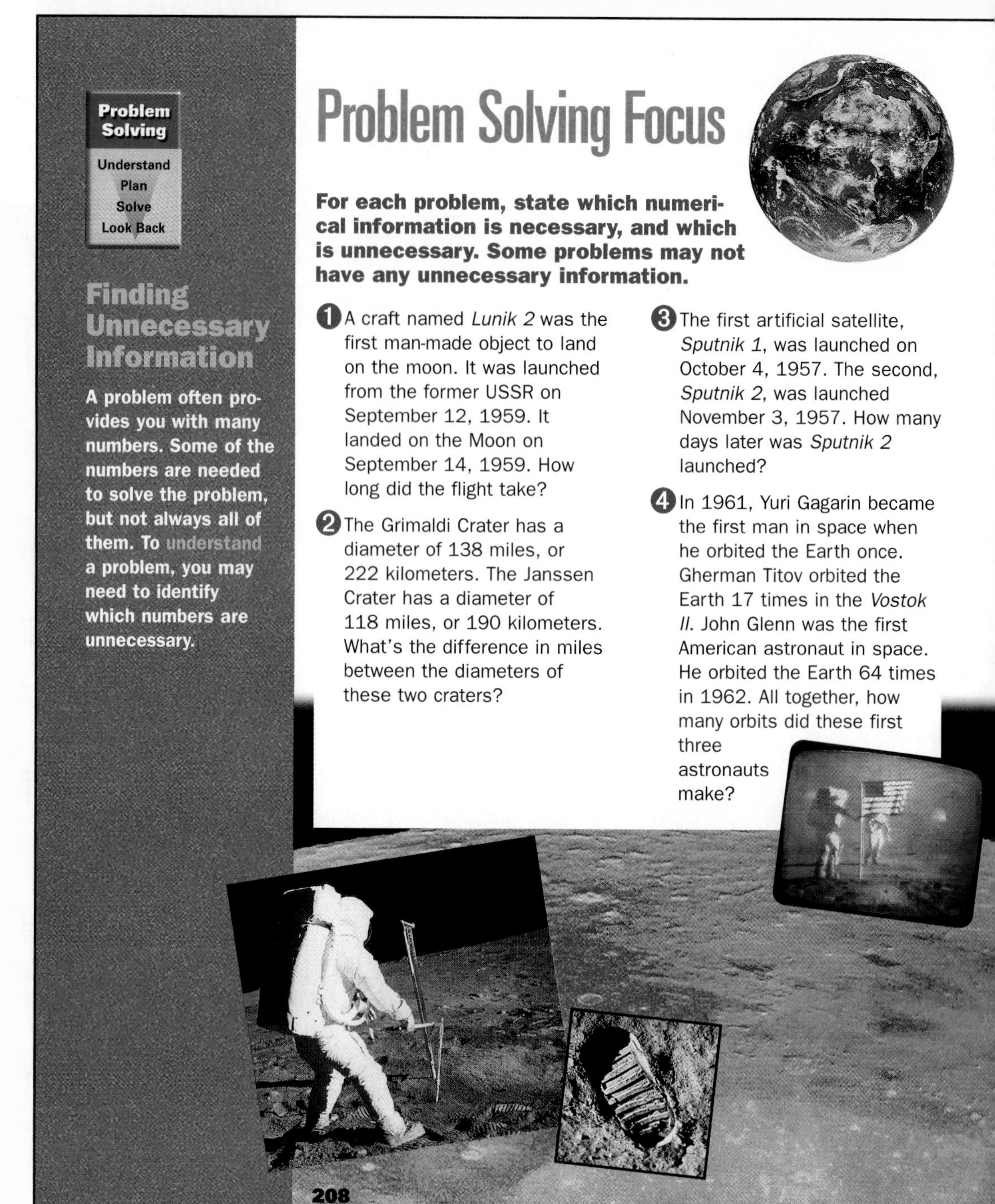

Problem Solving

Understand
Plan
Solve
Look Back

Finding Unnecessary Information

A problem often provides you with many numbers. Some of the numbers are needed to solve the problem, but not always all of them. To understand a problem, you may need to identify which numbers are unnecessary.

Problem Solving Focus

For each problem, state which numerical information is necessary, and which is unnecessary. Some problems may not have any unnecessary information.

1. A craft named *Lunik 2* was the first man-made object to land on the moon. It was launched from the former USSR on September 12, 1959. It landed on the Moon on September 14, 1959. How long did the flight take?
2. The Grimaldi Crater has a diameter of 138 miles, or 222 kilometers. The Janssen Crater has a diameter of 118 miles, or 190 kilometers. What's the difference in miles between the diameters of these two craters?
3. The first artificial satellite, *Sputnik 1*, was launched on October 4, 1957. The second, *Sputnik 2*, was launched November 3, 1957. How many days later was *Sputnik 2* launched?
4. In 1961, Yuri Gagarin became the first man in space when he orbited the Earth once. Gherman Titov orbited the Earth 17 times in the *Vostok II*. John Glenn was the first American astronaut in space. He orbited the Earth 64 times in 1962. All together, how many orbits did these first three astronauts make?

208

Additional Problem

Kareem is planning a birthday party. He will invite 12 friends. The party will be held on Saturday afternoon. He has planned four games for the party. He plans to serve cake and ice cream. The cake will cost $8.95 and the ice cream will cost $4.98. He also is purchasing party favors that cost $22.50. About how much is he spending per person for the party? About $2.80

1. What is the problem about? Kareem's birthday party.
2. What is the problem asking for? The approximate cost for each person.
3. How many people are involved? 13, including Kareem.
4. What information is not needed to solve the problem? The day the party will be held and the number of games.

Section 4A

Linear Measurements

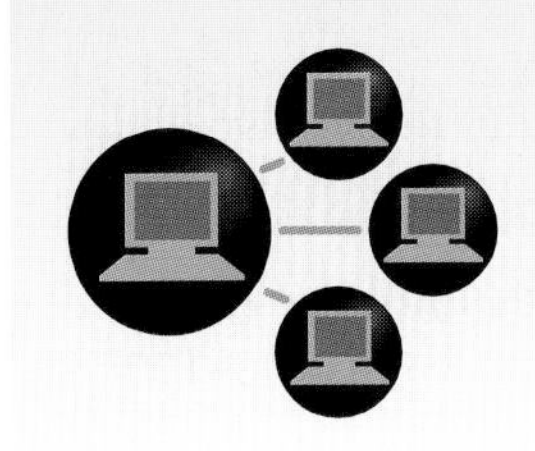

Visit www.teacher.mathsurf.com for links to lesson plans from teachers and other professionals, NCTM information, and other sites.

LESSON PLANNING GUIDE

Student Edition / Ancillaries*

LESSON		MATERIALS	VOCABULARY	DAILY	OTHER
	Chapter 4 Opener				Ch. 4 Project Master Ch. 4 Community Project Teaching Tool Trans. 1
	Problem Solving Focus				Teaching Tool Trans. 18 *Interactive CD-ROM Journal*
	Section 4A Opener				
4-1	Perimeter		perimeter	4-1	Lesson Enhancement Trans. 12 Ch. 4 Project Master *WW Math*–Middle School
4-2	Converting in the Metric System	calculator	metric system, meter, gram, liter, kilo-, centi-, milli-	4-2	Lesson Enhancement Transparencies 13, 14 Technology Master 16
4-3	Using Conversion Factors	calculator	inch, foot, yard, mile, ounce, pound, quart, gallon, conversion factor	4-3	Lesson Enhancement Trans. 15
	Connect	ruler, colored pencils/pens			Lesson Enhancement Trans. 16 Interdisc. Team Teaching 4A
	Review				Practice 4A; Quiz 4A; *TestWorks*

* Daily Ancillaries include Practice, Reteaching, Problem Solving, Enrichment, and Daily Transparency. Teaching Tool Transparencies are in *Teacher's Toolkits*. Lesson Enhancement Transparencies are in *Overhead Transparency Package*.

SKILLS TRACE

LESSON	SKILL	FIRST INTRODUCED GR. 4	GR. 5	GR. 6	DEVELOP	PRACTICE/ APPLY	REVIEW
4-1	Finding perimeter.	✗			pp. 210–212	pp. 213–214	pp. 262, 327, 456
4-2	Converting between metric units.			✗ p. 215	pp. 215–217	pp. 218–219	pp. 262, 369, 456
4-3	Using conversion factors.			✗ p. 220	pp. 220–222	pp. 223–224	pp. 262, 301, 374, 378, 386, 502

CONNECTED MATHEMATICS

The unit *Covering and Surrounding (2-D Measurement)* and Investigation 4 in the unit *Bits and Pieces I (Understanding Rational Numbers)*, from the **Connected Mathematics** series, can be used with Section 4A.

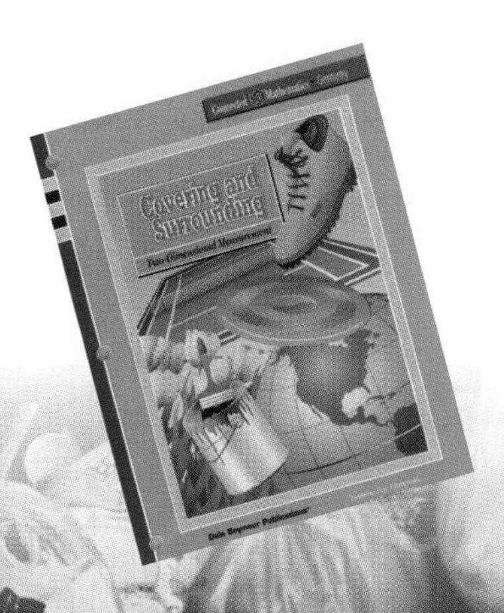

INTERDISCIPLINARY TEAM TEACHING

Math and Science/Technology

(Worksheet pages 19–20: Teacher pages T19–T20)

In this lesson, students convert measurements for space travel.

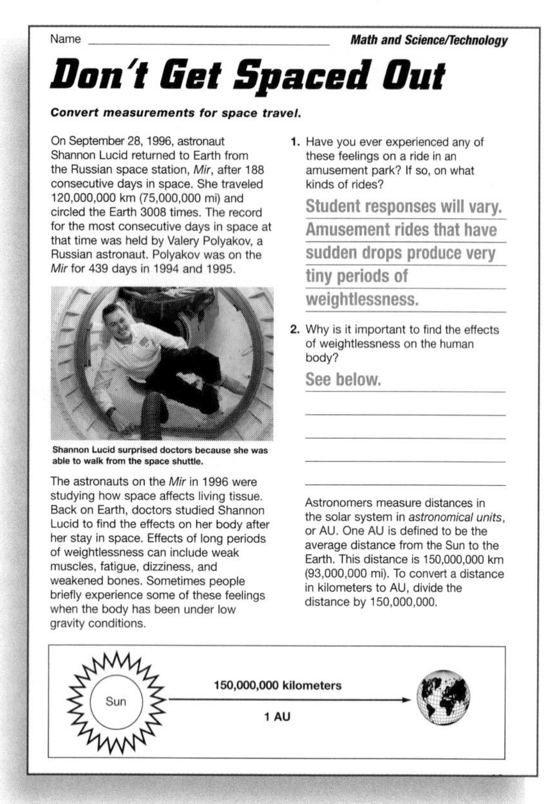

Name ______________________ *Math and Science/Technology*

Don't Get Spaced Out

Convert measurements for space travel.

On September 28, 1996, astronaut Shannon Lucid returned to Earth from the Russian space station, *Mir*, after 188 consecutive days in space. She traveled 120,000,000 km (75,000,000 mi) and circled the Earth 3008 times. The record for the most consecutive days in space at that time was held by Valery Polyakov, a Russian astronaut. Polyakov was on the *Mir* for 439 days in 1994 and 1995.

Shannon Lucid surprised doctors because she was able to walk from the space shuttle.

The astronauts on the *Mir* in 1996 were studying how space affects living tissue. Back on Earth, doctors studied Shannon Lucid to find the effects on her body after her stay in space. Effects of long periods of weightlessness can include weak muscles, fatigue, dizziness, and weakened bones. Sometimes people briefly experience some of these feelings when the body has been under low gravity conditions.

1. Have you ever experienced any of these feelings on a ride in an amusement park? If so, on what kinds of rides?
   Student responses will vary. Amusement rides that have sudden drops produce very tiny periods of weightlessness.

2. Why is it important to find the effects of weightlessness on the human body?
   See below.

Astronomers measure distances in the solar system in *astronomical units*, or AU. One AU is defined to be the average distance from the Sun to the Earth. This distance is 150,000,000 km (93,000,000 mi). To convert a distance in kilometers to AU, divide the distance by 150,000,000.

Sun — 150,000,000 kilometers — 1 AU

Name ______________________ *Math and Science/Technology*

3. The table below shows the mean distance of each planet from the Sun. Write the conversion calculation, and then compute the AU for each planet. The conversion calculation and the AU for Mercury are given. Note that since the mean distance is given in millions of kilometers, you simply divide 58 by 150.

4. How many AU did Shannon Lucid travel on the *Mir*?
   $120 \div 150 = 0.8$; Shannon Lucid traveled 0.8 AU orbiting the Earth.

5. On a separate sheet of paper, draw a scale model of the solar system, in astronomical units, to show the relative distance of each planet from the Sun. If you use the scale 1 cm = 1 AU, you will be able to draw the solar system on a piece of construction paper. With a scale of 1 cm = 1 AU, Mercury would be drawn 0.4 cm, or 4 mm, from the Sun.
   See below.

6. a. Since AU are distances measured from the Sun, show on your scale drawing how far Shannon Lucid would have traveled if she had traveled in a line from the Sun toward the far end of the solar system.
   See below.

   b. Between which two planets is Shannon Lucid on your model?
   Shannon Lucid would have been just past Venus on her way to Earth.

Planet	Mean Distance from Sun (in millions of km)	Conversion Calculation (distance from Sun ÷ 150)	AU (rounded to nearest tenth)
Mercury	58	58 ÷ 150	0.4
Venus	108	108 ÷ 150	0.7
Earth	150	150 ÷ 150	1
Mars	228	228 ÷ 150	1.5
Jupiter	778	778 ÷ 150	5.2
Saturn	1427	1427 ÷ 150	9.5
Uranus	2871	2871 ÷ 150	19.1
Neptune	4497	4497 ÷ 150	30.0
Pluto	5914	5914 ÷ 150	39.4

Answers

2. Student responses will vary, but students should recognize that this will affect the length of future space explorations and that knowing the effects of long periods of weightlessness might help improve medical treatments and procedures on Earth.

5.–6a.

Mercury, Venus, Earth, Mars, Jupiter, Saturn

Dr. Lucid (0.8 AU)

Note: If students use the scale given, 1 cm = 1 AU, a sheet of paper 30 cm x 45 cm (12 in. x 18 in.) can be used (since the largest measurement will be 39.4 cm, or about 15.75 inches). If a larger scale is desired, use larger paper or draw the distances on the chalkboard.

BIBLIOGRAPHY

FOR TEACHERS

Bonnet, Robert L. and Keen, G. Daniel. *Space & Astronomy: Forty-Nine Science Fair Projects.* Blue Ridge Summit, PA: Tab Books, 1992.

Couper, Heather. *The Space Atlas.* Fort Worth, TX: Harcourt Brace Jovanovich, 1992.

Parker, Steve. *The Random House Book of How Things Work.* New York, NY: Random House, 1991.

FOR STUDENTS

The Earth Works Group. *50 Simple Things Kids Can Do to Recycle.* Berkeley, CA: Earthworks Press, 1994.

Foster, Joanna. *Cartons, Cans and Orange Peels.* New York, NY: Clarion Books, 1991.

Isaacson, Philip M. *Round Buildings, Square Buildings, and Buildings That Wiggle Like a Fish.* New York, NY: Knopf, 1990.

Theme: Garbage

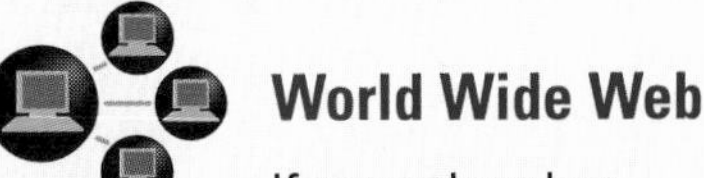

If your class has access to the World Wide Web, you might want to use the information found at the Web site address given. The interdisciplinary links relate to topics discussed in this section.

About the Page

This page introduces the theme of the section, garbage, and discusses ways to reduce, reuse, and recycle garbage.

Ask ...

- Does your family recycle?
- What do we use daily that is made from recycled products?

Extensions

The following activities do not require access to the World Wide Web.

Science
People are searching for ways to dispose of trash that do not harm the environment. Have students investigate uses of recycled trash.

Industry
Many companies are involved in recycling. Ask students to investigate and identify the companies in their community that are involved in recycling.

Answers for Questions

1. Broken tire treads: Sandals; Empty tin cans: Briefcases; Used license plates: Dust pans; Old hub caps: Artistic sculptures; Burned-out light bulbs: Headdress jewels; Cement bags: Dolls.
2. In order to conserve the Earth's resources.
3. Calculating amounts of garbage; Determining how to move it or where to put it.

Connect

On page 225, students will use their knowledge of perimeter to plan an efficient truck route.

Where are we now?

In Section 3C, students solved equations using decimals.

They learned how to

- multiply and divide using decimals.
- use mental math to solve multiplication and division equations with decimals.
- solve decimal equations with multiplication and division.

Where are we going?

In Section 4A, students will

- use addition of whole numbers and decimals to find perimeter.
- use metric measure to find length.
- convert units within the metric system.
- use the customary system of measurement to find length, weight, and capacity.

4-1 Lesson Organizer

Objective

- Find the perimeter of a geometric figure.

Vocabulary

- Perimeter

NCTM Standards

- 1–4, 7, 12, 13

Review

Find each sum.

1. 34.58 + 22.1 + 10 66.68
2. 22.01 + 3 + 5.3 30.31
3. 120 + 45.44 + 3.902 169.342

Available on Daily Transparency 4-1

1 Introduce

Explore  

You may wish to use Lesson Enhancement Transparency 12 with **Explore**.

The Point
Students practice finding the total length of the sides of a polygon. Completing the table helps them to identify a pattern and use the pattern to solve the problem: What is the distance around a figure made up of 100 triangles?

Ongoing Assessment
Be sure that students include only the outside of each figure and not every side of each triangle.

For Groups That Finish Early
Make a similar table that starts with a square, each of whose sides measures 6 units, and gives the perimeter of one square, two squares together, three squares together, and so on. Perimeters for 1, 2, 3, 4, 5, 10, and 100 squares will be 24, 36, 48, 60, 72, 132, 1212.

4-1 Perimeter

You'll Learn ...

- to find the perimeter of a geometric figure

... How It's Used

Homeowners calculate a perimeter when building a fence for their yard.

Vocabulary

perimeter

▶ Lesson Link You know how to add decimals and whole numbers. Now you will apply those skills to find the distance around geometric figures. ◀

Explore Perimeter

Watching the Side Lines

The chart below is based upon a row of triangles with equal sides of 4 units. The chart lists the distance around one triangle, two triangles, and so on.

Number of Triangles	Sketch	Distance Around Outside
1	4 4 4	12
2	4 4 4 4	
3		
4		
5		
10	—	
100	—	

1. Copy and complete the chart. Don't sketch the last two figures.
2. The distance around a triangle is 12 units. Why doesn't the distance around the figure go up by 12 units when you add a new triangle?
3. What would the distance around the outside be for the first five rows if the figure was a square measuring 4 units on each side?

Learn Perimeter

The distance around the outside of a figure is known as the **perimeter**. To determine the perimeter of a geometric figure, you add the lengths of each side.

MEETING INDIVIDUAL NEEDS

Resources

- 4-1 Practice
- 4-1 Reteaching
- 4-1 Problem Solving
- 4-1 Enrichment
- 4-1 Daily Transparency
  - Problem of the Day
  - Review
  - Quick Quiz
- Lesson Enhancement Transparency 12
- Chapter 4 Project Master
-  *Wide World of Mathematics* Middle School: Student Engineers

Learning Modalities

Verbal Have students research the meaning of the root words in perimeter: *peri* and *meter.*

Kinesthetic Have students outline a geometric figure on the floor with masking tape or string. Have them walk around the figure to "experience" perimeter.

Challenge

Have students use geoboards to find as many different-sized squares, rectangles, and triangles as they can. Have students make a list of the perimeters of each shape.

Example 1

Find the perimeter.

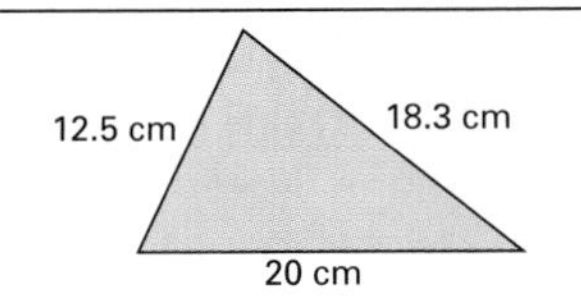

The perimeter equals
12.5 cm + 18.3 cm + 20 cm, or 50.8 cm.

Sometimes, a figure does not give all the side lengths. You can often determine the length of an unlabeled side by looking at the opposite side.

Examples

2 Antwon wants to build a composter out of 1-yard high wire mesh. He wants it to be a rectangle with the front measuring 4 ft and the right side 3 ft. How much 1-yard high wire mesh does he need?

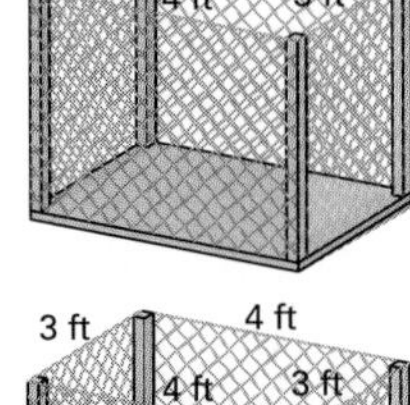

3 ft 4 ft 4 ft 3 ft

The composter has the shape of a rectangle. If the front is 4 ft, the back is also 4 ft. If the right side is 3 ft, the left side is also 3 ft.

Perimeter = 4 + 3 + 4 + 3, or 14 ft

Antwon needs 14 ft of 1-yard high wire mesh.

3 Find the perimeter.

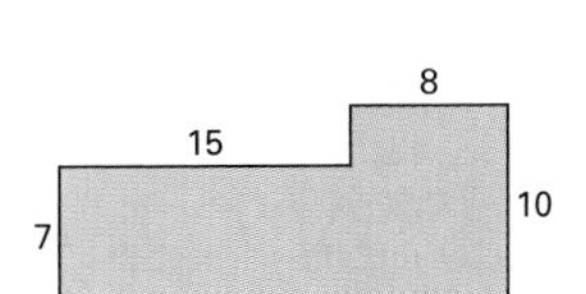

The bottom side is equal to the top two sides. Since the top two sides are 8 and 15, the bottom is 23.

The smallest side plus 7 is equal to 10. The smallest side is therefore 10 − 7, or 3.

8 15 7 10 10 − 7 = 3 15 + 8 = 23

Perimeter = 15 + 3 + 8 + 10 + 23 + 7, or 66

Try It

Find each perimeter.

a. 27

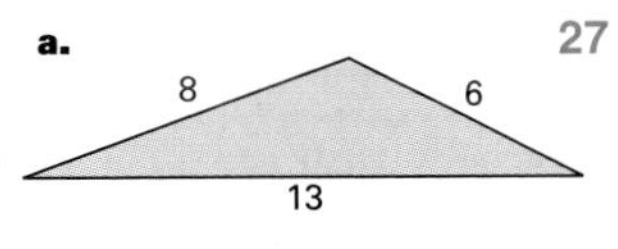

b. 46

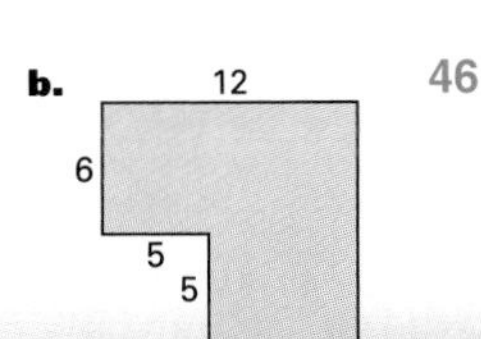

Remember

When adding decimals, line up the decimal points. This helps you to be sure that you are adding digits with the same place value.
[Page 165]

▶ Science Link

Composting allows organic garbage such as peels and grass to break down quickly and naturally. This leaves more room in landfills to store the garbage that cannot be recycled or broken down quickly.

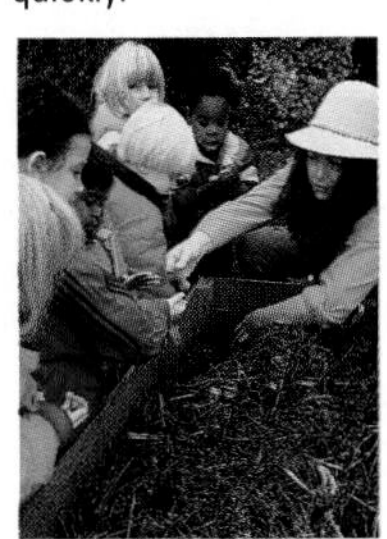

MATH EVERY DAY

▶ Problem of the Day

Each of Hector's two grandmothers has four children. Each of their children has five children. How many cousins does Hector have? 30 cousins; Each grandmother has 20 grandchildren including Hector and his siblings. So 20 + 20 − 5 − 5 = 30.

Available on Daily Transparency 4-1

An Extension is provided in the transparency package.

Fact of the Day

In 1965, Americans discarded 38,000,000 tons of paper and paperboard. By 1993 the figure had more than doubled to almost 78,000,000 tons.

Estimation

Estimate.

1. 315 × 4.8 1500
2. 1,199 ÷ 203 6
3. 8,902 + 550 + 3,228 12,700
4. 20,888 − 3,231 17,700

Answers for Explore

1. Row 2: 16

   Row 3: 20

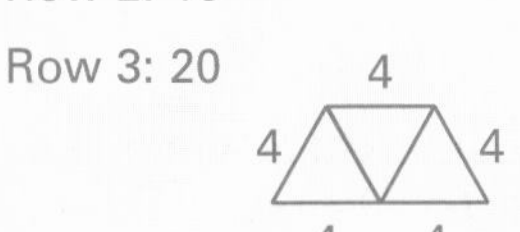

   Row 4: 24

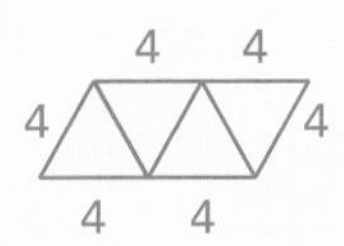

   Row 5: 28

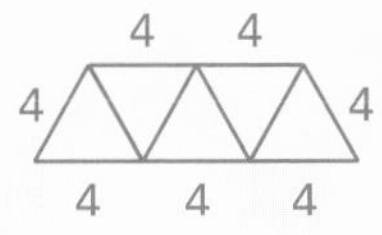

   Row 6: 48

   Row 7: 408
2. Some sides are inside so you don't count them.
3. 16, 24, 32, 40, 48

2 Teach

Learn

Alternate Examples

1. Find the perimeter of a triangle whose sides are 3.4 cm, 4.6 cm, and 7 cm long.

   The perimeter equals 3.4 + 4.6 + 7, or 15 cm.

2. A garden is built in the shape of a rectangle with a length of 12 feet and a width of 8 feet. The garden has a fence all around it. How long is the fence?

   Perimeter = 12 + 8 + 12 + 8, or 40 ft

   The fence is 40 ft long.

3. Find the perimeter of the figure shown.

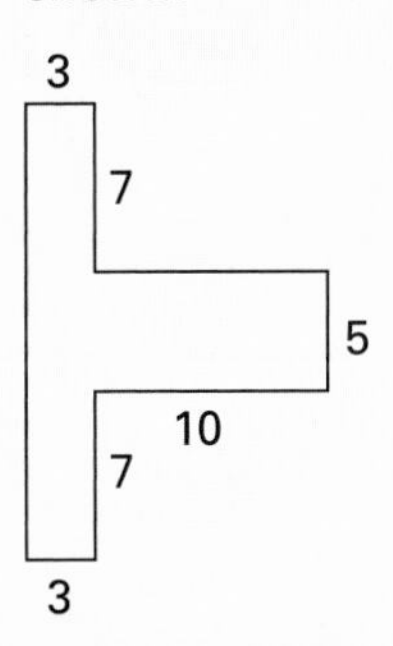

   The left side is equal to the length of the other three vertical sides. 7 + 5 + 7 = 19

   The side opposite the 10 is also 10.

   Perimeter = 3 + 7 + 10 + 5 + 10 + 7 + 3 + 19, or 64

Two different methods of finding the perimeter of a rectangle are presented. Students should discuss whether or not each method always works and why. Use of a calculator should be encouraged.

Answers for What Do You Think?

1. Answers may vary.
2. Larry writes down all 4 lengths; Catherine multiplies by 2.

3 Practice and Assess

Check

Students should understand that every polygon has a perimeter which can be found by adding the lengths of all the sides of the figure. They should also understand that sometimes shortcuts can be found for calculating perimeter.

Answers for Check Your Understanding

1. There are 4 equal sides on a square, so multiply the length of one side by 4.
2. Possible answer: No; The sides of the first shape could be longer.

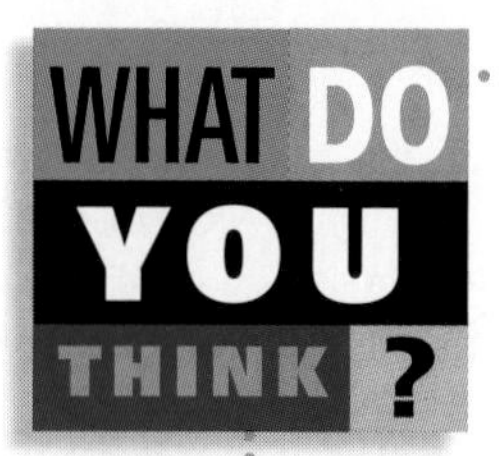

Larry and Catherine run laps around the school playground. The playground is 290 feet long and 150 feet wide. They want to know how many laps it takes to equal 5280 feet, or 1 mile.

Larry thinks ...

I'll sketch the shape of the playground and label all four sides.

P = length + width + length + width

$P = 290 + 150 + 290 + 150$

$P = 880$

290 ft, 150 ft, 150 ft, 290 ft

The perimeter of the playground is 880 feet.

$5280 \div 880 = 6$

It takes 6 laps to equal a mile.

Catherine thinks ...

I'll add the length and width of the rectangle. I know there are two lengths and widths, so I will multiply the sum by 2 to find the perimeter.

$$\text{Perimeter} = 2 \times (290 + 150)$$
$$= 2 \times (440)$$
$$= 880$$

The perimeter of the playground is 880 feet.

$5280 \div 880 = 6$

It takes 6 laps to equal a mile.

What do you think?

1. Which method would you prefer if the lengths were decimals?
2. How does each method prevent the mistake of using only one length and width?

MEETING MIDDLE SCHOOL CLASSROOM NEEDS

Tips From Middle School Teachers

I ask my students to find the perimeter of something at home. They bring in their answers, and we try to guess what they measured. If they made a mistake, either in measuring or adding, it can be really difficult to identify the object. This activity demonstrates the importance of measuring carefully.

Team Teaching

Ask other teachers on your team to point out situations in which perimeter is used, such as putting up a fence for a dog run, putting in a baseboard in a room, deciding how much framing material is needed for a picture, or buying fringe for a bedspread.

Health Connection

Reaction time is the amount of time needed to move or to react to something. A person can reduce reaction time by practicing responding to the stimulus. Fast reaction time is important in most sports. Fast reaction time can also help in avoiding accidents.

Check Your Understanding

1. If you know the length of one side of a square, how can you use multiplication to find the perimeter? Explain.
2. If one figure has a larger perimeter than another, does the first figure have to have more sides than the second? Explain.

4-1 Exercises and Applications

Practice and Apply

Getting Started Use mental math to find each perimeter.

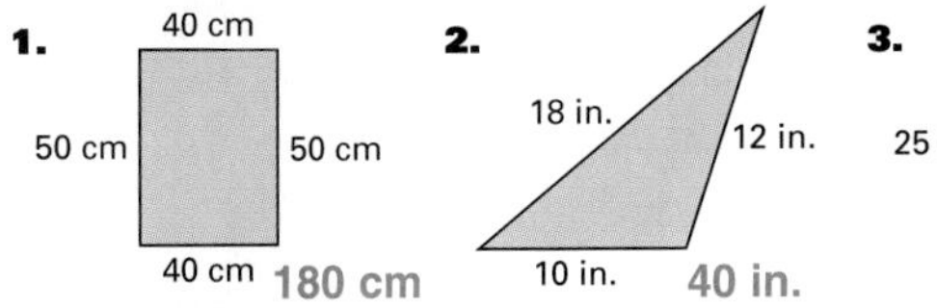

1. 40 cm, 50 cm, 50 cm, 40 cm **180 cm**
2. 18 in., 12 in., 10 in. **40 in.**
3. 25 in., 25 in., 25 in., 25 in. **100 in.**
4. 65 yd, 35 yd, 35 yd, 65 yd **200 yd**

Find each perimeter.

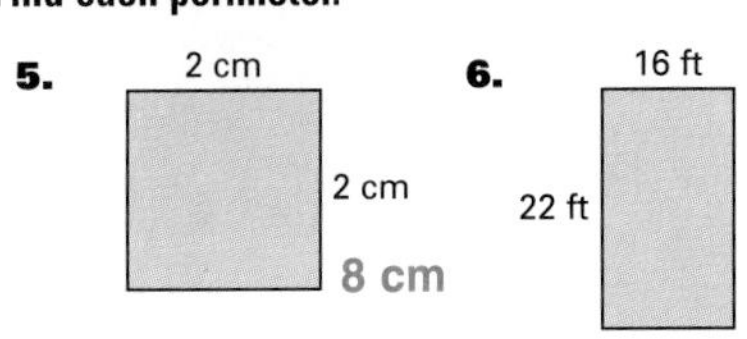

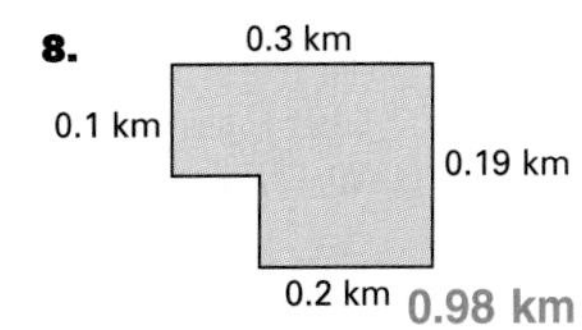

5. 2 cm, 2 cm **8 cm**
6. 16 ft, 22 ft **76 ft**
7. 6 in., 5 in., 5 in. **16 in.**
8. 0.3 km, 0.1 km, 0.19 km, 0.2 km **0.98 km**

Find the lengths of each unknown side.

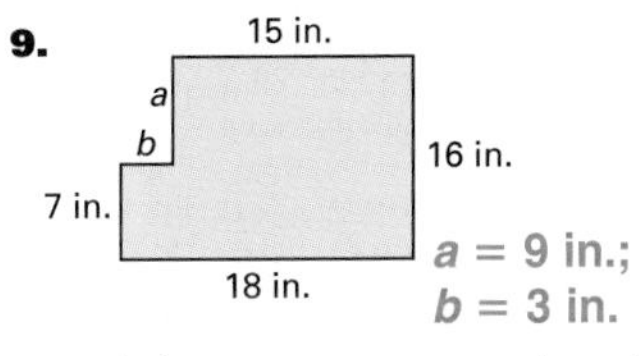

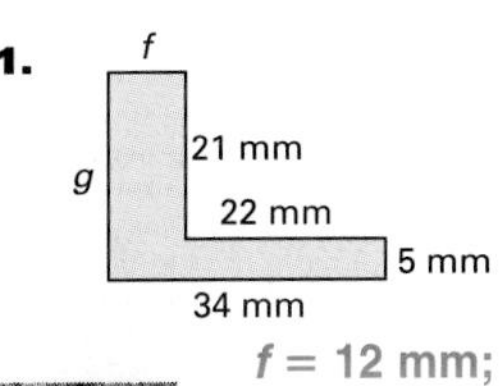

9. 15 in., *a*, *b*, 7 in., 16 in., 18 in. $a = 9$ in.; $b = 3$ in.
10. *c*, 30, 25, *e*, *d*, 20, 50, 70 $c = 20$; $d = 50$; $e = 25$
11. *f*, *g*, 21 mm, 22 mm, 5 mm, 34 mm $f = 12$ mm; $g = 26$ mm

12. Kristin wants to put organic garbage in a compost pile. She staked out a triangular area on the ground that has two sides of 6 and 8 feet. If the perimeter of the pile is 21 feet, how long is the third side? **7 ft**

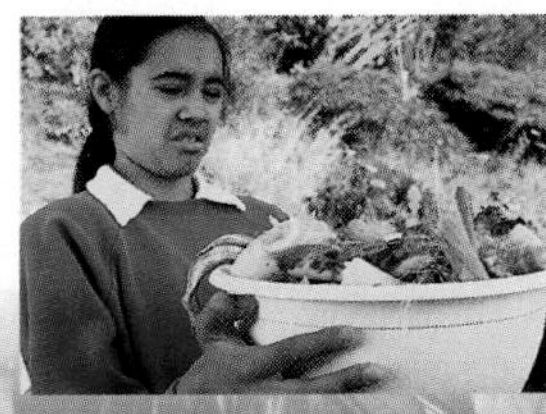

PRACTICE 4-1

PRACTICE

Name ______________________ **Practice 4-1**

Perimeter

Find the perimeter.

1. 20 cm 2. 36 ft 3. 12 m

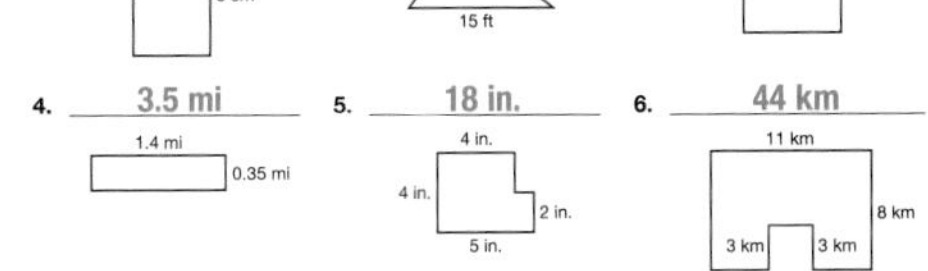

4. 3.5 mi 5. 18 in. 6. 44 km

Find the lengths of each unkown side.

7. $a =$ 2 cm $b =$ 4 cm 8. $c =$ 8 in. $d =$ 28 in. 9. $x =$ 3 ft $y =$ 2 ft

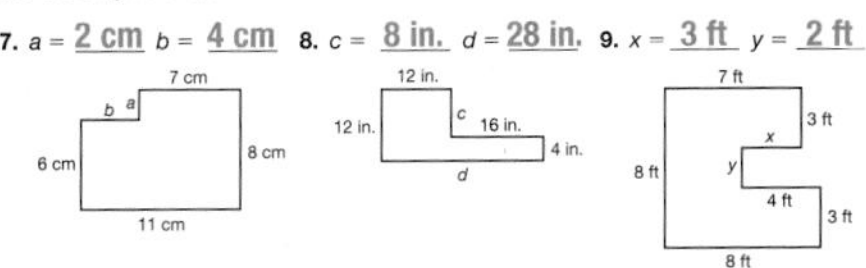

10. $p =$ 3 m $q =$ 6 m 11. $f =$ 21 cm $g =$ 12 cm 12. $t =$ 5 mi $u =$ 4 mi

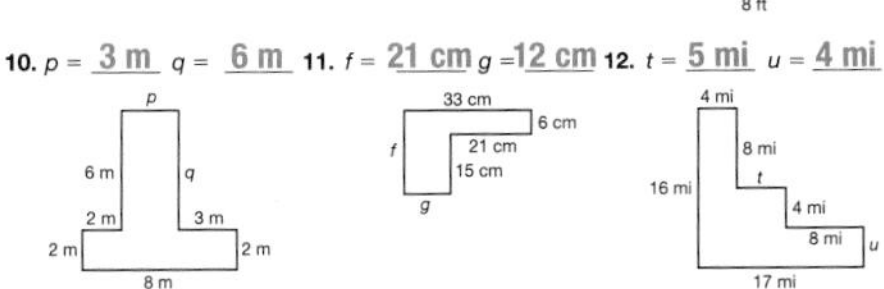

13. The triangular base of a skyscraper has a perimeter of 89 m. If two of the sides have lengths 30 m and 35 m, what is the length of the third side? 24 m

RETEACHING

Name ______________________ **Alternative Lesson 4-1**

Perimeter

The distance around the outside of a figure is known as the **perimeter**. To find the perimeter of a given geometric figure, you add the lengths of the sides.

Example 1

Find the perimeter.

Add the lengths of the four sides.

$6 + 8 + 6 + 8 = 28$

The perimeter is 28 inches.

Try It Find each perimeter by adding the lengths of the sides.

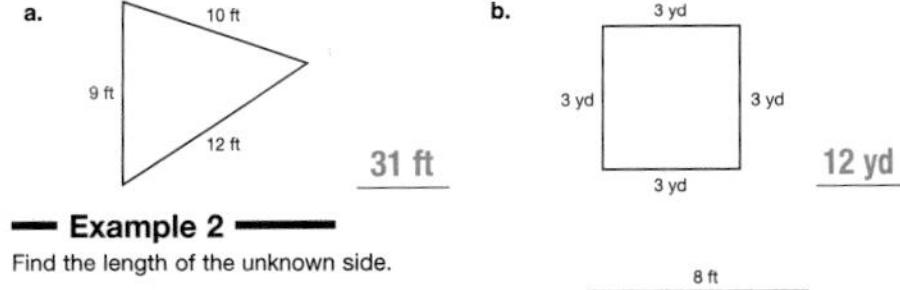

a. 31 ft b. 12 yd

Example 2

Find the length of the unknown side.

In a rectangle, opposite sides are equal, so the right side is equal to the left side.

The left side is 5 ft, so the two segments on the right side also equal 5 ft. One segment is 3 ft. Therefore, the other is equal to 5 − 3, or 2 ft. The unknown length is 2 ft.

Try It Find the length of each unknown side.

c. In a rectangle, opposite sides are equal.

6 − 2 = 4

The unknown side is 4 in.

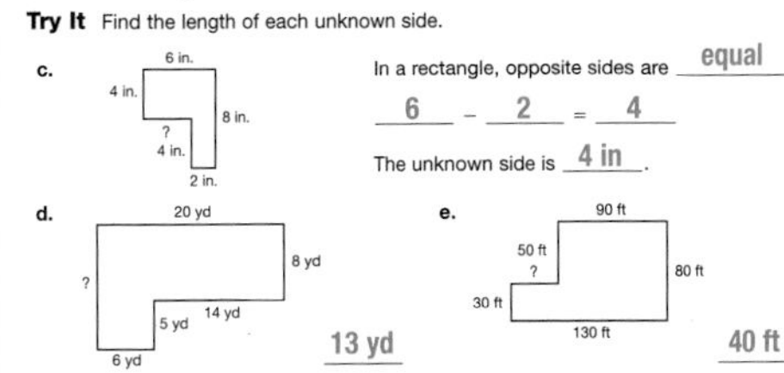

d. 13 yd e. 40 ft

4-1 Exercises and Applications

Assignment Guide

- Basic
  1–13, 15, 18, 21–24
- Average
  1–15, 18–28 evens
- Enriched
  1–19, 20–28 evens

Exercise Notes

Exercises 9–11

Error Prevention If students are not getting the correct answer, remind them that they are to find the lengths of the missing sides, not the perimeter, of each figure.

Reteaching

Activity

Materials: Unit tiles or 1 × 1 squares

- Arrange the tiles in three rows of five to make a rectangle. Find the perimeter. 16
- Move one tile so that its side lines up with another tile. You will not have a rectangle any more. Find the perimeter of the new shape. Answers may vary.
- Repeat Step 2 three more times. Find the perimeter of each figure. Answers may vary.
- What is the smallest perimeter you can have with 15 tiles? 16 What is the largest perimeter? 32

Exercise Notes

■ Exercise 13

Test Prep Students may choose C if they subtract 7 from 13, the length of the base. Point out that the unknown side is horizontal, but the side with length 7 is not. Explain that figures on tests are often not drawn to scale and that answers should not be based on what appears to be correct from looking at a figure.

■ Exercise 14

Error Prevention If students have difficulty with this problem, suggest that they draw a diagram to help them.

Project Progress

You may want to have students use Chapter 4 Project Master.

Exercise Answers

15. Sketches may vary; Perimeter of shapes must be 36 ft.

16. Yes; Doubling all the lengths will double the perimeter.

17. Subtract 7 in. and 9 in. from 30 in. to get 14 in.

Alternate Assessment

You may want to use the *Interactive CD-ROM Journal* with this assessment.

Journal Have students write a definition of perimeter and explain how to find the perimeter of a geometric figure. Their explanation should include three examples of when they would need to use perimeter.

Quick Quiz

1. Find the perimeter of a square whose side is 5 cm long. 20 cm
2. Find the perimeter of a triangle with sides of 6 m, 8 m, and 10 m. 24 m
3. Find the perimeter of a rectangular-shaped window that is 6 ft high by 3.5 ft wide. 19 ft

Available on Daily Transparency 4-1

PROBLEM SOLVING 4-1

13. **Test Prep** If the perimeter of this figure is 48 mm, how long is the unknown side? A

Ⓐ 3 mm Ⓑ 5 mm

Ⓒ 6 mm Ⓓ None of these

7 mm, x, 15 mm, 10 mm, 13 mm

14. Major league baseball diamonds have 90 feet between bases. Little League baseball diamonds have 60 feet between bases. Find the difference in running distance for a home run on the two diamonds. 120 ft

Problem Solving and Reasoning

15. **Critical Thinking** The students of Twin Creeks Middle School planted a rectangular garden. Thirty-six feet of decorative material was used for the border. Sketch two possible figures for the garden. Explain your sketches.

16. Journal If the length and width of a rectangle are doubled, is the perimeter also doubled? Explain.

17. **Communicate** Explain the steps needed to find the unknown side of a triangle if the other two sides are 7 inches and 9 inches, and the perimeter is 30 inches.

Mixed Review

For Exercises 18–20, use the Reaction Time graph. *[Lesson 1-1]*

18. At what age is the reaction time slowest for females? For males? 60; 60

19. What is the difference between male and female reaction times at age 50? 90 milliseconds

20. What do you think the reaction times for 70-year-old females will be? about 500 milliseconds

Reaction Time

Time (msec): 220, 260, 300, 340, 380, 420, 460

Age (yr): 10, 20, 30, 40, 50, 60, 70

Key: Female, Male

Write in scientific notation. *[Lesson 3-4]*

21. 56,000 5.6×10^4 **22.** 72,300,000 7.23×10^7 **23.** 2 trillion 2×10^{12} **24.** 6 thousand 6×10^3

25. 1,600 1.6×10^3 **26.** 48 billion 4.8×10^{10} **27.** 94,560,000 9.456×10^7 **28.** 874,870,000,000 8.7487×10^{11}

Project Progress

Draw sketches of the first four golf holes. Make the shapes interesting and challenging but keep the sides straight. Using a ruler, measure the perimeters in cm. If 1 cm = 2 feet, are your sketches a reasonable size?

Problem Solving: Understand, Plan, Solve, Look Back

PROBLEM SOLVING

Name ____

Guided Problem Solving 4-1

GPS PROBLEM 12, STUDENT PAGE 213

Kristin wants to put organic garbage in a compost pile. She staked out a triangular area on the ground that has two sides of 6 and 8 feet. If the perimeter of the pile is 21 feet, how long is the third side?

— Understand —

1. What are you asked to find? The length of the third side.
2. What are the lengths of two of the sides? 6 feet and 8 feet.
3. What is the perimeter? 21 feet
4. How do you find the perimeter of a triangle? Add lengths of 3 sides.

— Plan —

5. Write an addition equation to help you solve the problem. Let s = the length of the side you do not know. $6 + 8 + s = 21$
6. Which of the following is a reasonable range for the length of the third side? b

   a. Less than 5 feet b. Between 5 and 10 feet c. More than 10 feet

— Solve —

7. Solve the equation. What is the length of the unknown side? 7 feet
8. Write a sentence describing the size and shape of the compost pile. Possible answer: The compost pile is a triangle with sides measuring 6 feet, 7 feet, and 8 feet.

— Look Back —

9. Write a subtraction equation that you could use to find the length of the third side. Possible answer: $21 - 6 - 8 = s$

SOLVE ANOTHER PROBLEM

Kristin staked out a rectangular area on the ground that has one side measuring 6 feet. If the perimeter of the pile is 28 feet, how long are the other sides?
6 feet, 8 feet, and 8 feet.

ENRICHMENT

Name ____

Extend Your Thinking 4-1

Patterns in Geometry

You have learned that perimeter is the distance around the outside of a figure. Consider how the perimeter of a rectangle changes when you change the lengths of its sides.

(4 ft by 2 ft rectangle)

1. What is the perimeter of the rectangle? 12 ft
2. Write the length of each side of the rectangle when each side is doubled. (8 ft by 4 ft rectangle)
3. Find the perimeter of the new rectangle. 24 ft
4. What happens to the perimeter of the rectangle if the length of each side is doubled? It also is doubled.
5. Write the length of each side of the rectangle when each side is tripled. (12 ft by 6 ft rectangle)
6. Find the perimeter of the new rectangle. 36 ft
7. What happens to the perimeter of the rectangle if the length of each side is tripled? It also is tripled.
8. Write the length of each side of the rectangle when each side is halved. (2 ft by 1 ft rectangle)
9. Find the perimeter of the new rectangle. 6 ft
10. What happens to the perimeter of the rectangle if the length of each side is halved? It is also halved.
11. What happens to the perimeter of a rectangle when each side is multiplied by the same factor? The perimeter is multiplied by the same factor.
12. Do you think the relationship will be the same if the length of each side is increased by 2 units? Give an example to prove or disprove your theory. No, the rectangle above would have a perimeter of 20 units, which is 8 units more than that of the original rectangle.

Converting in the Metric System

4-2

▶ Lesson Link You know the decimal system is based on 10. Now you will use metric measurement, which is also based on 10. ◀

You'll Learn ...

■ to measure using the metric system and to convert units within that system

... How It's Used

Endodontists convert units in the metric system when selecting tools to perform root canals.

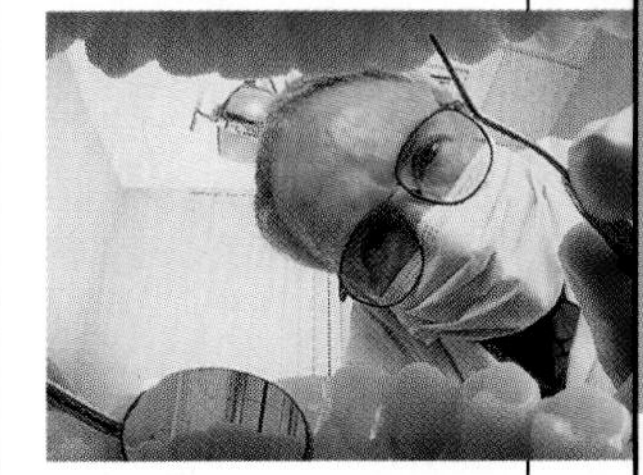

Vocabulary

metric system

meter

gram

liter

kilo-

centi-

milli-

Explore Converting in the Metric System

Super Powers of 10

Materials: Calculator

1. Using a calculator, copy and complete the chart.

÷ 1000	÷ 100	÷ 10	Base Unit	× 10	× 100	× 1000
	0.05	0.5	5	50	500	
		1.7	17	170		
			2.1			
			0.55			
			36.7			

2. If these were the next three lines in the chart, what would be the values of *a*, *b*, and *c*? Explain.

		0.0045			*a*	
b				270		
	0.00021					*c*

3. How could you fill out the chart without using a calculator?
4. If the numbers 0.034 and 34,000 were in the same row, how many columns would be in between them? How can you tell?

Learn Converting in the Metric System

The **metric system** is a system of measurements used to describe how long, how heavy, or how big something is. The base unit for measuring length is the **meter**. The base unit for measuring mass is the **gram**. The base unit for measuring volume is the **liter**.

MEETING INDIVIDUAL NEEDS

Resources

- **4-2** Practice
- **4-2** Reteaching
- **4-2** Problem Solving
- **4-2** Enrichment
- **4-2** Daily Transparency
  - Problem of the Day
  - Review
  - Quick Quiz
- Lesson Enhancement Transparencies 13, 14
- Technology Master 16

Learning Modalities

Verbal Have students research the origins of the prefixes used in the metric system.

Logical Students may find it useful to write out the prefixes (kilo-, hecto-, deka-, deci-, centi-, milli-) as headings for columns. They can start with the units they are given and count how many places left or right they need to move the decimal point.

English Language Development

Some students may be more familiar with the metric system because of its common use outside the United States. Encourage these students to share their knowledge of the metric system with the class, perhaps giving examples of how each measure is commonly used.

4-2 Lesson Organizer

Objective

- Measure using the metric system and convert units within that system.

Vocabulary

- Metric system, meter, gram, liter, kilo-, centi-, milli-

Materials

- Explore: Calculator

NCTM Standards

- 1–4, 7, 13

▶ Review

Write each fraction as a decimal.

1. $\frac{3}{10}$ 0.3
2. $\frac{53}{100}$ 0.53
3. $\frac{289}{1000}$ 0.289

Available on Daily Transparency 4-2

1 Introduce

Explore

You may wish to use Lesson Enhancement Transparencies 13 and 14 with **Explore**.

The Point

Students multiply and divide a series of numbers by 10, 100, and 1000.

Ongoing Assessment

Check that students who need to use a calculator are completing the table row-by-row rather than column-by-column. This will help them see how the decimal point "moves" as numbers are divided or multiplied by powers of 10.

For Groups That Finish Early

Add a column for × 10,000 and one for ÷ 10,000.

× 10,000 column: 50,000; 170,000; 21,000; 5500; 367,000.

÷ 10,000 column: 0.0005; 0.0017; 0.00021; 0.000055; 0.00367.

Answers for Explore on next page.

Answers for Explore

1. Row 1: 0.005; 5000

   Row 2: 0.017; 0.17; 1700; 17,000

   Row 3: 0.0021; 0.021; 0.21; 21; 210; 2100

   Row 4: 0.00055, 0.0055; 0.055; 5.5; 55; 550

   Row 5: 0.0367; 0.367; 3.67; 367; 3670; 36,700
2. $a = 4.5$; $b = 0.027$; $c = 21$; Multiply or divide by the appropriate power of 10.
3. Possible answer: For each column to the left of the number, move decimal point one place to the left: For each column to the right of the number, move decimal point one place to the right.
4. 5; The decimal moved 6 places so there would be 5 columns between the numbers.

2 Teach

Learn

Students may be interested to know that the metric system is the system used in almost every country in the world. Ask them if they can provide examples of metric measurements used in the United States.

Alternate Examples

1. Complete. Use the abbreviation for the most appropriate metric unit.
   Weight of a 12-year-old boy:

   40 _____

   Since weight is being measured, the metric unit should be based on a gram. Since a boy weighs about the same as 40 cantaloupes, the appropriate unit is kilograms, which is abbreviated kg. The weight is 40 kg.

History Link

The meter was originally defined as $\frac{1}{10,000,000}$ of the distance from the equator to the North Pole. It took the French from 1792 to 1798 to measure and calculate this distance. Today's satellites confirm that their measurements were only off by 0.2 mm.

The metric system also uses prefixes to describe amounts that are much larger or smaller than the base unit. The prefixes used most often are **kilo-**, meaning 1000; **centi-**, meaning $\frac{1}{100}$; and **milli-**, meaning $\frac{1}{1000}$.

	Name	Abbreviation	Number of Base Units	Approximate Comparison
Length	**Kilo**meter	km	1000	10 city blocks
	Meter	m	1	Half the height of a door
	Centimeter	cm	$\frac{1}{100}$	Length of a raisin
	Millimeter	mm	$\frac{1}{1000}$	Width of a period at the end of a sentence
Mass	**Kilo**gram	kg	1000	Mass of a cantaloupe
	Gram	g	1	Mass of a raisin
Volume	Liter	L	1	Half a large bottle of soda
	Milliliter	mL	$\frac{1}{1000}$	Half an eyedropper

The prefixes allow you to choose a convenient unit when something is too large or too small to be easily measured in meters, grams, or liters.

Science Link

Glass never wears out. It can be recycled forever.

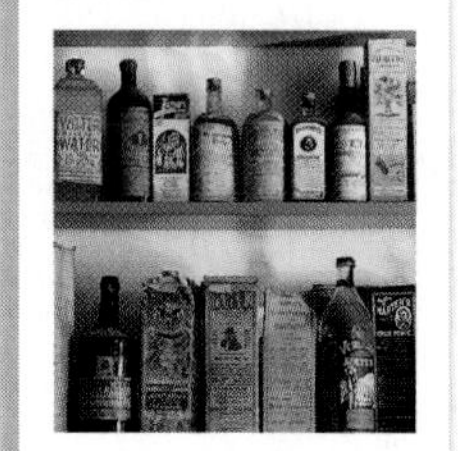

Example 1

Complete. Use the abbreviation for the most appropriate metric unit.

Height of a single-serving bottle: 17 _____

Since length (height) is being measured, the base unit should be the meter. Since a bottle is about 17 raisins tall, the appropriate unit is centimeters, abbreviated as cm. The height is 17 cm.

Try It

Complete. Use the abbreviation for the most appropriate metric unit.

a. Length of a marathon route: 42 km

b. Width of a thumbnail: 1.5 cm

c. Mass of a dog: 15 kg

d. Amount of water in a small fishbowl: 2 L

MATH EVERY DAY

Problem of the Day

Nancy plants 3 rows of cacti. Each row is 4 ft long. How many can she plant if the cacti in each row are 8 inches apart? Hint: There will be a plant at the beginning and at the end of each row. 21 plants

Available on Daily Transparency 4-2

An Extension is provided in the transparency package.

Fact of the Day

In 1975, Americans recycled about 100,000 tons of aluminum. By 1993, 10 times as much, 1,000,000 tons, was being recycled.

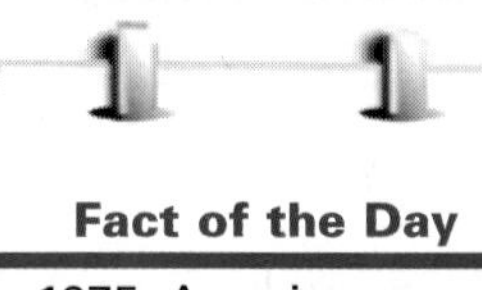

Mental Math

Do these mentally.

1. 51×6 306
2. $612 \div 6$ 102
3. $475 + 56 + 25$ 556
4. $702 - 299$ 403

To convert a unit in the metric system, you multiply or divide by a power of 10. The table below lists the powers of 10 to use when converting.

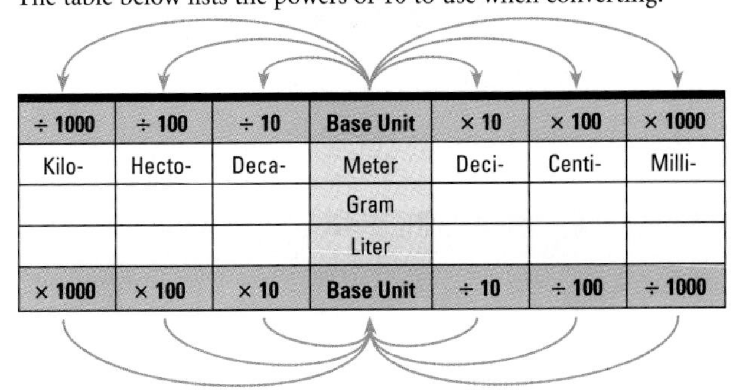

÷ 1000	÷ 100	÷ 10	Base Unit	× 10	× 100	× 1000
Kilo-	Hecto-	Deca-	Meter	Deci-	Centi-	Milli-
			Gram			
			Liter			
× 1000	× 100	× 10	Base Unit	÷ 10	÷ 100	÷ 1000

DID YOU KNOW?

Some metric measurements have names but are rarely used. These include the hectometer, which equals 100 meters, the decameter, which equals 10 meters, and the decimeter, which equals 0.1 meter.

Examples

2 The Danville Stroller Derby is 5 km long. How many meters is that?

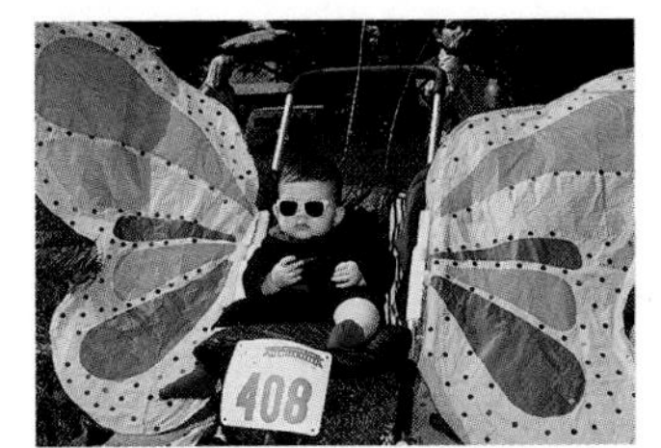

The first unit given is kilometers. To convert from kilometers to meters, you multiply by 1000.

$5 \text{ km} \times 1000 = 5000 \text{ m}$

3 60,000 cm = _____ km

First, to convert from centimeters to meters, you divide by 100. Then, to convert meters to kilometers, you divide by 1000.

$60{,}000 \text{ cm} \div 100 = 600 \text{ m}$

$600 \text{ m} \div 1000 = 0.6 \text{ km}$

Remember

A shortcut for multiplying by 1000 is to move the decimal point three places to the right. **[Page 178]** A shortcut for dividing by 1000 is to move the decimal point three places to the left. **[Page 187]**

Try It

Convert.

a. 7.36 km = _____ m 7360 **b.** 0.008 L = _____ mL 8 **c.** 325 g = _____ kg 0.325

Number sense can help determine if a conversion is reasonable. When converting to a larger unit, your answer gets smaller. When converting to a smaller unit, your answer gets larger. For example, if you have a given distance in millimeters, it will take fewer centimeters to equal that same distance.

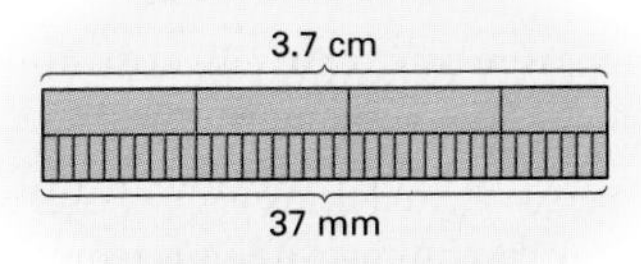

Alternate Examples

2. The distance to the next exit on the freeway is 1.6 km. How many meters is this?

   The first unit given is kilometers. To convert from kilometers to meters, you multiply by 1000.

   $1.6 \text{ km} \times 1000 = 1600 \text{ m}$

3. 1340 mL = _____ kL

   First, to convert from milliliters to liters, you divide by 1000. Then, to convert liters to kiloliters, you divide by 1000.

   $1340 \div 1000 = 1.34 \text{ L}$

   $1.34 \text{ L} \div 1000 = 0.00134 \text{ kL}$

MEETING MIDDLE SCHOOL CLASSROOM NEEDS

Tips from Middle School Teachers

I like to set up length, weight/mass, and capacity centers. At each center I provide instruction sheets, a variety of objects to measure, and appropriate measuring tools such as rulers, tape measures, balance scales, and beakers. The instruction sheet asks students to select an object from the center, estimate its measure in the given unit, measure it, and compare the estimate to the actual measurement. As students continue to estimate and measure objects, I find that their estimates get closer to the actual measure.

Team Teaching

Work with the foods teacher or the health teacher to help students read nutrition labels on food. Have them note the metric units used for such items as amounts of carbohydrates, protein, and sodium.

Science Connection

The metric system is also know as SI, or International System, from the French *Système International d'Unités*. The meter is defined as the distance light travels in a vacuum in $\frac{1}{299{,}792{,}458}$ of a second.

4-2 Exercises and Applications

Assignment Guide

- **Basic**
  1–12, 18–25, 30–33, 35, 38–52 evens
- **Average**
  1–27 odds, 29–35, 39–51 odds
- **Enriched**
  1–27 odds, 28–36, 38–52 evens

3 Practice and Assess

Check

Answers for Check Your Understanding

1. Similarities: They're both 1000 times the base unit; They have different base units: Kilograms measure weight, while kilometers measure distance.
2. Yes; Milliliters and liters have the same base unit; No; Milligrams and meters don't have the same base unit.

Reteaching

Activity

Materials: Index cards or pieces of paper, tape

- Make a visual display of the metric units for length, mass, and volume. Write each metric unit on an index card or piece of paper.
- Arrange the units of length, mass, and volume in decreasing order, such as kilometers, meters, centimeters, and so on.
- Tape the cards to the chalkboard in the correct order. There should be three columns of units.
- Next to the cards draw arrows and indicate the operation, such as "× 10" or "÷ 10," needed to make the conversion from larger units to smaller units and vice versa.
- Practice making conversions from one metric unit to another.

PRACTICE 4-2

Check Your Understanding

1. How are kilograms and kilometers similar? How are they different?
2. Can any measure in milliliters be converted to liters? Can any measure in milligrams be converted to meters? Explain.

4-2 Exercises and Applications

Practice and Apply

Getting Started For each pair of measurements, choose the larger.

1. 1 meter, 1 kilometer **1 kilometer**
2. 1 kilogram, 1 gram **1 kilogram**
3. 1 centimeter, 1 meter **1 meter**
4. 1 liter, 1 milliliter **1 liter**
5. 1 centimeter, 1 millimeter **1 centimeter**
6. 1 kilometer, 1 millimeter **1 kilometer**

For Exercises 7–12, name an appropriate metric unit of measure.

7. Weight of a 6th grader **Kilogram**
8. Amount of water in a swimming pool **Liter**
9. Distance from New York to Washington, DC **Kilometer**
10. Amount of water in a raindrop **Milliliter**
11. Weight of an aluminum can **Gram**
12. Height of a stack of daily newspapers read in one month **Meter**

Convert.

13. 90 g = ☐ kg **0.09**
14. 32.6 mm = ☐ m **0.0326**
15. 0.1 L = ☐ mL **100**
16. 5.3 m = ☐ mm **5300**
17. 7.88 mL = ☐ L **0.00788**
18. 1 m = ☐ cm **100**
19. 0.0042 kg = ☐ g **4.2**
20. 3 L = ☐ mL **3000**
21. 5 g = ☐ kg **0.005**
22. 25 kg = ☐ g **25,000**
23. 13.1 cm = ☐ mm **131**
24. 8 mL = ☐ L **0.008**
25. 2.67 km = ☐ cm **267,000**
26. 18 cm = ☐ m **0.18**
27. 42.9 kg = ☐ g **42,900**
28. **Career** Which measurement unit, millimeters or meters, would an optometrist use when measuring patients' eyes? **Millimeters**
29. **Estimation** A person should drink eight glasses of water every day. Estimate if this is more than or less than 1 liter. **More**

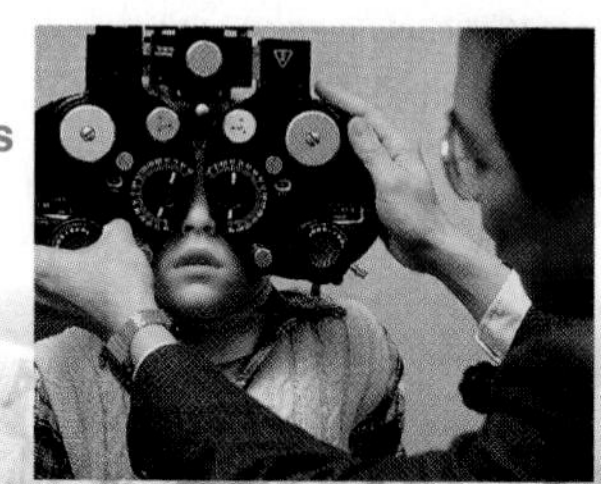

PRACTICE

Name ____________________

Practice 4-2

Converting in the Metric System

For Exercises 1–10, name an appropriate metric unit of measure.

1. Weight of a calculator **Possible answer: Grams**
2. Height of a woman **Possible answer: Centimeters**
3. Amount of gasoline in a car **Possible answer: Liters**
4. Distance from Hong Kong to Beijing, China **Possible answer: Kilometers**
5. Weight of a paper clip **Possible answer: Grams**
6. Length of an airplane **Possible answer: Meters**
7. Amount of coffee in a cup **Possible answer: Milliliters**
8. Weight of a golden retriever **Possible answer: Kilograms**
9. Width of a playing card **Possible answer: Centimeters**
10. Amount of glue used to repair a plate **Possible answer: Milliliters**

Convert.

11. 4 m = **400** cm
12. 39 g = **0.039** kg
13. 87 cm = **0.87** m
14. 2.7L = **2,700** mL
15. 4.3 km = **4,300** m
16. 14.2 kg = **14,200** g
17. 538 mL = **0.538** L
18. 3.7 g = **0.0037** kg
19. 7.4 m = **0.0074** km
20. 21 cm = **210** mm
21. 42 m = **0.042** km
22. 0.8 km = **80,000** cm
23. 43 mm = **4.3** cm
24. 8.26 kg = **8260** g
25. 2.3 km = **230,000** cm
26. **Science** A tornado typically moves about 64,400 meters in an hour. Convert this distance to kilometers. **64.4 km**
27. **Geography** Kazakhstan has about 2,320 km of coastline. Convert this distance to millimeters. **2,320,000,000 mm**
28. A Cessna 185 flies an average of 208 km in one hour. How many meters can the Cessna fly in one hour. **208,000 m**

RETEACHING

Name ____________________

Alternative Lesson 4-2

Converting in the Metric System

The **metric system** is a system of measurements used to describe how long, how heavy, or how big something is. The metric system uses **prefixes** to describe amounts that are much larger or smaller than the base unit. The base units for measuring length, mass, and volume are shown in the table below. The prefixes used most often are **kilo-**, meaning 1000; **centi-**, meaning $\frac{1}{100}$; and **milli-**, meaning $\frac{1}{1000}$.

To **convert** a unit in the metric system, you need to multiply or divide by a power of 10. The table below lists the powers of 10 to use when converting. When converting to a larger unit, your answer gets smaller. When converting to a smaller unit, your answer gets larger. For example, if you are given a distance in millimeters, it will take fewer centimeters to equal that same distance.

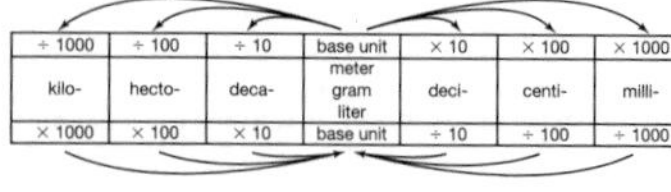

÷ 1000	÷ 100	÷ 10	base unit	× 10	× 100	× 1000
kilo-	hecto-	deca-	meter gram liter	deci-	centi-	milli-
× 1000	× 100	× 10	base unit	÷ 10	÷ 100	÷ 1000

Example

Convert 34,000 milliliters to liters.

You are converting from a smaller unit to a larger unit, so you will divide. Refer to the conversion table to find the divisor. When converting from milliliters to liters, divide by 1000.

34,000 ÷ 1,000 = 34

So, 34,000 milliliters = 34 liters.

Try It Convert.

a. 16 grams = ? milligrams

Are you converting from a smaller unit to a larger unit or a larger unit to a smaller unit? **Larger to smaller unit.**

Will you multiply or divide? **Multiply.**

What number will you multiply or divide by? **1000**

16 grams = **16,000** milligrams

b. 6 meters = **600** centimeters

c. 162 kilograms = **162,000** grams

d. 4000 milliliters = **4** liters

e. 25,000 millimeters = **25** meters

30. Every year, a person creates 163,300 grams of food and yard waste. Convert this amount to kilograms. 163.3

31. Test Prep In the 1996 Summer Olympics, Michael Johnson broke a world track record with a time of 19.32 seconds. Which distance did he most likely run? B

Ⓐ 2 meters Ⓑ 200 meters

Ⓒ 200 liters Ⓓ 20 kilometers

32. Newspapers make up the largest part of trash in landfills. A 30.48 cm stack of newspapers weighs about 15.87 kg. Convert the measurements to meters and grams. 0.3048 m; 15,870 g

Problem Solving and Reasoning

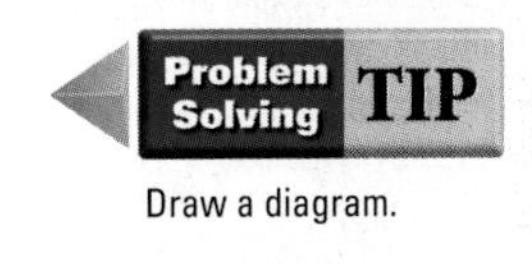

Draw a diagram.

33. Communicate State the perimeter of a square whose sides are each 12 cm in millimeters, centimeters, and meters. Explain your reasoning.

34. Journal Describe a situation in which you would use liters and one in which you would use milliliters. Explain why each measurement is appropriate.

35. Critical Thinking Robert and his granddaughter Bailey built a playhouse. The foundation of the playhouse was a 1.86 m-by-95 cm rectangle. What was the perimeter of Bailey's playhouse? Explain.

36. Critical Thinking As part of a statistics experiment, seven students measured the approximate distance around a bus token. Find the average measurement rounded to the hundredths of a cm. Explain your reasoning.

Jon	3.6 cm
Diane	34.2 mm
Wu-Lin	3.4 cm
Shelly	3.8 cm
Truc	37.5 mm
Mary	32.1 mm
Jason	3.5 cm

PROBLEM SOLVING 4-2

Mixed Review

Write in standard form. *[Lesson 2-1]*

37. one hundred three 103 **38.** 8 trillion 8,000,000,000,000 **39.** 45 billion 45,000,000,000 **40.** two thousand, five 2005

41. forty-five thousand, six hundred twelve 45,612 **42.** one million, sixty-one thousand, twenty-two 1,061,022

Write each fraction as a decimal. *[Lesson 3-1]*

43. $\frac{55}{100}$ 0.55 **44.** $\frac{2}{10}$ 0.2 **45.** $\frac{67}{1000}$ 0.067 **46.** $\frac{532}{1000}$ 0.532 **47.** $\frac{4}{10}$ 0.4

48. $\frac{9}{10}$ 0.9 **49.** $\frac{2}{100}$ 0.02 **50.** $\frac{10}{10}$ 1.0 **51.** $\frac{8}{1000}$ 0.008 **52.** $\frac{99}{100}$ 0.99

Exercise Notes

Exercises 7 and 11

Error Prevention Students may be confused by the use of "weight" in these exercises since gram is a unit of mass. You may wish to tell them that the weight of something or someone can be measured in grams as well as pounds.

Exercise 31

Test Prep If students select A, show them a meter stick to convince them that this is not the correct choice. If students select D, remind them that kilometers are often compared to $\frac{1}{2}$ miles. Therefore, 20 km is an unrealistic distance to run in 19.32 seconds.

Exercise Answers

33. 480 mm; 48 cm; 0.48 m. Possible answer: Find the perimeter in centimeters, then convert. 12 cm = 120 mm = 0.12 m.

34. Possible answer: Use liters to calculate volume of water in a swimming pool; Use milliliters to calculate the amount of medicine to give a child per day.

35. 562 cm; Convert to one measurement, then add the dimensions and double the sum.

36. 3.53 cm; Convert all measurements to cm, then find the average.

Alternate Assessment

Self Assessment Ask students to identify what they find the easiest and what they find the most difficult about working with the metric system.

PROBLEM SOLVING

Name ______ **Guided Problem Solving 4-2**

GPS PROBLEM 35, STUDENT PAGE 219

Robert and his granddaughter Bailey built a playhouse. The foundation of the playhouse was a 1.86 m-by-95 cm rectangle. What was the perimeter of Bailey's playhouse? Explain.

— Understand —

1. What are you asked to find? The perimeter of the playhouse.
2. What size and shape is the foundation? 1.86 m by 95 cm; rectangle.
3. How would you find the perimeter of the foundation? Possible answer: Add the lengths of the four sides.

— Plan —

4. Both dimensions should be in the same unit. What will you do to convert meters to centimeters? Multiply by 100.
5. How many centimeters equal 1.86 meters? 186 centimeters.

— Solve —

6. Find the perimeter of the foundation in centimeters. 562 centimeters.
7. Explain. How did you find your answer? Convert to one measurement and then add to find the perimeter.

— Look Back —

8. What is another way you could find the perimeter of the playhouse? Possible answer: Convert cm to m and then find the perimeter.

SOLVE ANOTHER PROBLEM

Allan and Yolanda built a bookcase. The base of the bookcase was a 1.5 m-by-62 cm rectangle. What was the perimeter of their bookcase? Explain.

424 cm or 4.24 m; convert to like units of measure and then find

ENRICHMENT

Name ______ **Extend Your Thinking 4-2**

Visual Thinking

Optical illusions occur when the human eye and brain perceive something that is not really true. Look at the pictures below. Answer the questions. Then check your answers by measuring.

1. Circle the railroad tie that is longest.

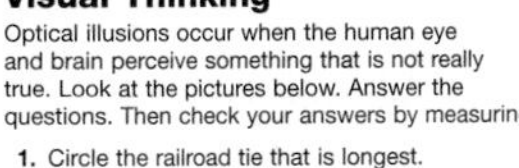

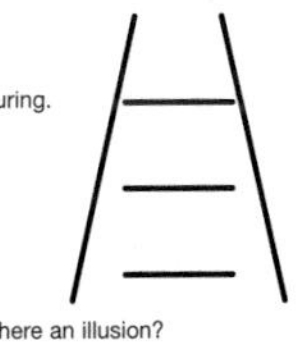

2. Measure the ties. Which is longest? Was there an illusion? If so, what was the illusion? The ties are the same length. The illusion is that the ties get longer as the track recedes.

3. Circle the square that is larger.

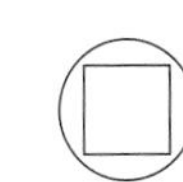

4. Measure the squares. Which is larger? Was there an illusion? If so, what was the illusion? The squares are the same size. The illusion is that the square on the right is larger.

5. Shade the center circle that is larger.

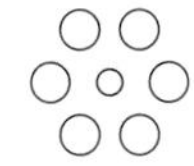

6. Measure the center circles. Which is larger? Was there an illusion? If so, what was the illusion? The center circles are the same size. The illusion is that the circle surrounded by smaller circles is larger.

Quick Quiz

Name an appropriate unit of measure for each item.

1. Weight of an apple grams
2. Height of a giraffe meters
3. Amount of juice in a carton liters

Convert:

4. 0.53 kg = ______ g 530
5. 56 mm = ______ m 0.056

Available on Daily Transparency 4-2

4-3 Lesson Organizer

Objective

- Convert units within the customary system of measurement.

Vocabulary

- Inch, foot, yard, mile, ounce, pound, quart, gallon, conversion factor

Materials

- Explore: Calculator

NCTM Standards

- 1–5, 13

Review

Find the value of x in each equation.

1. $145x = 290$ $x = 2$
2. $\frac{480}{x} = 40$ $x = 12$
3. $\frac{1428}{x} = 7$ $x = 204$
4. $125x = 1000$ $x = 8$

Available on Daily Transparency 4-3

1 Introduce

Explore

You may wish to use Lesson Enhancement Transparency 15 with **Explore.**

The Point

Students use the values in a table to find the conversion factors, first for conversions that would apply to customary units and then for ones that would apply to metric units.

Ongoing Assessment

Most students should be able to recognize the pattern in the second table as similar to the one in the last lesson.

For Groups That Finish Early

What measurements might the numbers in the tables represent? Possible answer: The first table might be miles, furlongs (6 feet), yards, feet, or inches. The second table might be any metric unit.

4-3 Using Conversion Factors

You'll Learn ...

- to convert units within the customary system of measurement

... How It's Used

Chefs convert units in the customary system when preparing meals for a large number of people.

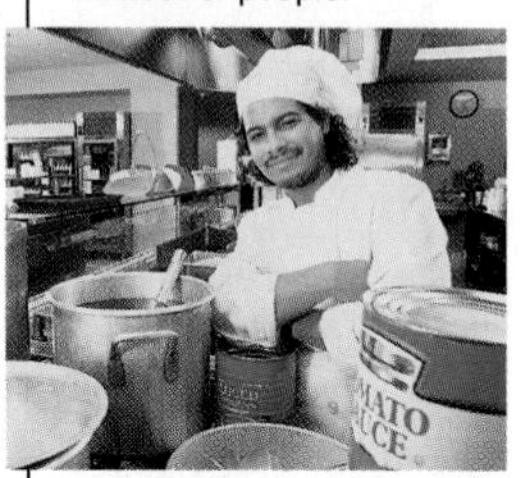

Vocabulary

inch
foot
yard
mile
ounce
pound
quart
gallon
conversion factor

▶ Lesson Link You have learned how to use the metric system of measurement. Now you will learn how to use the customary system of measurement for length, mass, and volume. ◀

Explore Using Conversion Factors

Go to the Head of the Table!

Materials: Calculator

1. Each column of numbers in the table below is the result of taking the base number and multiplying or dividing it by some factor. For each column, determine the factor used.

÷ ???	÷ ???	Base	× ???	× ???
2	1,760	3,520	10,560	126,720
5	4,400	8,800	26,400	316,800
7	6,160	12,320	36,960	443,520
		14,080		

2. What are the missing values in the bottom row of the chart?
3. For each column in the table below, determine the factor used.

÷ ???	÷ ???	Base	× ???	× ???
35.2	352	3,520	35,200	352,000
88	880	8,800	88,000	880,000
123.2	1,232	12,320	123,200	1,232,000
		14,080		

4. What are the missing values in the bottom row of the chart?
5. In which chart is it easier to go from one column to the next? Why?

MEETING INDIVIDUAL NEEDS

Resources

4-3 Practice
4-3 Reteaching
4-3 Problem Solving
4-3 Enrichment
4-3 Daily Transparency
Problem of the Day
Review
Quick Quiz
Lesson Enhancement Transparency 15

Learning Modalities

Musical Have students make up a song that will help them remember the conversion factors for the customary units.

Kinesthetic Have students actually measure objects using different units in order to get a better intuitive understanding of the size of the units.

Social Students could work in pairs to answer the questions in **Explore.**

Inclusion

Ask students to practice holding their hands about 1 inch apart, 1 foot apart, and 1 yard apart. Have them find something they think weighs about 1 ounce or 1 pound and then check it by weighing it. Have them identify containers that hold about 1 quart or about 1 gallon.

Have students add new vocabulary to their reference books.

Learn Using Conversion Factors

The customary system is another system of measurement used in the United States to describe how long, how heavy, or how big something is. The customary system does not use a base unit and prefixes. Each unit has a separate name.

	Name	Abbreviation	Approximate Comparison
Length	Inch	in.	Length of half a thumb
Length	Foot	ft	Length of adult male foot
Length	Yard	yd	Length from nose to outstretched fingertip
Length	Mile	mi	Length of 16 city blocks
Weight	Ounce	oz	Weight of birthday card
Weight	Pound	lb	Weight of three apples
Volume	Quart	qt	Amount in a medium container of milk
Volume	Gallon	gal	Amount in a small bucket

Inches can be abbreviated with quotation marks: 15" means 15 inches. Feet can be abbreviated with an apostrophe: 21' means 21 feet.

Example 1

Complete. Use the abbreviation for the most appropriate customary unit.

Height of a plastic water bottle: 11 ____

Since length is being measured, the customary unit should be inches, feet, yards, or miles. Since a bottle is about 11 half-thumbs, the appropriate unit is inches, which is abbreviated "in."

Try It

Complete. Use the abbreviation for the most appropriate customary unit.

a. Length of a marathon route: 26 Miles

b. Weight of a dog: 45 Pounds

c. Amount of water in a small fishbowl: 2 Quarts

DID YOU KNOW?

There is more than one type of ounce. For example, Avoirdupois ounces are used to measure solid things. Fluid ounces are used to measure liquid things.

▶ Science Link

Plastics of different types cannot be recycled together. In order to help sort plastics, bottle manufacturers label the plastic type on the bottle. Polyethylene terephthalate, one of the most common types, is labeled "1 PET" or "1 PETE."

MATH EVERY DAY

▶ Problem of the Day

Jeff placed six equilateral triangles together to form a six-sided figure called a hexagon. The perimeter of each triangle is 21 mm. What is the perimeter of the hexagon?
42 mm

Available on Daily Transparency 4-3

An Extension is provided in the transparency package.

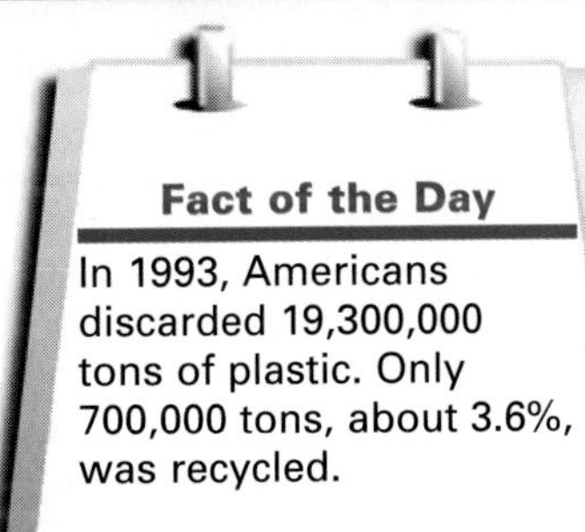

Fact of the Day

In 1993, Americans discarded 19,300,000 tons of plastic. Only 700,000 tons, about 3.6%, was recycled.

Estimation

Estimate.

1. 3.96 + 2.01 6
2. 6.02 − 1.88 4
3. 3.99 × 5.11 20
4. 55.789 ÷ 7.88 7

Answers for Explore

1. 1760; 2; 3; 36
2. 8; 7,040; 42,240; 506,880
3. 100; 10; 10; 100
4. 140.8; 1,408; 140,800; 1,408,000
5. The second chart; The factors are all powers of 10.

2 Teach

Learn

Ask students to make a list of everything they know about measuring length, weight, and liquid capacity in the customary system. Have them share their lists, writing each item under one of three categories: *Everyone Knows, About Half Know, Only a Few Know.* For each measure that they know, ask them to identify something that is about that size.

Alternate Examples

1. Complete. Use the abbreviation for the most appropriate customary unit. Weight of a pumpkin = 10 ____

   Since weight is being measured, the customary unit should be ounces or pounds. Since a pumpkin is heavier than 3 apples, the appropriate unit is pounds, which is abbreviated "lbs."

Alternate Examples

2. The average person in the United States uses about 20 gallons of water each day taking showers and baths. How many quarts is this?

   One gallon equals 4 quarts. Gallons are being converted to a smaller unit, so the number of gallons should be multiplied by the conversion factor.

   $20 \times 4 = 80$ quarts

3. The average person in the United States walks about 18,000 feet each day. How many miles is this?

   One mile equals 5280 feet. Feet are being converted to a larger unit, so the number of feet should be divided by the conversion factor.

   $18{,}000 \div 5{,}280 = 3.41$ miles

3 Practice and Assess

Check

Have students think about each of the questions, then discuss the questions with a partner. Finally, have them share their responses.

Answers for Check Your Understanding

1. Possible answer: Metric; The measurements are all powers of 10, so it's easy to move the decimal, multiply, or divide.
2. When converting to smaller units, multiply by a conversion factor. When converting to larger units, divide by a conversion factor.

History Link

In the 1300s, the standard for the foot was often the length of the king's foot. This length was usually copied inaccurately, and so the foot varied from village to village.

MENTAL MATH

When dividing a number with several zeros at the end, you can divide the whole number part and annex the zeros to your answer.

The customary system is not based on powers of 10. In order to convert from one unit to another, you need to know the **conversion factor**, or the number of units that another unit is equal to.

Length	Weight	Liquid Capacity
1 foot = 12 inches	1 pound = 16 ounces	1 gallon = 4 quarts
1 yard = 3 feet		
1 mile = 5280 feet		

To convert to a smaller unit, *multiply* by the appropriate conversion factor. The unit in the answer is smaller, so the number of units will be bigger. To convert to a larger unit, *divide* by the appropriate conversion factor. The unit in the answer is bigger, so the number of units will be smaller.

Examples

2 The average adult in the United States generates 8 pounds of newspaper garbage in a month. How many ounces is this?

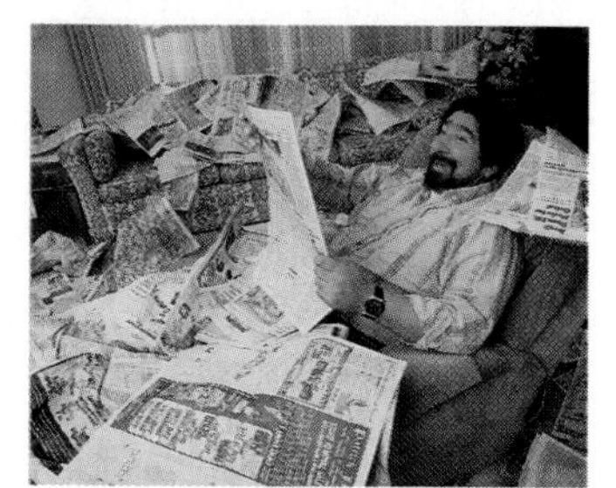

One pound equals 16 ounces. Pounds are being converted to smaller units, so the number of pounds should be multiplied by the conversion factor.

$8 \times 16 = 128$ ounces

3 An oil company can re-refine 62 gallons of new oil from every 400 quarts of recycled oil. 400 quarts is equal to how many gallons?

One gallon equals 4 quarts. Quarts are being converted to larger units, so the number of quarts should be divided by the conversion factor.

$400 \div 4 = 100$ gallons

Try It

Convert. **a.** 7 gal = 28 qt **b.** 64 oz = 4 lb **c.** 2 mi = 10,560 ft

Check Your Understanding

1. Is it easier to convert in the metric or the customary system? Why?
2. How can you tell when to multiply by a conversion factor and when to divide by a conversion factor?

MEETING MIDDLE SCHOOL CLASSROOM NEEDS

Tips from Middle School Teachers

I find that my students understand the customary units when they see real-life examples. I ask each student to bring in empty milk, juice, and soft drink containers in gallon, half-gallon, quart, pint, and cup sizes. We fill the containers with water so that students gain an understanding of the capacity of containers of various sizes.

Cooperative Learning

Have students work in groups of three or four to create flashcards of conversion facts. Using the flashcards, students can quiz each other on the conversions.

History Connection

The customary system of measurement is based on the British imperial system. Units were developed in medieval days, long before there were uniform standards. The inch was equal to 3 kernels of corn or wheat laid end to end. The foot was the equivalent of a human foot.

4-3 Exercises and Applications

Practice and Apply

Getting Started Convert to feet.

1. 36 inches 3 **2.** 24 inches 2 **3.** 96 inches 8 **4.** 144 inches 12 **5.** 60 inches 5

Convert.

6. 496 ounces = ☐ pounds 31 **7.** 252 inches = ☐ feet 21 **8.** 15 pounds = ☐ ounces 240

9. 36 feet = ☐ yards 12 **10.** 4 feet = ☐ inches 48 **11.** 2 pounds = ☐ ounces 32

12. 48 quarts = ☐ gallons 12 **13.** 12 yards = ☐ feet 36 **14.** 10,560 feet = ☐ miles 2

15. 24 pounds = ☐ ounces 384 **16.** 9 gallons = ☐ quarts 36 **17.** 4 miles = ☐ feet 21,120

18. 192 inches = ☐ feet 16 **19.** 21,120 feet = ☐ yards 7040 **20.** 44 quarts = ☐ gallons 11

21. **Number Sense** You can double the height of a 2-year-old child to get an estimate of how tall he or she will be as an adult. Grant is 2 years old and 36 inches tall. How tall will he be as an adult? Give the answer in feet and in inches. 72 in.; 6 ft

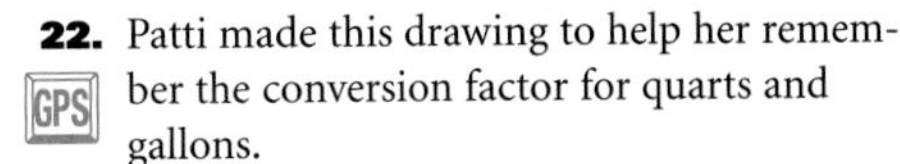

22. GPS Patti made this drawing to help her remember the conversion factor for quarts and gallons.

a. How many quarts are in a gallon? 4

b. How many quarts are in 4 gallons? 16

c. How many gallons are in 32 quarts? 8

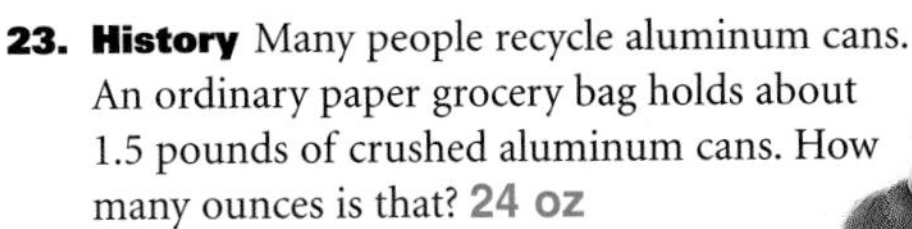

23. **History** Many people recycle aluminum cans. An ordinary paper grocery bag holds about 1.5 pounds of crushed aluminum cans. How many ounces is that? 24 oz

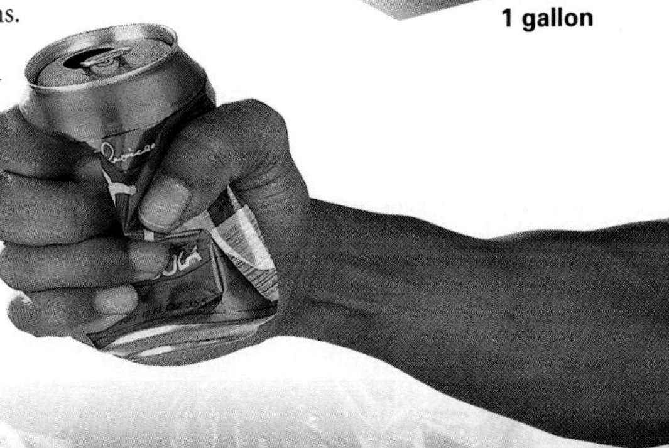

24. Order the following distances from shortest to longest distance: 2 miles; 15,840 feet; 63,360 inches; 7,040 yards.
63,360 inches; 2 miles; 15,840 feet; 7,040 yards

PRACTICE 4-3

4-3 Exercises and Applications

Assignment Guide

- **Basic**
  1–5, 6–16 evens, 21–22, 25, 28, 34–38 evens
- **Average**
  1–21 odds, 22–26, 27–39 odds
- **Enriched**
  6–22 evens, 23–30, 31–39 odds

Exercise Notes

Exercise 21

Extension Have students see if they can find out how tall they were when they were 2 years old. Students might find it interesting to get an estimate of their height as an adult.

Reteaching

Activity

Materials: Ruler, yardstick, tape or string

A prize-winning pumpkin was 72 inches around.

- Lay out a piece of tape or string that is 72 inches long. Use a ruler to measure its length in feet. 6 feet
- How could you find the length in feet without measuring? Divide by 12.
- Use a yardstick to measure its length in yards. 2 yards
- How could you find the length in yards without measuring? Divide number of feet by 3 or number of inches by 36.

The vine the pumpkin grew on was 5.5 yards long.

- Lay out a piece of tape or string that is 5.5 yards long. Measure its length in feet, using the ruler. 16.5 feet
- How could you find the length in feet without measuring? Multiply by 3.
- Measure its length in inches. 198 inches
- How could you find the length in inches without measuring? Multiply by 12.

PRACTICE

Name ____________________

Practice 4-3

Using Conversion Factors

Convert.

1. 21 feet = 252 inches
2. 21 feet = 7 yards
3. 4 miles = 21,120 feet
4. 15 pounds = 240 ounces
5. 36 quarts = 9 gallons
6. 252 inches = 21 feet
7. 48 ounces = 3 pounds
8. 31 gallons = 124 quarts
9. 35 yards = 105 feet
10. 8 quarts = 2 gallons
11. 21,120 feet = 4 miles
12. 80 ounces = 5 pounds
13. 63 gallons = 252 quarts
14. 32 quarts = 8 gallons
15. 39 feet = 13 yards
16. 18 miles = 95,040 feet
17. 23 gallons = 92 quarts
18. 96 ounces = 6 pounds
19. 132 inches = 11 feet
20. 71 yards = 213 feet
21. 60 quarts = 15 gallons
22. 31 pounds = 496 ounces
23. 63,360 feet = 12 miles
24. 47 feet = 564 inches
25. 23 gallons = 92 quarts
26. 42 feet = 14 yards
27. 288 ounces = 18 pounds
28. 73 miles = 385,440 feet
29. 84 quarts = 21 gallons
30. 46 pounds = 736 ounces
31. 276 inches = 23 feet
32. 51 yards = 153 feet
33. 7 gallons = 28 quarts
34. 656 ounces = 41 pounds
35. 79,200 feet = 15 miles
36. 53 feet = 636 inches
37. 26 pounds = 416 ounces
38. 127 miles = 670,560 feet
39. **Science** A gray whale can be up to 540 inches in length. How many feet is that? How many yards? 45 ft; 15 yd
40. In 1986, G. Graham of Edmond, Oklahoma, grew a pumpkin weighing 7.75 lb. How many ounces is that? 124 oz

RETEACHING

Name ____________________

Alternative Lesson 4-3

Using Conversion Factors

The customary system is another system of measurement. It is not based on powers of 10. In order to convert from one unit to another, you need to know the **conversion factor,** or the number of units that another unit is equal to.

Length	Weight	Liquid Capacity
1 foot (ft) = 12 inches (in.) 1 yard (yd) = 3 feet (ft) 1 mile (mi) = 5280 feet (ft)	1 pound (lb) = 16 ounces (oz)	1 gallon (gal) = 4 quarts (qt)

To convert from a larger unit to a smaller unit, you *multiply* by the appropriate conversion factor. To convert from a smaller unit to a larger unit, you *divide* by the appropriate conversion factor.

Example

How many feet are in 3 yards? In 24 inches?

When you convert from a larger unit (yard) to a smaller unit (foot), multiply the number of yards by the number of feet in a yard.

1 yard = 3 feet
$3 \times 3 = 9$

There are 9 feet in 3 yards.

When you convert from a smaller unit (inches) to a larger unit (feet), divide the number of feet by the number of inches in a foot.

1 foot = 12 inches
$24 \div 12 = 2$

There are 2 feet in 24 inches.

Try It Convert.

a. 48 ounces = ? pounds

Are you converting from a smaller unit to a larger unit or a larger unit to a smaller unit? Smaller to larger unit.

Will you multiply or divide? Divide.

What number will you multiply or divide by? 16

48 ounces = 3 pounds

b. 16 quarts = 4 gallons **c.** 10 miles = 52,800 feet

d. 5 feet = 60 inches **e.** 100 pounds = 1600 ounces

f. 10,560 feet = 2 miles **g.** 16 gallons = 64 quarts

Exercise Notes

■ Exercise 26

Extension Ask students to find the perimeter of the top part of the balance beam at the Olympic Games. Perimeter = 96 + 96 + 4 + 4, or 200 in.

■ Exercise 30

Extension Ask students to find other examples of equations which can be used to convert between customary units. Possible answers: $12f = i$, f = feet, i = inches; $5280m = f$, m = miles, f = feet; $4g = q$, g = gallons, q = quarts.

Exercise Answers

27. a. one
    b. 4 ft 5 in., 4 ft 9 in., 5 ft, 5ft 3 in., 6 ft.
28. Possible answers: 24 inches is 2 feet, so 30 inches is 2 feet, 6 inches or 2 and one-half feet; 30 ÷ 12 = 2.5 feet.
29. 12 × 5280 = 63,360 inches in 1 mile.
30. x = pounds; y = ounces; You have to multiply the number of pounds by 16 to find the number of ounces.

Alternate Assessment

Performance Have students create a visual overview of the different units of measure in the metric and customary systems by establishing benchmarks for each unit of measure. For example, students could describe a meter as about the height of the doorknob to the floor and an inch as one-half the length of a thumb.

Quick Quiz

Convert.

1. 480 ounces = ______ pounds 30
2. 60 feet = ______ yards 20
3. 11 gallons = ______ quarts 44
4. 8 miles = ______ feet 42,240

Available on Daily Transparency 4-3

PROBLEM SOLVING 4-3

25. **Test Prep** To change 16 quarts into gallons, you should D

Ⓐ multiply by 2. Ⓑ multiply by 4. Ⓒ divide by 2. Ⓓ divide by 4.

26. To perform well on the balance beam, a gymnast must always be aware of the length of the beam. The length of the balance beam at the Olympic Games is 96 inches, and it is 4 inches wide. How many feet long is the balance beam? 8

Problem Solving and Reasoning

27. Critical Thinking

a. Estimate how many heights in the table are between 5 and 6 feet.

b. Convert the heights in the table to feet. How close was your estimate?

Name	Height (in.)
Allison	53
Clive	57
Alberto	60
Maurice	63
Tanya	72

28. Communicate Explain how to convert 30 inches to feet.

29. Communicate There are 12 inches in a foot and 5280 feet in a mile. What is the conversion factor between inches and miles? Explain.

30. Critical Thinking There are 16 ounces in a pound. You can use the equation $16x = y$ to convert ounces to pounds or pounds to ounces. Which variable is ounces and which is pounds? Explain.

Mixed Review

For Exercises 31–33, use the scatterplot. *[Lesson 1-3]*

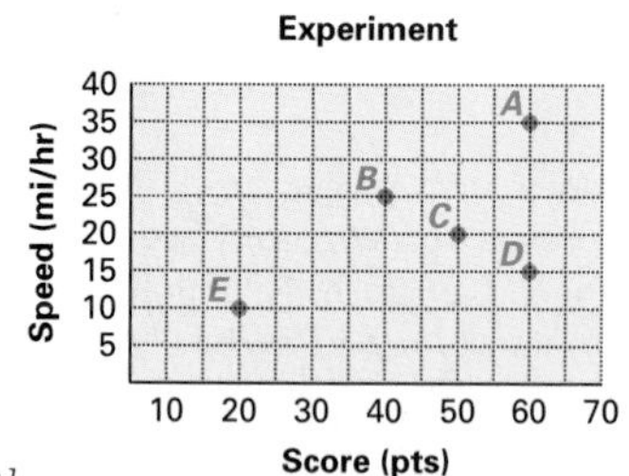

31. What was the highest score? Who received it? 60 points; A and D

32. What was the speed of person B? 25 mi/hr

33. If another person, G, scored a 45, between which two scores was that score? B and C

For Exercises 33–38, order from least to greatest. *[Lesson 3-3]*

34. 0.77, 0.7777, 1.77, 0.777 — 0.77, 0.777, 0.7777, 1.77

35. 1.34, 1.06, 1.36, 1.66 — 1.06, 1.34, 1.36, 1.66

36. 55.64, 0.564, 5.64, 5.06 — 0.564, 5.06, 5.64, 55.64

37. 0.678, 0.0349, 0.982, 0.56 — 0.0349, 0.56, 0.678, 0.982

38. 3.005, 3.011, 3.002, 3.01 — 3.002, 3.005, 3.01, 3.011

39. 67.1, 68.3, 66.3, 67.4, 67.5 — 66.3, 67.1, 67.4, 67.5, 68.3

PROBLEM SOLVING

Name ______________________ **Guided Problem Solving 4-3**

GPS PROBLEM 22, STUDENT PAGE 223

Patti made this drawing to help her remember the conversion factor for quarts and gallons.

1 quart / 1 quart / 1 quart / 1 quart — 1 gallon

a. How many quarts are in a gallon?
b. How many quarts are in 4 gallons?
c. How many gallons are in 32 quarts?

— Understand —

1. How many conversions are you asked to make? 3 conversions.
2. What information is given in the chart? Number of quarts in a gallon.

— Plan —

3. Will you multiply or divide to convert quarts to gallons? Divide.
4. Will you multiply or divide to convert gallons to quarts? Multiply.
5. By which number will you multiply or divide by? 4

— Solve —

6. Use your answers to Items 3, 4, and 5.
   a. How many quarts are in a gallon? 4 quarts.
   b. How many quarts are in 4 gallons? 16 quarts.
   c. How many gallons are in 32 quarts? 8 gallons.

— Look Back —

7. How could you have found the answer with a different method? Possible answer: Draw a picture; add instead of multiply.

SOLVE ANOTHER PROBLEM

Curtis made this drawing to help him remember the conversion factor for ounces and pounds.

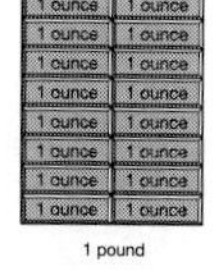

a. How many ounces are in a pound? 16 ounces.
b. How many ounces are in 8 pounds? 128 ounces.
c. How many pounds are in 176 ounces? 11 pounds.

ENRICHMENT

Name ______________________ **Extend Your Thinking 4-3**

Critical Thinking

Working with different units of measurement requires an understanding of conversion factors. Use the chart at the right to help you answer these questions.

Conversion Factors
1 foot = 12 inches
3 feet = 1 yard
5280 feet = 1 mile

1. There are 3 feet in 1 yard. You could use the equation $y = \frac{f}{3}$ to convert feet to yards. Which variable is feet and which is yards? Explain.
   f represents ft and y represents yd because 3 ft = 1 yd.
2. Write an equation to convert feet to miles. Explain what the variables represent in your equation. $m = \frac{f}{5280}$; f represents feet and m represents miles.
3. Can you use the equation you wrote in Question 2 to convert miles to feet? Explain. Yes, you can solve for f and rewrite the equation as $f = 5280m$.
4. Write an equation to convert inches into yards. Explain what the variables represent in your equation and how you decided which numbers to use.
   $y = \frac{i}{36}$; i represents inches and y represents yards; Since 36 in. = 3 ft and 3 ft = 1 yd, 12 × 3, or 36 in. = 1 yd.
5. Rewrite the equation to convert yards into inches. $i = 36y$
6. Write an equation to convert inches to miles. Explain what the variables represent in your equation and how you decided which numbers to use.
   $m = \frac{i}{63{,}360}$; i represents inches, m represents miles; Since 12 in. = 1 ft and 5280 ft = 1 mi, 12 × 5280, or 63,360 in. = 1 mi.

4A Connect

Section 4A Connect

In this section you've learned how to calculate perimeters and how to convert from one type of unit to another. Now you'll use this knowledge to decide on the most efficient route for a recyclables collection truck.

One Person's Trash Is Another Person's ...?

Materials: Ruler, Colored pencils/pens

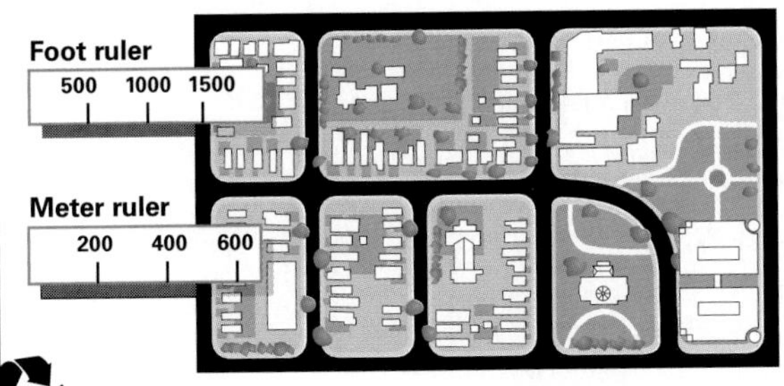

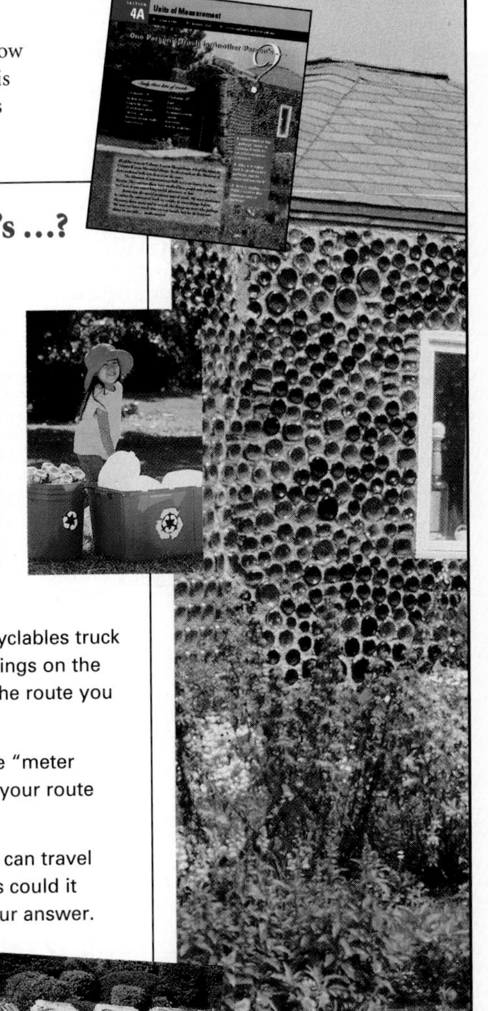

1. You need to determine the shortest possible route a recyclables truck can take to pick up recyclable material from all the buildings on the neighborhood map. Trace a copy of the map and label the route you think is best.
2. On another sheet of paper, trace the "foot ruler" and the "meter ruler" above. Use these rulers to measure the length of your route in feet and in meters.
3. Convert your measurement from feet to miles. If a truck can travel 150 miles on one tank of gas, how many neighborhoods could it collect recyclables from? Explain how you calculated your answer.
4. Convert your measurement from meters to kilometers. How many kilometers would a truck need to travel to collect recyclables from 20 neighborhoods? Explain how you calculated your answer.

225

One Person's Trash is Another Person's ...?

The Point

In *One Person's Trash is Another Person's ...?* on page 209, the importance of recycling and reusing garbage was discussed. Now, students analyze a map to determine the most efficient route for a recyclables truck.

Materials

Ruler, colored pencils or pens

Resources

Lesson Enhancement Transparency 16

About the Page

- Review the map with students to check that they can read and understand it.
- Explain that the "foot ruler" and "meter ruler" they are asked to use are drawn to the scale of the map so they can measure more easily.
- Review the number of feet in a mile and the number of meters in a kilometer.

Ongoing Assessment

Check students' measurements of a possible route to assure that they are reasonable before students calculate their answers to Questions 3 and 4.

Extension

If the recyclables truck in Question 3 travels 7.5 miles on each gallon of gas, how many gallons of gas does it take to fill the tank? 20 gallons If gasoline costs $1.39 per gallon, how much does it cost to fill the tank? $27.80

Answers for Connect

1. Answers may vary.
2. Possible answers: 34,000 ft; 11,147.541 m.
3. Possible answers: 6.4393 miles; About 25 neighborhoods; Divide 150 by 6.44.
4. Possible answers: 11.148 km; 222.96 km; Multiply 11.148 by 20.

4A Review

Review Correlation

Item(s)	Lesson(s)
1–10	4-1
11–13	4-2
14–16	4-3
17	4-2

Test Prep

Test-Taking Tip

Tell students to visualize relationships whenever possible. Here, students can visualize a kilometer as being longer than a meter, so it should take *fewer* of these units to make up a given length. This eliminates answer D, even though the decimal is moved the correct number of places.

Section 4A Review

REVIEW 4A

For Exercises 1–5, find each perimeter. Give the answer in centimeters.

1. 35.6 cm

5.2 cm
12.6 cm

2. 1200 cm

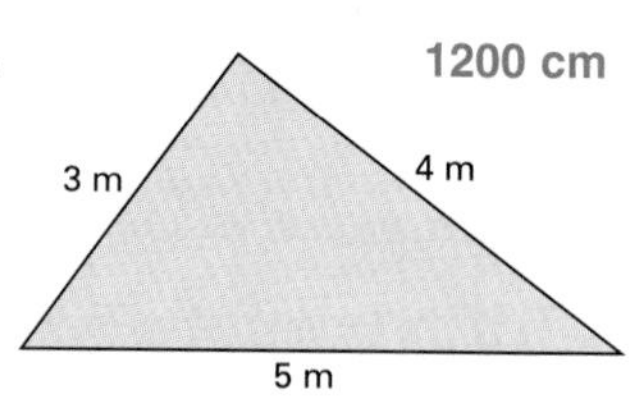

3. A square with a side length of 7.8 meters **3120 cm**

4. A 6-sided figure with all sides 6.8 mm long **4.08 cm**

5. An 8-sided figure with half of the sides 32 m and half 48 m **32,000 cm**

For Exercises 6–10, find each perimeter. Give the answer in feet.

6. 36 ft

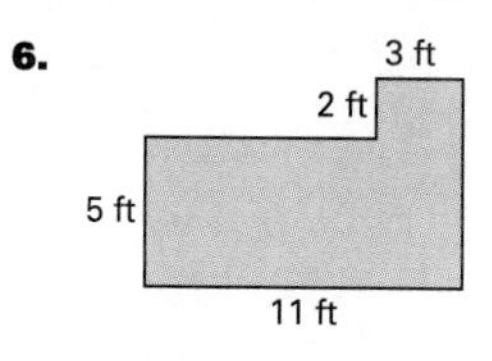

7. 42,240 ft

2 mi
2 mi

8. A triangle with sides of 6, 8, and 8 feet **22 ft**

9. A square with 5-yard sides **60 ft**

10. A rectangle where three of the sides are 12, 18, and 12 inches **5 ft**

Convert.

11. 8 L = □ mL **8000** **12.** 1963.7 g = □ kg **1.9637** **13.** 38 km = □ mm **38,000,000**

14. 128 ounces = □ pounds **8** **15.** 116 quarts = □ gallons **29** **16.** 180 feet = □ inches **2160**

Test Prep

You can convert from meters to kilometers by moving the decimal 3 places.

17. Convert 394.2 meters to kilometers. **A**

Ⓐ 0.3942 km Ⓑ 3.942 km Ⓒ 39.42 km Ⓓ 394200 km

Resources

Practice Masters
Section 4A Review

Assessment Sourcebook
Quiz 4A

TestWorks
Test and Practice Software

PRACTICE

Name ______________________

Practice

Section 4A Review

For Exercises 1–5, find the perimeter and give the answer in meters.

1. 54 m (15 m, 8 m, 12 m, 8 m) 2. 0.6 m (21 cm, 9 cm) 3. 21 m (8 m, 4 m, 4 m, 5 m)

4. A square with sides of length 18 km 72,000 m

5. A 7-sided figure with all sides 33 mm 0.231 m

For Exercises 6–10, find the perimeter and give the answer in feet.

6. 46 ft (12 ft, 7 ft, 3 ft, 16 ft) 7. 7.25 ft (42 in., 20 in., 25 in.) 8. 48 ft (4 yd, 3 yd, 3 yd, 6 yd)

9. A square with sides of length of 15 yards 180 ft

10. A rectangle with sides of length 2 mi and 5 mi 73,920 ft

Use the conversion factor to find the missing measurement.

11. 5 kilograms in 5000 grams
8.3 kilograms in 8300 grams

12. 5280 feet in 1 mile
19,008 feet in 3.6 miles

Convert.

13. 18 qt = 4.5 gal 14. 700 mL = 0.7 L 15. 87 ft = 29 yd

16. A sign at an amusement park says "You must be at least 56 in. tall to ride the Super Swoosh." Roger rounds this to 60 in., or 5 ft, and concludes that he cannot ride since he is only 4 ft 10 in. tall. Do you agree with his reasoning? Explain. *[Lesson 2-2]*

No. He is 58 in. tall, so he can ride.

17. Estimate the length of the lizard to the nearest centimeter and tenth of a centimeter. *[Lesson 3-2]*

5 cm; 5.3 cm

0 1 2 3 4 5 6
Centimeters

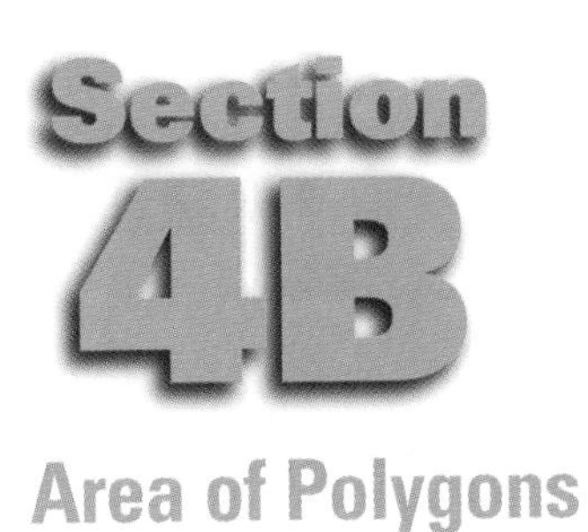

Section 4B

Area of Polygons

Visit www.teacher.mathsurf.com for links to lesson plans from teachers and other professionals, NCTM information, and other sites.

LESSON PLANNING GUIDE

Student Edition / Ancillaries*

LESSON		MATERIALS	VOCABULARY	DAILY	OTHER
	Section 4B Opener				
4-4	Area of Squares and Rectangles	transparent 10 x 10 grids	area, square inch, square centimeter, base, height, right angle	4-4	Teaching Tool Trans. 11 Lesson Enhancement Trans. 17 Technology Master 17 *WW Math*–Middle School
4-5	Area of Parallelograms		parallelogram	4-5	Teaching Tool Trans. 2, 3
4-6	Area of Triangles	dot paper		4-6	Teaching Tool Trans. 10 Technology Master 18 Ch. 4 Project Master *Interactive CD-ROM Lesson*
	Technology	geometry software			*Interactive CD-ROM Geometry Tool*
	Connect	ruler, colored pencils or pens			Interdisc. Team Teaching 4B
	Review				Practice 4B; Quiz 4B; *TestWorks*

* Daily Ancillaries include Practice, Reteaching, Problem Solving, Enrichment, and Daily Transparency. Teaching Tool Transparencies are in *Teacher's Toolkits*. Lesson Enhancement Transparencies are in *Overhead Transparency Package*.

SKILLS TRACE

LESSON	SKILL	FIRST INTRODUCED GR. 4	GR. 5	GR. 6	DEVELOP	PRACTICE/ APPLY	REVIEW
4-4	Finding areas of squares and rectangles.	✗			pp. 228–230	pp. 231–232	pp. 263, 332, 517
4-5	Finding areas of parallelograms.		✗		pp. 233–234	pp. 235–236	pp. 263, 338, 522
4-6	Finding areas of triangles.		✗		pp. 237–239	pp. 240–241	pp. 263, 345, 526

CONNECTED MATHEMATICS

The unit *Covering and Surrounding (2-D Measurement)*, from the **Connected Mathematics** series, can be used with Section 4B.

INTERDISCIPLINARY TEAM TEACHING

Math and Social Studies

(Worksheet pages 21–22: Teacher pages T21–T22)

In this lesson, students use modern and ancient units to calculate area.

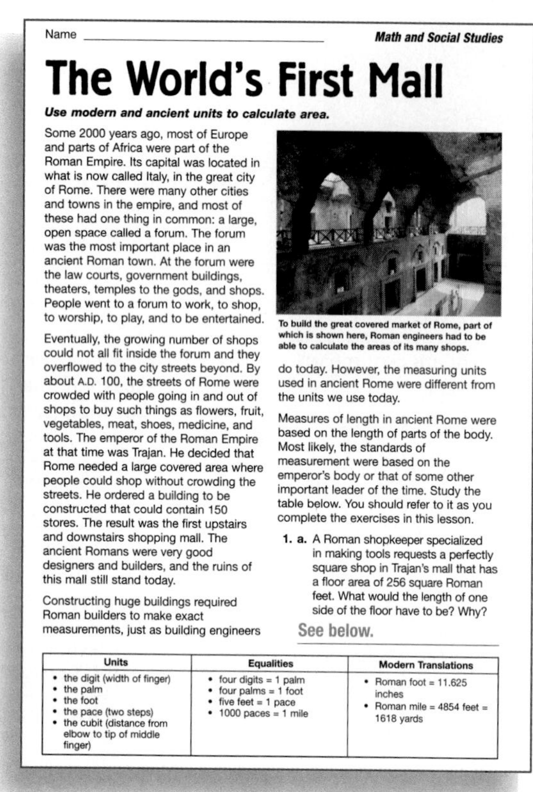

Name ______________________ *Math and Social Studies*

The World's First Mall

Use modern and ancient units to calculate area.

Some 2000 years ago, most of Europe and parts of Africa were part of the Roman Empire. Its capital was located in what is now called Italy, in the great city of Rome. There were many other cities and towns in the empire, and most of these had one thing in common: a large, open space called a forum. The forum was the most important place in an ancient Roman town. At the forum were the law courts, government buildings, theaters, temples to the gods, and shops. People went to a forum to work, to shop, to worship, to play, and to be entertained.

To build the great covered market of Rome, part of which is shown here, Roman engineers had to be able to calculate the areas of its many shops.

Eventually, the growing number of shops could not all fit inside the forum and they overflowed to the city streets beyond. By about A.D. 100, the streets of Rome were crowded with people going in and out of shops to buy such things as flowers, fruit, vegetables, meat, shoes, medicine, and tools. The emperor of the Roman Empire at that time was Trajan. He decided that Rome needed a large covered area where people could shop without crowding the streets. He ordered a building to be constructed that could contain 150 stores. The result was the first upstairs and downstairs shopping mall. The ancient Romans were very good designers and builders, and the ruins of this mall still stand today.

Constructing huge buildings required Roman builders to make exact measurements, just as building engineers do today. However, the measuring units used in ancient Rome were different from the units we use today.

Measures of length in ancient Rome were based on the length of parts of the body. Most likely, the standards of measurement were based on the emperor's body or that of some other important leader of the time. Study the table below. You should refer to it as you complete the exercises in this lesson.

1. a. A Roman shopkeeper specialized in making tools requests a perfectly square shop in Trajan's mall that has a floor area of 256 square Roman feet. What would the length of one side of the floor have to be? Why?

See below.

Units	Equalities	Modern Translations
• the digit (width of finger) • the palm • the foot • the pace (two steps) • the cubit (distance from elbow to tip of middle finger)	• four digits = 1 palm • four palms = 1 foot • five feet = 1 pace • 1000 paces = 1 mile	• Roman foot = 11.625 inches • Roman mile = 4854 feet = 1618 yards

Name ______________________ *Math and Social Studies*

b. Calculate the area of the floor of the store in palms.

See below.

2. Design and sketch a Roman shop whose walls, floor, and ceiling are rectangles or squares. Show the length and width of each surface in feet. Calculate the total area of the room's surfaces, so ancient Roman construction workers will know how many stones they will need. Don't forget to calculate the area of a doorway and to subtract it from the total. You may add other openings, such as windows. Subtract the areas of these openings from the total.

See below.

3. The emperor has asked that two triangular openings be cut in each of his palace's two front doors. Each triangle should have a base of one cubit and a height of 1.5 cubits.

a. His woodworker calculated the area of one triangle in cubits. What was his answer?

See below.

b. In 1997, an archaeologist, a specialist in ancient peoples, discovers the plans for the doors. She wants to describe the area of each triangle in inches. She knows that 1 cubit equaled 18 inches. What is the area of each triangle in inches?

See below.

c. In inches, what is the total area of wood the woodworker will remove from the emperor's doors?

See below.

4. Complete the table below by measuring the items according to the standards given. Use your own palm size, foot size, and length of step as "ancient units." Use a ruler to convert these units to modern units. An example has been provided.

See below.

5. In your opinion, are the ancient standards of measurement better, worse, or as good as modern units of measurement? Explain.

See below.

6. Why is it important for historians to understand ancient units of measurement?

See below.

7. How does a mall you have visited compare with Trajan's mall (shown in the photograph on page 21)?

See below.

Object to be Measured	Area in Ancient Units	Area in Modern Units
dictionary	4 square palms	64 square inches
math book		
table top		
classroom floor		

Answers

1. a. 16 Roman feet. All four sides of a square are equal. One side is measured and squared to determine the area. $16 \times 16 = 256$ square feet.

   b. 1 Roman foot = 4 palms; therefore, 16 Roman feet = 64 palms (4×16).
   $64 \times 64 = 4096$ square palms

2. Students' responses will vary. Check that they have a floor, ceiling, and four walls. Also check that they have a door and have subtracted the door's area from the total area. Finally, if students included other openings, the area of these must also be calculated and subtracted from the total area.

3. a. $1 \times 1.5 \div 2 = 0.75$ square cubits

   b. $18 \times 27 \div 2 = 243$ square inches

   c. $243 \times 4 = 972$ square inches

4. Students' responses will vary, depending on the sizes of the objects they measure and the sizes of their palms, feet, and paces. Check that students have reasonable answers and that their calculations include multiplying length $\times$ width.

5. Students may suggest that the standards are basically the same. They may say, however, that because measurements were based on a particular person's body, problems could arise. For example, the standards could change in the middle of a building project if one emperor replaced another.

6. Students may suggest that historians analyzing ancient documents, such as building plans, can only determine the dimensions of ancient objects if the relationship between ancient and modern units is known.

7. Students' responses will vary. Students may mention such things as differences in total area, building materials, use of color, lighting, shapes of stores, and sizes of individual stores.

BIBLIOGRAPHY

FOR TEACHERS

Bonnet, Robert L. and Keen, G. Daniel. *Space & Astronomy: Forty-Nine Science Fair Projects.* Blue Ridge Summit, PA: Tab Books, 1992.

Couper, Heather. *The Space Atlas.* Fort Worth, TX: Harcourt Brace Jovanovich, 1992.

Parker, Steve. *The Random House Book of How Things Work.* New York, NY: Random House, 1991.

FOR STUDENTS

Hutchinson, Brian. "Trouble in Big Mall Country." *Canadian Business*, Vol. 67 (September 1994), pp. 68–71.

New York Times, August 31, 1992, p. B1. "The Shopping Mall That Ate Minnesota."

Section 4B

Theme: Malls

World Wide Web

If your class has access to the World Wide Web, you might want to use the information found at the Web site address given. The interdisciplinary links relate to topics discussed in this section.

About the Page

This page introduces the theme of the section, malls, and describes the mathematics involved in planning and designing a shopping mall.

Ask ...

- Estimate the number of stores in a local shopping mall.
- What type of planning is necessary before a mall is built?
- What might happen if a mall is not planned carefully?

Extensions

The following activities do not require access to the World Wide Web.

Consumer
Have students research the local shopping mall. Ask students to describe the stores and services available and to estimate the number of parking spaces provided.

Industry
Have students prepare a report describing the education and training needed, the job opportunities, and the salary range of some of the professionals whose skills are necessary to plan and design a mall.

Answers for Questions

1. Possible answer: So people can go to one place to buy many things.
2. Possible answer: How big it should be and who will use it.
3. Possible answer: To make sure everything will fit in the space you have.

Connect

On page 243, students will use geometry to design a shopping mall.

Where are we now?

In Section 4A, students learned how to

- use addition of whole numbers and decimals to find perimeter.
- use metric measure to find length.
- convert units within the metric system.
- use the customary system of measurement to find length, weight, and capacity.

Where are we going?

In Section 4B, students will

- find the area of squares and rectangles.
- find the area of parallelograms.
- find the area of triangles.

4-4 Lesson Organizer

Objective

- Find the area of squares and rectangles.

Vocabulary

- Area, square inch, square centimeter, base, height, right angle

Materials

- Explore: Transparent 10 x 10 grids

NCTM Standards

- 1–5, 12, 13

► Review

Find the perimeter of each shape.

1. A square with sides of 5 cm. 20 cm
2. A rectangle 3 inches long and 5 inches wide. 16 in.
3. A triangle with sides of 10 m, 10 m and 5 m. 25 m

Available on Daily Transparency 4-4

1 Introduce

Explore

You may wish to use Teaching Tool Transparency 11: 10 × 10 Grids and Lesson Enhancement Transparency 17 with **Explore**.

The Point
Students estimate the areas of six different shapes and then use grids to find the number of squares needed to cover each shape.

Ongoing Assessment
Watch for students who try to calculate, instead of estimate, areas.

For Groups That Finish Early
List the rectangles you see in your classroom. Use a unit such as a ceiling or floor tile to estimate the area of the figures.

4-4 Area of Squares and Rectangles

You'll Learn ...

- to find the area of squares and rectangles

... How It's Used

Employees at art stores must work with area when framing and putting protective glass on a customer's purchase.

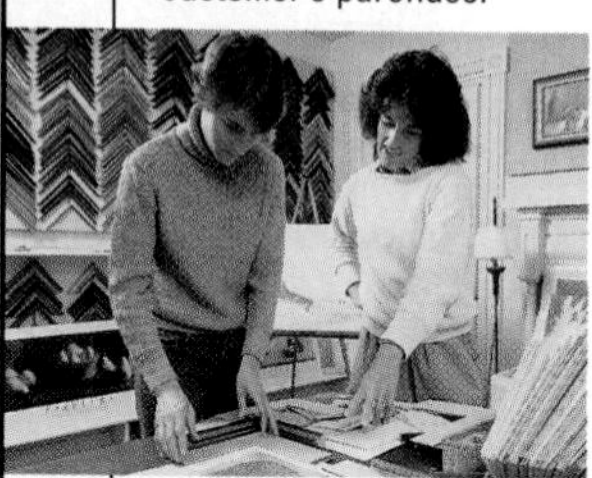

Vocabulary

area
square inch
square centimeter
base
height
right angle

► Lesson Link You have calculated the distance around the outside of squares and rectangles. Now you'll calculate the amount of surface they cover. ◄

Explore Area of Squares and Rectangles

Grid Lock

Materials: Transparent 100-grids

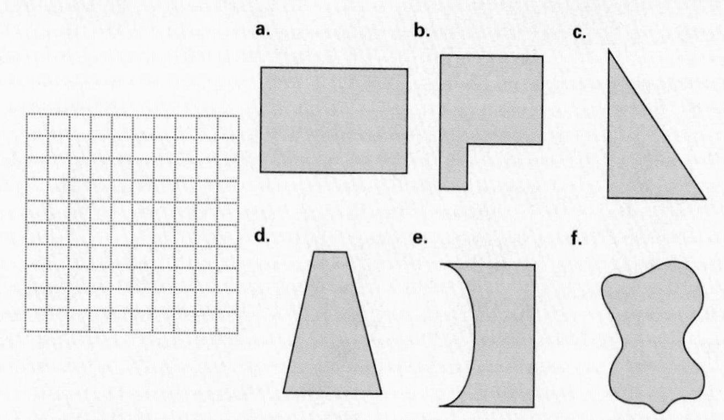

1. The grid contains 100 small squares. Estimate the number of small squares it takes to cover each gray figure.
2. When you have written all your estimates, get a transparent copy of the grid. Place it on top of each figure, and record the actual number of squares needed to cover the figure. For some figures, you may still need to make an estimate.
3. For which figure was your estimate without the grid closest to your measurement with the grid? Why was your estimate so accurate?
4. For which figure was your estimate without the grid furthest from your measurement with the grid? Why was your estimate so inaccurate?
5. Why were some of your measurements with the grids still estimates?

MEETING INDIVIDUAL NEEDS

Resources

- 4-4 Practice
- 4-4 Reteaching
- 4-4 Problem Solving
- 4-4 Enrichment
- 4-4 Daily Transparency
  - Problem of the Day
  - Review
  - Quick Quiz
- Teaching Tool Transparency 11
- Lesson Enhancement Transparency 17
- Technology Master 17

Wide World of Mathematics Middle School: Huge Mall Opens

Learning Modalities

Visual Have students draw pictures of each rectangle in Exercises 5–12 on page 231 on graph paper before trying to solve each problem.

Logical Have students use square tiles to model rectangles in the exercises.

Individual Ask students to decide if manipulatives or grids help them to solve problems involving areas of rectangles.

Challenge

Have students find as many different rectangles as they can with a given perimeter, such as 20 cm. Ask them to graph the length versus the area and use the graph to find the rectangle with the smallest area.

Learn Area of Squares and Rectangles

The **area** of a figure is the amount of surface it covers. Area is usually measured by the number of unit squares of the same size that fit into the figure.

Example 1

Which rectangle has a bigger area?

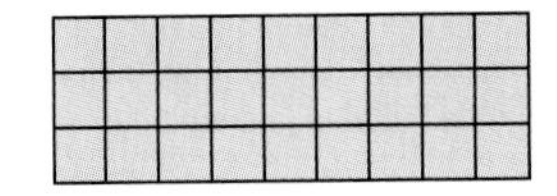

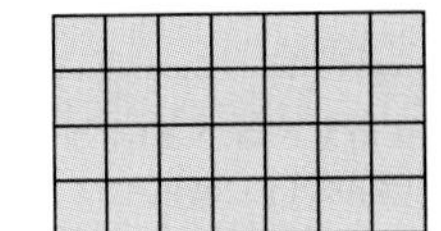

The first rectangle contains 27 squares. It has an area of 27 square units. The second rectangle contains 28 squares. It has an area of 28 square units.

The second rectangle has a bigger area.

If a figure is labeled with inches, the area is expressed in **square inches** (in^2). A square inch is a square whose sides measure 1 inch. A **square centimeter** (cm^2) is a square whose sides measure 1 centimeter. A figure without labels is measured in square units ($units^2$).

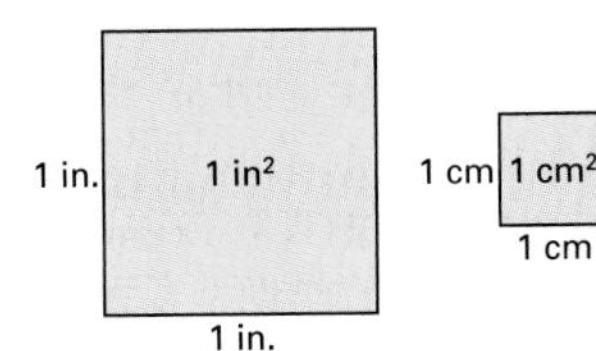

When a number is raised to the second power, like 5^2, the expression can be read "five squared." That's because the answer, 25, is the area of a square with sides of 5 units.

Example 2

Each square shown on the wall is a square meter. How much wallpaper would you need to cover the wall?

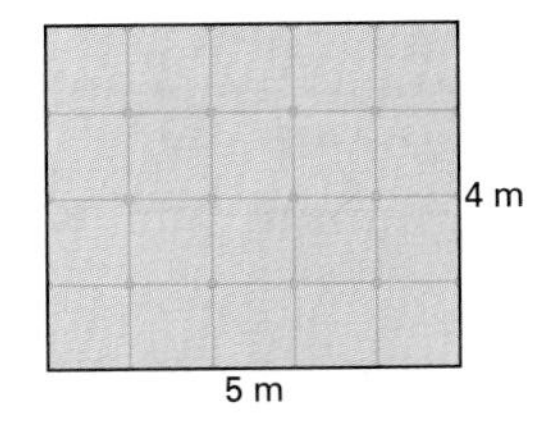

There are 20 squares in the rectangle. You would need 20 m^2 of wallpaper.

Try It

Find the area of each figure. Use the appropriate unit.

a.

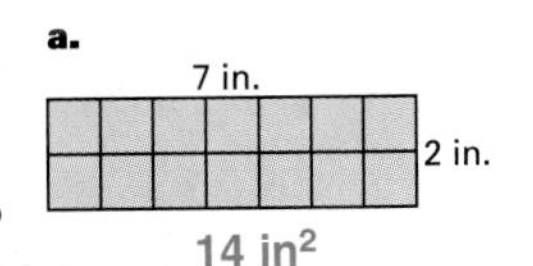

14 in^2

b.

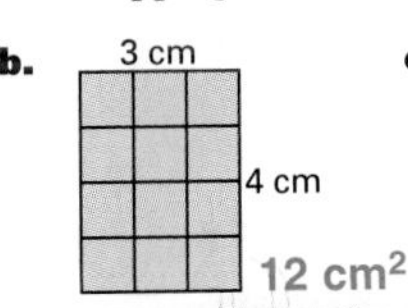

12 cm^2

c.

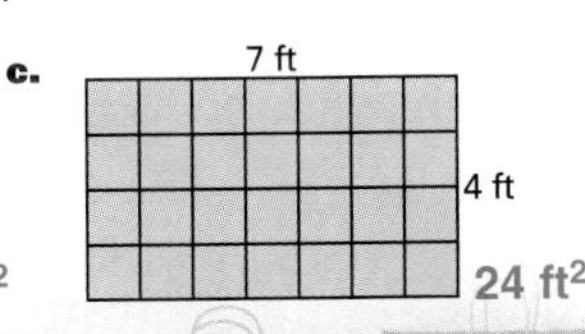

24 ft^2

Answers for Explore

1. Possible answer: a. 35; b. 22; c. 18; d. 21; e. 20; f. 20.
2. a. 35; b. 23; c. 17.5; d. 20; e. 21.5; f. 24.
3. Possible answer: a; It is a rectangle.
4. Possible answer: f; There are no straight sides.
5. Possible answer: It is difficult to determine how many squares it takes to cover a figure with curved sides.

2 Teach

Learn

Ask students to write about what they already know about area. Have a few volunteers share what they wrote, using this as a springboard for this lesson.

Alternate Examples

1. Which two rectangles have the same area?

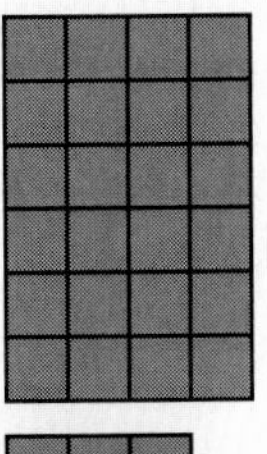

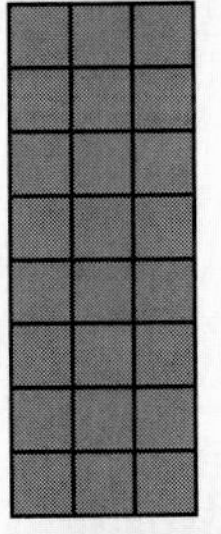

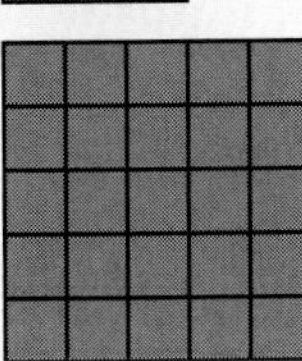

The first rectangle contains 24 squares. The second contains 24 squares. The third contains 25 squares. The first and the second have the same areas.

2. A window is made up of 1-foot square panes. The window is 10 ft wide by 6 ft high. Find the area of the window.

There are 6 rows of panes with 10 panes in each row. The window has $6 \times 10 = 60$ panes, so the area is 60 square feet.

MATH EVERY DAY

Problem of the Day

Arrange the numbers 1-7 so that each row adds to 12. Use each number one time only.

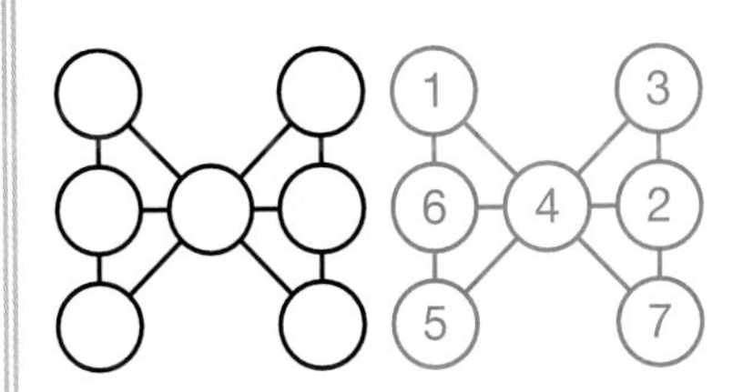

Available on Daily Transparency 4-4

An Extension is provided in the transparency package.

Fact of the Day

In 1945 there were fewer than a dozen shopping centers. By 1990 about 35,000 shopping centers had been built.

Mental Math

Do these mentally.

1. $175 \div 25$ 7
2. $4 \times 56 \times 25$ 5600
3. $78 + 35 + 22$ 135
4. $704 - 199$ 505

Alternate Examples

3. Beth is buying a new rug for her bedroom. Her room is in the shape of a rectangle that is 11 feet long and 13 feet wide. How big will the rug need to be?

   Base $\times$ height = area

   $11 \times 13 = 143$ ft^2

4. A square measures 8.5 feet on each side. Find the area of the square.

   Base $\times$ height = area

   $8.5 \times 8.5 = 72.25$ ft^2

3 Practice and Assess

Check

For Question 2, ask students to think about shapes they have seen in tiled floors.

Answers for Check Your Understanding

1. No; You still multiply the same two measures.
2. Possible answer: Squares are easy to draw, count, and measure.

Base and height are also known as length and width.

You can determine the area of a square or rectangle without counting the squares inside by using a formula.

The **base** of a square or rectangle is the distance across the bottom. The **height** is the distance along a side. A **right angle** is an angle as wide as the corner of a page. The height of a shape always forms a right angle with the base.

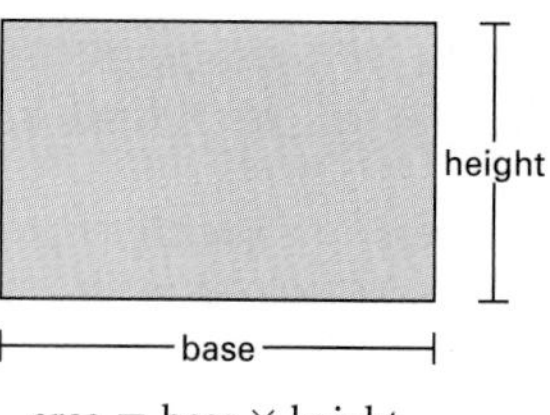

area = base $\times$ height

Examples

3 Karen is designing the layout for the customer area of her clothing store. The area is a square. Each side is 21 ft long. How big is the customer area?

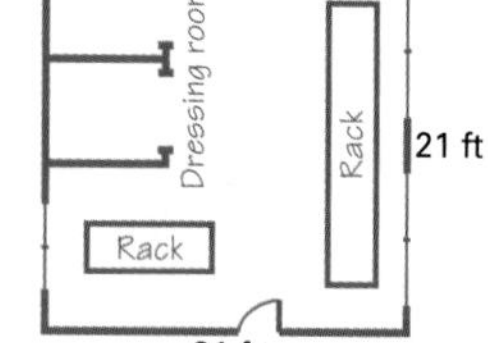

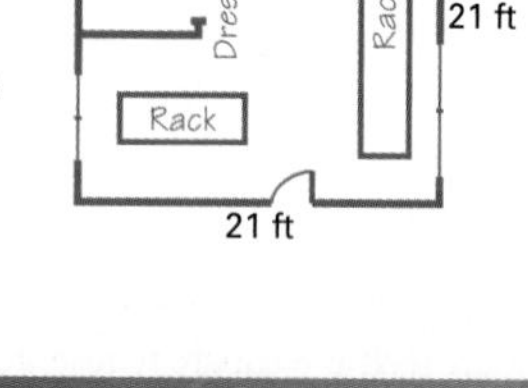

The base and height of the customer area are both 21 ft.

Base $\times$ height = area

$21 \times 21 = 441$ ft^2

Problem Solving TIP

When multiplying with decimals, check your answer to make sure the number of digits after the decimal point in the product are the same as the total number of digits after the decimal points in the factors.

4 Jaymo wants to buy a cover for his pool. The pool is a rectangle with a base of 9 m and a height of 5.5 m. How big will the cover need to be?

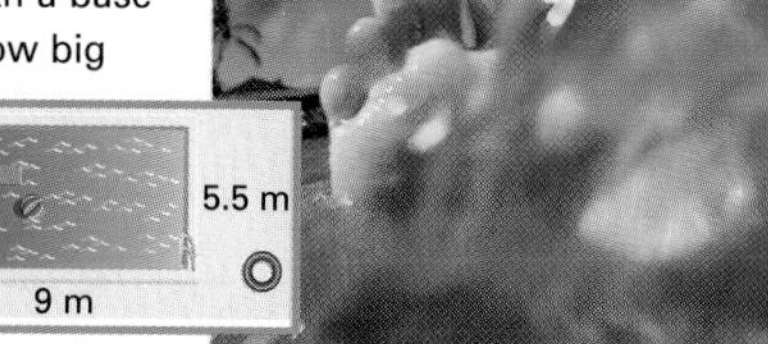

Base $\times$ height = area

$9 \times 5.5 = 49.5$ m^2

Try It

Find each area.

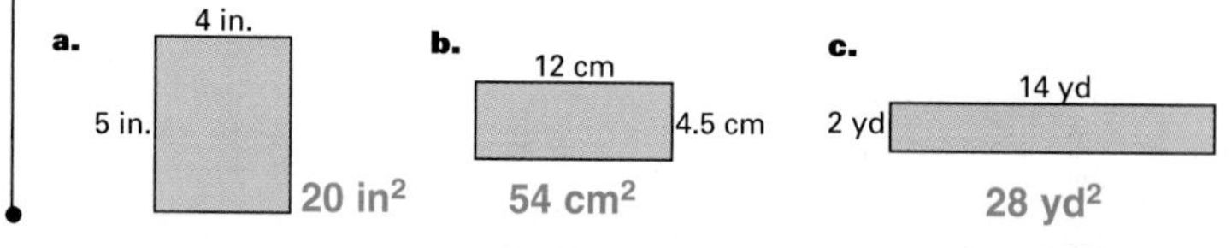

Check Your Understanding

1. For a given rectangle, if you switch the numbers for base and height, do you get a different area? Explain.
2. Why is area usually measured with squares, and not some other figure?

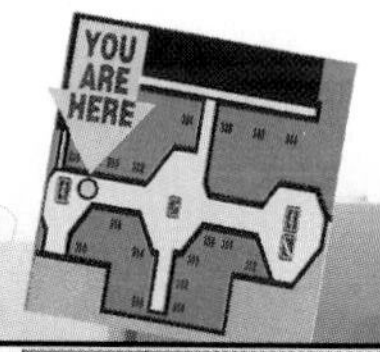

MEETING MIDDLE SCHOOL CLASSROOM NEEDS

Tips from Middle School Teachers

My students enjoy exploring what happens to the area of a rectangle when the base is doubled and the height remains the same, when the height is doubled and the base remains the same, and when both the base and the height are doubled. I have each student draw a rectangle of any size on graph paper and then draw three rectangles with the dimension changes described. Students compare their results and make generalizations about what happens to the area in each case.

Team Teaching

Work with the art teacher to show students the paintings of Piet Mondrian, which are composed of geometric shapes. Have students use rectangles to make their own drawings and then challenge each other to find the area of each rectangle that they used.

Sports Connection

Football, soccer, tennis, basketball, hockey, and many other sports are played on standard-sized rectangular playing fields. Have students find the dimensions and then compute the area of each field.

4-4 Exercises and Applications

Practice and Apply

Getting Started Find each area.

1. 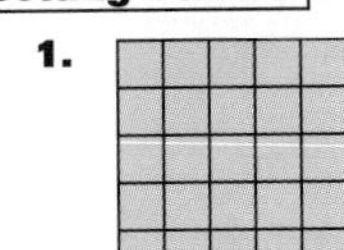 25

2. 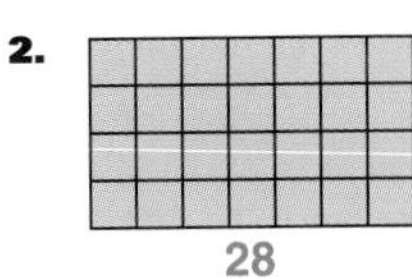 28

3. 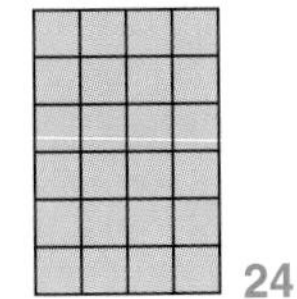 24

4. 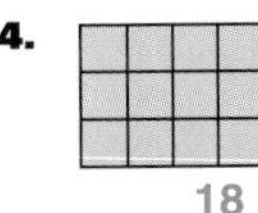 18

Find the missing measurement for each rectangle.

5. Area = 48 cm^2
Base = 2 cm
Height = ? 24 cm

6. Area = 12.96 ft^2
Base = ? 1.8 ft
Height = 7.2 ft

7. Area = ? 27 ft^2
Base = 3 ft
Height = 9 ft

8. Area = 28.8 in^2
Base = ? 3 in.
Height = 9.6 in.

9. Area = ? 1.2 km^2
Base = 0.8 km
Height = 1.5 km

10. Area = 33 yd^2
Base = 6 yd
Height = ? 5.5 yd

11. Area = ? 132 mm^2
Base = 12 mm
Height = 11 mm

12. Area = 300 in^2
Base = 30 in.
Height = ? 10 in.

13. **Test Prep** Cristina's painting is 2 feet tall. What else must she know to calculate how many square feet the painting occupies? C

Ⓐ The number of paintings on the wall
Ⓑ The length of the room
Ⓒ The width of the painting
Ⓓ The height of the ceiling

Johnson, William H.. "Man in Vest," 1939-40. National Museum of American Art, Smithsonian Institute, Gift of the Harmon Foundation.

Find the area of each figure.

14. Rectangle with base 3 and height 6 18

15. Square with side 2 cm 4 cm^2

16. Rectangle with sides 4 and 12 in. 48 in^2

17. Square centimeter 1 cm^2

18. **Geometry** For the dance fundraiser, Janet and Paul need a piece of tarp to cover and protect the gym floor. The floor is 90 by 100 feet. What size rectangular tarp is needed? 9000 ft^2

19. **Fine Arts** *Young Man in a Vest,* painted by William H. Johnson, is 30 inches tall and 24 inches wide. Find the area of the painting. 720 in^2

PRACTICE

Name ____________

Practice 4-4

Area of Squares and Rectangles

Find the missing measurement for each rectangle.

1. Area = 63 ft^2; Base = 7 ft; Height = 9 ft
2. Area = 24 cm^2; Base = 4 cm; Height = 6 cm
3. Area = 84 in^2; Base = 7 in.; Height = 12 in.
4. Area = 11.5 m^2; Base = 5 m; Height = 2.3 m
5. Area = 23.5 in^2; Base = 5.875 in.; Height = 4 in.
6. Area = 12.46 cm^2; Base = 1.78 cm; Height = 7 cm

Find the area of each figure.

7. Square with sides of length 8 ft 64 ft^2
8. Rectangle with sides 4.7 m and 7.3 m 34.31 m^2
9. Square with sides of length 21 cm 441 cm^2
10. Rectangle with sides 8.3 m and 5.2 m 43.16 m^2
11. Rectangle with sides 9 in. and 4 in. 36 in^2

Use the scatterplot for Exercises 12–14.

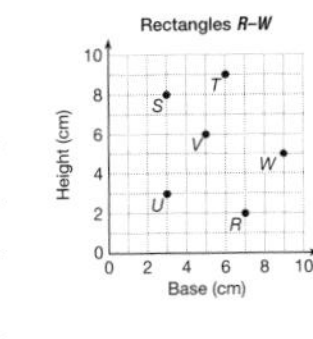

12. What is the area of each rectangle?
R 14 cm^2 S 24 cm^2 T 54 cm^2
U 9 cm^2 V 30 cm^2 W 45 cm^2
13. Which rectangle is also a square? U
14. What is the area of the rectangle with the greatest height? 54 cm^2
15. Shelly plans to paint a wall in her bedroom. The wall is 11 ft long and 8 ft high. She needs enough paint to cover how much area? 88 ft^2
16. In 1993, the Food Bank for Monterey County (California) set a record by baking a lasagne with an area of 490 ft^2. If the lasagne was 70 ft long, how wide was it? 7 ft

RETEACHING

Name ____________

Alternative Lesson 4-4

Area of Squares and Rectangles

The **area** of a figure is the amount of surface it covers. Area is usually measured by the number of unit squares of the same size that fit into the figure. If a figure is labeled with inches, then the area is expressed in **square inches (in^2)**. A square inch is a square whose sides measure one inch. A **square centimeter (cm^2)** is a square whose sides measure one centimeter.

The **base** of a square or rectangle is the distance across the bottom. The **height** is the distance up a side. The area of any square or rectangle is equal to the base times the height.

Example

Find the area of the rectangle.

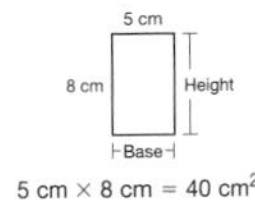

Each side is measured in centimeters, so the area will be measured in square centimeters (cm^2).

Find the area by multiplying base and height. 5 cm × 8 cm = 40 cm^2

The area of the rectangle is 40 square centimeters.

Try It Find the area of each rectangle.

a. (10 mi by 6 mi) What is the base? 10 mi
What is the height? 6 mi
Multiply base and height to find the area. 60 mi^2

b. (9 m by 4 m) 36 m^2

c. (3 yd by 7 yd) 21 yd^2

d. (25 in. by 4 in.) 100 in^2

e. (3 cm by 6 cm) 18 cm^2

f. (200 in. by 200 in.) 40,000 in^2

g. (5 cm by 4 cm) 20 cm^2

Assignment Guide

- **Basic**
  1–4, 5–13 odds, 16–19, 25, 26–34 evens
- **Average**
  1–13 odds, 14–19, 23, 25–28, 29–35 odds
- **Enriched**
  5–13 odds, 14–22 evens, 23–25, 26–36 evens

Exercise Notes

Exercises 1–4

Error Prevention If students have difficulty counting squares accurately, suggest that they use tracing paper to trace the drawings in the book. Have them check or number each square as it is counted.

Exercise 13

Test Prep Answers for multiple-choice questions often contain information that is not related to the question being asked. Encourage students to carefully read the question and identify exactly what is being asked.

Reteaching

Activity

Materials: One-inch squares

- Work in groups of two or three.
- Cut out 100 one-inch squares. Draw each of the following rectangles or squares: 6 × 8, 3 × 10, 4 × 6, 5 × 6, 9 × 9.
- Find the area of each figure by filling it with the squares and counting. 48; 30; 24; 30; 81.
- Look for a pattern that will help you find the area of each rectangle without counting. base × height = area.
- Make as many rectangles as you can with an area of 36 square units. Find the perimeter of each.
  1 × 36, P = 74;
  2 × 18, P = 40;
  3 × 12, P = 30;
  4 × 9, P = 26;
  6 × 6, P = 24.

Exercise Notes

■ Exercise 25

Problem-Solving Tip You may need to point out to students that in order to solve this problem they must first find the width of the rectangle.

Exercise Answers

20. A: 4 in^2; B: 7.5 in^2; C: 0.25 in^2; D: 19 in^2; E: 8 in^2; F: 2.5 in^2.
21. C; The base and height are the same length.
23. a. 12,800 ft.^{2}; 8(40 × 40)
    b. Low: 35(1 × 40 ft × 40) = \$56,000; High: 35(8 × 40 ft. × 40 ft.) = \$448,000.
24. There are an infinite number; The base and the height can be decimal numbers.
25. \$60,000; The bookstore is 60 ft by 50 ft, so it is 3000 square feet. Multiply 3000 by \$20 to find the rent.
27. Mean; The median is 22 and the mean is 23.526.

Alternate Assessment

Performance Have students make a table listing the base, height, and area of ten rectangles or squares they find around their homes. Items they might include are tables, computer or television screens, books, floors, or place mats.

► Quick Quiz

Find the missing measurement for each rectangle.

1. Area = 45 cm^2
   Base = 4.5 cm
   Height = ? 10 cm
2. Area = ? 21.3 m^2
   Base = 7.1 m
   Height = 3 m
3. Area = 56 ft^2
   Base = ? 16 ft
   Height = 3.5 ft

Available on Daily Transparency 4-4

PROBLEM SOLVING 4-4

Use the scatterplot for Exercises 20–22.

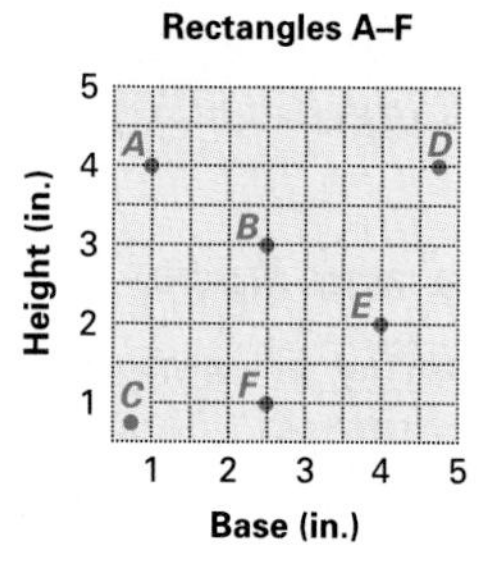

20. What is the area of each rectangle?

21. Which rectangle is also a square? How can you tell?

22. What is the area of the rectangle with a height of 3 inches? 7.5 in^2

Problem Solving and Reasoning

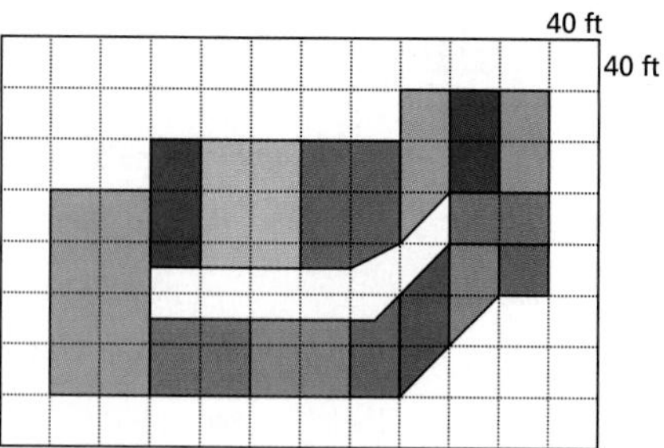

23. Critical Thinking Use the map of the shopping mall to answer these questions.

a. What is the area of the largest store? Explain.

b. The annual rent for each store is \$35 per square foot. Find the range of rental costs. Explain your method.

24. Communicate A rectangle has an area of 120 cm^2. How many possible base/height pairs are there? Explain.

25. Critical Thinking The perimeter of a rectangular bookstore is 220 ft, and its length is 50 ft. What is the annual rent for the bookstore if the rent is \$20 per square foot each year? Explain.

Mixed Review

For Exercises 26–28, use the stem-and-leaf diagram. *[Lesson 1-6]*

26. What is the range of values? 32

27. Is the median or the mean of the data larger? Explain.

28. What is the largest number in the data that is less than 25? 23

Stem	Leaf
0	9
1	2 5 6 6 7 9
2	1 1 2 3 5 7 7 8 8
4	0 0 1

Estimate each sum, difference, product, or quotient. *[Lesson 3-5]*

29. 67.29 + 3.01 70 **30.** 14.76 ÷ 6.12 2.5 **31.** 13.546 × 1.68 28 **32.** 0.886 − 0.324 0.6

33. 52,395 ÷ 9,546 5 **34.** \$16.34 − \$5.49 \$11 **35.** 87.003 + 56.31 143 **36.** 23.3 × 4.37 100

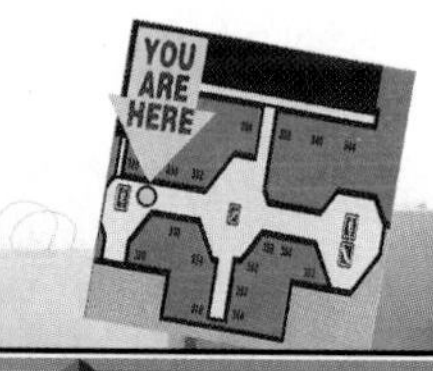

PROBLEM SOLVING

Name ______

Guided Problem Solving 4-4

GPS PROBLEM 25, STUDENT PAGE 232

The perimeter of a rectangular bookstore is 220 ft, and its length is 50 ft. What is the annual rent for the bookstore if the rent is \$20 per square foot each year? Explain.

— Understand —

1. Circle the perimeter, length, and annual rent of the bookstore.
2. The rent is per square foot. How do you find the number of square feet in a rectangular figure? Find length × width.

— Plan —

3. You are given the length of one side of the bookstore. What is the length of the opposite side of the bookstore? 50 ft
4. Given the perimeter, how can you use the length of two opposite sides to find the length of the other two sides in a rectangle? Find: perimeter minus the two sides...divide difference by 2.
5. What is the width of the bookstore? 60 ft
6. What operation will you use to find the annual rent? Multiplication.

— Solve —

7. Write a number sentence to find the number of square feet. 50 × 60 = 3000
8. Find the annual rent for the bookstore. \$60,000
9. Explain why it was necessary to follow the steps above. Need to find the width of store to find area. Need area to find rent.

— Look Back —

10. Explain how drawing a diagram could help you solve this problem. Possible answer: It could be easier to visualize the dimensions.

SOLVE ANOTHER PROBLEM

The perimeter of a rectangular bookstore is 180 ft, and its length is 50 ft. What is the annual rent for the bookstore if the rent is \$25 per square foot each year? Explain.
Width is 40 ft, area is 2000 ft^2, 2000 × 25 = \$50,000.

ENRICHMENT

Name ______

Extend Your Thinking 4-4

Patterns in Geometry

The area of a rectangle equals the measurement of the base times the measurement of the height. What happens to the area when you change the measurements of the base and height?

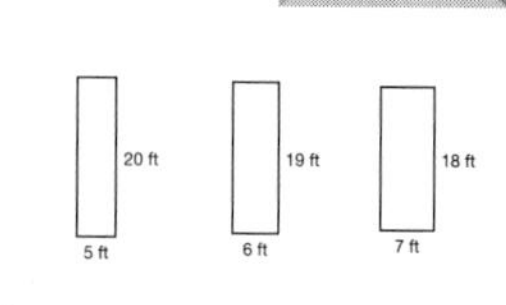

1. What is the sum of the length and width in each of the three rectangles above? 25 ft
2. What pattern do you see in the lengths and widths of the three rectangles? The width increases by 1 foot and the length decreases by 1 foot.
3. Find the area of each rectangle.
   a. 5 ft by 20 ft 100 ft^2 b. 6 ft by 19 ft 114 ft^2 c. 7 ft by 18 ft 126 ft^2
   d. 8 ft by 17 ft 136 ft^2 e. 9 ft by 16 ft 144 ft^2 f. 10 ft by 15 ft 150 ft^2
4. What pattern do you see in the areas of these six rectangles? Area increases by an even number that is 2 less than the prior increase. Pattern is +14, +12, +10....
5. Draw and label the next three rectangles in the pattern. Predict the area of each. Check students' work. Rectangles: 11 × 14, 12 × 13, 13 × 12. Predictions will vary.
6. Calculate the areas of the rectangles you drew in Question 5. Were your predictions on target? Explain. 154 ft^2, 156 ft^2, 156 ft^2; Yes, because increases followed the pattern.
7. How would you predict the areas of the next three rectangles in the pattern? Explain. Possible answers: Add −2, −4, −6 to the previous areas because each increase is 2 less than the prior change.

Area of Parallelograms

4-5

▶ Lesson Link You know how to find the area of squares and rectangles. Now you will learn how to find the area of parallelograms. ◀

Explore Area of Parallelograms

Is It Still the Same?

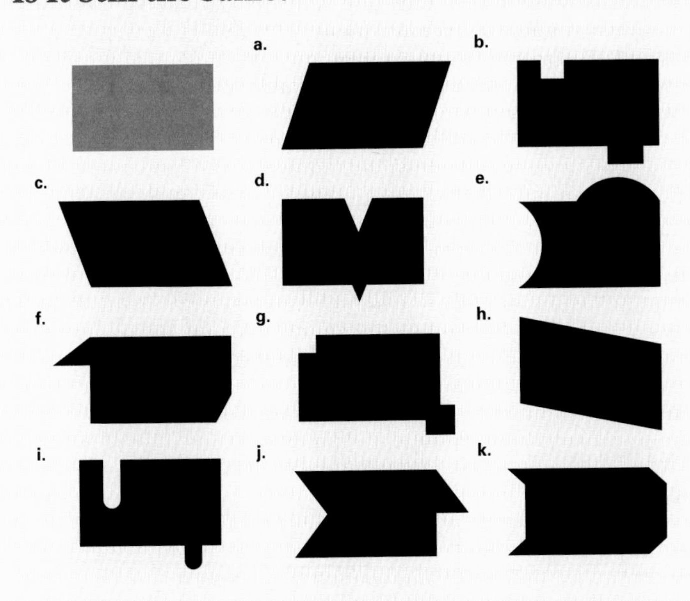

1. State whether the area of each black figure is equal to, more than, or less than the area of the red rectangle. Explain your reasoning.
2. Can two different figures have the same area? Explain.
3. If you cut a piece from a figure and attach it to another side of the figure, does it still have the same area? Explain.

You'll Learn ...

■ to find the area of parallelograms

... How It's Used

City planners must calculate area when planning parking structures for public use.

Vocabulary

parallelogram

MEETING INDIVIDUAL NEEDS

Resources
4-5 Practice
4-5 Reteaching
4-5 Problem Solving
4-5 Enrichment
4-5 Daily Transparency
Problem of the Day
Review
Quick Quiz
Teaching Tool Transparencies 2, 3

Learning Modalities

Kinesthetic Some students may confuse the height of a parallelogram with the length of one of its sides when finding area. Have students use models to compare the lengths and see that they are different.

Visual Have students use geoboards to model parallelograms.

Individual Ask students to decide whether they prefer using manipulatives or graph paper to help them solve problems involving areas of parallelograms.

English Language Development

Have students sort pictures or cut-outs of quadrilaterals by shape: squares, rectangles, parallelograms, and others. Be sure they understand that squares are special rectangles and rectangles are special parallelograms.

4-5

Lesson Organizer

Objective

- Find the area of parallelograms.

Vocabulary

- Parallelogram

NCTM Standards

- 1–4, 7, 8, 12, 13

Review

Write each decimal as a fraction.

1. 0.45 $\frac{9}{20}$
2. 0.04 $\frac{1}{25}$
3. 1.1 $\frac{11}{10}$ or $1\frac{1}{10}$

Available on Daily Transparency 4-5

1 Introduce

Explore

The Point

Students compare different figures to a standard rectangle to develop the idea that rearranging a figure does not change its area.

Ongoing Assessment

Some students may find it difficult to begin with the parallelograms. They may find it easier to work with the other shapes first and then see if the same type of strategy, cutting off a piece and moving it, can help them with the parallelograms.

For Groups That Finish Early

Which figures were easiest to work with and which were most difficult? Why? Answers may vary.

Answers for Explore on next page.

Answers for Explore

1. Equal to: a, c, e, h, k;
   More than; b, f, g;
   Less than; d, i, j.
2. Yes; A rectangle with length x and height y has the same area as a parallelogram with length x and height y.
3. Yes; The same amount of space is still covered.

2 Teach

Learn

You may wish to have students actually cut apart a parallelogram as described in **Learn**. You might have three or four different sizes of parallelograms for students to work with.

Alternate Examples

Find the area of a parallelogram with a base of 10 inches and a height of 3 inches.

Base × height = area

$10 \times 3 = 30$ in^2

3 Practice and Assess

Check

It may be helpful to give students some visual examples of quadrilaterals that are not parallelograms in Question 2.

Answers for Check Your Understanding

1. Yes; Cut along a vertical line from one corner to the opposite side, then move that triangle to the other end of the figure.
2. No; For example, this shape cannot be changed into a rectangle by moving a section.

Study TIP

Parallel lines are straight lines that never meet, just like the two l's next to each other in the word *parallel*.

Learn Area of Parallelograms

A **parallelogram** is a four-sided figure whose opposite sides are parallel.

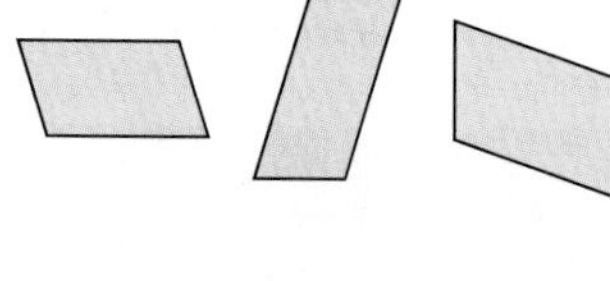

A parallelogram has the same area as a rectangle of equal base and height. You can cut a triangle-shaped piece from one side of a parallelogram and move it to the other side to form a rectangle.

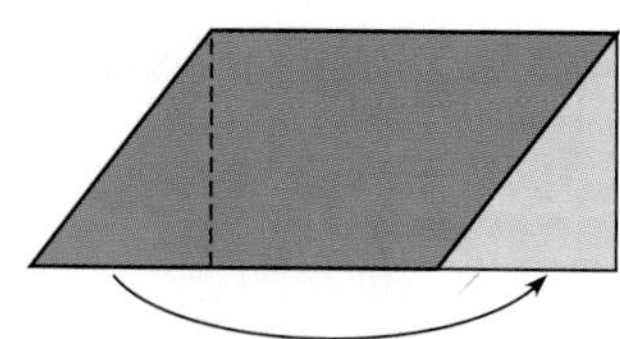

To find the area of a parallelogram, use the same formula for the area of a rectangle: base × height = area. The height of a parallelogram is always a vertical measure from the base, not a slanted measure. It is usually shown as a dashed line.

Example 1

Find the area.

Base × height = area

$7 \times 4 = 28$ units^2

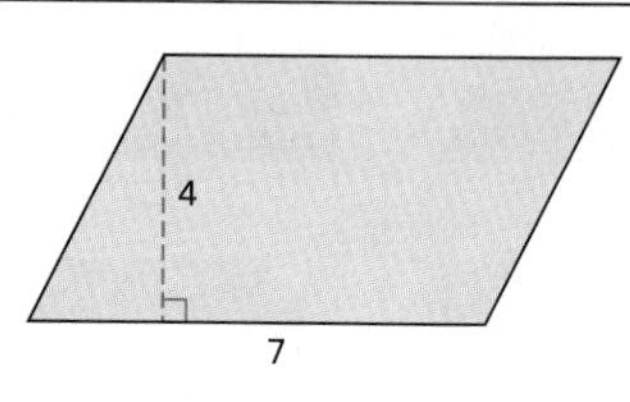

Try It

Find the area.

a.

18

b.

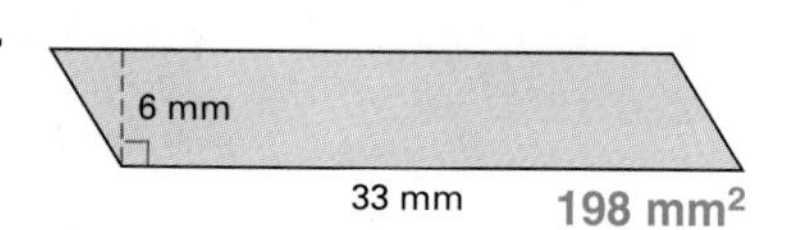

198 mm^2

Check Your Understanding

1. Can every parallelogram be changed into a rectangle by moving a section? Explain.
2. Can every four-sided figure be changed into a rectangle by moving a section? Explain.

MATH EVERY DAY

Problem of the Day

Korean children and young adults enjoy flying kites (yeon) like the one shown below, especially during the first lunar month of the year. The area of an average Korean rectangular kite is 300 in^2. Its length is 20 in. What is its perimeter?

70 in.

Available on Daily Transparency 4-5

An Extension is provided in the transparency package.

Fact of the Day

In 1994, the population of Tennessee was 5,175,240, ranking it 17th in the United States in population and 34th in total area.

Estimation

Estimate.

1. $1\frac{2}{3} + 2\frac{3}{7}$ 4
2. $4\frac{8}{9} - 2\frac{1}{16}$ 3
3. $3\frac{1}{5} \times 2\frac{7}{8}$ 9
4. $4\frac{4}{5} \div 2\frac{1}{20}$ $2\frac{1}{2}$

4-5 Exercises and Applications

Practice and Apply

Getting Started Find each area.

1.

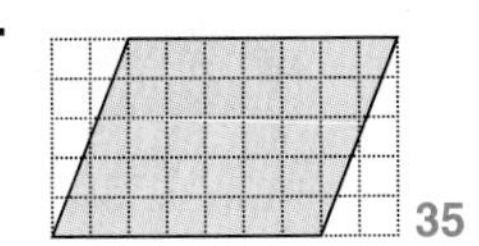

35

2.

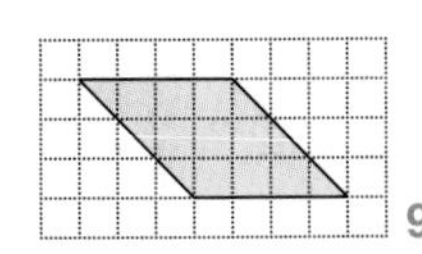

9

3.

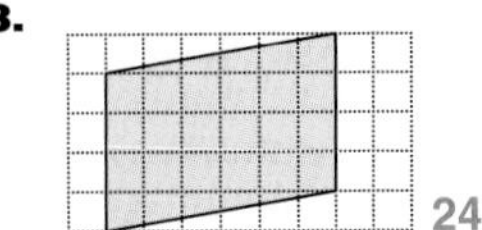

24

Find each area.

4.

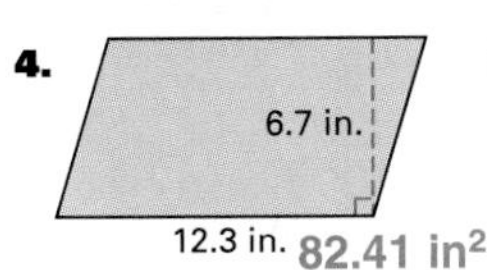

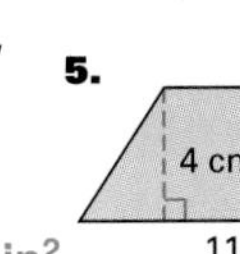

82.41 in^2

5.

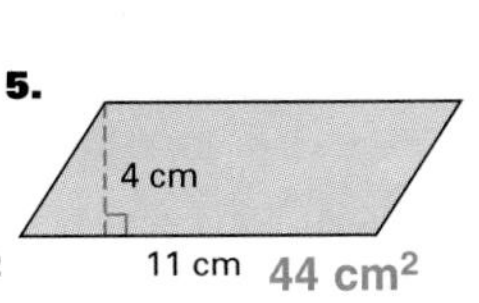

44 cm^2

6.

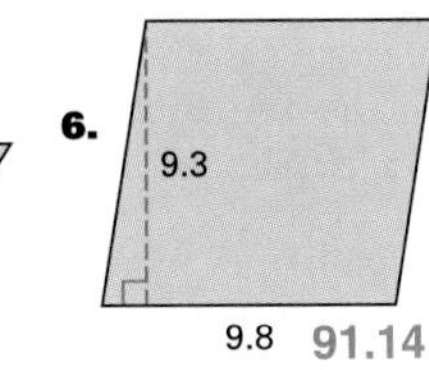

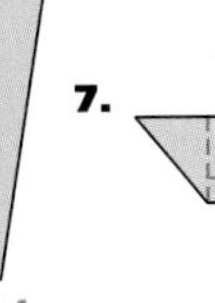

91.14

7.

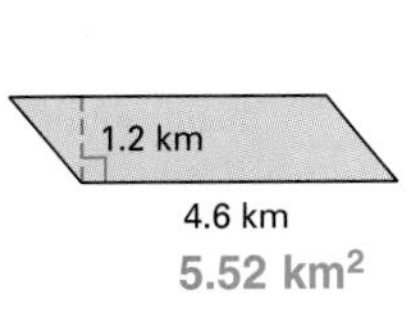

5.52 km^2

8.

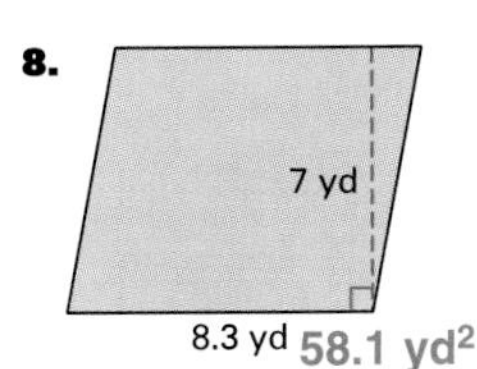

58.1 yd^2

9.

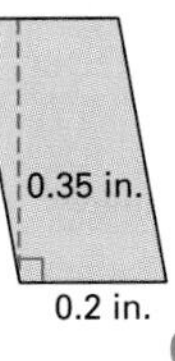

0.07 in^2

10.

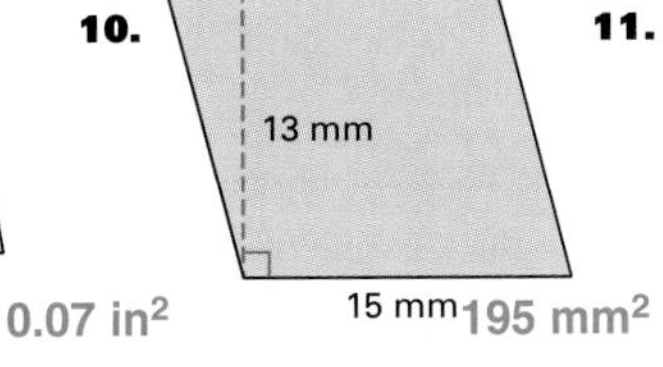

195 mm^2

11.

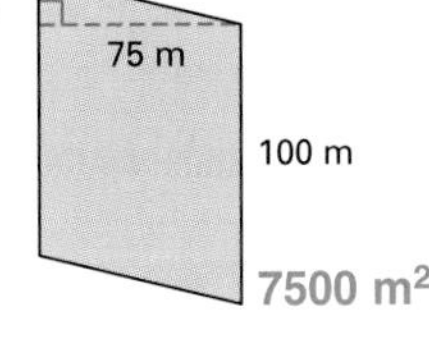

7500 m^2

Find each area if b is the base and h is the height of a parallelogram.

12. $b = 20, h = 6$ 120

13. $b = 12$ yd, $h = 7$ yd 84 yd^2

14. $h = 25$ ft, $b = 25$ ft 625 ft^2

15. $h = 14.7$ cm, $b = 18.1$ cm 266.07 cm^2

16. $h = 13.2$ m, $b = 0.5$ m 6.6 m^2

17. $b = 1000$ km, $h = 1000$ km 1,000,000 km^2

18. **Test Prep** Choose the correct units for the area of a figure. C

Ⓐ Centimeters   Ⓑ Meters

Ⓒ Square centimeters   Ⓓ Feet

19. **Geography** The state of Tennessee is shaped roughly like a parallelogram. Its northern border is about 442 miles long and the shortest distance between the northern and southern borders is about 115 miles. Estimate the area of Tennessee. 50,830 mi^2

PRACTICE

Name ______________ **Practice 4-5**

Area of Parallelograms

Find each area.

1. 28 cm^2
2. 120 yd^2
3. 72 km^2

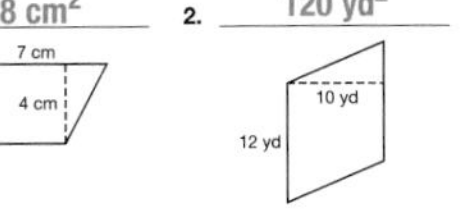

4. 2646 in^2
5. 476 mm^2
6. 26.27 ft^2

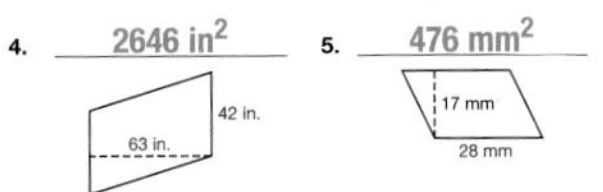

7. 40.95
8. 7.13 cm^2
9. 91.53 in^2

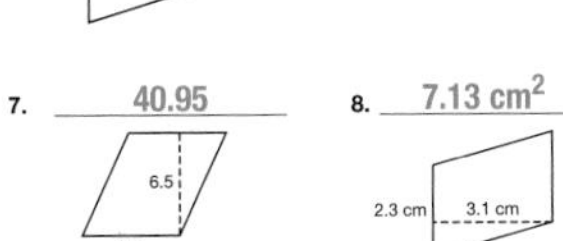

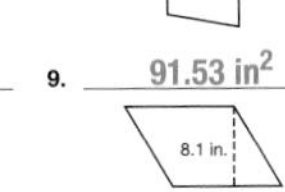

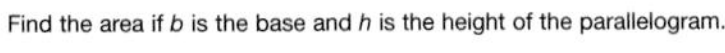

Find the area if b is the base and h is the height of the parallelogram.

10. $b = 5$ cm, $h = 7$ cm 35 cm^2
11. $b = 8.6$ m, $h = 12.0$ m 103.2 m^2
12. $b = 8.4$ m, $h = 5.3$ m 44.52 m^2
13. $h = 83$ in., $b = 104$ in. 8632 in^2
14. $b = 23$ cm, $h = 8.7$ cm 200.1 cm^2
15. $h = 2.1$ mi, $b = 2.5$ mi 5.25 mi^2
16. A beginning woodworking student accidentally built a picture frame in the shape of a parallelogram with base 8 in. and height 9.5 in. What was the area of the frame? 76 in^2
17. An unusual tabletop has the shape of a parallelogram with base 147 cm and height 136 cm. What is the area of the tabletop? 19,992 cm^2

RETEACHING

Name ______________ **Alternative Lesson 4-5**

Area of Parallelograms

A **parallelogram** is a four-sided figure whose opposite sides are parallel. A parallelogram has the same area as a rectangle of equal base and height.

To find the area of a parallelogram, use the same formula as that for the area of a rectangle: base × height = area. The height of a parallelogram is always a vertical measure from the base, not a slanted measure. Area is always represented in square units.

Example

Find the area of the parallelogram.

Use the formula base × height = area.
The base of the parallelogram is 12 cm.
The height of the parallelogram is 6 cm.
The area of the parallelogram is 72 cm^2.

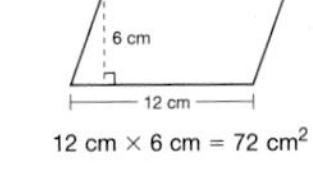

12 cm × 6 cm = 72 cm^2

Try It Find each area. Remember to write each area in square units.

a. (7 m, 5 m)
The base is 5 m.
The height is 7 m.
Multiply. The area is 35 m^2.

b. (100 ft, 100 ft)
The base is 100 ft.
The height is 100 ft.
Multiply. The area is 10,000 ft^2.

c. (8 in., 4 in.) 32 in^2

d. 45 cm^2

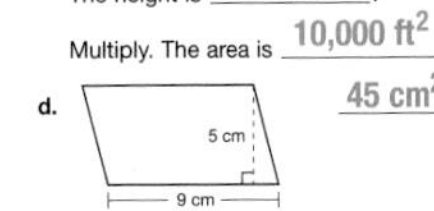

e. 45 m^2

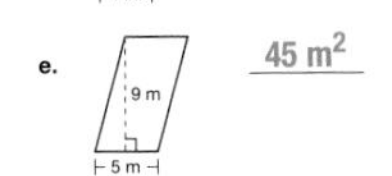

f. 9 yd^2

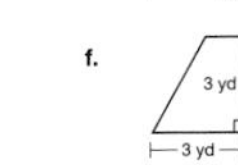

g. (2 ft, 15 ft) 30 ft^2

h. 63 cm^2

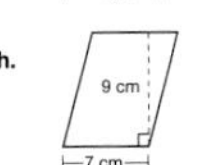

Assignment Guide

- **Basic** 1–11, 12–18 evens, 19, 20, 22–42 evens
- **Average** 1–17 odds, 18–23, 25, 28–44 evens
- **Enriched** 1–17 odds, 18–25, 31–43 odds

PRACTICE 4-5

Exercise Notes

Exercises 9 and 11

Error Prevention Have students turn their books a quarter turn if they have difficulty recognizing the shape as a parallelogram.

Reteaching

Activity

Materials: Graph paper

- Draw as many different parallelograms as you can with a base of 14 units and a height of 4 units.
- Find the area of each by counting squares and by using the formula Base × height = area. Areas will all equal 56 square units.
- Draw as many different parallelograms as you can with an area of 36 square units.
- Find the base and height of each.

Possible answers:
base = 1, height = 36;
base = 2, height = 18;
base = 3, height = 12;
base = 4, height = 9;
base = 4.5, height = 8;
base = 6, height = 6;
base = 9, height = 4;
base = 12, height = 3;
base = 18, height = 2;
base = 36, height = 1.

Exercise Notes

■ Exercise 22

Problem-Solving Tip You may wish to use Teaching Tool Transparencies 2 and 3: Guided Problem Solving, pages 1–2.

■ Exercises 26–37

Extension Before actually doing the problems, have students discuss which ones require the use of a calculator and which ones can be done mentally.

Exercise Answers

22. 12 in.; 12 inches is four times longer that 3 inches, and $3 \times 12 = 36$.
23. Possible answer: They have the same area, but different shapes.
24. Rectangle; If the slanted side of the parallelogram is 20, then the height is less than 20.
25. Convert to the same units first, then multiply base by height.
    a. 2.36 m² or 23,6000 cm²
    b. 384 in² or $2\frac{2}{3}$ ft²
    c. 1.32 cm² or 132 mm²
    d. 0.456 cm² or 45.6 mm²

Alternate Assessment

Interview Ask students to explain how to find the area of a parallelogram. Then have them describe the similarities and differences between finding the area of a rectangle and finding the area of a parallelogram.

▶ Quick Quiz

Find each area if b is the base and h is the height of a parallelogram.

1. $b = 11$ cm, $h = 4$ cm
   area = 44 cm²
2. $b = 2.1$ mm, $h = 1.1$ mm
   area = 2.31 mm²
3. $b = 100$ in., $h = 55$ in.
   area = 5500 in²

Available on Daily Transparency 4-5

PROBLEM SOLVING 4-5

20. Patterns GPS Jaspar drew a parallelogram with a base of 2 cm and a height of 2 cm. He drew another with base 2 cm and height 4 cm and a third with base 2 cm and height 8 cm. If Jaspar continues drawing parallelograms in this pattern, what will the area of the sixth figure be? 128 cm²

21. Geometry At some malls, parking spots are shaped like parallelograms. If a spot is 3.1 meters wide and 4.7 meters long, what is its area? 14.57 m²

Problem Solving and Reasoning

Problem Solving STRATEGIES

- Look for a Pattern
- Make an Organized List
- Make a Table
- Guess and Check
- Work Backward
- Use Logical Reasoning
- Draw a Diagram
- Solve a Simpler Problem

22. Choose a Strategy Violet wants to add parallelograms to the design of her Native American drum. Each parallelogram should be about 36 square inches. If she wants the height to be four times longer than the base, what should the height of each parallelogram be? Explain.

23. Journal Describe the similarities and differences between a 2 cm by 4 cm rectangle and a parallelogram with base 2 cm and height 4 cm.

24. Communicate Which figure has the larger area, a rectangle with a base of 50 and a height of 20, or a parallelogram with a base of 50 and a slanted side of 20? Explain.

25. Critical Thinking Find each area. Explain your reasoning.

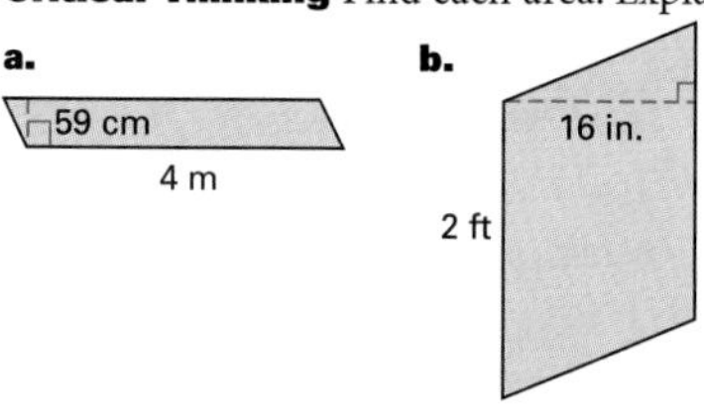

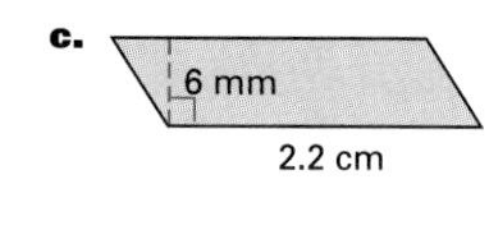

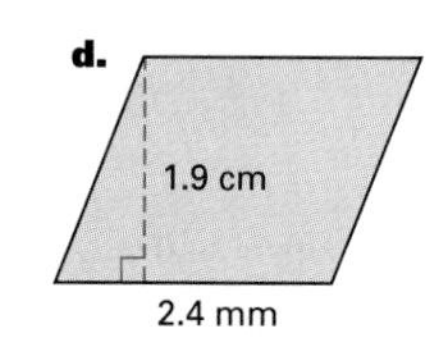

Mixed Review

Write in standard form. *[Lesson 2-4]*

26. 5^9 1,953,125 **27.** 3^4 81 **28.** 9^5 59,049 **29.** 12^2 144 **30.** 2^6 64 **31.** 4^3 64

32. 10^{13} 10,000,000,000,000 **33.** 1^{29} 1 **34.** 6^1 6 **35.** 8^7 2,097,152 **36.** 20^2 400 **37.** 7^8 5,764,801

Simplify. *[Lesson 3-6]*

38. 108.93 − 72.41 36.52 **39.** 0.5678 + 1.3452 1.913 **40.** 6.25 + 7.36 13.61 **41.** 238.14 − 5.67 232.47

42. 1.5 + 0.5 2 **43.** 2.3 + 4.5 6.8 **44.** 87.003 − 56.31 30.693

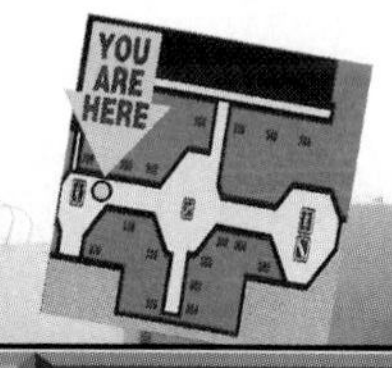

PROBLEM SOLVING

Name ____________________

Guided Problem Solving 4-5

GPS **PROBLEM 20, STUDENT PAGE 236**

Jaspar drew a parallelogram with a base of 2 cm and a height of 2 cm. He drew another with base 2 cm and height 4 cm and a third with base 2 cm and height 8 cm. If Jaspar continues drawing parallelograms in this pattern, what will the area of the sixth shape be?

— Understand —

1. Circle the information you need.
2. You are to find the area of the parallelogram in the sixth place in the pattern.
3. What is the formula for finding the area of a parallelogram? Area = base × height

— Plan —

4. Draw a picture of the three shapes in the pattern. Label each base and height.

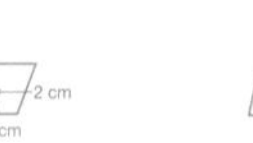

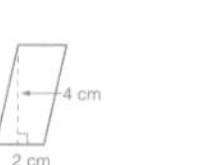

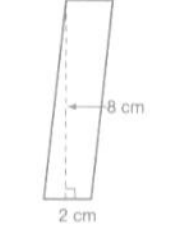

5. What pattern do you see? Possible answer: Height and area doubles.

— Solve —

6. What are the measures of the base and height of the sixth parallelogram? 2 cm and 64 cm
7. What is the area of the sixth parallelogram? 128 cm²

— Look Back —

8. What other strategy could you use to find the pattern? Possible answer: Make a Table.

SOLVE ANOTHER PROBLEM

Toi drew a parallelogram with a base of 3 cm and a height of 2 cm. She drew another with base 4 cm and height 3 cm and a third with base 5 cm and height 4 cm. If Toi continues drawing parallelograms in this pattern, what will the area of the seventh shape be? 72 cm²

ENRICHMENT

Name ____________________

Extend Your Thinking 4-5

Critical Thinking

Use the formula for the area of a parallelogram $A = b \cdot h$, where b stands for base and h stands for height. Find each missing length. The total area for each figure is given.

1. 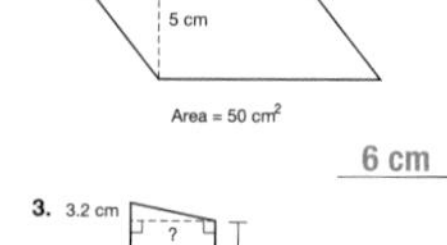

Area = 50 cm² — 6 cm

2. 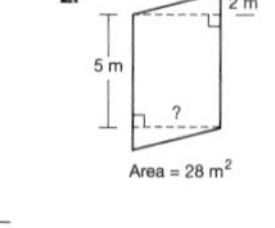

Area = 28 m² — 4 m

3. 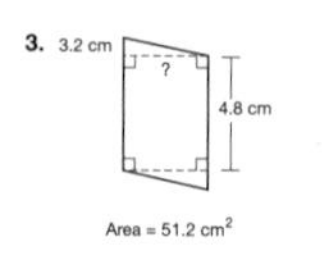

Area = 51.2 cm² — 6.4 cm

4. 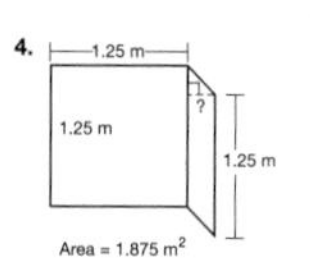

Area = 1.875 m² — 0.25 m

5. 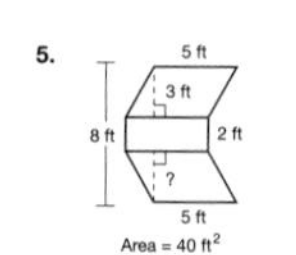

Area = 40 ft² — 3 ft

6. 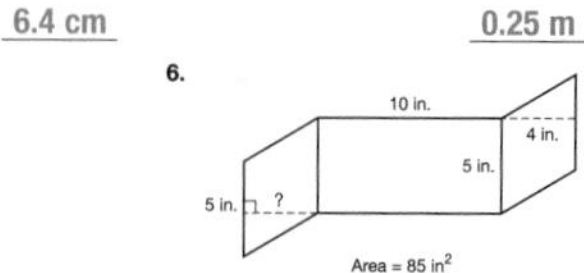

Area = 85 in² — 3 in.

7. 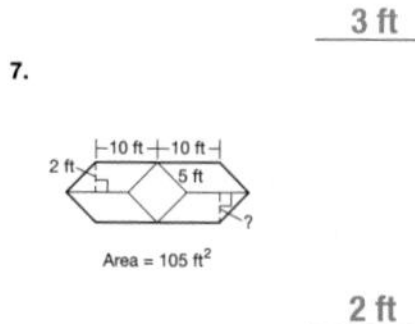

Area = 105 ft² — 2 ft

8. 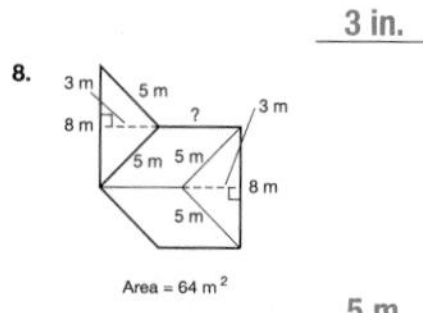

Area = 64 m² — 5 m

Area of Triangles

4-6

▶ Lesson Link You know how to find the area of several types of four-sided figures. Now you will find the area of a triangle. ◀

You'll Learn ...

■ to find the area of a triangle

... How It's Used

Carpet layers calculate areas in order to determine how much carpet they need.

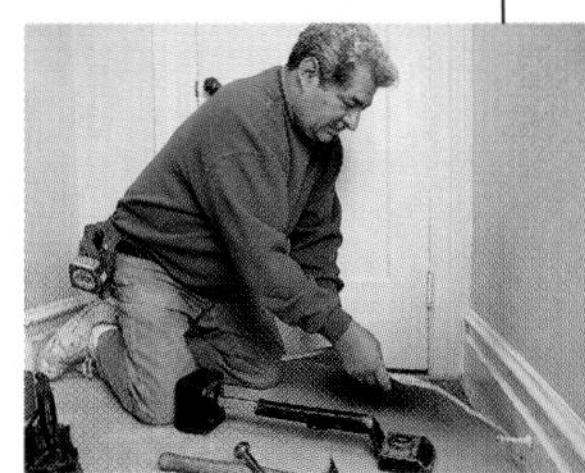

Explore Area of Triangles

Size Wise

Materials: Dot paper

Area of Rectangle	Sketch	Area of Corner-to-Corner Triangle
1		$\frac{1}{2}$
2		
3		
4		
5		
6		
7		
8		
9		
10		
11		
12		

1. Copy the chart on dot paper. For each row, sketch one rectangle that has the given area. Some rectangles can be sketched in more than one way.
2. On each sketch, shade in a triangle that goes from one corner of the rectangle to the opposite corner. Estimate the area of the triangle.
3. Describe any patterns you see in comparing the areas of the rectangles and the areas of the corner-to-corner triangles.
4. For a rectangle with an area of 50 square units, what do you think the area of the corner-to-corner triangle would be? Explain.

MEETING INDIVIDUAL NEEDS

Resources

4-6 Practice
4-6 Reteaching
4-6 Problem Solving
4-6 Enrichment
4-6 Daily Transparency
Problem of the Day
Review
Quick Quiz
Teaching Tool Transparency 10
Technology Master 18
Chapter 4 Project Master

Interactive CD-ROM Lesson

Learning Modalities

Logical Some students may prefer to focus on the numerical relationship between the area of a triangle and the area of a rectangle with the same base and height rather than looking at the geometry involved.

Visual Have students use geoboards to model triangles and the rectangles that surround them.

Social Have students work in teams to develop games that test students' ability to find areas of rectangles, squares, parallelograms, and triangles.

Inclusion

Some students may have difficulty deciding which side of a triangle is the base when they are presented with triangles that vary in their orientation. Have them draw each triangle on graph paper and enclose the triangle in a rectangle in order to find the area.

INTERACTIVE LESSON

4-6 Lesson Organizer

Objective

- Find the area of a triangle.

Materials

- Explore: Dot paper

NCTM Standards

- 1–4, 12, 13

Review

Divide.

1. 567 ÷ 14 40.5
2. 31.8 ÷ 1.2 26.5
3. 1004 ÷ 0.8 1255

Available on Daily Transparency 4-6

1 Introduce

Explore

You may wish to use Teaching Tool Transparency 10: Dot Paper with **Explore**.

The Point
Students explore how the area of a triangle is half the area of a rectangle with the same base and height.

Ongoing Assessment
Check that students understand that the areas of the two triangles in any sketch are the same.

For Groups That Finish Early
Find the area of the triangle formed by connecting the opposite corners of a parallelogram with base 8 and height 4. 16 square units.

Answers for Explore on next page.

Answers for Explore

1–2.

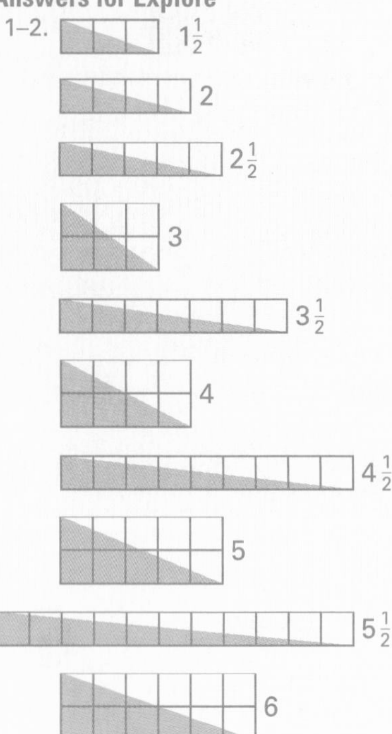

3. The area of the triangle is half of the area of the rectangle.
4. 25 units; 25 is one-half of 50.

2 Teach

Learn

Alternate Examples

1. Find the area.

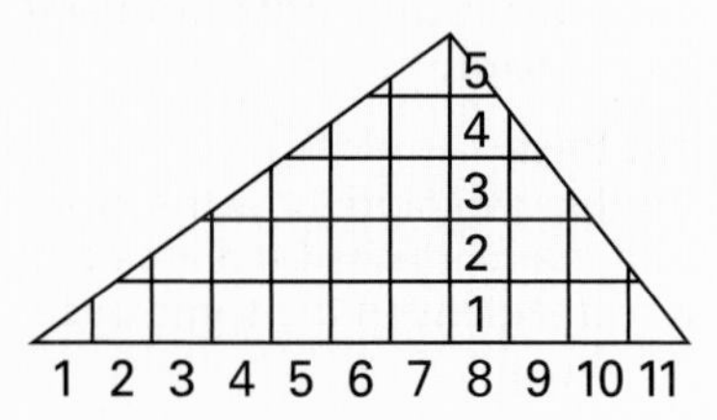

There are 11 squares across the base. The triangle is 5 squares tall.

base × height ÷ 2 = area

11 × 5 ÷ 2 = 27.5 units^2

2. Find the area.

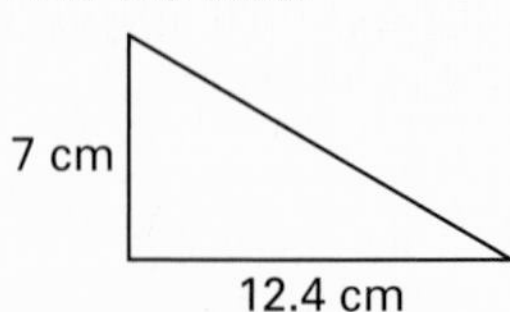

base × height ÷ 2 = area

12.4 × 7 ÷ 2 = 43.4 cm^2

3. A scarf is designed in the shape of a triangle with base 36 inches and height 18 inches. Find the area of the scarf.

36 × 18 ÷ 2 = 324

The area of the scarf is 324 in^2.

Learn Area of Triangles

The area of a triangle equals half the area of a rectangle whose base and height are the same as the triangle's. You can find the area of a triangle by calculating the area of the rectangle that surrounds it and dividing that in half. You can also use the area formula for a triangle.

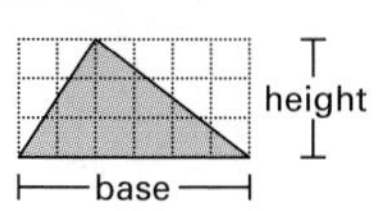

base × height ÷ 2 = area

Remember

When you divide a number by a number that doesn't go into the first number evenly, you get a decimal answer. The decimal point in the quotient should be placed directly above the decimal point in the dividend. **[Page 186]**

Examples

1 Find the area.

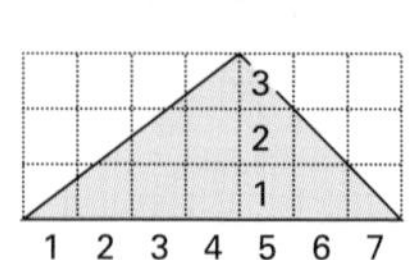

There are 7 squares across the base. The triangle is 3 squares tall.

base × height ÷ 2 = area

7 × 3 ÷ 2 = 10.5 units^2

2 Find the area.

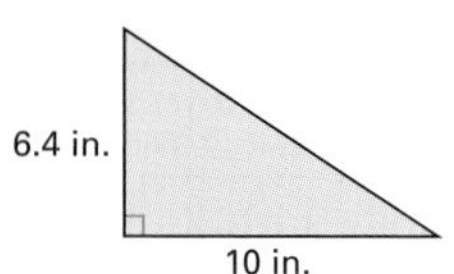

base × height ÷ 2 = area

10 × 6.4 ÷ 2 = 32 in^2

3 Devon wants to make a kite that measures 4 ft high and 5 ft at the base. How much fabric does she need?

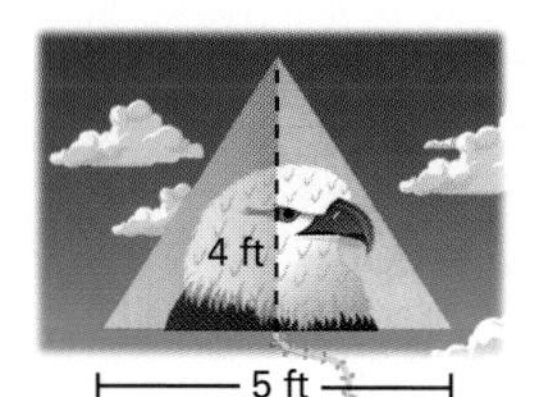

base × height ÷ 2 = area

5 × 4 ÷ 2 = 10

Devon needs 10 ft^2 of fabric.

History Link

Kites are the oldest form of aircraft.

Try It

Find the area.

a. 6

b. 2 yd, 4.75 yd — 4.75 yd^2

c. 3.5 in., 1 in. — 1.75 in^2

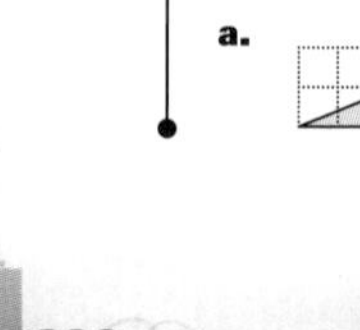

MATH EVERY DAY

Problem of the Day

Rosa drew this figure on folded paper as shown below. Draw the figure as it will appear when the holes are punched and the paper unfolded.

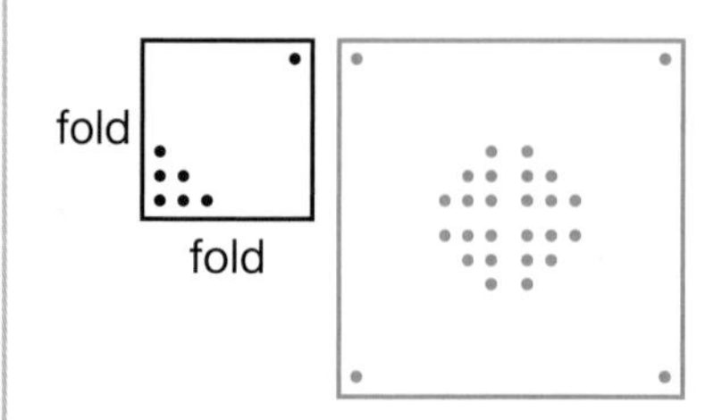

Available on Daily Transparency 4-6

An Extension is provided in the transparency package.

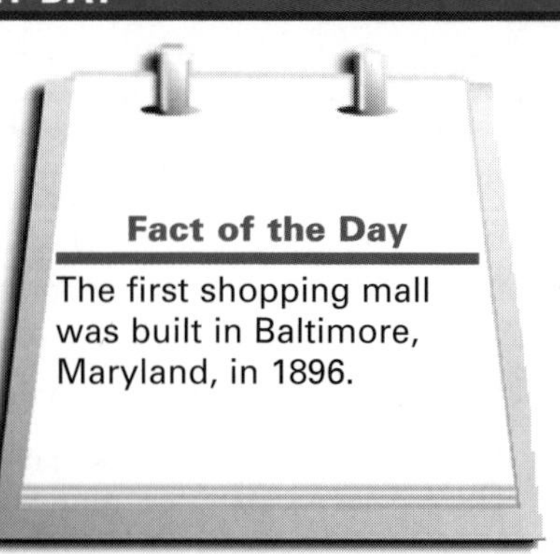

Fact of the Day

The first shopping mall was built in Baltimore, Maryland, in 1896.

Mental Math

Do these mentally.

1. 4.9 + 4.4 + 3.1 12.4
2. 6.5 − 3.3 3.2
3. 4 × 3.2 12.8
4. 7.77 ÷ 7 1.11

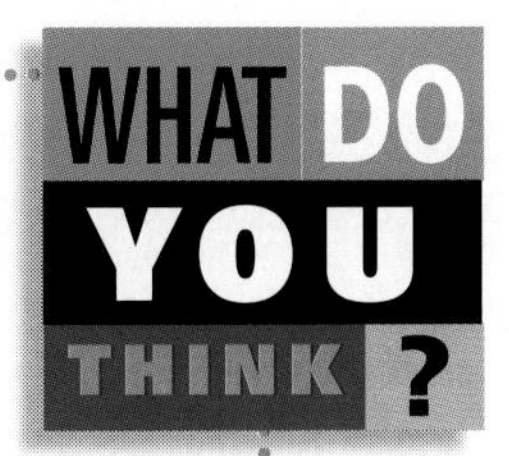

Sonia and Aaron are building the set for a play about ancient Egypt. They need to paint a large cardboard triangle to look like an Egyptian pyramid. The triangle measures 14 ft wide by 8 ft high. They have enough paint for about 60 square feet of cardboard. Do they have enough paint?

Sonia thinks ...

I'll imagine there's a rectangle around the triangle. I'll find the area of the rectangle and cut it in half.

Area of a rectangle = base × height

$= 14 \times 8$

$= 112\ ft^2$

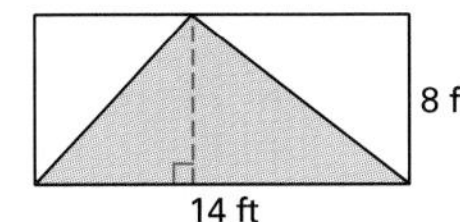

Half of 112 is 56. The cardboard is 56 square feet, so we have enough paint.

Aaron thinks ...

I'll use the area formula for a triangle.

Area of a triangle = base × height ÷ 2

$= 14 \times 8 \div 2$

$= 56\ ft^2$

The area is $56\ ft^2$. We have enough paint.

What do you think?

1. What information did Sonia and Aaron need to solve the problem?
2. Would Sonia and Aaron's answer change if the estimate of enough paint for 60 square feet was an overestimate? Explain.

Check Your Understanding

1. Why do you need to divide by 2 when finding the area of a triangle?
2. Do two triangles with the same height have the same area?

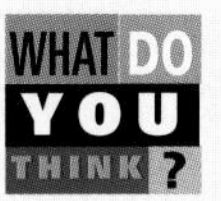

Students see two methods of solving the problem. Sonia finds the area of the related rectangle and divides it by 2 to get the area of the triangle. Aaron finds the area of the triangle using the formula.

Answers for What Do You Think?

1. The base and height of the triangle, how to find area, and the amount of paint they have.
2. Yes; Since the triangle is $56\ ft^2$, they might not have enough paint if $60\ ft^2$ was an overestimate.

3 Practice and Assess

Check

Some students may find it helpful to use examples to try out their answers to these questions.

Answers for Check Your Understanding

1. Possible answer: Base × height gives the area of a rectangle, a triangle is only half of that area.
2. Not necessarily; If the bases are not the same, two triangles with the same height will not have the same area.

MEETING MIDDLE SCHOOL CLASSROOM NEEDS

Tips from Middle School Teachers

Each year, I have my students work in groups to make a 3 foot by 5 foot "quilt" from construction paper squares, rectangles, parallelograms, and triangles. I show them some of the traditional quilt designs and then have them create designs of their own.

Team Teaching

Work with the social-studies teacher and have students find the areas of parts of flags from different countries.

Science Connection

Oysters are closely related to scallops, clams, and mussels. These bivalves are protected by two shells. Adult oysters live attached to rocks and other hard surfaces. Many bivalves are edible and a valuable asset to the commercial fishing industry.

4-6 Exercises and Applications

Assignment Guide

- **Basic**
  1–7, 12–17, 20–30
- **Average**
  1–11 odds, 12–22, 23–29 odds
- **Enriched**
  1–11 odds, 12–22, 24–30 evens

Exercise Notes

Exercises 1–12

Error Prevention Remind students to include the units in each answer.

Exercise 12

Geography The disappearance of airplanes and ships in the area known as the Bermuda Triangle has led to numerous scientific studies. Even though downward air currents and violent storms occur often in this area, research has not revealed any important peculiarities about the area.

Reteaching

Activity

Materials: Dot paper

- Draw each of the following right triangles on dot paper.

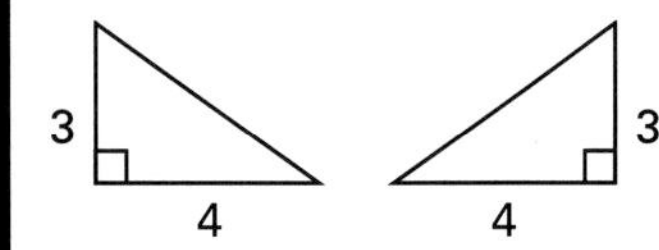

- Sketch the related rectangle with the same height and base and cut it out.
- Fold the rectangle along a diagonal and then cut so that you have two triangles.
- Turn the two triangles until one fits exactly on top of the other so that you can see that the area of the triangle is half that of the rectangle.
- Find the area of each triangle given below.

Base	Height	
4 cm	6 cm	12 cm²
8 cm	10 cm	40 cm²
2 cm	4 cm	4 cm²

4-6 Exercises and Applications

PRACTICE 4-6

Practice and Apply

Getting Started Find the area of each triangle.

1. 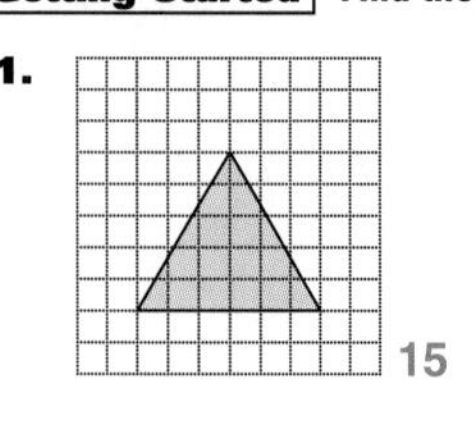 15
2. 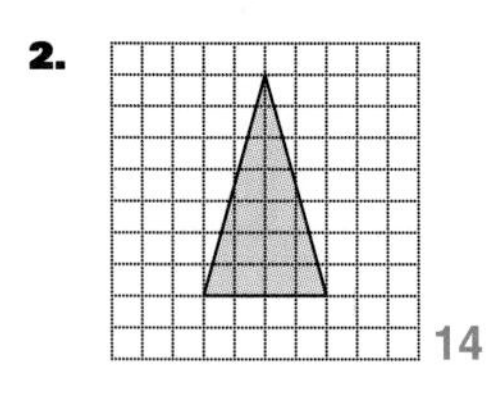 14
3. 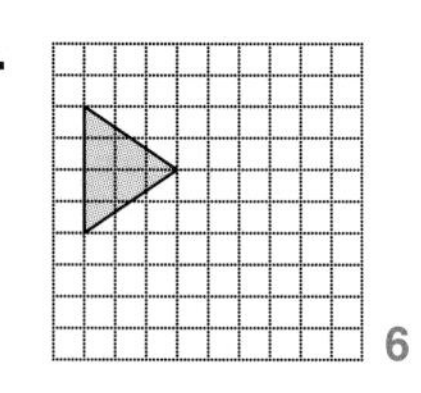 6

Find the area of each triangle.

4. 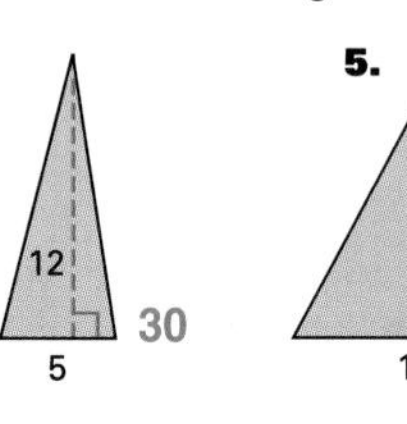

30

5. 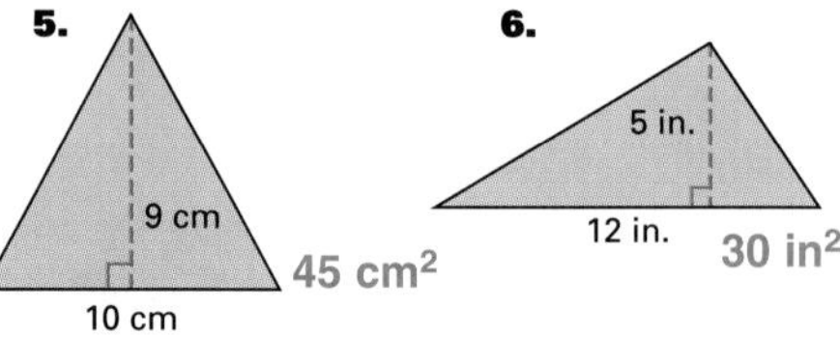

45 cm²

6.

30 in²

7. 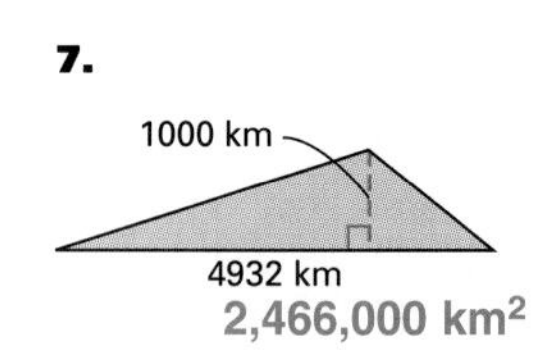

2,466,000 km²

8. 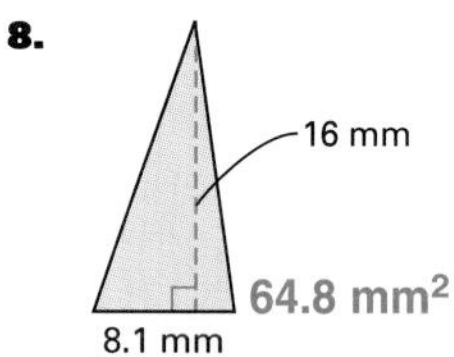

64.8 mm²

9. 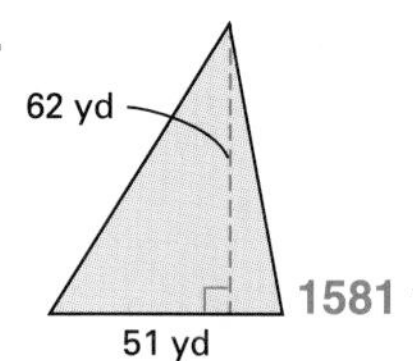

1581 yd²

10. 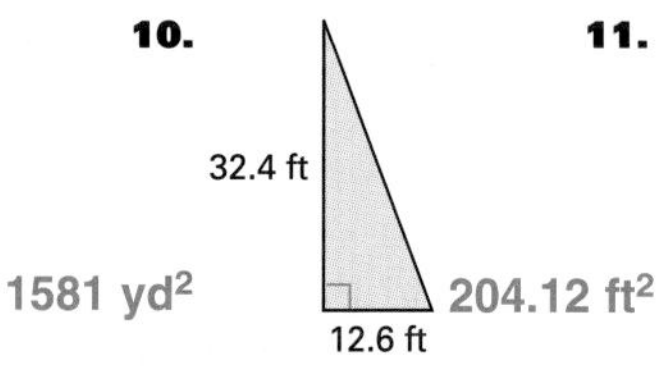

204.12 ft²

11. 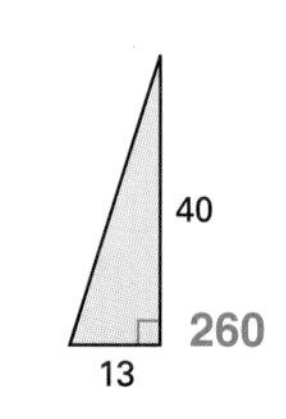

260

12. **Geography** The Bermuda Triangle is a region in the Atlantic Ocean where ships and airplanes are reported to have mysteriously disappeared since the 1940s. Use the diagram to find the area of the Bermuda Triangle. 434,700 mi²

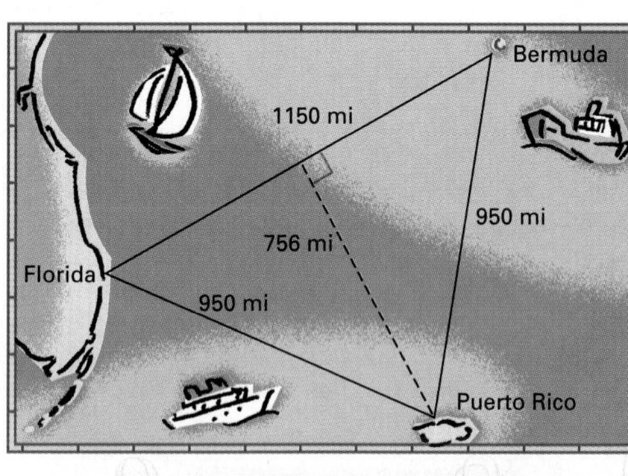

PRACTICE

Name ______

Practice 4-6

Area of Triangles

Find the area of each triangle.

1. 63 m²
2. 24 in²
3. 71.5 cm²

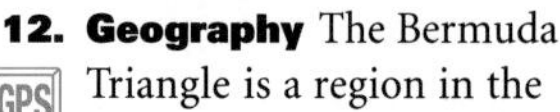

4. 100.44
5. 192.24 yd²
6. 75.465 m²

7. 29.05 ft²
8. 8.48 cm²
9. 18.33 mi²

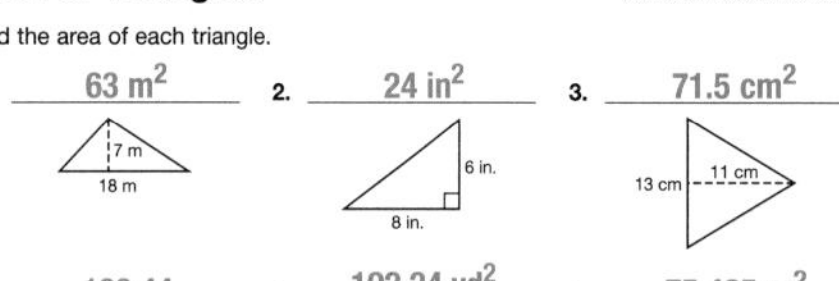

Find the area if b is the base and h is the height of the triangle.

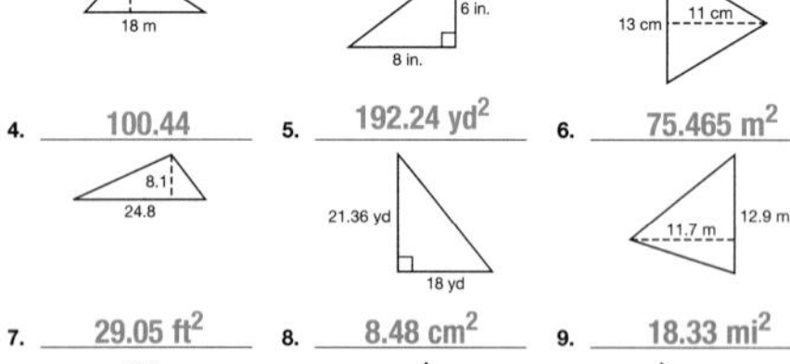

10. $b = 12$ ft, $h = 5$ ft — 30 ft²
11. $h = 9$ cm, $b = 11$ cm — 49.5 cm²
12. $b = 4.2$ mi, $h = 6$ mi — 12.6 mi²
13. $h = 7.3$, $b = 12.4$ — 45.26
14. $b = 8.37$ in., $h = 10.4$ in. — 43.524 in²
15. $h = 2.8$ km, $b = 5.8$ km — 8.12 km²
16. $b = 9.6$ yd, $h = 6.42$ yd — 30.816 yd²
17. $h = 20.6$ cm, $b = 6.4$ cm — 65.92 cm²
18. $b = 3.8$ ft, $h = 9.1$ ft — 17.29 ft²

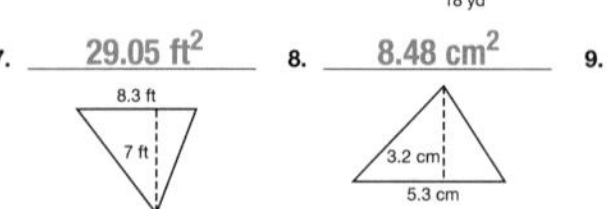

19. **Geography** The state of New Hampshire has the approximate shape of a triangle with base 90 mi and height 180 mi. Estimate the area of New Hampshire. 8100 mi²

RETEACHING

Name ______

Alternative Lesson 4-6

Area of Triangles

The area of a triangle equals half the area of a rectangle whose base and height are the same as the triangle's. You can find the area of a triangle by calculating the area of the rectangle that surrounds it and dividing that in half. You can also use the area formula for a triangle.

Example

Find the area of this triangle.

Method One: The area of the rectangular grid is 5 × 8, or 40 square units. Since the triangle on the grid covers only half of the squares, the area of the triangle is half of 40, or 20 square units.

Method Two: Use the formula base × height ÷ 2 = area. The base of the triangle is 5 units. The height of the triangle is 8 units.

5 × 8 ÷ 2 = 20

The area of the triangle is 20 square units.

Try It Find each area.

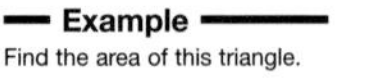

a. 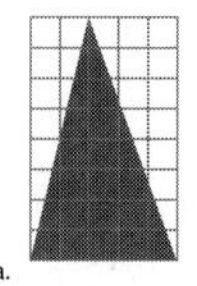

Base 4 units Height 5 units
4 × 5 ÷ 2 = 10
Area 10 square units

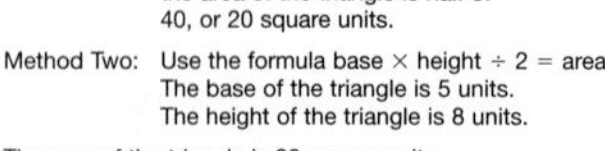

b.

Base 10 ft Height 7 ft
10 × 7 ÷ 2 = 35
Area 35 square feet

c. 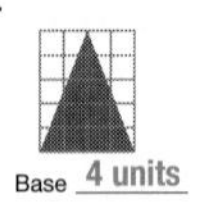

9 m²

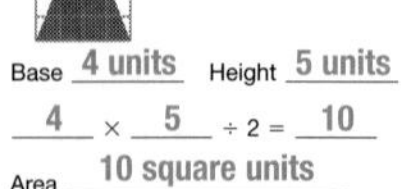

d. 

14 cm²

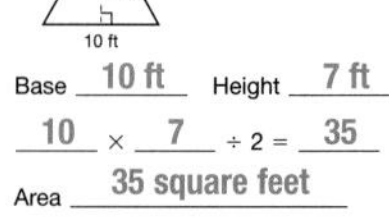

e. 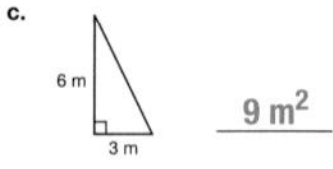 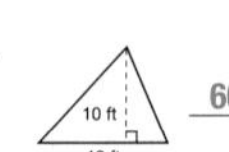

60 ft²

f. 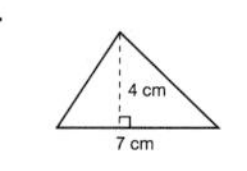 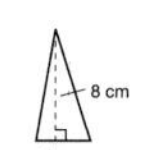

16 cm² 

Find the area if b is the base and h is the height of a triangle.

13. $b = 6$ in., $h = 9$ in. $27\ in^2$ **14.** $b = 62$ ft, $h = 3$ ft $93\ ft^2$ **15.** $h = 9$ in., $b = 7$ in. $31.5\ in^2$

16. **Test Prep** Find the area of the triangle. A

Ⓐ $11.25\ in^2$ Ⓑ $15.4\ in^2$

Ⓒ $62.7\ in^2$ Ⓓ None of these

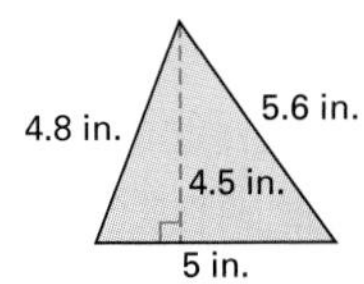

Problem Solving and Reasoning

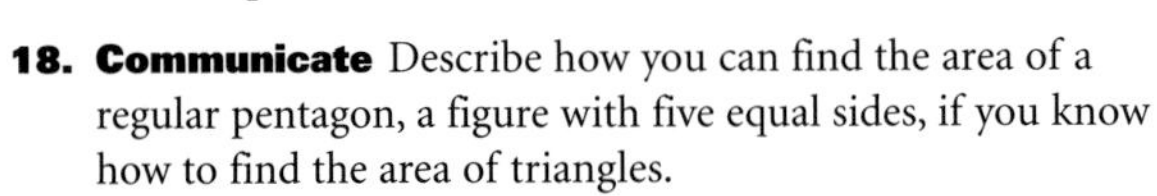

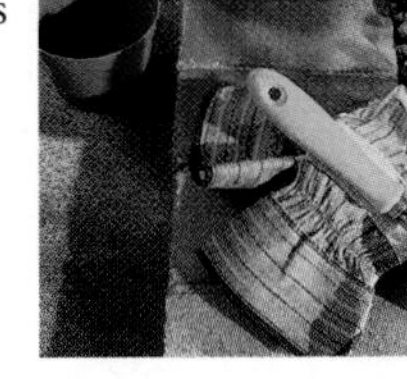

17. Critical Thinking The central plaza of a shopping mall has four triangular flower beds. Each bed has a base of 60 inches and a height of 48 inches. If one plant can be planted every 4 square inches, how many are needed to fill the flower beds? Explain.

18. Communicate Describe how you can find the area of a regular pentagon, a figure with five equal sides, if you know how to find the area of triangles.

19. 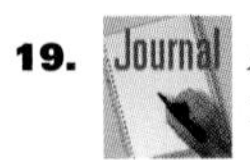

A triangular plot of land has a base of 1 mile and an area of 1 square mile. Explain how they can both have a measure of 1.

Mixed Review

For Exercises 20–22, use the Shucked Oysters graph. *[Lesson 1-1]*

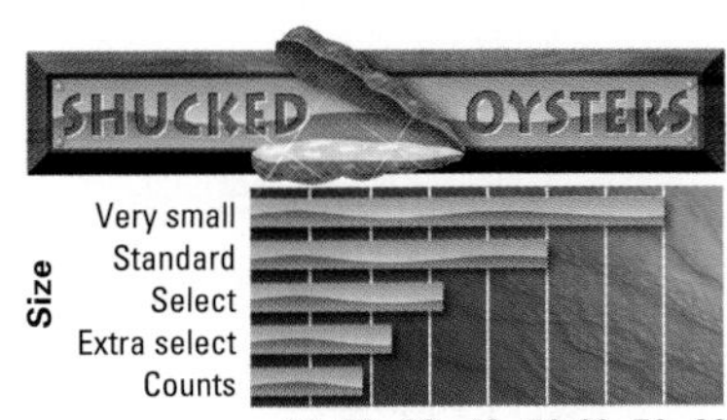

20. How many select oysters are in a pint? 32

21. How many more very small oysters than counts oysters are there in a pint? 52

22. Which size oyster gives the most number per pint? Very small

Write each expression using exponents. *[Lesson 2-4]*

23. $6 \times 6 \times 6 \times 6 \times 6$ 6^5 **24.** $435 \times 435 \times 435$ 435^3 **25.** $7 \times 7 \times 7 \times 7$ 7^4 **26.** $5 \times 5 \times 9 \times 9 \times 9$ $5^2 \times 9^3$

27. $10 \times 10 \times 10 \times 10$ 10^4 **28.** $1 \times 1 \times 1 \times 1 \times 1 \times 1$ 1^6 **29.** $3 \times 3 \times 3 \times 3 \times 8$ $3^4 \times 8$ **30.** 68×68 68^2

Project Progress

Return to your rough sketches and calculate the area of your golf holes. Make sure that at least two holes use rectangles and at least two holes use triangles in their shapes.

Problem Solving
Understand
Plan
Solve
Look Back

Project Progress

You may want to have students use Chapter 4 Project Master.

Exercise Answers

17. 1440; The area of one bed is $1440\ in^2$ so there are 360 plants in one bed.
18. Divide the pentagon into five triangles and add the areas of the triangles together.
19. The height of the triangular plot is 2 miles; $(1)(2) \div 2 = 1$.

Alternate Assessment

Self Assessment Have students write and solve problems involving finding the area of a square, a rectangle, a parallelogram, and a triangle. Have them rate their own understanding of these concepts.

Quick Quiz

Find the area if b is the base and h is the height of the triangle.

1. $b = 4$ units, $h = 4$ units
   8 $units^2$
2. $b = 22$ cm, $h = 18$ cm
   $198\ cm^2$
3. $b = 9$ in., $h = 10$ in. $45\ in^2$
4. A triangular flag has a base of 7 m and a height of 4 m. What is the area of the flag? $14\ m^2$

Available on Daily Transparency 4-6

PROBLEM SOLVING

Name ______

Guided Problem Solving 4-6

GPS PROBLEM 12, STUDENT PAGE 240

The Bermuda Triangle is a region in the Atlantic Ocean where ships and airplanes are reported to have mysteriously disappeared since the 1940's. Use the diagram to find the area of the Bermuda Triangle.

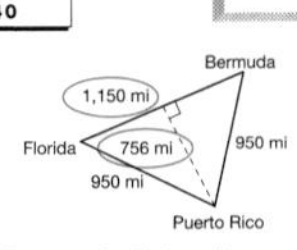

— Understand —

1. What are you asked to find? Area of Bermuda Triangle.
2. Circle the information in the picture which will help you solve the problem.

— Plan —

3. What is the formula for finding the area of a triangle? $Area = b \times h \div 2$
4. a. What is the base of the Bermuda Triangle? 1150 mi
   b. What is the height of the Bermuda Triangle? 756 mi
5. Which of the following is a reasonable answer? b
   a. About 200,000 mi^2 b. About 400,000 mi^2 c. About 800,000 mi^2

— Solve —

6. Substitute the values for base and height in the formula.
   1150 × 756 ÷ 2 = 434,700
7. Write a sentence stating the area of the Bermuda Triangle. Possible answer: The Bermuda Triangle's area is 434,700 mi^2.

— Look Back —

8. Why did you write your answer in square miles? Possible answer: Area is always measured in square units.

SOLVE ANOTHER PROBLEM

Find the area of the triangle.

13,081.5 mi^2

ENRICHMENT

Name ______

Extend Your Thinking 4-6

Decision Making

A tessellation is the repetition of a shape or shapes to completely fill a space without leaving any gaps. Experiment with some of the shapes you have been working with to create some interesting tessellations. You might like to try some designs with pattern blocks and then record them on this sheet by making drawings of your designs.

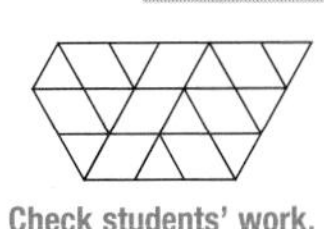

Check students' work.

1. Make a tessellation using any one shape.
2. Make a tessellation using any two 4-sided shapes.
3. Make a tessellation using any 4-sided shape and one triangle.
4. Make a tessellation using any three shapes.
5. What did you discover about creating tessellate? Do all shapes tessellate? Give examples to support your decision.
   Possible answer: All shapes do not tesselate. An example is a pentagon.

Technology

Using Dynamic Geometry Software • Finding the Sum of the Angles inside a Quadrilateral

The Point
Students use geometry software to find patterns in the sum of the angles in a quadrilateral.

Materials
Dynamic geometry software

Resources

Interactive CD-ROM Geometry Tool

About the Page

- You may want to demonstrate how to use the dynamic geometry software to draw figures, measure angles, and use the calculator feature.
- You might want to point out that a quadrilateral can be divided into two triangles. Note that the sum of the angle measures of a quadrilateral is 2 × 180°, or 360°.

Ask ...

- Once the figure is drawn, what is to be measured? The angles inside the figure.
- Is there a difference in how a five- or six-sided figure is drawn, compared to a four-sided figure?

Try It

- Remind students that the figures described should not have dents.

Answers for Try It

a. 540°

b. 720°

On Your Own
In the third question, point out that the angle where the dent is has a measure greater than 180°. The software may give the measure of this outside angle.

Answers for On Your Own

- Answers may vary. The sum of the angles is 900°.
- (The number of sides − 2) × 180°
- The sum is the same, but the software may give a smaller answer if it calculates the exterior measure of the dent angle.

TECHNOLOGY

Using Dynamic Geometry Software • Finding the Sum of the Angles inside a Quadrilateral

Problem: How can you determine the sum of the angles inside every quadrilateral, or four-sided polygon?

You can use dynamic geometry software to determine the sums of the angles inside a four-sided polygon. At first, the investigation will focus only on convex polygons. These are polygons with no "dents".

1 Using your geometry software draw a four-sided figure. Do not draw a figure with a "dent", like this one.

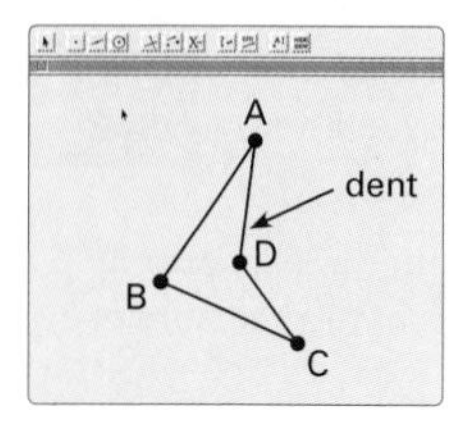

2 Use the measure tool to measure the angles.

m∠DAB = 125°
m∠ABC = 63°
m∠BCD = 102°
m∠CDA = 70°

3 Use the calculator feature of the software to find the sum of the measures of the angles.

4 Without creating a dent, stretch the figure to see if the sum changes.

Solution: The sum of the angles inside a quadrilateral is 360°.

TRY IT

a. Find the sum of the angles inside a five-sided figure.

b. Find the sum of the angles inside a six-sided figure.

ON YOUR OWN

- Predict the sum of the angles inside a seven-sided figure. Explain your prediction. Draw a seven-sided figure with the software and check to see if your guess was correct.
- Write a rule or formula that predicts the sum of the inside angles for any figure, no matter how many sides it has.
- Draw a four-sided concave polygon—a polygon that has a "dent" in it. Is the sum of the interior angles different for this type of polygon? Explain.

Section 4B Connect

In this section you learned how to find the area of squares, rectangles, parallelograms, and triangles. Now you will use your knowledge of area to decide how to design your own shopping mall.

The Monster That Ate Minnesota!

Materials: Ruler, Colored pencils or markers

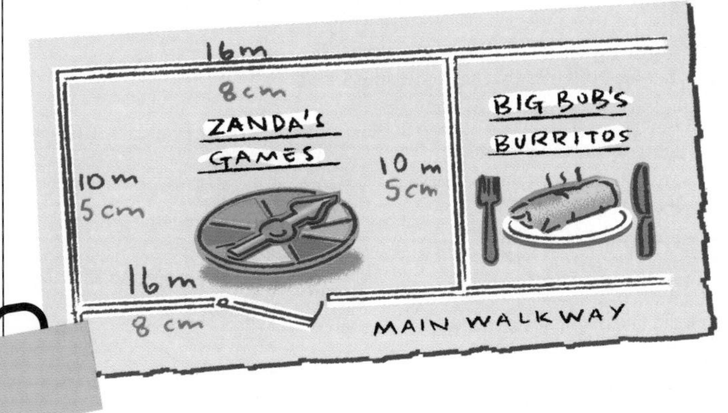

1. You need to design a mini-mall that meets the following conditions:
   a. It must have at least six stores.
   b. It must have a central area with benches and a fountain. Customers can walk through the area from store to store.
   c. It must have restrooms and an elevator to a restaurant on the roof.
   d. Its area must be at least 1800 m^2.
2. Use a cm ruler to make a diagram of your mall. In one color, label the length of each line in centimeters. In a different color, label the length that each wall will be when the mall is built. Assume that 1 cm on your diagram equals 2 m of wall.
3. Calculate the area for each store, the central area, the restrooms, and the elevator. Your calculations should be in square meters. Write these areas on your diagram.

4B Connect

The Monster That Ate Minnesota!

The Point

In *The Monster That Ate Minnesota!* on page 227, shopping malls are discussed. Now students are given an opportunity to design their own mini-mall.

Materials

Ruler, colored pencils or pens

About the Page

- Review metric measurement with students. They will use metric measurements as they design this mall.
- Discuss the scale they will use, 1 cm = 2m.
- Tell students not to include the restaurant or its area in their design because it is on another floor. They do need to be sure that their design includes an elevator so people can get to the restaurant.
- Suggest that students measure each line in the plan in centimeters and write those measurements on the map first. Then use another color to write the actual measurements on their plan.

Ongoing Assessment

Check that students have drawn a reasonable floor plan before they calculate the areas.

Extension

Shopping malls try to create "one-stop shopping" for the consumer. Ask students what stores they will have in their mall. Ask them to give the store names and tell which products they will sell. Have them add this information to their floor plan.

Answers for Connect

1–3. Answers may vary.

4B Review

Review Correlation

Item(s)	Lesson(s)
1	4-5
2	4-6
3–5	4-4
6	4-6
7, 8	4-3
9	4-2
10–13	4-1
14	4-4

Test Prep

Test-Taking Tip

Stress the importance of reading each answer choice carefully. Many students should be able to mentally multiply 20 and 40 correctly and get an answer of 800. However, point out to students that the units are part of the answer as well. Answer choice C is incorrect, because area is measured in *square* centimeters, not centimeters.

Section 4B Review

REVIEW 4B

Find the area of each figure.

1. 12 in. 4 in. **48 in²**

2. 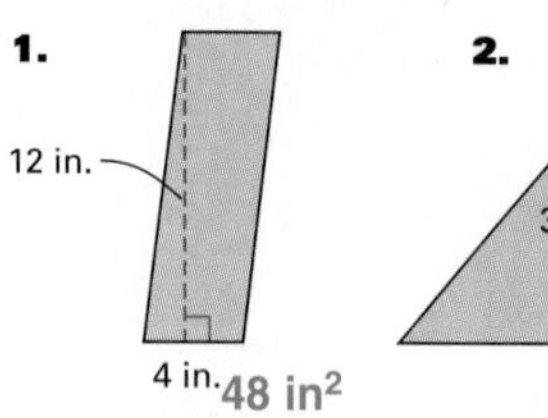

9.25 cm²

3. 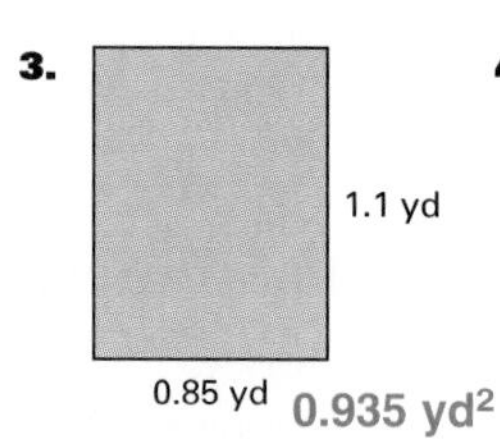

0.935 yd²

4. 36 mm 36 mm **1296 mm²**

5. **Number Sense** Bob wants to cover his patio with tiles. The patio measures 12.5 by 7.5 feet. If Bob has 100 tiles that each measure 1 foot by 1 foot, does he have enough to cover the patio? **Yes**

6. **History** The game of shuffleboard started as a small board game in which coins were shoved onto a scoring pattern. Cruise ships enlarged the game into a deck game for passengers. What is the area of the large triangle on a single shuffleboard court? **27 ft²**

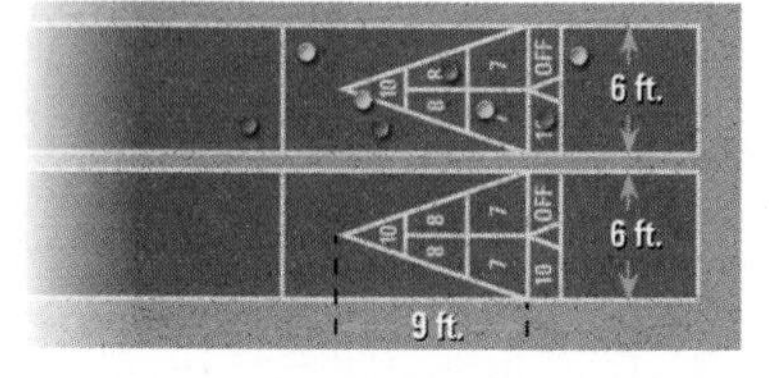

Use the conversion factor to find the missing measurement.

7. 16 ounces in 1 pound
☐ ounces in 6 pounds **96**

8. 4 cups in 1 quart
32 cups in ☐ quarts **8**

9. 1 knot is 1.15 mi/hr
☐ knots = 3.68 mi/hr **3.2**

Find the perimeter of each figure.

10. 34 cm, 67 cm **202 cm**

11. 6 in. **48 in.**

12. 25 yd, 25 yd **100 yd**

13. 11 mm **110 mm**

Test Prep

You can eliminate an answer if it has the wrong units of measurement.

14. Find the area of a rectangle that is 20 cm by 40 cm. **D**

Ⓐ 60 cm Ⓑ 60 cm² Ⓒ 800 cm Ⓓ 800 cm²

Resources

Practice Masters
Section 4B Review

Assessment Sourcebook
Quiz 4B

TestWorks
Test and Practice Software

PRACTICE

Name ______________________ Practice

Section 4B Review

Find the area of each figure.

1. 204 km² (17 km, 12 km)
2. 112 m² (8 m, 14 m)
3. 170.4 (21.3, 16.0)

Find the perimeter of each figure.

4. 29.4 ft (8.4 ft, 6.3 ft, 6.3 ft, 8.4 ft)
5. 77.6 in (21.6 in., 28 in., 28 in.)
6. 18.4 cm (4.6 cm, 4.6 cm)

7. Rhonda wants to carpet a room measuring 8 ft by 10 ft. She has a piece of carpet measuring 12 ft by 6 ft. Is it possible to cut the carpet into several pieces and assemble a piece large enough to carpet the room? Explain.
No, the room has area 80 ft², but the carpet area is only 72 ft².

8. A board for the game of Chinese checkers has the shape of 12 triangles placed together. If each of the 12 triangles has base 10 cm and height 17.3 cm, what is the area of the board?
1038 cm²

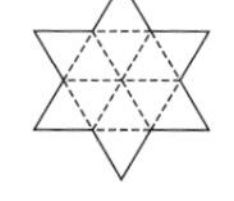

9. In 1980, the population of Texas was about 3^{15}. Use a calculator to write this number in standard form. *[Lesson 2-4]*
14,348,907

10. There are about 4,014,500,000 square inches in a square mile. Write this number in scientific notation. *[Lesson 3-4]*
4.0145×10^9

Section 4C

Area of Circles

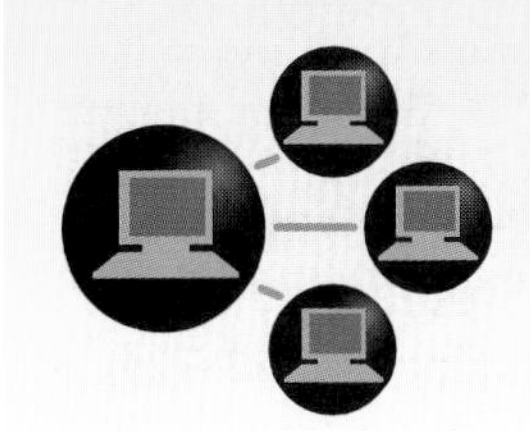

Visit **www.teacher.mathsurf.com** for links to lesson plans from teachers and other professionals, NCTM information, and other sites.

LESSON PLANNING GUIDE

Student Edition / Ancillaries*

LESSON		MATERIALS	VOCABULARY	DAILY	OTHER
	Section 4C Opener				
4-7	**Discovering Pi**	tape measures, calculators, several circular objects	radius, diameter, circumference, pi	4-7	Teaching Tool Trans. 23 Technology Master 19 Ch. 4 Project Master
4-8	**Area of Circles**			4-8	Lesson Enhancement Trans. 18 Technology Master 20
4-9	**Area of Irregular Figures**			4-9	Lesson Enhancement Trans. 19
	Connect	rulers			Interdisc. Team Teaching 4C
	Review				Practice 4C; Quiz 4C; *TestWorks*
	Extend Key Ideas	graph paper			Teaching Tool Trans. 7
	Chapter 4 Summary and Review				
	Chapter 4 Assessment				Ch. 4 Tests Forms A–F *TestWorks*; Ch. 4 Letter Home
	Cumulative Review, Chapters 1–4				Cumulative Review Ch. 1-4

* Daily Ancillaries include Practice, Reteaching, Problem Solving, Enrichment, and Daily Transparency. Teaching Tool Transparencies are in *Teacher's Toolkits*. Lesson Enhancement Transparencies are in *Overhead Transparency Package*.

SKILLS TRACE

LESSON	SKILL	FIRST INTRODUCED GR. 4	GR. 5	GR. 6	DEVELOP	PRACTICE/APPLY	REVIEW
4-7	**Discovering pi.**			✘ p. 246	pp. 246–247	pp. 248–249	pp. 263, 349, 390, 533
4-8	**Finding areas of circles.**			✘ p. 250	pp. 250–251	pp. 252–253	pp. 263, 537
4-9	**Finding areas of irregular shapes.**			✘ p. 254	pp. 254–256	pp. 257–258	pp. 263, 354, 542

CONNECTED MATHEMATICS

The unit *Covering and Surrounding (2-D Measurement)*, from the **Connected Mathematics** series, can be used with Section 4C.

INTERDISCIPLINARY TEAM TEACHING

Math and Social Studies

(Worksheet pages 23–24: Teacher pages T23–T24)

In this lesson, students find the area of a circle as it relates to houses that have circular bases.

Name ______________________ ***Math and Social Studies***

Welcome to the Round House

Find the area of a circle as it relates to houses that have circular bases.

Look around at your classroom. Then picture the different rooms in your home. These rooms, whether large or small, share some things. They usually have four walls, a floor, and a ceiling. While most rooms around the world are built this way, there are some exceptions, such as the *igloo* and the *teepee.*

The Inuit people (once called Eskimos) who live in central and western Canada used to build snow igloos as their permanent winter homes. Today, few Inuit people build snow igloos unless they are taking long journeys and need a temporary shelter.

Igloos are built from blocks of snow. Typically, each block is 2 to 3 feet long and 1 to 2 feet wide. The igloo is dome-shaped, and its base is circular. It usually has a diameter of about 8 feet and a height of 12 feet. A sheet of ice covering a hole in the side of the igloo forms a window. The igloo has a narrow tunnel opening. The tunnel stops the cold wind from coming inside the igloo. Seal oil lamps are used for light and heat. A small hole punched through the top of the igloo allows just enough fresh air to come into the igloo. A platform, built inside the igloo and covered with furs, is used as a bed.

Like the igloo, the teepee also has a circular base. The Plains Indians of North America lived in teepees, which are portable, cone-shaped tents. Portable homes were important for the Plains Indians, because they often moved their camps to follow the animals they hunted, such as buffalo and deer. Their teepees were constructed of three long poles tied at the top and stuck in the ground as a tripod. The Indians stretched buffalo hides across the poles. Typically, the Indians covered a teepee with as many as 20 buffalo hides. The teepee was about 10 feet high and had a diameter of 15 feet.

Type of Housing	Diameter of Base of Structure	Circumference of Base of Structure
snow igloo	8 feet	$8 \times 3.14 \approx 25.12$ feet
teepee	15 feet	$15 \times 3.14 \approx 47.1$ feet

1. Determine the circumference of the snow igloo and the teepee and record your answers in the table above: Use 3.14 for π.
2. Knowing the diameter of the floor of the snow igloo and the teepee, you can also determine the floor area of each structure. Calculate and write the radius and area of each structure in the table below. Use 3.14 for π.

Type of Housing	Radius of Circular Floor	Area of Circular Floor
snow igloo	4 feet	$3.14 \times (4 \times 4)$ ≈ 50.24 square feet
teepee	7.5 feet	$3.14 \times (7.5 \times 7.5)$ ≈ 176.625 square feet

Name ______________________ ***Math and Social Studies***

3. The snow igloo and the teepee are one-room structures. One family unit of Inuit people lived in an igloo, and one family unit of Plains Indians lived in a teepee. A family unit usually included a husband, a wife, and their children. Calculate the area of your bedroom and compare it to the areas of the snow igloo and the teepee. Would the circular floor of a snow igloo or a teepee fit in your bedroom? Explain your answer. Can you imagine your home consisting of just the room in which you sleep?

   See below.

4. The Plains Indians also built a dome-shaped structure called a sweat lodge. Tree branches were used to form the dome, and hides were placed over the branches. Sweat lodges were usually 4 feet high and had circular bases. In the middle of the lodge was a circular fire pit. Hot rocks were placed in the pit. Water was poured over the rocks to make steam. A group of men or women crowded into the lodge, where they sat around the fire pit and meditated, prayed, or chanted. Imagine that you are in a sweat lodge that has a floor area of 78.5 square feet.

   a. What is the diameter of the floor area? Explain how you got your answer. Use 3.14 for π.

   10 feet. Students' explanations will vary, but they should use the following formula: $a = \pi r^2$; $78.5\ ft^2 = 3.14\ r^2$; $78.5 \div 3.14 = r^2$; $25 = r^2$; $r = \sqrt{25} = 5$; $d = 10$

   b. If the fire pit in this sweat lodge had a diameter of 1.5 feet, how much floor area was left on which to sit?

   area of fire pit: $3.14 \times (0.75)^2 \approx 1.77$ square feet; $78.5 - 1.77 \approx 76.73$ square feet

   c. To get a sense of how close Native Americans sat in the sweat lodge, you decide to sit with several of your friends on 78.5 square feet of floor space. On your classroom floor, use chalk or tape to create a circle that encloses 78.5 square feet. In the middle of the circle, use chalk or tape to create a circle that encloses the area of the fire pit. Sitting as close together as possible, find out how many people will fit within the circle and around the fire pit.

   The number of students will vary according to their size.

5. What factors determined the size of the igloo and teepee?

   See below.

6. Why do you suppose the Inuits and the Plains Indians chose structures with circular bases?

   See below.

7. Why is an understanding of how to find the area of a circle useful to someone studying the Inuit and Plains Indians?

   See below.

Answers

3. Students' responses will vary. Their answers must demonstrate that they compared the diameter of the circular bases with the length and width of their rooms.
5. Students' responses will vary. Students may suggest any of the following: Available materials, amount of time available to build the structure, and number of people who will occupy the structure.
6. Students' responses will vary. Students may suggest that these structures are easy to build, can be built quickly, and require fewer materials than a rectangular structure. Since they were temporary structures, the ease with which they could be built was important.
7. Students' responses will vary. Students may suggest that, among many other things, it is important to study the homes in which these people lived. To determine how much space the people had and to compare this space to other structures, one must know how to calculate the area of a circle.

BIBLIOGRAPHY

FOR TEACHERS

Bonnet, Robert L. and Keen, G. Daniel. *Space & Astronomy: Forty-Nine Science Fair Projects.* Blue Ridge Summit, PA: Tab Books, 1992.

Couper, Heather. *The Space Atlas.* Fort Worth, TX: Harcourt Brace Jovanovich, 1992.

Parker, Steve. *The Random House Book of How Things Work.* New York, NY: Random House, 1991.

FOR STUDENTS

Asseng, Nathan. *Better Mousetraps.* Minneapolis, MN: Lerner Publications, 1990.

Giscard d'Estaing, Valerie-Anne. *Inventions and Discoveries.* New York, NY: Facts on File, 1993.

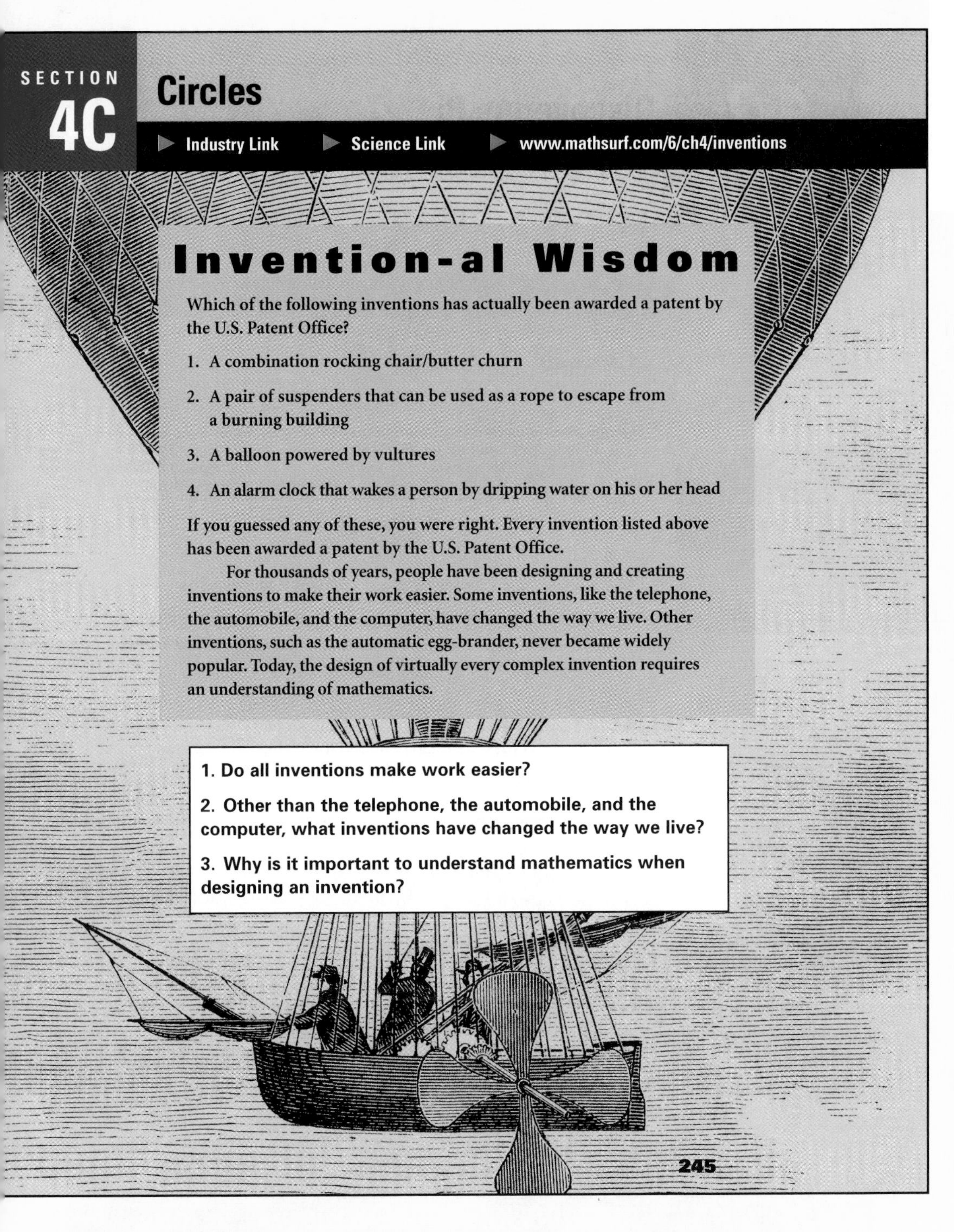

SECTION 4C

Circles

▶ Industry Link ▶ Science Link ▶ www.mathsurf.com/6/ch4/inventions

Invention-al Wisdom

Which of the following inventions has actually been awarded a patent by the U.S. Patent Office?

1. A combination rocking chair/butter churn
2. A pair of suspenders that can be used as a rope to escape from a burning building
3. A balloon powered by vultures
4. An alarm clock that wakes a person by dripping water on his or her head

If you guessed any of these, you were right. Every invention listed above has been awarded a patent by the U.S. Patent Office.

For thousands of years, people have been designing and creating inventions to make their work easier. Some inventions, like the telephone, the automobile, and the computer, have changed the way we live. Other inventions, such as the automatic egg-brander, never became widely popular. Today, the design of virtually every complex invention requires an understanding of mathematics.

1. Do all inventions make work easier?
2. Other than the telephone, the automobile, and the computer, what inventions have changed the way we live?
3. Why is it important to understand mathematics when designing an invention?

245

Where are we now?

In Section 4B, students learned to find the area of geometric figures and to better distinguish between perimeter and area.

They learned how to

- find the area of squares and rectangles.
- find the area of parallelograms.
- find the area of triangles.

Where are we going?

In Section 4C, students will

- use an activity to develop the value of pi.
- find the circumference of circles.
- find the area of circles.
- find the area of irregular figures.

Theme: Inventions

World Wide Web

If your class has access to the World Wide Web, you might want to use the information found at the Web site address given. The interdisciplinary links relate to topics discussed in this section.

About the Page

This page introduces the theme of the section, inventions, and describes some unusual inventions.

Ask ...

- What is a patent? Why should an inventor patent his or her invention? A patent is a grant made by the government to an inventor, assuring the owner the sole right to make, use, and sell the invention for a certain period of time.
- How would your life be different if the airplane had never been invented? Answers may vary.

Extensions

The following activities do not require access to the World Wide Web.

Industry
Ask students to find out about the United States Patent Office. They should report on its purpose, the steps, and the time required to patent an invention, as well as the cost involved.

Science
The National Inventors Hall of Fame is located in Akron, Ohio. Have students research and report on several scientists who are members of this Hall of Fame.

Answers for Questions

1. Answers may vary.
2. Possible answer: Television, refrigerator, electric light.
3. Possible answer: Math is necessary to understand how many inventions work.

Connect

On page 259, students will design an invention.

4-7 Lesson Organizer

Objective

- Find the circumference of a circle.

Vocabulary

- Radius, diameter, circumference, pi

Materials

- Explore: Tape measures, calculators, several circular objects

NCTM Standards

- 1–5, 12, 13

Review

Solve each equation.

1. $5x = 35$ $x = 7$
2. $14 + x = 28$ $x = 14$
3. $55 - x = 20$ $x = 35$
4. $\frac{x}{11} = 3$ $x = 33$

Available on Daily Transparency 4–7

1 Introduce

Explore

The Point
Students develop the concept of pi by measuring and then dividing the circumference by the diameter of at least five different objects.

Ongoing Assessment
Check that students are measuring the largest distance across each object when finding the diameter.

For Groups That Finish Early
Make a bar graph showing the result of dividing the circumference by the diameter for each object.

Answers for Explore

1. Check students' tables.
2. Answers may vary.
3. Answers should be around 3.14.
4. They are all near 3.

4-7 Discovering Pi

You'll Learn ...

- to find the circumference of a circle

... How It's Used

Bicycle riders need to calculate the circumference of their bicycle wheels when adjusting their speedometers.

Vocabulary

radius
diameter
circumference
pi

Lesson Link You've worked with the distance around shapes that have straight sides. Now you'll look at the distance around circles. ◄

Explore Discovering Pi

Circular Thinking

Materials: Tape measures, Calculators, Several circular objects

Object	Distance Around Outside	Distance Across Middle	Distance Around Outside ÷ Distance Across Middle

1. Copy the table. Your table should have at least five rows.
2. Using the tape measure, measure in centimeters the distance around the outside of five objects. Also measure the distance across the middle of each object. Make sure your distances across the middle go through the center.
3. Using a calculator, divide the distances around the outside by the distances across the middle. Round the results to 2 decimal places.
4. Describe any patterns you see in the values in the last column.

Learn Discovering Pi

Language Link
The prefix *di-* means "two." The diameter cuts a circle into two equal sections.

The **radius** of a circle is any line from the center to any point on the circle.

The **diameter** of a circle is any line from one point on the circle to another point on the circle that passes through the center.

The **circumference** of a circle is the distance around the circle.

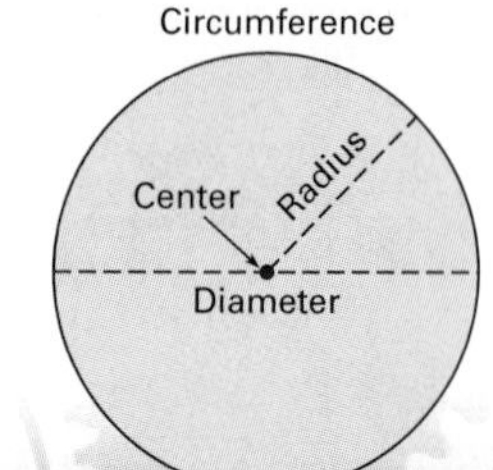

MEETING INDIVIDUAL NEEDS

Resources

4-7 Practice
4-7 Reteaching
4-7 Problem Solving
4-7 Enrichment
4-7 Daily Transparency
  Problem of the Day
  Review
  Quick Quiz
Teaching Tool Transparency 23
Technology Master 19
Chapter 4 Project Master

Learning Modalities

Musical Have students make up a jingle to help them remember the relationships among the radius, diameter, circumference, and pi.

Visual Show students several different shapes on the overhead or on the chalkboard, and ask them to sort the shapes into two groups: those that they know how to find the distance around and those that they do not know how to find the distance around without measuring directly. Most likely, they will sort them into one group with straight sides and one with curved sides.

English Language Development

It is helpful to reinforce pictorially the meaning of new terms. Have students draw diagrams to illustrate the meaning of *circle, diameter, center,* and *radius.* Have students identify the names of these terms in their native language and point out any similarities and differences.

For any circle, the circumference divided by the diameter always equals 3.14159265.... This value is called **pi** and is represented by the Greek letter π. Because the digits in π go on forever, the number 3.14 is used as an approximation.

If you know the circumference of a circle, you can use π to find the diameter. If you know the diameter, you can use π to find the circumference.

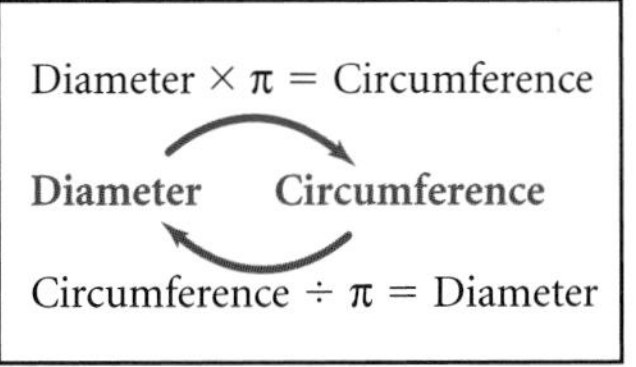

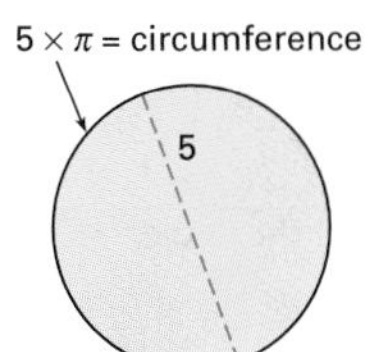

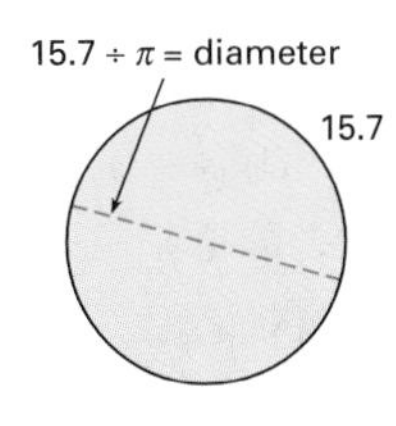

▶ Science Link

When building a computer, hardware engineers need to verify that the computer is doing calculations correctly. One method of checking a computer's accuracy is to have it calculate the value of π to one thousand digits.

Example 1

The diameter of one lens in the chicken eye-protector is 0.5 cm. What is the circumference?

Diameter × π = circumference

$0.5 \times 3.14 = 1.57$

The circumference is 1.57 cm.

Try It

a. Find the circumference of a compact disc with a diameter of 12 cm. *37.68 cm*

b. Find the diameter of a merry-go-round with a circumference of 75 ft. *23.9 ft*

c. Find the circumference. *18.84 ft* **d.** Find the diameter. *25.16 cm*

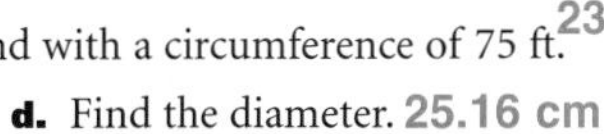

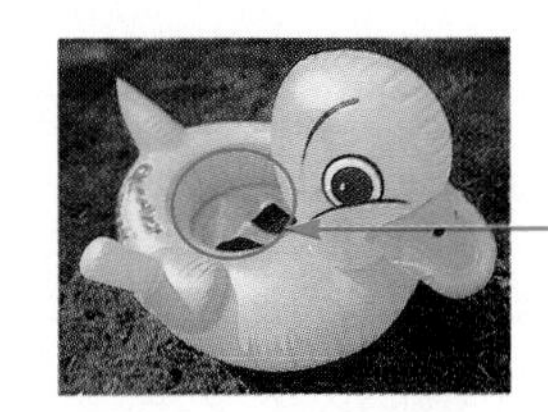

HINT

Some calculators have a [π] button that enters an approximation for π. If a circle has a diameter of 15.7, entering 1 5 [.] 7 [×] [π] [=] will give you the circumference.

Check Your Understanding

1. Why do we use 3.14 as an estimate for π?

2. Will you get a more accurate estimate for π by measuring the circumference and diameter of a big circle like a tire, or a small circle like a penny? Why?

2 Teach

Learn

You may wish to use Teaching Tool Transparency 23: Scientific Calculator with this lesson.

Have students explore the [π] key on their calculators; record the different values they get on different calculators and discuss why this happens.

Alternate Examples

The diameter of a bicycle wheel is 27 inches. What is the circumference?

Diameter × π = circumference

$27 \times 3.14 = 84.78$ inches

The circumference of the wheel is 84.78 inches.

3 Practice and Assess

Check

Have students look at the accuracy of their results in **Explore** in preparation for answering Question 2.

Answers for Check Your Understanding

1. 3.14 is a good approximation of π because π has an infinite number of place values.
2. Big circle; If your measurements are off a little, it won't make a big difference.

MATH EVERY DAY

▶ Problem of the Day

Blair, Donna, and Carol are going to marry Ken, Mark, and Dan. Blair will marry Ken's brother, and Dan will marry Blair's sister. Carol hopes that Ken doesn't quarrel with her husband. Name the three couples who are getting married.
Donna and Ken, Carol and Dan, Blair and Mark

Available on Daily Transparency 4-7

An Extension is provided in the transparency package.

Fact of the Day

In the 1995 Tour de France bicycle race, the winner rode 2270 miles in 92 hours, 44 minutes, and 59 seconds.

Mental Math

Do these mentally.

1. 15 + 5.6 + 5 25.6
2. 30 − 4.5 25.5
3. 5.5 × 10 55
4. 2.5 ÷ 0.5 5

4-7 Exercises and Applications

Assignment Guide

- **Basic**
  1–11, 17–22, 26–44 evens
- **Average**
  1–7, 8–14 evens, 16–22, 25–43 odds
- **Enriched**
  1–7, 11–14, 16–24, 25–43 odds

Exercise Notes

Exercises 4, 7–15

Error Prevention Some students will use the radius of the circle instead of the diameter to find the circumference. It may be helpful to review the relationships among the radius, diameter, and circumference frequently.

Exercise Answers

18. Diameter: 6.8;
Circumference: 21.352;
Pi: 3.14;
Radius: 3.4.

Reteaching

Activity

Materials: String, scissors, a variety of circular objects

- Measure the diameter of each circular object in centimeters.
- Multiply each diameter by 3.14 to find the circumference.
- Cut a piece of string the length of the circumference of each object.
- Check to see if the string fits around the object.

4-7 Exercises and Applications

PRACTICE 4-7

Practice and Apply

Getting Started State whether each sentence is true or false.

1. The radius of a circle is always smaller than the diameter. True
2. The circumference of a circle is equal to π. False
3. The diameter of a circle is the distance around the circle. False

Find each circumference. Use 3.14 for π.

4. 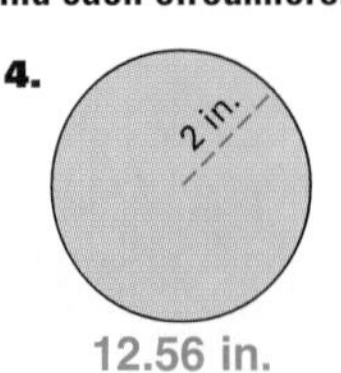

12.56 in.

5. 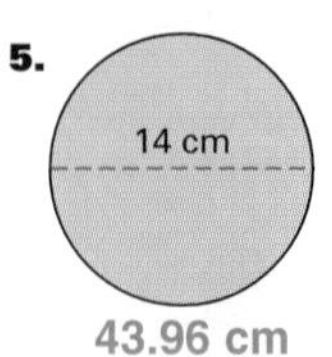

43.96 cm

6. 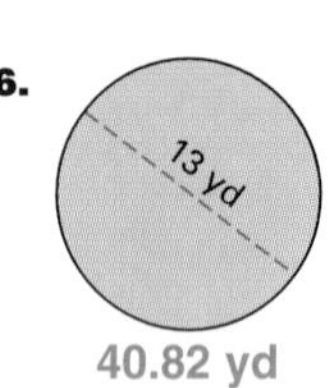

40.82 yd

7. 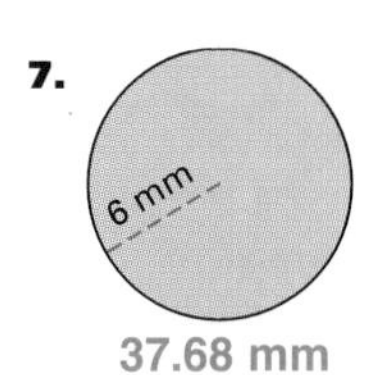

37.68 mm

Find the missing measurements for each circle, where r = radius, d = diameter, and C = circumference.

8. $r = 3$ mm, $d = 6$ mm, $C = \square$ 18.84 mm
9. $r = 4.5$, $d = \square$, $C = 28.26$ 9
10. $r = 0.62$ in., $d = \square$, $C = \square$ 1.24 in.; 3.8936 in.
11. $r = \square$, $d = \square$, $C = 47.1$ yd 7.5 yd; 15 yd
12. $r = \square$, $d = 17.2$ yd, $C = \square$ 8.6 yd; 54.008 yd
13. $r = \square$, $d = 11$ m, $C = \square$ 5.5 m; 34.54 m
14. $r = \square$, $d = \square$, $C = 0.942$ km 0.15 km; 0.3 km
15. $r = \square$, $d = 18.6$, $C = 58.404$ 9.3
16. Karteek is making a pencil holder. The bottom of the holder is a circle with a diameter of 7 cm. How long must the felt strip be to go around the bottom? 21.98 cm
17. The drawing shows a chewing gum locket. What is the circumference of the locket? 6.28 cm
18. **Number Sense** In an experiment, Abel measured a circle but separated the data from the labels. The data is 6.8, 21.352, 3.14, and 3.4. The labels are Radius, Diameter, Circumference, and Pi. Match the data items with the correct labels.

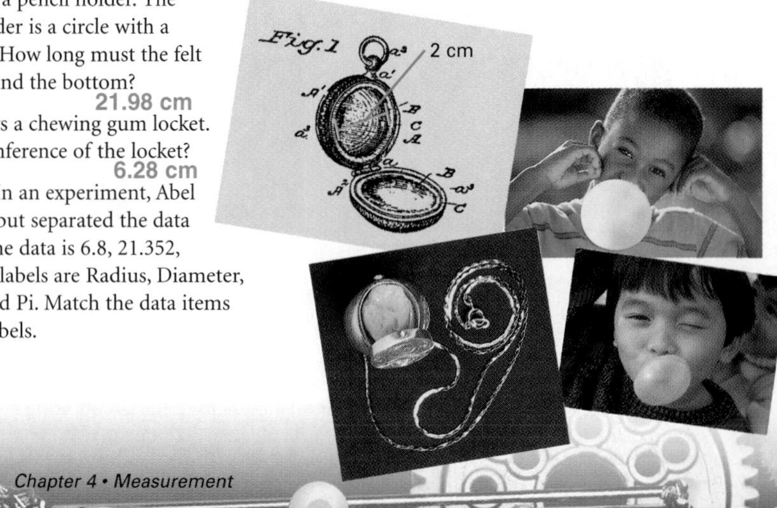

PRACTICE

Name ______________________

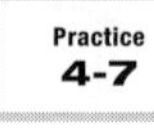

Discovering π

Find the circumference. Use 3.14 for π.

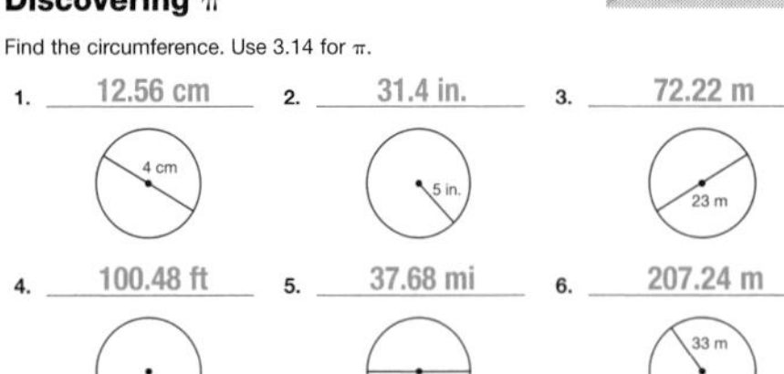

1. 12.56 cm
2. 31.4 in.
3. 72.22 m
4. 100.48 ft (16 ft)
5. 37.68 mi (12 mi)
6. 207.24 m (33 m)

Find the missing measurements for each circle where r = radius, d = diameter, and c = circumference.

7. $r = 8$ cm, $d = 16$ cm, $c =$ 50.24 cm
8. $r =$ 14, $d = 28$, $c = 87.92$
9. $r = 16$ in., $d =$ 32 in., $c = 100.48$ in.
10. $r = 2.5$ mm, $d =$ 5 mm, $c =$ 15.7 mm
11. $r = 18$ cm, $d =$ 36 cm, $c =$ 113.04 cm
12. $r =$ 17 mi, $d = 34$ mi, $c =$ 106.76 mi
13. $r =$ 12 ft, $d =$ 24 ft, $c = 75.36$ ft
14. $r = 10$ yd, $d =$ 20 yd, $c =$ 62.8 yd
15. $r = 40$ mi, $d =$ 80 mi, $c =$ 251.2 mi
16. $r =$ 1.9, $d =$ 3.8, $c = 11.932$
17. A circular track has a circumference of 0.4082 km. Find the diameter of the track. 0.13 km
18. **Geometry** The radius of the earth is about 3960 mi. Estimate the length of the equator. About 25,000 mi

RETEACHING

Name ______________________

Alternative Lesson 4-7

Discovering Pi

The **radius** of a circle is any segment from the center to any point on the circle. The **diameter** of a circle is any segment from one point on the circle to another point on the circle, that passes through the center.

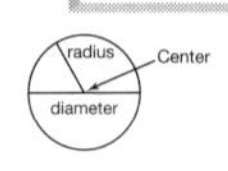

The **circumference** of a circle is the distance around the circle. For any circle, the circumference divided by the diameter always equals 3.14159265.... This value is called **pi** and is represented by the Greek letter π. If you know the diameter, you can use π to find the circumference. 3.14 is used as an approximation for π.

Diameter $\times \pi$ = circumference

Example 1

Find the diameter of this circle.

The diameter is equal to 2 times the radius.
The radius of this circle is 6 inches.

The diameter is 12 inches. $2 \times 6 = 12$

Try It Find the diameter of each circle.

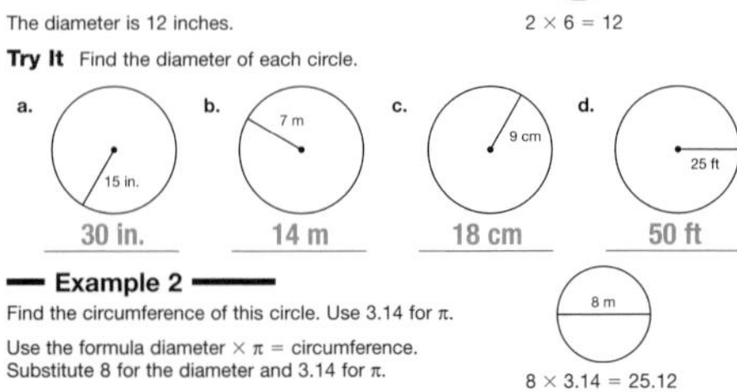

a. 30 in. b. 14 m c. 18 cm d. 50 ft

Example 2

Find the circumference of this circle. Use 3.14 for π.

Use the formula diameter $\times \pi$ = circumference.
Substitute 8 for the diameter and 3.14 for π. (8 m) $8 \times 3.14 = 25.12$

The circumference is 25.12 m.

Try It Find the circumference of each circle. Use 3.14 for π.

e. 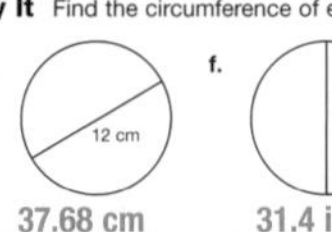

37.68 cm

f. 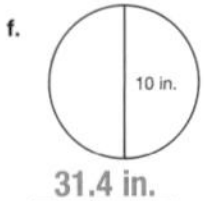

31.4 in.

g. 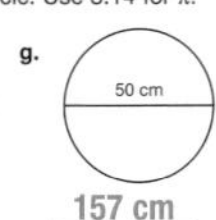

157 cm

h. 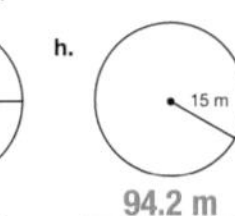

94.2 m

19. Hula hoops were popular during the 1960s and are still used today. A hula hoop is made by bending 2.6 meters of plastic tubing to form a circle. Find the diameter of the hula hoop, rounded to hundredths of a meter. 0.83 m

20. **Test Prep** A circle's circumference is 53 in. What is its radius rounded to the nearest tenth of an inch? A

Ⓐ 8.4 in. Ⓑ 16.8 in. Ⓒ 26.5 in. Ⓓ None of these

PROBLEM SOLVING 4-7

Problem Solving and Reasoning

21. Communicate When you multiply the diameter of a circle by π to get the circumference, why is the answer never exact?

22. Critical Thinking Pat's bicycle wheel has a radius of 13 inches. If she rides the bicycle 1 mile (63,360 inches), how many times has the wheel rotated? Explain.

23. Critical Thinking A grass fire is burning a circular region with a radius of 65 feet. How many firefighters are needed to surround the fire if they stand 10 feet apart from each other and 2 feet from the fire? Explain.

24. Critical Thinking An ice skater is following a path of two circles shaped like a figure eight. One loop has a diameter of 8 meters, and the other loop has a diameter of 10 meters. How far does the skater travel in one complete figure eight? Explain.

Mixed Review

Write in expanded form. *[Lesson 2-4]*

25. 11658^1 11,658 **26.** 28^4 **27.** 3^5 **28.** 56^2 56 × 56 **29.** 9^6 **30.** 7^3 7 × 7 × 7

31. 12^5 **32.** 36^8 **33.** 6^3 6 × 6 × 6 **34.** 41^7 **35.** 13^{11} **36.** 8^5

Estimate each sum or difference. *[Lesson 2-6]*

37. 567 + 324 900 **38.** 49 + 52 + 53 + 50 200 **39.** 23 − 12 10 **40.** 227 + 225 + 224 675

41. 452 − 262 200 **42.** 9324 + 675 10,000 **43.** \$16 − \$9 \$6 **44.** 6218 − 3281 2900

Project Progress

Sketch the final golf hole. Make sure it uses a circle, or part of a circle, in its shape. Calculate the perimeter of the final golf hole. If 1 cm = 2 feet, is the sketch a reasonable size?

Problem Solving
Understand
Plan
Solve
Look Back

PROBLEM SOLVING

Name ________

Guided Problem Solving 4-7

GPS PROBLEM 23, STUDENT PAGE 249

Pat's bicycle has a wheel of radius 13 inches. If she rides the bicycle 1 mile (63,360 inches), how many times has the wheel rotated? Explain.

— Understand —

1. What are you asked to find? Number of wheel rotations in 1 mile.
2. The circumference of the bicycle wheel is the same as one rotation of the wheel.
3. What is the value of pi? Approximately 3.14.
4. Circle the information you need.

— Plan —

5. What is the diameter of the wheel? 26 inches.
6. What is the circumference of the wheel? 81.64 inches.
7. Write an expression for the number of rotations. 63,360 ÷ 81.64

— Solve —

8. How many times does the wheel rotate? 776.09 times.
9. Explain how you can find the answer. Possible answer: Divide distance ridden by distance in one rotation.

— Look Back —

10. How could you find the number of rotations only using division? Possible answer: 63,360 ÷ 3.14 ÷ 26 = 776.09.

SOLVE ANOTHER PROBLEM

If the radius of Pat's bicycle wheel were 15 inches and she rode her bicycle for 2 miles, how many times would the wheel rotate? Explain.

1,345.22 times; 2 × 63,360 = 126,720; 126,720 ÷ (30 × 3.14)

ENRICHMENT

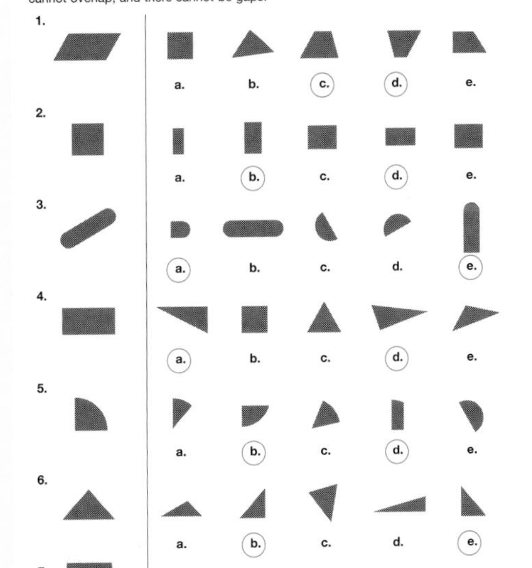
Name ________

Extend Your Thinking 4-7

Visual Thinking

Circle the letters of the two figures on the right that will form the figure on the left when joined. The figures may be flipped or turned, but they cannot overlap, and there cannot be gaps.

1. a. b. (c.) (d.) e.
2. a. (b.) c. (d.) e.
3. (a.) b. c. d. (e.)
4. (a.) b. c. (d.) e.
5. a. (b.) c. (d.) e.
6. a. (b.) c. d. (e.)
7. a. b. (c.) (d.) e.

Exercise Notes

■ Exercise 20

Test Prep Have students decide what mistake someone would make in order to get each of the wrong answers.

Project Progress

You may want to have students use Chapter 4 Project Master.

Exercise Answers

21. Because π is only approximated by 3.14.
22. About 776 times. The circumference of the wheel is 81.64 inches, so it rotates once every 81.64 inches. Divide 63,360 by 81.64 to find the total number of rotations, 776.09015.
23. 42; The firefighters stand in a circle with a circumference of 420.76 ft, so there must be 42 of them to stand 10 ft apart.
24. 56.52 m; Add the two circumferences together.
26. 28 × 28 × 28 × 28
27. 3 × 3 × 3 × 3 × 3
29. 9 × 9 × 9 × 9 × 9 × 9
31. 12 × 12 × 12 × 12 × 12
32. 36 × 36 × 36 × 36 × 36 × 36 × 36 × 36
34. 41 × 41 × 41 × 41 × 41 × 41 × 41
35. 13 × 13 × 13 × 13 × 13 × 13 × 13 × 13 × 13 × 13 × 13
36. 8 × 8 × 8 × 8 × 8

Alternate Assessment

Interview Have students explain the relationship between the diameter and the circumference of a circle.

► Quick Quiz

Find the missing measurements.

1. $r = 4$ mm, $d = ?$, $C = ?$
   8 mm, 25.12 mm
2. $r = ?$, $d = 10$ in, $C = ?$
   5 in., 31.4 in
3. $r = ?$, $d = ?$, $C = 200$ cm
   31.85 cm, 63.69 cm

Available on Daily Transparency 4-7

4-8

Lesson Organizer

Objective

- Find the area of circles.

NCTM Standards

- 1–5, 7, 12, 13

Review

Find the perimeter and area of each figure.

1. Rectangle: 3 cm, 5 cm

Perimeter = 16 cm; Area = 15 cm^2

2. Right triangle: 4 in., 5 in., 3 in.

Perimeter = 12 in; Area = 6 in^2

Available on Daily Transparency 4-8

1 Introduce

Explore

You may wish to use Lesson Enhancement Transparency 18 with **Explore**.

The Point
Students investigate how the area of a circle is a little more than three times the area of the radius squared.

Ongoing Assessment
Have students explain the relationship between the diameter and radius of a circle.

For Groups That Finish Early
Divide the estimated area of each circle (Step 1) by the area of the radius square (Step 2). Compare your answers to the answers you got for Step 3.

4-8 Area of Circles

You'll Learn ...

- to find the area of circles

... How It's Used

Umpires use the area of a circle to verify that the pitcher's mound in a baseball diamond is the right size.

▶ Lesson Link You know how to find the distance around the outside of a circle. Now you'll learn how to find the area inside a circle. ◀

Explore Area of Circles

A Square Peg in a Round Hole

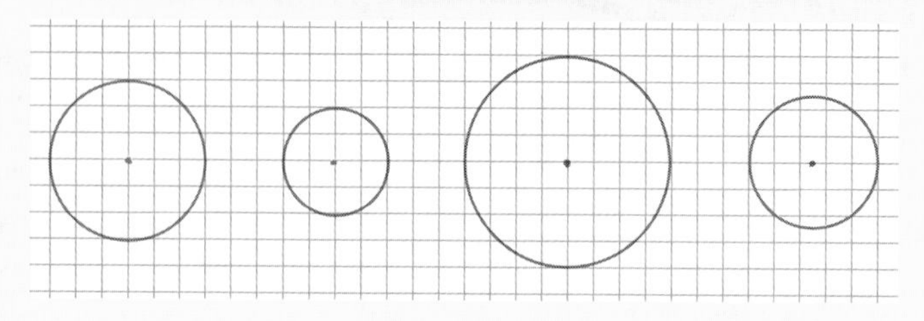

1. Estimate the area of each circle.
2. For each circle, draw a square whose sides are as long as the radius of the circle. Label it "radius square," and find the area.
3. For each circle, estimate the number of radius squares that would fit inside the circle.
4. Describe any patterns you observe in your results for Step 3.

Learn Area of Circles

The circumference and the diameter of a circle are related by the number π. The radius and the area of a circle are also related by the number π. If you know the radius of a circle, you can use π to find the area.

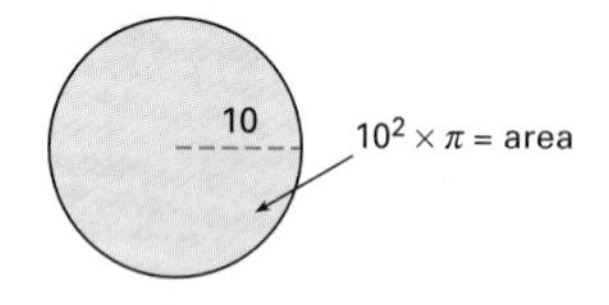

This can also be described by the formula: Area = $\pi \times r^2$, where r is the radius.

MEETING INDIVIDUAL NEEDS

Resources

- 4-8 Practice
- 4-8 Reteaching
- 4-8 Problem Solving
- 4-8 Enrichment
- 4-8 Daily Transparency
  - Problem of the Day
  - Review
  - Quick Quiz
- Lesson Enhancement Transparency 18
- Technology Master 20

Learning Modalities

Verbal Have students make up a poem to help them remember the relationships among the radius, diameter, area, circumference, and pi.

Logical Ask students how many numbers it takes to describe a rectangle and a triangle. 2 (base and height); 2 (base and height) or 3 (sides) Discuss how many numbers it takes to describe a circle. 1 (radius, diameter, or circumference)

Kinesthetic Some students may have difficulty counting parts of squares. Others may have difficulty visualizing how the squares fit inside the circles. It may be helpful to have students make copies of the radius squares and cut them apart so they can fit them on the circles.

Inclusion

Some students may have difficulty seeing patterns because they do not transfer information to new situations readily. Give these students extra practice in recognizing patterns before they are asked to generalize.

Examples

Find the area.

1

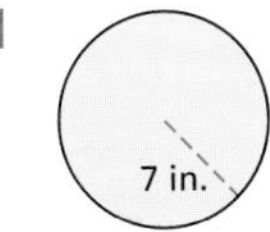

$$
\begin{aligned}
\text{Area} &= \pi \times r^2\\
&= 3.14 \times 7^2\\
&= 3.14 \times 49\\
&= 153.86 \text{ in}^2
\end{aligned}
$$

2

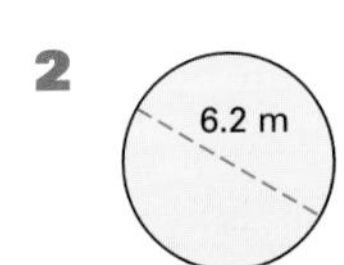

The diameter is 6.2 m. The radius is half the diameter, or 3.1 m.

$$
\begin{aligned}
\text{Area} &= \pi \times r^2\\
&= 3.14 \times 3.1^2\\
&= 3.14 \times 9.61\\
&= 30.1754 \text{ m}^2
\end{aligned}
$$

Remember

7^2 doesn't mean 7×2. The two is an exponent, and the expression equals 7×7. **[Page 80]**

3 The "Combined Grocer's Package, Grater, Slicer, and Mouse and Fly Trap" has a lid with a 4-inch diameter. What is the area of the lid?

The radius is half of the diameter, or 2 in.

$$
\begin{aligned}
\text{Area} &= \pi \times r^2\\
&= 3.14 \times 2^2\\
&= 3.14 \times 4\\
&= 12.56 \text{ in}^2
\end{aligned}
$$

The person who holds the most U.S. patents is Thomas Edison, inventor of the light bulb and the phonograph. He received 1093 patents from the U.S. Patent Office.

Try It

Find the area.

a.

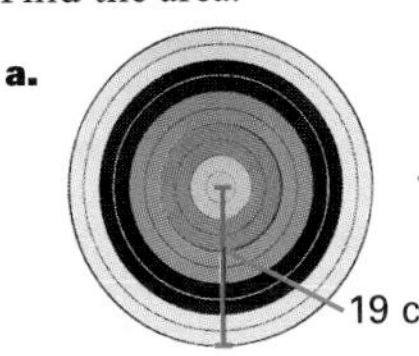

1133.54 cm^2

b.

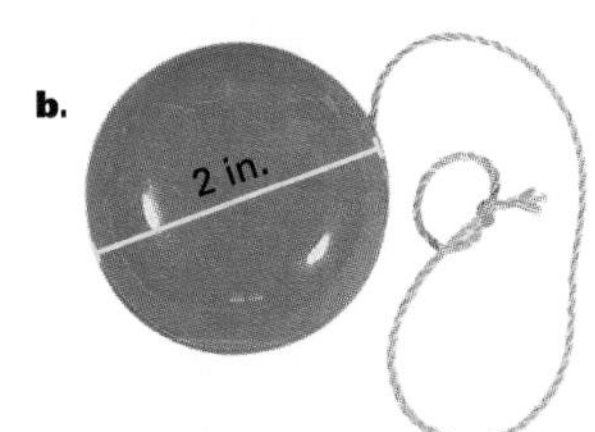

3.14 in^2

Check Your Understanding

1. Why is the area of a circle calculated in square units?

2. If you know the radius of a circle, how do you find the circumference? The area?

MATH EVERY DAY

Problem of the Day

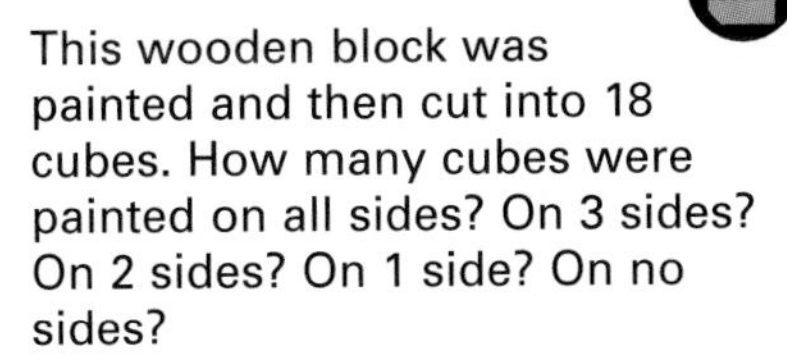

This wooden block was painted and then cut into 18 cubes. How many cubes were painted on all sides? On 3 sides? On 2 sides? On 1 side? On no sides?

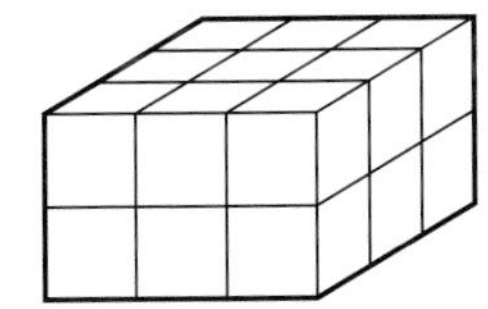

All sides: none; three sides: 8 cubes; two sides: 8 cubes; one side: 2 cubes; no sides: none

Available on Daily Transparency 4-8

An Extension is provided in the transparency package.

Fact of the Day

Lewis Latimer's work on carbon filaments made electric light bulbs safe and inexpensive for ordinary households.

Estimation

Estimate.

1. 27×5 125 or 150
2. $703 \div 24$ 35
3. 83×9 800
4. $803 \div 79$ 10

Answers for Explore

1. Possible answers: 28; 13; 50; 20.
2. 9; 4; 16; 6.25
3. Possible answers: 3.1; 3.25; 3.125; 3.2.
4. They are all near 3 or π.

2 Teach

Learn

Alternate Examples

1. Find the area.

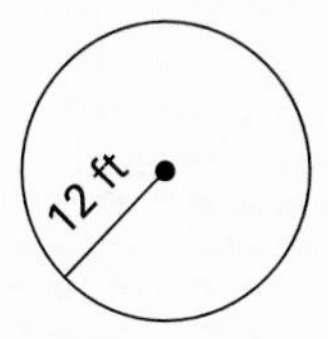

$$
\begin{aligned}
\text{Area} &= \pi \times r^2\\
&= 3.14 \times 12^2\\
&= 3.14 \times 144\\
&= 452.16 \text{ ft}^2
\end{aligned}
$$

2. Find the area.

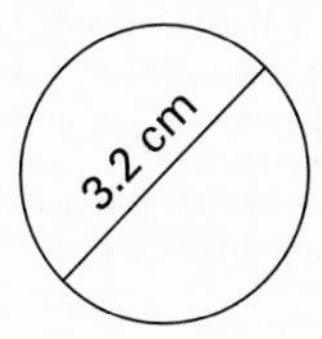

The radius is half the diameter, or 1.6 cm.

$$
\begin{aligned}
\text{Area} &= 3.14 \times 1.6^2\\
&= 3.14 \times 2.56\\
&= 8.0384 \text{ cm}^2
\end{aligned}
$$

3. The lid from a jar of peanut butter has a diameter of 5 in. What is the area of the lid?

The radius is half of the diameter, or 2.5 in.

$$
\begin{aligned}
\text{Area} &= 3.14 \times 2.5^2\\
&= 3.14 \times 6.25\\
&= 19.625 \text{ in}^2
\end{aligned}
$$

The area of the lid is 19.625 in^2.

3 Practice and Assess

Check

Answers for Check Your Understanding

1. The radius is squared to find the area. All area is calculated in square units.
2. $C = 2\pi r$; $A = \pi r^2$.

4-8 Exercises and Applications

Assignment Guide

- **Basic**
  1–3, 5–19 odds, 26, 27, 33–43 odds
- **Average**
  1–3, 5–23 odds, 24–27, 30–36, 37–43 odds
- **Enriched**
  1–3, 4–22 evens, 25–36, 38–44 evens

Exercise Notes

Exercises 16–23

Error Prevention Some students may have difficulty with these problems. Remind them to first find the radius, and then find the area.

Exercise 24

History Each of the stones in the outer circle in Stonehenge weighs about 25 metric tons and stands about 4 meters high. Researchers have estimated that about 30 million hours went into the construction of Stonehenge. The monument was built over a 500-year period.

Reteaching

Activity

Materials: Circle patterns, scissors, rulers

- Cut out a circle and cut it into eight equal wedges.
- Arrange the wedges to form a shape that looks like a parallelogram as shown below.

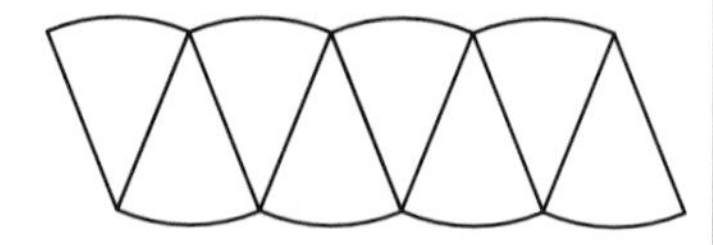

- Measure the base and the height of the shape.
- Multiply the base and the height to find the area.
- Compare the area obtained to the area obtained by using the formula $A = \pi r^2$.

PRACTICE 4-8

4-8 Exercises and Applications

Practice and Apply

Getting Started State whether each sentence is true or false.

1. If you know the circumference of a circle, you can find the area. **True**
2. The area of a circle is twice the radius. **False**
3. The units of measure for the area of a circle are always cm^2. **False**

Find the area of each circle. Use 3.14 for π.

4. (55 mm) **9498.5 mm^2**

5. 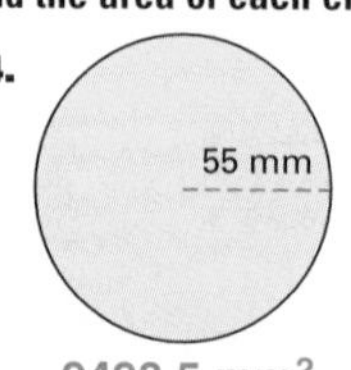

803.84 yd^2

6. 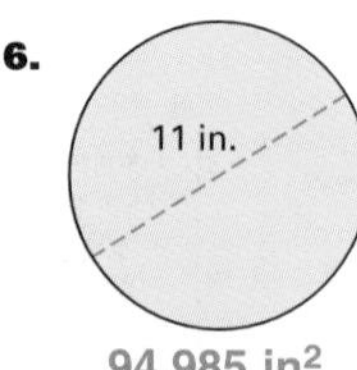

94.985 in^2

7. 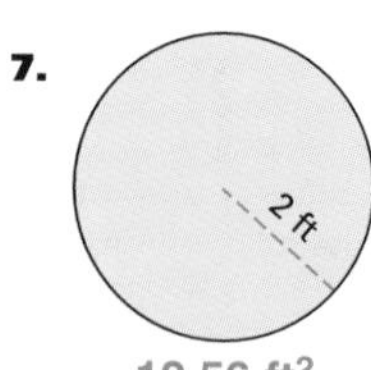

12.56 ft^2

Find the area of each circle, where r = radius and d = diameter.

8. $r = 4$ cm **50.24 cm^2**
9. $d = 12.8$ feet **128.6144 ft^2**
10. $d = 62$ cm **3017.54 cm^2**
11. $r = 17$ feet **907.46 ft^2**
12. $r = 10$ inches **314 in^2**
13. $r = 50$ mm **7850 mm^2**
14. $d = 16$ yards **200.96 yd^2**
15. $r = 0.6$ miles **1.1304 mi^2**

Given the circumference of a circle, find the radius and the area rounded to the nearest tenth.

16. $C = 12$ feet **1.9 ft; 11.5 ft^2**
17. $C = 8.2$ km **1.3 km; 5.4 km^2**
18. $C = 63$ cm **10.0 cm; 316.0 cm^2**
19. $C = 3.14$ mm **0.5 mm; 0.8 mm^2**
20. $C = 7$ inches **1.1 in.; 3.9 in^2**
21. $C = 1.33$ miles **0.2 mi; 0.1 mi^2**
22. $C = 21$ yards **3.3 yd; 35.1 yd^2**
23. $C = 18$ meters **2.9 m; 25.8 m^2**

24. **History** Stonehenge is a group of stones set in circles in southwestern England. Built almost 5000 years ago, the stones may have been used to determine when astronomical events would occur. The largest ring of stones is 30 m in diameter. What is its area? **706.5 m^2**

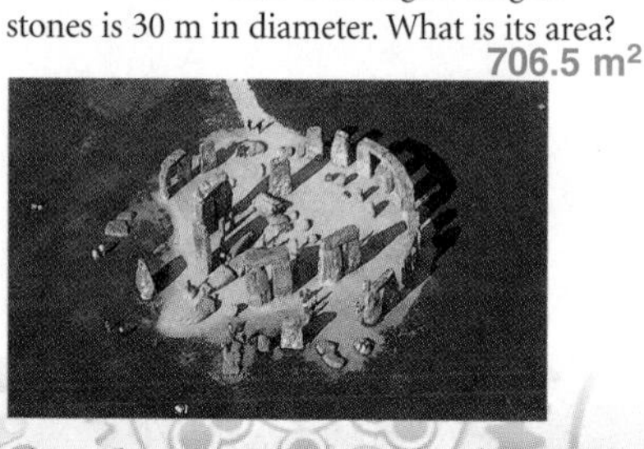

25. In 1879 a fire-escape device for safely jumping out of windows was invented. It used a parachute and padded shoes. If the opened and flattened parachute is a circle with a diameter of 1.3 yards, what is the area? **1.32665 yd^2**

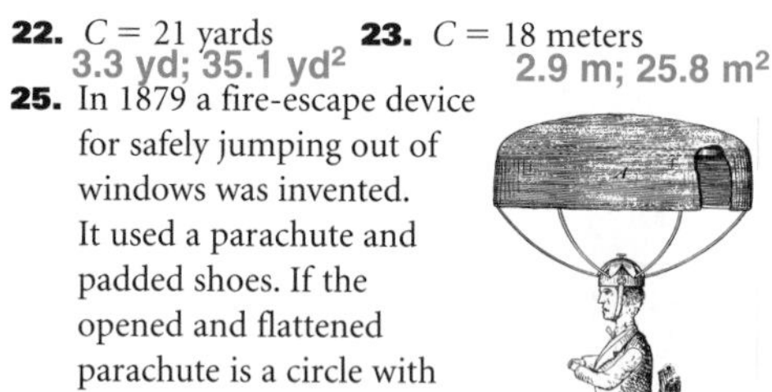

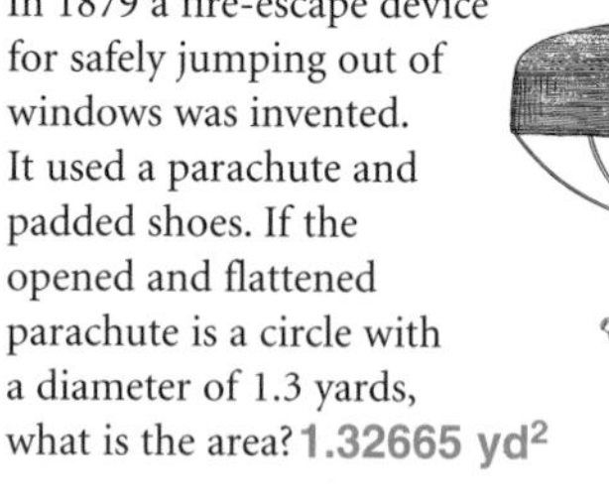

PRACTICE

Name ____________

Practice 4-8

Area of Circles

Find the area. Use 3.14 for π.

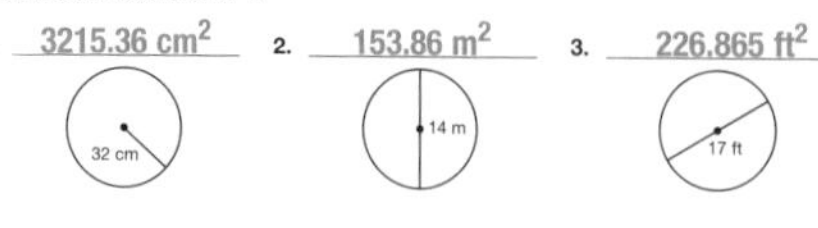

1. **3215.36 cm^2**
2. **153.86 m^2**
3. **226.865 ft^2**

Find the area of each circle where r = radius and d = diameter.

4. $r = 7$ in. **153.86 in^2**
5. $d = 22$ cm **379.94 cm^2**
6. $r = 5$ mi **78.5 mi^2**
7. $d = 40$ m **1256 m^2**
8. $d = 9$ yd **63.585 yd^2**
9. $r = 100$ km **31,400 km^2**
10. $d = 75$ in. **4415.625 in^2**
11. $r = 62$ mm **12,070.16 mm^2**

Given the circumference of a circle, find the radius and the area rounded to the nearest tenth.

12. $c = 43.96$ cm; $r =$ **7 cm**; $A =$ **153.9 cm^2**
13. $c = 16.96$ in.; $r =$ **2.7 in.**; $A =$ **22.9 in^2**
14. $c = 72.22$ m; $r =$ **11.5 m**; $A =$ **415.3 m^2**
15. $c = 11.32$ yd; $r =$ **1.8 yd**; $A =$ **10.2 yd^2**
16. $c = 229.9$ mm; $r =$ **36.6 mm**; $A =$ **4206.2 mm^2**
17. $c = 103$ ft; $r =$ **16.4 ft**; $A =$ **844.5 ft^2**
18. $c = 34.63$ km; $r =$ **5.5 km**; $A =$ **95.0 km^2**
19. $c = 25.1$ in.; $r =$ **4.0 in.**; $A =$ **50.2 in^2**

Use the scatterplot for Exercises 20–22. Assume all plates are circular.

Plate Comparison (Price ($) vs. Area ($in^2$); points P, Q, R, S, T)

20. Find the cost of the plate with diameter 13 in. **\$6.00**
21. Find the radius of the most expensive plate. **≈ 7 in.**
22. Which plate has the smallest circumference? **P**
23. The diameter of a compact disc is about 12 cm. Find the approximate area of a compact disc. **113 cm^2**

RETEACHING

Name ____________

Alternative Lesson 4-8

Area of Circles

The circumference and the diameter of a circle are related by the number π. The radius and the area of a circle are also related by the number π. If you know the radius of a circle, you can use π to find the area.

Area $= \pi \times r^2$, where r is the radius.

Example 1

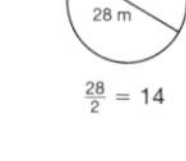

Find the radius of this circle.

The radius is one half of the diameter of a circle. The radius of this circle is 14 m.

$\frac{28}{2} = 14$

The radius is 14 m.

Try It Find the radius of each circle.

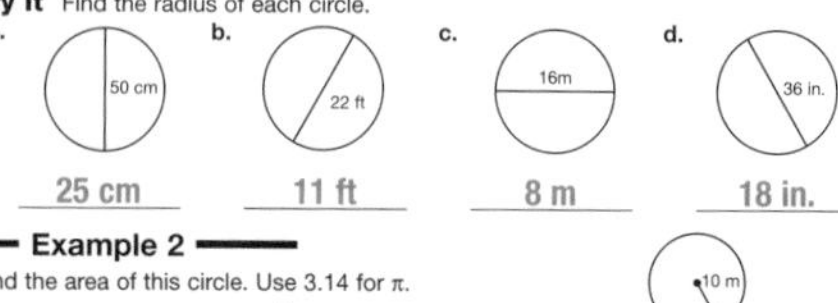

a. **25 cm**
b. **11 ft**
c. **8 m**
d. **18 in.**

Example 2

Find the area of this circle. Use 3.14 for π.

Use the formula area $= \pi \times r^2$.
Substitute 10 for r, the radius, and 3.14 for π.

$3.14 \times 10^2 = 3.14 \times 100 = 314$

The area is 314 square meters, or 314 m^2.

Try It Find the area of each circle. Use 3.14 for π.

e. (3 in.) **28.26 in^2**
f. (4 ft) **50.24 ft^2**
g. (1 m) **3.14 m^2**
h. (6 cm) **113.04 cm^2**

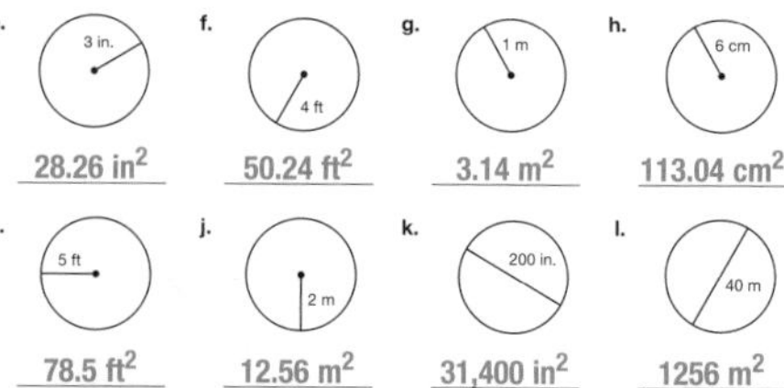

i. **78.5 ft^2**
j. **12.56 m^2**
k. **31,400 in^2**
l. **1256 m^2**

26. **Science** A sand dollar is an animal that lives slightly buried in the sand of shallow coastal waters. Its thin, circular body is about 2 to 4 inches wide. What are the smallest and largest areas of sand dollars? 3.14 in2; 12.56 in^2

27. **Test Prep** On a water ride at the amusement park, a rotating valve sprays water for 15 feet in all directions. How large is the area that gets wet? Round to the nearest tenth. C

Ⓐ 31.4 ft^2 Ⓑ 94.2 ft^2

Ⓒ 706.5 ft^2 Ⓓ 2220.7 ft^2

Use the Carpet Comparison scatterplot for Exercises 28–30. All of the carpets are circles.

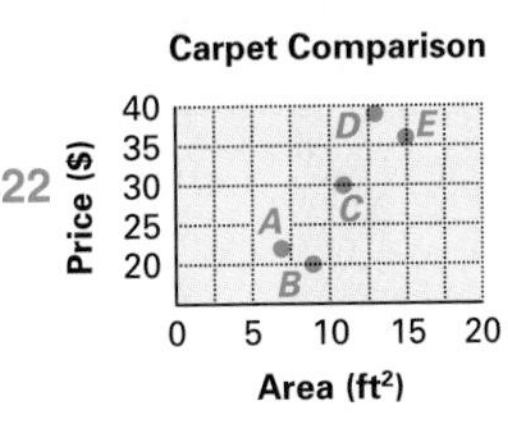

28. How much does the carpet with a diameter of 3 feet cost? $22

29. Which carpet costs the most per square foot? A

30. Which carpet has the largest circumference? E

Problem Solving and Reasoning

31. **Critical Thinking** Charlene has a circular rug in a square room. The area of the rug is about 113 ft^2. The rug reaches from wall to wall. Estimate the area of the room. Explain your estimate.

32. Journal Is the area of a circle with a diameter of 2 inches greater than or less than the area of a 2-inch square? Explain without using numbers.

33. **Communicate** Circle A has a radius of 12 feet; Circle B, 7 feet; Circle C, 36 inches; Circle D, 132 inches.

a. Order the circles by area from least to greatest. Explain.

b. Does the list change if the circles are ordered by circumference? Explain.

Mixed Review

For each scatterplot, determine if there is a trend. *[Lesson 1-3]*

34.

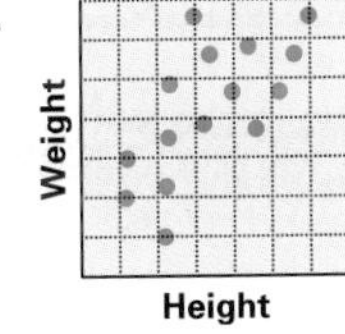

35.

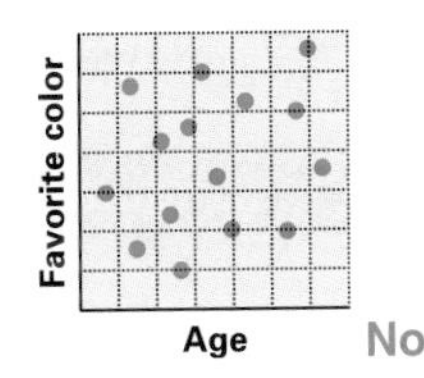

No

36.

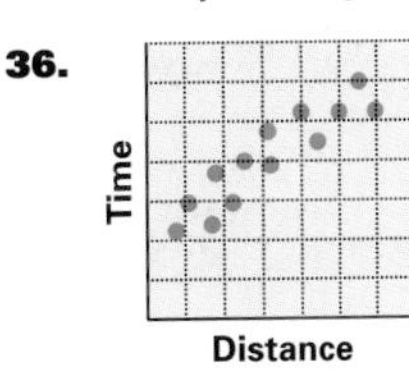

Estimate each product or quotient. *[Lesson 2-7]*

37. 26×3 75   38. $92 ÷ 31 $3   39. 78×3 240   40. $565 \div 53$ 11

41. 82×16 1600   42. $678 \div 35$ 20   43. 2056×439 800,000   44. $729 \div 96$ 7

Exercise Notes

Exercises 28–30

Error Prevention Students may have difficulty remembering what the axes indicate. It may be helpful for them to find the radius of each circle before answering the questions.

Exercise Answers

31. 144 ft^2; The radius of the rug is about 6 ft. It fits wall to wall, so the room is about 12 ft wide. The area of the square room is 12 ft × 12 ft.

32. The circle has a smaller area; The diameter of the circle and the side of the square are the same, so the circle can fit inside the square and there will be extra space.

33. a. C, B, D, A; Convert all measurements to inches or to feet and then order. The larger the radius, the larger the area.

b. No; A circle with a larger radius will also have the larger circumference.

34. Yes; As height increases, so does weight.

36. Yes; As distance increases, so does time.

Alternate Assessment

Interview Ask students to explain how the following terms are related: radius, diameter, area, circumference, pi. Have students give examples as part of their response.

Quick Quiz

Find the area of each circle.

1. $r = 5$ cm 78.5 cm^2
2. $r = 7.2$ cm 162.7776 cm^2
3. $d = 20$ cm 314 cm^2

Available on Daily Transparency 4-8

PROBLEM SOLVING

Name ____________ **Guided Problem Solving 4-8**

GPS PROBLEM 26, STUDENT PAGE 253

A sand dollar is an animal that lives slightly buried in the sand of shallow coastal waters. Its thin, circular body is about 2 to 4 inches wide. What are the smallest and largest areas of sand dollars?

— Understand —

1. Which mathematical term describes the "width" of a circle? Diameter.
2. You need to find the area of how many sand dollars? 2 sand dollars.

— Plan —

3. What is the formula for finding the area of a circle? Area = $\pi \times r^2$
4. To convert diameter to radius, you divide the diameter by 2.
5. What is the value of pi to the nearest hundredth? 3.14

— Solve —

6. What is the radius of the smallest sand dollar? 1 inch

Substitute the values of the radius and pi in the formula for finding area of a circle.

3.14 × 1^2 = 3.14

7. What is the area of the smallest sand dollar? 3.14 in^2
8. What is the radius of the largest sand dollar? 2 inches

Substitute the values of the radius and pi in the formula for finding area of a circle.

3.14 × 1^2 = 12.56

9. What is the area of the largest sand dollar? 12.56 in^2

— Look Back —

10. How could you estimate to see if your answer is reasonable? Possible answer: Use 3 for π. Multiply radius squared by 3.

SOLVE ANOTHER PROBLEM

What is the area of a sand dollar that has a circular body that is 3 inches wide? 7.065 in^2

ENRICHMENT

Name ____________

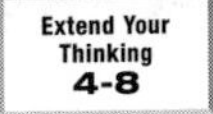

Patterns in Geometry

The area of a circle can be determined using the formula area = $\pi \times r^2$, where r is the radius. What happens to the area of the circle when the measurements of the radius change? Use 3.14 for π.

1. Find the area of the circles with the following radii.

1 inch 3.14 in^2 2 inches 12.56 in^2 3 inches 28.26 in^2

4 inches 50.24 in^2 5 inches 78.5 in^2 6 inches 113.04 in^2

2. What is the difference between the areas of circles with these radii?

1 and 2 inches 9.42 in^2 2 and 3 inches 15.7 in^2

3 and 4 inches 21.98 in^2 4 and 5 inches 28.26 in^2

5 and 6 inches 34.54 in^2

3. Write the differences in order from least to greatest. Then find the difference between the differences.

9.42 in^2, 15.7 in^2, 21.98 in^2, 28.26 in^2, 34.54 in^2

6.28 in^2, 6.28 in^2, 6.28 in^2, 6.28 in^2

All the differences are 6.28 in^2.

4. What pattern do you see? All the differences are 6.28 in^2.

9.42 $in.^2$, 15.7 $in.^2$, 21.98 $in.^2$, 28.26 $in.^2$, 34.54 $in.^2$

5. How is the number 6.28 related to the radii or to π. 6.28 = 2 × 3.14 = 2 × π.

6. What is the area of a circle with a 9-inch radius? 254.34 in^2

7. Would you rather use the pattern or the formula to find area? Why? Possible answer: The formula, because you can use it for any circle without calculating areas of other circles.

4-9 Lesson Organizer

Objective

- Find the area of irregular figures.

NCTM Standards

- 1–4, 7, 12, 13

Review

Find the missing number.

1. $\frac{1}{2}, \frac{2}{4}, ?, \frac{4}{8}$ $\frac{3}{6}$
2. 2, 2.1, 2.01, ?, 2.0001 2.001
3. 800, 400, 200, ?, 50 100
4. $\frac{5}{8}, \frac{3}{4}, \frac{7}{8}, 1, ?, 1\frac{1}{4}, 1\frac{3}{8}$ $1\frac{1}{8}$

Available on Daily Transparency 4-9

1 Introduce

Explore

You may wish to use Lesson Enhancement Transparency 19 with **Explore**.

The Point
Students explore how the area of an irregular shape is equal to the sum of the areas of its component shapes.

Ongoing Assessment
Check that students understand that they need to double the area of the triangular piece.

For Groups That Finish Early
Explain your answers for each step. Describe different strategies that could be used to solve the problem.

Answers for Explore

1. The first ramp; Find the area of the middle rectangular piece of each ramp and compare.
2. The second ramp; Find the area of the triangular piece of each ramp and compare.
3. The first ramp; For each ramp, add together the areas of the rectangular piece and the triangular pieces, and compare.

4-9 Area of Irregular Figures

You'll Learn ...

- to find the area of irregular figures

... How It's Used

Surveyors calculate the area of irregular figures when surveying property.

▶ Lesson Link You know how to find the area of squares, rectangles, parallelograms, triangles and circles. Now you will see how to use this knowledge to find the area of an irregular figure. ◀

Explore Area of Irregular Figures

View Points

The three designs below are for portable ramps. Each ramp is made of three pieces of wood, each of the same thickness. The rectangular piece is the surface, and the two triangular pieces are the supports. The supports are connected to the surface by hinges so that the ramp can easily be folded and carried away.

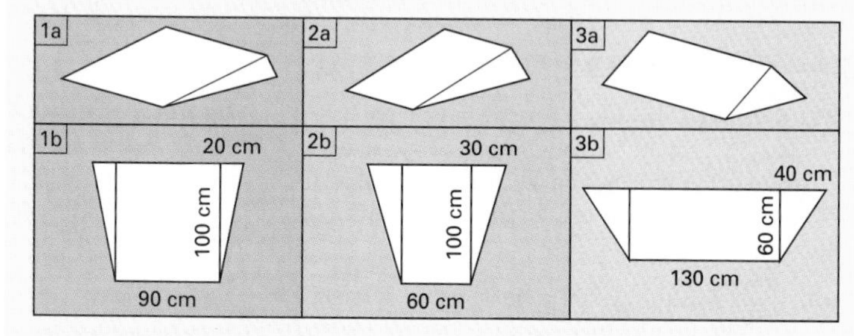

1. Which ramp has the largest surface (rectangular piece)? Explain how you got your answer.
2. Which ramp has the largest support (triangular piece)? Explain how you got your answer.
3. Which ramp uses the most wood? Explain how you got your answer.

Learn Area of Irregular Figures

Figures are not always perfect rectangles, triangles, or circles. To find the area of an irregular figure, you may need to break it down into smaller familiar figures. Then you can find the area of each smaller figure.

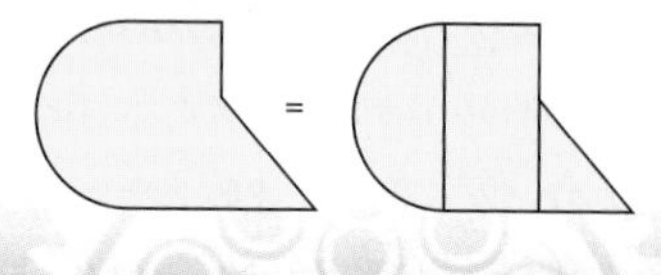

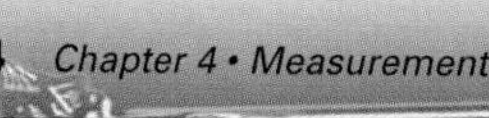

MEETING INDIVIDUAL NEEDS

Resources

- **4-9** Practice
- **4-9** Reteaching
- **4-9** Problem Solving
- **4-9** Enrichment
- **4-9** Daily Transparency
  - Problem of the Day
  - Review
  - Quick Quiz
- Lesson Enhancement Transparency 19

Learning Modalities

Kinesthetic Have students use tangrams, pattern blocks, or Power Polygons to make irregular shapes and find the area. They can trace around the shapes and then challenge each other to find the area.

Visual Have students find two or more ways to find the area of irregular shapes.

Social Have students share different ways they solved different problems either by explaining their solution, showing it on the board, or writing it on a transparency.

Challenge

Have students find the area of each room in their home. Alternatively, have them design their "dream apartment" and find the area of each room. Require that no room be a square.

Example 1

Find the area.

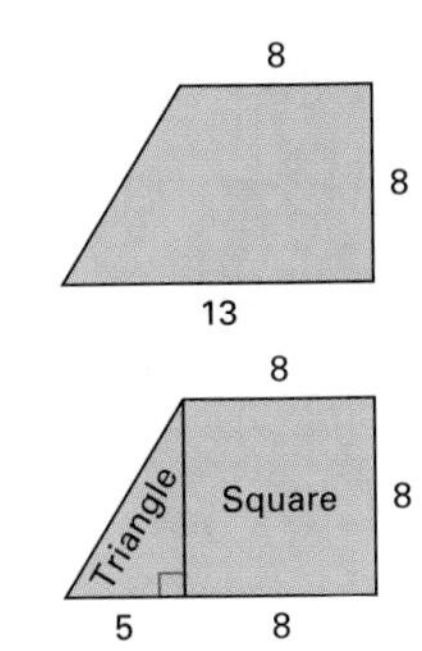

The figure can be divided into a triangle and a square.

The square has a base of 8 and a height of 8. The area is base × height, or 8 × 8, which is 64 units^2.

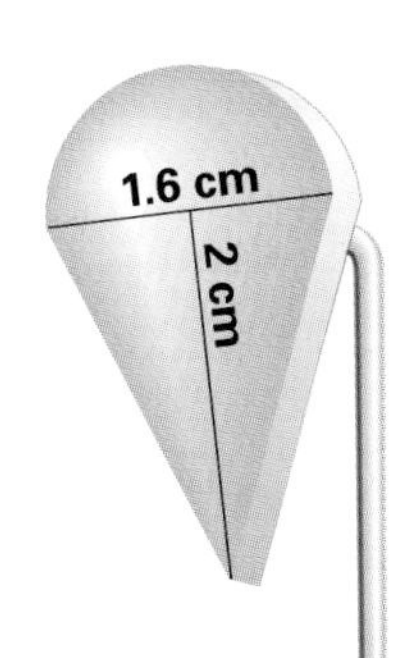

The triangle has a height of 8. The base is 13 − 8, or 5. The area is base × height ÷ 2, or 8 × 5 ÷ 2, which is 20 units^2.

The total area is 64 + 20, or 84 units^2.

Sometimes, part of an irregular figure is a semicircle, or half of a circle. To find the area of half a circle, find the area of a whole circle with the same radius, and then divide the area in half.

Language Link

The prefix *semi-* means "half." A semiannual event happens once every half year.

Example 2

What is the area of the candy part of the "candy pin"?

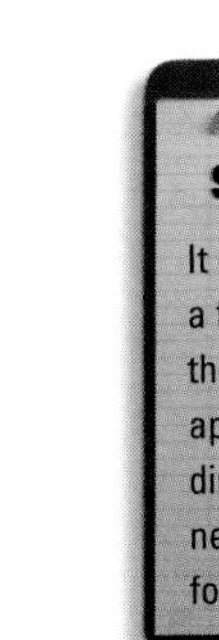

The top part of the badge is a semicircle with a radius of 0.8 cm.

Area of circle = $\pi \times \text{radius}^2$

$= 3.14 \times 0.8^2$

$= 2.0096 \text{ cm}^2$

Since the figure is only a semicircle, you must divide the area in half.

Area of semicircle = 2.0096 ÷ 2, or 1.0048 cm^2

The bottom part is a triangle with a base of 1.6 cm and a height of 2 cm.

Area of triangle = base × height ÷ 2

= 1.6 × 2 ÷ 2

= 1.6 cm^2

The total area = 1.0048 + 1.6, or 2.6048 cm^2.

Study TIP

It often helps to write a formula down, and then write the appropriate numbers directly underneath the formula.

2 Teach

Learn

Alternate Examples

1. Find the area.

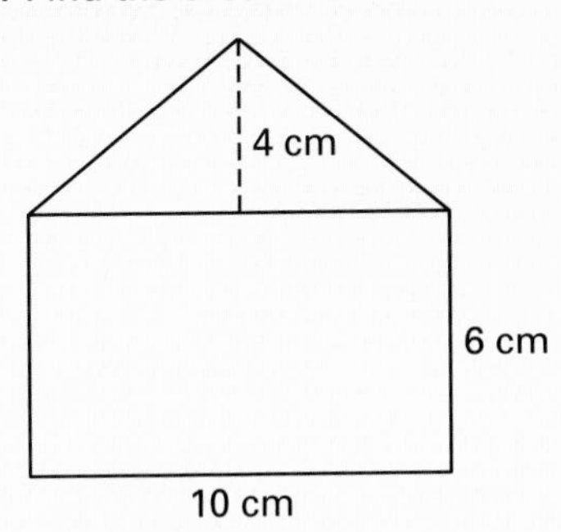

The figure can be divided into a triangle and a rectangle.

The rectangle has a base of 10 and a height of 6. The area is base × height, or 10 × 6, which is 60 cm^2.

The triangle has a base of 10 and a height of 4. The area is base × height ÷ 2, or 10 × 4 ÷ 2, which is 20cm^2.

The total area is 60 + 20, or 80 cm^2.

2. What is the area of this figure?

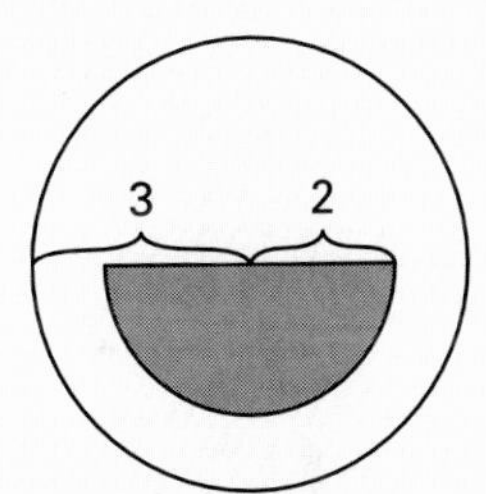

The figure is a circle with a semicircle cut out.

Area of circle = $\pi \times r^2$
$= 3.14 \times 3^2$
$= 28.26 \text{ cm}^2$

Area of semicircle = $\pi \times r^2 \div 2$
$= 3.14 \times 2^2 \div 2$
$= 6.28 \text{ cm}^2$

The area of the figure is the area of the circle minus the area of the semicircle, or 28.26 − 6.28 = 21.98 cm^2.

MATH EVERY DAY

Problem of the Day

Twenty-four students bought either one or two snacks at the movie theater. Thirteen bought popcorn, ten bought raisins, and fourteen bought peanuts. How many more students bought two snacks than bought just one snack? 2 more students

Available on Daily Transparency 4-9

An Extension is provided in the transparency package.

Fact of the Day

Ancient Egyptians used ramps to raise huge stone blocks for building pyramids. The stones weighed 2 to 15 tons each.

Estimation

Estimate.

1. 378 + 1,294 1,700
2. 39,222 − 2,988 36,000
3. 828 × 19 16,000
4. 9,930 ÷ 24 400

Students see two different ways of finding the area of an irregular shape. Ricardo divides the shape into two rectangles and adds the areas of each. Peggy thinks of the shape as the difference between two shapes and subtracts their areas. Students have an opportunity to discuss which method they prefer and why.

Answers for What Do You Think?

1. Yes; No
2. Ricardo's; He must subtract twice. Peggy subtracts only once.

3 Practice and Assess

Check

Students may need additional practice in breaking irregular shapes down into familiar shapes before responding to the following questions.

Answers for Check Your Understanding

1. Possible answer: Find the area of a whole circle with the same radius, and then divide the area in half.
2. Possible answer: No; Some figures have very irregular shapes which do not break down easily into smaller figures.

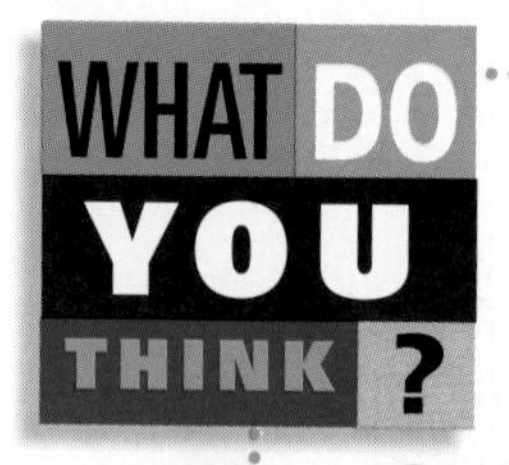

Ricardo and Peggy are planning how to plant their garden. The sketch shows the shape of the garden. All of the measurements are in feet. What is the area of the garden?

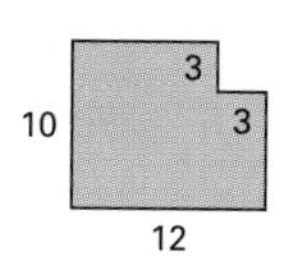

Ricardo thinks . . .

I'll divide the garden into two rectangles. I'll find the missing measurements, and the area of each rectangle. Then I'll add the areas together.

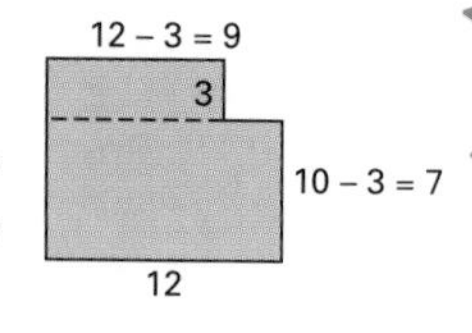

The area of the top rectangle equals $3 \times 9 = 27$.

The area of the bottom equals $12 \times 7 = 84$.

The total area is $27 + 84$, which is 111 ft^2.

Peggy thinks . . .

The garden looks like a rectangle with a missing piece. I'll find the area of the rectangle, and then subtract the area of the piece missing from the top corner.

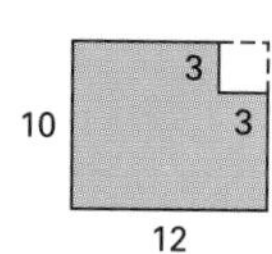

The area of the whole rectangle is $10 \times 12 = 120$.

The area of the missing piece is $3 \times 3 = 9$.

The total area $= 120 - 9$, or 111 ft^2.

What do you think?

1. Could Ricardo have split the garden into two rectangles in a different way? Would he get a different answer?
2. Which method requires more subtraction? Explain.

MEETING MIDDLE SCHOOL CLASSROOM NEEDS

Tips from Middle School Teachers

Sometimes I send my students on a scavenger hunt for objects with given areas or perimeters. For example, I might ask them to find something with an area of about 100 square inches or to find an irregular shape with an area greater than 50 square centimeters. The students must sketch the object and show their computations.

Cooperative Learning

Have students work in pairs on the problems in this lesson. Frequently, one student will not be able to "see" how to do a problem, but the other one will.

Social Studies Connection

Have students use aerial photographs to find the area of fields, playgrounds, businesses, factories, or parking lots around your community. They may be interested to see, for example, how much parkland there is in your community. The library in your community or a local historical society often have aerial photographs.

Check Your Understanding

1. How can you find the area of a semicircle?
2. Can every figure be broken down into smaller figures that are easy to find the area of? Explain.

4-9 Exercises and Applications

Practice and Apply

Getting Started List the familiar figures each object could be broken into.

1. 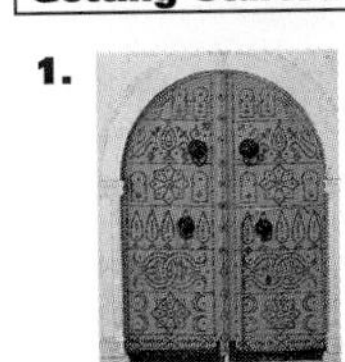
2. 
3. 

Find the area of each irregular figure.

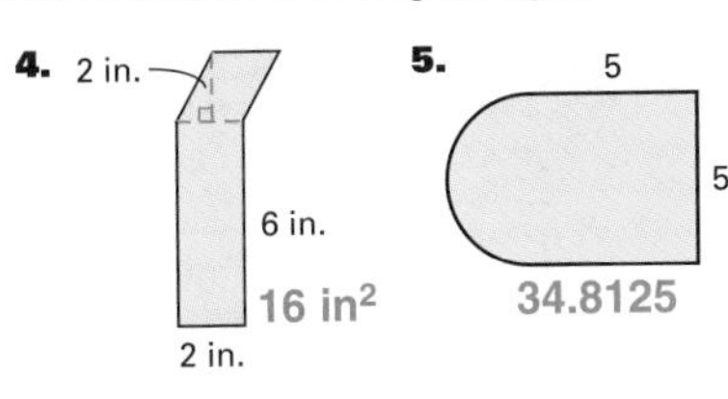

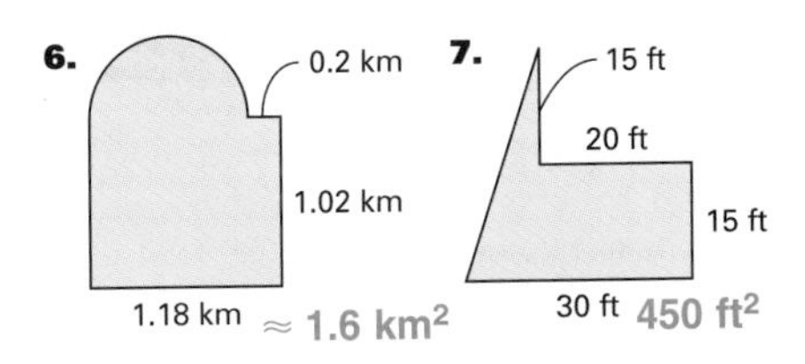

Find the area of each object.

8. 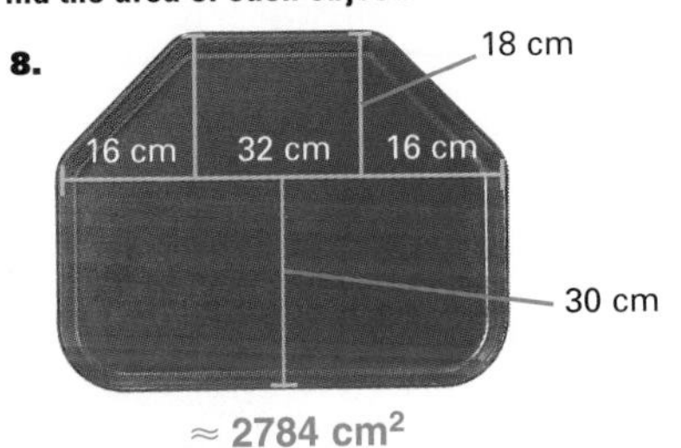

≈ 2784 cm²

9. 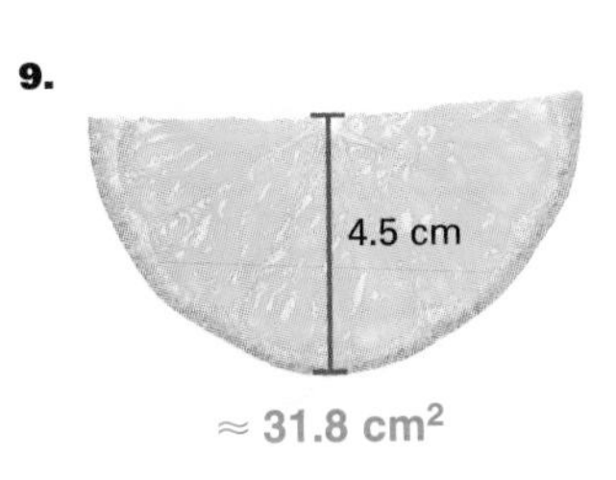

≈ 31.8 cm²

10. **Test Prep** Each square in a hopscotch pattern with 10 squares is 0.3 yard by 0.3 yard. What is the total area of the pattern to the nearest hundredth? A

Ⓐ 0.90 yd² Ⓑ 1.23 yd² Ⓒ 1.56 yd² Ⓓ 1.79 yd²

PRACTICE 4-9

4-9 Exercises and Applications

Assignment Guide

- **Basic** 2–12 evens, 13, 14, 17–31 odds
- **Average** 1–11, 13, 14, 17–31 odds
- **Enriched** 1–16, 18–32 evens

Exercise Notes

Exercises 4–7

Error Prevention Encourage students to write down their plan for finding the area of the shape. Suggest that students write a sentence such as "Area = rectangle + parallelogram" before beginning computations.

Exercise Answers

1. Rectangle, semicircle
2. Triangle, rectangle
3. Semicircle, rectangle, semicircle

PRACTICE

Name ____________

Practice 4-9

Area of Irregular Shapes

Find the area of each irregular figure. Use 3.14 for π.

1. 200 m² 2. 120 ft² 3. 52

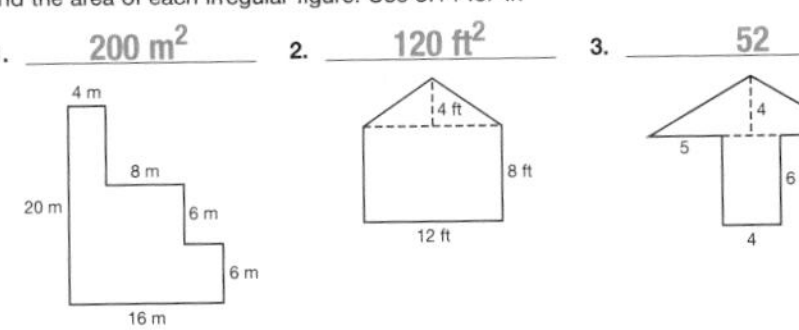

4. 108 in² 5. 349 in² 6. 147.25 yd²

7. 98 km² 8. 277.5625 9. 126 cm²

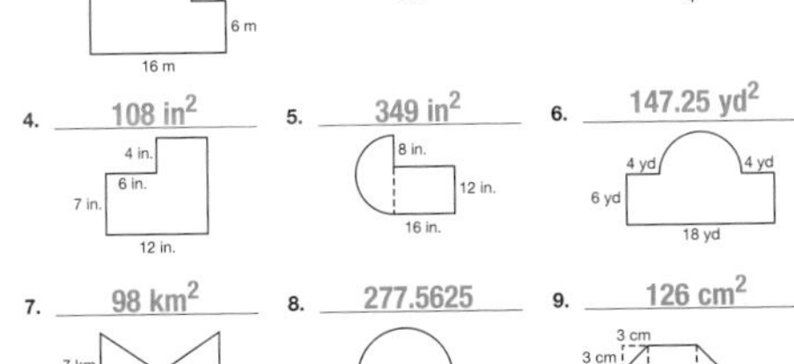

10. 1530.8125 cm² 11. 22.065 mm² 12. 421 ft²

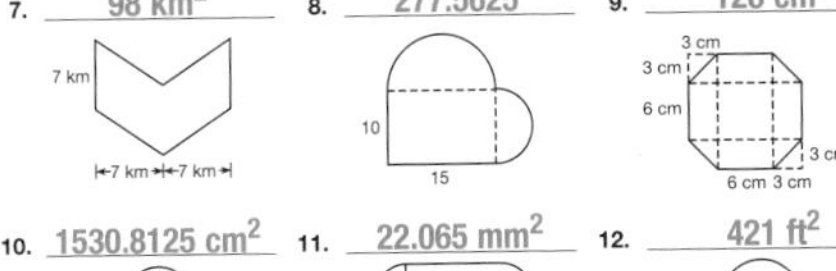

13. **Geography** Find the approximate area of Nevada.

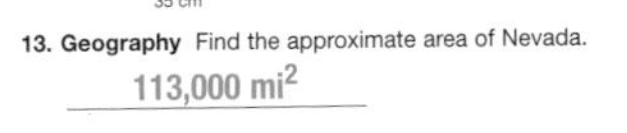

113,000 mi²

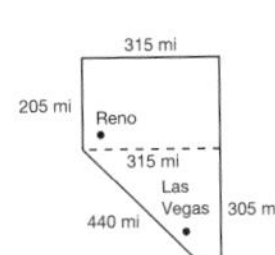

RETEACHING

Name ____________

Alternative Lesson 4-9

Area of Irregular Figures

Figures are not always perfect rectangles, triangles or circles. To find the area of an irregular figure, you may need to break it down into smaller familiar figures, and then find the area of each smaller figure.

Example

Find the area of this figure.

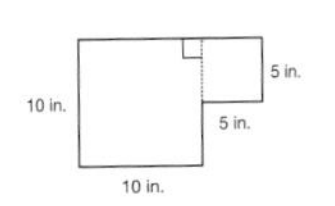

Step 1: Identify the smaller figures that make up the larger figure. The figure is made up of two squares.

Step 2: Find the area of each of the smaller figures. The area of a square is base times height.

The base and height of the larger square are 10 in. Substitute the values in the formula: 10 × 10. The area of the larger square is 100 in².

The base and height of the smaller square are 5 in. Substitute the values in the formula: 5 × 5. The area of the smaller square is 25 in².

Step 3: Decide how the figures make up the larger figure. Add the areas of the smaller figures to find the area of the larger figure.

100 + 25 = 125

So, the area of the figure is 125 in².

Try It Find the area of each figure.

a. Identify the figures in the drawing. Square, triangle.

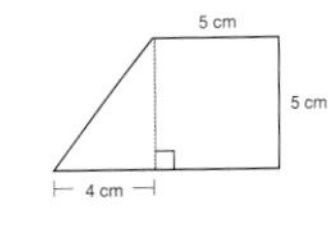

Find the area of one figure. 25 cm²

Find the area of the other figure. 10 cm²

Add both areas. 25 cm² + 10 cm² = 35 cm²

The area of the figure is 35 cm².

b. 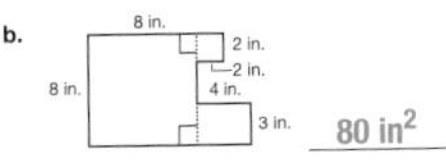

80 in²

c. 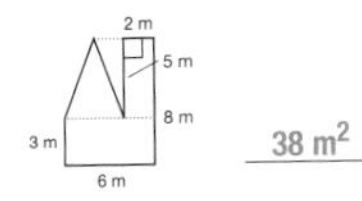

38 m²

Reteaching

Activity

Materials: Graph paper, rulers, scissors

- Work with a partner.
- Use graph paper to draw rectangles, triangles, and parallelograms of various sizes.
- Cut out the shapes and record the area of each shape on the back.
- Make three different irregular figures using the shapes.
- Place the shapes on a piece of graph paper and draw an outline around each figure.
- Exchange your figures with your partner and find the area of each figure.
- Check your partner's answers.

Exercise Notes

Exercise 13

Problem-Solving Tip Have students draw a picture before they try to solve the problems.

Exercises 17–24

Error Prevention Review order of operations with students before they do these problems.

Exercise Answers

13. Yes; The diameter of the circle is approximately 4.39 ft, which is shorter than the side of the square.
14. 20.5 ft^2; Subtract the area of the square, 4 ft^2, from the area of the triangle, 24.5 ft^2.
15. 289.56 ft^2; Add together the area of two rectangles and the quarter circle.
16. $52\frac{1}{3}$ cm^2; To find the area of one section, divide the total area by 6.

Alternate Assessment

Portfolio Have students sketch an irregular figure by using at least four different shapes. Students should then find the area and add these sketches to their portfolios.

Quick Quiz

Find the area of each shape.

1. 44.8125 cm^2
2. 66 cm^2

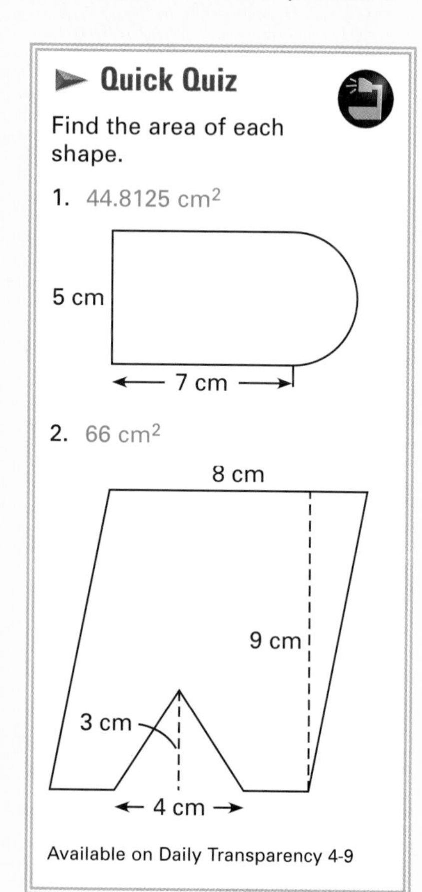

Available on Daily Transparency 4-9

PROBLEM SOLVING 4-9

11. Geography Find the approximate area of South Australia. All distances are in miles.

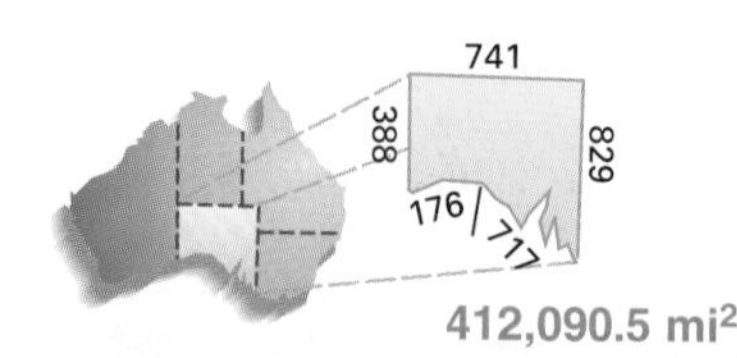

412,090.5 mi^2

12. Find the area of the combined clothes brush, bottle, and drinking cup.

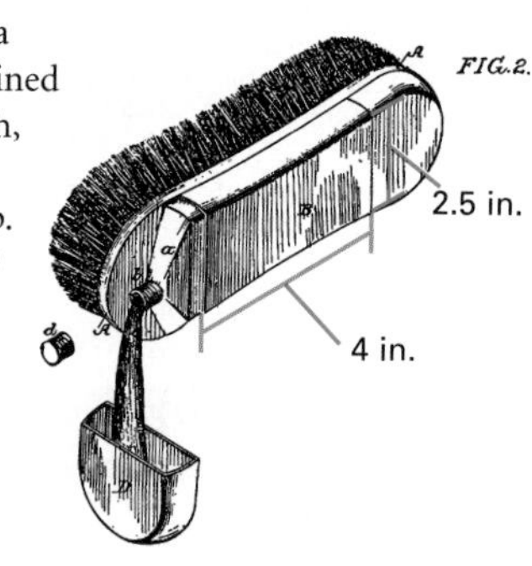

14.90625 in^2

Problem Solving and Reasoning

13. Critical Thinking Caitlin is making a tablecloth for a circular table. The circumference of the table is 13.8 feet. She has a square piece of cloth that is 4.5 feet on each side. If she cuts out the largest possible circle from the cloth, will it be big enough to cover the table? Explain.

14. Choose a Strategy GPS Sheetal is painting a cardboard cutout for her school's annual haunted house. The cardboard is a triangle 7 feet tall and 7 feet wide. It has a square opening as shown. How many square feet does Sheetal need to paint? Explain your reasoning.

Problem Solving STRATEGIES

- Look for a Pattern
- Make an Organized List
- Make a Table
- Guess and Check
- Work Backward
- Use Logical Reasoning
- Draw a Diagram
- Solve a Simpler Problem

15. Critical Thinking Joe and his dad are redoing the tile in the kitchen and living room. According to the picture, how many square feet do they have to retile? Explain.

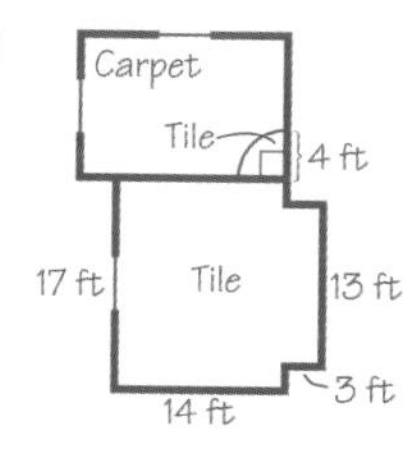

16. Journal A spinner is divided into six equal sections. The radius of the spinner is 10 cm. What is the area of each section? Explain.

Mixed Review

Simplify. *[Lesson 2-8]*

17. $14 + 10 - 3$ 21 **18.** $62 \div (1 + 1)$ 31 **19.** $2^8 \div 2 + 6$ 134 **20.** $5 \times 6 - 25$ 5

21. $18 + 18 \div 3$ 24 **22.** $2 \times 10 - 4 \div 2$ 18 **23.** $2 \times (10 - 4) \div 2$ 6 **24.** $8 + 3^3 \times 4$ 116

Solve. *[Lesson 3-7]*

25. $16.1 - f = 9.1$ 7 **26.** $r + 25.3 = 50.73$ 25.43 **27.** $56.04 + k = 64.06$ 8.02 **28.** $m - 7.25 = 19.75$ 27

29. $e - 86.5 = 76$ 162.5 **30.** $86.8 + q = 100.9$ 14.1 **31.** $47.34 - g = 42.04$ 5.3 **32.** $z + 0.13 = 6.68$ 6.55

PROBLEM SOLVING

Name ______

Guided Problem Solving 4-9

GPS PROBLEM 15, STUDENT PAGE 258

Sheetal is painting a cardboard cutout for her school's annual haunted house. The cardboard is a triangle 7 feet tall and 7 feet wide. It has a square opening as shown. How many square feet does Sheetal need to paint? Explain your reasoning.

— Understand —

1. What are you asked to find? The area Sheetal needs to paint.
2. Underline the measurements of the triangle's height and width.

— Plan —

3. What is the formula for the area of the triangle? Area = base × height ÷ 2
4. What is the formula for the area of the square? Area = base × height
5. Will you add or subtract to find the area to be painted? Subtract.

— Solve —

6. What is the area of the triangle? 24.5 ft^2 Of the square? 4 ft^2
7. Write a number sentence to show how to find the painted area. 24.5 – 4 = 20.5
8. How many square feet will Sheetal paint? Explain. 20.5 ft^2; She will paint the area of the triangle minus the area of the square opening.

— Look Back —

9. Draw an example of what the cardboard might look like if Sheetal needed to paint the combined areas of the square and the triangle. Possible answer:

SOLVE ANOTHER PROBLEM

Liam is painting a cardboard cutout. The cardboard is a square with 8-ft sides, and it has a circular opening as shown. About how many square feet does Liam need to paint? Explain your reasoning.

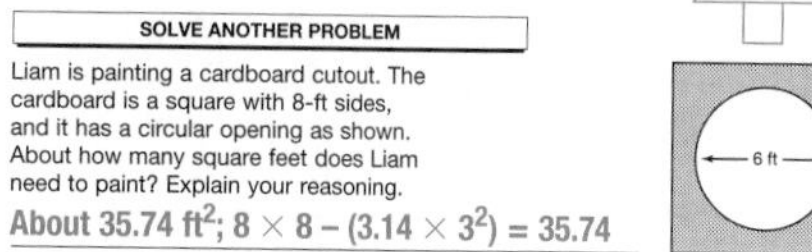

About 35.74 ft^2; $8 \times 8 - (3.14 \times 3^2) = 35.74$

ENRICHMENT

Name ______

Extend Your Thinking 4-9

Decision Making

You want to make a small pool in your yard. You want the pool to cover 30 square feet. What dimensions could you use for your pool? Use whole numbers unless otherwise noted.

1. Record the base and height of all possible rectangular pools. 1 × 30, 2 × 15, 3 × 10, 5 × 6, 6 × 5, 10 × 3, 15 × 2, 30 × 1
2. Record the base and height of all possible triangular pools. 1 × 60, 2 × 30, 3 × 20, 4 × 15, 5 × 12, 6 × 10, 10 × 6, 12 × 5, 15 × 4, 20 × 3, 30 × 2, 60 × 1
3. What are the radii of any circular pools? What value of π will you use? Make the area as close to 30 square feet as you can. Record the radii and the areas. You do not have to use whole numbers for the radii. Possible answers: 3 ft (28.26 ft^2), 3.1 ft (30.18 ft^2)
4. Draw a diagram of an irregularly shaped pool that covers about 30 square feet. Make the area as close to 30 square feet as you can. Record the dimensions and the area.

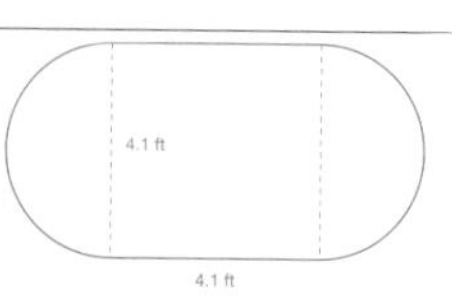

Possible answer: 2 semi-circles with diameter 4.1 ft, square 4.1ft by 4.1ft; area = 30.01 square feet

5. Which shape that you created would you choose for your own pool? Why would you choose it? Possible answer: Irregular shape; The oval looks larger and more attractive.

Section 4C Connect

In this section you learned how to find the area of several different types of figures. Now, you will make decisions about the best way to design an invention.

Invention-al Wisdom

Materials: Rulers

1. You need to design an invention. The invention can be ordinary or weird, but it must meet the following conditions:
   - **a.** It must serve some function.
   - **b.** It must be made up of flat surfaces.
   - **c.** The design must use at least one rectangle, one triangle, and either one circle or one semicircle.
2. Use a ruler to make a diagram of your invention. Label its parts clearly, and label the length of all the materials. Be sure to include appropriate units of measurement, such as centimeters or feet.
3. Calculate the amount of material needed to construct your invention.
4. Write a brief description of what the invention does.

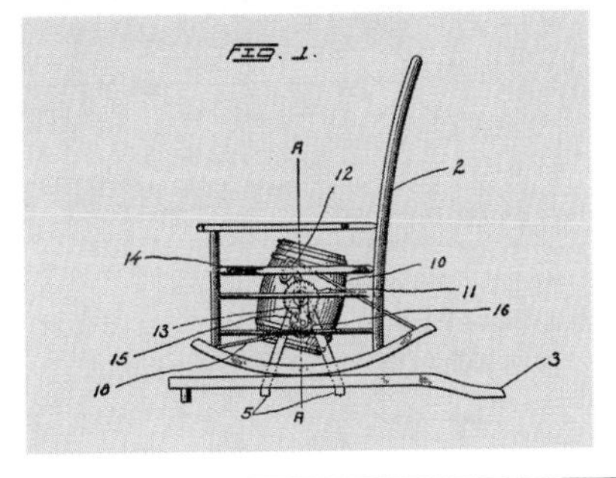

Invention-al Wisdom

The Point

In *Invention-al Wisdom* on page 245, students learned that the design of every complex invention requires an understanding of mathematics. Now they will design their own invention.

Materials

Ruler

About the Page

- You may want to have students work in groups.
- Brainstorm ideas for inventions with the class.
- Ask students if they have ever seen something new or different and thought, "What a good idea. Why didn't I think of that?"
- Many inventors improve on or add a unique twist to something we already use. Suggest that students may want to improve something that already exists.
- Remind students that their invention should include the geometric figures listed in the assignment.

Ongoing Assessment

Check that students have drawn a reasonable design containing the appropriate geometric figures.

Extension

Now that students have created some new invention, have them estimate the cost of producing a prototype of their invention. Have students give their invention a unique name.

Answers for Connect

1–4. Answers may vary.

4C Review

Review Correlation

Item(s)	Lesson(s)
1–3	4-3
4	4-1, 4-4
5	4-1, 4-5
6	4-9
7	4-7, 4-8
8	4-1, 4-6
9	4-7, 4-8
10	4-1, 4-4
11	4-9
12–13	4-1
14	4-7

Test Prep

Test-Taking Tip

Tell students they can use easier numbers than those given to help them solve some problems. Here, students could use 3 for π to find the circumference.

Answers for Review

4. A: 256 in^2; P: 64 in
5. A: 43.2 mm^2; P: 28 mm
6. A: 22 units^2; P: 20 units
7. A: 0.5024 km^2; C: 2.512 km
8. A: 15 yd^2; P: 23.44 yd
9. A: 153.86 in^2; C: 43.96 in.
10. A: 108 ft^2; P: 42 ft
11. A: 119.065 units^2 ; P: 42.71 units
13. The perimeter of a square; Square: 16in., triangle: 12 in.

Section 4C Review

REVIEW 4C

Use the conversion factor to find each missing measurement.

1. 2000 pounds in 1 ton
   ☐ pounds in 6 tons **12,000**
2. 8 quarts in 2 gallons
   37 quarts in ☐ gallons **9.25**
3. 3 feet in 1 yard
   27.6 feet in ☐ yards **9.2**

Find the area and the distance around each figure.

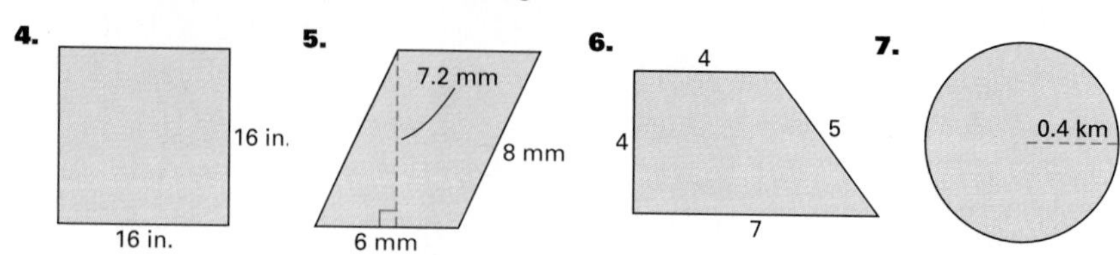

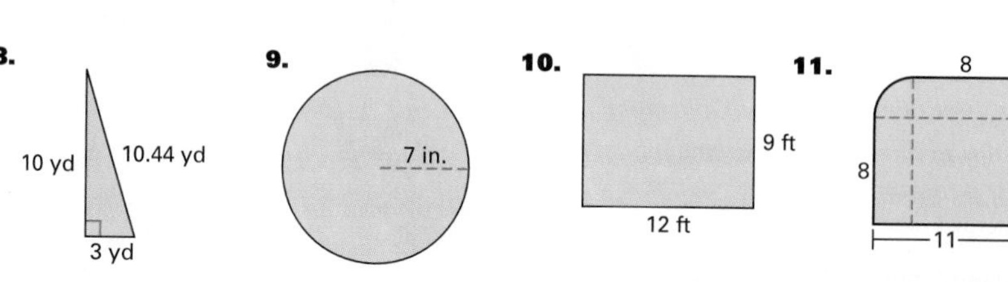

12. Scott wants to place trees around the perimeter of his model train setup. If the trees are placed 2 feet apart, how many trees does he need? **12**

13. **Number Sense** Which is larger, the perimeter of a square with sides 4 inches long or the perimeter of a triangle with sides 4 inches long? Explain.

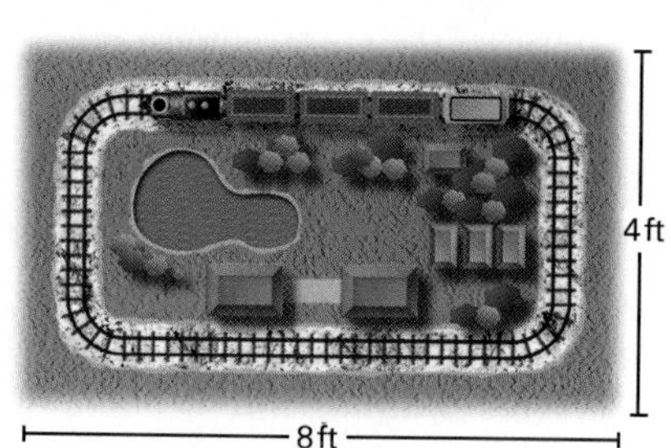

Test Prep

When finding the circumference of a circle, you can estimate the answer by using 3 for π.

14. What is the circumference of a circle with a diameter of 9 cm? **B**
   Ⓐ 2.87 cm Ⓑ 28.26 cm Ⓒ 150.72 cm Ⓓ 254.34 cm

Resources

Practice Masters
Section 4C Review

Assessment Sourcebook
Quiz 4C

TestWorks
Test and Practice Software

PRACTICE

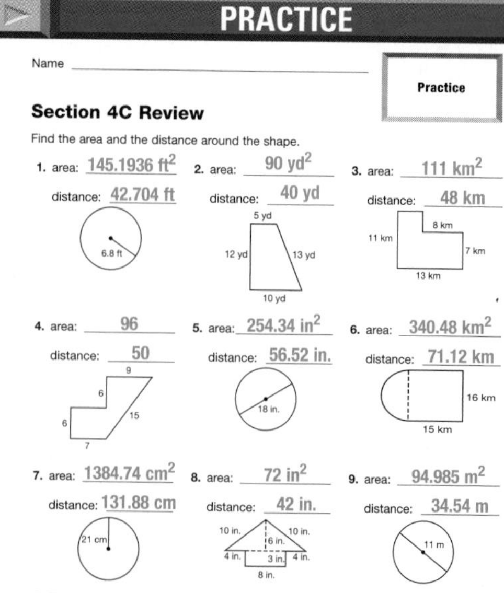

Name ____________ Practice

Section 4C Review

Find the area and the distance around the shape.

1. area: 145.1936 ft^2 distance: 42.704 ft
2. area: 90 yd^2 distance: 40 yd
3. area: 111 km^2 distance: 48 km
4. area: 96 distance: 50
5. area: 254.34 in^2 distance: 56.52 in.
6. area: 340.48 km^2 distance: 71.12 km
7. area: 1384.74 cm^2 distance: 131.88 cm
8. area: 72 in^2 distance: 42 in.
9. area: 94.985 m^2 distance: 34.54 m

10. The table shows a snail's progress as it moves along a telephone pole. Complete the table by assuming that the pattern continues.

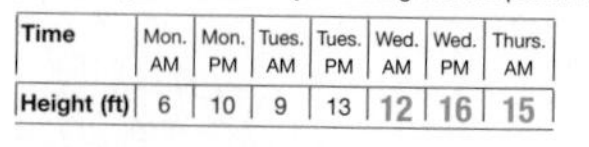

Time	Mon. AM	Mon. PM	Tues. AM	Tues. PM	Wed. AM	Wed. PM	Thurs. AM
Height (ft)	6	10	9	13	12	16	15

11. The lot shown has perimeter 319.8 ft. Write and solve an equation to find the length of the unknown side. [Lesson 3-7] Possible equation:
$x + 103.7 + 56.2 + 81.3 = 319.8$; $x = 78.6$ ft

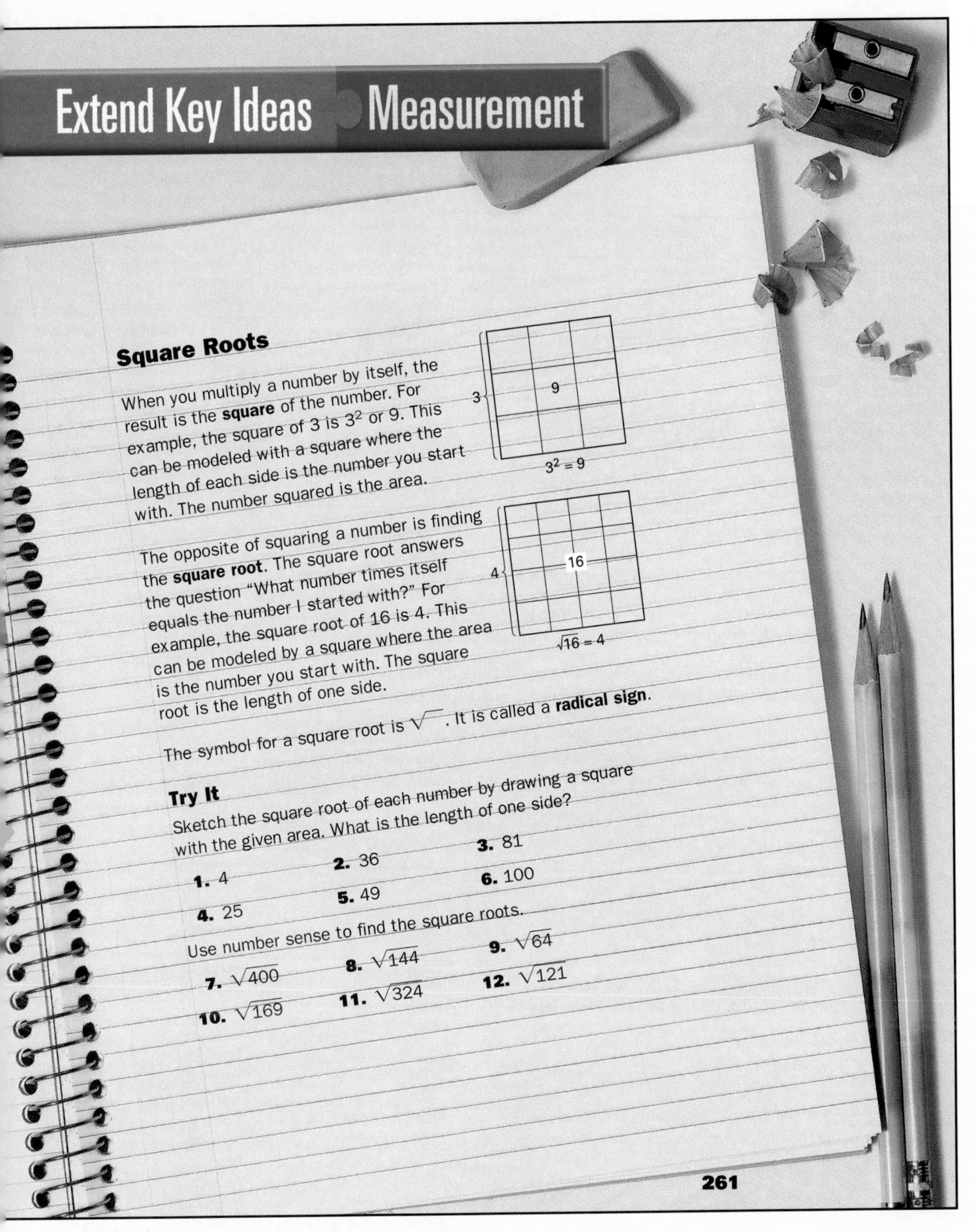

Extend Key Ideas Measurement

Square Roots

When you multiply a number by itself, the result is the **square** of the number. For example, the square of 3 is 3^2 or 9. This can be modeled with a square where the length of each side is the number you start with. The number squared is the area.

The opposite of squaring a number is finding the **square root**. The square root answers the question "What number times itself equals the number I started with?" For example, the square root of 16 is 4. This can be modeled by a square where the area is the number you start with. The square root is the length of one side.

The symbol for a square root is $\sqrt{}$. It is called a **radical sign**.

Try It

Sketch the square root of each number by drawing a square with the given area. What is the length of one side?

1. 4 **2.** 36 **3.** 81

4. 25 **5.** 49 **6.** 100

Use number sense to find the square roots.

7. $\sqrt{400}$ **8.** $\sqrt{144}$ **9.** $\sqrt{64}$

10. $\sqrt{169}$ **11.** $\sqrt{324}$ **12.** $\sqrt{121}$

261

Extend Key Ideas

Square Roots

The Point

Students use diagrams to show the relationship between perfect squares and their square roots.

Materials

Graph paper

Resources

Teaching Tool Transparency 7: $\frac{1}{4}$-Inch Graph Paper

About the Page

- Remind students that in the expression 3^2, 2 is the exponent and means that 3 should be used as a factor two times: $3^2 = 3 \times 3 = 9$.
- Point out to students that they can think of finding square roots as using the work backwards problem-solving strategy.

Ask ...

Is the square root of a whole number less than or greater than the number? Less than

Extension

Between what two whole numbers is each square root?

1. $\sqrt{11}$ Between 3 and 4
2. $\sqrt{30}$ Between 5 and 6
3. $\sqrt{93}$ Between 9 and 10

Answers for Try It

1. 2;

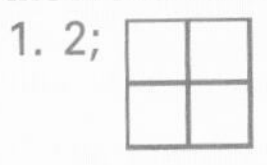

2. 6;

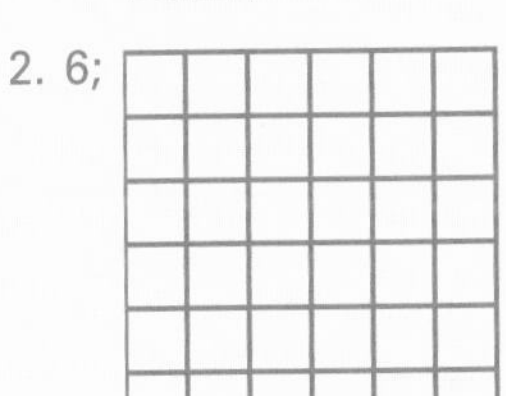

3. 9;

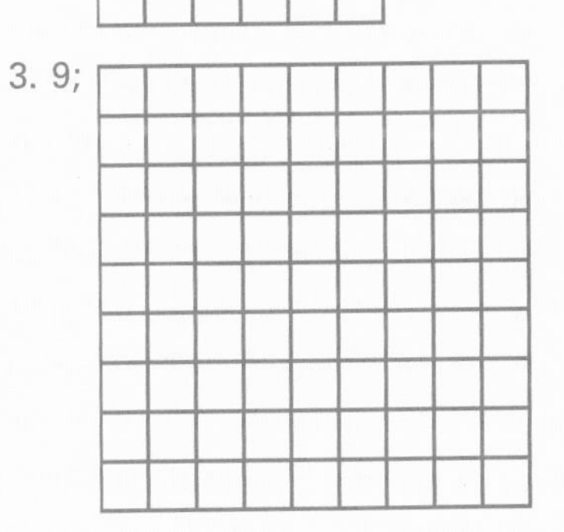

4. 5;

5. 7;

6. 10;

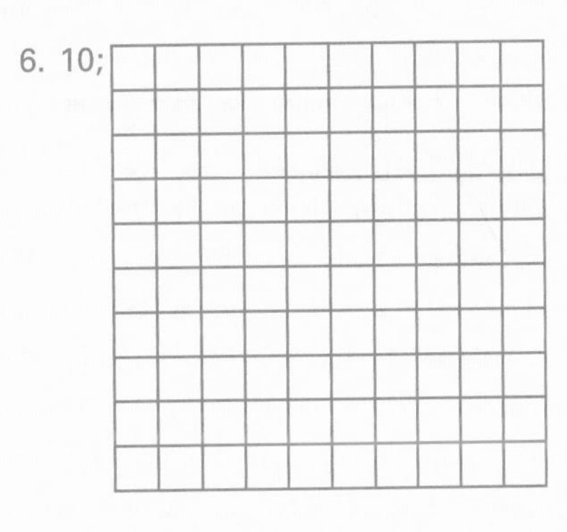

7. 20
8. 12
9. 8
10. 13
11. 18
12. 11

Chapter 4 Summary and Review

Review Correlation

Item(s)	Lesson(s)
1–3	4-1
4	4-2
5–7	4-3
8, 9	4-2
10	4-1
11	4-4
12	4-5
13	4-6
14, 15	4-4
16	4-6
17	4-7, 4-8
18	4-9

For additional review, see page 665.

Answers for Review

17. a. 9.42 yd

b. 7.065 yd^2

18. 167.13 $units^2$

Chapter 4 Summary and Review

Graphic Organizer

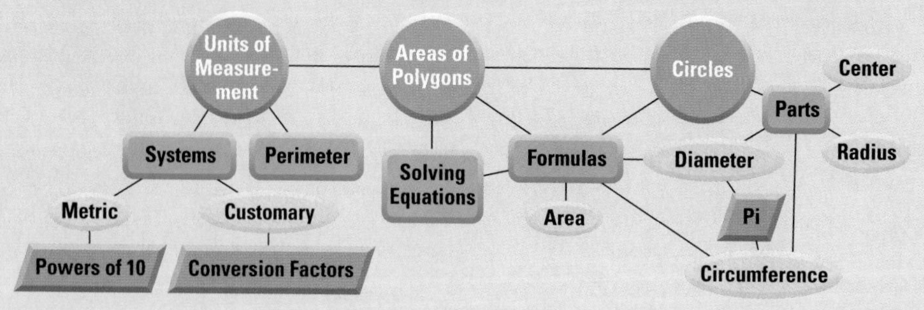

Section 4A Units of Measurement

Summary

- The **perimeter** is the distance around a figure.
- The basic units of measure of the **metric system** are the **meter,** used for length; the **gram,** used for mass; and the **liter,** used for volume.
- The customary system also has units of measure for length, weight, and capacity, such as **inch, foot, ounce, pound, quart,** and **gallon.**
- Use powers of 10 to convert from one related unit of metric measure to another. Use **conversion factors** to change from one related customary unit of measure to another.

Review

Find the perimeter of each figure.

1.

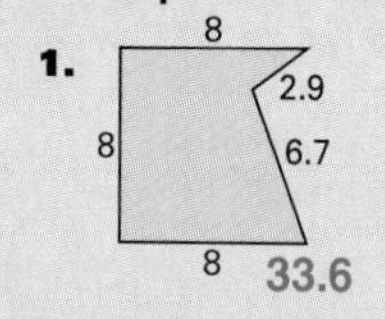

33.6

2.

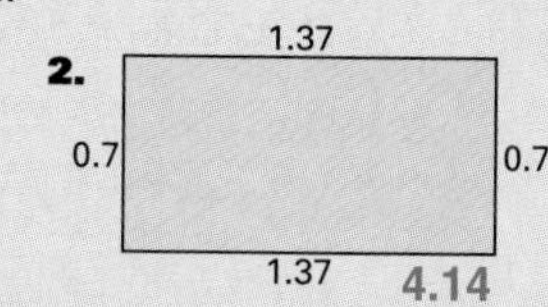

4.14

3.

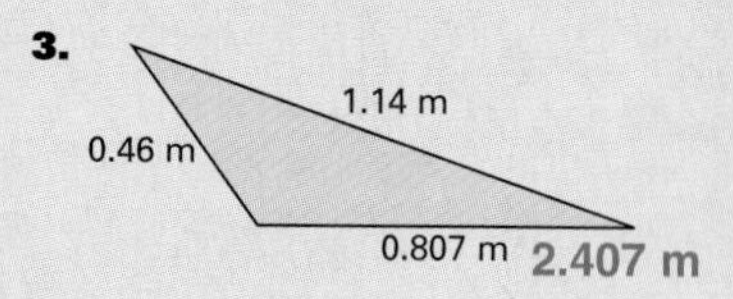

2.407 m

Use powers of 10 or conversion factors to find each measure.

4. 5.3 km = 5300 m **5.** 219 ft = 73 yd **6.** 4 ft = 48 in.

7. 3.5 gal = 14 qt **8.** 11.726 kg = 11,726 g **9.** 432 mm = 0.432 m

10. A rectangular dining room table is 44 in. by 66 in. What is the perimeter of the table? State your answer in feet. 18.3 ft

Resources

Practice Masters
Cumulative Review Chapters 1–4

PRACTICE

Name ______________________

Practice

Cumulative Review Chapters 1–4

Find the mean of each set of data. *[Lesson 1-8]*

1. 37, 43, 64, 53, 39, 28 — 44
2. 635, 842, 963, 612, 385 — 687.4
3. 8, 5, 8, 3, 9, 8, 8, 4, 3, 7 — 6.3
4. 8.6, 12.4, 7.3, 11.2, 13.1, 14.2, 13.0 — 11.4

Estimate. *[Lesson 2-6]*

5. 286 + 541 — ≈ 830
6. 8,912 − 4,371 — ≈ 4,500
7. 305 + 290 + 310 + 286 — ≈ 1,200
8. 914 − 352 — ≈ 560
9. 2,165 + 891 — ≈ 3,000
10. 6,140 + 5,912 + 6,041 — ≈ 18,000

Round to the underlined place value. *[Lesson 3-2]*

11. 38.465 — 38.47
12. 5.8364 — 5.8
13. 2.1759 — 2.18
14. 14.3755 — 14.38
15. 5.8149 — 5.81
16. 6.7431 — 6.743
17. 2.865 — 2.9
18. 56.413 — 56.41

Convert. *[Lesson 4-3]*

19. 17 feet = 204 inches
20. 32 pounds = 512 ounces
21. 14 miles = 73,920 feet
22. 136 quarts = 34 gallons

Find the area. *[Lesson 4-5]*

23. 143 m^2 24. 255 in^2 25. 12.04 cm^2

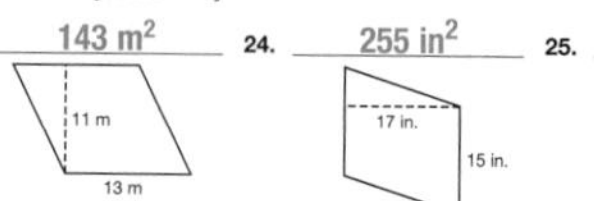

Chapter 4 Summary and Review

Section 4B Area of Polygons

Summary

- **Area** is the measure of how much surface is covered.
- You can also use formulas to find the area of some polygons.

  Rectangles and squares: $A = b \times h$, where b = base and h = height.

  Parallelogram: $A = b \times h$, where b = base and h = height.

  Triangle: $A = b \times h \div 2$, where b = base and h = height.

Review

Find the area of each figure.

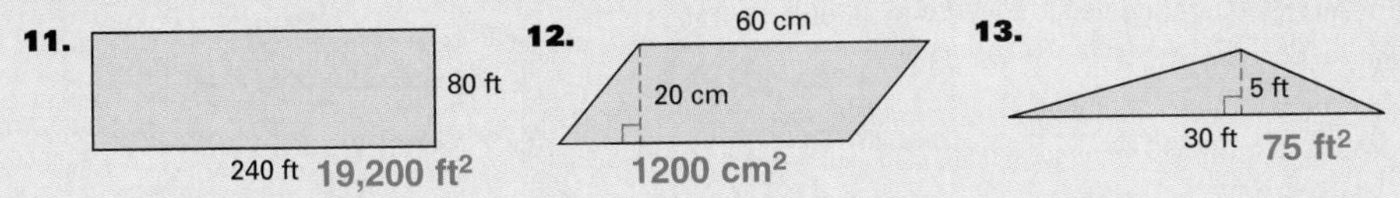

14. A square with a side 7.5 mm long 56.25 mm²

15. A door 3.5 ft wide and 6 ft high. 21 ft²

16. Find the height of a triangle with a base of 13.2 ft and an area of 198 ft². 30 ft

Section 4C Circles

Summary

- The **radius** of a circle is the distance from its center to any point on the circle. The **diameter** is the distance across a circle through its center. The **circumference** is the distance around a circle.
- For any circle, the circumference divided by the diameter equals about 3.14. This number is named **pi**, and its symbol is π.
- Use $C = \pi \times d$ to find a circumference, where C is the circumference and d is the diameter. Use $d = C \div \pi$ to find the diameter.
- Use the formula $A = \pi \times r^2$ to find the area of any circle, where r = the radius.
- To find the area of an irregular polygon, divide it into figures you recognize, find the area of each and add them together to get the total area.

Review

17. a. Find the circumference of a circle if its diameter is 3 yards.

b. Find its area.

18. Find the area of the irregular figure:

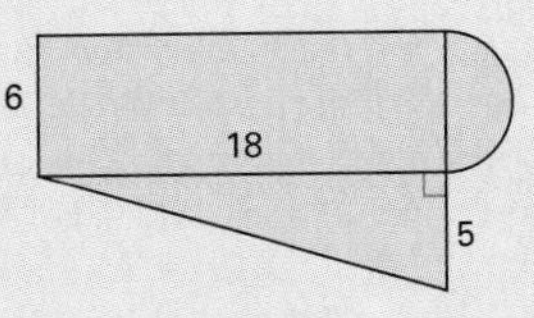

Chapter 4 Assessment

Assessment Correlation

Item(s)	Lesson(s)
1, 2	4-7
3	4-2
4	4-4, 4-5, 4-6
5	4-1, 4-4
6	4-1, 4-6
7	4-1, 4-5
8	4-3
9, 10	4-2
11	4-3
12	4-7
13	4-8
14	4-7
15, 16	4-9

Answer for Performance Task
Organized list should include triangles whose (base, height) measurements are: (1, 24), (2, 12), (3, 8), and (4, 6).

Chapter 4 Assessment

Supply the missing word in each sentence.

1. The distance from the center of a circle to any point on the circle is called the ______. Radius
2. The value of the symbol π is the circumference of any circle divided by its ______. Diameter
3. Powers of 10 are used to convert from one related measure to another in the ______ system. Metric
4. ______ measures the number of square units used to cover a surface. Area

For each figure, (a) find its perimeter and (b) find its area.

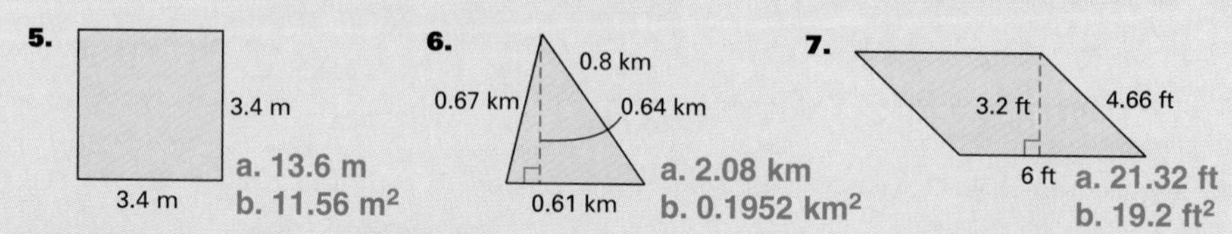

Use powers of 10 or conversion factors to find each measure.

8. 12 yd = __36__ ft **9.** 75 mm = __7.5__ cm **10.** 1 km = __1000__ m **11.** 360,000 in. = __30,000__ ft

12. Find the diameter of a circle whose circumference is 28.26 mi. 9 mi
13. Find the area of a circle to the nearest tenth if its radius is 2.5 kilometers. 19.6 km²
14. **a.** What is the diameter of the semicircle? 8 in. **b.** What is its radius? 4 in.
 c. How long is the perimeter of the semicircle? 20.56 in.
 d. What is its area? 25.12 in²

8 in.

Find the area of each irregular figure.

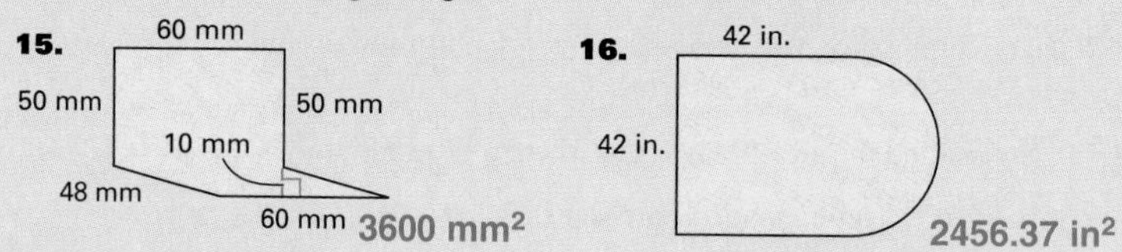

Performance Task

Using graph paper, draw as many triangles as possible whose area is 12 square units and whose base and height dimensions are whole numbers. As you find each triangle, label the dimensions of its base and height. When you are finished, make an organized list of the bases and heights of your triangles.

Resources

Assessment Sourcebook
Chapter 4 Tests
- Forms A and B (free response)
- Form C (multiple choice)
- Form D (performance assessment)
- Form E (mixed response)
- Form F (cumulative chapter test)

TestWorks
Tests and Practice Software

Home and Community Connections
Letter Home for Chapter 4 in English and Spanish

Cumulative Review Chapters 1–4

Test Prep

Multiple Choice

Choose the best answer.

1. Which of the following would make you think a bar graph might be misleading? *[Lesson 1-2]* B

Ⓐ All bar heights start from zero.

Ⓑ The data values are not equally spaced.

Ⓒ A broken graph symbol showing a break in the values.

Ⓓ Not here

2. What number in a frequency chart represents this set of tally marks? *[Lesson 1-4]* A

卌 卌 ||

Ⓐ 12 Ⓑ 10 Ⓒ 2 Ⓓ Not here

3. What is the place value of the digit 7 in 31,076,123? *[Lesson 2-1]* C

Ⓐ millions Ⓑ thousands

Ⓒ ten-thousands Ⓓ Not here

4. Use the order of operations to evaluate the expression $(18 + 9^2) \div 3$. *[Lesson 2-8]* B

Ⓐ 9 Ⓑ 33

Ⓒ 45 Ⓓ 243

5. There are m marbles arranged in 7 equal groups. Write an expression to show the number of marbles in each group. *[Lesson 2-11]* D

Ⓐ $m + 7$ Ⓑ $m - 7$

Ⓒ $7m$ Ⓓ $\frac{m}{7}$

6. Round 32.874 to the nearest tenth. *[Lesson 3-2]* B

Ⓐ 40 Ⓑ 32.9

Ⓒ 32.87 Ⓓ Not here

7. If you rank these decimals from smallest to largest, which will come second: 302.607, 3026.07, 302.067, 3020.67? *[Lesson 3-3]* C

Ⓐ 3026.07 Ⓑ 3020.67

Ⓒ 302.607 Ⓓ 302.067

8. Solve for x, if $x + 41.5 = 43.2$. *[Lesson 3-7]* A

Ⓐ 1.7 Ⓑ 2.7

Ⓒ 2.8 Ⓓ Not here

9. Simplify 3.76×0.08. *[Lesson 3-9]* B

Ⓐ 0.2968 Ⓑ 0.3008

Ⓒ 2.968 Ⓓ 3.008

10. How many millimeters are in 432.6 cm? *[Lesson 4-3]* D

Ⓐ 4.326 Ⓑ 43.26

Ⓒ 432.6 Ⓓ 4326

11. Find the area of the triangle. *[Lesson 4-6]* A

Ⓐ 24 m^2

Ⓑ 14 m^2

Ⓒ 12 m^2

Ⓓ 10 m^2

4 m

12 m

12. What is the area of a circle with a radius of 3 yd? *[Lesson 4-8]* A

Ⓐ 28.26 yd^2 Ⓑ 18.84 yd^2

Ⓒ 9.42 yd^2 Ⓓ Not here

Cumulative Review Test Prep

About Multiple-Choice Tests

The Cumulative Review found at the end of Chapters 2, 4, 6, 8, 10, and 12 can be used to prepare students for standardized tests.

Students sometimes do not perform as well on standardized tests as they do on other tests. There may be several reasons for this, related to the format and content of the test.

- **Format**
Students may have limited experience with multiple-choice tests. For some questions, such tests are harder because having options may confuse the students.

- **Content**
A standardized test may cover a broader range of content than normally covered on a test, and the relative emphasis given to various strands may be different than given in class. Also, some questions may assess general aptitude or thinking skills and not include specific pieces of mathematical content.

It is important not to let the differences between standardized tests and other tests shake your students' confidence.

Chapter 5

OVERVIEW

Patterns and Number Theory

Section 5A

Number Theory: Students learn that the quotient of two whole numbers may or may not have a remainder. They use divisibility rules to find the prime factorization of a number. Then students learn to find the least common multiple of two numbers.

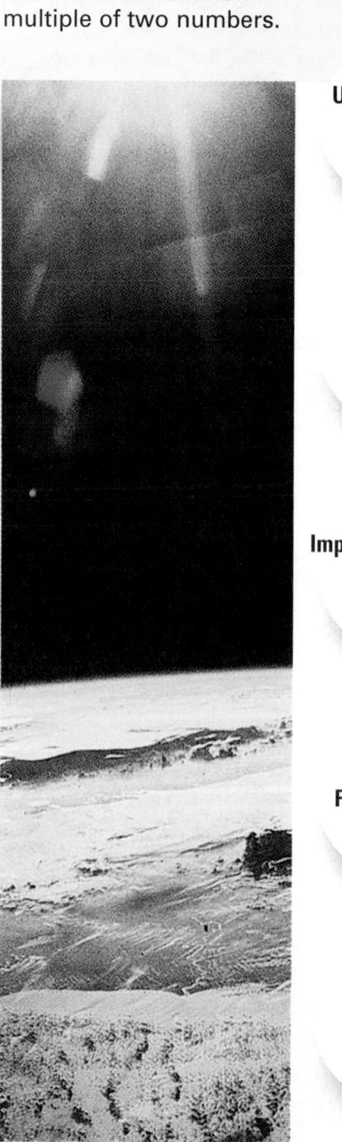

Section 5B

Connecting Fractions and Decimals: Students learn that different fractions have equivalent values. They learn to express numbers in decimal notation and in fraction notation, and to convert between the two forms. Students compare and order fractions.

Meeting NCTM Standards

Curriculum Standards

STANDARD			pages
1	**Problem Solving**	Skills and Strategies	268, 274, 284, 297, 306, 312
		Applications	273–274, 278–279, 283–284, 285, 291–292, 296–297, 300, 305–306, 311–312, 313, 315
		Exploration	270, 275, 280, 288, 293, 298, 302, 308
2	**Communication**	Oral	269, 273, 278, 282, *284*, 287, 290, *292*, 295, *297*, 300, *301*, 305, *306*, 310
		Written	274, 279, 284, 292, 297, 301, 306, 312
		Cooperative Learning	*270, 272, 275, 280, 288, 293, 295, 298, 302, 308*
3	**Reasoning**	Critical Thinking	274, 284, 292, 297, 301, 306, 312
4	**Connections**	Mathematical	See Standards 5, 6, 8, 12, and 13 below.
		Interdisciplinary	Career 306; Arts & Literature 266; Fine Arts 314; Industry 289, 292, 303, *310*, 312; Science 267, *269*, 277, 285, *290*, 300, *304*; Language 290; Entertainment 267; History *269*, 270, 272, 274, 277, 281, 282, 297; Social Studies 266, *282*, 286; Consumer *304, 306*
		Technology	270, 272, 280, 304, 307
		Cultural	266, *272*, 290, *295*
5	**Number and Number Relationships**		273, 286, 288–315
6	**Number Systems and Number Theory**		269–315
8	**Patterns and Functions**		267, *302*, 307
12	**Geometry**		291
13	**Measurement**		300, 305, 311

Italic type indicates Teacher Edition reference.

Teaching Standards

Focus on Questioning

The teacher has a central role in orchestrating discourse in the classroom. Teachers should

- pose questions that elicit, engage, and challenge each student's thinking.
- ask students to clarify and justify their ideas orally and in writing.

Assessment Standards

Focus on Inferences

Journal The Inferences Standard encourages the use of multiple sources of evidence of students' performance in order to make valid inferences about their learning. It also cautions that new forms of assessment, such as journal writing, may create sources of bias which need to be addressed. Journal writing in Chapter 5 has students write

- a paragraph.
- rules for divisibility.
- definitions.

TECHNOLOGY

For the Teacher

- **Teacher Resource Planner CD-ROM**
  Use the teacher planning CD-ROM to view resources available for Chapter 5. You can prepare custom lesson plans or use the default lesson plans provided.

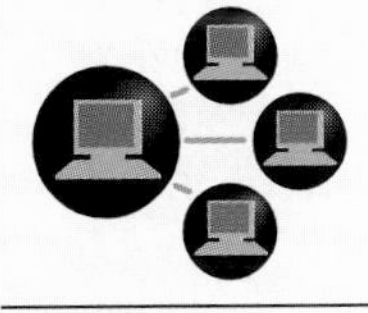

- **World Wide Web**
  Visit **www.teacher.mathsurf.com** for links to lesson plans from teachers and other professionals, NCTM information, and other sites.

- **TestWorks**
  TestWorks provides ready-made tests and can create custom tests and practice worksheets.

For the Parent

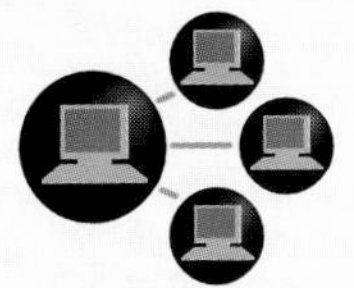

- **World Wide Web**
  Parents can use the Web site at **www.parent.mathsurf.com.**

For the Student

- **Interactive CD-ROM**
  Lesson 5-3 has an *Interactive CD-ROM Lesson*. The *Interactive CD-ROM Journal* and *Interactive CD-ROM Spreadsheet/Grapher Tool* are also used in Chapter 5.

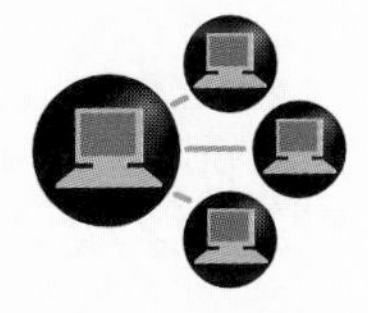

- **World Wide Web**
  Use with Chapter and Section Openers; Students can go online to the Scott Foresman-Addison Wesley Web site at **www.mathsurf.com/6/ch5** to collect information about chapter themes.

STANDARDIZED - TEST CORRELATION

SECTION 5A

LESSON	OBJECTIVE	ITBS Form M	CTBS 4th Ed.	CAT 5th Ed.	SAT 9th Ed.	MAT 7th Ed.	Your Form
5-1	• Know the rules of divisibility.	✘	✘				
5-2	• Recognize the difference between prime and composite numbers.		✘	✘		✘	
	• Find the prime factorization of a number.		✘	✘		✘	
5-3	• Find the least common multiple for two numbers.			✘	✘	✘	

SECTION 5B

LESSON	OBJECTIVE	ITBS Form M	CTBS 4th Ed.	CAT 5th Ed.	SAT 9th Ed.	MAT 7th Ed.	Your Form
5-4	• Represent values between whole numbers as fractions.	✘		✘	✘	✘	
5-5	• Write a fraction in lowest terms.	✘		✘	✘	✘	
5-6	• Convert between improper fractions and mixed numbers.			✘	✘	✘	
5-7	• Convert between fractions and decimals.			✘	✘	✘	
5-8	• Compare and order fractions.	✘		✘	✘	✘	

Key: ITBS - Iowa Test of Basic Skills; CTBS - Comprehensive Test of Basic Skills; CAT - California Achievement Test; SAT - Stanford Achievement Test; MAT - Metropolitan Achievement Test

ASSESSMENT PROGRAM

Traditional Assessment

QUICK QUIZZES	SECTION REVIEW	CHAPTER REVIEW	CHAPTER ASSESSMENT FREE RESPONSE	CHAPTER ASSESSMENT MULTIPLE CHOICE	CUMULATIVE REVIEW
TE: pp. 274, 279, 284, 292, 297, 301, 306, 312	SE: pp. 286, 314 *Quiz 5A, 5B	SE: pp. 316–317	SE: p. 318 *Ch. 5 Tests Forms A, B, E	*Ch. 5 Tests Forms C, E	SE: p. 319 *Ch. 5 Test Form F

Alternate Assessment

INTERVIEW	JOURNAL	ONGOING	PERFORMANCE	PORTFOLIO	PROJECT	SELF
TE: pp. 297, 301, 306	SE: pp. 279, 284, 292, 297, 301, 306, 312 TE: pp. 268, 274	TE: pp. 270, 275, 280, 288, 293, 298, 302, 308	SE: pp. 318–319 TE: pp. 284, 292 *Ch. 5 Tests Forms D, E	TE: p. 312	SE: pp. 267, 279, 301 TE: p. 267	TE: p. 279

*Tests and quizzes are in *Assessment Sourcebook.* Test Form E is a mixed response test. Forms for Alternate Assessment are also available in *Assessment Sourcebook.*

TestWorks: Test and Practice Software

MIDDLE SCHOOL PACING CHART

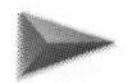

REGULAR PACING

Day	5 classes per week
1	Chapter 5 Opener; Problem Solving Focus
2	Section **5A** Opener; Lesson **5-1**
3	Lesson **5-2**
4	Lesson **5-3**
5	**5A** Connect; **5A** Review
6	Section **5B** Opener; Lesson **5-4**
7	Lesson **5-5**
8	Lesson **5-6**
9	Lesson **5-7**; Technology
10	Lesson **5-8**
11	**5B** Connect; **5B** Review; Extend Key Ideas
12	Chapter 5 Summary and Review
13	Chapter 5 Assessment Cumulative Review, Chapters 1–5

BLOCK SCHEDULING OPTIONS

Block Scheduling for Complete Course

Chapter 5 may be presented in

- eight 90-minute blocks
- eleven 75-minute blocks

Each block consists of a combination of

- Chapter and Section Openers
- Explores
- Lesson Development
- Problem Solving Focus
- Technology
- Extend Key Ideas
- Connect
- Review
- Assessment

For details, see *Block Scheduling Handbook.*

Block Scheduling for Interdisciplinary Course

Each block integrates math with another subject area.

In Chapter 5, interdisciplinary topics include

- Clocks
- Tools

Themes for Interdisciplinary Team Teaching 5A and 5B are

- Gardening
- Horseshoe Pitching

For details, see *Block Scheduling Handbook.*

Block Scheduling for Lab-Based Course

In each block, 30–40 minutes is devoted to lab activities including

- Explores in the Student Edition
- Connect pages in the Student Edition
- Technology options in the Student Edition
- Reteaching Activities in the Teacher Edition

For details, see *Block Scheduling Handbook.*

Block Scheduling for Course with *Connected Mathematics*

In each block, investigations from **Connected Mathematics** replace or enhance the lessons in Chapter 5.

Connected Mathematics topics for Chapter 5 can be found in

- *Prime Time*
- *Bits and Pieces I*

For details, see *Block Scheduling Handbook.*

INTERDISCIPLINARY BULLETIN BOARD

Set Up

Provide a set of dominoes or make some "dominoes" from index cards. Explain that for hundreds of years, people have played a game by matching the numbers or blanks on the tiles. The tiles probably were brought to Italy from China in the 14th century.

Procedure

- Groups of 4 students play a game. Tell students to stop matching domino halves when the 2 parts of an end of an arrangement equals 5.
- Each group should draw a copy of the arrangement its members made. Students should write a fraction for each domino in the arrangement.
- Each group hangs its arrangement and fraction labels on the bulletin board.

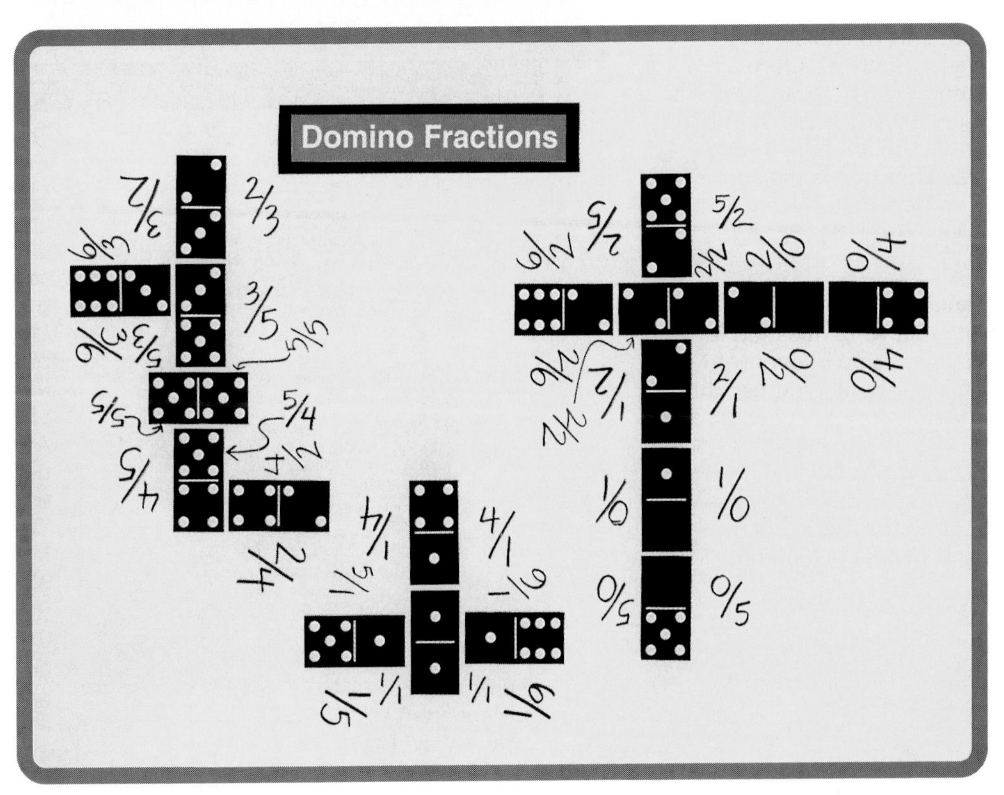

Chapter 5

The information on these pages shows how patterns and fractions are used in real-life situations.

World Wide Web

If your class has access to the World Wide Web, you might want to use the information found at the Web site addresses given.

Extensions

The following activities do not require access to the World Wide Web.

People of the World
Ask students to research the history of chopsticks and forks and knives. Discuss why different cultures might use different eating implements.

Arts & Literature
Have students find examples of Japanese *haiku* poems and verify that the pattern described here does exist. Then ask them to create such a poem themselves.

Social Studies
Have the students find out where Angel Falls is in Venezuela and locate it on a map or globe. Have them share any interesting facts they discover.

Science
Ask students to explain the Fibonacci number pattern and to extend the pattern to 12 or 14 numbers. The first two numbers in the pattern are both 1. Each number after that is the sum of the two numbers that precede it; 1, 1, 2, 3, 5, 8, 13, 21, 34, 55, 89, 144, 233, 377, ...

Entertainment
Use the following question for discussion: If you interviewed 3000 people, could you use the given data to predict how many people would be listening to news or talk stations? No, the given data are based on the people listening to the radio, not on a group of people in general.

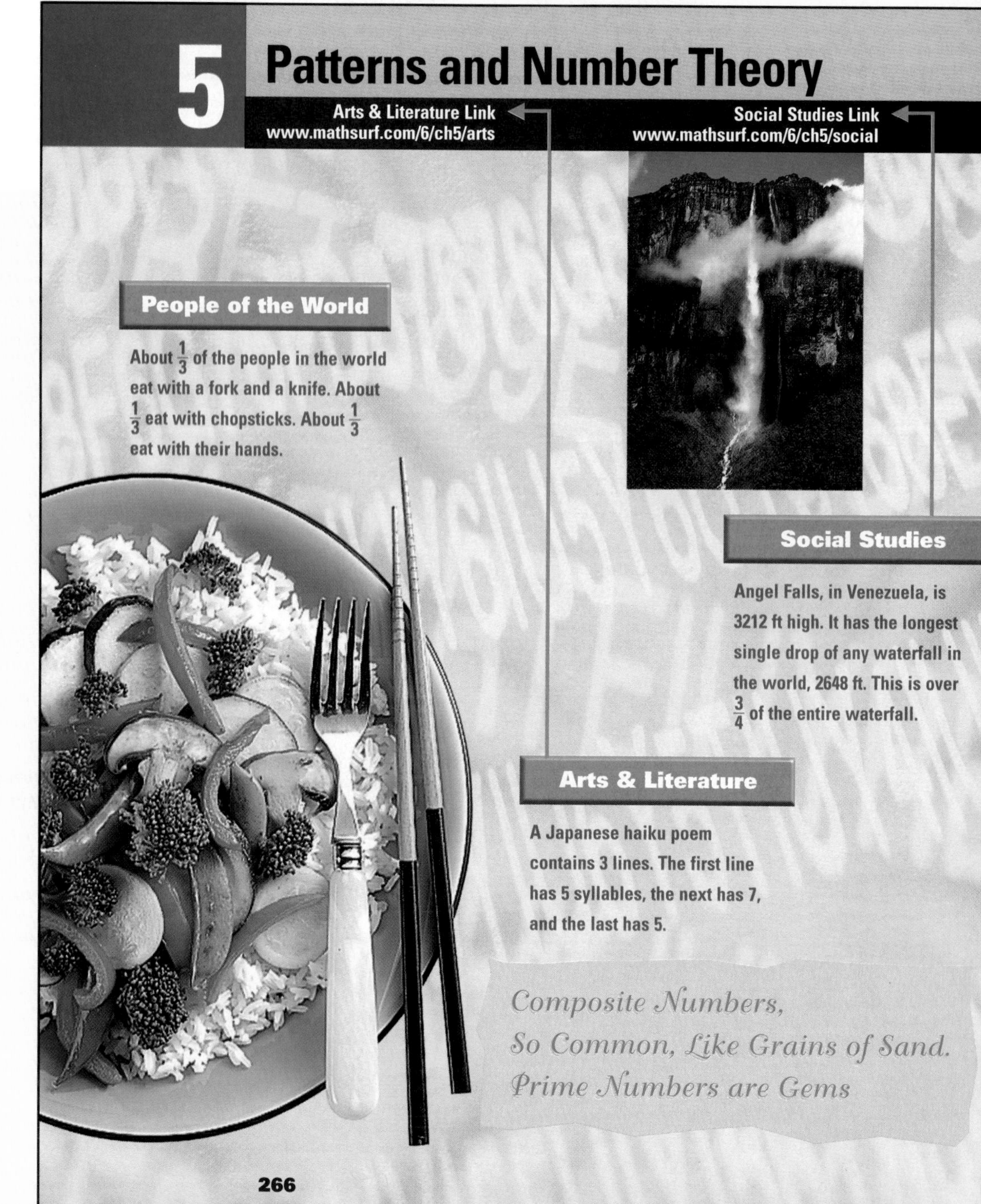

TEACHER TALK

Meet Madelaine Gallin

Manhattan District #5
New York, NY

To introduce a lesson in number theory, my class plays "What's In My Circle?" I begin by drawing a large circle. The class suggests numbers which I place either inside or outside the circle. For example, sometimes I put only even numbers, or only numbers that are factors of a specific number, or only prime numbers in the circle. After they have given me at least 10 numbers, I have them analyze what they see. After a while some students may deduce the rule for themselves as to which numbers belong inside my circle. These students call out numbers and indicate where the number should be placed. When at least half the class thinks they know the rule, I ask them to discuss what the numbers inside the circle have in common and what the numbers outside the circle have in common. As an extension, I draw two intersecting circles and have students find the rule for each circle and their intersections.

Entertainment Link
www.mathsurf.com/6/ch5/ent

KEY MATH IDEAS

The rules of divisibility describe patterns that can help you determine if a number can be divided evenly by another given number.

Every whole number greater than 1 is either a prime number or a composite number. A prime number has exactly two factors, the number itself and 1.

Fractions can be used to describe some part of a whole.

Fractions can describe amounts that are greater than one.

Decimal numbers can be converted to fraction numbers, and fraction numbers can be converted to decimal numbers.

Entertainment

On an average day, $\frac{16}{100}$ of the people listening to the radio are listening to news or talk stations. $\frac{9}{100}$ of the people are listening to Top 40 stations.

Science

The Fibonacci number pattern, 1, 1, 2, 3, 5, 8, ..., describes many things in nature, including how tree branches grow and what the surface of a pineapple looks like.

CHAPTER PROJECT

Problem Solving
Understand
Plan
Solve
Look Back

In this project, you will create a visual presentation of your favorite number. Begin by thinking about all the different ways a single number can be written.

267

PROJECT ASSESSMENT

You may choose to use this project as a performance assessment for the chapter.

Performance Assessment Key

Level 4 Full Accomplishment

Level 3 Substantial Accomplishment

Level 2 Partial Accomplishment

Level 1 Little Accomplishment

Suggested Scoring Rubric

Level	Criteria
4	• Visual is well organized and contains several relationships between favorite number and other numbers. • Several correct alternate forms of the favorite number are included.
3	• Visual is easy to read and contains some relationships between favorite number and other numbers. • Correct alternate forms of the favorite number are included.
2	• Visual is presentable and contains few relationships between favorite number and other numbers. • Very few correct alternate forms of the favorite number are included.
1	• Visual is not well organized nor does it contain any relationships between favorite number and other numbers. • No other correct alternate forms of the favorite number are included.

Chapter Project

In this chapter students will use their imaginations to create a visual representation of a number of their choice.

Resources
Chapter 5 Project Master

Introduce the Project

- Ask students if they have a favorite number and why it is their favorite. Make a list of students' favorite numbers and tally the number of students who chose each number.
- Talk about some of the ways students can think of to represent a given number. Remind them that numbers can be represented by sums or differences, for example, or by symbols used in other number systems.
- Talk about where students might find information about different ways to represent numbers, such as in encyclopedias, books about numbers, and the Internet.

Project Progress
Section A, page 279 Students explore prime numbers, multiples and factors, and least common multiple.

Section B, page 301 Students change a number to its fraction and decimal forms, and compare numbers written in fraction form.

Community Project

A community project for Chapter 5 is available in *Home and Community Connections.*

Cooperative Learning

You may want to use Teaching Tool Transparency 1: Cooperative Learning Checklist with **Explore** and other group activities in this chapter.

Problem Solving Focus

Identifying Missing Information

The Point
Students focus on identifying missing information needed to solve the problem.

Resources
Teaching Tool Transparency 18: Problem-Solving Guidelines

 *Interactive CD-ROM Journal*

About the Page

Using the Problem-Solving Process
A critical element in problem solving is the ability to identify the information that is needed to solve the problem. Discuss these four steps for identifying necessary, but missing, information.

- Determine what the problem is asking.
- Identify the information needed to solve the problem.
- Determine whether the necessary information is given or whether it can be deduced.
- Identify missing information.

Ask ...
- In Problem 3, suppose Ronisha bought 2 gallons of green paint and one gallon of white paint. How much did she spend on paint? $13.95
- In Problem 4, if Terrance painted for 3 hours, how much time did it take to paint the treehouse? $15\frac{1}{2}$ hours

Answers for Problems
1. No missing information.
2. How long are the rungs? How long is the ladder? How thick are the side pieces?
3. How much paint does Ronisha need?
4. For how long did Terrance paint? Did anyone else help?

Journal

Ask students to write a paragraph describing how they would find the information needed to solve Problem 2.

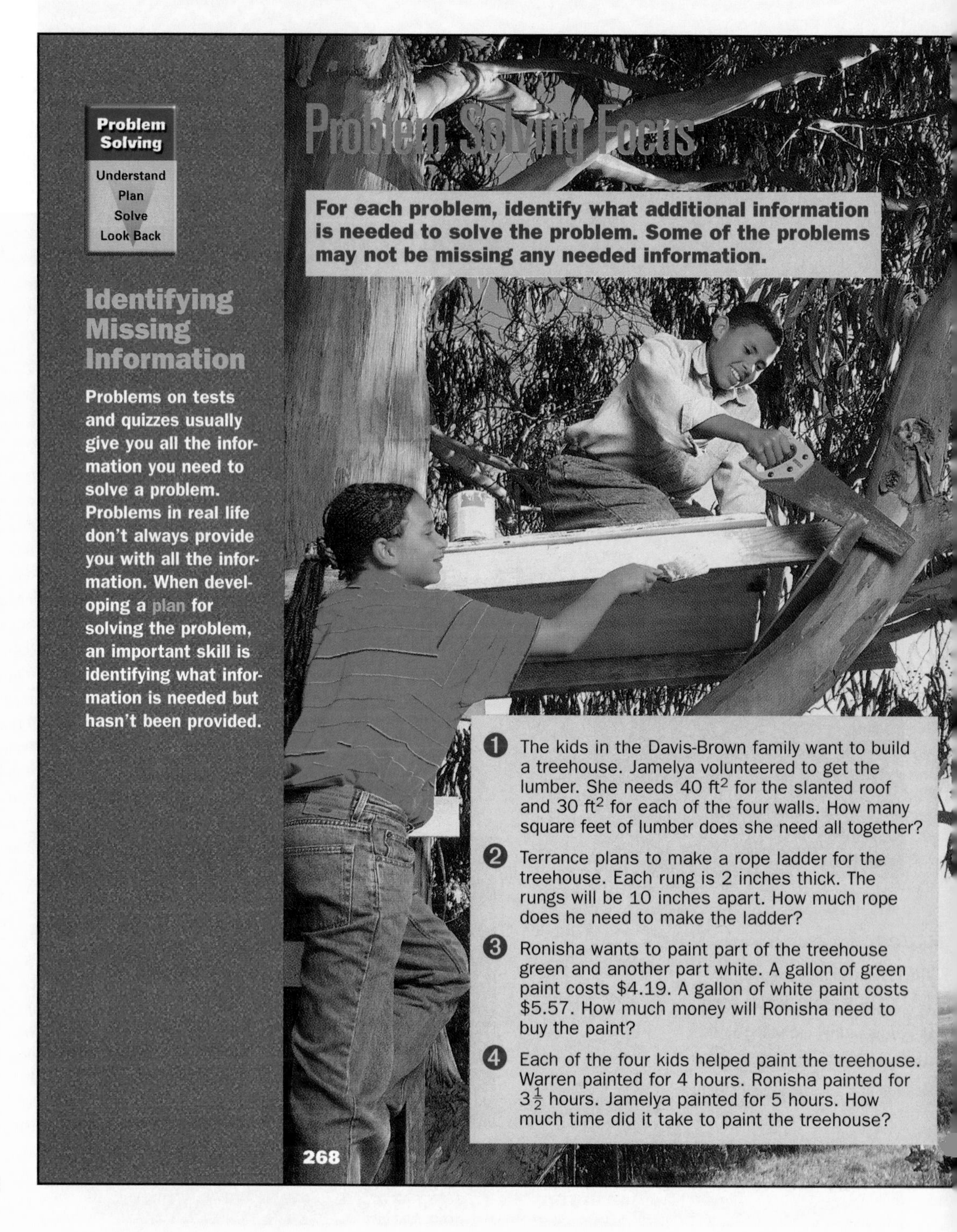

Problem Solving
Understand
Plan
Solve
Look Back

Problem Solving Focus

For each problem, identify what additional information is needed to solve the problem. Some of the problems may not be missing any needed information.

Identifying Missing Information

Problems on tests and quizzes usually give you all the information you need to solve a problem. Problems in real life don't always provide you with all the information. When developing a plan for solving the problem, an important skill is identifying what information is needed but hasn't been provided.

1. The kids in the Davis-Brown family want to build a treehouse. Jamelya volunteered to get the lumber. She needs 40 ft^2 for the slanted roof and 30 ft^2 for each of the four walls. How many square feet of lumber does she need all together?
2. Terrance plans to make a rope ladder for the treehouse. Each rung is 2 inches thick. The rungs will be 10 inches apart. How much rope does he need to make the ladder?
3. Ronisha wants to paint part of the treehouse green and another part white. A gallon of green paint costs $4.19. A gallon of white paint costs $5.57. How much money will Ronisha need to buy the paint?
4. Each of the four kids helped paint the treehouse. Warren painted for 4 hours. Ronisha painted for $3\frac{1}{2}$ hours. Jamelya painted for 5 hours. How much time did it take to paint the treehouse?

268

Additional Problem

Kenisha planned a party for her friends. She bought birthday hats for $1.19 each, favors for $3 each, and a cake for $8.95. She planned to spend $2.50 more per person for juice and snacks. How much did she spend in all?

1. What is the problem about? Planning a party.
2. What does the problem ask you to find? The total amount Kenisha spent.
3. If birthday hats cost $1.19 each, how do you find the total spent on hats? Multiply the number of hats needed by $1.19.
4. How much will Kenisha spend for each person, excluding the cake? $6.69
5. Is there any missing information? The number of people invited to the party.

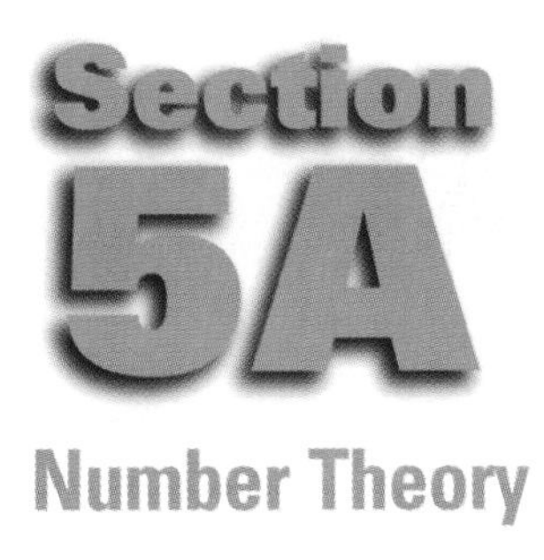

Section 5A

Number Theory

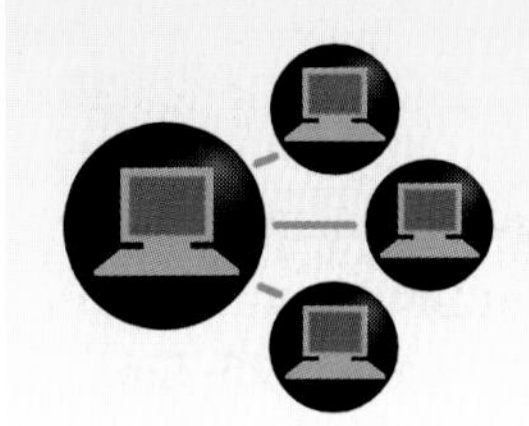

Visit **www.teacher.mathsurf.com** for links to lesson plans from teachers and other professionals, NCTM information, and other sites.

LESSON PLANNING GUIDE

Student Edition / Ancillaries*

LESSON		MATERIALS	VOCABULARY	DAILY	OTHER
	Chapter 5 Opener				Ch. 5 Project Master Ch. 5 Community Project Teaching Tool Trans. 1
	Problem Solving Focus				Teaching Tool Trans. 18 *Interactive CD-ROM Journal*
	Section 5A Opener				
5-1	**Divisibility**	calculators	divisible	5-1	Technology Master 21
5-2	**Prime Factorization**	graph paper	prime number, composite number, prime factorization	5-2	Teaching Tool Trans. 7 Technology Master 22 Ch. 5 Project Master
5-3	**Least Common Multiples**	spreadsheet software	multiple, common multiple, least common multiple (LCM)	5-3	Teaching Tool Trans. 2, 3 Lesson Enhancement Trans. 20 *Interactive CD-ROM Lesson*
	Connect				Interdisc. Team Teaching 5A
	Review				Practice 5A; Quiz 5A; *TestWorks*

* Daily Ancillaries include Practice, Reteaching, Problem Solving, Enrichment, and Daily Transparency. Teaching Tool Transparencies are in *Teacher's Toolkits*. Lesson Enhancement Transparencies are in *Overhead Transparency Package*.

SKILLS TRACE

LESSON	SKILL	FIRST INTRODUCED GR. 4	GR. 5	GR. 6	DEVELOP	PRACTICE/ APPLY	REVIEW
5-1	**Using rules of divisibility.**			✘ p. 270	pp. 270–272	pp. 273–274	pp. 316, 369, 546
5-2	**Finding prime factorizations.**			✘ p. 275	pp. 275–277	pp. 278–279	pp. 316, 374, 553
5-3	**Finding least common multiples.**			✘ p. 280	pp. 280–282	pp. 283–284	pp. 316, 378, 557

CONNECTED MATHEMATICS

Investigations 1–6 from the unit *Prime Time (Factors and Multiples)*, from the **Connected Mathematics** series, can be used with Section 5A.

INTERDISCIPLINARY TEAM TEACHING

Math and Science/Technology

(Worksheet pages 25–26: Teacher pages T25–T26)

In this lesson, students use number theory to help with gardening.

Name ______________________ *Math and Science/Technology*

Gardening By the Numbers

Use number theory to help with gardening.

There are many people who grow their own vegetables in "backyard" gardens. Even so, the majority of vegetables that we eat today are grown on farms. The people who grow these vegetables are professionals. They have studied *agriculture*, which is the science of farming. Through experimentation, they have learned what works best. Here are examples of things backyard gardeners have learned from professionals and from their own experiments:

- The soil in which vegetables are planted should be loose, so roots, air, and water can travel through it easily.
- The planting beds must be located where they will get the most sun. They need at least a half day of full sun each sunny day.
- Fertilizer should be placed on the bottom of each planting area. The planting mix is then placed on top of the fertilizer. This will prompt the roots to grow deep.
- The top inch of soil should be free of fertilizer. This will keep weed seedlings from growing quickly.
- Vegetables should be planted when the threat of frost has passed.
- Planted seeds or seedlings should be fertilized from time to time.
- Plants that will grow tall, such as tomatoes, must be able to attach themselves to tall posts, poles, stakes, or trellises.
- Plants should be watered regularly if not enough rain falls.

Backyard gardeners must also put their math skills to work. They must know how to make correct calculations when they divide their garden and arrange seeds and seedlings.

1. Though you can plant onion seeds or seedlings, it is better to buy little onions called onion sets because they are easier to plant and grow faster. If you want to share 81 onion sets with two other vegetable gardeners, explain why you can or cannot divide the sets evenly among the three of you?

   Yes. 81 is divisible by 3 because 8 + 1 = 9, and 9 is divisible by 3.

2. Peter Chan is a well-known vegetable gardener. Chan likes to use raised vegetable beds in his garden. The planting area looks like a box. The border is filled with planting mix. Seeds or seedlings are then planted in the mix. Chan prefers the raised bed because it enables the gardener to grow the most vegetables in the smallest amount of space. Here are the reasons why: The dirt in a raised bed warms faster in the spring, since it is on top of the earth. That means that the gardener can start planting earlier in the spring. The dirt also drains better, so plants do not decay from being in too much water. Furthermore, if a raised bed is long and narrow, the gardener can work from the side of the bed and not step into it. That way, the plants are not trampled accidentally. Chan uses $3\frac{1}{2}$ by 14-foot raised beds.

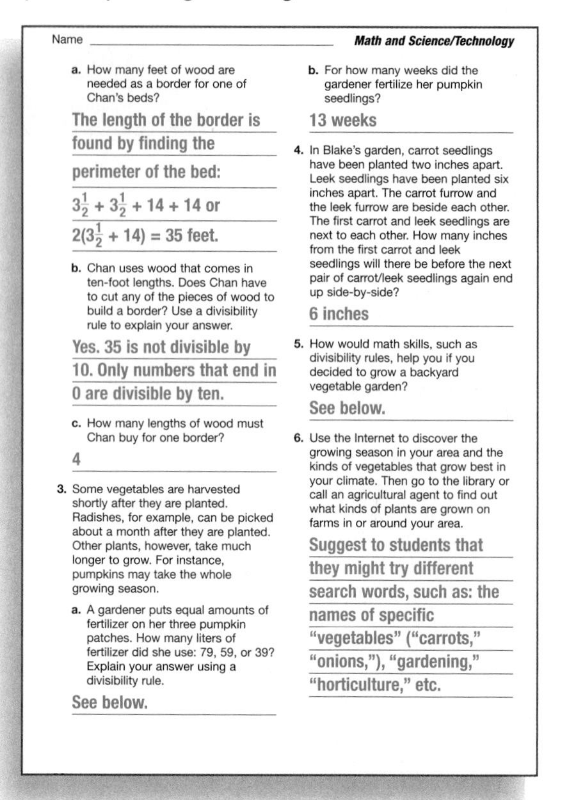

Name ______________________ *Math and Science/Technology*

a. How many feet of wood are needed as a border for one of Chan's beds?

   The length of the border is found by finding the perimeter of the bed: $3\frac{1}{2} + 3\frac{1}{2} + 14 + 14$ or $2(3\frac{1}{2} + 14) = 35$ feet.

b. Chan uses wood that comes in ten-foot lengths. Does Chan have to cut any of the pieces of wood to build a border? Use a divisibility rule to explain your answer.

   Yes. 35 is not divisible by 10. Only numbers that end in 0 are divisible by ten.

c. How many lengths of wood must Chan buy for one border?

   4

3. Some vegetables are harvested shortly after they are planted. Radishes, for example, can be picked about a month after they are planted. Other plants, however, take much longer to grow. For instance, pumpkins may take the whole growing season.

   a. A gardener puts equal amounts of fertilizer on her three pumpkin patches. How many liters of fertilizer did she use: 79, 59, or 39? Explain your answer using a divisibility rule.

   See below.

   b. For how many weeks did the gardener fertilize her pumpkin seedlings?

   13 weeks

4. In Blake's garden, carrot seedlings have been planted two inches apart. Leek seedlings have been planted six inches apart. The carrot furrow and the leek furrow are beside each other. The first carrot and leek seedlings are next to each other. How many inches from the first carrot and leek seedlings will there be before the next pair of carrot/leek seedlings again end up side-by-side?

   6 inches

5. How would math skills, such as divisibility rules, help you if you decided to grow a backyard vegetable garden?

   See below.

6. Use the Internet to discover the growing season in your area and the kinds of vegetables that grow best in your climate. Then go to the library or call an agricultural agent to find out what kinds of plants are grown on farms in or around your area.

   Suggest to students that they might try different search words, such as: the names of specific "vegetables" ("carrots," "onions,"), "gardening," "horticulture," etc.

Answers

3. a. 39. 3 will not evenly divide into 79 or 59. But 3 will divide evenly into 39 because 3 + 9 = 12, which is evenly divisible by 3.

5. Students' responses will vary. Math skills help the gardener divide the garden, the seeds, and the fertilizer. The rules of divisibility make division a faster operation. Math skills also help the gardener when he or she buys supplies for the garden, such as wood for a raised planting bed.

BIBLIOGRAPHY

FOR TEACHERS

Muirden, James. *Stars and Planets.* New York, NY: Kingfisher Books, 1993.

Blair, Harry and Bob Knauff. *Not Strictly by the Numbers.* Palo Alto, CA: Dale Seymore, 1996.

FOR STUDENTS

Ericksen, Aase and Marjorie Wintermute. *Students, Structures, Spaces.* Reading, MA: Innovative Learning Publications, 1996.

Scarre, Chris. *Smithsonian Timelines of the Ancient World.* London, England: Dorling Kindersley Ltd., 1993.

Macvey, John W. *Time Travel.* Chelsea, MI: Scarborough House, 1990.

Brackin, A. J. *Clocks: Chronicling Time.* San Diego, CA: Lucent Books, 1991.

SECTION 5A

Number Theory

▶ Science Link ▶ History Link ▶ www.mathsurf.com/6/ch5/clocks

02.28.98 01.00.23

A Switch in Time ...

Thirty days hath September,
April, June, and November.
All the rest have 31,
Excepting February alone,
Which hath by 28, in fine,
Till leap year gives it 29.

As the poem suggests, time is not a regular thing. One month doesn't always equal another. (July has more days than June.) One year doesn't always equal another. (Leap years have an extra day.) One century doesn't always equal another. (Earth is slowing down by about $\frac{1}{2}$ second each century.)

We have often changed how we keep track of time in an effort to create simpler clocks and calendars. In the 1200s, an hour was $\frac{1}{12}$ of the time from sunrise to sunset, regardless of how long that was. In the 1700s, there were no time zones. Each town kept its own time. In the early 1900s, according to Greenwich Mean Time, the day began and ended at noon. Every change has been an effort to make timekeeping more accurate and more convenient. And every change has involved mathematics.

1 Before the invention of mechanical clocks, how did humans keep track of time?

2 Why doesn't a year always equal exactly 365 days?

3 What sort of mathematics do you need to know to create an accurate clock or calendar?

Where are we now?

In Grade 5, students used division to explore other concepts.

They learned how to

- factor and determine divisibility.
- distinguish between prime and composite numbers.

Where are we going?

In Grade 6, Section 5A, students will

- test for divisibility.
- distinguish between prime and composite numbers.
- use prime factorization.
- find the least common multiple for two numbers.

Section 5A

Theme: Clocks

World Wide Web

If your class has access to the World Wide Web, you might want to use the information found at the Web site address given. The interdisciplinary links relate to topics discussed in this section.

About the Page

This page introduces the theme of the section, clocks, and discusses the changes in the way people have measured and kept track of time.

Ask ...

- What is Greenwich Mean Time?
  By agreement, nearly all world time calculations are counted from the meridian which passes through Greenwich, England. When it is noon on this meridian, it is midnight exactly 180° east or west, on the opposite side of the Earth.

Extensions

The following activities do not require access to the World Wide Web.

Science
Every year that is divisible by 4 is a leap year, except century years. Century years, such as 1800, 1900, and 2000 are leap years only if they are divisible by 400. Have students research how and why rules for leap years were established.

History
The months of the year and the days of the week were given special names for a variety of reasons. Have students investigate how the names of the months and days were chosen.

Answers for Questions

1. Possible answers: They used the sun, shadows, water, sand.
2. Because leap years have an extra day.
3. Counting, division.

Connect

On page 285, students use their knowledge of factors and multiples to create a calendar for the planet Venus.

Lesson Organizer

Objective

- Learn rules of divisibility.

Vocabulary

- Divisible

Materials

- Explore: Calculator

NCTM Standards

- 1–6

Review

Find each quotient.

1. 135 ÷ 9 15
2. 84 ÷ 6 14
3. 108 ÷ 9 12
4. 102 ÷ 6 17

Available on Daily Transparency 5-1

1 Introduce

Explore

The Point
Students develop intuitive rules of divisibility by looking for patterns in a table of division problems.

Ongoing Assessment
Check that students understand that numbers to the right of the decimal point in a quotient indicate a remainder.

For Groups That Finish Early
Write a list of three-digit numbers and determine whether there are remainders when the numbers are divided by the numbers 2 through 10.

5-1 Divisibility

You'll Learn ...

- the rules of divisibility

... How It's Used

Shipping company employees use the rules of divisibility to determine if a given number of packages can be evenly packed into a given crate.

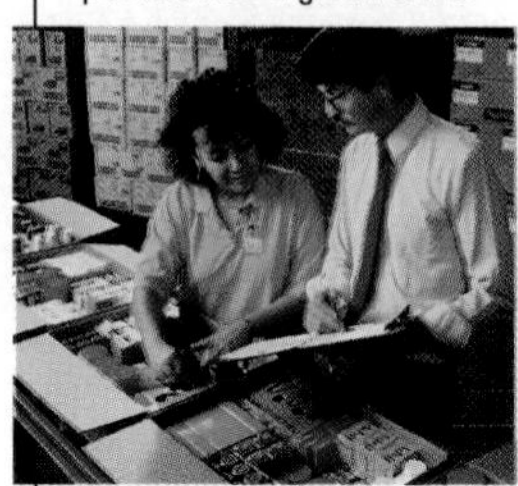

Vocabulary

divisible

History Link

In 1795, the French adopted a decimal time system, with 10-day weeks, 10-hour days, 100-minute hours, and 100-second minutes. It was abandoned in 1805 because the public didn't like a 10-day week.

Lesson Link You've learned that the quotient of two whole numbers may or may not have a remainder. In this lesson, you'll learn ways to determine if a quotient will have a remainder without actually dividing. ◄

Explore Divisibility

Let's Take a Vacation!

Materials: Calculator

Vacations often last an exact number of weeks. ("I'm taking a 4-week vacation.") But how long is a week? In most countries, it is 7 days. But ancient Rome had an 8-day week, France once had a 10-day week, and Russia had 5- and 6-day weeks.

	Week Length (days)								
Vacation (days)	2	3	4	5	6	7	8	9	10
32									
42									
60									
75									
117									
180									

1. Using a calculator, divide each vacation length by each of the week lengths. If your answer is a whole number, the week length divides evenly into the vacation length. Write "yes" in the matching square. If your answer is not a whole number, the week length does not divide evenly into the vacation length. Write "no" in the matching square.
2. Suppose you have to fill out one column without a calculator. Which would be easier, the 2 column or the 7 column. Why?
3. Did you discover any shortcuts that allowed you to write "yes" or "no" without actually dividing? If so, describe them.
4. If a week were one day long, what would the answers in that column be? Why?

MEETING INDIVIDUAL NEEDS

Resources

5-1 Practice
5-1 Reteaching
5-1 Problem Solving
5-1 Enrichment
5-1 Daily Transparency
Problem of the Day
Review
Quick Quiz
Technology Master 21

Learning Modalities

Verbal Discussing mathematics is an invaluable aid to understanding, so have students verbalize the divisibility rules.

Social Have students work in groups of three on **Explore**. Have one student find the quotients for 32 and 75 days, the second student finds the quotients for 42 and 117 days, and the third student finds the quotients for 60 and 180 days.

English Language Development

Be sure that students understand the meaning of *even* and *odd* as whether or not a number is divisible by 2. Point out, however, that when we speak of a division problem "coming out even," we do not mean the quotient is an even number, we mean that there is no remainder.

Learn Divisibility

A whole number is **divisible** by another whole number if you can divide the first number by the second without leaving a remainder.

$3\overline{)21}$ = 7 → 21 is divisible by 3.

$4\overline{)21}$ = 5 R 1 → 21 is *not* divisible by 4.

For any number, you can list all of the numbers that are divisible by that number. Sometimes you will see patterns that can help you determine if a number is divisible by another number without actually needing to divide.

Some patterns depend upon the ones digit in the number.

DIVISIBILITY RULES

A whole number is divisible by	Examples
• 2 if the ones digit is even.	2, 4, 6, 8, 10, 12, 14, 16, 18, 20, ...
• 5 if the ones digit is 5 or 0.	5, 10, 15, 20, 25, 30, 35, 40, 45, ...
• 10 if the ones digit is 0.	10, 20, 30, 40, 50, 60, 70, 80, ...

DID YOU KNOW?

There are also rules of divisibility for 4, 7, and 8. But the rules are more complicated, so it's usually faster to just divide the number and see if there is a remainder.

Remember

An *even* number ends in 0, 2, 4, 6, or 8. An *odd* number ends in 1, 3, 5, 7, or 9.
[Previous Course]

Example 1

Mr. Ashman is planning a lesson. He wants his students to work first in groups of 2, then in groups of 5, and finally in groups of 10. There should never be any students left over. He has 30 students in his first class, and 25 in his second class. Will the lesson work in both classes?

Is 30 divisible by 2, 5, and 10?

2? Yes The ones digit is even.

5? Yes The ones digit is 0.

10? Yes The ones digit is 0.

Is 25 divisible by 2, 5 and 10?

2? No The ones digit is not even.

5? Yes The ones digit is 5.

10? No The ones digit is not 0.

The lesson will work for the first class, but not the second.

Answers for Explore

1. Row 1: Yes, No, Yes, No, No, No, Yes, No, No

   Row 2: Yes, Yes, No, No, Yes, Yes, No, No, No

   Row 3: Yes, Yes, Yes, Yes, Yes, No, No, No, Yes

   Row 4: No, Yes, No, Yes, No, No, No, No, No

   Row 5: No, Yes, No, No, No, No, No, Yes, No

   Row 6: Yes, Yes, Yes, Yes, Yes, No, No, Yes, Yes
2. Possible answer: The "2" column would be easier; Only even numbers are divisible by 2.
3. Even numbers are divisible by 2; Numbers ending in 0 or 5 are divisible by 5; Numbers ending in 0 are divisible by 10.
4. The vacation-length column and the column for a 1-day week would have the same values; The number of days and the number of weeks would be the same.

2 Teach

Learn

Alternate Examples

1. Mrs. Taubner wants to make a $60 "money tree" for her mom, who is 60 years old, and an $85 money tree for her grandmother, who is 85 years old. She will use bills of the same denomination on the trees. Will $2, $5, or $10 bills work?

   Is 60 divisible by 2, 5, and 10?

   2? Yes, the ones digit is 0.
   5? Yes, the ones digit is 0.
   10? Yes, the ones digit is 0.

   Is 85 divisible by 2, 5, and 10?

   2? No, the ones digit is not even.
   5? Yes, the ones digit is 5.
   10? No, the ones digit is not 0.

   Mrs. Taubner can make a $60 money tree with $2, $5, or $10 bills and an $85 money tree with $5 bills.

MATH EVERY DAY

Problem of the Day

Copy this clock on a piece of paper. Use two straight lines to divide the clockface into three parts. Each part should have a sum of 26.

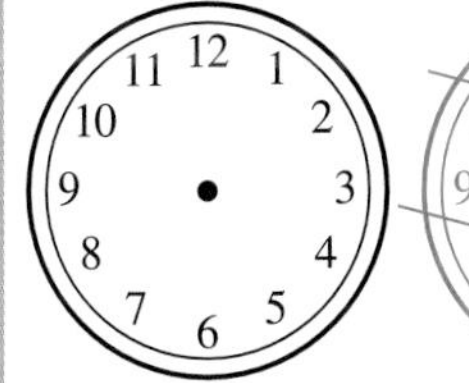

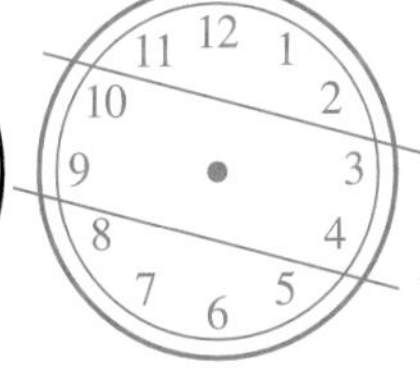

Available on Daily Transparency 5-1

An Extension is provided in the transparency package.

Fact of the Day

There is only a 26-second difference between a calendar year and the time the Earth takes to go around the Sun.

Mental Math

Find each quotient mentally.

1. 250 ÷ 5 50
2. 360 ÷ 9 40
3. 244 ÷ 4 61
4. 444 ÷ 2 222

Alternate Examples

2. Test 840 for divisibility by 2, 3, 5, 9, and 10.

   2? Yes, the ones digit is even.

   3? Yes, 8 + 4 + 0 = 12, which is divisible by 3.

   5? Yes, the ones digit is 0.

   9? No, 8 + 4 + 0 = 12, which is not invisible by 9.

   10? Yes, the ones digit is 0.

3. A square mile is 640 acres. Can a square mile be separated into equal-sized parcels of 2, 3, 5, 6, and 10 acres?

   Test 640 for divisibility by 2, 3, 5, 6, and 10.

   640 is even, so it is divisible by [2].

   6 + 4 = 10, and 10 is not divisible by 3, so 640 is not divisible by 3.

   640 ends in 0, so it is divisible by [5] and by [10].

   640 is divisible by 2 but not by 3, so it is not divisible by 6.

   A square mile can be separated into equal-sized parcels of 2, 5, and 10 acres.

3 Practice and Assess

Check

Students may be intrigued by the divisibility tests for 3 and 9. Point out that when the sum of the digits of a number being tested has two or more digits, they can add the digits as many times as possible to get a one-digit sum, and the test is still valid.

Answers for Check Your Understanding

1. Possible answer: You can know if a number divides another evenly without actually dividing.
2. Possible answer: 2, 5, 9, and 10 are easiest to remember.

HINT

You can also use a calculator to test for divisibility. If the quotient of two numbers has no digits after the decimal, the first number is divisible by the second.

Some patterns depend upon the sum of the digits.

A whole number is divisible by	Examples
• 3 if the sum of its digits is divisible by 3.	3, 6, 9, 12, 15, 18, 21, 24, ...
• 9 the sum of its digits is divisible by 9.	9, 18, 27, 36, 45, 54, 63, ...

Example 2

Test 945 for divisibility by 2, 3, 5, 9 and 10.

2? No, the ones digit is not even.

3? Yes, 9 + 4 + 5 = 18, which is divisible by 3.

5? Yes, the ones digit is 5.

9? Yes, 9 + 4 + 5 = 18, which is divisible by 9.

10? No, the ones digit is not 0.

Some patterns depend upon other patterns.

A whole number is divisible by	Examples
• 6 if it is divisible by both 2 and 3.	6, 12, 18, 24, 30, 36, 42, ...

▶ History Link

The oldest known document on number theory was written in Babylon some time between 1900 B.C. and 1600 B.C. It was written using sexagecimal notation, which is based on the number 60.

Example 3

The ancient Babylonians recognized the value of the number 60 in timekeeping. We have 60-second minutes and 60-minute hours because 60 is easily divided into smaller parts. Test 60 for divisibility by 2, 3, 5, 6, 9, and 10.

0 is even, so it's divisible by [2].

6 + 0 = 6, and 6 is divisible by 3, so 60 is divisible by [3].
60 ends in 0, so it's divisible by [5] and by [10].

60 is divisible by both 2 and 3, so it is divisible by [6].
6 + 0 = 6, and 6 is not divisible by 9, so 60 is not divisible by 9.

Try It

Tell whether the number is divisible by 2, 3, 5, 6, 9, or 10.

a. 141 3 **b.** 455 5 **c.** 684 2, 3, 6, 9 **d.** 555 3, 5 **e.** 2700 2, 3, 5, 6, 9, 10

MEETING MIDDLE SCHOOL CLASSROOM NEEDS

Tips from Middle School Teachers

Number theory is a topic that encourages the study of patterns and conjecturing about patterns. Students need to be comfortable with taking risks, so I often use the think-pair strategy when teaching the lessons in this chapter. Students solve problems individually. Then they discuss their solutions with a partner. Finally, partners share their solutions with the class.

Cooperative Learning

Have students work in groups of three or four and give a number that has 3 as its last digit, but that is not divisible by 3. Possible answers: 13, 23, 43. Repeat the process using the number 9. Possible answers: 19, 29, 39. Then ask students to give 2-, 3-, 4-, or 5-digit numbers that end in each of the digits from 0 through 9 and that are divisible by 3.

Cultural Connection

The year 46 B.C. was called the Year of Confusion. It was 445 days long. The Romans added an extra 90 days to the year to bring it in line with the solar year.

Check Your Understanding

1. What are the advantages of knowing divisibility rules?
2. Which divisibility rules do you think are easiest to use? Explain.

5-1 Exercises and Applications

Practice and Apply

1. **Getting Started** Tell whether each number is divisible by 2, 5, or 10.

a. 66 2 **b.** 228 2 **c.** 45 5 **d.** 120 2, 5, 10 **e.** 985 5 **f.** 30 2, 5, 10

Tell whether each number is divisible by 2, 3, 5, 6, 9, or 10.

2. 63 3, 9 **3.** 55 5 **4.** 117 3, 9 **5.** 81 3, 9 **6.** 621 3, 9 **7.** 1360 2, 5, 10

8. 35 5 **9.** 42 2, 3, 6 **10.** 104 2 **11.** 4320 **12.** 10 **13.** 90

14. 27 3, 9 **15.** 68 2 **16.** 180 **17.** 135 3, 5, 9 **18.** 282 2, 3, 6 **19.** 56 2

20. 5555 5 **21.** 48 2, 3, 6 **22.** 362 2 **23.** 1110 **24.** 9 3, 9 **25.** 24 2, 3, 6

26. 66 2, 3, 6 **27.** 75 3, 5 **28.** 85 5 **29.** 695 5 **30.** 1587 3 **31.** 96 2, 3, 6

11. 2, 3, 5, 6, 9, 10 12. 2, 5, 10 13. 2, 3, 5, 6, 9, 10 16. 2, 3, 5, 6, 9, 10

Tell whether the first number is divisible by the second. 23. 2, 3, 5, 6, 10

32. 33, 3 Yes **33.** 132, 11 Yes **34.** 41, 5 No **35.** 105, 8 No **36.** 63, 4 No

37. 92, 9 No **38.** 65, 10 No **39.** 99, 11 Yes **40.** 78, 6 Yes **41.** 60, 4 Yes

42. 93, 2 No **43.** 115, 5 Yes **44.** 171, 9 Yes **45.** 109, 7 No **46.** 52, 6 No

47. 160, 8 Yes **48.** 54, 7 No **49.** 30, 4 No **50.** 52, 11 No **51.** 58, 8 No

52. 84, 7 Yes **53.** 76, 2 Yes **54.** 30, 10 Yes **55.** 120, 12 Yes **56.** 37, 3 No

57. Number Sense A leap year occurs in every year that is divisible by 4, unless the year ends in 2 zeros. Then, to be a leap year, it must be divisible by 400. Which of the following are leap years?

a. 1900 No **b.** 1999 No **c.** 1066 No **d.** 1776 Yes **e.** 2000 Yes

58. Test Prep By how many whole numbers is 24 divisible? D

Ⓐ 3 Ⓑ 6 Ⓒ 7 Ⓓ 8

PRACTICE 5-1

5-1 Exercises and Applications

Assignment Guide

- **Basic** 1–57 odds, 58–59, 61–62, 70–80 evens
- **Average** 2–56 evens, 57–60, 62–80 evens
- **Enriched** 3–57 odds, 58, 60–64, 65–79 odds

Exercise Notes

Exercise 57

Extension Have interested students research the need for leap years in our current calendar.

Exercise Answers

23. 2, 3, 5, 6, 10

PRACTICE

Name ____________________ **Practice 5-1**

Divisibility

Tell whether the number is divisible by 2, 3, 5, 6, 9, or 10.

1. 75 3, 5 **2.** 532 2 **3.** 625 5 **4.** 39 3

5. 118 2 **6.** 354 2, 3, 6 **7.** 585 3, 5, 9 **8.** 408 2, 3, 6

9. 235 5 **10.** 105 3, 5 **11.** 186 2, 3, 6 **12.** 73 None

13. 69 3 **14.** 317 None **15.** 200 2, 5, 10 **16.** 366 2, 3, 6

17. 306 2, 3, 6, 9 **18.** 645 3, 5 **19.** 223 None **20.** 326 2

Tell whether the first number is divisible by the second.

21. 46, 7 No **22.** 65, 2 No **23.** 43, 10 No **24.** 165, 3 Yes

25. 133, 5 No **26.** 66, 11 Yes **27.** 85, 3 No **28.** 185, 5 Yes

29. 99, 6 No **30.** 106, 7 No **31.** 150, 3 Yes **32.** 196, 2 Yes

33. 99, 5 No **34.** 128, 4 Yes **35.** 39, 6 No **36.** 33, 3 Yes

37. 110, 6 No **38.** 129, 9 No **39.** 37, 5 No **40.** 126, 7 Yes

41. 117, 8 No **42.** 96, 8 Yes **43.** 63, 2 No **44.** 192, 10 No

45. 74, 4 No **46.** 55, 5 Yes **47.** 171, 8 No **48.** 165, 11 Yes

49. There are 365 days in a non-leap year. Test 365 for divisibility by 2, 3, 5, 6, and 10. Divisible by 5 only

50. Social Science During an election year, the U.S. President is chosen by 538 electoral votes. Test 538 for divisibility by 2, 3, 5, 6, and 10. Divisible by 2 only

RETEACHING

Name ____________________ **Alternative Lesson 5-1**

Divisibility

A whole number is **divisible** by another whole number if the first number can be divided by the second number without leaving a remainder. Twelve is divisible by two since 12 ÷ 2 = 6. Twelve is not divisible by five since 12 ÷ 5 = 2 R2.

— Example 1 —

Is 35 divisible by 2, 5, and 10? To decide if a whole number is divisible by 2, 5, or 10, you can start at zero and count by 2s, 5s, or 10s. You can also use divisibility rules.

If the ones digit is even, the number is divisible by 2.
If the ones digit is 0 or 5, the number is divisible by 5.
If the ones digit is 0, the number is divisible by 10.

The ones digit is 5, so 35 is divisible by 5. It is not divisible by 2 or 10.

Try It Tell whether the number is divisible by 2, 5, or 10. Use the rules above.

a. 40 What is the ones digit? 0

Is the number divisible by 2? Yes. By 5? Yes. By 10? Yes.

40 is divisible by 2, 5, 10.

b. 85 5 **c.** 50 2, 5, 10 **d.** 136 2

— Example 2 —

Is 108 divisible by 3 and 9? To decide if a whole number is divisible by 3 or 9, you can count by 3s, or 9s. You can also use divisibility rules.

If the sum of the digits is divisible by 3, the number is divisible by 3.
If the sum of the digits is divisible by 9, the number is divisible by 9.

The sum of the digits in 108 is 1 + 0 + 8 = 9. Since 9 is divisible by both 3 and 9, 108 is divisible by both 3 and 9.

Try It Tell whether the number is divisible by 3 or 9. Use the rules above.

e. 342 Find the sum of the digits. 9

Is the sum divisible by 3? Yes. By 9? Yes.

342 is divisible by 3, 9.

f. 255 3 **g.** 204 3 **h.** 441 3, 9

Reteaching

Activity

Materials: Counters

- Separate 18 counters into groups of 2 and then 3. Are there are any counters left over? No
- Continue to separate the 18 counters into groups of 4, 5, 6, 7, 8, 9, and 10. If a group has no left-over counters, 18 is divisible by that number.
- Which numbers is 18 divisible by? 2, 3, 6, 9
- Repeat the process with 24, 30, and 36 counters. Determine what numbers each is divisible by.
  24: 2, 3, 4, 6, 8
  30: 2, 3, 5, 6, 10
  36: 2, 3, 4, 6, 9

Exercise Notes

■ Exercise 60

History Abraham Lincoln gave the Gettysburg Address on November 19, 1863, to dedicate a national cemetery on the battlefield at Gettysburg, PA. He took less than 3 minutes to deliver fewer than 300 words in 10 sentences.

Exercise Answers

59. No; It is important if you want to know if there are an even number of weeks in a month.
62. 4 model cars per carton; 4 is the only number between 3 and 10 that 53,716 is divisible by.
63. 10; A number divisible by 2 and 5 must end in 0, which is the rule for divisibility by 10.
64. Possible answer: Five months of 73 days; 365 is only divisible by 1, 5, 73, and 365.
65. Fifty-four thousand, seven
66. Five hundred thousand, two hundred
67. One hundred one thousand, one hundred ten
68. Two thousand, three hundred forty-five
69. Thirty-two thousand, three hundred two
70. Six hundred forty thousand
71. Five hundred thousand, seven
72. Six thousand, two hundred nineteen

Alternate Assessment

You may want to use the *Interactive CD-ROM Journal* with this assessment.

Journal Have students write the rules for divisibility, along with examples, in their journals.

▶ Quick Quiz

Test each number for divisibility by 2, 3, 5, 6, 9, and 10.

1. 357 3
2. 525 3, 5
3. 1500 2, 3, 5, 6, 10
4. 256 2
5. 216 2, 3, 6, 9

Available on Daily Transparency 5-1

---

59. There are approximately 52 weeks in a year. Is this number divisible by 12? Why would it be important for you to know this?

60. History Abraham Lincoln's Gettysburg Address begins "Four score and seven years ago ..." A score is 20 years, so "four score" is 80 years. A score is divisible by what numbers? 1, 2, 4, 5, 10, 20

61. Determine if the number of years in each of following is divisible by 2, 3, 5, 6, 9, or 10.

a. A decade (10 years) 2, 5, 10

b. A century (100 years) 2, 5, 10

c. A millennium (1000 years) 2, 5, 10

Problem Solving and Reasoning

62. Critical Thinking Marvel Models produces 53,716 model cars each month. They want to design shipping cartons that hold more than 3 but fewer than 10 models each. They want to pack each month's cars in the cartons, with no cars left over. What are their choices? Explain.

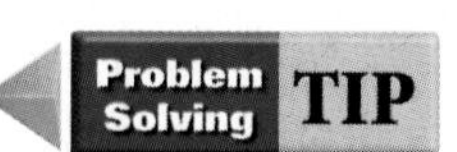

Use the rules of divisibility to find numbers that can evenly divide 53,716.

63. Communicate If a number is divisible by both 2 and 3, it is divisible by 6. If a number is divisible by 2 and 5, what other number is it divisible by? Explain.

64. Critical Thinking The solar calendar of the Aztec people had 365 days, which was 18 months of 20 days and 5 "unlucky" extra days. How could the Aztecs have rearranged their calendar so that each month had the same number of days and no "unlucky" days? Explain.

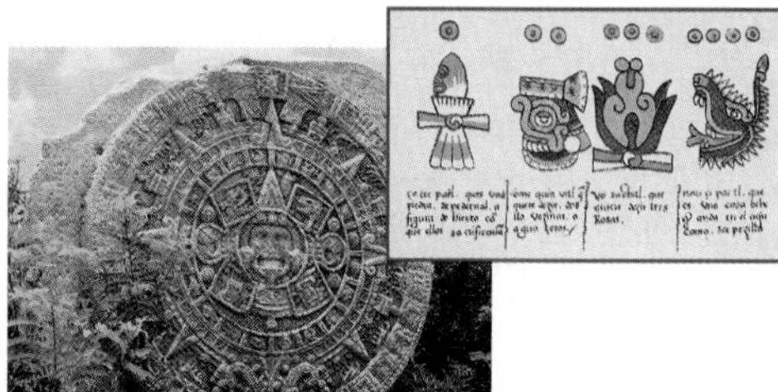

PROBLEM SOLVING 5-1

Mixed Review

Write each number in word form. *[Lesson 2-1]*

65. 54,007 **66.** 500,200 **67.** 101,110 **68.** 2345

69. 32,302 **70.** 640,000 **71.** 500,007 **72.** 6219

Multiply. *[Lesson 3-9]*

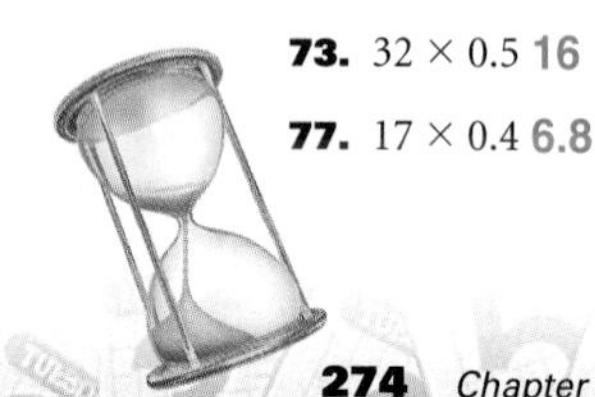

73. 32×0.5 16 **74.** 15×0.9 13.5 **75.** 8.1×0.6 4.86 **76.** 5.5×1.4 7.7

77. 17×0.4 6.8 **78.** 21×0.3 6.3 **79.** 68×0.2 13.6 **80.** 51×1.2 61.2

PROBLEM SOLVING

Name ______________

Guided Problem Solving 5-1

GPS PROBLEM 62, STUDENT PAGE 274

Marvel Models produces 53,716 model cars each month. They want to design shipping cartons that hold more than 3 but fewer than 10 models each. They want to pack each month's cars in their cartons, with no cars left over. What are their choices? Explain.

— Understand —

1. Underline what you are asked to find.
2. Circle the information you need.

— Plan —

3. To find which carton sizes to use for shipping, use divisibility rules or division to test 53,716 for divisibility by 4, 5, 6, 7, 8, and 9. If 53,716 is evenly divisible by the carton size, then all the models can be shipped using that sized carton.

Is 53,716 evenly divisible

a. by 4? Yes. b. by 5? No. c. by 6? No.

d. by 7? No. e. by 8? No. f. by 9? No.

— Solve —

4. Which number is 53,716 evenly divisible by? 4
5. Write a sentence to tell which size cartons can be used by Marvel Models.
Marvel Models should design a carton that holds 4 cars.

— Look Back —

6. How do you know that you checked all the possible carton sizes given in the problem?
Possible answer: All of the whole numbers between 3 and 10 have been checked.

SOLVE ANOTHER PROBLEM

The Pool Company is shipping 5325 wading pools. They want to design shipping cartons that hold 2, 3, 5, 6, 9, or 10 pools each. They want to pack each month's pools in their cartons with no pools left over. What are their choices? Explain.

Shipping cartons can hold either 3 or 5 pools since 5325 is evenly divisible only by 3 or 5.

ENRICHMENT

Name ______________

Extend Your Thinking 5-1

Patterns in Numbers

1. Is each number divisible by 4? Write *yes* or *no*.

a. 108 Yes. b. 212 Yes. c. 250 No.

d. 316 Yes. e. 625 No. f. 1020 Yes.

2. List the numbers in Question 1 that were divisible by 4.
108, 212, 316, 1020
3. Choose one of the numbers that was divisible by 4. Change the hundreds digit. Write the new number. Is the number still divisible by 4? How do you know?
Possible answer: Change 108 to 208. The new number is divisible by 4 since there is no remainder when divided by 4.
4. Look at the number formed by the last two digits in each of the numbers you listed in Question 2. What pattern do you see in these digits?
The numbers increase by 4, and all are evenly divisible by 4.
5. Write a divisibility rule for dividing by 4.
If the number formed by the last two digits of a given number is divisible by 4, then the number is divisible by 4.
6. Test your rule. Is each number divisible by 4? Write *yes* or *no*.

a. 111 No. b. 128 Yes. c. 296 Yes.

d. 332 Yes. e. 548 Yes. f. 1,036 Yes.

g. 3,456 Yes. h. 65,728 Yes. i. 362,042 No.

Prime Factorization

5-2

▶ Lesson Link You've learned to use divisibility rules to decide if one number is divisible by another. Now you'll use those rules to express whole numbers in terms of their simplest factors. ◀

You'll Learn ...

- the difference between prime and composite numbers
- to find the prime factorization of a number

... How It's Used

Programmers use prime numbers when developing security programs that make it difficult to read information from other people's computers.

Vocabulary

prime number

composite number

prime factorization

Explore Factorization

The Great Rectangle Search

Materials: Graph paper

Any number of squares can be arranged into a rectangle. Some can be arranged into only one rectangle, and some can be arranged into several different rectangles.

1. On a sheet of graph paper, copy and complete the table down to 20 squares. Two rectangles are the same if one can be turned to look like the other.

Number of Squares	Number of Rectangles	Sketches
1	1	
2	1	
3	1	
4	2	

2. Make a list of the numbers for which you could draw only one rectangle. Make a second list of the numbers for which you could draw more than one.
3. How many factors does each number in your first list have? How many does each number in your second list have? What can you conclude about the numbers that can be made into only one rectangle?
4. Is there a number of squares that cannot be arranged into a rectangle? Explain.

MEETING INDIVIDUAL NEEDS

Resources

5-2 Practice
5-2 Reteaching
5-2 Problem Solving
5-2 Enrichment
5-2 Daily Transparency
Problem of the Day
Review
Quick Quiz
Teaching Tool Transparency 7
Technology Master 22
Chapter 5 Project Master

Learning Modalities

Kinesthetic Using counters to make rectangular arrays offers students another medium in which to explore prime and composite numbers.

Social Have students work in pairs on **Explore**. Have one partner work on the entries for the odd numbers and the other the entries for the even numbers.

Challenge

Ask students the following question and have them explain their answer. What is the greatest number of prime numbers that can occur in a set of ten consecutive numbers? The numbers 2–11 contain five prime numbers. All other sets contain at most four prime numbers because each set has five even numbers that cannot be prime and five odd numbers. The odd number that ends in five (except five itself) is not prime.

5-2 Lesson Organizer

Objectives

- Learn the difference between prime and composite numbers.
- Find the prime factorization of a number.

Vocabulary

- Prime number, composite number, prime factorization

Materials

- Explore: Graph paper

NCTM Standards

- 1–2, 4, 6

Review

Test each number for divisibility by 2, 3, 5, 6, 9, and 10.

1. 630 2, 3, 5, 6, 9, 10
2. 405 3, 5, 9
3. 324 2, 3, 6, 9

Available on Daily Transparency 5-2

1 Introduce

Explore

You may wish to use Teaching Tool Transparency 7: $\frac{1}{4}$-Inch Graph Paper with **Explore**.

The Point
Students draw rectangular arrays on graph paper to find patterns between prime and composite numbers.

Ongoing Assessment
Check that students are able to find all the rectangles for the given numbers. Explain to students that vertical or horizontal rectangular sketches are acceptable.

For Groups That Finish Early
Follow Steps 1–3 with the numbers 21 through 25. Remember that 21, 22, 24, and 25 each have more than one rectangular representation.

Answers for Explore on next page.

Answers for Explore

1. Sketches of rectangles for the numbers 15–20 on page C3.

   5; 1;

   6; 2; 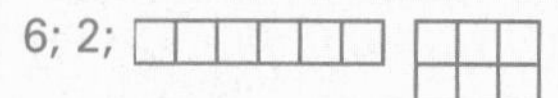

   7; 1; 

   8; 2; 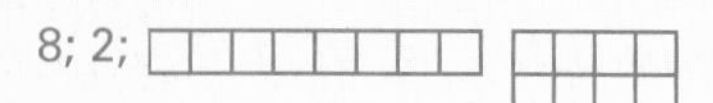

   9; 2; 

   10; 2;

   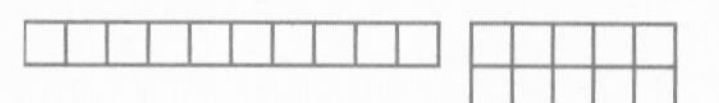

   11; 1;

   12; 3; 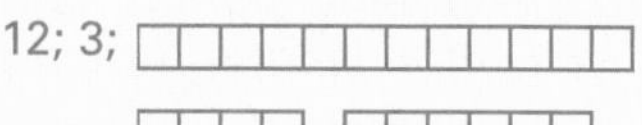

   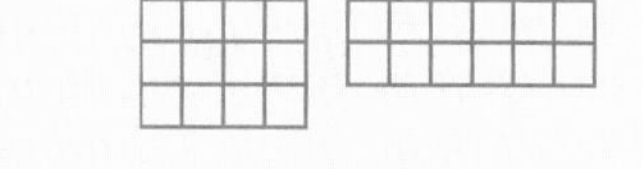

   13; 1;

   14; 2;

   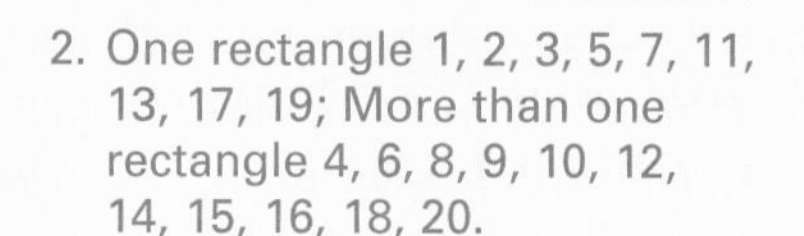

2. One rectangle 1, 2, 3, 5, 7, 11, 13, 17, 19; More than one rectangle 4, 6, 8, 9, 10, 12, 14, 15, 16, 18, 20.
3. 1 or 2; 3, 4, 5 or 6; They have only 1 or 2 factors.
4. 0; Any whole number of squares can be arranged into a single-row rectangle.

2 Teach

Learn

After discussing prime and composite numbers, have students identify the prime numbers between 30 and 40. 31, 37

Alternate Examples

Find the prime factorization of 300.

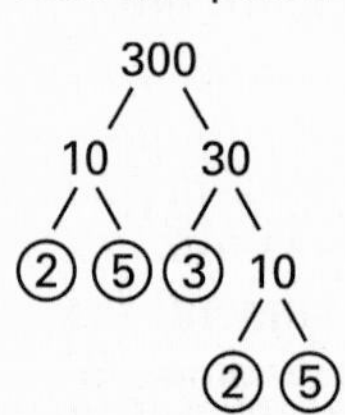

The prime factorization is $2 \times 2 \times 3 \times 5 \times 5$, or $2^2 \times 3 \times 5^2$.

DID YOU KNOW?

The smallest number that is either composite or prime is 2. Mathematicians consider 0 and 1 to be neither prime nor composite.

Learn Prime Factorization

Every whole number greater than 1 is either a **prime number** or a **composite number**. A prime number has exactly two factors, 1 and itself. A composite number has more than two factors.

	4	7	10	25	29
Factors	1, 2, 4	1, 7	1, 2, 5, 10	1, 5, 25	1, 29
Type	composite	prime	composite	composite	prime

The first ten prime numbers are: 2, 3, 5, 7, 11, 13, 17, 19, 23, and 29.

Every human has a unique fingerprint. Similarly, every composite number has a unique "factorprint." It is called the **prime factorization**. It's the set of primes whose product equals the number.

You can use a "factor tree" to find a prime factorization. Find two numbers whose product equals the original number, and write them below. If a number is prime, circle it. If a number is composite, continue to break it apart until you only have prime numbers left. Rewrite the prime factors at the bottom from least to greatest.

30
③ 10
② ⑤

$30 = 2 \times 3 \times 5$

Remember

3^2 is in exponential notation. It means 3×3. The exponent, in this case 2, tells you how many times the base, in this case 3, is used as a factor.

[Page 78]

Example 1

Find the prime factorization of 630.

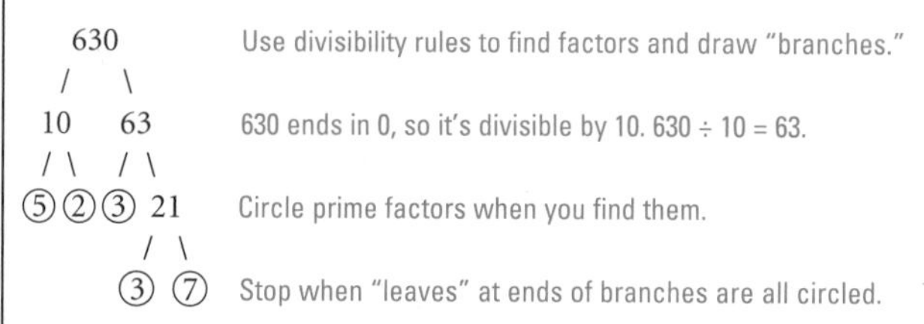

The prime factorization is $2 \times 3 \times 3 \times 5 \times 7$, or $2 \times 3^2 \times 5 \times 7$.

Try It

Find the prime factorization of each number.

a. 12 $2^2 \times 3$ **b.** 20 $2^2 \times 5$ **c.** 36 $2^2 \times 3^2$ **d.** 45 $3^2 \times 5$ **e.** 210 $2 \times 3 \times 5 \times 7$

MATH EVERY DAY

Problem of the Day

A rowboat can carry only 150 pounds safely. How can a woman weighing 150 pounds and her two daughters, each weighing 75 pounds, use the boat to cross the river? Each of them can row the boat.

The two daughters row the boat from River Bank 1 to River Bank 2. One of the daughters rows back to River Bank 1. The mother rows the boat from River Bank 1 to River Bank 2. The other daughter rows back to River Bank 1, picks up her sister, and rows to River Bank 2.

Available on Daily Transparency 5-2

An Extension is provided in the transparency package.

Fact of the Day

There are 168 prime numbers between 1 and 1000. The largest prime number less than 1000 is 997.

Mental Math

Give the prime factorization mentally.

1. 33 3×11
2. 44 $2^2 \times 11$
3. 63 $3^2 \times 7$
4. 30 $2 \times 3 \times 5$

Skye and Erica need to plant a rectangular garden. Its length times its width equals 90 ft². They want to determine all the ways they could lay out the garden with whole-number dimensions.

Skye thinks ...

I'll use the divisibility rules and number sense to list the pairs of factors that multiply to make 90.

Every whole number is divisible by 1.	1×90
90 ends in 0, so it's divisible by 2.	2×45
$9 + 0 = 9$, so 90 is divisible by 3.	3×30
90 ends in 0, so it's divisible by 5.	5×18
90 is divisible by 2 and 3, so also 6.	6×15
90 ends in 0, so it's divisible by 10.	9×10

Since $90 \div 2$ is an odd number, 90 is not divisible by 4 or 8.
Since 7×13 is 91, 90 is not divisible by 7.

There are six ways we can lay out the garden.

Erica thinks ...

I'll use the prime factors and an organized list to help me find all the factors.

```
     90
    /  \
   9    10
  / \   / \
 (3)(3)(5)(2)
```

1 prime factor
2, 3, 5

2 prime factors
6 (2 × 3), 9 (3 × 3), 10 (2 × 5), 15 (3 × 5)

3 prime factors
18 (2 × 3 × 3), 30 (2 × 3 × 5), 45 (3 × 3 × 5)

Including 1 and 90, there are 12 factors. So, there are 6 pairs of factors that will make 90. There are 6 ways we can lay out the garden.

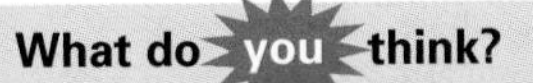

1. Which method works better for large numbers? Why?
2. How can Skye be certain 90 isn't divisible by 4 or 8?

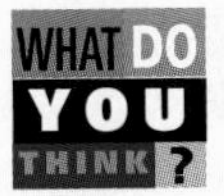

Students see two methods of solving a problem involving factorization. One involves listing possible factors and the other involves using a factor tree to find the prime factorization.

Answers for What Do You Think?

1. For large numbers, using prime factors is faster.
2. 4 and 8 both have more than one factor of 2, and since $90 \div 2$ is 45 (an odd number), 90 can't be divisible by 4 or 8.

MEETING MIDDLE SCHOOL CLASSROOM NEEDS

Tips from Middle School Teachers

When teaching this lesson, I have students arrange themselves in all the possible arrangements of equal-length rows. We then discuss the arrangements and the ideas of prime and composite numbers. If there are a prime number of students in the class, I have students repeat the activity, including me in the arrangements. As an extension, we discuss if it is possible for two consecutive numbers, other than 2 and 3, to be prime.

Team Teaching

Have the music teacher explain to students how rectangular arrays can be used to plan marching-band assignments.

Science Connection

In addition to his work with prime and composite numbers, Eratosthenes calculated the Earth's circumference. He figured the angle of shadows cast by the Sun in different cities and measured how far apart they were. He calculated the circumference of the Earth as more than 28,000 miles. The actual circumference is 24,860 miles.

5-2 Exercises and Applications

Assignment Guide

- **Basic** 1–37 odds, 38, 40, 44–45, 48–58 evens
- **Average** 1, 2–44 evens, 45, 46–58 evens
- **Enriched** 3–37 odds, 38–47, 49–59 odds

3 Practice and Assess

Check

Answers for Check Your Understanding

1. Use any factors.
2. Every other even number is divisible by 2.

Exercise Notes

Exercises 8–37

Extension You may wish to allow the use of calculators. Encourage students to use exponents when writing the prime factorizations.

Reteaching

Activity

Materials: Counters

- Make a rectangular array with 6 counters to show a pair of numbers whose product is 6. Do not use 1×6.
- What two numbers give a product of 6? 2 and 3 Are these numbers prime? Yes What is the prime factorization of 6? 2×3
- Now make an array to show a pair of numbers whose product is 18. Do not use 1×18. Are both numbers prime? No
- For the numbers that are composite, make another array with the counters.
- The array should show that 18 is the product $2 \times 3 \times 3$ which is the prime factorization of 18.
- Use this method to find the prime factorization of 36, 45, and 54. $2^2 \times 3^2$; 5×3^2; 2×3^3

Check Your Understanding

1. When you draw a factor tree, how can you tell which two factors to use to start the tree?
2. Why is 2 the only even prime number?

5-2 Exercises and Applications

Practice and Apply

1. **Getting Started** Use mental math to find the prime factorization.
   a. 15 5×3 b. 33 11×3 c. 14 7×2 d. 21 7×3 e. 6 2×3 f. 35 5×7

Given the number and its factors, tell whether it is prime or composite.

2. 45: 1, 3, 5, 9, 15, 45 Composite
3. 67: 1, 67 Prime
4. 37: 1, 37 Prime
5. 26: 1, 2, 13, 26 Composite
6. 53: 1, 53 Prime
7. 65: 1, 5, 13, 65 Composite

Find the prime factorization.

12. $3^4 \times 5$ 16. $2^5 \times 3^2$ 21. $2^2 \times 3^2 \times 19$
23. $2^2 \times 3 \times 5$ 30. $3^3 \times 11$ 32. $2 \times 3^4 \times 5 \times 7$

8. 58 2×29 9. 25 5^2 10. 26 2×13 11. 95 5×19 12. 405 13. 125 5^3
14. 56 $2^3 \times 7$ 15. 6 2×3 16. 288 17. 88 $2^3 \times 11$ 18. 87 3×29 19. 72 $2^3 \times 3^2$
20. 50 2×5^2 21. 684 22. 27 3^3 23. 60 24. 32 2^5 25. 105 $3 \times 5 \times 7$
26. 96 $2^5 \times 3$ 27. 48 $2^4 \times 3$ 28. 13 prime 29. 85 5×17 30. 297 31. 162 2×3^4
32. 5670 33. 165 $3 \times 5 \times 11$ 34. 693 $3^2 \times 7 \times 11$ 35. 468 $2^2 \times 3^2 \times 13$ 36. 10 2×5 37. 42 $2 \times 3 \times 7$

38. Mr. Armond has 36 students in his math class. He wants to put them into groups of the same size. He also wants the number in each group to be a prime factor of 36. What are his choices? 2 or 3 students per group.

39. **Chance** Tran dropped a marker on the board. Was it more likely to fall on a prime number or on a composite number? Explain.

40. **Test Prep** Which number appears more than once in the prime factorization of 100? C
   Ⓐ Only 2 Ⓑ Only 5 Ⓒ 2 and 5 Ⓓ There are no repeated factors.

41. Olivia has three friends who live in her apartment building. One day, she noticed that she and her friends all had apartment numbers that were three-digit prime numbers less than 110. If everyone lived in a different apartment, what were the four apartment numbers? 101, 103, 107, 109

39. Composite; There are more of them.

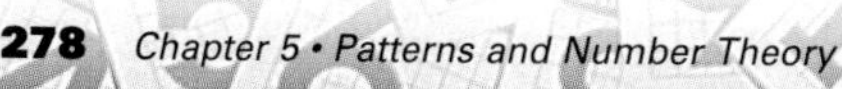

PRACTICE

Name ______ **Practice 5-2**

Prime Factorization

Given the number and its factors, tell whether it is prime or composite.

1. 92: 1, 2, 4, 23, 46, 92 Composite
2. 121: 1, 11, 121 Composite
3. 83: 1, 83 Prime
4. 129: 1, 3, 43, 129 Composite
5. 52: 1, 2, 4, 13, 26, 52 Composite
6. 55: 1, 5, 11, 55 Composite
7. 29: 1, 29 Prime
8. 57: 1, 3, 19, 57 Composite
9. 63: 1, 3, 7, 9, 21, 63 Composite

Find the prime factorization.

10. 12 $2^2 \times 3$
11. 40 $2^3 \times 5$
12. 64 2^6
13. 36 $2^2 \times 3^2$
14. 60 $2^2 \times 3 \times 5$
15. 65 5×13
16. 20 $2^2 \times 5$
17. 30 $2 \times 3 \times 5$
18. 56 $2^3 \times 7$
19. 21 3×7
20. 18 2×3^2
21. 16 2^4
22. 630 $2 \times 3^2 \times 5 \times 7$
23. 1001 $7 \times 11 \times 13$
24. 625 5^4

25. The prime factorization of a number is $2 \times 2 \times 3 \times 3 \times 3 \times 5 \times 5 \times 5 \times 5 \times 5$. What is the number? 337,500

26. **Social Science** The House of Representatives has 435 members. If a committee has a prime number of members, and that number is a factor of 435, then how many members can be on the committee? 3, 5, or 29

RETEACHING

Name ______ **Alternative Lesson 5-2**

Prime Factorization

Every whole number greater than 1 is either a **prime number** or a **composite number**. A prime number has exactly two factors: 1 and itself. A composite number has more than two factors. The numbers 0 and 1 are neither prime nor composite.

Example 1

The factors of 185 are 1, 5, 37, and 185. Is 185 a prime number or a composite number?

Since there are more than two factors of 185, the number is a composite number.

Try It Given the number and its factors, tell whether it is prime or composite.

a. 25: 1, 5, 25 Composite.
b. 83: 1, 83 Prime.
c. 54: 1, 2, 3, 6, 9, 18, 27, 54 Composite.
d. 68: 1, 2, 4, 17, 34, 68 Composite.

Example 2

Write the prime factorization of 50. Tell whether it is prime or composite.

To decide if a number is prime or composite, you need to find the factors. You can use a factor tree to find the prime factors. If the prime factorization is 1 × the number, the number is a prime number. If the prime factorization is **not** 1 × the number, the number is a composite number.

Here are two factor trees that show the prime factors of 50.

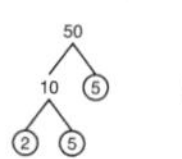

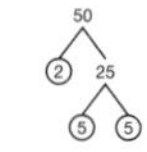

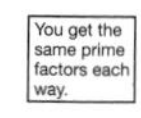

You get the same prime factors each way.

$50 = 2 \times 5 \times 5$ ← Prime Factorization

Since the prime factorization is **not** 1 × the number, 50 is a composite number.

Try It Write the prime factorization of each number. Then tell whether the number is prime or composite.

e. 18 = $2 \times 3 \times 3$, composite
f. 23 = 1×23, prime
g. 27 = $3 \times 3 \times 3$, composite
h. 60 = $2 \times 2 \times 3 \times 5$, composite
i. 93 = 3×31, composite
j. 115 = 5×23, composite

42. The prime factorization of a number is $2 \times 3 \times 5 \times 5 \times 7 \times 13 \times 29$. What is the number? 395,850

43. **History** Eratosthenes designed a method, called the Sieve of Eratosthenes, to find prime numbers. Between the numbers 40 and 80, he found 10 prime numbers. What are they? 41, 43, 47, 53, 59, 61, 67, 71, 73, 79

APRIL

S	M	T	W	T	F	S
			1	2	3	4
5	6	7	8	9	10	11
12	13	14	15	16	17	18
19	20	21	22	23	24	25
26	27	28	29	30		

Johnson, William H.. Untitled (Soapbox Racing), 1939-40. National Museum of American Art, Smithsonian Institute, Washington, D.C..

Problem Solving and Reasoning

44. **Communicate** An April calendar shows 30 days, labeled 1 through 30. How many days have a prime number date? How many have a composite number date? If your friend was born on a day in April, would it more likely be a prime date or a composite date? Explain.

45. **Communicate** Would you prefer your teacher to assign the odd-numbered problems or the prime-numbered problems for homework? Explain. Prime; There are fewer of them.

46. **Communicate** What is the smallest composite number that has all of the first 5 prime numbers as factors? Explain. $2 \times 3 \times 5 \times 7 \times 11 = 2310$

47.  A prime number is any whole number with exactly two factors, itself and 1. Explain why 1 isn't a prime number. 1 has only one factor.

PROBLEM SOLVING 5-2

Mixed Review

Round each number to the given place value. *[Lesson 2-2]*

48. 456,892; thousands 457,000

49. 5,678,022; hundred-thousands 5,700,000

50. 923,894; hundreds 923,900

51. 5,890,324,331; millions 5,890,000,000

Divide. *[Lesson 3-10]*

52. $10 \div 6$ 1.666...

53. $12 \div 10$ 1.2

54. $4 \div 8$ 0.5

55. $14 \div 56$ 0.25

56. $1 \div 5$ 0.2

57. $1 \div 4$ 0.25

58. $1 \div 10$ 0.1

59. $1 \div 2$ 0.5

Project Progress

Figure out your favorite number's prime factors. Find numbers by which your favorite number is divisible and some common multiples of your number. Pair your number with other numbers to find the least common multiple of each pair. Record all the data in a chart.

Problem Solving: Understand, Plan, Solve, Look Back

PROBLEM SOLVING

Name ____________

Guided Problem Solving 5-2

GPS PROBLEM 38, STUDENT PAGE 278

Mr. Armond has 36 students in his math class. He wants to put them into groups of the same size. He also wants the number in each group to be a prime factor of 36. What are his choices?

— Understand —

1. What are you asked to find? The size group Mr. Armond can use for student groups when the group size is a prime factor of 36.

— Plan —

2. To find the possible group sizes, find the prime factors of 36.

Complete the factor tree to find the prime factors.

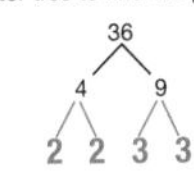

36 = 2 × 2 × 3 × 3

— Solve —

3. Which numbers are the prime factors of 36? 2 and 3

4. Write a sentence to tell how many students could be in each group. There can be 2 or 3 students in each group.

— Look Back —

5. How could you have found the answer using another method? Possible answer: Make an organized list. Divide 36 by all prime numbers from 2 to 17 to see which are factors of 36.

SOLVE ANOTHER PROBLEM

Cassie is lining up 45 students in the pep squad. She wants each row to have the same number of students. She also wants the number of students in each row to be a prime number. What are her options? 15 rows of 3 students or 9 rows of 5 students.

ENRICHMENT

Name ____________

Extend Your Thinking 5-2

Critical Thinking

Goldbach's Conjecture

Christian Goldbach, an eighteenth-century Russian mathematician, believed that every even number greater than 4 could be written as the sum of two odd primes. For example 16 = 5 + 11. He also believed that every even number greater than 4 could be written as the sum of three primes. For example, 16 = 2 + 3 + 11 or 16 = 2 + 7 + 7.

1. Complete the table. Possible answers:

Number	Sum of two odd primes	Sum of three primes
6	3 + 3	2 + 2 + 2
8	3 + 5	2 + 3 + 3
14	7 + 7	2 + 5 + 7
30	11 + 19	2 + 11 + 17
38	7 + 31	2 + 5 + 31
40	17 + 23	2 + 7 + 31
50	19 + 31	2 + 7 + 41
88	5 + 83	2 + 3 + 83
100	47 + 53	2 + 31 + 67
116	19 + 97	2 + 53 + 61
132	23 + 109	2 + 59 + 71
150	71 + 79	2 + 59 + 89
152	73 + 79	2 + 61 + 89

Choose a composite number between 60 and 70 and write the number as the sum of Possible answers:

2. two primes. 23 + 41 = 64

3. three primes. 2 + 31 + 31 = 64

Choose a composite number between 135 and 150 and write the number as the sum of Possible answers:

4. two primes. 67 + 73 = 140

5. three primes. 2 + 67 + 71 = 140

Exercise Notes

Exercise 43

Extension Have students use the following steps to make a list of the prime numbers from 1–100. Tell students this method is called the Sieve of Eratosthenes.

a. Write the numbers from 1–100.

b. Cross out 1; it is not prime.

c. Circle 2 and cross out all other multiples of 2.

d. Circle 3 and cross out all other multiples of 3.

e. Circle 5 and cross out all other multiples of 5.

f. Continue in the same way. When you have finished, the circled numbers are prime.

The prime numbers from 1–100 are 2, 3, 5, 7, 11, 13, 17, 19, 23, 29, 31, 37, 41, 43, 47, 53, 59, 61, 67, 71, 73, 79, 83, 89, 97.

Exercise 44

Error Prevention Some students may include the number 1 as they find the number of prime-number days. Remind students that 1 is neither prime nor composite.

Project Progress

You may want to have students use Chapter 5 Project Master.

Exercise Answers

44. 10 prime; 19 composite; Composite; Because there are more of them.

Alternate Assessment

Self Assessment Have students identify any steps they find difficult to accomplish or do not understand when finding the prime factorization of a composite number and include an example.

Quick Quiz

Give the prime factorization of each number.

1. 84 $2^2 \times 3 \times 7$
2. 48 $2^4 \times 3$
3. 27 3^3
4. 42 $2 \times 3 \times 7$
5. 75 3×5^2

Available on Daily Transparency 5-2

INTERACTIVE LESSON

5-3 Lesson Organizer

Objective

- Find the least common multiple for two numbers.

Vocabulary

- Multiple, common multiple, least common multiple (LCM)

Materials

- Explore: Spreadsheet software

NCTM Standards

- 1–4, 6

Review

Count by the indicated number.

1. By 5s to 60 5, 10, 15, 20, 25, 30, 35, 40, 45, 50, 55, 60
2. By 4s to 48 4, 8, 12, 16, 20, 24, 28, 32, 36, 40, 44, 48
3. By 6s to 60 6, 12, 18, 24, 30, 36, 42, 48, 54, 60
4. By 8s to 80 8, 16, 24, 32, 40, 48, 56, 64, 72, 80

Available on Daily Transparency 5-3

5-3 Least Common Multiples

You'll Learn ...

- to find the least common multiple for two numbers

... How It's Used

Astronomers use least common multiples to determine when celestial objects will pass Earth at the same time.

Vocabulary

multiple

common multiple

least common multiple (LCM)

Lesson Link You've learned about the numbers that divide a given number. Now you'll learn about the numbers that a given number divides.

Explore Common Multiples

Going In Evenly

Materials: Spreadsheet software

1. On a blank spreadsheet, enter the following information. The numbers in column A should go through 30.

	A	B	C
1		First Divisor	Second Divisor
2		2	3
3			
4	Dividend	First Quotient	Second Quotient
5	1	=A5/$B$2	=A5/$C$2
6	2		
7	3		
8	4		

2. Copy the formulas in B5 and C5 down each column to the bottom of the list in column A.
3. Columns B and C contain the number of times 2 and 3 go into the numbers from 1 to 30. How many numbers does 2 go into evenly? How many does 3 go into evenly? How many numbers do both 2 and 3 go into evenly? What's the first number they both go into evenly?
4. Change the number in B2 to 4. How many numbers do both 3 and 4 go into evenly? What's the first number they both go into evenly?
5. Change the numbers in B2 and C2 to numbers of your choice. Find a pair of numbers that both go evenly into only one of the numbers from 1 to 30.

1 Introduce

Explore

You may wish to use Lesson Enhancement Transparency 20 with **Explore**.

The Point
Students use spreadsheet software to investigate numbers with factors of 2, 3, and 4 as well as numbers of their choice.

Ongoing Assessment
Be sure that students understand the information being provided by the spreadsheet.

For Groups That Finish Early
Repeat Steps 1–4 with the numbers 31 through 40.

MEETING INDIVIDUAL NEEDS

Resources

5-3 Practice
5-3 Reteaching
5-3 Problem Solving
5-3 Enrichment
5-3 Daily Transparency
Problem of the Day
Review
Quick Quiz
Teaching Tool Transparencies 2, 3
Lesson Enhancement Transparency 20

Interactive CD-ROM Lesson

Learning Modalities

Visual When students make their lists of multiples for pairs of numbers, have them put circles around each pair of common multiples.

Social Have students work in groups of 3 or 4 on **Explore**. If enough computers are available, you could have students work in pairs to maximize their experience.

English Language Development

Give students additional help with the terms in this lesson. Be sure they understand that, in these contexts, *common* means *shared*, not *ordinary* or *usual*. Also discuss what it means for two people to "have something in common."

Learn Least Common Multiple

A **multiple** of a number is the product of the number and a whole number.

Multiples of 6: 6, 12, 18, **24,** 30, 36, 42, **48,** 54, 60, 66, **72,** ...

Multiples of 8: 8, 16, **24,** 32, 40, **48,** 56, 64, **72,** 80, ...

Numbers that appear on both lists are **common multiples**. The **least common multiple (LCM)** of two numbers is the *smallest* common multiple of the numbers.

One way to find the LCM of two numbers is to list multiples of both numbers. Then choose the smallest multiple that appears on both lists.

Study TIP

Factors and multiples have related meanings. The multiples of 6 are 6, 12, 18, and so on. The factors of 6 are 1, 2, 3, and 6.

Examples

1 Find the least common multiple of 10 and 12.

Multiples of 10: 10, 20, 30, 40, 50, **60,** 70, 80, 90, 100, ...

Multiples of 12: 12, 24, 36, 48, **60,** ...

The least common multiple of 10 and 12 is 60.

2 A U.S. President is elected every 4 years. A U.S. senator is elected every 6 years. If a senator is elected the same year as the President, how many years will it be until the senator could run for reelection during a presidential campaign?

"When I said, 'term limits,' I was speaking in dog years."

History Link

According to the U.S. Constitution, a person can be elected to serve only two 4-year terms as President. There is no limit to the number of times a person can be elected to serve as a senator.

Multiples of 4: 4, 8, **12,** 16, 20, 24, 28, 32, ...

Multiples of 6: 6, **12,** 18, 24, 30, 36, ...

The senator will run for reelection during a presidential campaign in another 12 years.

Try It

Find the LCM of each pair of numbers.

a. 5, 7 35 **b.** 3, 10 30 **c.** 4, 10 20 **d.** 9, 15 45

MATH EVERY DAY

Problem of the Day

The people at a meeting of Team Sports are forming teams with an equal number of players. When they form groups of 2, 3, 4, 5, or 6, there is always exactly one person left. What is the smallest number of players that could be part of the Team Sports group? 61 people

Available on Daily Transparency 5-3

An Extension is provided in the transparency package.

Fact of the Day

The number 1 followed by 100 zeros is called a *googol*. The number 1 followed by a googol zeros is called a *googolplex*.

Mental Math

Find the least common multiple for each pair of numbers mentally.

1. 10, 90 90
2. 4, 5 20
3. 8, 48 48
4. 3, 8 24

Answers for Explore

1–2. Check students' entries.

3. 15; 10; 5; 6
4. 2; 12
5. Possible answer: 4 and 5

2 Teach

Learn

Using the lists of numbers from **Review** on page 280, have students identify some common multiples and the least common multiple of each pair of numbers:

4 and 6: 12, 24, 36, 48; LCM: 12

4 and 8: 8, 16, 24, 32, 40, 48; LCM: 8

Alternate Examples

1. Find the least common multiple of 18 and 24.

   Multiples of 18: 18, 36, 54, **72,** 90, ...

   Multiples of 24: 24, 48, **72,** 96, 120, ...

   The least common multiple of 18 and 24 is 72.

2. Nate plays in a soccer game every 6 days and in a baseball game every 8 days. If he plays in soccer and baseball games on the same day, how many days will it be before he plays in both games again?

   Multiples of 6: 6, 12, 18, **24,** 30, 36, ...

   Multiples of 8: 8, 16, **24,** 32, 40, 48, ...

   Nate will play in both games again in 24 days.

Alternate Examples

3. Nancy and Gary want to spend the same amount of money on tapes and CDs for the local library. If tapes cost $10 each and CDs cost $14 each, what is the least amount of money they can spend for each?

   Find the least common multiple of 10 and 14.

   Multiples of 10: 10, 20, 30, 40, 50, 60, **70**, 80, 90, ...

   Multiples of 14: 14, 28, 42, 56, **70**, 84, ...

   The least amount of money they can spend for each is $70.

3 Practice and Assess

Check

Students should recognize from the examples that the LCM of two numbers is never less than the larger of the two numbers, but it may be the greater of the two numbers.

Answers for Check Your Understanding

1. No; The LCM can be equal to one of the numbers.
2. Yes; Since two prime numbers have no factors in common, the smallest number that can be divided evenly by both prime numbers is the product of the prime numbers.
3. Possible answer: A factor of a number is a number that evenly divides a given number. A multiple of a number is the product of the number and a whole number. 8 has four factors and an infinite number of multiples.

▶ History Link

Clepsydras were used in courts of law. Corrupt lawyers sometimes bribed the timekeepers to put muddy water in the clepsydra. This water would flow more slowly, and the lawyer would have more time to speak.

Example 3

The clepsydra (KLEP-suh-druh), or water clock, and the hourglass were among the first clocks. In a clepsydra, water pours from one container into another at a regular rate to mark the passage of time. In an hourglass, sand flows from the top container to the bottom one.

One ancient clepsydra had to be refilled every 12 minutes. One kind of hourglass had to be turned over every 30 minutes. If you start both clocks at the same time, when will you need to restart them at the same time?

Find the least common multiple of 12 and 30.

Multiples of 30: 30, **60,** 90, 120, 150, 180, 210, 240, 270, 300, ...

Multiples of 12: 12, 24, 36, 48, **60,** ...

The least common multiple of 12 and 30 is 60. You will restart both clocks at the same time every 60 minutes.

Try It

Find the LCM of each pair of numbers.

a. 6, 9 18 **b.** 8, 2 8 **c.** 20, 25 100 **d.** 10, 12 60
e. 5, 11 55 **f.** 6, 15 30 **g.** 6, 54 54 **h.** 1297, 1 1297

Check Your Understanding

1. For any pair of numbers, is the least common multiple always greater than either number? Explain.
2. Terrence believes that the least common multiple of two prime numbers is always the product of those numbers. Do you think Terrence is correct? Explain.
3. What's the difference between a factor and a multiple? How many factors does 8 have? How many multiples?

MEETING MIDDLE SCHOOL CLASSROOM NEEDS

Tips from Middle School Teachers

Because number-theory concepts are of such great importance in the study of algebra, I work especially hard to ensure that all students have a thorough understanding of the topics in this chapter.

Team Teaching

Have the social-studies teacher discuss with students the makeup of the Senate and the House of Representatives. Discuss number of members, the length of their terms, eligibility requirements, and so on.

History Connection

Franklin D. Roosevelt is the only American President elected more than twice. He was elected four times. Roosevelt died after only $2\frac{1}{2}$ months into his fourth term, so he served just over 12 years, from 1933 to 1945.

5-3 Exercises and Applications

Practice and Apply

1. **Getting Started** List the first five multiples of each number.

a. 3 **b.** 10 **c.** 11 **d.** 8 **e.** 4 **f.** 5

List the first three common multiples of each pair of numbers.

2. 4, 6 12, 24, 36
3. 1, 5 5, 10, 15
4. 6, 2 6, 12, 18
5. 12, 5 60, 120, 180
6. 3, 9 9, 18, 27
7. 6, 7 42, 84, 126
8. 8, 11 88, 176, 264
9. 8, 4 8, 16, 24
10. 10, 15 30, 60, 90
11. 16, 4 16, 32, 48
12. 5, 3 15, 30, 45
13. 4, 7 28, 56, 84

Find the LCM of each pair.

14. 7, 11 77 **15.** 3, 33 33 **16.** 8, 16 16

17. 5, 13 65 **18.** 2, 15 30 **19.** 10, 5 10

20. 15, 7 105 **21.** 4, 3 12 **22.** 6, 9 18

23. 14, 21 42 **24.** 4, 6 12 **25.** 6, 7 42

26. 6, 8 24 **27.** 10, 20 20 **28.** 3, 11 33

29. 7, 2 14 **30.** 88, 4 88 **31.** 15, 3 15

32. Victoria wears slacks every 2 days. She wears her jogging shoes every 3 days. If she wears slacks with jogging shoes on June 1, what are the next three dates on which she will wear both slacks and jogging shoes? June 7, 13, 19

33. The Blue Line bus arrives at Chesapeake Parkway every 20 minutes. The Express Shuttle arrives at the same stop every 3 minutes. How often do both buses arrive at the same time? Every 60 minutes

34. The key on the Race Times pictograph is missing. If the key is a whole number, give three possible times that Marty could have run. Possible answer: 3 min, 6 min, 9min

Race Times	
David	⏱ ⏱ ⏱ ⏱ (partial)
Marty	⏱ ⏱ ⏱
Joel	⏱ ⏱ ⏱ ⏱ ⏱ (partial)

⏱ = ? min.

35. **Test Prep** Chuck has baseball practice every 5 days and trumpet practice every 6 days. How often does he have baseball practice and trumpet practice on the same day? D

Ⓐ Every 5 days

Ⓑ Every 6 days

Ⓒ Every 15 days

Ⓓ Every 30 days

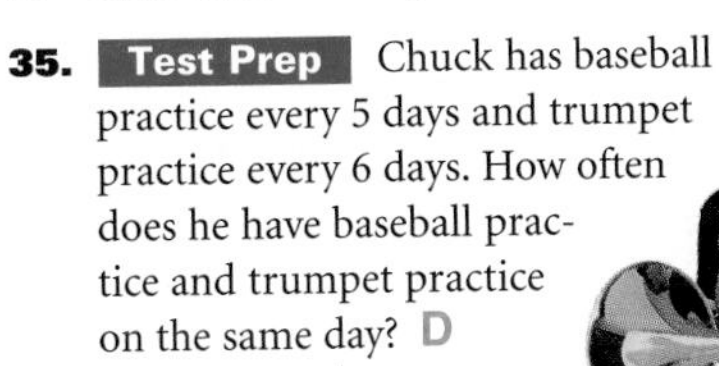

PRACTICE 5-3

5-3 Exercises and Applications

Assignment Guide

- **Basic**
  1–35 odds, 36–38, 41–47 odds
- **Average**
  1, 2–32 evens, 35–41, 44–48 evens
- **Enriched**
  3–33 odds, 34–42, 43–47 odds

Exercise Notes

Exercises 14–31

Extension Ask students to explain how they would find the LCM of 3 or more numbers. List common multiples of the numbers until you find the least number that appears in all the lists.

Exercise 34

Error Prevention If students have difficulty answering this exercise, remind them that each symbol represents the same amount of time and that parts of the symbol represent corresponding partial amounts of time.

Exercise Answers

1. a. 3, 6, 9, 12, 15
   b. 10, 20, 30, 40, 50
   c. 11, 22, 33, 44, 55
   d. 8, 16, 24, 32, 40
   e. 4, 8, 12, 16, 20
   f. 5, 10, 15, 20, 25

PRACTICE

Name ____________________ **Practice 5-3**

Least Common Multiples

List the first three common multiples of the given numbers.

1. 3, 2 6, 12, 18 **2.** 3, 4 12, 24, 36 **3.** 5, 4 20, 40, 60 **4.** 2, 8 8, 16, 24

5. 3, 5 15, 30, 45 **6.** 2, 7 14, 28, 42 **7.** 6, 5 30, 60, 90 **8.** 13, 2 26, 52, 78

Find the LCM of each pair.

9. 6, 23 138 **10.** 3, 21 21 **11.** 9, 5 45 **12.** 17, 3 51

13. 7, 5 35 **14.** 21, 7 21 **15.** 2, 12 12 **16.** 15, 11 165

17. 4, 19 76 **18.** 6, 28 84 **19.** 14, 18 126 **20.** 23, 2 46

21. 15, 14 210 **22.** 11, 33 33 **23.** 5, 15 15 **24.** 8, 5 40

25. 26, 22 286 **26.** 3, 22 66 **27.** 2, 34 34 **28.** 15, 8 120

29. 10, 15 30 **30.** 12, 4 12 **31.** 6, 10 30 **32.** 43, 13 559

33. 24, 3 24 **34.** 36, 45 180 **35.** 17, 2 34 **36.** 24, 7 168

37. 29, 5 145 **38.** 27, 2 54 **39.** 9, 10 90 **40.** 31, 5 155

41. 62, 9 558 **42.** 2, 7 14 **43.** 6, 4 12 **44.** 10, 2 10

45. 4, 10 20 **46.** 6, 11 66 **47.** 11, 2 22 **48.** 7, 12 84

49. 7, 16 112 **50.** 16, 6 48 **51.** 10, 14 70 **52.** 22, 4 44

53. Marti works Monday through Saturday, so she has a day off once every 7 days. She needs to give her dog some medicine every 5 days. How often does she give her dog medicine on her day off? Every 35 days

54. The traffic signal at 4th and Main turns green every 6 minutes. The signal at 5th and Broadway turns green every 4 minutes. If both turned green at 12:15 P.M., when are the next three times that both will turn green at the same time?

12:27 P.M., 12:39 P.M., 12:51 P.M.

RETEACHING

Name ____________________ **Alternative Lesson 5-3**

Least Common Multiples

A **multiple** of a number is the product of the number and a whole number. When the same number is a multiple of two or more numbers, it is a **common multiple**. The smallest common multiple of two numbers is the **least common multiple (LCM)**.

Example

Find the least common multiple (LCM) of 15 and 20.

List the common multiples of 15 and 20.

Multiples of 15:	15 1×15	30 2×15	45 3×15	**60** 4×15	…
Multiples of 20:	20 1×20	40 2×20	**60** 3×20	80 4×20	…

The LCM is the smallest number that appears on both lists. The LCM of 15 and 20 is 60.

Try It Find the least common multiple (LCM) of each pair of numbers.

a. 6 and 9 Multiples of 6: 6, 12, 18, 24, 30 LCM: 18
Multiples of 9: 9, 18, 27, 36, 45

b. 12 and 18 Multiples of 12: 12, 24, 36, 48, 60 LCM 36
Multiples of 18: 18, 36, 54, 72, 90

Find the least common multiple (LCM) of 8 and 10.

c. Write the first five multiples of each number.

Multiples of 8: 8, 16, 24, 32, 40

Multiples of 10: 10, 20, 30, 40, 50

d. Choose the smallest number that appears on both lists. 40

Find the least common multiple (LCM) of each pair of numbers.

e. 5, 7
Multiples of 5: 5, 10, 15, 20, 25, 30, 35
Multiples of 7: 7, 14, 21, 28, 35
LCM: 35

f. 4, 6
Multiples of 4: 4, 8, 12, 16
Multiples of 6: 6, 12, 18, 24
LCM: 12

Reteaching

Activity

- To find the least common multiple of 9 and 15, make a table like the one shown.

Multiples of 15	15	30	45
Divisible by 9	No	No	Yes

- In the top row, list multiples of 15, checking whether the multiple is divisible by 9. Stop when you answer yes. 45 is the LCM of 15 and 9.
- Use this method to find the least common multiples of other pairs of numbers. The greater number is in the first row, and the lesser number is in the second row.

Exercise Notes

■ Exercises 36–39

Problem-Solving Tip You may wish to use Teaching Tool Transparencies 2 and 3: Guided Problem Solving, pages 1–2.

■ Exercise 39

Extension Have students find the delivery date prior to January 1 when all four employees made deliveries on the same date. November 2

Alternate Assessment

Performance Have students demonstrate at the chalkboard their methods for finding the least common multiple of a pair of numbers.

➤ Quick Quiz

Find the least common multiple of each pair of numbers.

1. 18, 9 18
2. 4, 15 60
3. 10, 7 70
4. 9, 12 36
5. 15, 25 75

Available on Daily Transparency 5-3

PROBLEM SOLVING 5-3

Problem Solving and Reasoning

Choose a Strategy For Exercises 36–39, use the following delivery schedule.

Mr. Storrit manages a warehouse. Each employee makes deliveries based on a pattern of days. Every employee made a delivery on January 1.

Employee	Delivers
Landry	Every 5 days
Melancon	Every 2 days
Norton	Every 6 days
O'Hare	Every 4 days

36. How often will both Norton and Melancon make deliveries? Every 6 days.

37. How often will both Norton and O'Hare make deliveries? Every 12 days.

38. How often will all the employees make deliveries on the same day? Every 60 days.

39. All four employees make a delivery on January 1 of a year that's not a leap year. What's the next date when all four employees will make deliveries on the same day? March 2

40. Journal Explain why there is no greatest common multiple for any pair of numbers. Multiples are infinite.

41. Critical Thinking In a middle school, the principal plans to hide prizes in the new lockers for the students. The principal plans to put a binder in every 10th locker, a school tee shirt in every 15th locker, and a new backpack in every 50th locker. If she starts counting at locker number 1, what is the number of the first locker in which the principal will put all three prizes? 150

42. Communicate What is the LCM of 0.3 and 0.7? Explain. 2.1; The smallest number that is a whole-number multiple of both 0.3 and 0.7.

Problem Solving STRATEGIES

- Look for a Pattern
- Make an Organized List
- Make a Table
- Guess and Check
- Work Backward
- Use Logical Reasoning
- Draw a Diagram
- Solve a Simpler Problem

Mixed Review

Compare, using > or <. *[Lesson 2-3]*

43. 23,301 [>] 23,103 **44.** 7,377 [<] 73,777 **45.** 501,501 [>] 501,105

Divide. *[Lesson 3-11]*

46. $42 \div 0.7$ 60 **47.** $100 \div 0.05$ 2000 **48.** $6.32 \div 0.01$ 632

PROBLEM SOLVING

Name ______________________

Guided Problem Solving 5-3

GPS PROBLEM 41, STUDENT PAGE 284

In a middle school, the principal plans to hide prizes in the new lockers for the students. The principal plans to put a binder in every 10th locker, a school tee shirt in every 15th locker, and a new backpack in every 50th locker. If she starts counting at locker number 1, what is the number of the first locker in which the principal will put all three prizes?

— Understand —

1. Restate the problem in your own words. Possible answer: Every 10th locker has a binder, every 15th locker has a tee shirt, and every 50th locker has a backpack. Find the first locker that will have all three prizes.
2. Underline the information you need.

— Plan —

3. Find the least common multiple for 10, 15, and 50.
   a. List multiples of 10: 10, 20, 30, 40, 50, 60, 70, 80, 90, 100, 110, 120, 130, 140, 150
   b. List multiples of 15: 15, 30, 45, 60, 75, 90, 105, 120, 135, 150
   c. List multiples of 50: 50, 100, 150, 200

— Solve —

4. What is the least common multiple of 10, 15, and 50? 150
5. Which will be the first locker to contain a binder, a tee shirt, and a backpack? The 150th locker.

— Look Back —

6. What is another way you could solve the problem? Use this strategy: Draw a Diagram.

SOLVE ANOTHER PROBLEM

Ernesto, Michelina, and Kale volunteer at the zoo. Ernesto works every 5 days. Michelina works every 6 days. Kale works every 15 days. They work together today. How many days will it be until the next time they work together? 30 days.

ENRICHMENT

Name ______________________

Extend Your Thinking 5-3

Decision Making

Alyshia and Tamara went to the Neighborhood Cafe for lunch. They each chose one of the Lunch Specials, a beverage, and a dessert from the list printed on the menu board.

Lunch Specials		Desserts	
Caesar Salad	$5.25	Carrot Cake	$1.50
Nature Salad	$4.75	Chocolate Mousse	$2.25
Club Sandwich	$4.75		
Mushroom Cheeseburger	$4.50	**Beverages**	
Gyro	$3.75	Cocoa	$1.25
		Milk	$1.00

1. Tamara has $7 to spend for lunch. If she wants a special, a beverage, and a dessert, what items could she choose for her lunch? Possible answers: gyro, carrot cake, milk; gyro, carrot cake, cocoa; gyro, chocolate mousse, milk; mushroom cheeseburger, carrot cake, milk.
2. Alyshia has $10 to spend for lunch. If she wants a special, a beverage, and a dessert, what items could she choose for her lunch? Any combination of a special, drink, and dessert.
3. Together, Tamara and Alyshia have $17. They want to leave a $3.00 tip for the waitress. How will this affect what they can order? How will each girls' order change from the selections above? Possible answer: If they share equally, each girl will have $7 to spend after deducting the tip and can choose from the options in Item 1.
4. Eight students are going to the Neighborhood Cafe to celebrate the end of the semester. Each student orders a special, a beverage, and a dessert. About how much will the eight lunches cost? How did you decide on that amount? About $64 since a special costs about $5, a dessert costs about $2, and a drink costs about $1 for a total of $8 per meal. $8 \times \$8 = \$64$ for 8 students.

Section 5A Connect

Our calendar is based on the number 365, the approximate number of days it takes Earth to orbit the sun. What might the calendar be like if you lived on a planet with a different orbital period? In this investigation, you'll use factors and multiples to find out.

A Switch in Time ...

The planet Venus orbits the sun once for every 225 days on Earth. So a Venus-year equals 225 Earth days.

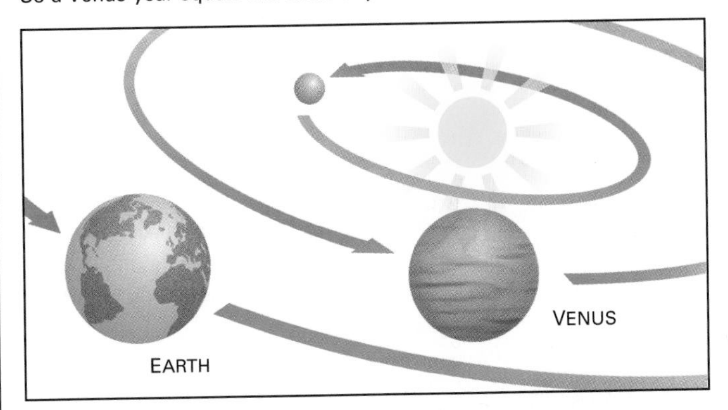

1. Divide Venus's 225-day year into months, all with the same number of days. Divide each month into weeks, all with the same number of days. Give names to the months and to the days of the week. Explain how you decided on the length of a month and a week.
2. Draw a calendar for a sample month on Venus.
3. Venus begins a new year every 225 days. Earth begins a new year every 365 days. Suppose both planets begin a new year on the same day. How many days will pass before that happens again? How many years is that on Earth? On Venus?
4. Earth children on their 12th birthdays are 4383 days old. This is equal to 12 Earth years, 144 Earth months, or about 626 Earth weeks. According to your Venus calendar, 4383 days equals how many years on Venus? How many months? How many weeks?

285

Answers for Connect

1. Possible answer: 9 months, 25 days; 5 weeks, 5 days per week; 1st month: Jenian; 1st day of the week: Uno; The length of a month and a week must be factors of 225.
2.

Jenian				
U	D	T	Q	C
1	2	3	4	5
6	7	8	9	10
11	12	13	14	15
16	17	18	19	20
21	22	23	24	25

3. 16,425 days; 45 Earth years; 73 Venus years.
4. About 19.5 Venus years; About 175.3 months; 876.6 weeks.

A Switch in Time ...

The Point

In *A Switch in Time ...* on page 269, students discussed different methods people have used to keep track of time. Now they will use factors and multiples to draw a calendar for the planet Venus.

About the Page

- Since the calendar must have months of equal length, ask students what numbers are factors of 225.
- Suggest that students use a theme or pattern for naming the months and days on their calendars.

Ongoing Assessment

Some students may not know how to solve Question 3. Discuss how finding the least common multiple will help them find the solution.

Extension

Suppose our calendar has the following:

- 360 days.
- 5 vacation days per year.
- an extra vacation day every fourth year. These vacation days are "extra" days and do not appear on the calendar.
- months with an equal number of days.
- no month with 30 days.

Decide how many months, weeks, and days this new calendar will have. Draw a sample month of this new calendar. Name the days and the months. Possible answers: 10 months, 36 days per month, 6 days per week; 18 months, 20 days per month, 5 days per week.

5A Review

Review Correlation

Item(s)	Lesson(s)
1–12	5-1
13–24	5-2
25–38	5-3
39–42	5-2

Test Prep

Test-Taking Tip
Tell students that making an organized list can help them solve some problems. Here, students can eliminate numbers divisible by 2, then by 3, then by 5, and so on, until they find the prime number.

Answers for Review

25. 2, 4, 6, 8, 10, 12, 14
26. 6, 12, 18, 24, 30, 36, 42
27. 7, 14, 21, 28, 35, 42, 49
28. 9, 18, 27, 36, 45, 54, 63
29. 0, 0, 0, 0, 0, 0, 0
30. 12, 24, 36, 48, 60, 72, 84
40. 180; Write the prime factorization of each number. Find the product of the prime numbers represented, where each should be multiplied by itself the greatest number of times in any one factorization.
41. 5; Every fifth number is divisible by 5, whereas every seventh number is divisible by 7.

Section 5A Review

REVIEW 5A

Tell whether the first number is divisible by the second.

1. 6, 4 No **2.** 31, 7 No **3.** 48, 2 Yes **4.** 63, 9 Yes **5.** 22, 6 No **6.** 80, 10 Yes

7. 175, 5 Yes **8.** 882, 9 Yes **9.** 78, 6 Yes **10.** 16, 8 Yes **11.** 72, 3 Yes **12.** 54, 11 No

Find the prime factorization.

13. 76 $2^2 \times 19$ **14.** 24 $2^3 \times 3$ **15.** 22 2×11 **16.** 59 59 is prime **17.** 12 $2^2 \times 3$ **18.** 44 $2^2 \times 11$

19. 114 $2 \times 3 \times 19$ **20.** 243 3^5 **21.** 73 73 is prime **22.** 85 5×17 **23.** 81 3^4 **24.** 32 2^5

List the first seven multiples of each number.

25. 2 **26.** 6 **27.** 7 **28.** 9 **29.** 0 **30.** 12

Find the LCM of each pair.

31. 3, 6 6 **32.** 5, 15 15 **33.** 6, 9 18 **34.** 8, 12 24 **35.** 10, 20 20 **36.** 9, 2 18

37. Social Studies Members of the House of Representatives are elected in years divisible by 2. Which years between 1996 and 2006 will have congressional elections? 1998, 2000, 2002, 2004

38. Number Sense A short way of writing May 10, 1962, is 5/10/62. When Mrs. Ahearn writes the date of her birth in this way, the numbers are the first three odd multiples of 7. When is her birthday? 7/21/35

39. The prime factorization of a number is $3 \times 3 \times 5 \times 13$. What is the number? 585

40. What is the smallest number that is divisible by 2, 3, 4, 5, 6, 9, and 10? Explain how you found your answer.

41. If you choose a two-digit number at random, is it more likely that the number will be divisible by 5 or by 7? Explain.

Test Prep

You can use the rules of divisibility to help determine if a number is prime or composite.

42. Which number is a prime number? C

Ⓐ 63 Ⓑ 78 Ⓒ 109 Ⓓ 115

Resources

Practice Masters
Section 5A Review

Assessment Sourcebook
Quiz 5A

TestWorks
Test and Practice Software

PRACTICE

Name ____________

Practice

Section 5A Review

Tell whether the first number is divisible by the second.

1. 95, 5 Yes 2. 72, 6 Yes 3. 38, 4 No 4. 48, 9 No

Find the prime factorization.

5. 85 5×17 6. 72 $2^3 \times 3^2$ 7. 220 $2^2 \times 5 \times 11$

8. 231 $3 \times 7 \times 11$ 9. 128 2^7 10. 148 $2^2 \times 37$

List the first seven multiples of the number.

11. 3 3, 6, 9, 12, 15, 18, 21
12. 11 11, 22, 33, 44, 55, 66, 77
13. 8 8, 16, 24, 32, 40, 48, 56
14. 60 60, 120, 180, 240, 300, 360, 420

Find the LCM of each pair.

15. 2, 9 18 16. 15, 10 30 17. 7, 63 63 18. 22, 4 44

19. A certain city holds elections for mayor in years divisible by 3. These elections will be held in which years between 1996 and 2015?
1998, 2001, 2004, 2007, 2010, 2013

20. Margo's locker combination consists of the first three even multiples of 9, in order. What is her combination? 18–36–54

21. The prime factorization of a number is $5 \times 7 \times 7 \times 17$. What is the number? 4165

22. **Health** A serving of stir fried mung bean sprouts has 3 times as much iron as a serving of boiled mung bean sprouts. The stir fried sprouts have 2.4 mg of iron. Write and solve an equation to find the amount of iron in a serving of boiled bean sprouts. *[Lesson 3-12]*
Possible equation: $3x = 2.4$; 0.8 mg

23. A certain brand of washing machine uses 140 liters of water to do a load of laundry. Convert this amount to milliliters. *[Lesson 4-2]* 140,000 mL

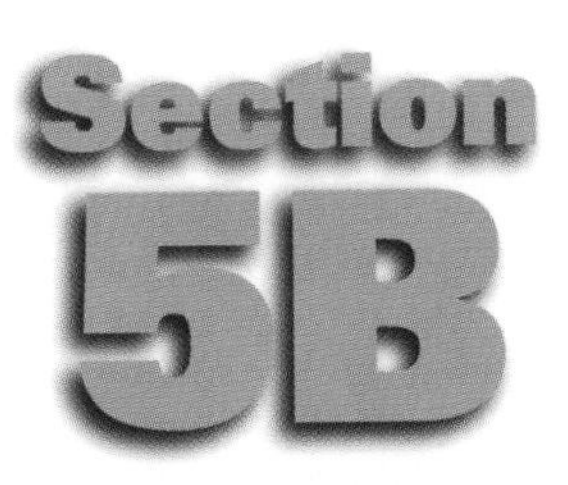

Connecting Fractions and Decimals

Visit www.teacher.mathsurf.com for links to lesson plans from teachers and other professionals, NCTM information, and other sites.

LESSON PLANNING GUIDE

Student Edition / Ancillaries

LESSON		MATERIALS	VOCABULARY	DAILY	OTHER
	Section 5B Opener				
5-4	Understanding Fractions	4 sheets of paper of different colors, scissors	fraction, denominator, numerator, equivalent fractions	5-4	Lesson Enhancement Trans. 21 Technology Master 23
5-5	Fractions in Lowest Terms		lowest terms, greatest common factor (GCF)	5-5	Lesson Enhancement Trans. 22 Technology Master 24
5-6	Improper Fractions and Mixed Numbers	pattern blocks or power polygons	improper fraction, mixed number	5-6	Teaching Tool Trans. 19 Lesson Enhancement Trans. 23 Ch. 5 Project Master
5-7	Converting Fractions and Decimals	tenth grids, 10 x 10 grids	terminating decimal, repeating decimal	5-7	Teaching Tool Trans. 11, 12
	Technology	spreadsheet software			*Interactive CD-ROM Spreadsheet/Grapher Tool*
5-8	Comparing and Ordering	Fraction Bars®	common denominator	5-8	Teaching Tool Trans. 2, 3, 14 Technology Master 25
	Connect	calculator			Interdisc. Team Teaching 5B Lesson Enhancement Trans. 24
	Review				Practice 5B; Quiz 5B; *TestWorks*
	Chapter 5 Summary and Review				
	Chapter 5 Assessment				Ch. 5 Tests Forms A–F *TestWorks*; Ch. 5 Letter Home
	Cumulative Review, Chapters 1–5	10 x 10 grid			Cumulative Review Ch. 1–5

SKILLS TRACE

LESSON	SKILL	FIRST INTRODUCED GR. 4	GR. 5	GR. 6	DEVELOP	PRACTICE/ APPLY	REVIEW
5-4	Writing equivalent fractions.	✘			pp. 288–290	pp. 291–292	pp. 306, 317, 386, 390, 396, 562
5-5	Writing fractions in lowest terms.	✘			pp. 293–295	pp. 296–297	pp. 317, 396, 567
5-6	Converting improper fractions and mixed numbers.			✘ p. 298	pp. 298–299	pp. 300–301	pp. 317, 411, 415, 567
5-7	Converting fractions and decimals.		✘		pp. 302–304	pp. 305–306	pp. 317, 420, 427, 583
5-8	Comparing and ordering fractions.	✘			pp. 308–310	pp. 311–312	pp. 317, 431, 435, 439, 447, 587

CONNECTED MATHEMATICS

The unit *Bits and Pieces I (Understanding Rational Numbers)*, from the **Connected Mathematics** series, can be used with Section 5B.

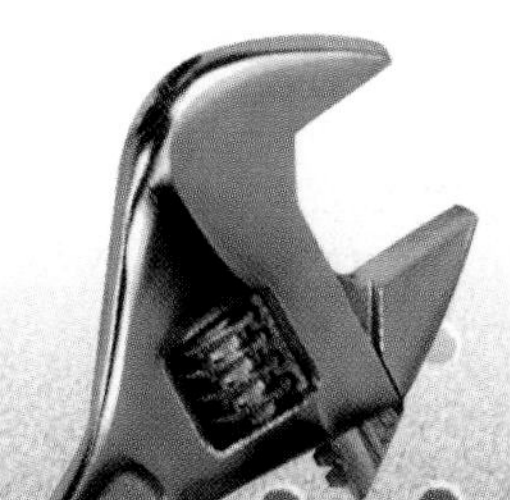

INTERDISCIPLINARY TEAM TEACHING

Math and Social Studies

(Worksheet pages 27–28: Teacher pages T27–T28)

In this lesson, students convert fractions and decimals related to horseshoe pitching.

Name ______________________ ***Math and Social Studies***

Horseshoe Pitching

Convert fractions and decimals related to horseshoe pitching.

Horseshoe pitching is a game that was invented around A.D. 100, when Roman soldiers first put horseshoes on their horses. It is likely that the soldiers began tossing, or pitching, the horseshoes as a way to amuse themselves. More than 1500 years later, the English brought horseshoe pitching to colonial America. The game has been popular ever since.

In the game of horseshoe pitching, players toss horseshoes at a stake. A stake is a length of metal that is pointed at one end and pounded into the ground. Two, three, or four players can play at one time. Players score points by pitching the horseshoe within six inches of the stake or completely around it.

People pitch horseshoes on a rectangular court that is six feet wide and fifty feet long. There is a pitching box at each end of the court. A pitching box has an area of six square feet. Within each pitching box is a stake. Players stand behind a foul line at one end of the court. They pitch their horseshoes at the stake at the other end.

There are many strict rules in horseshoe pitching. Most of the rules involve measurement. For example, each stake must be one inch in diameter. The stake must be driven into the ground so that it stands fifteen inches high in the pitching box. There are also distance regulations.

For instance, men pitch from a distance of forty feet. Women and young players pitch from a distance of thirty feet.

1. The table on this page contains details about the kind of horseshoe that can be used in a horseshoe pitching game. Fill in the table's blanks by converting the fractions to decimals and the decimals to fractions. Express fractions in lowest terms.

	Measurement Expressed As a Fraction or Mixed Number	Measurement Expressed As a Decimal
Maximum Width of Horseshoe	$7\frac{1}{4}$ inches	7.25 inches
Maximum Length of Horseshoe	$7\frac{5}{8}$ inches	7.625 inches
Maximum Weight of Horseshoe	$2\frac{5}{8}$ pounds	2.625 pounds
Space Between Open Ends of Horseshoe	$3\frac{1}{2}$ inches	3.5 inches

Name ______________________ ***Math and Social Studies***

Turn	Player A (Best Throw)	Player B (Best Throw)	Winner	Score: Player A	Score: Player B
1	$\frac{2}{3}$ inch	0.6 inch	B	0	1
2	$\frac{3}{4}$ inch	0.34 inch	B	0	1
3	$\frac{1}{7}$ inch	0.7 inch	A	1	0
4	ringer	1.2 inches	A	3	0
5	$2\frac{3}{10}$ inches	ringer	B	0	3
6	$4\frac{5}{6}$ inches	4.6 inches	B	0	1
7	$\frac{4}{5}$ inch	0.070 inch	B	0	1
8	$\frac{7}{8}$ inch	ringer	B	0	3
9	$\frac{4}{9}$ inch	0.4 inch	B	0	1
10	ringer	2.1 inches	A	3	0

2. A "ringer" is made when a player throws a horseshoe that encircles a stake. A ringer counts three points in scoring. If no player throws a ringer, one point is scored for the shoe closest to the stake. A player throws two horseshoes each turn. Study the table above. Who is the better player, Player A or Player B? After you have picked the winner of each turn and given the winner a score, score the whole game and write the totals for each player and the winner of the contest in the spaces provided. A player's "Best Throw" represents the least amount of distance between a landed horseshoe and the stake.

Total Score for Player A 7

Total Score for Player B 11

Winner Player B

3. In the early 1920s, the National Horseshoe Pitchers' Association of America was created. The association holds world championship games for both men and women every year. How do strict rules about sizes and distances make a contest fair?

See below.

4. How might the ability to convert fractions to decimals and decimals to fractions be important to horseshoe pitchers and the people who judge horseshoe pitching contests?

See below.

5. When is the ability to convert fractions to decimals and decimals to fractions helpful to you in your daily life?

See below.

Answers

3. Students' responses may vary. Students may suggest that all things must be equal so that a player wins only because of his or her skill.
4. Students' responses may vary. Students may suggest that since horseshoe pitching is played all over the world, some people may measure distances using fractions, and some may measure using decimals. In order for comparisons to be made easily, all numbers must be expressed the same way, either all in fractions or all in decimals.
5. Students' responses may vary. Students may suggest sports statistics (1 hit in 3 at bats = .333 batting average), money ($\frac{1}{2}$ dollar equals \$0.50), and the prices of shares on the stockmarket ($3\frac{1}{2}$ = \$3.50).

BIBLIOGRAPHY

FOR TEACHERS

Muirden, James. *Stars and Planets.* New York, NY: Kingfisher Books, 1993.

Blair, Harry and Bob Knauff. *Not Strictly by the Numbers.* Palo Alto, CA: Dale Seymore, 1996.

FOR STUDENTS

Ericksen, Aase and Marjorie Wintermute. *Students, Structures, Spaces.* Reading, MA: Innovative Learning Publications, 1996.

Thomas, David A. *Math Projects for Young Scientists.* New York, NY: Watts, 1988.

Brownridge, Dennis R. *Metric in Minutes.* Belmont, CA: Professional Publications, 1994.

Fowler, Allan. *The Metric System.* Chicago, IL: Childrens Press, 1995.

Section 5B

Connecting Fractions and Decimals

Visit **www.teacher.mathsurf.com** for links to lesson plans from teachers and other professionals, NCTM information, and other sites.

LESSON PLANNING GUIDE

Student Edition / Ancillaries

LESSON		MATERIALS	VOCABULARY	DAILY	OTHER
	Section 5B Opener				
5-4	**Understanding Fractions**	4 sheets of paper of different colors, scissors	fraction, denominator, numerator, equivalent fractions	5-4	Lesson Enhancement Trans. 21 Technology Master 23
5-5	**Fractions in Lowest Terms**		lowest terms, greatest common factor (GCF)	5-5	Lesson Enhancement Trans. 22 Technology Master 24
5-6	**Improper Fractions and Mixed Numbers**	pattern blocks or power polygons	improper fraction, mixed number	5-6	Teaching Tool Trans. 19 Lesson Enhancement Trans. 23 Ch. 5 Project Master
5-7	**Converting Fractions and Decimals**	tenth grids, 10 x 10 grids	terminating decimal, repeating decimal	5-7	Teaching Tool Trans. 11, 12
	Technology	spreadsheet software			*Interactive CD-ROM Spreadsheet/Grapher Tool*
5-8	**Comparing and Ordering**	Fraction Bars®	common denominator	5-8	Teaching Tool Trans. 2, 3, 14 Technology Master 25
	Connect	calculator			Interdisc. Team Teaching 5B Lesson Enhancement Trans. 24
	Review				Practice 5B; Quiz 5B; *TestWorks*
	Chapter 5 Summary and Review				
	Chapter 5 Assessment				Ch. 5 Tests Forms A–F *TestWorks*; Ch. 5 Letter Home
	Cumulative Review, Chapters 1–5	10 x 10 grid			Cumulative Review Ch. 1–5

SKILLS TRACE

LESSON	SKILL	FIRST INTRODUCED GR. 4	GR. 5	GR. 6	DEVELOP	PRACTICE/ APPLY	REVIEW
5-4	**Writing equivalent fractions.**	✘			pp. 288–290	pp. 291–292	pp. 306, 317, 386, 390, 396, 562
5-5	**Writing fractions in lowest terms.**	✘			pp. 293–295	pp. 296–297	pp. 317, 396, 567
5-6	**Converting improper fractions and mixed numbers.**			✘ p. 298	pp. 298–299	pp. 300–301	pp. 317, 411, 415, 567
5-7	**Converting fractions and decimals.**		✘		pp. 302–304	pp. 305–306	pp. 317, 420, 427, 583
5-8	**Comparing and ordering fractions.**	✘			pp. 308–310	pp. 311–312	pp. 317, 431, 435, 439, 447, 587

CONNECTED MATHEMATICS

The unit *Bits and Pieces I (Understanding Rational Numbers)*, from the **Connected Mathematics** series, can be used with Section 5B.

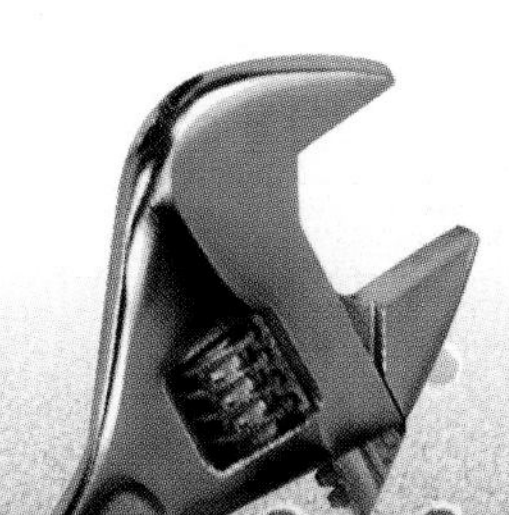

INTERDISCIPLINARY TEAM TEACHING

Math and Social Studies

(Worksheet pages 27–28: Teacher pages T27–T28)

In this lesson, students convert fractions and decimals related to horseshoe pitching.

Name ______________________ ***Math and Social Studies***

Horseshoe Pitching

Convert fractions and decimals related to horseshoe pitching.

Horseshoe pitching is a game that was invented around A.D. 100, when Roman soldiers first put horseshoes on their horses. It is likely that the soldiers began tossing, or pitching, the horseshoes as a way to amuse themselves. More than 1500 years later, the English brought horseshoe pitching to colonial America. The game has been popular ever since.

In the game of horseshoe pitching, players toss horseshoes at a stake. A stake is a length of metal that is pointed at one end and pounded into the ground. Two, three, or four players can play at one time. Players score points by pitching the horseshoe within six inches of the stake or completely around it.

People pitch horseshoes on a rectangular court that is six feet wide and fifty feet long. There is a pitching box at each end of the court. A pitching box has an area of six square feet. Within each pitching box is a stake. Players stand behind a foul line at one end of the court. They pitch their horseshoes at the stake at the other end.

There are many strict rules in horseshoe pitching. Most of the rules involve measurement. For example, each stake must be one inch in diameter. The stake must be driven into the ground so that it stands fifteen inches high in the pitching box. There are also distance regulations.

For instance, men pitch from a distance of forty feet. Women and young players pitch from a distance of thirty feet.

1. The table on this page contains details about the kind of horseshoe that can be used in a horseshoe pitching game. Fill in the table's blanks by converting the fractions to decimals and the decimals to fractions. Express fractions in lowest terms.

	Measurement Expressed As a Fraction or Mixed Number	Measurement Expressed As a Decimal
Maximum Width of Horseshoe	$7\frac{1}{4}$ inches	7.25 inches
Maximum Length of Horseshoe	$7\frac{5}{8}$ inches	7.625 inches
Maximum Weight of Horseshoe	$2\frac{5}{8}$ pounds	2.625 pounds
Space Between Open Ends of Horseshoe	$3\frac{1}{2}$ inches	3.5 inches

Name ______________________ ***Math and Social Studies***

Turn	Player A (Best Throw)	Player B (Best Throw)	Winner	Score: Player A	Score: Player B
1	$\frac{2}{3}$ inch	0.6 inch	B	0	1
2	$\frac{3}{4}$ inch	0.34 inch	B	0	1
3	$\frac{1}{7}$ inch	0.7 inch	A	1	0
4	ringer	1.2 inches	A	3	0
5	$2\frac{3}{10}$ inches	ringer	B	0	3
6	$4\frac{5}{6}$ inches	4.6 inches	B	0	1
7	$\frac{4}{5}$ inch	0.070 inch	B	0	1
8	$\frac{7}{8}$ inch	ringer	B	0	3
9	$\frac{4}{9}$ inch	0.4 inch	B	0	1
10	ringer	2.1 inches	A	3	0

2. A "ringer" is made when a player throws a horseshoe that encircles a stake. A ringer counts three points in scoring. If no player throws a ringer, one point is scored for the shoe closest to the stake. A player throws two horseshoes each turn. Study the table above. Who is the better player, Player A or Player B? After you have picked the winner of each turn and given the winner a score, score the whole game and write the totals for each player and the winner of the contest in the spaces provided. A player's "Best Throw" represents the least amount of distance between a landed horseshoe and the stake.

   Total Score for Player A 7

   Total Score for Player B 11

   Winner Player B

3. In the early 1920s, the National Horseshoe Pitchers' Association of America was created. The association holds world championship games for both men and women every year. How do strict rules about sizes and distances make a contest fair?

   See below.

4. How might the ability to convert fractions to decimals and decimals to fractions be important to horseshoe pitchers and the people who judge horseshoe pitching contests?

   See below.

5. When is the ability to convert fractions to decimals and decimals to fractions helpful to you in your daily life?

   See below.

Answers

3. Students' responses may vary. Students may suggest that all things must be equal so that a player wins only because of his or her skill.
4. Students' responses may vary. Students may suggest that since horseshoe pitching is played all over the world, some people may measure distances using fractions, and some may measure using decimals. In order for comparisons to be made easily, all numbers must be expressed the same way, either all in fractions or all in decimals.
5. Students' responses may vary. Students may suggest sports statistics (1 hit in 3 at bats = .333 batting average), money ($\frac{1}{2}$ dollar equals \$0.50), and the prices of shares on the stockmarket ($3\frac{1}{2}$ = \$3.50).

BIBLIOGRAPHY

FOR TEACHERS

Muirden, James. *Stars and Planets.* New York, NY: Kingfisher Books, 1993.

Blair, Harry and Bob Knauff. *Not Strictly by the Numbers.* Palo Alto, CA: Dale Seymore, 1996.

FOR STUDENTS

Ericksen, Aase and Marjorie Wintermute. *Students, Structures, Spaces.* Reading, MA: Innovative Learning Publications, 1996.

Thomas, David A. *Math Projects for Young Scientists.* New York, NY: Watts, 1988.

Brownridge, Dennis R. *Metric in Minutes.* Belmont, CA: Professional Publications, 1994.

Fowler, Allan. *The Metric System.* Chicago, IL: Childrens Press, 1995.

Section 5B

SECTION 5B

Connecting Fractions and Decimals

▶ Industry Link ▶ www.mathsurf.com/6/ch5/tools

Meanwhile, Back at the WRENCH

Using a tool can make your work easy...but choosing a tool can make your work hard! That's because there are so many tools to choose from. A recent book listed nearly a thousand tools used by workers. Take wrenches, which are used to tighten or loosen bolts or other fasteners. Some wrenches adjust to different sizes, like monkey wrenches, spud wrenches, and chain wrenches.

Other wrenches have fixed sizes, like box wrenches, open-end wrenches, and crow's foot wrenches. There are wrenches that are designed for special purposes, like spark plug wrenches, basin wrenches, and bicycle wrenches.

To make matters even more complicated, every type of wrench comes in a variety of sizes. In this section, you'll learn how we use both fractions and decimals to measure such sizes. And you'll learn about special tools we use to measure the sizes of items as different as bones, fabric, flour, and rain.

1 Name a tool you have used to measure the size of an item. What units were used? Were they fractional or decimal measurements?

2 What problems might occur if your wrenches were sized in inches and the bolts you wanted to tighten were sized in millimeters?

3 Why do we have so many different kinds of tools? Why are different systems of measurement used to size them?

287

Where are we now?

In Section 5A, students learned how to

- test for divisibility.
- distinguish between prime and composite numbers.
- use prime factorization.
- find the least common multiple for two numbers.

Where are we going?

In Section 5B, students will

- represent values between whole numbers as fractions.
- simplify fractions.
- convert between improper fractions and mixed numbers.
- convert between fractions and decimals.
- compare and order fractions.

Theme: Tools

World Wide Web

If your class has access to the World Wide Web, you might want to use the information found at the Web site address given. The interdisciplinary link relates to topics discussed in this section.

About the Page

This page introduces the theme of the section, tools, and discusses the many sizes of and uses for tools.

Ask ...

- What is a wrench? A long-handled tool with jaws used for gripping objects.
- Why are tools made using both metric and customary units? The United States uses customary units, but most other countries use the metric system.

Extension

The following activity does not require access to the World Wide Web.

Industry

Ask students which tools they think are most commonly found in the average household. Have them count and classify the tools in their own homes. Ask students to compile the results of their research into a classroom graph. Then ask them to find data about how many of each of the common tools are manufactured and sold each year in the United States.

Answers for Questions

1. Possible answer: Tape measure; Inches and feet; Fractional
2. Possible answer: The wrench would not fit exactly.
3. Different tools do different things; Different countries use different systems of measurement.

Connect

On page 313, students use fractions and decimals to order wrenches by size.

Lesson Organizer

Objective

- Represent values between whole numbers as fractions.

Vocabulary

- Fraction, denominator, numerator, equivalent fractions

Materials

- Explore: 4 sheets of paper of different colors, scissors

NCTM Standards

- 1–6, 12

Review

Write the number for the word name given.

1. Three-fourths $\frac{3}{4}$
2. Two-thirds $\frac{2}{3}$
3. Four-fifths $\frac{4}{5}$
4. Seven-eighths $\frac{7}{8}$
5. Nine-tenths $\frac{9}{10}$

Available on Daily Transparency 5-4

1 Introduce

Explore

You may wish to use Lesson Transparency 21 with **Explore**.

The Point

Students cut colored paper to model halves, fourths, eighths, and sixteenths. They then use their models to find equivalent fractions.

Ongoing Assessment

Watch for students who have difficulty cutting congruent pieces. You might suggest that they fold the paper before cutting.

For Groups That Finish Early

Repeat Steps 1 and 2 with halves, thirds, sixths, and twelfths. Do not expect that the fractions will be exact.

5-4 Understanding Fractions

You'll Learn ...

- to represent values between whole numbers as fractions

... How It's Used

Plumbers use fractions when measuring pipes and fittings.

Vocabulary

fraction

denominator

numerator

equivalent fractions

Lesson Link In the last chapter, you learned to use decimals, which name amounts using place values less than one. Now you'll learn to use fractions, which express numbers as equal parts of the whole.

A **fraction** describes part of a whole when the whole is cut into equal pieces. On this ruler, the inches are divided into 4 equal parts. Each part is 1 of the 4 parts, or $\frac{1}{4}$.

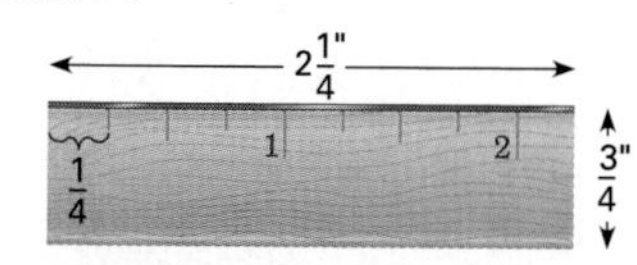

Explore Fractions

Halve It Your Way

Materials: 4 sheets of paper of different colors, Scissors

1. Cut the first sheet of paper into halves and label each piece $\frac{1}{2}$. Cut the second sheet into fourths and label each piece $\frac{1}{4}$. Cut the third sheet into eighths and label each piece $\frac{1}{8}$. Cut the fourth sheet into sixteenths and label each piece $\frac{1}{16}$.

$\frac{1}{2}$ $\frac{1}{2}$ $\frac{1}{4}$ $\frac{1}{4}$ $\frac{1}{4}$ $\frac{1}{4}$

each = $\frac{1}{8}$ each = $\frac{1}{16}$

2. Notice that two of your $\frac{1}{4}$ pieces fit perfectly on a $\frac{1}{2}$ piece. This shows that 2 fourths, or $\frac{2}{4}$, equal $\frac{1}{2}$. Use your pieces to find five other pairs of equal fractions. Make a sketch like the one shown for each pair of equal fractions. Do not use $\frac{2}{4} = \frac{1}{2}$ as one of your pairs.

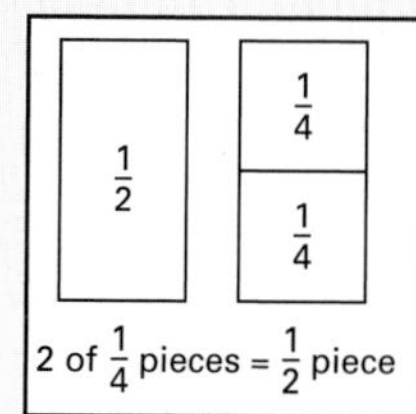

3. A rain gauge at City Hall showed that $\frac{1}{2}$ in. of rain fell during the night. A rain gauge at the airport showed that $\frac{4}{8}$ in. of rain had fallen. Which gauge recorded more rain? Explain.
4. Two cars have the same-size gas tank. One car has $\frac{3}{4}$ of a tank of gas. The other car has $\frac{11}{16}$ of a tank of gas. Which car has more gas? Explain.

MEETING INDIVIDUAL NEEDS

Resources

- **5-4** Practice
- **5-4** Reteaching
- **5-4** Problem Solving
- **5-4** Enrichment
- **5-4** Daily Transparency
  - Problem of the Day
  - Review
  - Quick Quiz
- Lesson Enhancement Transparency 21
- Technology Master 23

Learning Modalities

Visual It may be helpful for some students to repeat **Explore** using four paper circles.

Individual Ask students to describe situations in which they have used fractions.

Inclusion

Have students fold a piece of paper in half and shade one-half of it. Then have them fold the paper again to show that $\frac{1}{2} = \frac{2}{4}$. Point out that folding the halves into two equal parts is like doubling the numerator and the denominator. Have the students fold the paper again to show that $\frac{1}{2} = \frac{2}{4} = \frac{4}{8}$. Write these equivalent fractions on the board.

Learn Understanding Fractions

A fraction describes a portion of something that has been divided into equal parts. The bottom number, called the **denominator**, gives the number of parts in the whole. The top number, the **numerator**, tells how many of the parts are being named.

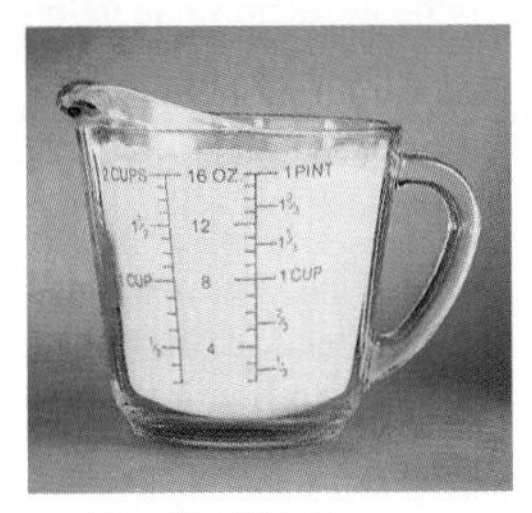

You can read the fraction $\frac{5}{8}$ three ways: "five eighths," "five over eight," or "five out of eight."

When the numerator and denominator are the same number, the fraction is equal to 1.

$\frac{6}{6}$ =  = one whole = 1

Example 1

A slotted screwdriver has an end that looks like a –. A Phillips screwdriver has an end that looks like a +. What fraction of all the screwdrivers shown are slotted screwdrivers? What fraction are Phillips screwdrivers?

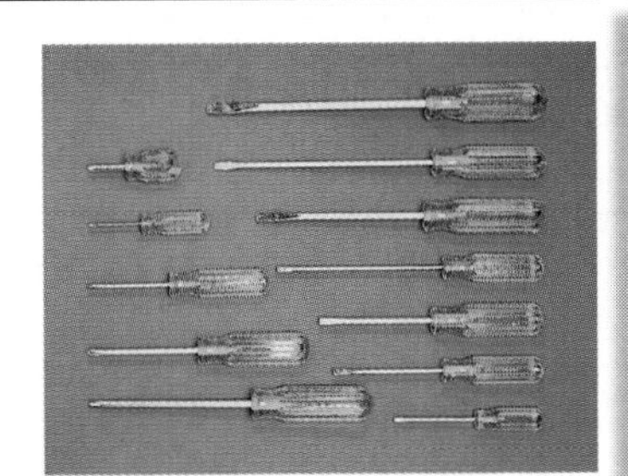

There are 12 screwdrivers. Seven of those are slotted. The fraction that are slotted is $\frac{7}{12}$. There are five Phillips screwdrivers, so $\frac{5}{12}$ of the screwdrivers are Phillips screwdrivers.

▶ Industry Link

Many screwdrivers have been invented for special purposes. Five-sided screwdrivers are used for caps and valves on fire hydrants. Hexagonal-head screwdrivers were used to put armor together in the 15th century.

Recall that the same number can be expressed in different ways using decimals. For example, 5.2 = 5.20 = 5.200 = 5.2000.

Fractions can also have different names. Two fractions that name the same amount are **equivalent fractions**. In the first rectangle, 2 of 3 equal parts are shaded. In the second rectangle, 4 of 6 equal parts are shaded. The same amount is shaded in both rectangles, so $\frac{2}{3} = \frac{4}{6}$.

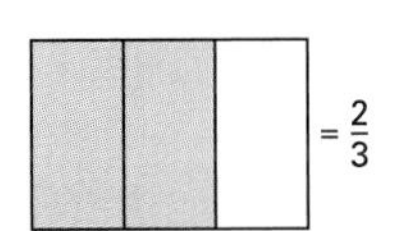 $= \frac{2}{3}$

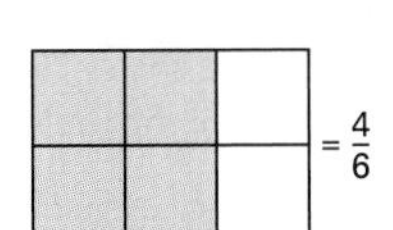 $= \frac{4}{6}$

Remember

When you annex zeros to the end of a decimal, you do not change its value. [Page 148]

MATH EVERY DAY

▶ Problem of the Day

On the first roll of a number cube, Nuru rolls the larger and Leon rolls the smaller of two numbers that have an LCM of 12. On the second roll, Leon rolls the larger and Nuru rolls the smaller of two numbers that have an LCM of 10. Leon then had a total of 2 more points than Nuru. How many points did each boy score on each roll? First roll: Nuru-4 points, Leon-3 points; Second roll: Nuru-2 points, Leon-5 points

Available on Daily Transparency 5-4

An Extension is provided in the transparency package.

Fact of the Day

The oldest known glass objects are beads produced in Egypt and Mesopotamia around 1500 B.C.

Mental Math

Give each decimal as a fraction.

1. 0.3 $\frac{3}{10}$
2. 0.23 $\frac{23}{100}$
3. 0.9 $\frac{9}{10}$
4. 0.59 $\frac{59}{100}$

Follow Up

Ask students to share their strategies for answering Step 4.

Answers for Explore

1. Check students' papers.
2. Possible answers: $\frac{1}{2} = \frac{4}{8}, \frac{1}{2} = \frac{8}{16}, \frac{2}{8} = \frac{1}{4}, \frac{4}{8} = \frac{2}{4}, \frac{1}{4} = \frac{4}{16}$
3. They recorded the same.
4. The car with $\frac{3}{4}$ of a tank of gas. $\frac{3}{4} > \frac{11}{16}$.

2 Teach

Learn

Write several fractions on the chalkboard and have students read the fractions out loud, and name the numerator and denominator.

Alternate Examples

1. Ms. Hayes has 24 students in her class. Eleven of the students are girls. What fraction of the class are girls? What fraction are boys?

   Since 11 of the 24 students are girls, the fraction that are girls is $\frac{11}{24}$. There are 13 boys, so $\frac{13}{24}$ of the class are boys.

Alternate Examples

2. $\frac{5}{8}$ of the rectangle has been shaded. Name a fraction equivalent to $\frac{5}{8}$.

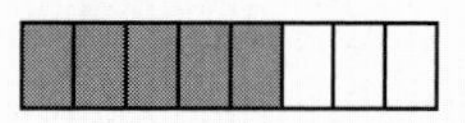

You can draw a line across the rectangle, cutting it into 16 pieces. Then 10 pieces are shaded. $\frac{5}{8} = \frac{10}{16}$.

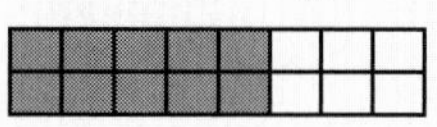

3. What fraction of the individual shoes are sandals? Give two equivalent fractions for your answer.

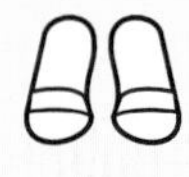

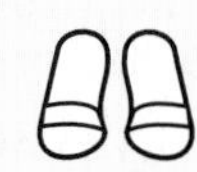

There are 16 shoes, and 6 of them are sandals. $\frac{6}{16}$ of the shoes are sandals. There are 8 pairs of shoes, and 3 pairs are sandals. $\frac{3}{8}$ of the pairs of shoes are sandals. $\frac{6}{16} = \frac{3}{8}$.

3 Practice and Assess

Check

Answers for Check Your Understanding

1. The top number tells how many parts are being named; The bottom gives the number of parts in the whole.
2. An infinite amount; After one fraction is used to describe the situation, there are infinitely many equivalent fractions that can describe the same situation.
3. Possible answer: Eating 1 slice of a pizza cut in fourths is the same as eating 2 slices of the same pizza cut in eighths.

Example 2

$\frac{3}{5}$ of the rectangle has been shaded. Name a fraction equivalent to $\frac{3}{5}$.

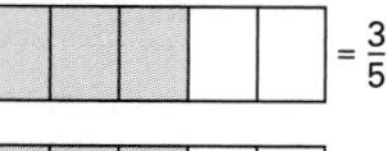

$= \frac{3}{5}$

You can draw a line across the rectangle, cutting it into 10 pieces. Then 6 pieces are shaded. $\frac{3}{5} = \frac{6}{10}$

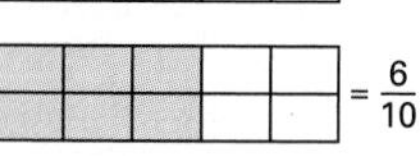

$= \frac{6}{10}$

In some situations, you may need to find one fraction equivalent to a given fraction. In other situations, it may be helpful to find two equivalent fractions.

DID YOU KNOW?

Japanese chopsticks come in "his" and "hers" sizes. The men's size is about eight inches long. The women's size is about seven inches long.

Example 3

Chinese chopsticks are 10 inches long with flat ends. Japanese chopsticks are 7 to 8 inches long with pointed ends. What fraction of the individual chopsticks are Chinese? Give two equivalent fractions for your answer.

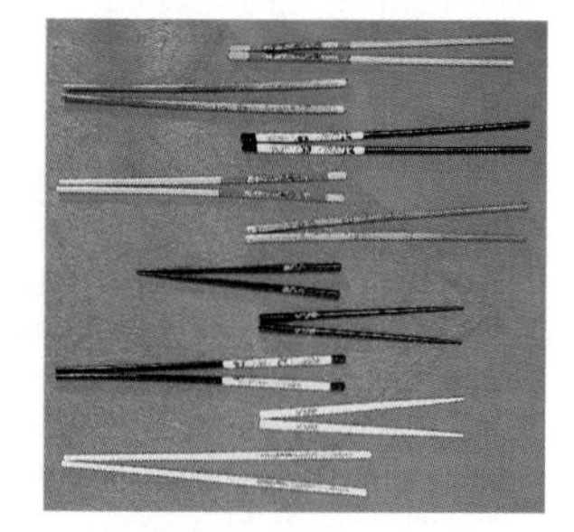

There are 20 chopsticks. 14 of them are Chinese. $\frac{14}{20}$ of the chopsticks are Chinese. There are 10 pairs of chopsticks. 7 of them are Chinese. $\frac{7}{10}$ of the chopstick pairs are Chinese. $\frac{14}{20} = \frac{7}{10}$.

▶ Language Link

The line above the *n* in "jalapeño" is called a *tilde.* The *ñ* sounds like an English *n* followed by a *y*, like the *n* in *unusual.*

Try It

a. What fraction of the jalapeño peppers are red? What fraction are not? $\frac{6}{11}$ are red; $\frac{5}{11}$ are not.

b. What fraction does the shaded part of the rectangle represent? Name an equivalent fraction. $\frac{7}{8}, \frac{14}{16}$

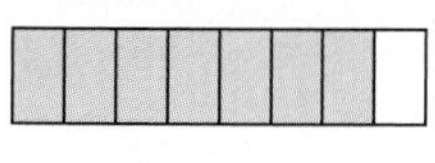

Check Your Understanding

1. How are the top number of a fraction and the bottom number different?
2. How many fractions can you use to describe a portion of a whole? Explain.
3. Give a real-world example to show that $\frac{1}{4} = \frac{2}{8}$.

MEETING MIDDLE SCHOOL CLASSROOM NEEDS

Tips from Middle School Teachers

Materials: Standard measuring cups

When explaining fractions to students, I find it helpful to use some real-life examples, such as standard measuring cups. I have students point out the markings on each cup, name the fraction, and identify the numerator and denominator. If the cups are marked for ounces, I extend the discussion to cover eighths.

Team Teaching

Have the industrial-arts teacher show students examples of various drill bits, types of screwdrivers, and other tools that might interest students.

Science Connection

Tools make it easier to do work. Tools with only a few parts are called simple machines. Screws, ramps, levers, pulleys, wedges, and wheel and axle are all simple machines.

5-4 Exercises and Applications

Practice and Apply

1. **Getting Started** What fraction does the shaded part represent?

a. $\frac{1}{2}$ b. $\frac{1}{4}$ c. $\frac{5}{8}$ d. $\frac{3}{4}$

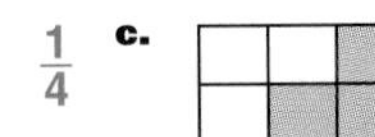

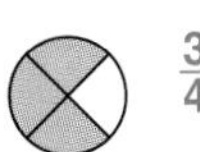

For each fraction, draw a model and name an equivalent fraction.

2. $\frac{3}{4}$	**3.** $\frac{7}{9}$	**4.** $\frac{1}{2}$	**5.** $\frac{12}{17}$	**6.** $\frac{5}{8}$	**7.** $\frac{2}{3}$
8. $\frac{12}{12}$	**9.** $\frac{8}{16}$	**10.** $\frac{11}{11}$	**11.** $\frac{4}{10}$	**12.** $\frac{6}{7}$	**13.** $\frac{3}{8}$
14. $\frac{1}{9}$	**15.** $\frac{6}{8}$	**16.** $\frac{2}{7}$	**17.** $\frac{2}{4}$	**18.** $\frac{8}{11}$	**19.** $\frac{9}{10}$

The window shown has equal-size sections made of both stained glass and clear glass.

20. What fraction of the window is made of stained glass? $\frac{7}{9}$

21. What fraction of the window is made of clear glass? $\frac{2}{9}$

22. Suppose three sections of the window need to be replaced. Name two fractions that describe this amount. $\frac{3}{9}, \frac{1}{3}$

23. **Test Prep** Which fraction expresses one out of seven equal pieces? B

Ⓐ $\frac{7}{1}$ Ⓑ $\frac{1}{7}$ Ⓒ $\frac{7}{7}$

Geometry **Use the shapes pictured to answer Exercises 24–26.**

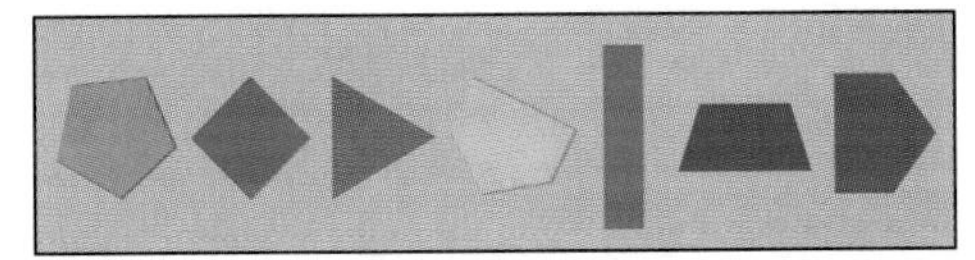

24. What fraction of the shapes shown have five sides? $\frac{3}{7}$

25. What fraction of the shapes do not have exactly three sides? $\frac{6}{7}$

26. Which fraction is larger, the fraction of the shapes with four sides or the fraction of the shapes with five sides? They are equal.

PRACTICE 5-4

5-4 Exercises and Applications

Assignment Guide

- **Basic**
  1–27 odds, 28, 29–41 odds
- **Average**
  1–23 odds, 24–30, 32–42 evens
- **Enriched**
  3–23 odds, 24–30, 31–41 odds

Exercise Notes

Exercises 24–26

Extension Ask students what a 5-sided polygon is called. Pentagon You may wish to have students identify the other polygons shown.

Exercise Answers

2. $\frac{6}{8}$;

3. $\frac{14}{18}$;

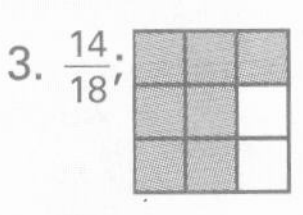

4. $\frac{2}{4}$;

5. $\frac{24}{34}$;

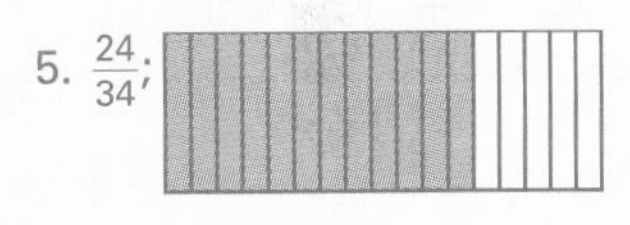

6. $\frac{10}{16}$;

7–19. See page C3.

PRACTICE

Name ______________________

Practice 5-4

Understanding Fractions

For each fraction, draw a model and name an equivalent fraction.

1. $\frac{1}{3}$ $\frac{2}{6}$	2. $\frac{3}{5}$ $\frac{6}{10}$	3. $\frac{8}{12}$ $\frac{2}{3}$
4. $\frac{5}{7}$ $\frac{10}{14}$	5. $\frac{5}{9}$ $\frac{10}{18}$	6. $\frac{8}{20}$ $\frac{2}{5}$
7. $\frac{15}{25}$ $\frac{3}{5}$	8. $\frac{2}{5}$ $\frac{4}{10}$	9. $\frac{1}{6}$ $\frac{3}{18}$
10. $\frac{5}{6}$ $\frac{10}{12}$	11. $\frac{1}{10}$ $\frac{3}{30}$	12. $\frac{3}{6}$ $\frac{1}{2}$

The picture shows how to set up the game of backgammon. The 24 triangular-shaped spaces on the board are called points.

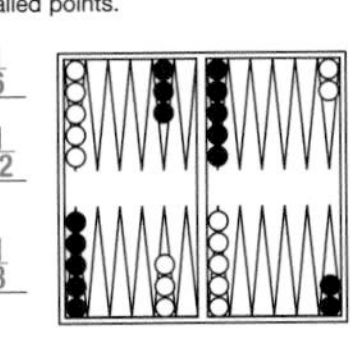

13. What fraction of the points have white playing pieces? $\frac{4}{24}$ or $\frac{1}{6}$

14. What fraction of the points have five black playing pieces? $\frac{2}{24}$ or $\frac{1}{12}$

15. What fraction of the white playing pieces are on the point shown at the upper left corner of the board? $\frac{5}{15}$ or $\frac{1}{3}$

16. Arturo has 3 dogs and 5 cats. What fraction of his pets are dogs? $\frac{3}{8}$

RETEACHING

Name ______________________

Alternative Lesson 5-4

Understanding Fractions

A **fraction** describes part of a whole when the whole is cut into equal pieces. The **numerator**, or top number, tells how many parts are named. The **denominator,** or bottom number, gives the number of parts in the whole.

$\frac{2}{3}$ ← numerator / ← denominator

Example

What fraction does the shaded part represent?

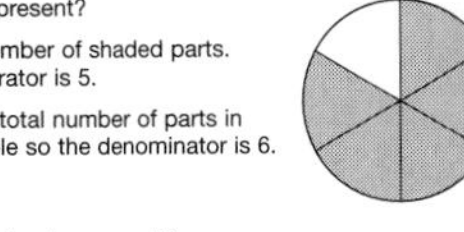

Find the numerator by counting the number of shaded parts. There are 5 shaded parts so the numerator is 5.

Find the denominator by counting the total number of parts in the whole. There are 6 parts in the whole so the denominator is 6.

The fraction is $\frac{5}{6}$.

Try It What fraction does the shaded part represent?

a.

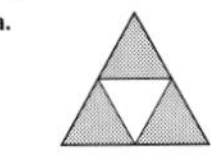

1. Count the shaded parts. What is the numerator? 3
2. Count the total number of parts. What is the denominator? 4
3. Write the fraction. $\frac{3}{4}$

b.

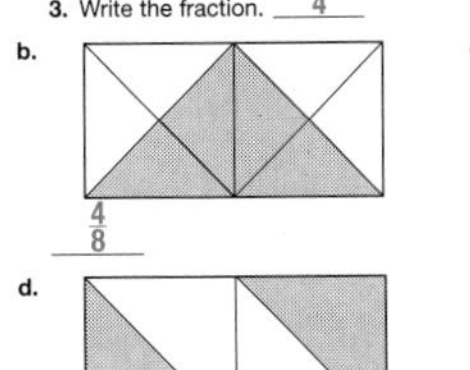

$\frac{4}{8}$

c.

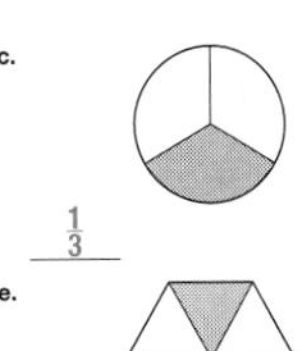

$\frac{1}{3}$

d. $\frac{2}{4}$

e.

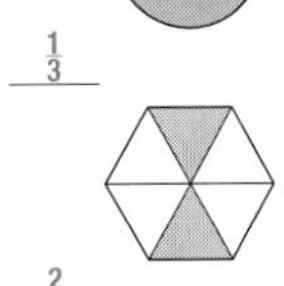

$\frac{2}{6}$

Reteaching

Activity

Materials: 20 index cards or small pieces of paper

- Work with a partner and make a list of 10 pairs of equivalent fractions. Write one fraction on each index card.
- Exchange index cards with another pair of students and then place the cards face down.
- Player 1 selects two cards. If the cards are equivalent fractions, Player 1 keeps them. If not, he or she returns the cards face down, and Player 2 selects two cards.
- The player with the most cards at the end of the game wins.

Exercise Notes

■ Exercise 28

Error Prevention Watch for students who are confused by the outside borders of some of the picture frames. Point out that they can look at the shape of the picture inside the frame to determine the number of square picture frames.

Exercise Answers

28. $\frac{6}{13}$: numerator 6, denominator 13; $\frac{12}{26}$: numerator 12, denominator 26

31. a, b; They are divided into four equal parts.

Alternate Assessment

Performance Have students draw a model for $\frac{1}{3}$ and then show how to use the model to find two or more equivalent fractions.

▶ Quick Quiz

For each fraction, name an equivalent fraction.

Possible answers are given.

1. $\frac{5}{6}$ $\frac{10}{12}$
2. $\frac{8}{12}$ $\frac{2}{3}$
3. $\frac{6}{10}$ $\frac{12}{20}$
4. $\frac{7}{8}$ $\frac{14}{16}$
5. $\frac{15}{25}$ $\frac{3}{5}$

Available on Daily Transparency 5-4

27. **Industry** Celia needs 20 nails and 8 screws to build a bookshelf. What fraction of the hardware she needs are screws? $\frac{8}{28}$ or $\frac{2}{7}$

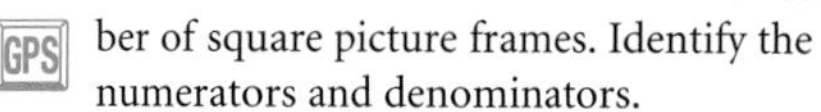

28. GPS Name two fractions that describe the number of square picture frames. Identify the numerators and denominators.

Problem Solving and Reasoning

Use the drill-bit size chart for Exercises 29–30.

Number	Bit Size
#4	$\frac{1}{4}$ in.
#5	$\frac{5}{16}$ in.
#6	$\frac{6}{16}$ in.
#7	$\frac{7}{16}$ in.
#8	$\frac{2}{4}$ in.

29. **Critical Thinking** The bit sizes increase according to a mathematical pattern. What will the size of the #10 drill bit be?

30. **Critical Thinking** What number bit would you need to drill a $\frac{3}{4}$-inch hole? #12

29. $\frac{10}{16}$ in. or $\frac{5}{8}$ in.

PROBLEM SOLVING 5-4

31. **Communicate** Which of these figures are divided into fourths? Explain.

a. 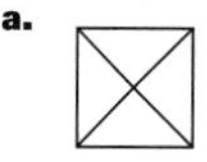

b. 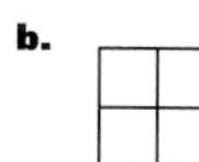

c. 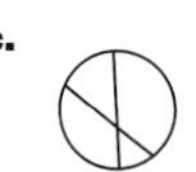

d. 

32. Journal Explain what happens to the value of a fraction when the numerator gets bigger and the denominator stays the same. What happens when the denominator gets bigger and the numerator doesn't change? Gets bigger; Gets smaller.

Mixed Review

Round to the underlined place value. *[Lesson 3-2]*

33. 101.93 101.9 **34.** 6.792 6.792 **35.** 48.25 48.3 **36.** 0.672 1 **37.** 8.7 9 **38.** 12.702 12.7

Solve. *[Lesson 3-12]*

39. $92.4n = 9240$ $n = 100$ **40.** $p \div 0.05 = 5$ $p = 0.25$

41. $1.45h = 2.9$ $h = 2$ **42.** $w \div 3 = 333.3$ $w = 999$

PROBLEM SOLVING

Name ____________

Guided Problem Solving 5-4

GPS PROBLEM 28, STUDENT PAGE 292

Name two fractions that describe the number of square picture frames. Identify the numerators and denominators.

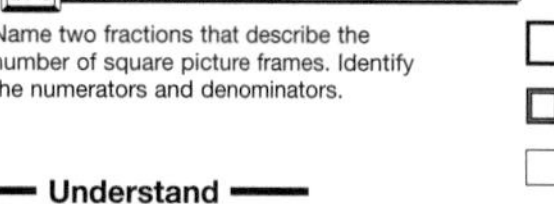

— Understand —

1. What are you asked to do? Possible answers: Items 6–9. Find two equivalent fractions that tell the number of square picture frames; identify numerators and denominators.

— Plan —

2. What will the numerator describe? The number of square frames.
3. What will the denominator describe? The total number of frames.

— Solve —

4. How many picture frames are shaped like squares? 6 frames
5. How many picture frames are there in all? 13 frames
6. What are two fractions that describe the number of square picture frames? $\frac{6}{13}, \frac{12}{26}$
7. What are the numerators in the two fractions you wrote? 6 and 12
8. What are the denominators in the two fractions you wrote? 13 and 26

— Look Back —

9. What two other equivalent fractions could you write for the number of square picture frames? $\frac{18}{39}, \frac{24}{52}$

SOLVE ANOTHER PROBLEM

Name two fractions that describe the number of shaded rectangles. One of the fractions should have 10 as the denominator. Identify the numerators and denominators.

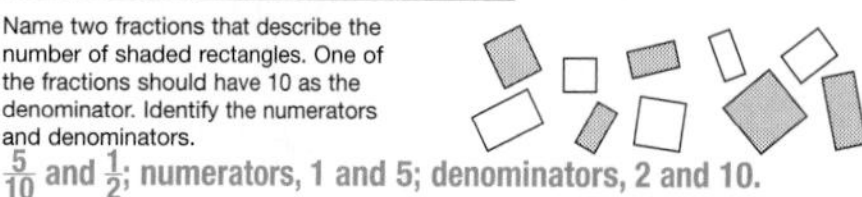

$\frac{5}{10}$ and $\frac{1}{2}$; numerators, 1 and 5; denominators, 2 and 10.

ENRICHMENT

Name ____________

Extend Your Thinking 5-4

Critical Thinking

The fraction $\frac{3}{4}$ can be modeled in a variety of ways. Two ways are shown below.

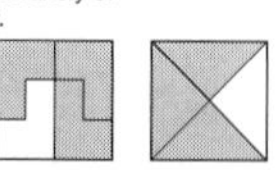

Divide the squares in column one into fourths. Show a different way to divide the square into fourths for each problem. Shade some parts. Write the fraction. Then use your model in column one to show an equivalent fraction in column two. Write the equivalent fraction.

Possible answers:

	Fourths	Equivalent fraction
1.	fraction $\frac{2}{4}$	fraction $\frac{4}{8}$
2.	fraction $\frac{1}{4}$	fraction $\frac{4}{16}$
3.	fraction $\frac{2}{4}$	fraction $\frac{6}{12}$
4.	fraction $\frac{3}{4}$	fraction $\frac{6}{8}$
5.	fraction $\frac{3}{4}$	fraction $\frac{12}{16}$

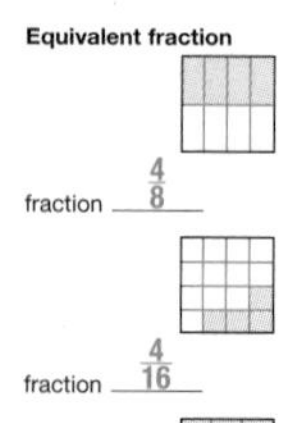

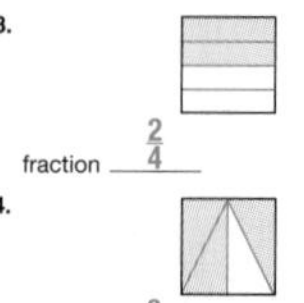

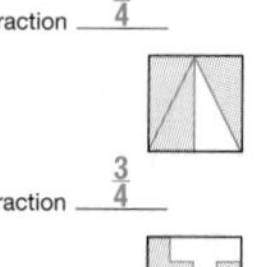

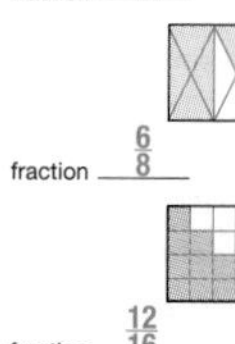

Fractions in Lowest Terms

5-5

▶ **Lesson Link** You've seen that different fractions can have equal values. Now you'll learn the simplest way to name a fraction. ◀

You'll Learn ...

■ to write a fraction in lowest terms

... How It's Used

Organic gardeners must write fractions in lowest terms in order to be certain they are caring for their crops correctly.

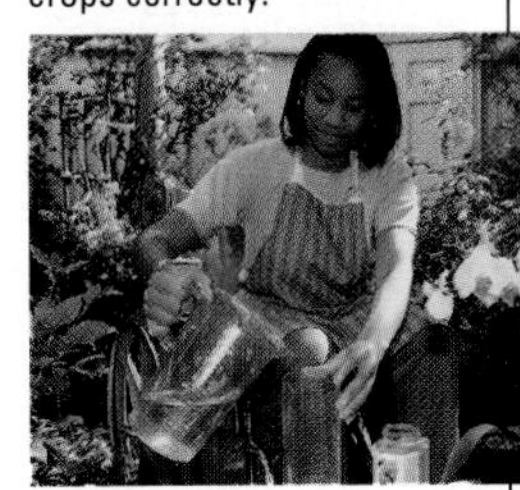

Vocabulary

lowest terms

greatest common factor (GCF)

Explore Equivalent Fractions

Fractions in Action

1. Complete the table. Every row should have equivalent fractions created by multiplying the shaded and total pieces by the same number.

Model	Fraction	$\frac{\times 2}{\times 2}$	$\frac{\times 3}{\times 3}$	$\frac{\times 4}{\times 4}$
	$\frac{1}{2}$	$= \frac{2}{4}$	$= \frac{?}{6}$	$= \frac{?}{?}$

2. Complete the table. Every row should have equivalent fractions created by dividing the shaded and total pieces by the same number. If a fraction can't be done, write "Can't do."

Model	Fraction	$\frac{\div 2}{\div 2}$	$\frac{\div 3}{\div 3}$	$\frac{\div 4}{\div 4}$
	$\frac{6}{12}$	$= \frac{3}{6}$	$= \frac{2}{4}$	Can't do

3. Can every fraction be turned into an equivalent fraction with larger numbers? With smaller numbers? Explain.

MEETING INDIVIDUAL NEEDS

Resources

- **5-5** Practice
- **5-5** Reteaching
- **5-5** Problem Solving
- **5-5** Enrichment
- **5-5** Daily Transparency
  - Problem of the Day
  - Review
  - Quick Quiz
- Lesson Enhancement Transparency 22
- Technology Master 24

Learning Modalities

Visual Have students represent fractions and equivalent fractions using circular fraction models.

Social Have students work in pairs, one partner on the first exercise and the other on the second. Have them agree on their solutions before proceeding.

Challenge

Have students find the greatest common factor of a set of numbers by finding the prime factorization of each number using exponents. Then have them identify any common factors and find the product of the least powers of any common factor identified. Have students use this method to find the greatest common factor of the following sets of numbers.

1. 36, 90, 126 $2 \times 3^2 = 18$
2. 96, 144, 240 $2^3 \times 3 = 24$
3. 60, 180, 300 $2^2 \times 3 \times 5 = 60$

5-5 Lesson Organizer

Objective

- Write a fraction in lowest terms.

Vocabulary

- Lowest terms, greatest common factor (GCF)

NCTM Standards

- 1–6

▶ Review

For each fraction, find an equivalent fraction.

Possible answers are given.

1. $\frac{3}{4}$ $\frac{6}{8}$
2. $\frac{2}{3}$ $\frac{4}{6}$
3. $\frac{4}{5}$ $\frac{12}{15}$
4. $\frac{7}{8}$ $\frac{14}{16}$
5. $\frac{9}{10}$ $\frac{90}{100}$

Available on Daily Transparency 5-5

1 Introduce

Explore

You may wish to use Lesson Enhancement Transparency 22 with **Explore**.

The Point

Students use simple fraction diagrams to determine how fractions can always be renamed using multiplication, but not always using division.

Ongoing Assessment

Check that students understand that there is no limit to the number of equivalent fractions they could model in Step 1.

For Groups That Finish Early

Give examples of fractions for which you cannot write equivalent fractions by dividing.

Answers for Explore on next page.

Answers for Explore

1. Row 1: $\frac{1}{2}, \frac{2}{4}, \frac{3}{6}, \frac{4}{8}$;

   Row 2: $\frac{2}{3}, \frac{4}{6}, \frac{6}{9}, \frac{8}{12}$;

   Row 3: $\frac{3}{4}, \frac{6}{8}, \frac{9}{12}, \frac{12}{16}$

2. Row 2: $\frac{4}{6}, \frac{2}{3}$, can't do, can't do;

   Row 3: $\frac{4}{8}, \frac{2}{4}$, can't do, $\frac{1}{2}$

3. Yes; No; There is an infinite number of multiples for a given number, but not an infinite number of factors.

2 Teach

Learn

Write the fraction $\frac{12}{24}$ on the chalkboard. Ask students to write equivalent fractions by multiplying. $\frac{24}{48}, \frac{36}{72}, \ldots$ Then ask other students to write equivalent fractions by dividing. $\frac{6}{12}, \frac{4}{8}, \frac{3}{6}$ Have them note that the number of fractions in the first list is infinite, while the number in the second list is limited.

Alternate Examples

1. Find two fractions equivalent to $\frac{12}{16}$.

$\frac{12}{16}$

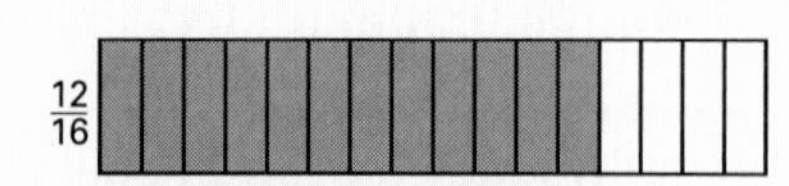

$\frac{24}{32}$

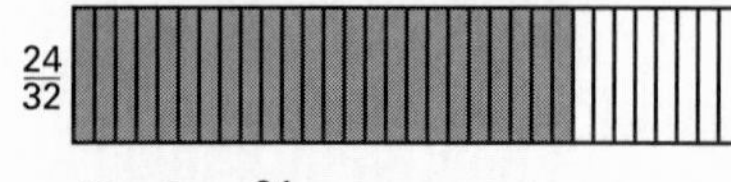

$\frac{12 \times 2}{16 \times 2} = \frac{24}{32}$

$\frac{12}{16}$

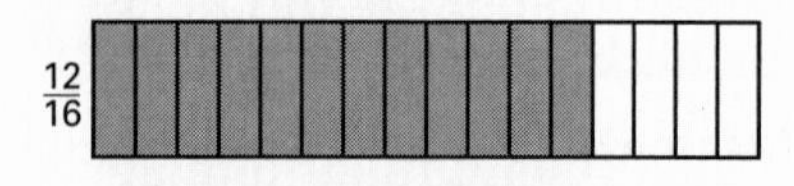

$\frac{3}{4}$

$\frac{12 \div 4}{16 \div 4} = \frac{3}{4}$

Two fractions equivalent to $\frac{12}{16}$ are $\frac{24}{32}$ and $\frac{3}{4}$.

2. The diameter of a drill bit measures $\frac{40}{64}$ inch. Give this fraction in lowest terms.

$\frac{40 \div 2}{64 \div 2} = \frac{20}{32}$

$\frac{20 \div 4}{32 \div 4} = \frac{5}{8}$

There are no numbers that divide into both 5 and 8. $\frac{40}{64}$ in lowest terms is $\frac{5}{8}$.

Learn | Fractions in Lowest Terms

You can find equivalent fractions by multiplying or dividing the numerator and denominator of a given fraction by the same number.

$\frac{2}{4} = \frac{4}{8}$ $\quad$ $\frac{2}{4} = \frac{1}{2}$

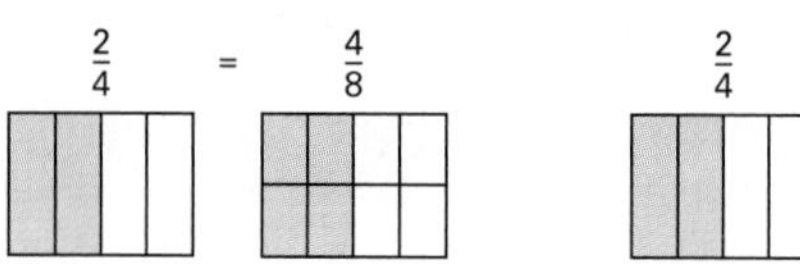

Problem Solving TIP

When looking for equivalent fractions, try multiplying and dividing by easy numbers like 2, 3, and 10.

Example 1

Find two fractions equivalent to $\frac{9}{12}$.

$\frac{9 \times 2}{12 \times 2} = \frac{18}{24}$ Multiply numerator and denominator by 2.

$\frac{9}{12}$ =

$\frac{18}{24}$ =

$\frac{9 \div 3}{12 \div 3} = \frac{3}{4}$ Divide numerator and denominator by 3.

$\frac{9}{12}$ =

$\frac{3}{4}$ =

Two fractions equivalent to $\frac{9}{12}$ are $\frac{18}{24}$ and $\frac{3}{4}$.

Remember

A fraction in lowest terms is also known as a fraction in simplest terms.
[Previous course]

When you multiply to find equivalent fractions, you can use any non-zero number as a multiplier. When you divide, you must find a number that divides both the numerator and the denominator. If there is no whole number that divides both the numerator and the denominator, the fraction is in **lowest terms**.

Example 2

A size-15 knitting needle measures about $\frac{24}{60}$ of an inch. What is this fraction in lowest terms?

$\frac{24 \div 4}{60 \div 4} = \frac{6}{15}$ Divide numerator and denominator by 4.

$\frac{6 \div 3}{15 \div 3} = \frac{2}{5}$ Divide numerator and denominator by 3.

There are no numbers that divide into both 2 and 5. $\frac{24}{60}$ in lowest terms is $\frac{2}{5}$.

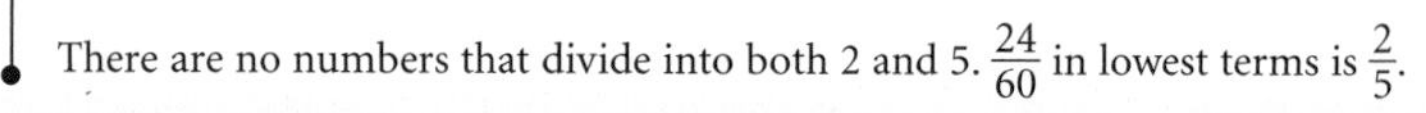

MATH EVERY DAY

Problem of the Day

Domingo has some change in his pocket. He cannot make change for a nickel, dime, quarter, half dollar, or dollar. Assuming he has no silver dollars, what is the greatest amount of money he can have? $1.19: 1 half-dollar, 1 quarter, 4 dimes, and 4 pennies

Available on Daily Transparency 5-5

An Extension is provided in the transparency package.

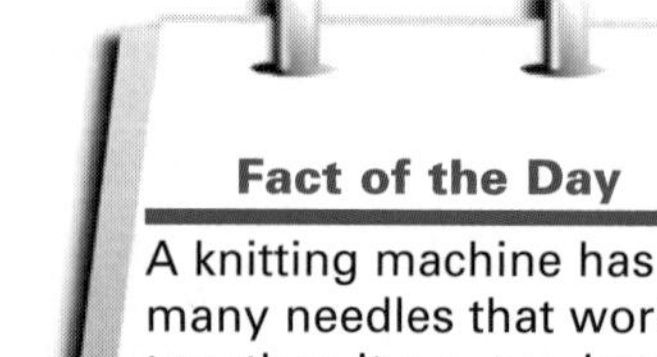

Fact of the Day

A knitting machine has many needles that work together. It can produce as many as 12,000,000 stitches a minute.

Mental Math

Do these mentally.

1. 1200 − 398 802
2. 25 + 65 + 35 125
3. 550 − 153 397
4. 198 + 98 296

You can reduce a fraction to lowest terms in one step if you divide by the greatest whole number that divides the numerator and the denominator. That number is called the **greatest common factor (GCF)**.

Examples

3 Find the GCF of 36 and 90.

Factors of 36: [1], [2], [3], 4, [6], [9], 12, [18], 36

Factors of 90: [1], [2], [3], 5, [6], [9], 10, 15, [18], 30, 45, 90

The common factors of 36 and 90 are 1, 2, 3, 6, 9, and 18. The *greatest* common factor is 18.

4 Find the GCF of 24 and 30, and use it to reduce $\frac{23}{40}$.

Factors of 24: [1], [2], [3], 4, [6], 8, 12, 24

Factors of 30: [1], [2], [3], 5, [6], 10, 15, 30

The common factors of 24 and 30 are 1, 2, 3, and 6. The *greatest* common factor is 6.

$\frac{24 \div 6}{30 \div 6} = \frac{4}{5}$

$\frac{24}{30}$ in lowest terms is $\frac{4}{5}$.

Try It

Find two fractions equivalent to the given fraction.

a. $\frac{6}{10}$ $\frac{3}{5}$, $\frac{12}{20}$ **b.** $\frac{12}{15}$ $\frac{4}{5}$, $\frac{24}{30}$ **c.** $\frac{7}{21}$ $\frac{1}{3}$, $\frac{14}{42}$

Find the GCF of the given pair of numbers.

d. 15, 20 5 **e.** 10, 12 2 **f.** 18, 45 9

Write in lowest terms.

g. $\frac{8}{10}$ $\frac{4}{5}$ **h.** $\frac{21}{28}$ $\frac{3}{4}$ **i.** $\frac{36}{54}$ $\frac{2}{3}$

Remember

Unlike the greatest common factor, the least common multiple is the smallest number that two numbers divide. [Page 279]

MENTAL MATH

Using the rules of divisibility can help you to find the factors of a number.

Check Your Understanding

1. How can you use the GCF when reducing a fraction to lowest terms?
2. You can write fractions in lowest terms. Can you also write them in "highest terms"? Explain.

Alternate Examples

3. Find the GCF of 28 and 42.

   Factors of 28: [1], [2], 4, [7], [14], 28

   Factors of 42: [1], [2], 3, 6, [7], [14], 21, 42

   The common factors of 28 and 42 are 1, 2, 7, and 14. The *greatest* common factor is 14.

4. Find the GCF of 32 and 48, and use it to reduce $\frac{32}{48}$.

   Factors of 32: [1], [2], [4], [8], [16], 32

   Factors of 48: [1], [2], 3, [4], 6, [8], 12, [16], 24, 48

   The common factors of 32 and 48 are 1, 2, 4, 8, and 16. The *greatest* common factor is 16.

   $\frac{32 \div 16}{48 \div 16} = \frac{2}{3}$

   $\frac{32}{48}$ in lowest terms is $\frac{2}{3}$.

3 Practice and Assess

Check

Refer students to Example 2. Have them identify the greatest common factor of 24 and 60 and use it to give the fraction in lowest terms. GCF is 12; $\frac{24 \div 12}{60 \div 12} = \frac{2}{5}$

Even though using the GCF requires only one division, some students may prefer to divide by factors that are more obvious to them.

Answers for Check Your Understanding

1. Divide the numerator and denominator by their GCF to reduce the fraction to lowest terms.
2. No; There are infinitely many equivalent fractions with larger numerators and denominators.

MEETING MIDDLE SCHOOL CLASSROOM NEEDS

Tips from Middle School Teachers

Students enjoy playing the following game of thumbs up or thumbs down. Make 20 or more fraction cards showing a pair of equal or unequal fractions on each card. Hold up one card at a time. Have students signal thumbs up if the fractions are equal and thumbs down if the fractions are not equal.

Cooperative Learning

Have students work in groups and list ten fractions equal to $\frac{10}{25}$. Then have groups combine their lists. Repeat the activity with other fractions.

Multicultural Connection

The earliest known tools were found at Hadar, Ethiopia, and date from about 2.5 million years ago. They were made of stone and used for chopping and slicing. Knives, scrapers, and spearheads made from *chert*, a flintlike rock, have been located in Washington County, Pennsylvania. It is estimated that they are about 11,000 to 16,000 years old.

5-5 Exercises and Applications

Assignment Guide

- **Basic**
  1–49 odds, 50–53, 54–60 evens
- **Average**
  1, 2–50 evens, 51, 53, 54, 57–61
- **Enriched**
  1–19 odds, 44–56, 58–61

Exercise Notes

Exercises 14–31

Extension For each exercise, have students give a different equivalent fraction.

Exercise 51

Test Prep Stress the importance of reading multiple-choice problems carefully. If students selected B, they found the fraction of hammers that have blue handles instead of the fraction of hammers that do *not* have blue handles.

Reteaching

Activity

- To find the greatest common factor of 36 and 90, first write the prime factorization of each number without using exponents. Then put a box around the common factors as shown.

  $36 = \boxed{2} \times 2 \times \boxed{3} \times \boxed{3}$

  $90 = \boxed{2} \times \boxed{3} \times \boxed{3} \times 5$

- The common factors of 36 and 90 are 2, 3, and 3. Find the product of these common factors: $2 \times 3 \times 3 = 18$. 18 is the *greatest* common factor.
- Use this method to find the GCF of each pair.

  48 and 64 16

  36 and 108 36

  64 and 96 32

5-5 Exercises and Applications

PRACTICE 5-5

Practice and Apply

1. Getting Started State if each fraction is in lowest terms.

a. $\frac{3}{7}$ Yes **b.** $\frac{4}{8}$ No **c.** $\frac{1}{10}$ Yes **d.** $\frac{1}{16}$ Yes **e.** $\frac{3}{9}$ No **f.** $\frac{2}{15}$ Yes

Find two fractions equivalent to each fraction. Possible answers:

2. $\frac{3}{5}$ $\frac{6}{10}, \frac{9}{15}$ **3.** $\frac{6}{18}$ $\frac{2}{6}, \frac{1}{3}$ **4.** $\frac{5}{20}$ $\frac{1}{4}, \frac{10}{40}$ **5.** $\frac{1}{6}$ $\frac{2}{12}, \frac{3}{18}$ **6.** $\frac{2}{7}$ $\frac{4}{14}, \frac{6}{21}$ **7.** $\frac{9}{21}$ $\frac{3}{7}, \frac{18}{42}$

8. $\frac{12}{24}$ $\frac{1}{2}, \frac{4}{8}$ **9.** $\frac{10}{25}$ $\frac{2}{5}, \frac{20}{50}$ **10.** $\frac{21}{35}$ $\frac{3}{5}, \frac{42}{70}$ **11.** $\frac{11}{33}$ $\frac{1}{3}, \frac{22}{66}$ **12.** $\frac{7}{11}$ $\frac{14}{22}, \frac{21}{33}$ **13.** $\frac{4}{9}$ $\frac{8}{18}, \frac{20}{45}$

Write in lowest terms.

14. $\frac{7}{14}$ $\frac{1}{2}$ **15.** $\frac{5}{25}$ $\frac{1}{5}$ **16.** $\frac{20}{30}$ $\frac{2}{3}$ **17.** $\frac{6}{18}$ $\frac{1}{3}$ **18.** $\frac{12}{36}$ $\frac{1}{3}$ **19.** $\frac{8}{10}$ $\frac{4}{5}$

20. $\frac{6}{8}$ $\frac{3}{4}$ **21.** $\frac{9}{15}$ $\frac{3}{5}$ **22.** $\frac{3}{21}$ $\frac{1}{7}$ **23.** $\frac{4}{24}$ $\frac{1}{6}$ **24.** $\frac{21}{35}$ $\frac{3}{5}$ **25.** $\frac{6}{9}$ $\frac{2}{3}$

26. $\frac{10}{12}$ $\frac{5}{6}$ **27.** $\frac{11}{44}$ $\frac{1}{4}$ **28.** $\frac{2}{8}$ $\frac{1}{4}$ **29.** $\frac{5}{30}$ $\frac{1}{6}$ **30.** $\frac{8}{36}$ $\frac{2}{9}$ **31.** $\frac{3}{18}$ $\frac{1}{6}$

Find the GCF of each pair.

32. 4, 8 4 **33.** 15, 25 5 **34.** 12, 15 3 **35.** 6, 8 2 **36.** 3, 7 1 **37.** 2, 5 1

38. 18, 27 9 **39.** 16, 24 8 **40.** 11, 23 1 **41.** 10, 100 10 **42.** 35, 24 1 **43.** 36, 16 4

44. 22, 66 22 **45.** 27, 72 9 **46.** 64, 32 32 **47.** 48, 28 4 **48.** 11, 17 1 **49.** 3, 105 3

50. Test Prep The head of a sledgehammer is shaped like a barrel. Which fraction in lowest terms describes the number of hammers that are sledgehammers? B

Ⓐ $\frac{1}{2}$ Ⓑ $\frac{1}{3}$ Ⓒ $\frac{4}{8}$ Ⓓ $\frac{4}{12}$

51. Test Prep Which fraction in lowest terms describes the number of hammers that don't have blue handles? C

Ⓐ $\frac{1}{6}$ Ⓑ $\frac{2}{12}$

Ⓒ $\frac{5}{6}$ Ⓓ $\frac{10}{12}$

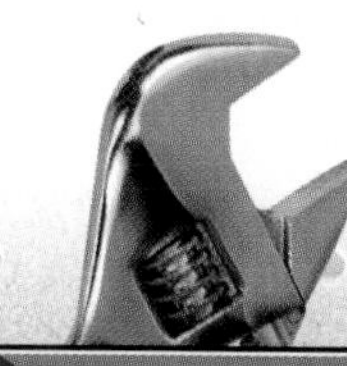

PRACTICE

Name ____________

Practice 5-5

Fractions in Lowest Terms

Find two fractions equivalent to each fraction. Possible answers:

1. $\frac{8}{10}$ $\frac{24}{30}, \frac{4}{5}$ 2. $\frac{3}{4}$ $\frac{6}{8}, \frac{12}{16}$ 3. $\frac{8}{24}$ $\frac{40}{120}, \frac{1}{3}$
4. $\frac{4}{7}$ $\frac{12}{21}, \frac{16}{28}$ 5. $\frac{18}{21}$ $\frac{36}{42}, \frac{6}{7}$ 6. $\frac{6}{8}$ $\frac{30}{40}, \frac{3}{4}$
7. $\frac{12}{14}$ $\frac{24}{28}, \frac{6}{7}$ 8. $\frac{5}{9}$ $\frac{10}{18}, \frac{15}{27}$ 9. $\frac{6}{9}$ $\frac{30}{45}, \frac{2}{3}$
10. $\frac{6}{14}$ $\frac{30}{70}, \frac{3}{7}$ 11. $\frac{12}{30}$ $\frac{48}{120}, \frac{2}{5}$ 12. $\frac{4}{13}$ $\frac{8}{26}, \frac{12}{39}$

Write in lowest terms.

13. $\frac{12}{24}$ $\frac{1}{2}$ 14. $\frac{6}{9}$ $\frac{2}{3}$ 15. $\frac{9}{21}$ $\frac{3}{7}$ 16. $\frac{8}{10}$ $\frac{4}{5}$
17. $\frac{6}{28}$ $\frac{3}{14}$ 18. $\frac{18}{20}$ $\frac{9}{10}$ 19. $\frac{30}{38}$ $\frac{15}{19}$ 20. $\frac{8}{20}$ $\frac{2}{5}$
21. $\frac{12}{18}$ $\frac{2}{3}$ 22. $\frac{14}{32}$ $\frac{7}{16}$ 23. $\frac{8}{12}$ $\frac{2}{3}$ 24. $\frac{12}{16}$ $\frac{3}{4}$
25. $\frac{12}{30}$ $\frac{2}{5}$ 26. $\frac{9}{15}$ $\frac{3}{5}$ 27. $\frac{6}{42}$ $\frac{1}{7}$ 28. $\frac{9}{12}$ $\frac{3}{4}$
29. $\frac{6}{15}$ $\frac{2}{5}$ 30. $\frac{6}{10}$ $\frac{3}{5}$ 31. $\frac{6}{12}$ $\frac{1}{2}$ 32. $\frac{24}{30}$ $\frac{4}{5}$

Find the GCF of each pair.

33. 16, 10 2 34. 11, 18 1 35. 15, 6 3 36. 8, 6 2
37. 3, 6 3 38. 20, 15 5 39. 12, 18 6 40. 3, 14 1
41. 8, 12 4 42. 10, 14 2 43. 21, 15 3 44. 49, 70 7
45. 36, 60 12 46. 70, 42 14 47. 32, 76 4 48. 64, 4 4
49. 15, 75 15 50. 63, 42 21 51. 30, 65 5 52. 32, 24 8

53. **Measurement** A kilometer is about $\frac{6}{10}$ of a mile. Write this distance in lowest terms. $\frac{3}{5}$ mi

54. $\frac{25}{30}$ of the students in Mrs. Lim's class went on last week's field trip. Write this fraction in lowest terms. $\frac{5}{6}$

RETEACHING

Name ____________

Alternative Lesson 5-5

Fractions in Lowest Terms

Equivalent fractions are two fractions that name the same amount. You can find equivalent fractions by multiplying or dividing the numerator and the denominator by the same nonzero number. This is the same as multiplying or dividing the fraction by 1.

Example 1

Find two fractions that are equivalent to $\frac{5}{10}$.

Numerator → / Denominator → $\frac{5 \times \mathbf{2}}{10 \times \mathbf{2}} = \frac{10}{20}$ $\frac{5}{10}$ is equivalent to $\frac{10}{20}$.

Numerator → / Denominator → $\frac{5 \div \mathbf{5}}{10 \div \mathbf{5}} = \frac{1}{2}$ $\frac{5}{10}$ is equivalent to $\frac{1}{2}$.

The fractions $\frac{5}{10}$, $\frac{10}{20}$, and $\frac{1}{2}$ are equivalent.

Try It Multiply to find an equivalent fraction.

a. $\frac{2}{6} = \frac{2 \times \square}{6 \times \square} = \frac{\square}{\square}$ b. $\frac{4}{5} = \frac{4 \times \square}{5 \times \square} = \frac{\square}{\square}$

Divide to find an equivalent fraction.

c. $\frac{6}{8} = \frac{6 \div \square}{8 \div \square} = \frac{\square}{\square}$ d. $\frac{3}{12} = \frac{3 \div \square}{12 \div \square} = \frac{\square}{\square}$

Possible answers:
a. $\frac{2}{2}$, $\frac{4}{12}$
b. $\frac{2}{2}$, $\frac{8}{10}$
c. $\frac{2}{2}$, $\frac{3}{4}$
d. $\frac{3}{3}$, $\frac{1}{4}$

Example 2

A fraction is in **lowest terms** when no whole number can be divided evenly into both the numerator and the denominator. A fraction in lowest terms is equivalent to the original fraction.

Write $\frac{8}{24}$ in lowest terms.

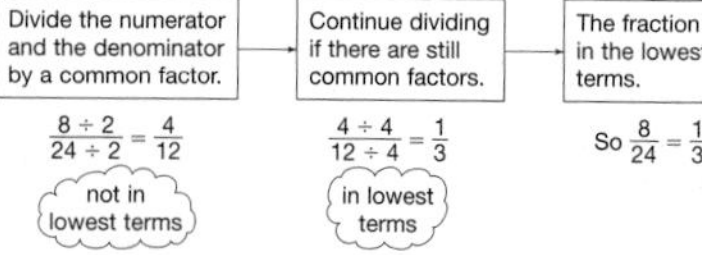

Try It Write each fraction in lowest terms.

e. $\frac{4}{10}$ $\frac{2}{5}$ f. $\frac{15}{60}$ $\frac{1}{4}$ g. $\frac{8}{28}$ $\frac{2}{7}$

52. **History** Medieval carpenters used tools with narrow cutting edges, called gouges, to shape their work. The width of one paring gouge was about $\frac{4}{16}$ in. Write the width in lowest terms.

Problem Solving and Reasoning

53. **Choose a Strategy** Marilyn sold $\frac{3}{6}$ of the raffle tickets at a carnival. Darren sold $\frac{2}{8}$ of them. Jamelya sold the rest. Who sold more tickets, Marilyn by herself, or Darren and Jamelya together? Explain.

54. Journal Explain the difference between LCM and GCF. Can the LCM and GCF of two numbers ever be equal? Explain.

55. **Critical Thinking** Explain why $\frac{2}{17}$, $\frac{11}{13}$, $\frac{2}{3}$, and $\frac{5}{7}$ cannot be written in lower terms. What do the numbers making up the fractions have in common?

56. **Communicate** What is the GCF of 1 and x? Explain.

Problem Solving STRATEGIES

- Look for a Pattern
- Make an Organized List
- Make a Table
- Guess and Check
- Work Backward
- Use Logical Reasoning
- Draw a Diagram
- Solve a Simpler Problem

PROBLEM SOLVING 5-5

Mixed Review

57. For each point in the graph, approximate the data represented by the point. *[Lesson 1-3]*

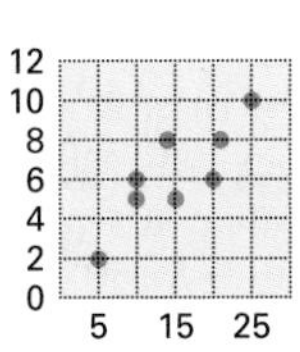

Use the Maximum Weight graph for Exercises 58–61. *[Lesson 1-1]*

58. What is the maximum weight for a flyweight boxer? 50 kg

59. What is the difference in the maximum weights for the cruiserweight and the welterweight? 25 kg

60. Tony weighs 76 kg. What weight class is he in? Cruiserweight

61. Which two weight classes have the largest difference? What is the difference between those two classes?

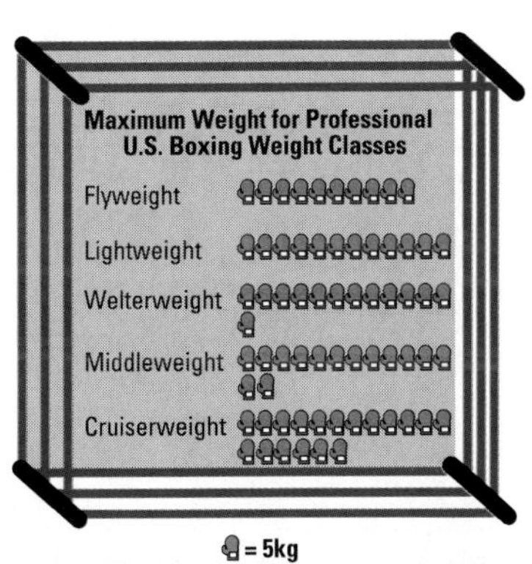

Exercise Notes

Exercise 53

Error Prevention Tell students to express the fractions in lowest terms before trying to solve the problem. It should be obvious that Marilyn sold the same number of tickets that the other two sold together.

Exercise Answers

52. $\frac{1}{4}$ in.

53. They sold the same; $\frac{3}{6} = \frac{1}{2}$.

54. The LCM is the least common multiple of the numbers, while the GCF is the greatest common factor; No; The GCF is less than or equal to the smaller number, and the LCM is greater than or equal to the larger number.

55. There are no numbers that divide both the numerator and the denominator; The numbers are prime.

56. 1; The only factor of 1 is 1.

57. (5, 2); (10, 5); (10, 6); (14, 8); (15, 5); (20, 6); (21, 8); (25, 10)

61. Flyweight and Cruiserweight; 40 kg.

Alternate Assessment

Interview Have students demonstrate two methods for reducing a fraction to lowest terms. Ask them if they prefer one method and have them explain why.

Quick Quiz

Write each fraction in lowest terms.

1. $\frac{9}{18}$ $\frac{1}{2}$
2. $\frac{14}{35}$ $\frac{2}{5}$
3. $\frac{18}{42}$ $\frac{3}{7}$
4. $\frac{24}{36}$ $\frac{2}{3}$
5. $\frac{15}{25}$ $\frac{3}{5}$

Available on Daily Transparency 5-5

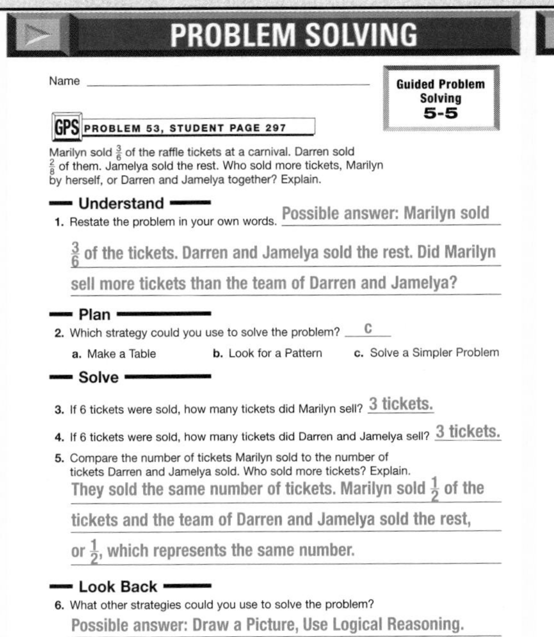

PROBLEM SOLVING

Name ____________ Guided Problem Solving 5-5

GPS PROBLEM 53, STUDENT PAGE 297

Marilyn sold $\frac{3}{6}$ of the raffle tickets at a carnival. Darren sold $\frac{2}{8}$ of them. Jamelya sold the rest. Who sold more tickets, Marilyn by herself, or Darren and Jamelya together? Explain.

— Understand —

1. Restate the problem in your own words. Possible answer: Marilyn sold $\frac{3}{6}$ of the tickets. Darren and Jamelya sold the rest. Did Marilyn sell more tickets than the team of Darren and Jamelya?

— Plan —

2. Which strategy could you use to solve the problem? C

a. Make a Table b. Look for a Pattern c. Solve a Simpler Problem

— Solve —

3. If 6 tickets were sold, how many tickets did Marilyn sell? 3 tickets.

4. If 6 tickets were sold, how many tickets did Darren and Jamelya sell? 3 tickets.

5. Compare the number of tickets Marilyn sold to the number of tickets Darren and Jamelya sold. Who sold more tickets? Explain. They sold the same number of tickets. Marilyn sold $\frac{1}{2}$ of the tickets and the team of Darren and Jamelya sold the rest, or $\frac{1}{2}$, which represents the same number.

— Look Back —

6. What other strategies could you use to solve the problem? Possible answer: Draw a Picture, Use Logical Reasoning.

SOLVE ANOTHER PROBLEM

Casey ate $\frac{3}{8}$ of a pizza. Ann ate $\frac{2}{8}$ of the pizza and Juan ate the rest. Who ate more pizza, Juan by himself, or Casey and Ann together? Casey and Ann together.

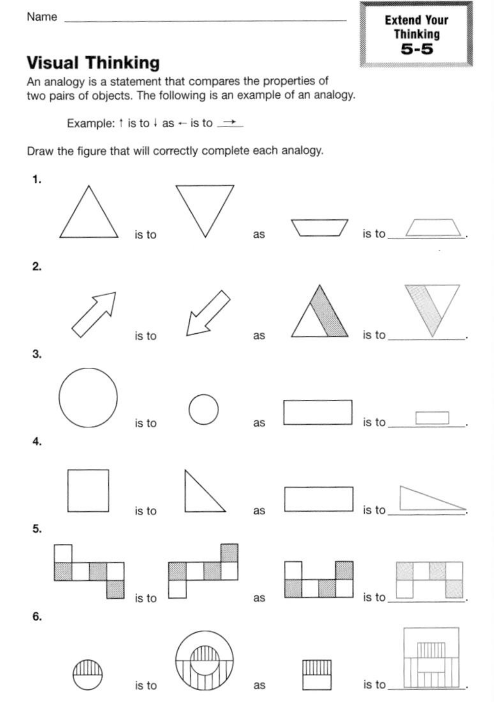

ENRICHMENT

Name ____________ Extend Your Thinking 5-5

Visual Thinking

An analogy is a statement that compares the properties of two pairs of objects. The following is an example of an analogy.

Example: ↑ is to ↓ as ← is to →

Draw the figure that will correctly complete each analogy.

1. is to as is to ____.
2. is to as is to ____.
3. is to as is to ____.
4. is to as is to ____.
5. is to as is to ____.
6. is to as is to ____.

5-6 Lesson Organizer

Objective

- Convert between improper fractions and mixed numbers.

Vocabulary

- Improper fraction, mixed number

Materials

- Explore: Pattern blocks or Power Polygons

NCTM Standards

- 1–6, 13

Review

Give the word name for each number.

1. $\frac{3}{4}$ Three fourths
2. $1\frac{2}{3}$ One and two-thirds
3. $3\frac{4}{5}$ Three and four-fifths
4. $5\frac{7}{8}$ Five and seven-eighths
5. $2\frac{9}{10}$ Two and nine-tenths

Available on Daily Transparency 5-6

1 Introduce

Explore

You may wish to use Teaching Tool Transparency 19: Power Polygons and Lesson Enhancement Transparency 23 with **Explore**.

The Point
Students use pattern blocks to investigate models of mixed numbers.

Ongoing Assessment
Ask students for examples of proper and improper fractions to be sure that they know the difference between them.

5-6 Improper Fractions and Mixed Numbers

You'll Learn ...

- to convert between improper fractions and mixed numbers

... How It's Used

Deli clerks use improper fractions and mixed numbers when weighing meats and cheeses.

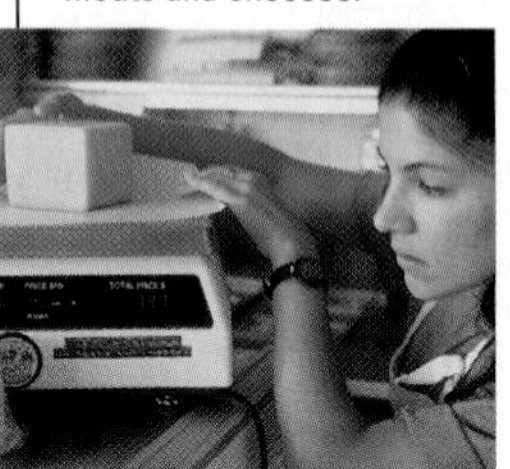

Vocabulary

improper fraction

mixed number

▶ Lesson Link So far in this section, you've worked mainly with fractions less than a whole. Now you'll look at fractions greater than a whole. ◀

An **improper fraction** has a numerator that is greater than or equal to its denominator. A **mixed number** combines a whole number and a fraction.

Proper $\frac{2}{3}$

Improper $\frac{20}{9}$

Mixed $3\frac{4}{5}$

Explore Improper Fractions and Mixed Numbers

Hexagons Plus

Materials: Pattern blocks or Power Polygons

1. Use pattern blocks to complete the table.

The "whole"	The "parts"	Fraction naming one "part"	Improper fraction: all "parts"	Mixed number: all "parts"
		$\frac{1}{6}$	$\frac{7}{6}$	$1\frac{1}{6}$

2. Can any improper fraction be written as a mixed number? Can any mixed number be rewritten as an improper fraction? Explain.

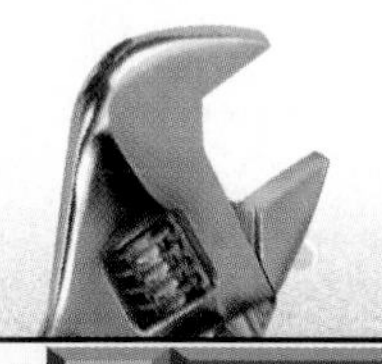

MEETING INDIVIDUAL NEEDS

Resources

- **5-6** Practice
- **5-6** Reteaching
- **5-6** Problem Solving
- **5-6** Enrichment
- **5-6** Daily Transparency
  - Problem of the Day
  - Review
  - Quick Quiz
- Teaching Tool Transparency 19
- Lesson Enhancement Transparency 23
- Chapter 5 Project Master

Learning Modalities

Logical Explain that a mixed number can be thought of as the sum of a whole number and a fraction. Show students the following method for writing mixed numbers as improper fractions.

$2\frac{3}{4} = 2 + \frac{3}{4} = \frac{8}{4} + \frac{3}{4} = \frac{11}{4}$

Visual Draw several different number lines on the chalkboard or use Teaching Tool Transparency 5: Number Lines. Mark the lines in fourths, sixths, and eighths. Indicate locations greater than 1, and have students identify both the mixed number and the improper fraction it represents.

Inclusion

Students may have difficulty with the various shapes made from the pattern blocks used in **Explore**. They might be better able to understand improper fractions and mixed numbers using circular models or Fraction Bars.

Learn: Mixed Numbers and Improper Fractions

A proper fraction has a value less than 1. Recall that a proper fraction can have many names.

Improper fractions and mixed numbers have values greater than or equal to 1. Improper fractions and mixed numbers can also have many names. Sometimes, one is easier to use than the other.

Proper Fractions

$\frac{1}{2} = \frac{2}{4} = \frac{3}{6} = \frac{4}{8}$

Improper Fractions

$\frac{4}{3} = \frac{8}{6} = \frac{12}{9} = \frac{16}{12}$

Mixed Numbers

$7\frac{1}{2} = 7\frac{2}{4} = 7\frac{3}{6} = 7\frac{4}{8}$

Remember

The order of operations states:

(1) do operations in parentheses;
(2) do operations with exponents;
(3) multiply and divide from left to right; and
(4) add and subtract from left to right.

[Page 99]

Divide the numerator by the denominator. The whole number part is the whole number in the mixed number. The remainder is the fraction.

$\frac{13}{4} = 13 \div 4 = 3\text{ R }1 = 3\frac{1}{4}$

Improper Fraction ⇄ **Mixed Number**

To get the improper fraction numerator, multiply the fraction denominator by the whole number, then add the mixed-number numerator.

$2\frac{1}{3} = \frac{(3 \times 2) + 1}{3} = \frac{7}{3}$

Examples

1 Rewrite $\frac{11}{4}$ cups as a mixed number.

$\frac{11}{4} = 11 \div 4 = 4\overline{)11}$ with quotient 2 R 3 — Divide numerator by denominator.

$\frac{11}{4} = 2\frac{3}{4}$

2 Write $4\frac{3}{5}$ as an improper fraction.

$4\frac{3}{5} = \frac{(5 \times 4) + 3}{5} = \frac{23}{5}$ — Multiply denominator and whole number and add numerator.

Try It

Write as a mixed number. **a.** $\frac{14}{3}$ $4\frac{2}{3}$ **b.** $\frac{26}{9}$ $2\frac{8}{9}$ **c.** $\frac{35}{4}$ $8\frac{3}{4}$

Write as an improper fraction. **d.** $1\frac{5}{6}$ $\frac{11}{6}$ **e.** $4\frac{1}{8}$ $\frac{33}{8}$ **f.** $2\frac{3}{5}$ $\frac{13}{5}$

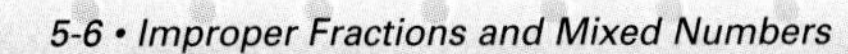

For Groups That Finish Early

Work with a partner to create models similar to those in Step 1. Analyze your partner's model.

Follow Up

Be sure that students have completed the table correctly before proceeding.

Answers for Explore

1. Row 2: $\frac{1}{3}$, $\frac{8}{3}$, $2\frac{2}{3}$

   Row 3: $\frac{1}{3}$, $\frac{4}{3}$, $1\frac{1}{3}$

   Row 4: $\frac{1}{2}$, $\frac{5}{2}$, $2\frac{1}{2}$

   Row 5: $\frac{2}{3}$, $\frac{6}{3}$, 2

2. Yes; Yes; Multiply the whole number by the denominator and add the result to the numerator to get a new numerator.

2 Teach

Learn

Alternate Examples

1. Rewrite $\frac{20}{8}$ cups as a mixed number.

   $\frac{20}{8} = 20 \div 8 = 8\overline{)20}$ with quotient 2 R 4

   $2\frac{4}{8} = 2\frac{1}{2}$

2. Write $3\frac{5}{8}$ as an improper fraction.

   $3\frac{5}{8} = \frac{(8 \times 3) + 5}{8} = \frac{29}{8}$

MATH EVERY DAY

Problem of the Day

Kay used this data to "prove" there are no days left to go to school. What is wrong with her conclusion?

Days in a year	365
Sleep 8 hr/day, $\frac{1}{3}$ year	−122
This leaves:	243
Days in weekends	−104
This leaves:	139
Vacation time	−109
This leaves:	30
Eat 2 hr/day, $\frac{1}{12}$ year	−30
Days left to go to school	0

Kay counted sleeping and eating hours twice.

Available on Daily Transparency 5-6

An Extension is provided in the transparency package.

Fact of the Day

A dripping faucet can waste more than 1000 gallons of water a year.

Mental Math

Give each improper fraction as a mixed number.

1. $\frac{3}{2}$ $1\frac{1}{2}$
2. $\frac{5}{4}$ $1\frac{1}{4}$
3. $\frac{7}{3}$ $2\frac{1}{3}$
4. $\frac{11}{8}$ $1\frac{3}{8}$

5-6 Exercises and Applications

Assignment Guide

- Basic
  1–29 odds, 30, 32, 33–45 odds
- Average
  1–28 evens, 29–31, 33, 36–46 evens
- Enriched
  1–29 odds, 30–34, 35–45 odds

3 Practice and Assess

Check

Answers for Check Your Understanding

1. No; A mixed number can be greater than 1.
2. Yes; The numerator can be a multiple of the denominator.

Exercise Notes

Exercises 14–25

Error Prevention Be sure that students give answers in lowest terms.

Exercise 29

Extension Ask students to find how much longer the tool box is than the hammer. $4\frac{1}{2}$ cm longer.

Reteaching

Activity

- *Materials:* Inch ruler or customary tape measure
- Choose any eighth mark on the ruler between 1 and 2 inches. How many eighths are there from 0 to 1 inch? 8 eighths How many eighths are there from zero to your mark? Answers may vary.
- Write an improper fraction for the mark you chose. Then write a mixed number. What will the whole-number part be? 1 Explain why. Because the number is between 1 and 2
- Choose other marks on the ruler and give both an improper fraction and a mixed number for each mark.

Check Your Understanding

1. Can a mixed number be equal to 1? Explain.
2. Can an improper fraction equal a whole number? Explain.

5-6 Exercises and Applications

PRACTICE 5-6

Practice and Apply

1. **Getting Started** Identify each fraction as proper or improper.

a. $\frac{9}{10}$ Proper **b.** $\frac{12}{3}$ Improper **c.** $\frac{3}{2}$ Improper **d.** $\frac{4}{6}$ Proper **e.** $\frac{17}{8}$ Improper **f.** $\frac{8}{2}$ Improper

Write each mixed number as an improper fraction.

2. $1\frac{8}{8}$ $\frac{16}{8}$ **3.** $1\frac{9}{5}$ $\frac{14}{5}$ **4.** $1\frac{6}{3}$ $\frac{9}{3}$ **5.** $3\frac{1}{3}$ $\frac{10}{3}$ **6.** $4\frac{9}{8}$ $\frac{41}{8}$ **7.** $2\frac{6}{4}$ $\frac{14}{4}$

8. $1\frac{2}{5}$ $\frac{7}{5}$ **9.** $2\frac{4}{5}$ $\frac{14}{5}$ **10.** $1\frac{1}{4}$ $\frac{5}{4}$ **11.** $3\frac{1}{10}$ $\frac{31}{10}$ **12.** $5\frac{4}{5}$ $\frac{29}{5}$ **13.** $2\frac{9}{12}$ $\frac{33}{12}$

Write each improper fraction as a mixed number.

14. $\frac{10}{3}$ $3\frac{1}{3}$ **15.** $\frac{14}{5}$ $2\frac{4}{5}$ **16.** $\frac{15}{8}$ $1\frac{7}{8}$ **17.** $\frac{11}{2}$ $5\frac{1}{2}$ **18.** $\frac{14}{3}$ $4\frac{2}{3}$ **19.** $\frac{23}{8}$ $2\frac{7}{8}$

20. $\frac{50}{7}$ $7\frac{1}{7}$ **21.** $\frac{99}{10}$ $9\frac{9}{10}$ **22.** $\frac{201}{2}$ $100\frac{1}{2}$ **23.** $\frac{805}{8}$ $100\frac{5}{8}$ **24.** $\frac{40}{9}$ $4\frac{4}{9}$ **25.** $\frac{29}{11}$ $2\frac{7}{11}$

Science **Write the mixed number as an improper fraction or the improper fraction as a mixed number.**

26. Washing the dishes with the water running wastes $25\frac{2}{3}$ gallons of water. $\frac{77}{3}$

27. A running faucet uses $3\frac{7}{8}$ gallons of water every minute. $\frac{31}{8}$

28. Flushing a toilet uses $\frac{28}{5}$ gallons of water. $5\frac{3}{5}$

29. **Measurement** Caesar has a tool box that is $15\frac{3}{4}$ in. long. His hammer is $\frac{45}{4}$ in. long. Will the hammer fit in the tool box? Yes

GPS

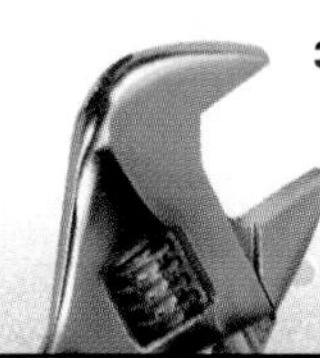

30. **Test Prep** Choose the mixed number equivalent to $\frac{10}{6}$. C

Ⓐ $\frac{5}{3}$ Ⓑ $\frac{6}{10}$ Ⓒ $1\frac{4}{6}$ Ⓓ $2\frac{2}{6}$

PRACTICE

Name ______________________

Practice 5-6

Improper Fractions and Mixed Numbers

Write each mixed number as an improper fraction.

1. $2\frac{1}{6}$ $\frac{13}{6}$ 2. $5\frac{1}{5}$ $\frac{26}{5}$ 3. $1\frac{2}{5}$ $\frac{7}{5}$ 4. $13\frac{1}{2}$ $\frac{27}{2}$

5. $8\frac{3}{4}$ $\frac{35}{4}$ 6. $3\frac{2}{3}$ $\frac{11}{3}$ 7. $1\frac{3}{5}$ $\frac{8}{5}$ 8. $4\frac{1}{2}$ $\frac{9}{2}$

9. $14\frac{2}{9}$ $\frac{128}{9}$ 10. $12\frac{2}{3}$ $\frac{38}{3}$ 11. $3\frac{5}{8}$ $\frac{29}{8}$ 12. $9\frac{1}{9}$ $\frac{82}{9}$

13. $5\frac{2}{3}$ $\frac{17}{3}$ 14. $7\frac{4}{5}$ $\frac{39}{5}$ 15. $8\frac{1}{3}$ $\frac{25}{3}$ 16. $4\frac{3}{4}$ $\frac{19}{4}$

Write each improper fraction as a mixed number.

17. $\frac{17}{4}$ $4\frac{1}{4}$ 18. $\frac{19}{2}$ $9\frac{1}{2}$ 19. $\frac{37}{3}$ $12\frac{1}{3}$ 20. $\frac{16}{7}$ $2\frac{2}{7}$

21. $\frac{32}{3}$ $10\frac{2}{3}$ 22. $\frac{77}{8}$ $9\frac{5}{8}$ 23. $\frac{101}{7}$ $14\frac{3}{7}$ 24. $\frac{33}{4}$ $8\frac{1}{4}$

25. $\frac{27}{2}$ $13\frac{1}{2}$ 26. $\frac{19}{3}$ $6\frac{1}{3}$ 27. $\frac{41}{9}$ $4\frac{5}{9}$ 28. $\frac{61}{6}$ $10\frac{1}{6}$

29. $\frac{59}{10}$ $5\frac{9}{10}$ 30. $\frac{19}{4}$ $4\frac{3}{4}$ 31. $\frac{5}{3}$ $1\frac{2}{3}$ 32. $\frac{26}{5}$ $5\frac{1}{5}$

Science Write the mixed number as an improper fraction or the improper fraction as a mixed number.

33. A geranosaurus was $1\frac{1}{5}$ m long. $\frac{6}{5}$ m

34. Each arm of a deinocherius was $\frac{17}{2}$ ft long. $8\frac{1}{2}$ ft

35. A hypsilophodon was $\frac{23}{10}$ m long. $2\frac{3}{10}$ m

36. A protoceratops was $\frac{9}{5}$ m long. $1\frac{4}{5}$ m

37. An anatosaurus was $13\frac{2}{3}$ m long. $\frac{41}{3}$ m

38. Heidi built a fort with a ceiling that was $\frac{21}{4}$ ft high. Marvin is $5\frac{3}{4}$ ft tall. Can Marvin stand up straight in Heidi's fort? No

RETEACHING

Name ______________________

Alternative Lesson 5-6

Improper Fractions and Mixed Numbers

An **improper fraction** has a numerator that is greater than or equal to its denominator. It has a value greater than or equal to one. A **mixed number** combines a whole number and a fraction.

Example

Write an improper fraction and a mixed number to describe the picture.

The shapes are divided into fifths, so the denominator of all fractions will be 5.

There are 12 shaded parts, so the numerator will be 12.

The improper fraction shown by the picture is $\frac{12}{5}$.

There are 2 wholes shaded. The third shape has 2 fifths shaded.

The mixed number shown by the picture is $2\frac{2}{5}$.

Try It Write an improper fraction and a mixed number to describe each picture.

a. $\frac{4}{3}$, $1\frac{1}{3}$

b. 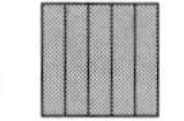 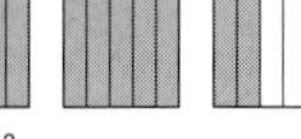

$\frac{10}{4}$, $2\frac{2}{4}$ or $2\frac{1}{2}$

c. 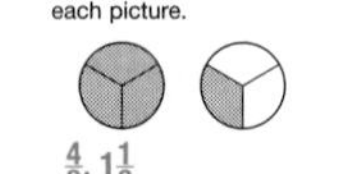

$\frac{22}{6}$, $3\frac{4}{6}$ or $3\frac{2}{3}$

d.  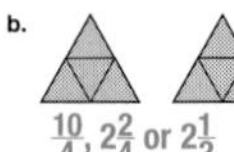 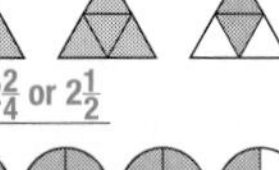

$\frac{7}{2}$ or $3\frac{1}{2}$

e. 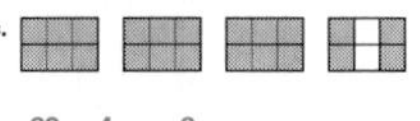

$\frac{20}{8}$, $2\frac{4}{8}$ or $2\frac{1}{2}$

f.  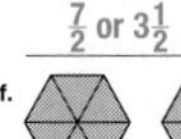 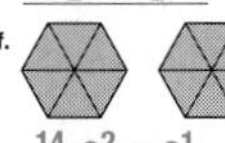

$\frac{14}{6}$, $2\frac{2}{6}$ or $2\frac{1}{3}$

g. 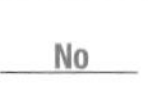

$\frac{16}{7}$, $2\frac{2}{7}$

h. 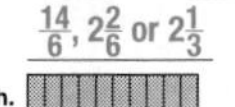 

$\frac{14}{10}$, $1\frac{4}{10}$ or $1\frac{2}{5}$

Problem Solving and Reasoning

31. Critical Thinking Darrell needs to measure a board about 6 feet long. He can't find his ruler, but he knows his hand is $\frac{1}{2}$ a foot long. How many hand lengths will he have to mark to get the length he needs? 12

32. Critical Thinking The picture models a number greater than one. Write the value it represents as a mixed number and as an improper fraction. Explain. $3\frac{3}{4}$, $\frac{15}{4}$; Each pie represents 1.

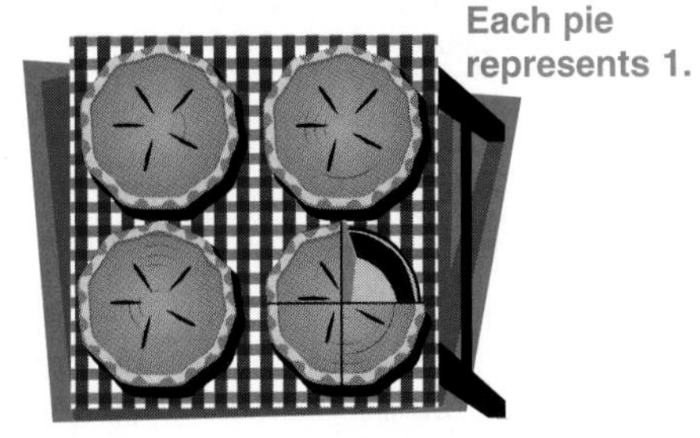

33. Journal Explain why an improper fraction can be written as a mixed number but a fraction less than 1 cannot.

34. Communicate Which is more, $\frac{9}{4}$ slices of cantaloupe or $1\frac{1}{2}$ slices? Explain your decision.

Mixed Review

Find the mean, median, and mode with and without the outlier. Which does the outlier affect the most? *[Lesson 1-9]*

35. 20, 31, 32, 34, 35, 35, 35, 36, 37

36. 7, 4, 3, 6, 20, 7, 7, 4, 5, 2, 2, 1, 2

37. Make a line plot of the data in Exercise 35. *[Lesson 1-4]*

38. Make a line plot of the data in Exercise 36. *[Lesson 1-4]*

Convert. *[Lesson 4-3]*

39. 2 mi = □ ft **40.** 60 in. = □ ft **41.** 27 ft = □ yd **42.** 3 lb = □ oz

43. 5 mi = □ ft **44.** 108 in. = □ ft **45.** 90 ft = □ yd **46.** 7 lb = □ oz

Project Progress

In your chart, write several versions of your favorite number as a fraction and as a decimal. Compare one of the fraction versions of your number to other fractions and record the comparisons in your chart.

Problem Solving
Understand
Plan
Solve
Look Back

PROBLEM SOLVING 5-6

PROBLEM SOLVING

Name ______________________

Guided Problem Solving 5-6

GPS PROBLEM 29, STUDENT PAGE 300

Caesar has a tool box that is $15\frac{3}{4}$ in. long. His hammer is $\frac{45}{4}$ in. long. Will the hammer fit in the tool box?

— Understand —

1. What do you need to find?
   Whether or not the hammer will fit in the tool box.
2. Circle the information you need.

— Plan —

3. For the hammer to fit in the tool box, should the length of the hammer be longer or shorter than the length of the tool box? Shorter than.
4. Write $\frac{45}{4}$ as a mixed number. $11\frac{1}{4}$
5. Compare the whole number of the number you wrote in Item 4 with the whole number in $15\frac{3}{4}$. Which is greater? 15

— Solve —

6. Will the hammer fit in the tool box? Explain how you know.
   The hammer will fit in the tool box since $15\frac{3}{4}$ in. is longer than $11\frac{1}{4}$ in. This assumes that the width of the hammer is also less than the width of the tool box.

— Look Back —

7. Can you think of another way to solve the problem? Explain.
   Possible answer: Convert the tool box length to an improper fraction and then compare the numerators.

SOLVE ANOTHER PROBLEM

Yoko has $2\frac{5}{8}$ pounds of trail mix in one bag. Sam has $\frac{10}{8}$ pounds of trail mix in ten bags. Who has more trail mix? Explain how you know.

Yoko has more trail mix since $2\frac{5}{8}$ is more than $1\frac{2}{8}$.

ENRICHMENT

Name ______________________

Extend Your Thinking 5-6

Decision Making

Marsha wants to take her dog, Duchess, on a 2-mile walk. In her city, 8 blocks are equal to one mile. Marsha and Duchess will walk only on the sidewalk.

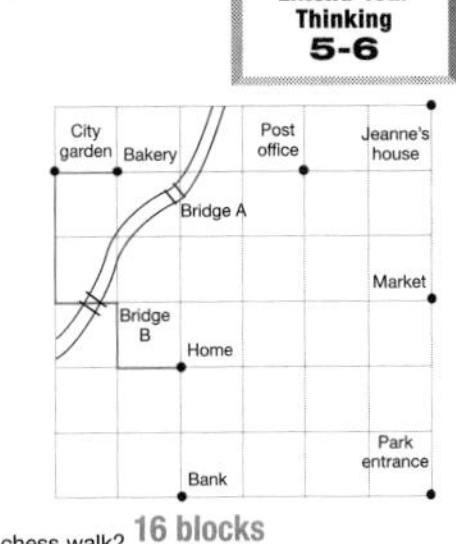

1. How many blocks will Marsha and Duchess walk? 16 blocks
2. If Marsha wants to go to the farthest point from her home, where would she and Duchess walk? Explain.
   Possible answer: Jeanne's house, because it is 8 blocks, or 1 mile, to her house. A round trip walk would be 2 miles.
3. If the route you chose in Question 2 took Marsha and Duchess up a steep hill, would you change the destination? Why or why not?
   Possible answer: Possibly, since there are other places to visit.
4. Can Marsha and Duchess walk by the post office, the market, and the bank on this walk? Why or why not?
   No. There is no way to pass all locations and walk 2 miles or less.
5. Bridge A is being repaired and is closed to walkers. Draw the most direct route to the bakery on the map above. Explain why you chose that route.
   Possible answer: It is one of the most direct routes, and it goes by the city garden so Marsha can see the flowers.

Project Progress

You may want to have students use Chapter 5 Project Master.

Exercise Answers

33. Possible answer: By definition, a mixed number must be greater than 1 and an improper fraction is also greater than 1.
34. $\frac{9}{4}$; $\frac{9}{4} = 2\frac{1}{4}$; $2\frac{1}{4} > 1\frac{1}{2}$
35. With outlier: mean ≈ 32.778, median 35, mode 35; Without outlier: mean 34.375, median 35, mode 35; Mean is most affected.
36. With outlier: mean 5.385, median 4, modes 2 and 7; No outlier: mean 4.167, median 4, modes 2 and 7; Mean is most affected.
37.

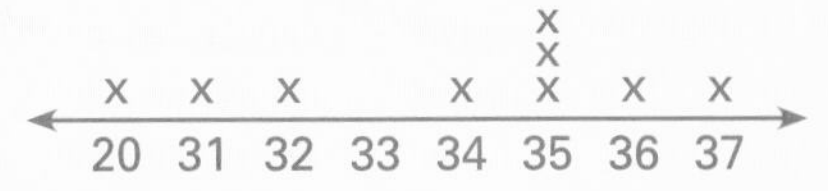

38.

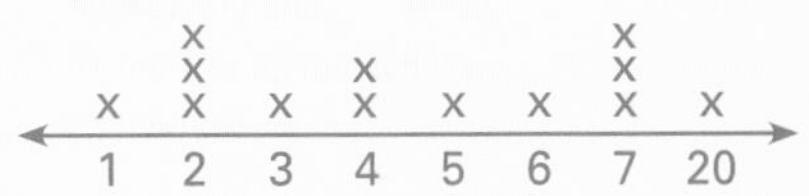

39. 10,560
40. 5
41. 9
42. 48
43. 26,400
44. 9
45. 30
46. 112

Alternate Assessment

Interview Have students define and give examples of mixed numbers and improper fractions.

Quick Quiz

Write each mixed number as an improper fraction.

1. $4\frac{7}{8}$ $\frac{39}{8}$
2. $2\frac{3}{10}$ $\frac{23}{10}$
3. $5\frac{1}{4}$ $\frac{21}{4}$

Write each improper fraction as a mixed number.

4. $\frac{12}{5}$ $2\frac{2}{5}$
5. $\frac{17}{3}$ $5\frac{2}{3}$

Available on Daily Transparency 5-6

5-7

Lesson Organizer

Objective

- Convert between fractions and decimals.

Vocabulary

- Terminating decimal, repeating decimal

Materials

- Explore: Tenths grids, 10 x 10 grids

NCTM Standards

- 1–6, 8, 13

Review

Give each quotient to the nearest hundredth.

1. 3 ÷ 4 0.75
2. 5 ÷ 3 1.67
3. 7 ÷ 8 0.88
4. 1 ÷ 6 0.17
5. 4 ÷ 7 0.57

Available on Daily Transparency 5-7

1 Introduce

Explore

You may wish to use Teaching Tool Transparencies 11: 10 × 10 Grids and 12: Tenths Grids with **Explore**.

The Point
Students use decimal models to express fractions as decimals and decimals as fractions.

Ongoing Assessment
Circulate around the class and check that students are modeling the numbers correctly.

For Groups That Finish Early
Name fractions and decimals for your group to model.

5-7 Converting Fractions and Decimals

You'll Learn ...

- to convert between fractions and decimals

... How It's Used

International travelers have to understand the connection between fractions and decimals when traveling to foreign countries.

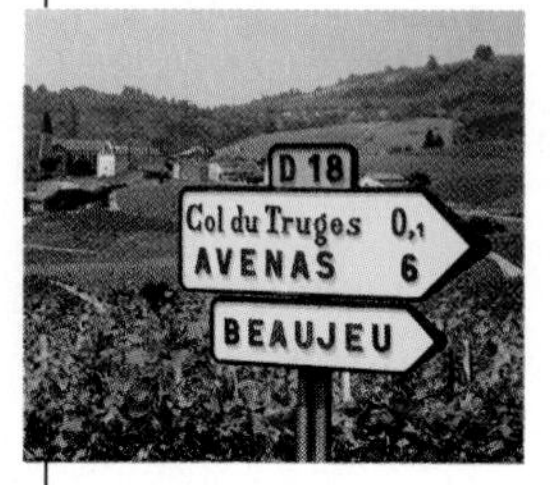

Vocabulary

terminating decimal

repeating decimal

▶ Lesson Link You've learned to write numbers using decimal notation and fraction notation. Now you'll learn to convert between the two notations. ◀

Explore Fractions and Decimals

Making the Grid

Materials: Tenths grids, 10 × 10 grids

Modeling Fractions on a Tenths Grid

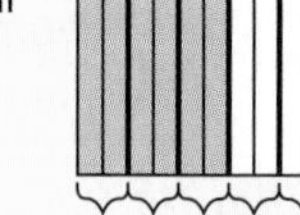

- Divide the strips into a number of groups equal to the denominator. Each group should have the same number of strips.
- Color in as many groups as the numerator.
- Describe the number modeled in the grid.

1. Model these fractions as decimals.

a. $\frac{1}{2}$ **b.** $\frac{2}{5}$ **c.** $\frac{7}{10}$ **d.** $\frac{4}{5}$

Modeling Fractions on a 10 × 10 Grid

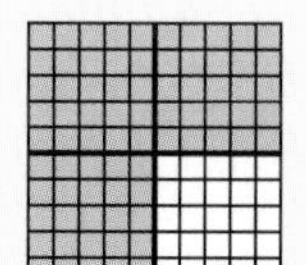

- Divide the squares into a number of groups equal to the denominator. Each group should have the same number of squares.
- Color in as many groups as the numerator.
- Describe the number modeled in the grid.

2. Model these fractions as decimals.

a. $\frac{4}{10}$ **b.** $\frac{1}{4}$ **c.** $\frac{3}{20}$ **d.** $\frac{13}{50}$

3. Could you model $\frac{1}{4}$ on a 10-strip grid? Explain.

4. Could you model $\frac{1}{3}$ on a 10-strip grid? Could you model it on a 100-strip grid? Explain.

5. Which of the following would have more shaded squares, a grid showing $\frac{3}{10}$ or a grid showing 0.3? Explain.

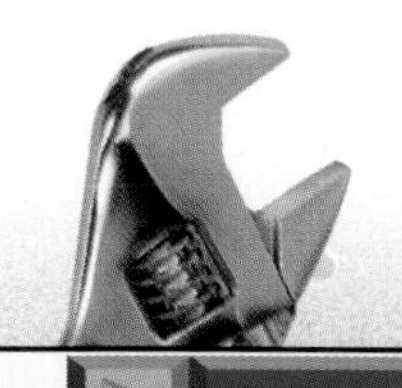

MEETING INDIVIDUAL NEEDS

Resources

5-7 Practice
5-7 Reteaching
5-7 Problem Solving
5-7 Enrichment
5-7 Daily Transparency
  Problem of the Day
  Review
  Quick Quiz
Teaching Tool Transparencies 11, 12

Learning Modalities

Kinesthetic Use money to illustrate fractional parts of a dollar.

Social Have pairs of students take turns modeling the fractions in **Explore** as decimals. Have them discuss and agree on their models before they work on the remaining exercises.

Challenge

Have students use calculators to investigate the repeating patterns found in fractions with denominators of 7, 9, and 11. Have them find decimal equivalents for several fractions with the same denominator and use the pattern to find decimal equivalents for other fractions with that denominator.

Learn Converting Fractions and Decimals

Fractions and decimals are two different ways of describing numbers in between whole numbers. It's important to be able to compare these numbers, even if some are written as decimals and some as fractions.

Rewrite the digits of the decimal as the numerator. Write the denominator equal to the place value of the decimal number.

$0.9 = \text{nine tenths} = \frac{9}{10}$

$0.013 = \text{thirteen thousandths} = \frac{13}{1000}$

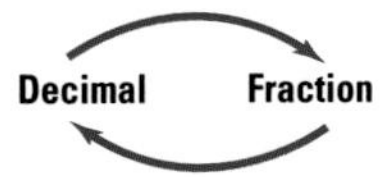

Decimal **Fraction**

Divide the numerator by the denominator. You may need to go several places past the decimal point.

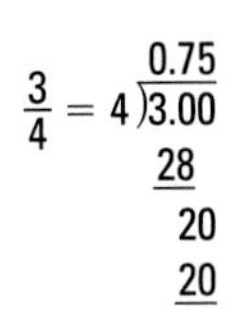

$$\frac{3}{4} = 4\overline{)3.00} = 0.75 \quad \begin{array}{r} 28 \\ 20 \\ 20 \end{array}$$

MENTAL MATH

Decimal numbers greater than 1 can be converted to mixed numbers. The digits to the left of the decimal are the whole-number part. The digits to the right of the decimal can be converted to the fraction part.

Examples

1 Write 0.775 as a fraction in lowest terms.

$0.775 = \frac{775}{1000}$ Write the fraction.

$= \frac{775 \div 25}{1000 \div 25}$ The greatest common factor of 775 and 1000 is 25.

$= \frac{31}{40}$ Divide.

2 Jane needs to drill a hole at least 0.7 inch wide. Her hand drill has a #10 auger bit, which is $\frac{5}{8}$ of an inch wide. Is the auger bit big enough?

$$\frac{5}{8} = 8\overline{)5.000} = 0.625 \quad \begin{array}{r} 48 \\ 20 \\ 16 \\ 40 \\ 40 \end{array}$$

Divide the numerator by the denominator.

The drill bit is 0.625 inches wide.
$0.625 < 0.7$. No, it is not big enough.

Industry Link

The point of a drill should be suited to the material being drilled. For the best results, metal and wood require completely different types of drill points.

Answers for Explore

1. a. b. 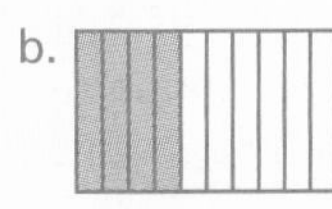
c. 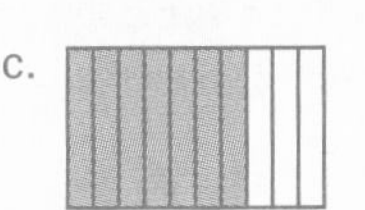 d. 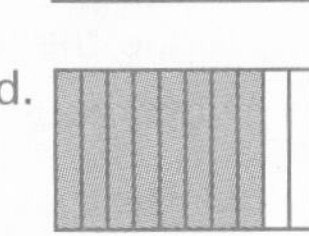

2. a. 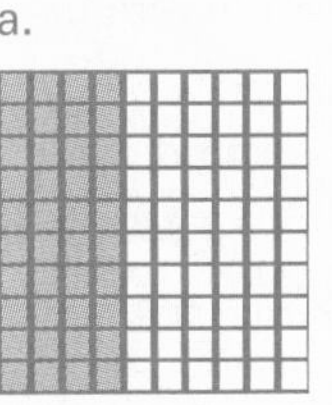 b. 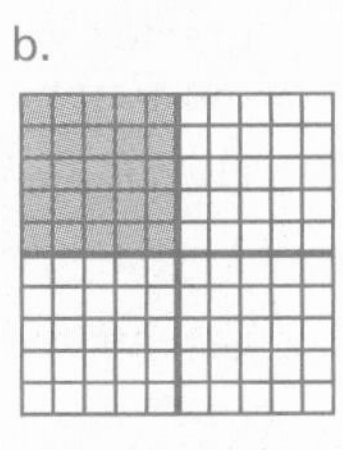
c. 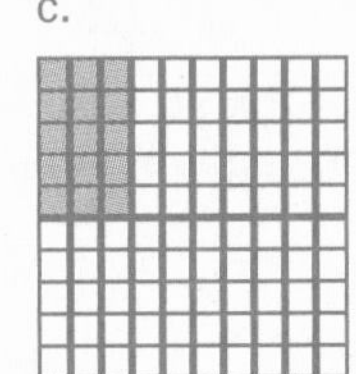 d. 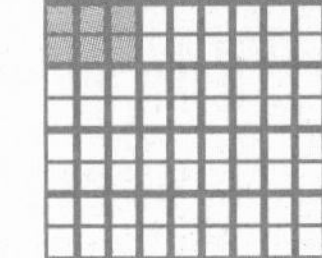

3. No; 10 is not divisible by 4.
4. No; No; Neither 10 nor 100 is divisible by 3.
5. Neither; They represent the same number.

2 Teach

Learn

Alternate Examples

1. Write 0.45 as a fraction in lowest terms.

$0.45 = \frac{45}{100}$

$= \frac{45 \div 5}{100 \div 5}$

$= \frac{9}{20}$

2. Ollie needs a nail at least 0.9 inch long. He has some nails which are $\frac{15}{16}$ inch long. Are they long enough?

$\frac{15}{16} = 15 \div 16 = 0.9375$

The nail is 0.9375 inch long. $0.9375 > 0.9$, so the nail is long enough.

MATH EVERY DAY

Problem of the Day

Select the drawing that best continues the pattern.

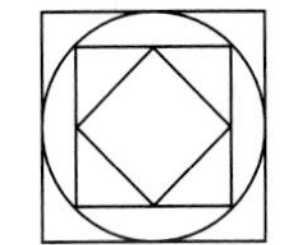 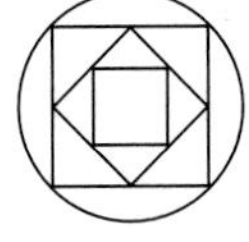 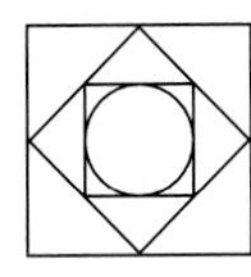

A. 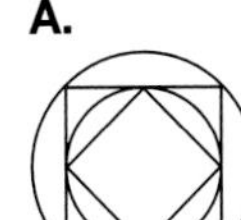 **B.** 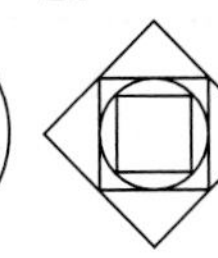 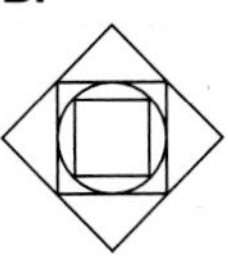 **C.** 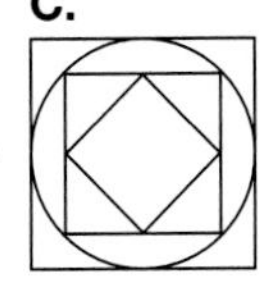

Figure B

Available on Daily Transparency 5-7

An Extension is provided in the transparency package.

Fact of the Day

There are more than five billion one-dollar bills in circulation and more than 180 million one-hundred dollar bills in circulation.

Mental Math

Give each fraction in lowest terms.

1. $\frac{2}{4}$ $\frac{1}{2}$
2. $\frac{4}{6}$ $\frac{2}{3}$
3. $\frac{5}{10}$ $\frac{1}{2}$
4. $\frac{25}{100}$ $\frac{1}{4}$

Alternate Examples

3. The pattern for a stuffed teddy bear calls for $\frac{1}{3}$ yard of ribbon, while the pattern for a stuffed dog requires $\frac{3}{8}$ yard of ribbon.

   Write these measures as decimals, and tell which is greater. Which toy requires more ribbon?

   Use a calculator to divide.

   1 [÷] 3 [=] 0.333 ..., so $\frac{1}{3}$ is the repeating decimal $0.\overline{3}$.

   3 [÷] 8 [=] 0.375, so $\frac{3}{8}$ is the terminating decimal 0.375.

   0.375 is greater than $0.\overline{3}$, so the stuffed dog requires more ribbon.

3 Practice and Assess

Check

Check that students know to place the bar over only the set of repeating digits in a repeating decimal. Tell them that this set of numbers is called the *repetend*, a term derived from the word *repeat*.

Answers for Check Your Understanding

1. Yes; To change a fraction to a decimal, divide the numerator by the denominator.
2. If the numerator is less than the denominator, the fraction is less than 1; If the numerator is equal to the denominator, the fraction is equal to 1; If the numerator is greater than the denominator, the fraction is greater than 1.

When you convert a fraction to a decimal, there are two kinds of answers you can get, a *terminating decimal* or a *repeating decimal*.

A **terminating decimal** ends:

$$\frac{5}{8} = 8\overline{)5.000} = 0.625$$

```
   0.625
8)5.000
  48
   20
   16
    40
    40
```

A **repeating decimal** repeats a pattern of digits continuously:

$$\frac{4}{11} = 11\overline{)4.000000}$$

```
    0.363636...
11)4.000000
   33
    70
    66
     40
     33
```

$\frac{5}{8} = 0.625$. The decimal ends.

$\frac{4}{11} = 0.3636\ldots$ The decimal repeats.

To represent a repeating decimal, draw a bar over the repeating digits. $\frac{4}{11} = 0.\overline{36}$.

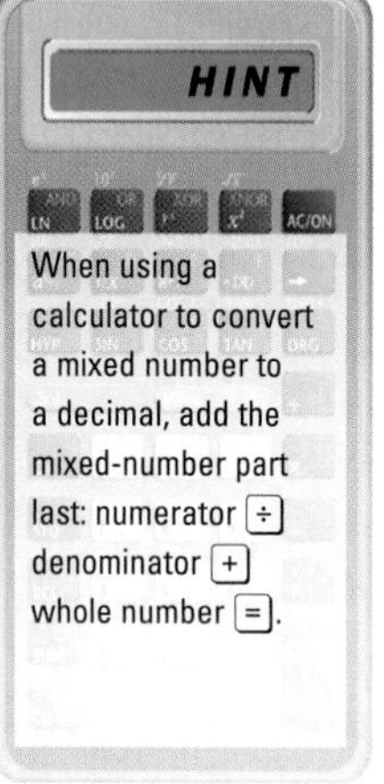

Example 3

Paleontologists use calipers to measure the width of solid objects. A paleontologist measures two bones as $\frac{1}{9}$ in. and $\frac{3}{32}$ in. Write these measures as decimals. Which decimal value is larger? Which bone is larger?

Use a calculator to divide.

1 [÷] 9 [=] 0.111111..., so $\frac{1}{9}$ is the repeating decimal $0.\overline{1}$.

3 [÷] 32 [=] 0.09375, so $\frac{3}{32}$ is the terminating decimal 0.09375.

$0.\overline{1}$ is larger than 0.09375. The first bone is larger.

Try It

Write as a fraction in lowest terms.

a. 0.8 $\frac{4}{5}$ **b.** 0.24 $\frac{6}{25}$ **c.** 0.375 $\frac{3}{8}$

Write as a decimal. State whether the decimal terminates or repeats.

d. $\frac{1}{5}$ 0.2; Terminates **e.** $\frac{13}{20}$ 0.65; Terminates **f.** $\frac{12}{33}$ $0.\overline{36}$; Repeats

MEETING MIDDLE SCHOOL CLASSROOM NEEDS

Tips from Middle School Teachers

Materials: Calculators

It is important for students to know how a calculator shows a repeating decimal. Have students use their calculators to find the decimal for $\frac{2}{3}$. Some calculators will display 0.6666666 and some will display 0.6666667. Write the two representations on the chalkboard and explain that the first calculator *truncated*, or cut off, the decimal after the seventh place, and that the second calculator rounded the decimal to that place.

Consumer Connection

Both wire and plastic sheeting are measured in *mils*, or thousandths of an inch. Have students give both the decimal and the fraction for 3 mils and 12 mils. 0.003, $\frac{3}{1000}$; 0.012, $\frac{12}{1000}$

Science Connection

Paleontologists study the forms of life existing in prehistoric times by investigating animal and plant fossils. They are mainly concerned with life during the Paleolithic period (Old Stone Age), which began around 2.5 million years ago, and the Neolithic period (New Stone Age), which began about 9000 B.C.

Check Your Understanding

1. Can all fractions be changed into decimals? Explain.
2. How can you tell if a fraction is less than, equal to, or greater than 1?

5-7 Exercises and Applications

Practice and Apply

1. **Getting Started** Write each decimal in fraction form.
   a. 0.3 $\frac{3}{10}$ **b.** 0.7 $\frac{7}{10}$ **c.** 0.11 $\frac{11}{100}$ **d.** 0.37 $\frac{37}{100}$ **e.** 0.121 $\frac{121}{1000}$ **f.** 0.333 $\frac{333}{1000}$

Rewrite using bar notation.

2. 0.33333333... $0.\overline{3}$ **3.** 0.14141414... $0.\overline{14}$ **4.** 0.827272727... $0.8\overline{27}$ **5.** 1.345345... $1.\overline{345}$

Write each fraction as a decimal. State whether the decimal terminates or repeats.

6. $\frac{2}{5}$ **7.** $\frac{2}{11}$ **8.** $\frac{7}{10}$ **9.** $\frac{9}{20}$ **10.** $\frac{2}{22}$ **11.** $\frac{7}{25}$

12. $\frac{17}{20}$ **13.** $\frac{4}{6}$ **14.** $\frac{11}{6}$ **15.** $\frac{5}{2}$ **16.** $\frac{62}{62}$ **17.** $\frac{5}{4}$

18. $\frac{7}{9}$ **19.** $\frac{72}{100}$ **20.** $\frac{5}{8}$ **21.** $\frac{3}{4}$ **22.** $\frac{5}{6}$ **23.** $\frac{4}{8}$

Write each decimal as a fraction in lowest terms.

24. 0.25 $\frac{1}{4}$ **25.** 0.4 $\frac{2}{5}$ **26.** 0.75 $\frac{3}{4}$ **27.** 0.44 $\frac{11}{25}$ **28.** 0.3 $\frac{3}{10}$ **29.** 0.67 $\frac{67}{100}$

30. 0.168 $\frac{21}{125}$ **31.** 0.35 $\frac{7}{20}$ **32.** 0.64 $\frac{16}{25}$ **33.** 0.52 $\frac{13}{25}$ **34.** 0.332 $\frac{83}{250}$ **35.** 0.192 $\frac{24}{125}$

36. 0.6 $\frac{3}{5}$ **37.** 0.7 $\frac{7}{10}$ **38.** 0.36 $\frac{9}{25}$ **39.** 0.128 $\frac{16}{125}$ **40.** 0.28 $\frac{7}{25}$ **41.** 0.88 $\frac{22}{25}$

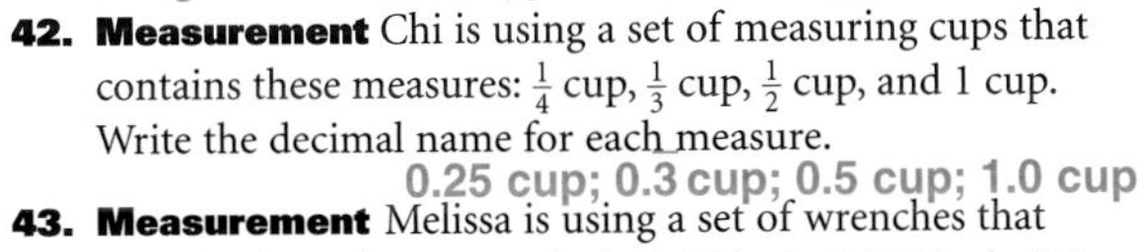

42. Measurement Chi is using a set of measuring cups that contains these measures: $\frac{1}{4}$ cup, $\frac{1}{3}$ cup, $\frac{1}{2}$ cup, and 1 cup. Write the decimal name for each measure.
0.25 cup; $0.\overline{3}$ cup; 0.5 cup; 1.0 cup

43. Measurement Melissa is using a set of wrenches that come in these sizes: 0.125 inch, 0.25 inch, 0.375 inch, 0.5 inch, 0.625 inch, 0.75 inch, and 0.875 inch. Write each wrench size as a fraction in lowest terms.
GPS
$\frac{1}{8}$ in., $\frac{1}{4}$ in., $\frac{3}{8}$ in., $\frac{1}{2}$ in., $\frac{5}{8}$ in., $\frac{3}{4}$ in., $\frac{7}{8}$ in.

PRACTICE 5-7

5-7 Exercises and Applications

Assignment Guide

- **Basic**
  1–41 odds, 42, 43, 45, 49–63 odds
- **Average**
  1, 2–42 evens, 43–46, 50–64 evens
- **Enriched**
  1–41 odds, 43–49, 50–64 evens

Exercise Answers

6. 0.4; Terminates
7. $0.\overline{18}$; Repeats
8. 0.7; Terminates
9. 0.45; Terminates
10. $0.\overline{09}$; Repeats
11. 0.28; Terminates
12. 0.85; Terminates
13. $0.\overline{6}$; Repeats
14. $1.8\overline{3}$; Repeats
15. 2.5; Terminates
16. 1.0; Terminates
17. 1.25; Terminates
18. $0.\overline{7}$; Repeats
19. 0.72; Terminates
20. 0.625; Terminates
21. 0.75; Terminates
22. $0.8\overline{3}$; Repeats
23. 0.5; Terminates

PRACTICE

Name ______________________

Practice 5-7

Converting Fractions and Decimals

Rewrite using bar notation.

1. 0.77777777 ... $0.\overline{7}$ 2. 0.58585858 ... $0.\overline{58}$ 3. 2.65656565 ... $2.\overline{65}$
4. 3.008008008 ... $3.\overline{008}$ 5. 4.876767676 ... $4.8\overline{76}$ 6. 12.12121212 ... $12.\overline{12}$
7. 4.93333333 ... $4.9\overline{3}$ 8. 7.50505050 ... $7.\overline{50}$ 9. 6.80888888 ... $6.80\overline{8}$

Write each fraction as a decimal. State whether the decimal terminates or repeats.

10. $\frac{2}{3}$ $0.\overline{6}$ Repeats 11. $\frac{7}{10}$ 0.7 Terminates 12. $\frac{3}{5}$ 0.6 Terminates 13. $\frac{15}{6}$ 2.5 Terminates
14. $\frac{23}{33}$ $0.\overline{69}$ Repeats 15. $\frac{1}{8}$ 0.125 Terminates 16. $\frac{5}{11}$ $0.\overline{45}$ Repeats 17. $\frac{36}{25}$ 1.44 Terminates
18. $\frac{41}{100}$ 0.41 Terminates 19. $\frac{5}{6}$ $0.8\overline{3}$ Repeats 20. $\frac{21}{40}$ 0.525 Terminates 21. $\frac{49}{50}$ 0.98 Terminates

Write each decimal as a fraction in lowest terms.

22. 0.25 $\frac{1}{4}$ 23. 0.74 $\frac{37}{50}$ 24. 0.5 $\frac{1}{2}$ 25. 0.47 $\frac{47}{100}$
26. 0.8 $\frac{4}{5}$ 27. 0.375 $\frac{3}{8}$ 28. 0.515 $\frac{103}{200}$ 29. 0.863 $\frac{863}{1000}$
30. 0.28 $\frac{7}{25}$ 31. 0.45 $\frac{9}{20}$ 32. 0.7 $\frac{7}{10}$ 33. 0.186 $\frac{93}{500}$
34. 0.504 $\frac{63}{125}$ 35. 0.84 $\frac{21}{25}$ 36. 0.775 $\frac{31}{40}$ 37. 0.868 $\frac{217}{250}$

38. **Measurement** Gilbert is using a set of drill bits that came in the following sizes: 0.0625 in., 0.125 in., 0.1875 in., 0.25 in., and 0.375 in. Write each drill bit size as a fraction in lowest terms.
$\frac{1}{16}$ in., $\frac{1}{8}$ in., $\frac{3}{16}$ in., $\frac{1}{4}$ in., $\frac{3}{8}$ in.

39. **Technology** A computer word processing program allows users to select a font size of 8 pt, 10 pt, 12 pt, or 16 pt. These sizes are equivalent to $\frac{1}{9}$ in., $\frac{5}{36}$ in., $\frac{1}{6}$ in., and $\frac{2}{9}$ in., respectively. Write each font size as a decimal.
$0.\overline{1}$ in., $0.13\overline{8}$ in., $0.1\overline{6}$ in., $0.\overline{2}$ in.

RETEACHING

Name ______________________

Alternative Lesson 5-7

Converting Fractions and Decimals

Fractions and decimals can be used to name the same number. Sometimes it is necessary to write a fraction as a decimal or a decimal as a fraction.

— Example 1 —

To write a fraction as a decimal, divide the numerator by the denominator. Your answer will be a **terminating decimal,** one with no remainder, or a **repeating decimal,** one that repeats a pattern.

a. Write $\frac{2}{5}$ as a decimal.

Divide 2 by 5.

```
  0.4
5)2.0
  2 0
```

The fraction $\frac{2}{5}$ and the decimal 0.4 name the same number.

b. Write $\frac{2}{9}$ as a decimal.

Divide 2 by 9.

```
  0.222...
9)2.000
  1 8
    20
    18
     20
```

The fraction $\frac{2}{9}$ and the decimal 0.222... name the same number.

Try It Write as a decimal.

a. $\frac{4}{5}$ 0.8 b. $\frac{2}{3}$ 0.666... c. $\frac{4}{9}$ 0.444... d. $\frac{3}{8}$ 0.375
e. $\frac{5}{25}$ 0.2 f. $\frac{5}{6}$ 0.8333... g. $\frac{5}{75}$ 0.0666... h. $\frac{2}{11}$ 0.181818...

— Example 2 —

To write a terminating decimal as a fraction, write the digits in the decimal as the numerator. Use the place value of the decimal to write the denominator. Then write your answer in lowest terms.

Write 0.3 as a fraction.

$0.3 = \frac{3}{10}$ ← place value of decimal

The fraction is in lowest terms, so the decimal 0.3 and the fraction $\frac{3}{10}$ name the same number.

Try It Write as a fraction in lowest terms.

i. 0.45 $\frac{9}{20}$ j. 0.25 $\frac{1}{4}$ k. 0.6 $\frac{3}{5}$ l. 0.52 $\frac{13}{25}$
m. 0.01 $\frac{1}{100}$ n. 0.24 $\frac{6}{25}$ o. 0.625 $\frac{5}{8}$ p. 0.440 $\frac{11}{25}$

Reteaching

Activity

Materials: 10 × 10 Grids

- Let one square on a 10 × 10 grid represent one cent. One cent is $\frac{1}{100}$ of a dollar. The decimal for one cent is 0.01, so $\frac{1}{100} = 0.01$.
- Use a 10 × 10 grid to represent 1 nickel. A nickel is 5 cents, the decimal is 0.05. So, $\frac{1}{20} = 0.05$.
- Use 10 × 10 grids to give a fraction and a decimal for the following amounts.
  1. 9 nickels $\frac{9}{20} = 0.45$
  2. 13 nickels $\frac{13}{20} = 0.65$
  3. 1 dime $\frac{1}{10} = 0.1$
  4. 7 dimes $\frac{7}{10} = 0.7$

Exercise Notes

Exercise 58

Consumer The United States Mint was established in 1792. The Mint manufactures all U.S. coins and distributes them through the Federal Reserve banks and branches.

Exercise Answers

46. 0.667; A number is more accurate if you round the decimals farther away from the decimal point.

47. $\frac{2}{99}$ has fewer steps; It uses more zeros.

48. Possible answer: It is a repeating decimal; $0.\overline{3}$.

49. Possible answer: A repeating decimal repeats digits continuously. A terminating decimal has an end.

58.

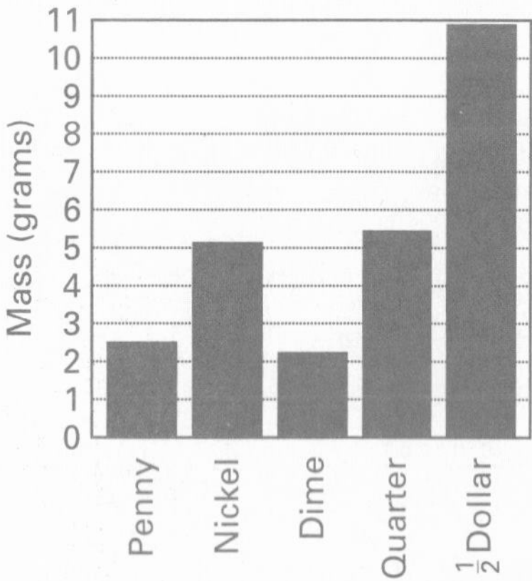

59–64. See page C3.

Alternate Assessment

Interview Have students verbalize the methods of writing fractions as decimals and decimals as fractions. Ask students to give examples on the chalkboard.

Quick Quiz

Write each decimal as a fraction in lowest terms.

1. 0.68 $\frac{17}{25}$
2. 0.275 $\frac{11}{40}$

Write each fraction as a decimal.

3. $\frac{3}{8}$ 0.375
4. $\frac{4}{9}$ $0.\overline{4}$
5. $\frac{4}{5}$ 0.8

Available on Daily Transparency 5-7

---

44. Career Jeff is entering data from the Measurement graph into a computer spreadsheet. It will be easier to enter the kilograms in decimal form. What values should Jeff enter for the following dates?

a. March 2 0.3 **b.** March 5 0.8

c. March 8 0.6 **d.** March 14 0.2

Measurement — March Data

Kilograms: 10/10, 5/10

Day: 2, 4, 6, 8, 10, 12, 14

45. **Test Prep** Choose the equivalent decimal for $\frac{5}{6}$. D

Ⓐ 0.3333 Ⓑ $0.\overline{3}$

Ⓒ 0.8 Ⓓ $0.8\overline{3}$

PROBLEM SOLVING 5-7

Problem Solving and Reasoning

46. Communicate Is $\frac{2}{3}$ closer to 0.67 or 0.667? Explain.

47. Critical Thinking Using long division, write $\frac{2}{99}$ and $\frac{37}{99}$ as decimals. Which process takes more steps? Explain why.

48. Communicate Mimi is converting $\frac{1}{3}$ to a decimal, using division, but the division problem never ends. Explain why this happens. How should Mimi write the decimal?

49. Journal Explain the difference between a terminating decimal and a repeating decimal.

Mixed Review

Simplify mentally. *[Lesson 2-5]*

50. 60×10 600 **51.** $175 + 425$ 600 **52.** $86 + 24$ 110 **53.** $3 \times 68 \times 10$ 2040

54. $8000 \div 200$ 40 **55.** 300×50 15,000 **56.** $17 + 70 + 30$ 117 **57.** 34×3 102

58. Make a bar graph of the data. *[Lesson 1-5]*

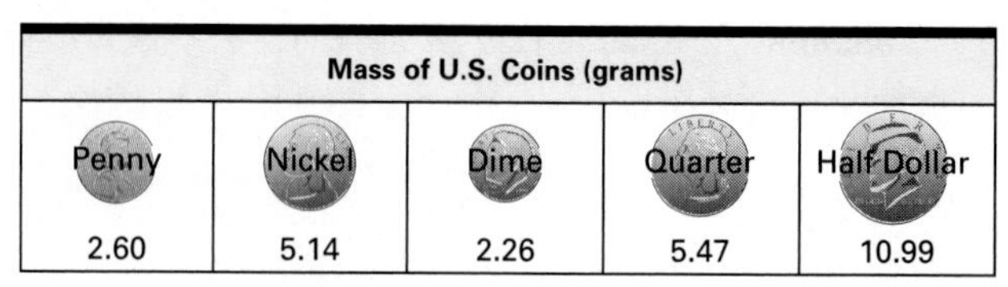

Mass of U.S. Coins (grams)				
Penny	Nickel	Dime	Quarter	Half Dollar
2.60	5.14	2.26	5.47	10.99

Draw a model for each of the fractions. *[Lesson 5-4]*

59. $\frac{1}{3}$ **60.** $\frac{2}{5}$ **61.** $\frac{3}{7}$ **62.** $\frac{9}{10}$ **63.** $\frac{3}{12}$ **64.** $\frac{1}{4}$

PROBLEM SOLVING

Name ______

Guided Problem Solving 5-7

GPS PROBLEM 43, STUDENT PAGE 305

Melissa is using a set of wrenches that come in these sizes: 0.125 inch, 0.25 inch, 0.375 inch, 0.5 inch, 0.625 inch, 0.75 inch, and 0.875 inch. Write each wrench size as a fraction in lowest terms.

Understand

1. What are you asked to find?
The size of each wrench as a fraction in lowest terms.

Plan

2. Write the steps to follow when you write a decimal as a fraction.
Write the digits in a decimal as the numerator. Use the place value of the decimal as the denominator.

3. Use your rule to write 0.125 as a fraction. $\frac{125}{1000}$

4. Find the greatest common factor for the numerator and denominator. 125

Solve

5. Use the greatest common factor to write the fraction in lowest terms. $\frac{1}{8}$

6. Repeat steps 3 through 5 for the remaining decimals.

a. 0.25 $\frac{1}{4}$ b. 0.375 $\frac{3}{8}$ c. 0.5 $\frac{1}{2}$

d. 0.625 $\frac{5}{8}$ e. 0.75 $\frac{3}{4}$ f. 0.875 $\frac{7}{8}$

Look Back

7. Check your answers by converting the fractions to decimals. Are the decimals you find the same as the original decimals?
$\frac{1}{8} = 0.125, \frac{1}{4} = 0.25, \frac{3}{8} = 0.375, \frac{1}{2} = 0.5, \frac{5}{8} = 0.625,$
$\frac{3}{4} = 0.75, \frac{7}{8} = 0.875$ Yes, they are the same.

SOLVE ANOTHER PROBLEM

Timothy bought some salads for a party. The salads weighed 0.6 pound, 0.25 pound, 0.15 pound, and 0.375 pound. Write each weight as a fraction in lowest terms.
0.6 lb = $\frac{3}{5}$ lb, 0.25 lb = $\frac{1}{4}$ lb, 0.15 lb = $\frac{3}{20}$ lb, 0.375 lb = $\frac{3}{8}$ lb

ENRICHMENT

Name ______

Extend Your Thinking 5-7

Patterns in Numbers

When some fractions are converted to decimals, they create a pattern.

1. Write each fraction as a decimal.

$\frac{1}{9}$ $0.\overline{1}$ $\frac{1}{11}$ $0.\overline{09}$

$\frac{2}{9}$ $0.\overline{2}$ $\frac{2}{11}$ $0.\overline{18}$

$\frac{3}{9}$ $0.\overline{3}$ $\frac{3}{11}$ $0.\overline{27}$

$\frac{4}{9}$ $0.\overline{4}$ $\frac{4}{11}$ $0.\overline{36}$

$\frac{5}{9}$ $0.\overline{5}$ $\frac{5}{11}$ $0.\overline{45}$

$\frac{6}{9}$ $0.\overline{6}$ $\frac{6}{11}$ $0.\overline{54}$

$\frac{7}{9}$ $0.\overline{7}$ $\frac{7}{11}$ $0.\overline{63}$

2. Look at the decimals you wrote for the fractions with a denominator of 9. What pattern do you see?
Possible answer: The decimal is a repeating decimal. The repeating part of the decimal is the same as the numerator of the fraction.

3. Look at the decimals you wrote for the fractions with a denominator of 11. What pattern do you see?
Possible answer: The decimal is a repeating decimal. The repeating part of the decimal is the product of 9 and the numerator of the fraction.

4. Use the patterns to write the decimal for each fraction.

a. $\frac{8}{9}$ $0.\overline{8}$ b. $\frac{8}{11}$ $0.\overline{72}$ c. $\frac{9}{11}$ $0.\overline{81}$ d. $\frac{10}{11}$ $0.\overline{90}$

TECHNOLOGY

Using a Spreadsheet • Finding Decimal Equivalents for Common Fractions

Problem: What patterns can you see in decimal equivalents for fifths?

You can use your spreadsheet to quickly calculate the decimal equivalents for fractions.

1 Enter the information into the spreadsheet as shown:

	A	B	C	D	E	F	G
1	Numerator	1	2	3	4	5	
2	Denominator	5	5	5	5	5	
3							
4	Decimal						
5							

2 In cell B4, enter the formula =B1/B2

	A	B	C	D	E	F	G
1	Numerator	1	2	3	4	5	
2	Denominator	5	5	5	5	5	
3							
4	Decimal	0.2	0.4	0.6	0.8	1.0	
5							

3 Copy the formula across the row to column F. You may need to format row 4 to see all the numbers after the decimal place.

Solution: Each decimal goes up by 0.2.

TRY IT

a. Find a decimal pattern for ninths.

b. Find a decimal pattern for sevenths.

ON YOUR OWN

- Why do you think the division formula uses a "/" and not a "÷" for division?
- Is the decimal value in C4 always twice as big as the decimal value in B4? Explain.
- When converting a fraction pattern with an even denominator into decimals, the number 0.5 always appears as one of the decimal equivalents. Why?

307

Technology

Using a Spreadsheet • Finding Decimal Equivalents for Common Fractions

The Point

Students use a spreadsheet to build tables showing decimal forms for fractions.

Materials

Spreadsheet software

Resources

Interactive CD-ROM Spreadsheet/Grapher Tool

About the Page

- Explain to students that the formula B1/B2 divides the entry in row 1 by the entry in row 2.
- If the pattern of a repeating decimal is not noticeable, the number of decimal places to be displayed has to be increased.

Ask ...

- How is a fraction converted to a decimal? Divide the numerator by the denominator.
- Which row in the spreadsheet will have the same number in each cell? Row 2

Answers for Try It

a. The decimal repeats the numerator of the fraction.

b. Each decimal repeats the numbers 1, 4, 2, 8, 5, and 7 in the same order but starts with a different number.

On Your Own

Refer to the third question. Ask students if the number 0.5 ever occurs for a fraction with an odd denominator. Explain. No; An integer numerator cannot be half of an odd number.

Answers for On Your Own

- Possible answer: The ÷ symbol is not shown on most computer keyboards.
- Yes; 2 parts of a whole are always twice as large as 1 part of the same whole.
- $0.5 = \frac{1}{2}$ and all fractions equivalent to $\frac{1}{2}$ have an even denominator.

5-8

Lesson Organizer

Objective

- Compare and order fractions.

Vocabulary

- Common denominator

Materials

- Explore: Fraction Bars

NCTM Standards

- 1–6, 13

Review

Order from least to greatest.

1. 365, 360, 402, 331
   331, 360, 365, 402
2. 4.1, 4.3, 4.07, 4.23
   4.07, 4.1, 4.23, 4.3
3. 0.05, 5.0, 0.005, 0.5
   0.005, 0.05, 0.5, 5.0
4. 0.928, 0.2895, 0.82, 0.2
   0.2, 0.2895, 0.82, 0.928

Available on Daily Transparency 5-8

1 Introduce

Explore  

You may wish to use Teaching Tool Transparency 14: Fraction Bars with **Explore**.

The Point
Students use Fraction Bars to model and order fractions with denominators of 2, 3, 4, 6, and 12. They then draw a graph to show that order.

Ongoing Assessment
After students have correctly ordered the Fraction Bars representing the R-values, they should be able to easily translate the bars to a graphical representation.

5-8 Comparing and Ordering

You'll Learn ...

■ to compare and order fractions

... How It's Used

Disc jockeys order fractions when determining which songs have been played the most.

Vocabulary

common denominator

▶ Lesson Link You've learned to compare and order decimals. In this lesson, you'll learn how to do the same with fractions. ◀

Explore Comparing and Ordering

The 3 Rs—Plus 7 More

Materials: Fraction Bars®

The "R-value" of a building material measures how well the material keeps heat in or out. The table gives the approximate R-values of ten common building materials in alphabetical order.

1. A building contractor has asked you to arrange the materials in order of their R-values. Use your number sense to guess the order of the ten fractions from least to greatest.
2. Use fraction bars to order the fractions. Compare the results with your guesses.
3. Use the fraction bars to help you sketch a bar graph of the ten R-values. On your graph, order the bars from least to greatest.

Material	R-Value
Asphalt roof shingle	$\frac{5}{12}$
Common brick	$\frac{1}{4}$
Half-inch gypsum board	$\frac{7}{12}$
Hardwood finish flooring	$\frac{2}{3}$
Lightweight gypsum plaster	$\frac{1}{3}$
Stucco	$\frac{1}{6}$
Three-eighths-inch plywood	$\frac{1}{2}$
Wood bevel siding	$\frac{3}{4}$
Wood roof shingles	$\frac{11}{12}$
Wood siding shingles	$\frac{5}{6}$

Learn Comparing and Ordering

Tools and building materials are commonly measured in inches and fractions of inches. In order to know which screw, nail, saw blade, or chisel is the largest or smallest, you must be able to compare fractions.

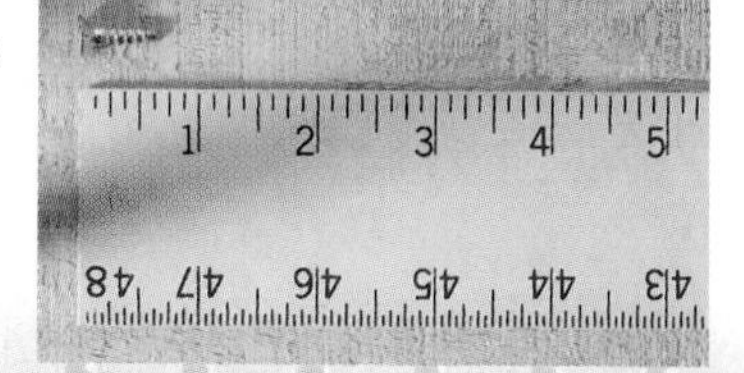

MEETING INDIVIDUAL NEEDS

Resources

5-8 Practice
5-8 Reteaching
5-8 Problem Solving
5-8 Enrichment
5-8 Daily Transparency
Problem of the Day
Review
Quick Quiz
Teaching Tool Transparencies 2, 3, 14
Technology Master 25

Learning Modalities

Logical Students may think that for fractions with the same numerator and different denominators, the fraction with the greater denominator is greater. To help them understand that the opposite is true, ask whether $\frac{3}{10}$ of a pizza or $\frac{3}{4}$ of the same pizza is a larger portion. It should be obvious that the fraction with the lesser denominator is the greater fraction.

Kinesthetic Circular fraction models work well for comparing fractions. Students can compare two fractions by placing the model for one fraction over the other.

Challenge

Show students this alternate method for comparing fractions. For example, to compare $\frac{3}{4}$ and $\frac{5}{6}$, cross-multiply: $3 \times 6 = 18$ and $4 \times 5 = 20$. Since $3 \times 6 < 4 \times 5$, $\frac{3}{4} < \frac{5}{6}$. In symbolic form, given fractions $\frac{a}{b}$ and $\frac{c}{d}$, if $ad < bc$, then $\frac{a}{b} < \frac{c}{d}$.

One way to do this is to convert the fractions so that they have the same denominator. Then compare the numerators. When two fractions have the same denominator, it is called a **common denominator**.

DID YOU KNOW?

The smallest common denominator is also known as the least common denominator, or LCD.

Examples

1 Compare $\frac{5}{6}$ and $\frac{7}{8}$.

Rewrite each fraction by multiplying the numerator and the denominator by the denominator of the *other* fraction.

$\frac{5}{6} = \frac{5 \times \mathbf{8}}{6 \times \mathbf{8}} = \frac{40}{48}$ Multiply numerator and denominator by the denominator of $\frac{7}{8}$.

$\frac{7}{8} = \frac{7 \times \mathbf{6}}{8 \times \mathbf{6}} = \frac{42}{48}$ Multiply numerator and denominator by the denominator of $\frac{5}{6}$.

Since $\frac{42}{48} > \frac{40}{48}$, $\frac{7}{8} > \frac{5}{6}$.

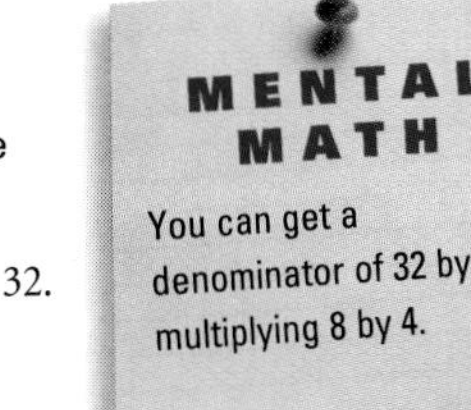

2 Mayra has drill bits measuring $\frac{5}{32}$ in., $\frac{3}{16}$ in., and $\frac{1}{8}$ in. She wants to use the largest bit. Which one should she use?

8 and 16 are factors of 32, so you can rewrite $\frac{1}{8}$ and $\frac{3}{16}$ with a denominator of 32.

$\frac{1}{8} = \frac{1 \times 4}{8 \times 4} = \frac{4}{32}$

$\frac{3}{16} = \frac{3 \times 2}{16 \times 2} = \frac{6}{32}$

The drill bits measure in order: $\frac{4}{32}$ in., $\frac{5}{32}$ in., and $\frac{6}{32}$ in. She should use the $\frac{3}{16}$ in. bit.

You can also compare fractions by rewriting them as decimals. Then compare the decimals.

Example 3

Clay needs $\frac{5}{8}$ yd of vinyl fabric to make a cover for his tennis racket. He found a piece marked as $\frac{2}{3}$ yd. Should he buy it?

5 [÷] 8 [=] 0.625

2 [÷] 3 [=] 0.6666... Use a calculator to write the fractions as decimals.

$0.\overline{6} > 0.625$, so $\frac{2}{3} > \frac{5}{8}$. Clay should buy the fabric.

Try It

Decide which fraction is greater. **a.** $\frac{3}{8}, \frac{7}{16}$ $\frac{7}{16}$ **b.** $\frac{3}{4}, \frac{5}{6}$ $\frac{5}{6}$ **c.** $\frac{8}{11}, \frac{5}{7}$ $\frac{8}{11}$

MATH EVERY DAY

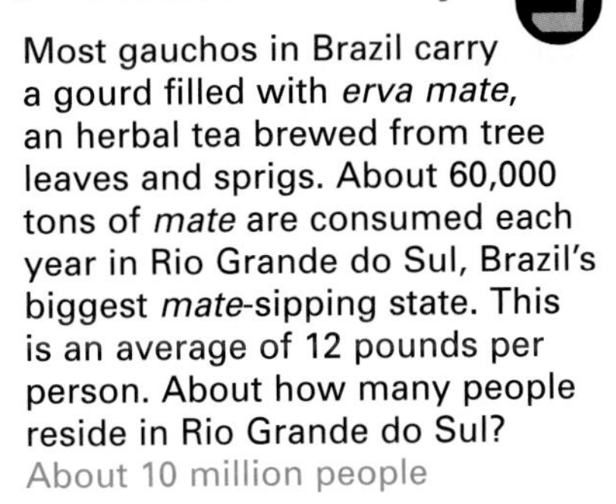

Problem of the Day

Most gauchos in Brazil carry a gourd filled with *erva mate*, an herbal tea brewed from tree leaves and sprigs. About 60,000 tons of *mate* are consumed each year in Rio Grande do Sul, Brazil's biggest *mate*-sipping state. This is an average of 12 pounds per person. About how many people reside in Rio Grande do Sul? About 10 million people

Available on Daily Transparency 5-8

An Extension is provided in the transparency package.

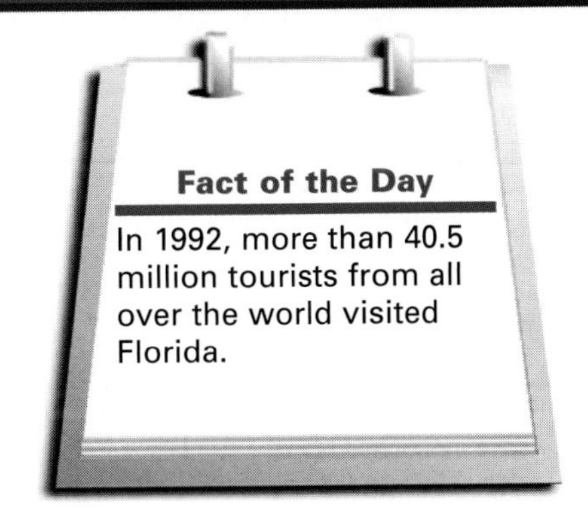

Fact of the Day

In 1992, more than 40.5 million tourists from all over the world visited Florida.

Mental Math

Tell which fraction is greater.

1. $\frac{3}{4}, \frac{1}{2}$ $\frac{3}{4}$
2. $\frac{5}{9}, \frac{7}{9}$ $\frac{7}{9}$
3. $\frac{5}{8}, \frac{5}{6}$ $\frac{5}{6}$
4. $\frac{13}{20}, \frac{13}{21}$ $\frac{13}{20}$

For Groups That Finish Early

Use your ordered Fraction Bars to find equivalent fractions. $\frac{1}{6} = \frac{2}{12}$,

$\frac{1}{4} = \frac{3}{12}$, $\frac{1}{3} = \frac{2}{6} = \frac{4}{12}$, $\frac{1}{2} = \frac{2}{4} = \frac{3}{6} = \frac{6}{12}$,

$\frac{2}{3} = \frac{4}{6} = \frac{8}{12}$, $\frac{3}{4} = \frac{9}{12}$, $\frac{5}{6} = \frac{10}{12}$

Do you think it is now easier to order the fractions in the R-value list? Why? Yes; The fractions all have the same denominator, 12.

Answers for Explore

1. $\frac{1}{6}, \frac{1}{4}, \frac{1}{3}, \frac{5}{12}, \frac{1}{2}, \frac{7}{12}, \frac{2}{3}, \frac{3}{4}, \frac{5}{6}, \frac{11}{12}$
2. $\frac{1}{6}, \frac{1}{4}, \frac{1}{3}, \frac{5}{12}, \frac{1}{2}, \frac{7}{12}, \frac{2}{3}, \frac{3}{4}, \frac{5}{6}, \frac{11}{12}$
3. See page C4.

2 Teach

Learn

Ask students where they have encountered the word *common* as part of a mathematical term. They should remember *common multiple, least common multiple, common factor,* and *greatest common factor.*

Alternate Examples

1. Compare $\frac{5}{6}$ and $\frac{3}{4}$.

   $\frac{5}{6} = \frac{5 \times \mathbf{4}}{6 \times \mathbf{4}} = \frac{20}{24}$

   $\frac{3}{4} = \frac{3 \times \mathbf{6}}{4 \times \mathbf{6}} = \frac{18}{24}$

   Since $\frac{20}{24} > \frac{18}{24}$, $\frac{5}{6} > \frac{3}{4}$.

2. Marge has brads measuring $\frac{9}{16}$ in. and $\frac{5}{8}$ in. If she wants to use the longer brad, which ones should she use?

   $\frac{5}{8} = \frac{5 \times 2}{8 \times 2} = \frac{10}{16}$

   Since $\frac{9}{16} < \frac{10}{16}$, the $\frac{5}{8}$-in. brads are longer than the $\frac{9}{16}$-in. brads.

   Marge should use the $\frac{5}{8}$-in. brads.

3. In the first game of the season, Nick made $\frac{8}{15}$ of the free throws he attempted and Nate made $\frac{6}{9}$. Which player had the better free-throw average?

   8 [÷] 15 [=] 0.5333 ...

   6 [÷] 9 [=] 0.6666 ...

   $0.5\overline{3} < 0.\overline{6}$, so $\frac{8}{15} < \frac{6}{9}$.

   Nate had the better free-throw average.

Students sees two methods for comparing fractions. The first uses a calculator to express the fractions as decimals, and the second expresses the fractions with a common denominator.

Answers for What Do You Think?

1. Possible answer: Peggy's is faster for $\frac{5}{18}$ and $\frac{3}{10}$; Zack's is faster for $\frac{2}{5}$ and $\frac{3}{5}$.
2. Possible answer: When measuring or cooking.

3 Practice and Assess

Check

Answers for Check Your Understanding

1. No; $\frac{5}{8} = 0.625$, $\frac{4}{3} = 1.\overline{3}$.
2. When numerators are equal, the fraction with the smaller denominator is larger in value.

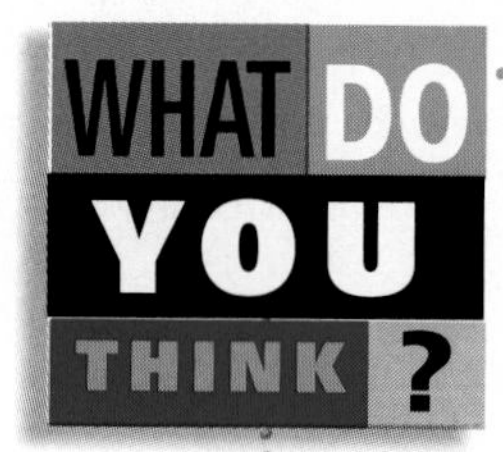

For a report on recycling, Peggy and Zack read that 8 out of every 21 aluminum cans were recycled in 1990. In 1993, 5 out every 14 aluminum cans were recycled. They wanted to know whether the fraction of cans recycled increased or decreased from 1990 to 1993.

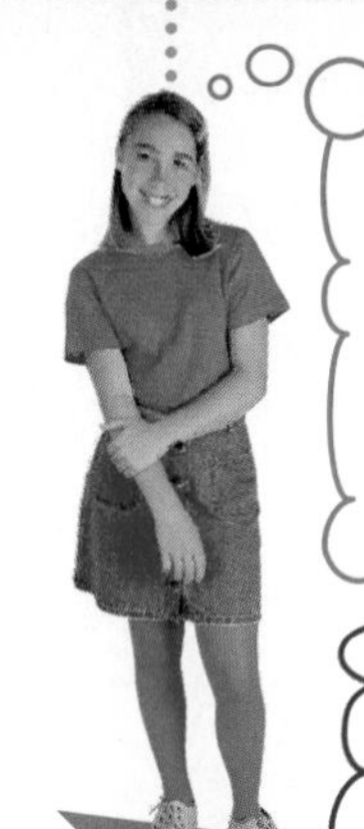

Peggy thinks ...

I'll rewrite the fractions as decimals using my calculator.

8 [÷] 21 [=] 0.3809524

5 [÷] 14 [=] 0.3571429

0.3809524 > 0.3571429, so the fraction decreased from 1990 to 1993.

I'll rewrite $\frac{8}{21}$ and $\frac{5}{14}$ with a common denominator.

$\frac{8 \times 14}{21 \times 14} = \frac{112}{294}$ $\quad$ $\frac{5 \times 21}{14 \times 21} = \frac{105}{294}$

$\frac{112}{294} > \frac{105}{294}$, so the fraction decreased from 1990 to 1993.

1. Name a pair of fractions for which Peggy's method would be faster than Zack's method. Name a pair of fractions for which Zack's method would be faster than Peggy's.
2. What other real-world situations might involve comparing fractions?

Check Your Understanding

1. Since 5 > 4, is $\frac{5}{8} > \frac{4}{3}$? Explain.
2. Two fractions have the same numerator. How can you use the denominators to compare the fractions?

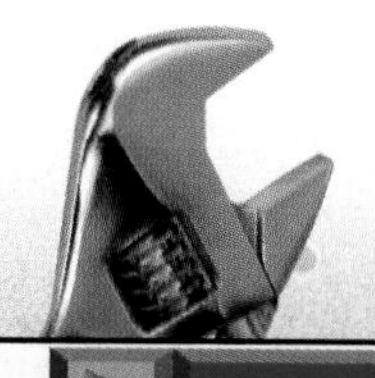

MEETING MIDDLE SCHOOL CLASSROOM NEEDS

Tips from Middle School Teachers

I used to be reluctant to allow students to use calculators in class, but I have found that they can be very beneficial in exploring various topics in number theory and in relating fractions and decimals. In our technological society it is important that students be able to use available tools, such as calculators, effectively.

Team Teaching

Ask the industrial-arts teacher to display samples of the materials in the R-value chart and discuss why some have higher ratings than others.

Industry Connection

Fiberglass is another material used for insulation. It consists of fine threads of glass bunched up in a fuzzy mass. Tiny spaces between the threads trap air and hold heat in or out. Commercial production of fiberglass in the United States started in the 1940s.

5-8 Exercises and Applications

Practice and Apply

1. **Getting Started** Compare using <, >, or =.

a. $\frac{1}{5} \boxed{<} \frac{2}{5}$ b. $\frac{3}{7} \boxed{>} \frac{2}{7}$ c. $\frac{3}{8} \boxed{<} \frac{9}{8}$

d. $\frac{16}{20} \boxed{>} \frac{7}{20}$ e. $\frac{7}{12} \boxed{<} \frac{11}{12}$ f. $\frac{5}{2} \boxed{<} \frac{8}{2}$

Give the least common denominator that could be used to compare each pair of fractions. Then compare using <, >, or =.

2. $\frac{2}{3} \boxed{=} \frac{8}{12}$ 3
3. $\frac{5}{6} \boxed{>} \frac{5}{8}$ 24
4. $\frac{1}{4} \boxed{<} \frac{5}{12}$ 12
5. $\frac{3}{6} \boxed{<} \frac{6}{9}$ 6
6. $\frac{4}{10} \boxed{=} \frac{6}{15}$ 5
7. $\frac{3}{4} \boxed{=} \frac{6}{8}$ 4
8. $\frac{5}{8} \boxed{>} \frac{10}{24}$ 24
9. $\frac{1}{11} \boxed{<} \frac{3}{12}$ 132
10. $\frac{3}{7} \boxed{<} \frac{6}{3}$ 7
11. $\frac{7}{11} \boxed{<} \frac{2}{3}$ 33
12. $\frac{9}{15} \boxed{=} \frac{3}{5}$ 5
13. $\frac{5}{10} \boxed{=} \frac{7}{14}$ 2

Order from smallest to largest.

14. $\frac{2}{3}, \frac{2}{6}, \frac{4}{9}$
15. $\frac{7}{9}, \frac{5}{6}, \frac{4}{8}$
16. $\frac{18}{4}, \frac{16}{5}, \frac{19}{20}$
17. $\frac{3}{11}, \frac{11}{3}, \frac{11}{11}$
18. $\frac{9}{12}, \frac{3}{6}, \frac{15}{18}$
19. $\frac{4}{5}, \frac{4}{6}, \frac{4}{7}$
20. $\frac{32}{10}, \frac{25}{100}, \frac{16}{1}$
21. $\frac{3}{5}, \frac{2}{7}, \frac{3}{8}$
22. $\frac{1}{2}, \frac{1}{4}, \frac{1}{3}$
23. $\frac{3}{22}, \frac{10}{11}, \frac{2}{33}$
24. $\frac{4}{10}, \frac{3}{5}, \frac{6}{7}$
25. $\frac{7}{36}, \frac{13}{4}, \frac{1}{6}$

26. **Measurement** Flannery has $3\frac{5}{8}$ yards of ribbon. Does she have enough to complete a project that calls for $3\frac{1}{2}$ yards? Yes

27. Order the wood screw lengths, in inches, from longest to shortest:
$\frac{1}{4}, \frac{3}{8}, \frac{10}{32}, \frac{10}{16}, \frac{7}{8}, \frac{2}{16}$

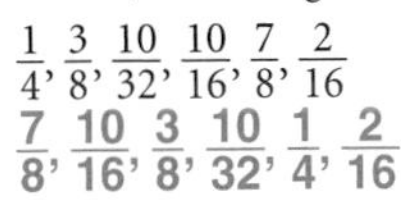
$\frac{7}{8}, \frac{10}{16}, \frac{3}{8}, \frac{10}{32}, \frac{1}{4}, \frac{2}{16}$

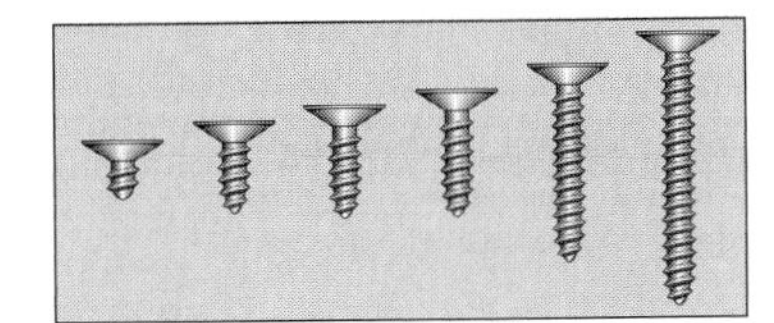

PRACTICE

Name ______________________ **Practice 5-8**

Comparing and Ordering

Compare using <, >, or =.

1. $\frac{1}{4} \bigcirc\!\!\!< \frac{4}{13}$ 2. $\frac{2}{4} = \frac{10}{20}$ 3. $\frac{5}{7} < \frac{6}{7}$ 4. $\frac{5}{12} < \frac{3}{5}$

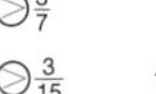

5. $\frac{2}{9} > \frac{1}{5}$ 6. $\frac{1}{7} < \frac{3}{18}$ 7. $\frac{4}{9} > \frac{3}{7}$ 8. $\frac{12}{18} < \frac{10}{14}$

9. $\frac{12}{16} > \frac{4}{6}$ 10. $\frac{7}{20} > \frac{1}{3}$ 11. $\frac{2}{8} > \frac{3}{15}$ 12. $\frac{2}{6} = \frac{4}{12}$

13. $\frac{2}{5} < \frac{5}{11}$ 14. $\frac{10}{16} < \frac{3}{4}$ 15. $\frac{7}{11} < \frac{9}{13}$ 16. $\frac{2}{7} > \frac{2}{9}$

Order from smallest to largest.

17. $\frac{3}{8}, \frac{3}{9}, \frac{3}{10}$ — $\frac{3}{10}, \frac{3}{9}, \frac{3}{8}$
18. $\frac{4}{5}, \frac{5}{4}, \frac{4}{4}$ — $\frac{4}{5}, \frac{4}{4}, \frac{5}{4}$
19. $\frac{7}{10}, \frac{18}{25}, \frac{3}{5}$ — $\frac{3}{5}, \frac{7}{10}, \frac{18}{25}$
20. $\frac{3}{4}, \frac{2}{5}, \frac{11}{20}$ — $\frac{2}{5}, \frac{11}{20}, \frac{3}{4}$
21. $\frac{2}{3}, \frac{3}{4}, \frac{5}{6}$ — $\frac{2}{3}, \frac{3}{4}, \frac{5}{6}$
22. $\frac{7}{15}, \frac{1}{3}, \frac{2}{5}$ — $\frac{1}{3}, \frac{2}{5}, \frac{7}{15}$
23. $\frac{1}{5}, \frac{1}{6}, \frac{7}{30}$ — $\frac{1}{6}, \frac{1}{5}, \frac{7}{30}$
24. $\frac{6}{11}, \frac{3}{7}, \frac{4}{9}$ — $\frac{3}{7}, \frac{4}{9}, \frac{6}{11}$
25. $\frac{1}{2}, \frac{2}{5}, \frac{1}{3}$ — $\frac{1}{3}, \frac{2}{5}, \frac{1}{2}$
26. $\frac{5}{8}, \frac{3}{4}, \frac{7}{10}$ — $\frac{5}{8}, \frac{7}{10}, \frac{3}{4}$
27. $\frac{33}{100}, \frac{3}{10}, \frac{33}{1000}$ — $\frac{3}{10}, \frac{33}{100}, \frac{333}{1000}$
28. $\frac{40}{49}, \frac{13}{28}, \frac{3}{14}$ — $\frac{3}{14}, \frac{13}{28}, \frac{40}{49}$

29. **Measurement** Ralph has $2\frac{1}{3}$ cups of milk. Does he have enough to prepare a recipe that uses $2\frac{1}{2}$ cups? No

30. **Measurement** Jody's Hardware stocks wooden dowels in the following widths: $\frac{3}{16}$ in., $\frac{1}{8}$ in., $\frac{3}{8}$ in., $\frac{1}{4}$ in., $\frac{1}{2}$ in. Write these widths in order from the least to the greatest.
$\frac{1}{8}$ in., $\frac{3}{16}$ in., $\frac{1}{4}$ in., $\frac{3}{8}$ in., $\frac{1}{2}$ in.

RETEACHING

Name ______________________ **Alternative Lesson 5-8**

Comparing and Ordering

Sometimes it is necessary to compare or order fractions. One way to do this is to write each fraction so that they have the same, or a **common, denominator.** For example, the fractions $\frac{4}{10}$ and $\frac{8}{10}$ have a common denominator, tenths.

Example 1

Find a common denominator for $\frac{3}{4}$ and $\frac{2}{3}$.

One way to find a common denominator of $\frac{3}{4}$ and $\frac{2}{3}$ is to list the multiples of both denominators.

Multiples of 4:	4,	8,	**12,**	16
Multiples of 3:	3,	6,	9,	**12**

A common multiple is 12, so a common denominator is also 12.

Try It Find a common denominator. Possible answers:

a. $\frac{1}{2}, \frac{3}{5}$ 10 b. $\frac{3}{4}, \frac{1}{7}$ 28 c. $\frac{4}{10}, \frac{3}{8}$ 40

d. $\frac{7}{10}, \frac{2}{3}$ 30 e. $\frac{3}{4}, \frac{3}{10}$ 20 f. $\frac{11}{20}, \frac{9}{15}$ 60

g. $\frac{3}{8}, \frac{1}{9}$ 72 h. $\frac{4}{5}, \frac{3}{4}$ 20 i. $\frac{5}{12}, \frac{7}{8}$ 24

Example 2

Compare $\frac{3}{4}$ and $\frac{5}{6}$.

$\frac{3}{4} \boxed{?} \frac{5}{6}$

Write the fractions using a common denominator → $\frac{9}{12} < \frac{10}{12}$ ← Since the denominators are the same, compare the numerators. $9 < 10$ so $\frac{9}{12} < \frac{10}{12}$ and $\frac{3}{4} < \frac{5}{6}$.

Try It Compare the fractions. Use >, <, or =.

j. $\frac{3}{12} < \frac{5}{12}$ k. $\frac{1}{6} < \frac{1}{4}$ l. $\frac{2}{3} > \frac{1}{2}$ m. $\frac{3}{8} < \frac{3}{4}$

n. $\frac{9}{10} > \frac{4}{5}$ o. $\frac{5}{12} > \frac{3}{8}$ p. $\frac{3}{6} = \frac{1}{2}$ q. $\frac{5}{8} > \frac{1}{3}$

r. $\frac{2}{5} < \frac{1}{2}$ s. $\frac{2}{3} > \frac{5}{8}$ t. $\frac{4}{7} < \frac{2}{3}$ u. $\frac{3}{4} < \frac{5}{6}$

PRACTICE 5-8

Assignment Guide

- **Basic**
  1–25 odds, 26–28, 30, 32, 35–45 odds
- **Average**
  1, 2–26 evens, 27–31, 33–45 odds
- **Enriched**
  1–27 odds, 28–33, 34–44 evens

Exercise Answers

14. $\frac{2}{6}, \frac{4}{9}, \frac{2}{3}$
15. $\frac{4}{8}, \frac{7}{9}, \frac{5}{6}$
16. $\frac{19}{20}, \frac{16}{5}, \frac{18}{4}$
17. $\frac{3}{11}, \frac{11}{11}, \frac{11}{3}$
18. $\frac{3}{6}, \frac{9}{12}, \frac{15}{18}$
19. $\frac{4}{7}, \frac{4}{6}, \frac{4}{5}$
20. $\frac{25}{100}, \frac{32}{10}, \frac{16}{1}$
21. $\frac{2}{7}, \frac{3}{8}, \frac{3}{5}$
22. $\frac{1}{4}, \frac{1}{3}, \frac{1}{2}$
23. $\frac{2}{33}, \frac{3}{22}, \frac{10}{11}$
24. $\frac{4}{10}, \frac{3}{5}, \frac{6}{7}$
25. $\frac{1}{6}, \frac{7}{36}, \frac{13}{4}$

Reteaching

Activity

- *Materials:* Two strips of paper, each about 8 inches long
- Fold one strip of paper in half, and then into fourths, eighths, and sixteenths.
- Fold the other strip in half, and then as carefully as possible into thirds, sixths, and twelfths. Label all the fold lines with the appropriate fraction.
- Use the first strip to compare fractions such as $\frac{3}{4}$ and $\frac{9}{16}$ and the second strip to compare fractions such as $\frac{2}{3}$ and $\frac{7}{12}$.
- Use the strips together to compare fractions such as $\frac{3}{4}$ and $\frac{7}{12}$ or $\frac{5}{8}$ and $\frac{5}{6}$.

Exercise Notes

■ Exercise 33

Problem-Solving Tip You may wish to use Teaching Tool Transparencies 2 and 3: Guided Problem Solving, pages 1–2.

Exercise Answers

32. $0.\overline{3}$ is greater; The 3 repeats and 0.333 ... > 0.30.

33. First meeting: $\frac{9}{12}$ of an hour;

Second meeting: $\frac{4}{2}$ of an hour;

Third meeting: $\frac{45}{30}$ of an hour;

Fourth meeting: $\frac{1}{2}$ of an hour.

43.

Stem	Leaf
0	1 4 4 5 7
1	1 1 2 2 3 4

44.

Stem	Leaf
10	1 2 5 5 8
11	1 2

45.

Stem	Leaf
2	6 7 8 8
3	0 1 1 1 2 3

Alternate Assessment

Portfolio Have students include a detailed explanation in their portfolio of how they would compare two fractions with different denominators. An example of their work that supports their explanation should be included.

▶ Quick Quiz

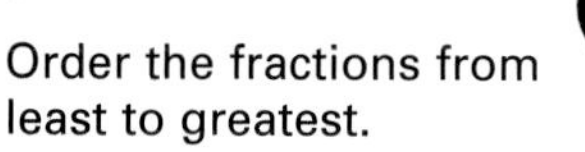

Order the fractions from least to greatest.

1. $\frac{3}{4}, \frac{7}{8}, \frac{2}{3}$ $\frac{2}{3}, \frac{3}{4}, \frac{7}{8}$
2. $\frac{2}{5}, \frac{1}{4}, \frac{1}{2}$ $\frac{1}{4}, \frac{2}{5}, \frac{1}{2}$
3. $\frac{5}{6}, \frac{7}{12}, \frac{5}{8}$ $\frac{7}{12}, \frac{5}{8}, \frac{5}{6}$
4. $\frac{3}{4}, \frac{4}{5}, \frac{5}{6}$ $\frac{3}{4}, \frac{4}{5}, \frac{5}{6}$

Available on Daily Transparency 5-8

---

28. Industry $\frac{3}{5}$ of the tourists who visit Florida come during the summer. $\frac{3}{10}$ travel to Florida during the winter. During which season does Florida get more tourists? **Summer**

GPS

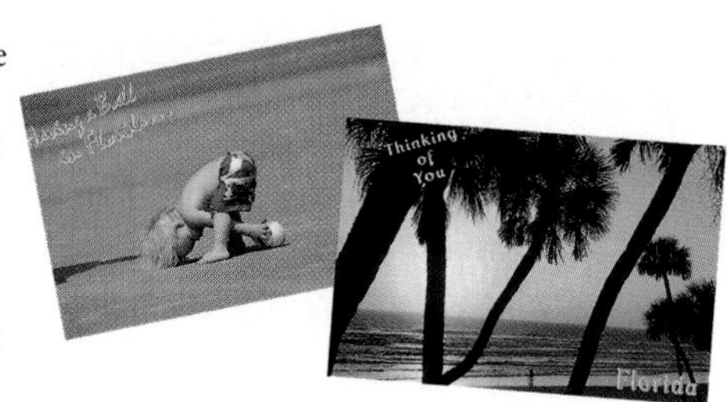

29. On a recent test, Renaldo got $\frac{5}{6}$ of the problems correct and Julius got $\frac{7}{9}$ of them correct. All the problems were worth the same amount. Who got the higher grade? **Renaldo**

Problem Solving and Reasoning

PROBLEM SOLVING 5-4

30. Critical Thinking Order from smallest to largest.

a. $0.34, \frac{2}{3}, 0.145$ **0.145, 0.34, $\frac{2}{3}$** **b.** $\frac{1}{2}, 0.23, \frac{2}{3}, 0.4$ **0.23, 0.4, $\frac{1}{2}, \frac{2}{3}$** **c.** $\frac{3}{4}, 0.77, \frac{1}{7}$ **$\frac{1}{7}, \frac{3}{4}$, 0.77**

31. Journal Can you always tell by looking at a calculator display if a decimal terminates or repeats? Explain your answer. **No; The repeating part could be longer than the calculator**

32. Communicate Explain which is bigger, 0.3 or $0.\overline{3}$.

33. Choose a Strategy Zoe is planning a conference. Here is the schedule for the day:
the first meeting, snack,
the second meeting, lunch,
the third meeting, an afternoon break,
and the last meeting.
The four meetings will be $\frac{1}{2}, \frac{4}{2}, \frac{45}{30}$, and $\frac{9}{12}$ of an hour long. The longest meeting should be after the snack and the second longest right after lunch. The shortest meeting should be after the break. How long is the first meeting? The second? The third? The fourth?

Problem Solving STRATEGIES
- Look for a Pattern
- Make an Organized List
- Make a Table
- Guess and Check
- Work Backward
- Use Logical Reasoning
- Draw a Diagram
- Solve a Simpler Problem

Mixed Review

Evaluate each expression for x = 5, 9, and 11. *[Lesson 2-10]*

34. $\frac{495}{x}$ **99; 55; 45** **35.** $x - 5$ **0; 4; 6** **36.** $8x$ **40; 72; 88**

37. $\frac{990}{x}$ **198; 110; 90** **38.** $5x$ **25; 45; 55** **39.** $7x$ **35; 63; 77**

40. $x + 10$ **15; 19; 21** **41.** $13 - x$ **8; 4; 2** **42.** $x + 101$ **106; 110; 112**

Make a stem-and-leaf diagram of the data. *[Lesson 1-6]*

43. 1, 4, 4, 5, 7, 11, 11, 12, 12, 13, 14 **44.** 101, 102, 105, 105, 108, 111, 112

45. 31, 31, 32, 30, 27, 28, 26, 33, 28, 31

312 *Chapter 5 • Patterns and Number Theory*

PROBLEM SOLVING

Name ______________

Guided Problem Solving 5-8

GPS PROBLEM 28, STUDENT PAGE 312

$\frac{3}{5}$ of the tourists who visit Florida come during the summer. $\frac{3}{10}$ travel to Florida during the winter. During which season does Florida get more tourists?

— Understand —

1. Underline the question.
2. What fraction of tourists visit Florida in the summer? $\frac{3}{5}$
3. What fraction of tourists visit Florida in the winter? $\frac{3}{10}$

— Plan —

4. Find a common denominator for $\frac{3}{5}$ and $\frac{3}{10}$. 10
5. Rewrite each fraction using the common denominator. $\frac{6}{10}, \frac{3}{10}$

— Solve —

6. Compare the fractions. Which fraction is greater? $\frac{6}{10}$
7. When do more tourists visit Florida—summer or winter? Summer.

— Look Back —

8. How could you have solved the problem in a different way?
Possible answers: Use the strategy Draw a Picture; write both fractions as decimals and compare the decimals.
9. Use your answer to the problem to make a generalization. If two fractions have the same numerator, which is the greater fraction?
The one with the lesser number in the denominator.

SOLVE ANOTHER PROBLEM

Manny, Anita, and Taylor shared the driving on a trip. Manny drove $\frac{1}{8}$ of the distance. Anita drove $\frac{1}{4}$ of the distance. Did Manny or Anita drive more miles? Explain how you know.
Anita, because $\frac{1}{4}$ is greater than $\frac{1}{8}$.

ENRICHMENT

Name ______________

Extend Your Thinking 5-8

Visual Thinking

a b c d e

One of the figures above is hidden in each of the figures below. Shade the hidden shape in each figure. Then write the letter of the hidden figure in the blank.

1. e 2. b 3. d 4. c
5. a 6. c 7. b 8. d
9. b 10. a 11. a 12. e

Section 5B Connect

In this section, you've seen that tools come in many sizes. In the United States, we use the customary system of measurement, so tools made here are sized with fractions. In countries that use the metric system, tools are sized with decimals. Now that you've studied both fractions and decimals, you're ready for a problem that faces anyone who uses tools: How do I deal with both fraction and decimal sizes?

Meanwhile, Back at the Wrench

Materials: Calculator

Otto Mechanic uses 32 wrenches to work on car engines. Sixteen of the wrenches were made in Europe and are sized in millimeters. Sixteen were made in the United States and are sized in fractions of an inch. One evening after finishing a difficult job, Otto tossed all of his wrenches onto a table and went home. Here, in no particular order, are the sizes of the wrenches. The metric sizes, given in millimeters, have also been converted to decimal inches.

Metric								
Size (mm)	9	16	20	3	25	7	4	12
Size (in.)	0.354	0.630	0.787	0.118	0.984	0.276	0.157	0.472
Size (mm)	17	13	8	22	6	18	14	10
Size (in.)	0.669	0.512	0.315	0.866	0.236	0.709	0.551	0.394

Customary								
Size (in.)	$\frac{5}{16}$	$\frac{7}{32}$	$\frac{5}{8}$	$\frac{1}{2}$	$\frac{3}{4}$	$\frac{9}{32}$	$\frac{9}{16}$	$\frac{1}{8}$
	$\frac{13}{16}$	$\frac{3}{8}$	$\frac{21}{32}$	$\frac{7}{8}$	$\frac{3}{16}$	$\frac{3}{32}$	$\frac{1}{4}$	$\frac{7}{16}$

Order Otto's 32 wrenches from the smallest size to the largest.

Meanwhile, Back at the Wrench

The Point

In *Meanwhile, Back at the Wrench* on page 287, students discussed the many sizes and uses of tools. Now they will use fractions and decimals to order the sizes of wrenches used to work on car engines.

Materials

Calculator

Resources

Lesson Enhancement Transparency 24

About the Page

- Ask students if they think it would be easier to order these numbers if they were all expressed as either fractions or as decimals.
- Review decimal place value and the rules for ordering decimals. Review ordering fractions.
- Review converting between fractions and decimals.
- Point out that the chart shows metric wrenches in both millimeters and inches while the wrenches made in the United States are shown only in inches.

Ongoing Assessment

Check that students have correctly ordered the wrenches from smallest to largest.

Extension

To order the wrenches from the smallest to the largest, students may have changed the fractions to decimals. Ask students to express the decimal inches as fractions in lowest terms.

$0.354 = \frac{177}{500}$, $0.630 = \frac{63}{100}$,

$0.787 = \frac{787}{1000}$, $0.118 = \frac{59}{500}$,

$0.984 = \frac{123}{125}$, $0.276 = \frac{69}{250}$,

$0.157 = \frac{157}{1000}$, $0.472 = \frac{59}{125}$,

$0.669 = \frac{669}{100}$, $0.512 = \frac{64}{125}$,

$0.315 = \frac{63}{200}$, $0.866 = \frac{433}{500}$,

$0.236 = \frac{59}{250}$, $0.709 = \frac{709}{1000}$,

$0.551 = \frac{551}{100}$, $0.394 = \frac{197}{500}$.

Answers for Connect

$\frac{3}{32}$, 0.118, $\frac{1}{8}$, 0.157, $\frac{3}{16}$, $\frac{7}{32}$, $\frac{1}{4}$, 0.236, 0.276, $\frac{9}{32}$, $\frac{5}{16}$, 0.315, 0.354, $\frac{3}{8}$, 0.394, $\frac{7}{16}$, 0.472, $\frac{1}{2}$, 0.512, 0.551, $\frac{9}{16}$, $\frac{5}{8}$, 0.630, $\frac{21}{32}$, 0.669, 0.709, $\frac{3}{4}$, 0.787, $\frac{13}{16}$, 0.866, $\frac{7}{8}$, 0.984.

5B Review

Review Correlation

Item(s)	Lesson(s)
1–6	5-1, 5-2
7–9	5-8
10–15	5-5, 5-7
16–21	5-6
22	5-3
23	5-4
24	5-8

Test Prep

Test-Taking Tip

Tell students that a diagram can be used for some problems. Here, students could draw a number line and estimate each fraction's position to find the true relationship.

Answers for Review

7. $\frac{1}{2}$; Numerator 1; Denominator 2

8. $\frac{1}{3}$; Numerator 1; Denominator 3

9. $\frac{3}{8}$; Numerator 3; Denominator 8

Section 5B Review

REVIEW 5B

Tell whether the first number is divisible by the second. Find the prime factorization of the first number.

1. 27, 9 Yes; 3^3 **2.** 180, 10 Yes; $2^2 \times 3^2 \times 5$ **3.** 32, 5 No; 2^5 **4.** 99, 6 No; $3^2 \times 11$ **5.** 48, 4 Yes; $2^4 \times 3$ **6.** 35, 3 No; 5×7

Determine what fraction each shaded part represents. Identify the numerator and denominator of each fraction.

7. **8.** **9.**

Write each fraction in lowest terms and as a decimal.

10. $\frac{4}{6}$ $\frac{2}{3}$; $0.\overline{6}$ **11.** $\frac{18}{24}$ $\frac{3}{4}$; 0.75 **12.** $\frac{2}{8}$ $\frac{1}{4}$; 0.25

13. $\frac{5}{15}$ $\frac{1}{3}$; $0.\overline{3}$ **14.** $\frac{8}{12}$ $\frac{2}{3}$; $0.\overline{6}$ **15.** $\frac{12}{24}$ $\frac{1}{2}$; 0.5

Write each mixed number as an improper fraction and each improper fraction as a mixed number.

16. $4\frac{1}{7}$ $\frac{29}{7}$ **17.** $\frac{32}{10}$ $3\frac{2}{10} = 3\frac{1}{5}$ **18.** $\frac{99}{11}$ 9

19. $7\frac{4}{5}$ $\frac{39}{5}$ **20.** $12\frac{7}{8}$ $\frac{103}{8}$ **21.** $\frac{42}{5}$ $8\frac{2}{5}$

22. Fine Arts Noriko and Ava are dancing together in the talent show. Noriko does a shuffle step every 5 steps and Ava does a shuffle every 7 steps. On what number step will they do the shuffle at the same time? 35

23. Beverly, Tom, and Maye are building a clubhouse. Beverly cut $\frac{2}{5}$ of the wood. Tom cut $\frac{3}{10}$ of the wood and Maye cut the rest. Who cut the most wood? The least? Tom and Maye; Beverly

Test Prep

To compare fractions, estimate to find out if they are near 0, $\frac{1}{2}$, or 1.

24. Which statement is true? B

Ⓐ $\frac{2}{9} > \frac{7}{8}$ Ⓑ $\frac{3}{6} > \frac{1}{5}$ Ⓒ $\frac{3}{4} > \frac{4}{3}$ Ⓓ $\frac{6}{7} > \frac{7}{8}$

Resources

Practice Masters
Section 5B Review

Assessment Sourcebook
Quiz 5B

TestWorks
Test and Practice Software

PRACTICE

Name ______________________

Practice

Section 5B Review

Determine what fraction the shaded part represents. Identify the numerator and denominator of each fraction.

1. fraction: $\frac{1}{4}$ numerator: 1 denominator: 4

2. fraction: $\frac{2}{5}$ numerator: 2 denominator: 5

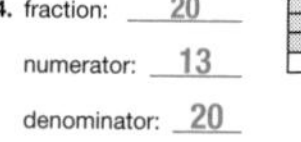

3. fraction: $\frac{7}{8}$ numerator: 7 denominator: 8

4. fraction: $\frac{13}{20}$ numerator: 13 denominator: 20

Write each fraction in lowest terms and as a decimal.

5. $\frac{16}{20}$ $\frac{4}{5}$, 0.8 6. $\frac{6}{16}$ $\frac{3}{8}$, 0.375 7. $\frac{8}{24}$ $\frac{1}{3}$, $0.\overline{3}$ 8. $\frac{21}{42}$ $\frac{1}{2}$, 0.5

9. $\frac{84}{100}$ $\frac{21}{25}$, 0.84 10. $\frac{9}{36}$ $\frac{1}{4}$, 0.25 11. $\frac{10}{12}$ $\frac{5}{6}$, $0.8\overline{3}$ 12. $\frac{45}{72}$ $\frac{5}{8}$, 0.625

Write each mixed number as an improper fraction or the improper fraction as a mixed number.

13. $3\frac{5}{6}$ $\frac{23}{6}$ 14. $\frac{23}{5}$ $4\frac{3}{5}$ 15. $7\frac{3}{8}$ $\frac{59}{8}$ 16. $\frac{47}{10}$ $4\frac{7}{10}$

17. Fred and Gina are baking cookies. Fred puts chocolate icing on every eighth cookie, and Gina puts colored sprinkles on every fifth cookie. Which cookies have both chocolate icing and colored sprinkles? Every 40th cookie

18. Bill correctly answered $\frac{3}{14}$ of the problems on an algebra test. Cheryl correctly answered $\frac{1}{7}$ of the problems, and Dana correctly answered $\frac{1}{4}$ of the problems. Order these students from the fewest correct answers to the most. Cheryl, Bill, Dana

19. A store owner obtained a compact stereo system for $86.72 and sold it for $97.95. What was the profit? *[Lesson 3-1]* $11.23

20. **Science** A king salmon can weigh up to 100 pounds or more. How many ounces is that? *[Lesson 4-3]* 1600 oz

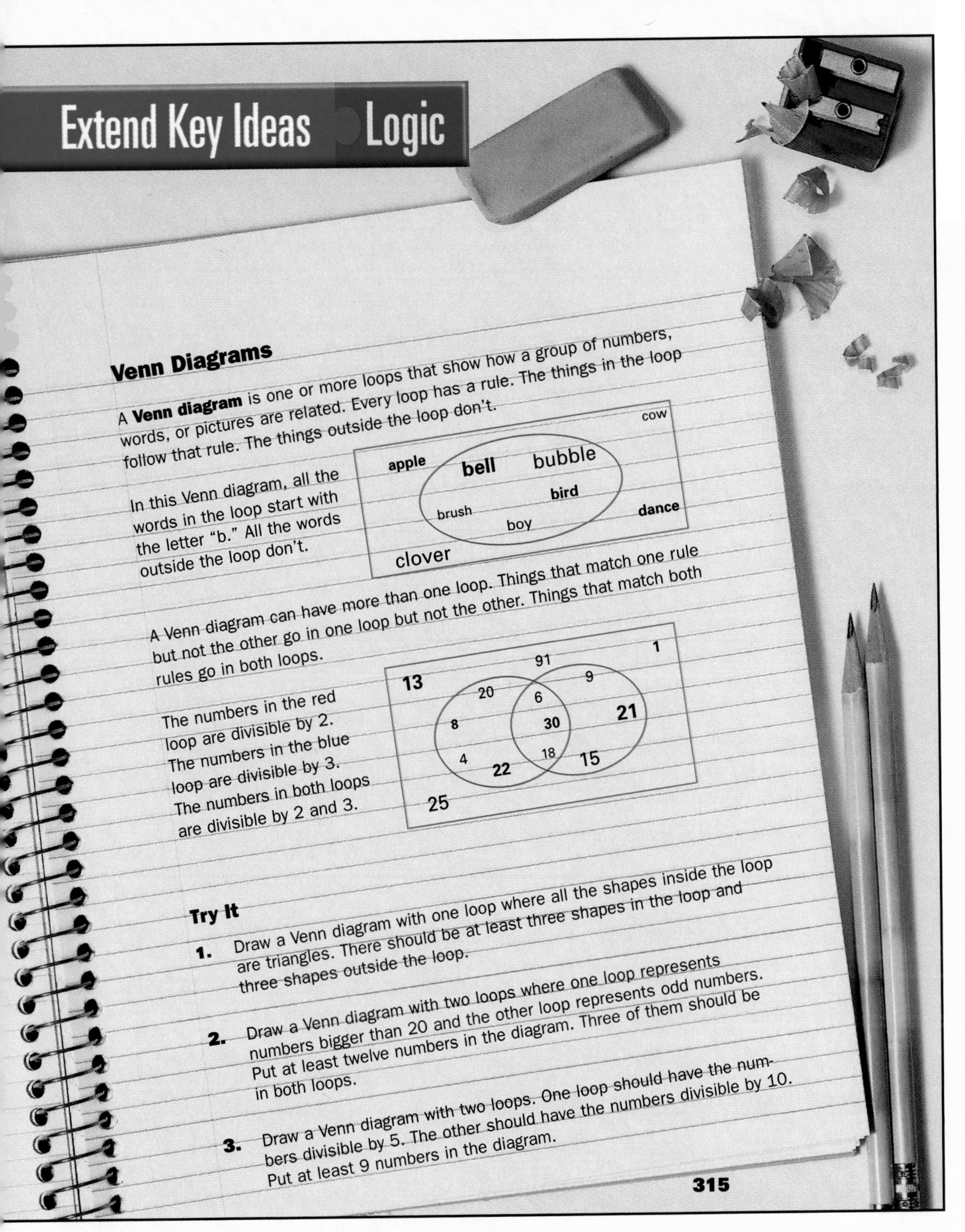

Extend Key Ideas Logic

Venn Diagrams

A **Venn diagram** is one or more loops that show how a group of numbers, words, or pictures are related. Every loop has a rule. The things in the loop follow that rule. The things outside the loop don't.

In this Venn diagram, all the words in the loop start with the letter "b." All the words outside the loop don't.

A Venn diagram can have more than one loop. Things that match one rule but not the other go in one loop but not the other. Things that match both rules go in both loops.

The numbers in the red loop are divisible by 2. The numbers in the blue loop are divisible by 3. The numbers in both loops are divisible by 2 and 3.

Try It

1. Draw a Venn diagram with one loop where all the shapes inside the loop are triangles. There should be at least three shapes in the loop and three shapes outside the loop.

2. Draw a Venn diagram with two loops where one loop represents numbers bigger than 20 and the other loop represents odd numbers. Put at least twelve numbers in the diagram. Three of them should be in both loops.

3. Draw a Venn diagram with two loops. One loop should have the numbers divisible by 5. The other should have the numbers divisible by 10. Put at least 9 numbers in the diagram.

315

Extend Key Ideas

Venn Diagrams

The Point

Students use Venn diagrams to show inclusions and exclusions to certain rules.

About the Page

Venn diagrams provide a useful way to visualize thoughts.

Ask ...

- Where, in the second diagram, would the number 14 be placed? 27? 12? 37? In the red loop; In the blue loop; In both loops; Outside both loops.
- What is another number that could be placed in the red loop? The black loop? Both loops? Neither loop? Answers may vary.

Extension

Refer to the second diagram shown. Have students add a third loop for numbers divisible by 5 and redraw the diagram. Add numbers so that each area has two or more numbers.

Possible answer:

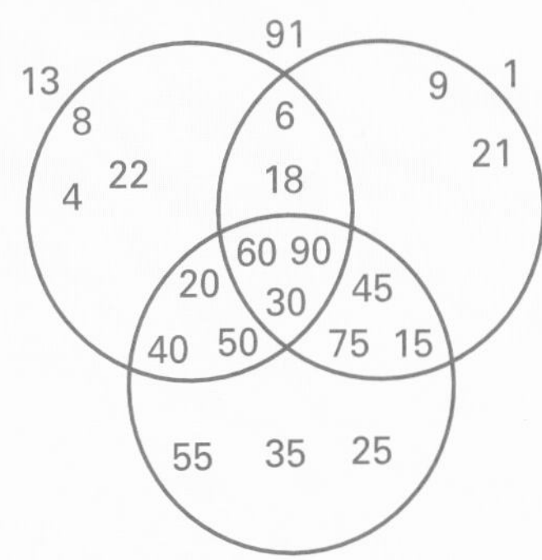

Answers for Try It

1. Possible answer:

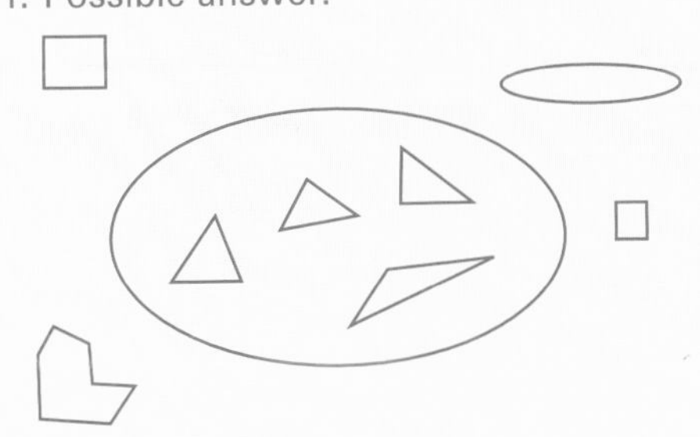

2. Possible answer:

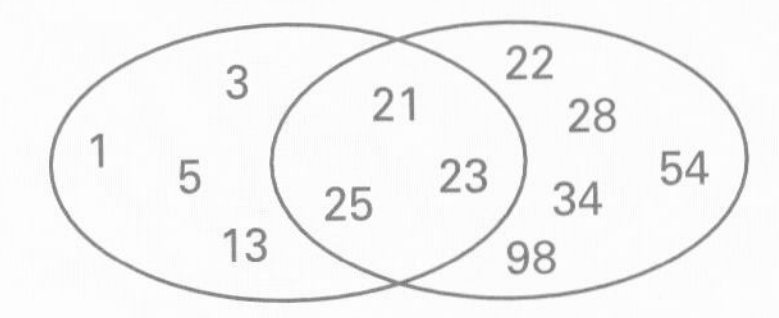

3. Possible answer:

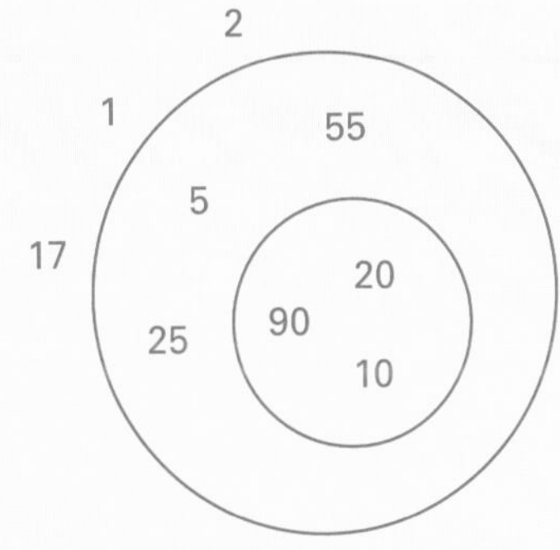

Chapter 5 Summary and Review

Review Correlation

Item(s)	Lesson(s)
1–4	5-1
5–8	5-2
9, 10	5-3
11–13	5-4
14–17	5-5
18–21	5-6
22	5-8
23–30	5-7

For additional review, see page 666.

Answers for Review

22. $\frac{7}{8}$, $1\frac{1}{4}$, $2\frac{3}{4}$, $\frac{7}{2}$

Chapter 5 Summary and Review

Graphic Organizer

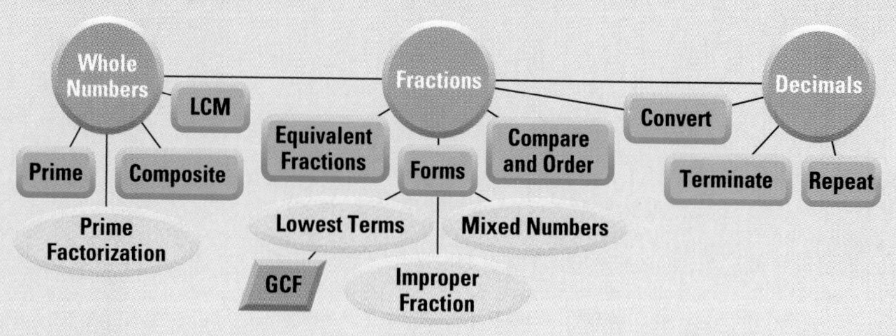

Section 5A Number Theory

Summary

- A whole number is **divisible** by another whole number if the first number can be divided by the second number without leaving a remainder.
- A **prime number** has exactly two factors, itself and 1. A **composite number** has more than two factors.
- The **prime factorization** of a number is the set of prime numbers whose product equals the number.
- To find the prime factorization of a number, you can use the divisibility rules and a factor tree.
- The **least common multiple** of two numbers is their smallest common multiple.

Review

Test each number for divisibility by 2, 3, 5, 6, 9, and 10.

1. 234 2, 3, 6, and 9 **2.** 68 2 **3.** 6000 2, 3, 5, 6, and 10 **4.** 255 3 and 5

Label each number as prime or composite.

5. $2 \times 2 \times 3 \times 3$ Composite **6.** 1×143 Prime **7.** $2 \times 3 \times 3 \times 7$ Composite **8.** 3×29 Composite

Find the least common multiple for each number pair.

9. 36, 54 108 **10.** 14, 18 126

Resources

Practice Masters
Cumulative Review Chapters 1–5

PRACTICE

Name ______________________ Practice

Cumulative Review Chapters 1–5

Order each group of numbers from least to greatest. *[Lesson 2-3]*

1. 3,333; 33,333; 333 — 333; 3,333; 33,333
2. 60,660; 60,606; 66,006 — 60,606; 60,660; 66,006
3. 7,000; 7,010; 7,009; 6,999 — 6,999; 7,000; 7,009; 7,010
4. 5 billion; 4 million; 6 hundred — 6 hundred; 4 million; 5 billion

Simplify. *[Lessons 3-6 and 3-11]*

5. 8.37 + 21 — 29.37
6. 5.43 − 1.9 — 3.53
7. 6.98 + 7.47 — 14.45
8. 12 − 5.63 — 6.37
9. 24.893 ÷ 3.1 — 8.03
10. 4.36 + 8.9 — 13.26
11. 1.4535 ÷ 0.085 — 17.1
12. 0.828 ÷ 3.6 — 0.23

Find the missing measurement for each rectangle. *[Lesson 4-4]*

13. Area = 66 in^2; Base = 11 in.; Height = 6 in.
14. Area = 90 ft^2; Base = 6 ft; Height = 15 ft
15. Area = 35 m^2; Base = 5 m; Height = 7 m
16. Area = 48 km^2; Base = 12 km; Height = 4 km
17. Area = 26.65 yd^2; Base = 6.5 yd; Height = 4.1 yd
18. Area = 9.25 mm^2; Base = 3.7 mm; Height = 2.5 mm

Find the prime factorization. *[Lesson 5-2]*

19. 350 — $2 \times 5^2 \times 7$
20. 135 — $3^3 \times 5$
21. 616 — $2^3 \times 7 \times 11$
22. 180 — $2^2 \times 3^2 \times 5$

Write as a fraction in lowest terms *[Lesson 5-7]*

23. 0.625 — $\frac{5}{8}$
24. 0.47 — $\frac{47}{100}$
25. 0.775 — $\frac{31}{40}$
26. 0.42 — $\frac{21}{50}$

Chapter 5 Summary and Review

Section 5B Connecting Fractions and Decimals

Summary

- The **denominator** of a fraction tells the number of parts in the whole. The **numerator** tells how many parts are being named.
- An **improper fraction** has a numerator greater than or equal to its denominator. A **mixed number** combines a whole number and a fraction.
- Fraction values can be written as decimals whose digits either terminate or repeat.
- **Equivalent fractions** name the same amount.
- A fraction is in **lowest terms** when its numerator and denominator have no common factors other than 1.
- The **greatest common factor** is the largest whole number that divides evenly into two numbers.
- If two fractions have the same denominator, it is called a **common denominator**.

Review

What fraction does the shaded part of each model represent?

11. $\frac{5}{8}$

12. $\frac{4}{6}$ or $\frac{2}{3}$

13. Identify the numerator and the denominator in the fraction $\frac{11}{3}$. The numerator is 11, the denominator is 3.

Write each fraction in lowest terms.

14. $\frac{16}{24}$ $\frac{2}{3}$ **15.** $\frac{125}{1000}$ $\frac{1}{8}$ **16.** $\frac{12}{72}$ $\frac{1}{6}$ **17.** $\frac{648}{810}$ $\frac{4}{5}$

Rewrite each fraction as a mixed number or an improper fraction.

18. $\frac{17}{4}$ $4\frac{1}{4}$ **19.** $8\frac{3}{5}$ $\frac{43}{5}$ **20.** $\frac{47}{7}$ $6\frac{5}{7}$ **21.** $2\frac{8}{9}$ $\frac{26}{9}$

22. Four rubber bands have lengths of $2\frac{3}{4}$, $\frac{7}{8}$, $1\frac{1}{4}$, and $\frac{7}{2}$ inches. List their lengths in order from shortest to longest.

Rewrite each fraction as a decimal.

23. $\frac{4}{6}$ $0.\overline{6}$ **24.** $\frac{11}{2}$ 5.5 **25.** $\frac{3}{8}$ 0.375 **26.** $\frac{7}{5}$ 1.4

Rewrite each decimal as a fraction in lowest terms or a mixed number.

27. 0.05 $\frac{1}{20}$ **28.** 3.8 $3\frac{4}{5}$ **29.** 0.625 $\frac{5}{8}$ **30.** 2.023 $2\frac{23}{1000}$

Chapter 5 Assessment

Assessment Correlation

Item(s)	Lesson(s)
1–3	5-1
4–7	5-2
8	5-4
9	5-2
10	5-4
11	5-3
12	5-2
13	5-4
14	5-3
15–18	5-5
19–22	5-7

Answers for Assessment

1. 3 and 9
2. 5
3. 2, 3, 5, 6, and 10
4. Composite
5. Prime
6. Composite
7. $2 \times 3 \times 3 \times 13$
8. Possible answers: $\frac{1}{4}$, $\frac{6}{24}$
9. 6 ways: groups of 2, 3, 5, 6, 10, and 15.
10. a. Numerator: 5; Denominator, 8

    b. 0.625
11. 36
12. 84
13. $\frac{2}{3}$ yard
14. Every twelfth day
15. $\frac{2}{7}$
16. $\frac{1}{3}$
17. 10
18. 14
19. 0.375
20. $3\frac{1}{4}$
21. $\frac{13}{20}$
22. $5\frac{7}{200}$

Answer for Performance Task

Possible answer for number patterns: Fractional values for nickels increase by twentieths, dimes by tenths, quarters by fourths, and half-dollars by halves. Equivalent fractional parts of the dollar for different coins have the same dollar value.

See table on page C4.

Chapter 5 Assessment

Tell whether each number is divisible by 2, 3, 5, 6, 9, and 10.

1. 3447 **2.** 485 **3.** 2400

Identify each number as prime or composite.

4. $2 \times 2 \times 2 \times 2 \times 2 \times 2$ **5.** 1×47 **6.** 3×109

7. Find the prime factorization of 234.

8. Find two fractions equivalent to $\frac{3}{12}$.

9. A pet store has 30 cages. The owner wants to arrange the cages in equal groups. How many ways can she do this?

10. **a.** Identify the numerator and denominator of the fraction $\frac{5}{8}$.

b. Write $\frac{5}{8}$ as a decimal number.

11. Find the least common multiple of 9 and 12.

12. The prime factorization of a number is $2 \times 2 \times 3 \times 7$. What is the number?

13. A yardstick was used to measure a fish. What fraction of a yard represents the length of the fish?

14. If John walks to the park every third day, and Sue walks to the park every fourth day, how often will they walk to the park on the same day?

Write each fraction in lowest terms.

15. $\frac{16}{56}$ **16.** $\frac{120}{360}$

Find the GCF of each pair of numbers.

17. 30, 50 **18.** 42, 70

Write each fraction as a decimal and each decimal as a fraction or mixed number.

19. $\frac{3}{8}$ **20.** $\frac{13}{4}$ **21.** 0.65 **22.** 5.035

Performance Task

Use U.S. coins whose values are more than a penny and less than a dollar. Think of all the different groups of the same kind of coins you could form and have a dollar or less. Organize your data for each coin in a table that shows the number of coins in each group, the fraction of a dollar each group represents, and its value written in dollars and cents: $0.75. What number patterns can you find?

Resources

Assessment Sourcebook

Chapter 5 Tests
- Forms A and B (free response)
- Form C (multiple choice)
- Form D (performance assessment)
- Form E (mixed response)
- Form F (cumulative chapter test)

TestWorks
Test and Practice Software

Home and Community Connections
- Letter Home for Chapter 5 in English and Spanish

Cumulative Review Chapters 1–5 — Test Prep

Performance Assessment

Choose one problem.

Stop and Go Patterns

Create a two-column table. Write these fractions in the first column: $\frac{1}{2}, \frac{1}{3}, \frac{1}{4}, \frac{1}{5}, \frac{1}{6}, \frac{1}{7}, \frac{1}{8}, \frac{1}{9}, \frac{1}{10}, \frac{1}{11}, \frac{1}{12}, \frac{1}{15}, \frac{1}{16}, \frac{1}{18}, \frac{1}{20}$. Use a calculator to fill in the second column with the decimal value equivalent to each fraction. Mark each decimal with an **R** if it repeats and with a **T** if it doesn't.

Fraction	Decimal	T or R?
$\frac{1}{2}$	0.5	T
⋮		
$\frac{1}{20}$		

Make a list of all the denominators of the fractions for which the equivalent decimals terminated. Find their prime factorizations. Describe a pattern that can help you predict which fractions convert to terminating decimals and which ones don't.

Prime Time

For each pair of numbers:
30 and 35   18 and 45

Find the prime factorization of the pair of numbers. Then find the LCM of the pair of numbers and the prime factorization of the LCM.

How can the prime factorization of each pair of numbers help you find their LCM?

AREA BREAK DOWN

Measure and record the floor areas of at least five rooms in your home. Find the total of the areas you measured. What fractional part is each floor area of the total areas you measured? What kind of graph would be used to show this data? Explain.

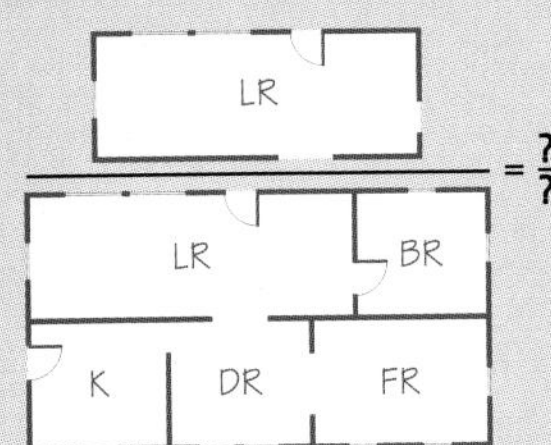

Number Strain

Use a 10 × 10 grid numbered from left to right from 1 through 100. Follow the steps to cross out numbers on the grid. As you go through the steps, some of the numbers may already be crossed out.

- Cross out the 1.
- Cross out the multiples of 2 (except 2 itself) and the multiples of 3 (except 3 itself).
- Cross out the multiples of 5 (except 5 itself) and the multiples of 7 (except 7 itself).

What are the numbers that have not been crossed out called?

Explain why there were no steps listed for crossing out the multiples of 4, 6, 8, or 9.

Answers for Assessment

• Stop and Go Patterns

Table entries: Fraction, Decimal, T or R; $\frac{1}{2}$: 0.5, T; $\frac{1}{3}$: $0.\overline{3}$, R; $\frac{1}{4}$: 0.25; T; $\frac{1}{5}$: 0.2, T; $\frac{1}{6}$: $0.\overline{16}$, R; $\frac{1}{7}$: 0.142857, R; $\frac{1}{8}$: 0.125, T; $\frac{1}{9}$: 0.1, R; $\frac{1}{10}$: 0.1, T; $\frac{1}{11}$: 0.09, R; $\frac{1}{12}$: $0.08\overline{3}$, R; $\frac{1}{15}$: $0.0\overline{6}$, R; $\frac{1}{16}$: 0.0625; T; $\frac{1}{18}$: $0.0\overline{5}$, R; $\frac{1}{20}$: 0.05, T.

Denominators and prime factorizations: 2, Prime; 4, 2 × 2; 5, Prime; 8, 2 × 2 × 2; 10, 2 × 5; 16, 2 × 2 × 2 × 2; 20, 2 × 2 × 5. Fractions with denominators whose prime factorizations contain only 2's and/or 5's convert to terminating decimals.

• Prime Time

30 = 2 × 3 × 5; 35 = 5 × 7; LCM of 30 and 35 is 210; 210 = 2 × 3 × 5 × 7. 18 = 2 × 3 × 3; 45 = 3 × 3 × 5; LCM of 18 and 45 is 90; 90 = 2 × 3 × 3 × 5. LCM of two numbers can be found by using the prime factors of each number pair as multipliers the maximum number of times each factor is found in the pair of numbers.

• Number Strain

The numbers not crossed out were not multiples of 2, 3, 5, or 7. They are called prime numbers. Multiples of 4, 6, 8, and 9 all contained more than one factor of 2 or 3 so they could not have been prime numbers.

Cumulative Review Test Prep

About Performance Assessment

The Performance Assessment options ...

- provide teachers with an alternate means of assessing students.
- address different learning modalities.
- allow students to choose one problem.

Teachers may encourage students to choose the most challenging problem.

Learning Modalities
Stop and Go Patterns **Social** Students compare fractions with their decimal equivalents and predict the decimal form of a fraction.
Area Breakdown **Kinesthetic** Students measure areas to compare fractions.
Prime Time **Logical** Students find prime factorizations and reason how these can be used to find the LCM.
Number Strain **Linguistic** Students explain the steps used or not used in determining prime numbers from a grid of numbers.

Suggested Scoring Rubric

See key on page 267.

Area Breakdown

Score	Criteria
4	•Computations are accurate and reflect recorded data for five rooms. •Explanations are clear and support choice of graph.
3	•Most computations are accurate and reflect recorded data for four rooms. •Explanations are adequate and support choice of graph.
2	•Computations are inaccurate and do not reflect recorded data. •Explanations are attempted, but are incomplete.
1	•Calculations are incomplete or incorrect. Explanations are incomplete or not included.

Chapter

6

▶ OVERVIEW

Adding and Subtracting Fractions

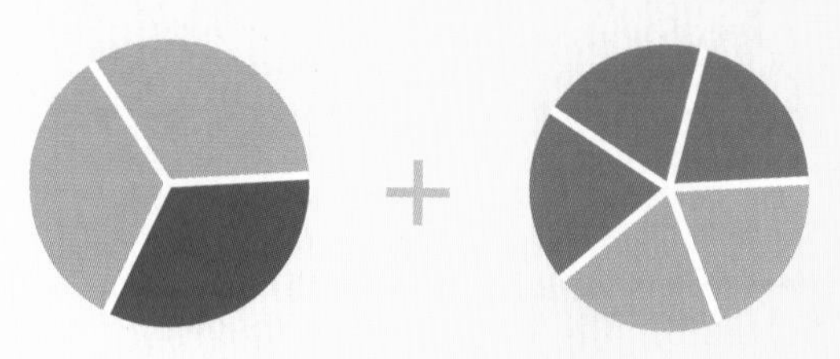

Section 6A

Adding and Subtracting Fractions: Students learn to add and subtract fractions. Then they learn to solve fraction equations by adding and subtracting fractions.

6-1 Adding and Subtracting Fractions with Like Denominators

6-2 Adding and Subtracting Fractions with Unlike Denominators

6-3 Solving Fraction Equations: Addition and Subtraction

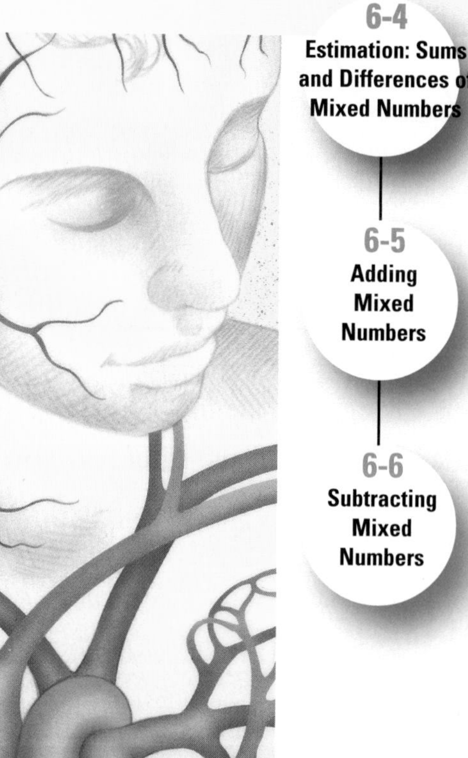

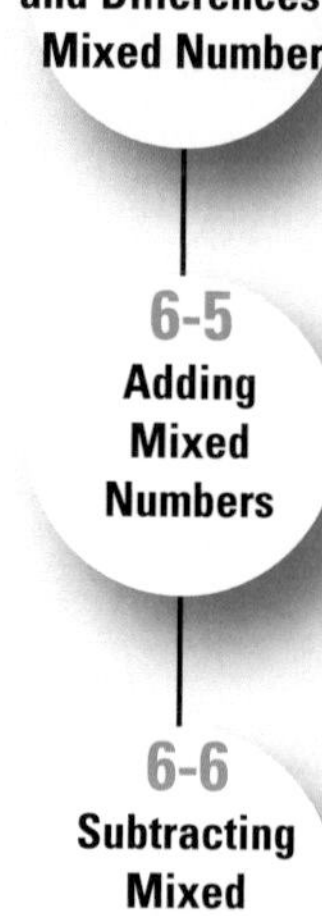

Section 6B

Adding and Subtracting Mixed Numbers: Students learn to add and subtract mixed numbers.

6-4 Estimation: Sums and Differences of Mixed Numbers

6-5 Adding Mixed Numbers

6-6 Subtracting Mixed Numbers

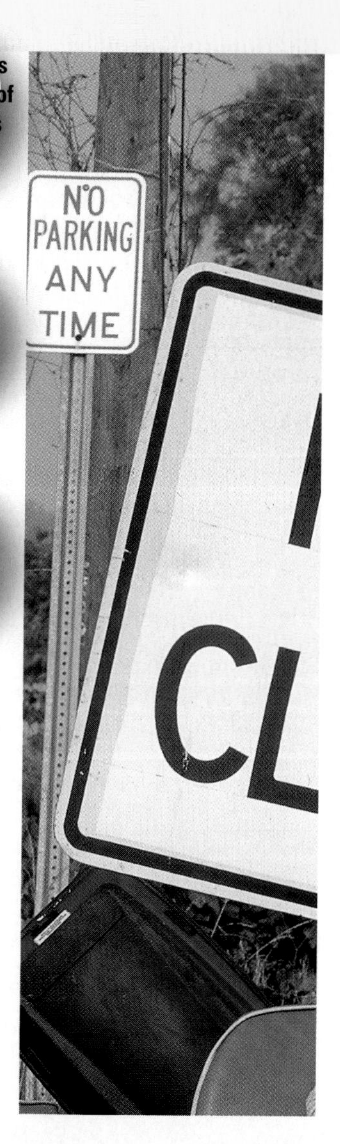

Meeting NCTM Standards

Curriculum Standards

STANDARD

	Standard		pages
1	**Problem Solving**	Skills and Strategies	322, 327, 332, 338, 345, 349, 354
		Applications	326–327, 331–332, 337–338, 339, 344–345, 348–349, 353–354, 355
		Exploration	324, 334, 338, 342, 346, 350
2	**Communication**	Oral	323, 325, 330, 336, *338*, 341, 343, *345*, 347, 352
		Written	327, 338, 345, 349, 354
		Cooperative Learning	*324, 328, 334, 342, 346, 350*
3	**Reasoning**	Critical Thinking	332, 338, 345, 354
4	**Connections**	Mathematical	See Standards 5, 6, 7, 9, 13 below.
		Interdisciplinary	Arts and Literature 320, 329, *330*; Entertainment 320; Science 321, *323*, 326, 331, 332, 335, 336, 338, 339, *341*; Social Studies 321; Health 323, *336*, 340, 354; Geography 327, *341*, 342, 343, *352*; Industry 340; Sports *348*; Language 347; Career 348; History 351
		Technology	333
		Cultural	320, *329*
5	**Number and Number Relationships**		345
6	**Number Systems and Number Theory**		324–332, 337, 342–354
7	**Computation and Estimation**		324–332, 342–354, 356
9	**Algebra**		334–338, 353
13	**Measurement**		*326*, 357

Italic type indicates Teacher Edition reference.

Teaching Standards

Focus on Inclusion

NCTM sees the comprehensive mathematics education of every child as its most compelling goal. By "every" child is meant

- students who have been denied access in any way to educational opportunities, as well as those who have not.
- students who have not been successful in mathematics, as well as those who have been successful.

Assessment Standards

Focus on Equity

Interviews Providing each student with the chance to demonstrate his or her mathematical understanding is a goal of the Equity Standard. A teacher/student interview enables the teacher to obtain a more complete picture of each student's knowledge of a given topic. Interviews in Chapter 6 have students

- give a detailed explanation.
- justify their choice.

TECHNOLOGY

For the Teacher

- **Teacher Resource Planner CD-ROM**
  Use the teacher planning CD-ROM to view resources available for Chapter 6. You can prepare custom lesson plans or use the default lesson plans provided.

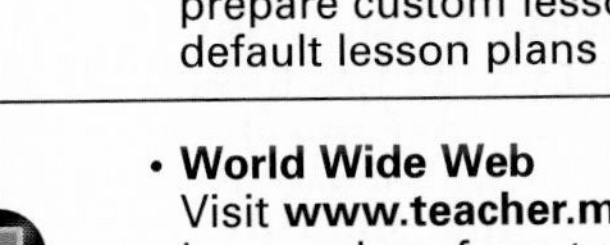

- **World Wide Web**
  Visit **www.teacher.mathsurf.com** for links to lesson plans from teachers and other professionals, NCTM information, and other sites.

- **TestWorks**
  TestWorks provides ready-made tests and can create custom tests and practice worksheets.

For the Parent

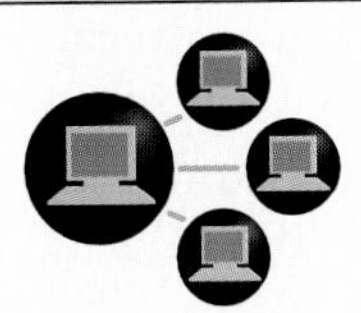

- **World Wide Web**
  Parents can use the Web site at **www.parent.mathsurf.com.**

For the Student

- **Interactive CD-ROM**
  Lesson 6-6 has an *Interactive CD-ROM Lesson*. The *Interactive CD-ROM Journal* is also used in Chapter 6.

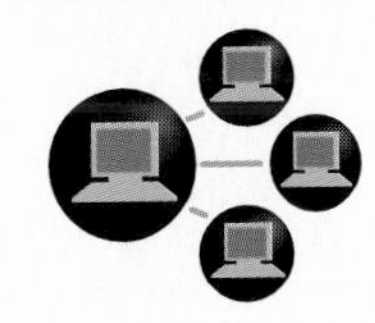

- **World Wide Web**
  Use with Chapter and Section Openers; Students can go online to the Scott Foresman-Addison Wesley Web site at **www.mathsurf.com/6/ch6** to collect information about chapter themes.

STANDARDIZED - TEST CORRELATION

SECTION 6A

LESSON	OBJECTIVE	ITBS Form M	CTBS 4th Ed.	CAT 5th Ed.	SAT 9th Ed.	MAT 7th Ed.	Your Form
6-1	• Add and subtract fractions with like denominators.	✘	✘	✘	✘	✘	
6-2	• Add and subtract fractions with unlike denominators.	✘	✘	✘	✘	✘	
6-3	• Solve equations by adding and subtracting fractions.			✘		✘	

SECTION 6B

LESSON	OBJECTIVE	ITBS Form M	CTBS 4th Ed.	CAT 5th Ed.	SAT 9th Ed.	MAT 7th Ed.	Your Form
6-4	• Estimate sums and differences of mixed numbers.				✘		
6-5	• Add mixed numbers.			✘	✘	✘	
6-6	• Subtract mixed numbers.			✘	✘	✘	

Key: ITBS - Iowa Test of Basic Skills; CTBS - Comprehensive Test of Basic Skills; CAT - California Achievement Test; SAT - Stanford Achievement Test; MAT - Metropolitan Achievement Test

ASSESSMENT PROGRAM

Traditional Assessment	QUICK QUIZZES	SECTION REVIEW	CHAPTER REVIEW	CHAPTER ASSESSMENT FREE RESPONSE	CHAPTER ASSESSMENT MULTIPLE CHOICE	CUMULATIVE REVIEW
	TE: pp. 327, 332, 338, 345, 349, 354	SE: pp. 340, 356 *Quiz 6A, 6B	SE: pp. 358–359	SE: p. 360 *Ch. 6 Tests Forms A, B, E	*Ch. 6 Tests Forms C, E	SE: p. 361 *Ch. 6 Test Form F; Quarterly Test Ch. 1–6

Alternate Assessment	INTERVIEW	JOURNAL	ONGOING	PERFORMANCE	PORTFOLIO	PROJECT	SELF
	TE: p. 338	SE: pp. 327, 338, 349, 354 TE: pp. 322, 327, 349	TE: pp. 324, 328, 334, 342, 346, 350	SE: p. 360 TE: p. 345 *Ch. 6 Tests Forms D, E	TE: p. 332	SE: pp. 338, 354	TE: p. 354

*Tests and quizzes are in *Assessment Sourcebook.* Test Form E is a mixed response test.
Forms for Alternate Assessment are also available in *Assessment Sourcebook.*

TestWorks: Test and Practice Software

MIDDLE SCHOOL PACING CHART

REGULAR PACING

Day	5 classes per week
1	Chapter 6 Opener; Problem Solving Focus
2	Section **6A** Opener; Lesson **6-1**
3	Lesson **6-2**; Technology
4	Lesson **6-3**
5	**6A** Connect; **6A** Review
6	Section **6B** Opener; Lesson **6-4**
7	Lesson **6-5**
8	Lesson **6-6**
9	**6B** Connect; **6B** Review; Extend Key Ideas
10	Chapter 6 Summary and Review
11	Chapter 6 Assessment Cumulative Review, Chapters 1–6

BLOCK SCHEDULING OPTIONS

Block Scheduling for Complete Course

Chapter 6 may be presented in

- five 90-minute blocks
- eight 75-minute blocks

Each block consists of a combination of

- Chapter and Section Openers
- Explores
- Lesson Development
- Problem Solving Focus
- Technology
- Extend Key Ideas
- Connect
- Review
- Assessment

For details, see *Block Scheduling Handbook.*

Block Scheduling for Interdisciplinary Course

Each block integrates math with another subject area.

In Chapter 6, interdisciplinary topics include

- Blood
- Floods

Themes for Interdisciplinary Team Teaching 6A and 6B are

- Music
- Woodworking

For details, see *Block Scheduling Handbook.*

Block Scheduling for Lab-Based Course

In each block, 30–40 minutes is devoted to lab activities including

- Explores in the Student Edition
- Connect pages in the Student Edition
- Technology options in the Student Edition
- Reteaching Activities in the Teacher Edition

For details, see *Block Scheduling Handbook.*

Block Scheduling for Course with *Connected Mathematics*

In each block, investigations from **Connected Mathematics** replace or enhance the lessons in Chapter 6.

Connected Mathematics topics for Chapter 6 can be found in

- *Bits and Pieces II*

For details, see *Block Scheduling Handbook.*

INTERDISCIPLINARY BULLETIN BOARD

Set Up

Put a large outline map of the United States on a bulletin board. Write the phrase, "Total Inches of Rain on (today's date)" on the bottom of the board.

Procedure

- Display a weather map from a newspaper. Point out where the map lists the amounts of rain that fell in major U.S. cities the previous day. If necessary, explain that the amounts are expressed as hundredths of an inch in decimal form.
- Assign partners one or two major cities and have them convert the decimals into fractions.
- Partners should write the name of each city in its correct location on the map and the fractional amount of rainfall it received.
- Volunteers might add the fractions to determine the total inches of rain that fell in the major cities.

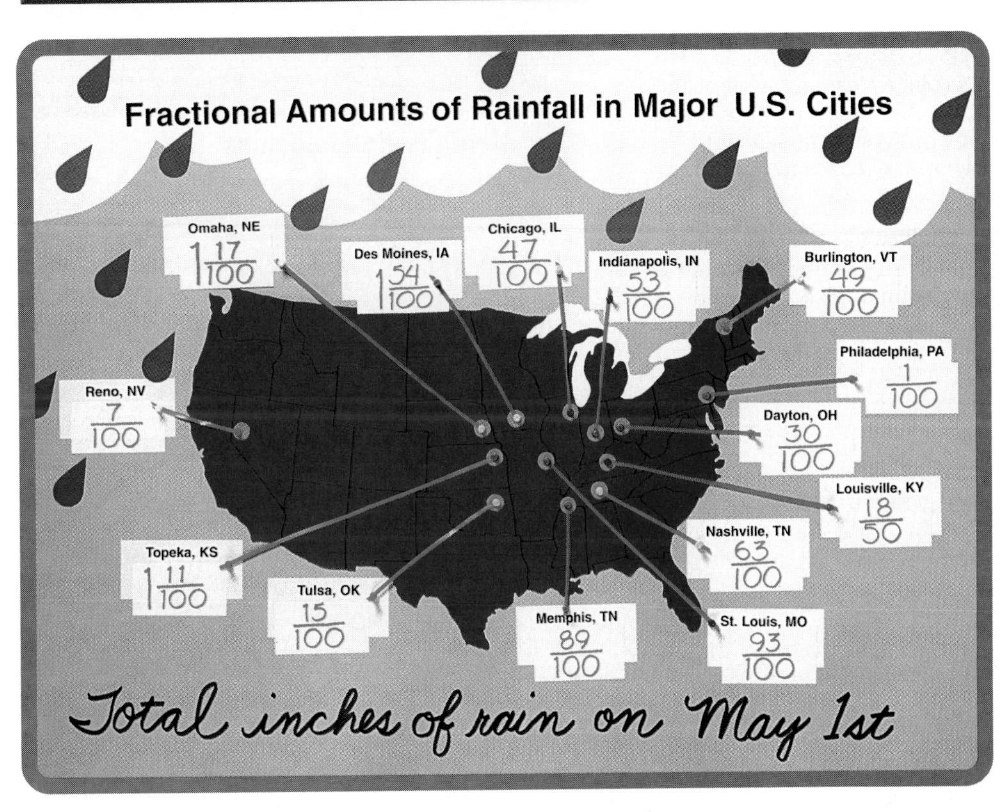

Chapter 6

The information on these pages shows how adding and subtracting fractions are used in real-life situations.

World Wide Web

If your class has access to the World Wide Web, you might want to use the information found at the Web site addresses given.

Extensions

The following activities do not require access to the World Wide Web.

People of the World
Have students predict which countries probably have the fewest telephones per person. Then ask them to see if they can find any data to support their predictions.

Arts & Literature
Ask students why they think the height of the walls was designed to be $\frac{1}{2}$, $\frac{2}{3}$, or $\frac{3}{4}$ the distance across the church. Answers may vary.

Entertainment
Ask groups of four students to create a comic book or comic strip of their own. Talk about what makes comic books appealing.

Science
Have students research California sea lions. Ask them to share their findings on where the sea lions live, what they eat, and how long they live.

Social Studies
Ask students to find information about tall buildings around the world. Ask them to try to find the height of the World Trade Center Towers. The twin towers are 110 stories (1350 ft) high.

6 Adding and Subtracting Fractions

Entertainment Link
www.mathsurf.com/6/ch6/ent

People of the World

The country with the most telephones per person is Sweden. If the telephones were evenly distributed, $\frac{17}{25}$ of Sweden's total population would have a telephone.

Entertainment

$\frac{1}{3}$ of the money spent on newly published comic books goes to Marvel Comics, the publishers of *The X-Men* and *Spider-Man*. $\frac{1}{5}$ goes to DC Comics, the publishers of *Batman* and *Superman*.

Arts & Literature

In 15th century Italy, church buildings were designed so that heights of the walls were either $\frac{1}{2}$, $\frac{2}{3}$, or $\frac{3}{4}$ the distance across the church.

320

TEACHER TALK

Meet Charlotte Jenkins

Ulysses S. Grant School
Chicago, Illinois

I use paper plate activities to introduce adding and subtracting fractions with different denominators. To find $\frac{5}{8} + \frac{1}{4}$, I give each student two paper plates. I ask students to draw lines to divide one plate into fourths and the other into eighths. Then I have them cut the plates to join $\frac{1}{4}$ of one to $\frac{5}{8}$ of the other, and ask them to describe the result.

To find $\frac{5}{8} - \frac{1}{4}$, I give each student one paper plate. I ask students to draw lines to divide the plate into eighths and shade five of the eighths. Then I have them cut $\frac{1}{4}$ of the plate from the shaded area and describe the shaded amount that is left. I have students repeat the activities to find other sums and differences.

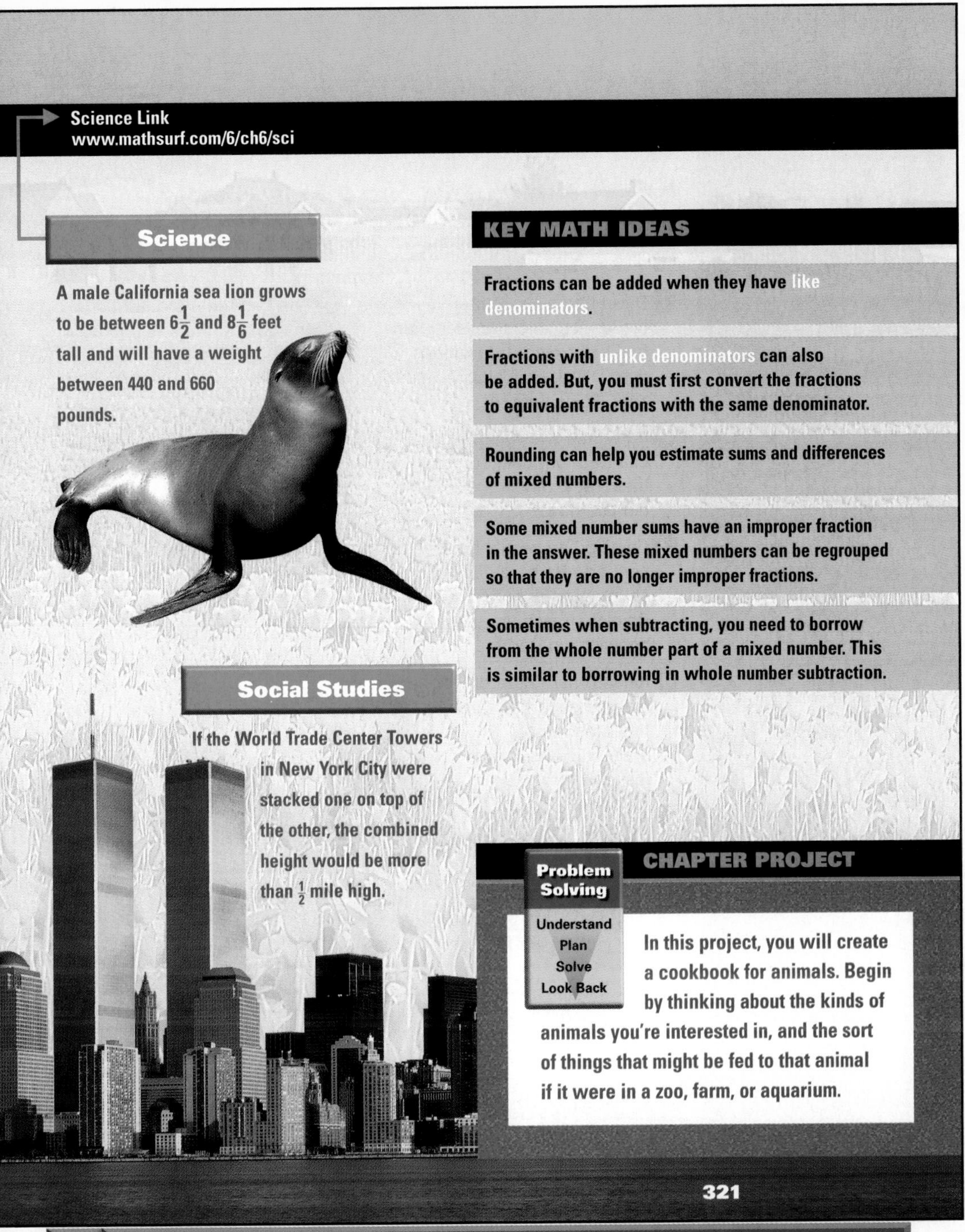

Science Link
www.mathsurf.com/6/ch6/sci

Science

A male California sea lion grows to be between $6\frac{1}{2}$ and $8\frac{1}{6}$ feet tall and will have a weight between 440 and 660 pounds.

Social Studies

If the World Trade Center Towers in New York City were stacked one on top of the other, the combined height would be more than $\frac{1}{2}$ mile high.

KEY MATH IDEAS

Fractions can be added when they have like denominators.

Fractions with unlike denominators can also be added. But, you must first convert the fractions to equivalent fractions with the same denominator.

Rounding can help you estimate sums and differences of mixed numbers.

Some mixed number sums have an improper fraction in the answer. These mixed numbers can be regrouped so that they are no longer improper fractions.

Sometimes when subtracting, you need to borrow from the whole number part of a mixed number. This is similar to borrowing in whole number subtraction.

CHAPTER PROJECT

Problem Solving
Understand
Plan
Solve
Look Back

In this project, you will create a cookbook for animals. Begin by thinking about the kinds of animals you're interested in, and the sort of things that might be fed to that animal if it were in a zoo, farm, or aquarium.

321

Chapter Project

Students use information about what animals eat to create a cookbook for animals.

Resources

Chapter 6 Project Master

Introduce the Project

- Discuss the types of animals students might be interested in.
- Talk about the kinds of foods different animals might eat. Differentiate between animals that eat meat and animals that eat only plants.
- Discuss places where students might find information about their chosen animals and what they eat, such as in encyclopedias, in books about animals, and on the Internet.

Project Progress

Section A, page 338 Students use operations with fractions to increase or decrease the amount of each ingredient in a recipe, depending on the number of servings needed.

Section B, page 354 Students use estimation and operations with mixed numbers to complete the recipes in their cookbook.

Community Project

A community project for Chapter 6 is available in *Home and Community Connections.*

Cooperative Learning

You may want to use Teaching Tool Transparency 1: Cooperative Learning Checklist with **Explore** and other group activities in this chapter.

PROJECT ASSESSMENT

You may choose to use this project as a performance assessment for the chapter.

Performance Assessment Key

Level 4 Full Accomplishment

Level 3 Substantial Accomplishment

Level 2 Partial Accomplishment

Level 1 Little Accomplishment

Suggested Scoring Rubric

4
- Food selections for animals indicate accurate research.
- Cookbook recipes are accurately calculated to yield correct servings.

3
- Food selections for animals indicate some research.
- Cookbook recipes are calculated to yield correct servings.

2
- Food selections for animals indicate limited research.
- Not all cookbook recipes are correctly calculated.

1
- Food selections for animals indicate no research.
- Cookbook recipes will not produce correct servings.

Problem Solving Focus

Interpreting Math Phrases

The Point
Students focus on interpreting comparison phrases in order to solve a problem.

Resources
Teaching Tool Transparency 18: Problem-Solving Guidelines

 *Interactive CD-ROM Journal*

About the Page

Using the Problem-Solving Process
Sometimes it is first necessary to interpret a phrase before beginning to solve the problem. Discuss these suggestions.

- Read the problem several times.
- Identify the phrases that are being used to ask the question.
- Determine what the problem is asking.
- Determine the meaning of any comparison phrases.

Ask ...
- In Problem 1, did Jennifer or David have more butterflies? How do you know? Jennifer; Problem states she had eight more.
- In Problem 3, did Barbara have more grasshoppers than Camille? Explain. No; She had half as many as Camille.

Answers for Problems
1. $7 + 8 = 15$
2. $12 - 4 = 8$
3. $20 \div 2 = 10$
4. $3 \times 3 = 9$
5. $10 + 14 = 24$
6. $6 \div 2 = 3$
7. $7 \times 2 = 14$

Journal

Have students write a list of phrases they have seen in problems that tell them what to do and then describe what the phrases mean.

Problem Solving
Understand
Plan
Solve
Look Back

Interpreting Math Phrases

In some problems, numerical information is given directly. At other times, numerical information is given as a comparison, such as "Neil had *three more than* Doreen". When making a plan to solve a problem, you must be able to correctly interpret these comparison phrases.

Problem Solving Focus

For each problem, write down the answer and the arithmetic for how you got the answer. For example, if you added 5 to 7 to get 12, write "5 + 7 = 12".

1. David had seven butterflies in his insect collection. Jennifer had eight more butterflies than David. How many butterflies did Jennifer have?
2. Patty had twelve crickets. Lila had four crickets less than Patty. How many crickets did Lila have?
3. Camille had twenty grasshoppers. Barbara had half as many grasshoppers as Camille. How many grasshoppers did Barbara have?
4. Richard had three dragonflies. Phoebe had three times as many dragonflies as Richard. How many did Phoebe have?
5. Ada had ten more ladybugs than Mark. Mark had fourteen ladybugs. How many did Ada have?
6. Jack had twice as many beetles as Lois. Jack had six beetles. How many did Lois have?
7. Kristen had half as many bees as Terri. Kristen had seven bees. How many did Terri have?

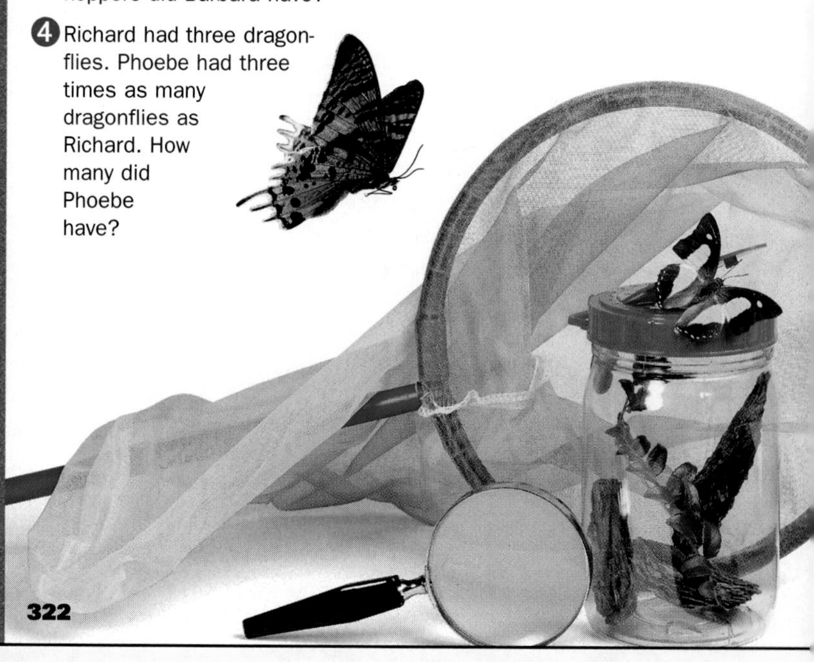

322

Additional Problem

The top speed of a prong-horned antelope is about 60 miles per hour. An ostrich can run about half as fast, and the fastest speed of a human is about 3 miles per hour slower than the ostrich. What is a human's fastest speed?

1. What is the problem about? Top speeds of animals.
2. What does the problem ask you to find? The top speed of a human.
3. Which animal is fastest? How can you tell? Antelope; The ostrich is only half as fast, which means you divide the antelope's speed by 2, and the human's speed is 3 miles per hour slower than the ostrich's.
4. What is a human's top speed? 27 miles per hour.

Adding and Subtracting Fractions

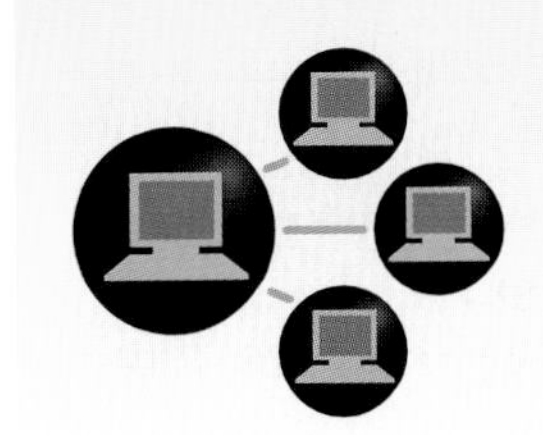

Visit www.teacher.mathsurf.com for links to lesson plans from teachers and other professionals, NCTM information, and other sites.

LESSON PLANNING GUIDE

Student Edition / Ancillaries*

LESSON		MATERIALS	VOCABULARY	DAILY	OTHER
	Chapter 6 Opener				Ch. 6 Project Master Ch. 6 Community Project Teaching Tool Trans. 1
	Problem Solving Focus				Teaching Tool Trans. 18 *Interactive CD-ROM Journal*
	Section 6A Opener				
6-1	**Adding and Subtracting Fractions with Like Denominators**	pattern blocks or, power blocks	like denominators	6-1	Teaching Tool Trans. 19 Lesson Enhancement Trans. 25 Technology Master 26
6-2	**Adding and Subtracting Fractions with Unlike Denominators**	Fraction Bars®	unlike denominators, least common denominator (LCD)	6-2	Teaching Tool Trans. 2, 3, 14 Lesson Enhancement Transparencies 26, 27 Technology Master 27
	Technology	fraction calculator			Teaching Tool Trans. 24
6-3	**Solving Fraction Equations: Addition and Subtraction**			6-3	Lesson Enhancement Trans. 28 Technology Master 28 Ch. 6 Project Master
	Connect				Interdisc. Team Teaching 6A
	Review				Practice 6A; Quiz 6A; *TestWorks*

* Daily Ancillaries include Practice, Reteaching, Problem Solving, Enrichment, and Daily Transparency. Teaching Tool Transparencies are in *Teacher's Toolkits*. Lesson Enhancement Transparencies are in *Overhead Transparency Package*.

SKILLS TRACE

LESSON	SKILL	FIRST INTRODUCED GR. 4	GR. 5	GR. 6	DEVELOP	PRACTICE/APPLY	REVIEW
6-1	**Adding and subtracting fractions with like denominators.**	✘			pp. 324–325	pp. 326–327	pp. 340, 358, 411, 592
6-2	**Adding and subtracting fractions with unlike denominators.**	✘			pp. 328–330	pp. 331–332	pp. 340, 358, 415, 592
6-3	**Solving equations by adding and subtracting fractions.**			✘ p. 334	pp. 334–336	pp. 337–338	pp. 340, 358, 420

CONNECTED MATHEMATICS

Investigation 4 in the unit *Bits and Pieces II (Using Rational Numbers)*, from the **Connected Mathematics** series, can be used with Section 6A.

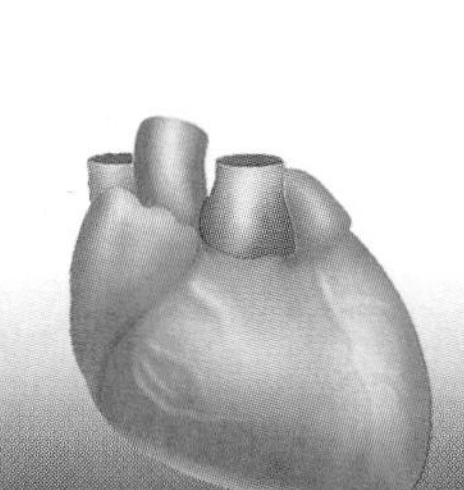

INTERDISCIPLINARY TEAM TEACHING

Math and Music

(Worksheet pages 29–30: Teacher pages T29–T30)

In this lesson, students add fractions in musical compositions.

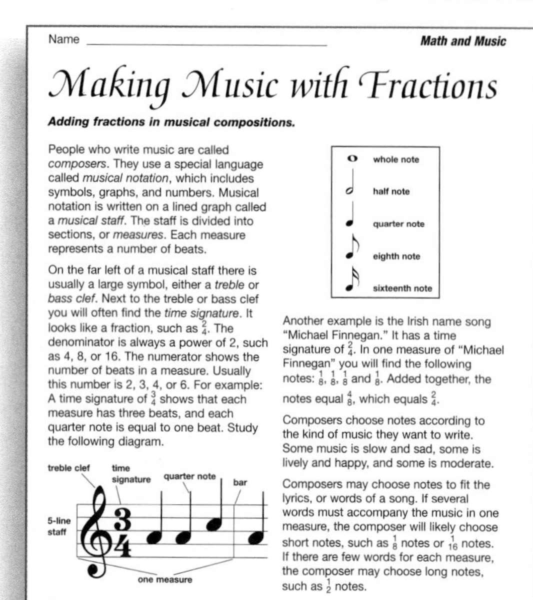

Name ______________________ **Math and Music**

Making Music with Fractions

Adding fractions in musical compositions.

People who write music are called *composers*. They use a special language called *musical notation*, which includes symbols, graphs, and numbers. Musical notation is written on a lined graph called a *musical staff*. The staff is divided into sections, or *measures*. Each measure represents a number of beats.

On the far left of a musical staff there is usually a large symbol, either a *treble* or *bass clef*. Next to the treble or bass clef you will often find the *time signature*. It looks like a fraction, such as $\frac{2}{4}$. The denominator is always a power of 2, such as 4, 8, or 16. The numerator shows the number of beats in a measure. Usually this number is 2, 3, 4, or 6. For example: A time signature of $\frac{3}{4}$ shows that each measure has three beats, and each quarter note is equal to one beat. Study the following diagram.

Composers write music using notes such as the sixteenth note, the eighth note, the quarter note, the half note, and the whole note (see chart). If you add the musical notes in a measure, the sum will equal the time signature. For example, in the song "This Ol' Man," the time signature is $\frac{4}{4}$. One measure of the song has the following notes: $\frac{1}{4}$, $\frac{1}{4}$, $\frac{1}{8}$, $\frac{1}{8}$, and $\frac{1}{4}$. Added together, the notes equal $\frac{8}{8}$ or 1, which is equal to $\frac{4}{4}$.

Another example is the Irish name song "Michael Finnegan." It has a time signature of $\frac{2}{4}$. In one measure of "Michael Finnegan" you will find the following notes: $\frac{1}{8}$, $\frac{1}{8}$, $\frac{1}{8}$ and $\frac{1}{8}$. Added together, the notes equal $\frac{4}{8}$, which equals $\frac{2}{4}$.

Composers choose notes according to the kind of music they want to write. Some music is slow and sad, some is lively and happy, and some is moderate.

Composers may choose notes to fit the lyrics, or words of a song. If several words must accompany the music in one measure, the composer will likely choose short notes, such as $\frac{1}{8}$ notes or $\frac{1}{16}$ notes. If there are few words for each measure, the composer may choose long notes, such as $\frac{1}{2}$ notes.

1. Why are time signatures not reduced to lowest terms?

   See below.

2. Why do composers choose fractions to represent notes or beats instead of whole numbers?

   See below.

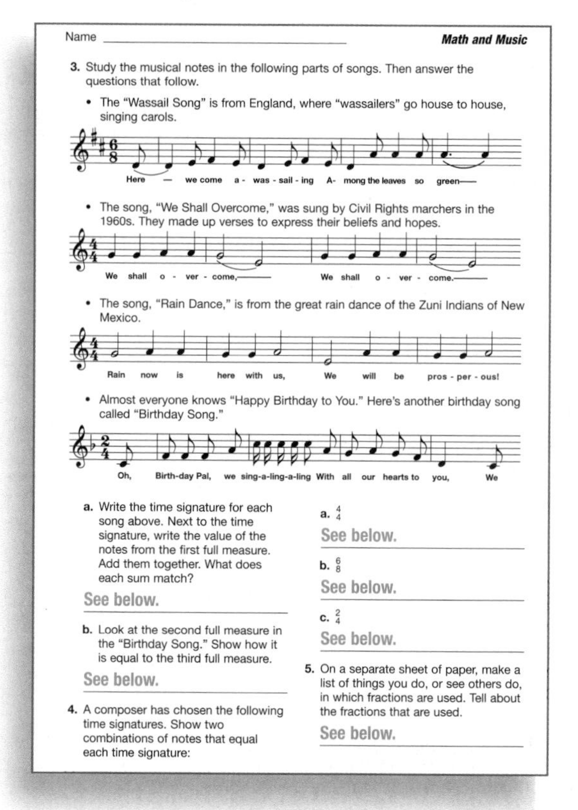

Name ______________________ **Math and Music**

3. Study the musical notes in the following parts of songs. Then answer the questions that follow.

   - The "Wassail Song" is from England, where "wassailers" go house to house, singing carols.

   - The song, "We Shall Overcome," was sung by Civil Rights marchers in the 1960s. They made up verses to express their beliefs and hopes.

   - The song, "Rain Dance," is from the great rain dance of the Zuni Indians of New Mexico.

   - Almost everyone knows "Happy Birthday to You." Here's another birthday song called "Birthday Song."

   a. Write the time signature for each song above. Next to the time signature, write the value of the notes from the first full measure. Add them together. What does each sum match?

   See below.

   b. Look at the second full measure in the "Birthday Song." Show how it is equal to the third full measure.

   See below.

4. A composer has chosen the following time signatures. Show two combinations of notes that equal each time signature:

   a. $\frac{4}{4}$ See below.

   b. $\frac{6}{8}$ See below.

   c. $\frac{2}{4}$ See below.

5. On a separate sheet of paper, make a list of things you do, or see others do, in which fractions are used. Tell about the fractions that are used.

   See below.

Answers

1. The purpose of the time signature is to show the number of beats per measure and which note equals one beat. If composers reduced all the time signatures to lowest terms, they'd be changing the number of beats per measure and the note that represented one beat.
2. Whole numbers could not be used to represent parts of a beat.
3. a. $\frac{6}{8}$; $\frac{1}{4}+\frac{1}{8}+\frac{1}{4}+\frac{1}{8}=\frac{6}{8}$. $\frac{4}{4}$; $\frac{1}{4}+\frac{1}{4}+\frac{1}{4}+\frac{1}{4}=\frac{4}{4}$. $\frac{4}{4}$; $\frac{1}{2}+\frac{1}{4}+\frac{1}{4}=\frac{4}{4}$. $\frac{2}{4}$; $\frac{1}{8}+\frac{1}{8}+\frac{1}{8}+\frac{1}{8}=\frac{4}{8}$; the time signature

   b. $\frac{1}{16}+\frac{1}{16}+\frac{1}{16}+\frac{1}{16}+\frac{1}{8}+\frac{1}{8}=\frac{8}{16}$, which equals $\frac{2}{4}$;

   $\frac{1}{8}+\frac{1}{8}+\frac{1}{8}+\frac{1}{8}=\frac{4}{8}$, which equals $\frac{2}{4}$

4. a. Students' responses will vary. Examples:

   $\frac{1}{4}+\frac{1}{4}+\frac{1}{4}+\frac{1}{4}$; $\frac{1}{2}+\frac{1}{8}+\frac{1}{8}+\frac{1}{8}+\frac{1}{8}$

   b. Students' responses will vary. Examples:

   $\frac{1}{8}+\frac{1}{8}+\frac{1}{16}+\frac{1}{16}+\frac{1}{16}+\frac{1}{16}+\frac{1}{8}+\frac{1}{8}$; $\frac{1}{4}+\frac{1}{4}+\frac{1}{4}$

   c. Students' responses will vary. Examples:

   $\frac{1}{4}+\frac{1}{4}$; $\frac{1}{16}+\frac{1}{16}+\frac{1}{8}+\frac{1}{8}+\frac{1}{8}$

5. Students' responses will vary, but may include such things as cooking (parts of a teaspoon), crafts, woodworking, and building things, (parts of an inch), sports events (quarters, halves), and the stock market (prices of shares).

BIBLIOGRAPHY

FOR TEACHERS

Willoughby, Stephen. *Mathematics Education for a Changing World.* Alexandria, VA: ASCD, 1990.

Room, Adrian, ed. *Guinness Book of Numbers.* New York, NY: Sterling, 1990.

Spangler, David. *Math for Real Kids.* Glenview, IL: Good Year Books, 1997.

FOR STUDENTS

Wagman, Richard J. *The New Complete Medical and Health Encyclopedia.* Chicago, IL: J. G. Ferguson Publications, 1992.

Sheehan, Angela, ed. *The Marshall Cavendish Encyclopedia of Health.* New York, NY: M. Cavendish, 1991.

SECTION 6A

Adding and Subtracting Fractions

▶ Science Link ▶ Health Link ▶ www.mathsurf.com/6/ch6/blood

What's Your Type?

Imagine sitting down at the dinner table while your mother is serving dinner.

"Can I have a potato please?"
"What's your type?"
"I'm O-negative."
"Sorry. I didn't cook any O-negative potatoes. All of these potatoes are AB-positive."
"Can you cook an O-negative potato for me?"
"I don't think we have any. Only 7 out of every 100 potatoes are O-negative."
"Can't I just eat one of the AB-positive potatoes?"
"Don't be ridiculous, dear. The wrong kind of potato could kill you."

Fortunately, there's no such thing as a food type. But there is such a thing as a blood type. If you ever need to have a blood transfusion, you may not be able to use just any blood. You need blood that matches your type and Rh factor. People with AB+ blood can use O– blood, but people with O– blood can't use AB+ blood.

People who work in the health care industry must have a good understanding of what blood is and how it works. Fractions are useful in describing the different parts of blood and the different ways it can be used.

1 **Why is it important for health care professionals to have a good understanding of blood?**

2 **How could fractions be used to describe blood?**

323

Where are we now?

In Section 5B, students represented fractions in equivalent forms. They explored the relationships between fractions, and between fractions and decimals.

They learned how to

- represent values between whole numbers as fractions.
- simplify fractions.
- convert between improper fractions and mixed numbers.
- convert between fractions and decimals.
- compare and order fractions.

Where are we going?

In Section 6A, students will

- add and subtract fractions with like denominators.
- add and subtract fractions with unlike denominators.
- solve equations by adding and subtracting fractions.

Theme: Blood

World Wide Web

If your class has access to the World Wide Web, you might want to use the information found at the Web site address given. The interdisciplinary links relate to topics discussed in this section.

About the Page

This page introduces the theme of the section, blood, and discusses blood types.

Ask ...

- Do you know your blood type?
- Why is it important for a health professional to know your blood type?

Extensions

The following activities do not require access to the World Wide Web.

Science
Blood is the life stream of the human body. Have students investigate the purpose that blood serves in our body. Carries oxygen and food to every part of the body; Fights disease.

Health
In 1918, during World War I, the use of stored blood for transfusions was first begun. The first large-scale blood bank was established at the Cook County Hospital in Chicago in 1937. Have students investigate the history of their local blood bank and report on the ways it serves the community.

Answers for Questions

1. Possible answer: They work with it a lot.
2. Possible answer: To describe amounts.

Connect

On page 339, students use addition and subtraction of fractions to compare blood types.

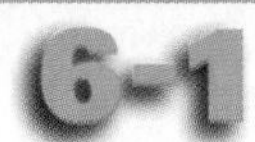

Lesson Organizer

Objective

- Add and subtract fractions with like denominators.

Vocabulary

- Like denominators

Materials

- Explore: Pattern blocks or Power Polygons

NCTM Standards

- 1–2, 4, 6, 7, 13

▶ Review

Write each fraction as a decimal.

1. $\frac{3}{5}$ 0.6
2. $\frac{7}{10}$ 0.7
3. $\frac{13}{8}$ 1.625
4. $\frac{14}{28}$ 0.5
5. $\frac{5}{20}$ 0.25

Available on Daily Transparency 6-1

1 Introduce

Explore

You may wish to use Teaching Tool Transparency 19: Power Polygons and Lesson Enhancement Transparency 25 with **Explore**.

The Point
Students use pattern blocks or Power Polygons to model addition of fractions with like denominators.

Ongoing Assessment
Check that students understand the relationships between the wholes and the fractions.

6-1 Adding and Subtracting Fractions with Like Denominators

You'll Learn ...

- to add and subtract fractions with like denominators

... How It's Used

Painters use fractions when mixing paints to get a particular color.

Vocabulary

like denominators

▶ Lesson Link You have learned how to work with individual fractions. Now you will add and subtract fractions that have the same denominator. ◀

Explore Fractions with Like Denominators

Block Heads!

Materials: Pattern blocks or Power Polygons

1. Copy the table below and use pattern blocks to complete the table.

The "Whole"	Group 1	Group 2	Fraction Names For Group 1 Plus Group 2	Sum
			$\frac{1}{2}+\frac{4}{2}$	$\frac{5}{2}$

	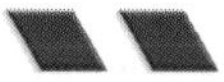			

2. The fraction names for Group 1 and Group 2 should always have the same denominator. Why?
3. For each problem, did the sum have the same denominator as the denominators in Group 1 and Group 2? Explain.

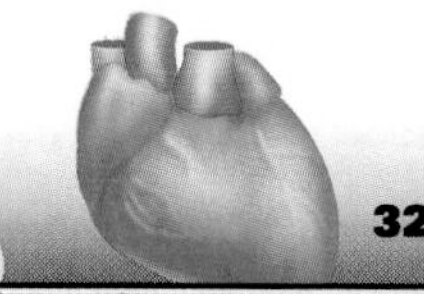

MEETING INDIVIDUAL NEEDS

Resources

6-1 Practice
6-1 Reteaching
6-1 Problem Solving
6-1 Enrichment
6-1 Daily Transparency
Problem of the Day
Review
Quick Quiz
Teaching Tool Transparency 19
Lesson Enhancement Transparency 25
Technology Master 26

Learning Modalities

Visual Having students draw models of the addition exercises in this lesson can greatly add to their understanding of the concepts.

Kinesthetic A variety of hands-on experiences can enhance the teaching of this lesson. Fraction Bars and play money can be used with this lesson.

Inclusion

Some students may have poor memory skills. Presenting the material in small steps and providing constant reinforcement may be helpful for these students.

Have students add new vocabulary with examples to their reference books.

Learn Fractions with Like Denominators

Two fractions with the same denominator have **like denominators**.

$\frac{1}{4}$ and $\frac{3}{4}$ = 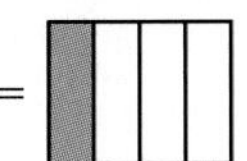 and 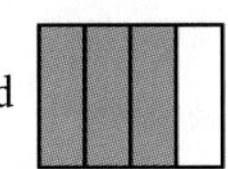

When you add and subtract fractions with like denominators, the denominator acts as a label. It tells you what size pieces you're using. The numerators tell the number of pieces you add or subtract.

Remember

Like denominators are also known as common denominators. [Page 309]

Examples

1 Add $\frac{2}{7} + \frac{4}{7}$.

 + 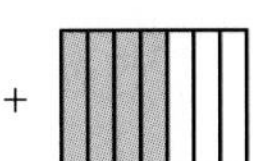 = 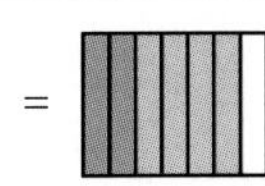

$\frac{2}{7} + \frac{4}{7} = \frac{2+4}{7}$ Add numerators only. Denominators do not change.

$= \frac{6}{7}$

2 When an adult man donates blood, he donates about $\frac{1}{2}$ of a quart. The body of an average man contains about 5, or $\frac{10}{2}$, quarts of blood. How much blood is in his body after donation?

$\frac{10}{2} - \frac{1}{2} = \frac{10-1}{2}$ Subtract numerators only. Denominators do not change.

$= \frac{9}{2}$

There are $\frac{9}{2}$ of a quart, or $4\frac{1}{2}$ quarts, left in his body.

Try It

Simplify. **a.** $\frac{3}{10} + \frac{4}{10}$ $\frac{7}{10}$ **b.** $\frac{5}{7} - \frac{3}{7}$ $\frac{2}{7}$ **c.** $\frac{8}{2} + \frac{9}{2}$ $\frac{17}{2}$ **d.** $\frac{4}{9} - \frac{4}{9}$ 0

Science Link

In 1940, Charles Drew revolutionized the way doctors cared for patients by devising a blood bank plan for adequate storage of blood.

Check Your Understanding

1. When you add or subtract fractions with like denominators, why doesn't the denominator change?
2. What values can n have to make the equation $\frac{3}{n} + \frac{5}{n} = \frac{8}{n}$ true?

MATH EVERY DAY

Problem of the Day

Adam has 8 times as many quarters as dimes, half as many pennies as quarters, 6 nickels, and twice as many half-dollars as dimes. Write an algebraic expression to represent the number of coins if d represents how many dimes.

$d + 8d + \frac{8d}{2} + 6 + 2d$

Available on Daily Transparency 6-1

An Extension is provided in the transparency package.

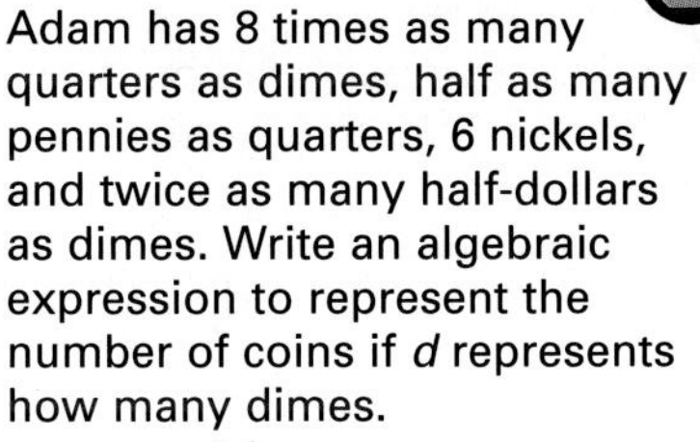

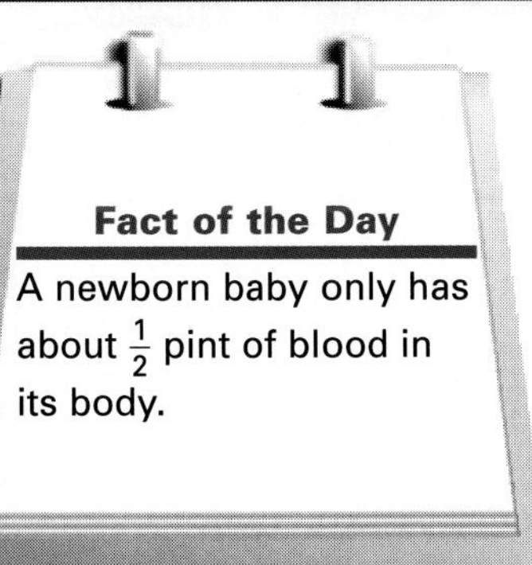

Fact of the Day

A newborn baby only has about $\frac{1}{2}$ pint of blood in its body.

Estimation

Estimate.

1. 12 + 19 30
2. 214 + 199 400
3. 58 − 28 30
4. 302 − 175 125

Answers for Explore

1. Row 2: $\frac{1}{3} + \frac{2}{3}; \frac{3}{3} = 1$

   Row 3: $\frac{2}{3} + \frac{5}{3}; \frac{7}{3}$

   Row 4: $\frac{2}{3} + \frac{2}{3}; \frac{4}{3}$

   Row 5: $\frac{2}{2} + \frac{3}{2}; \frac{5}{2}$
2. Possible answer: They are parts from the same whole.
3. Yes; The denominators do not change.

2 Teach

Learn

Alternate Examples

1. Add $\frac{1}{5} + \frac{3}{5}$.

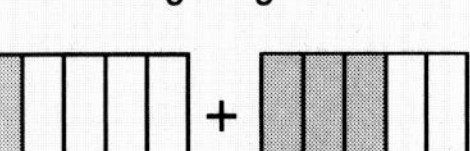

$\frac{1}{5} + \frac{3}{5} = \frac{1+3}{5}$

$= \frac{4}{5}$

2. Blood cells make up $\frac{9}{20}$ of blood, while the rest is a liquid called plasma. What part of the blood is plasma? The entire amount of blood is $\frac{20}{20}$.

$\frac{20}{20} - \frac{9}{20} = \frac{20-9}{20}$

$= \frac{11}{20}$

$\frac{11}{20}$ of blood is plasma.

3 Practice and Assess

Check

In Question 2, be sure students know that the same value must be substituted for every n. Remind students that division by zero is not possible.

Answers for Check Your Understanding

1. Possible answer: The whole is still divided into the same number of pieces.
2. Any value other than zero as long as each n is the same.

6-1 Exercises and Applications

Assignment Guide

- **Basic**
  1–31 odds, 32, 35, 36, 39–43 odds
- **Average**
  1, 2–42 evens
- **Enriched**
  6–26 evens, 27–37, 40–43

Exercise Notes

Exercise 31

Science Plasma, the liquid portion of the blood, is $\frac{9}{10}$ water. The remaining $\frac{1}{10}$ includes proteins, hormones, enzymes, nutrients, and wastes.

Reteaching

Activity

Materials: Inch ruler

- Use a ruler to add and subtract fractions with denominators of 2, 4, 8, and 16.
- To add $\frac{3}{4}$ and $\frac{3}{4}$, draw a segment $\frac{3}{4}$ inch long on your paper. Without moving the ruler, extend the segment by $\frac{3}{4}$ inch. At what point did your second segment end? $1\frac{1}{2}$
- Use a ruler to find the following sums.
  1. $\frac{11}{16} + \frac{15}{16}$ $1\frac{5}{8}$
  2. $\frac{5}{8} + \frac{1}{8}$ $\frac{3}{4}$
  3. $\frac{2}{4} + \frac{3}{4}$ $1\frac{1}{4}$
- To find the difference $\frac{7}{8} - \frac{5}{8}$, draw a segment $\frac{7}{8}$ inch long. Without moving the ruler, draw a heavier segment $\frac{5}{8}$ inch back from $\frac{7}{8}$ inch. At what point did your second segment end? $\frac{1}{4}$.
- Use a ruler to find the differences.
  4. $\frac{13}{16} - \frac{9}{16}$ $\frac{1}{4}$
  5. $\frac{7}{8} - \frac{3}{8}$ $\frac{1}{2}$
  6. $\frac{4}{4} - \frac{1}{4}$ $\frac{3}{4}$

6-1 Exercises and Applications

Practice and Apply

1. **Getting Started** Tell if the fractions have like denominators or not.

   a. $\frac{6}{7}, \frac{4}{7}$ Yes **b.** $\frac{9}{10}, \frac{13}{10}$ Yes **c.** $\frac{1}{2}, \frac{1}{3}$ No **d.** $\frac{22}{11}, \frac{11}{22}$ No **e.** $\frac{8}{8}, \frac{8}{8}$ Yes

Simplify. Write each answer in lowest terms.

2. $\frac{3}{5} + \frac{1}{5}$ $\frac{4}{5}$ **3.** $\frac{9}{10} - \frac{8}{10}$ $\frac{1}{10}$ **4.** $\frac{7}{8} + \frac{5}{8}$ $\frac{3}{2}$ **5.** $\frac{4}{3} + \frac{2}{3}$ 2 **6.** $\frac{23}{8} - \frac{13}{8}$ $\frac{5}{4}$

7. $\frac{4}{3} - \frac{3}{3}$ $\frac{1}{3}$ **8.** $\frac{98}{10} + \frac{2}{10}$ 10 **9.** $\frac{3}{4} - \frac{1}{4}$ $\frac{1}{2}$ **10.** $\frac{4}{11} + \frac{3}{11}$ $\frac{7}{11}$ **11.** $\frac{12}{18} - \frac{9}{18}$ $\frac{1}{6}$

12. $\frac{15}{19} + \frac{5}{19}$ $\frac{20}{19}$ **13.** $\frac{7}{9} - \frac{3}{9}$ $\frac{4}{9}$ **14.** $\frac{6}{8} - \frac{4}{8}$ $\frac{1}{4}$ **15.** $\frac{5}{13} + \frac{1}{13}$ $\frac{6}{13}$ **16.** $\frac{34}{12} - \frac{30}{12}$ $\frac{1}{3}$

State whether the answer is greater than, less than, or equal to 1.

17. $\frac{7}{9} + \frac{2}{9}$ = **18.** $\frac{1}{2} + \frac{3}{2}$ > **19.** $\frac{2}{7} + \frac{6}{7}$ > **20.** $\frac{3}{4} - \frac{2}{4}$ < **21.** $\frac{5}{6} - \frac{3}{6}$ <

22. $\frac{9}{5} - \frac{4}{5}$ = **23.** $\frac{7}{12} + \frac{7}{12}$ > **24.** $\frac{1}{10} - \frac{1}{10}$ < **25.** $\frac{16}{13} + \frac{4}{13}$ > **26.** $\frac{5}{4} - \frac{1}{4}$ =

Tillie's volleyball team had a picnic. Team members brought food or games. The bar graph represents the players who brought an item of food. Use the graph for Exercises 27–30.

27. What fraction of the students who brought food brought fruit or drinks? $\frac{7}{13}$

28. What fraction of the students who brought food brought fruit, drinks, or salad? $\frac{11}{13}$

29. If 17 students went to the picnic, what fraction brought games? $\frac{4}{17}$

30. If 17 students went to the picnic, what fraction of them brought fruit or bread? $\frac{5}{17}$

31. Science Plasma is the liquid part of blood. Blood is about $\frac{11}{20}$ plasma. What fraction represents the other components of blood? $\frac{9}{20}$

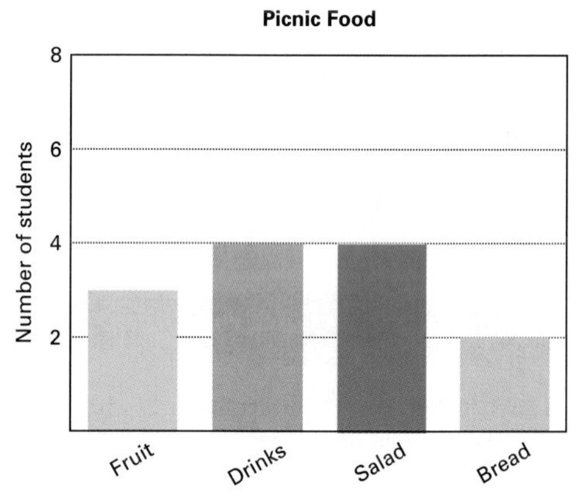

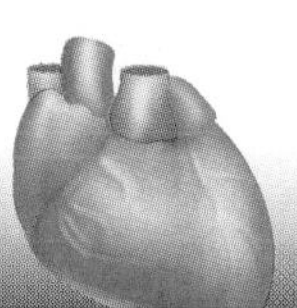

PRACTICE 6-1

PRACTICE

Name ______________________

Practice 6-1

Adding and Subtracting Fractions with Like Denominators

Simplify. Write each answer in lowest terms.

1. $\frac{3}{20} - \frac{1}{20}$ $\frac{1}{10}$ 2. $\frac{6}{15} + \frac{4}{15}$ $\frac{2}{3}$ 3. $\frac{3}{4} + \frac{3}{4}$ $\frac{3}{2}$ 4. $\frac{6}{8} + \frac{3}{8}$ $\frac{9}{8}$

5. $\frac{2}{13} + \frac{3}{13}$ $\frac{5}{13}$ 6. $\frac{6}{8} - \frac{5}{8}$ $\frac{1}{8}$ 7. $\frac{3}{15} + \frac{10}{15}$ $\frac{13}{15}$ 8. $\frac{8}{10} - \frac{4}{10}$ $\frac{2}{5}$

9. $\frac{7}{14} - \frac{3}{14}$ $\frac{2}{7}$ 10. $\frac{1}{4} + \frac{1}{4}$ $\frac{1}{2}$ 11. $\frac{6}{7} - \frac{1}{7}$ $\frac{5}{7}$ 12. $\frac{14}{19} - \frac{5}{19}$ $\frac{9}{19}$

13. $\frac{5}{6} + \frac{5}{6}$ $\frac{5}{3}$ 14. $\frac{2}{3} + \frac{1}{3}$ 1 15. $\frac{15}{18} + \frac{4}{18}$ $\frac{19}{18}$ 16. $\frac{10}{15} - \frac{6}{15}$ $\frac{4}{15}$

State whether the answer is greater than, less than, or equal to 1.

17. $\frac{7}{11} - \frac{3}{11}$ Less than 1 18. $\frac{4}{10} + \frac{6}{10}$ Equal to 1 19. $\frac{2}{4} + \frac{3}{4}$ Greater than 1

20. $\frac{1}{4} + \frac{2}{4}$ Less than 1 21. $\frac{5}{6} - \frac{1}{6}$ Less than 1 22. $\frac{2}{5} + \frac{4}{5}$ Greater than 1

Each guest at Tony's 8th birthday party brought one gift or a card. The bar graph shows the gifts that Tony received. Use the graph for Exercises 23–25.

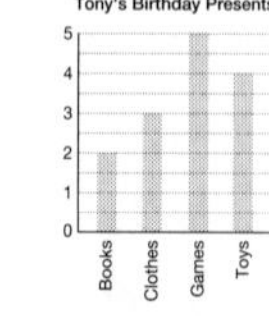

23. What fraction of the gifts were books or games? $\frac{1}{2}$

24. What fraction of the gifts were clothing, games, or toys? $\frac{6}{7}$

25. There were 18 guests at the party. What fraction brought cards only? $\frac{2}{9}$

26. In 1990, about $\frac{1}{8}$ of the American population was of age 65 or older. What fraction of the population was under 65? $\frac{7}{8}$

27. In 1993, $\frac{11}{20}$ of America's electricity was produced using coal, and $\frac{4}{20}$ of America's electricity was produced using nuclear power. What fraction was produced using other means such as natural gas or hydroelectric power? $\frac{1}{4}$

RETEACHING

Name ______________________

Alternative Lesson 6-1

Adding and Subtracting Fractions with Like Denominators

Two fractions with the same denominator have **like denominators**.

When adding and subtracting fractions with like denominators, the denominator acts like a label, telling you what size pieces you are using. The numerators are the number of pieces you add or subtract.

Example 1

Simplify $\frac{5}{8} + \frac{1}{8}$.

Add numerators only. $\frac{5}{8} + \frac{1}{8} = \frac{5+1}{8}$

Denominators do not change. $= \frac{6}{8}$

Write in lowest terms. $= \frac{3}{4}$

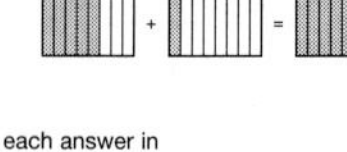

So, $\frac{5}{8} + \frac{1}{8} = \frac{3}{4}$.

Try It Simplify. Draw a picture if you like. Write each answer in lowest terms.

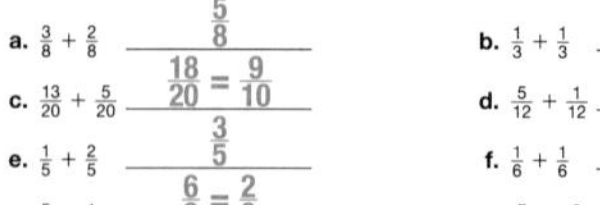
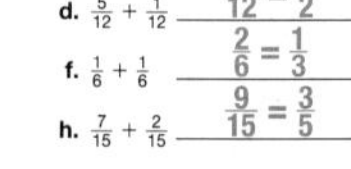

a. $\frac{3}{8} + \frac{2}{8}$ $\frac{5}{8}$ b. $\frac{1}{3} + \frac{1}{3}$ $\frac{2}{3}$

c. $\frac{13}{20} + \frac{5}{20}$ $\frac{18}{20} = \frac{9}{10}$ d. $\frac{5}{12} + \frac{1}{12}$ $\frac{6}{12} = \frac{1}{2}$

e. $\frac{1}{5} + \frac{2}{5}$ $\frac{3}{5}$ f. $\frac{1}{6} + \frac{1}{6}$ $\frac{2}{6} = \frac{1}{3}$

g. $\frac{5}{9} + \frac{1}{9}$ $\frac{6}{9} = \frac{2}{3}$ h. $\frac{7}{15} + \frac{2}{15}$ $\frac{9}{15} = \frac{3}{5}$

Example 2

Simplify $\frac{9}{10} - \frac{3}{10}$.

Subtract numerators only. $\frac{9}{10} - \frac{3}{10} = \frac{9-3}{10}$

Denominators do not change. $= \frac{6}{10}$

Write in lowest terms. $= \frac{3}{5}$

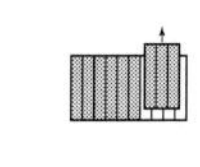

So, $\frac{9}{10} - \frac{3}{10} = \frac{3}{5}$.

Try It Simplify. Draw a picture if you like. Write each answer in lowest terms.

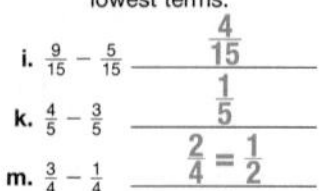
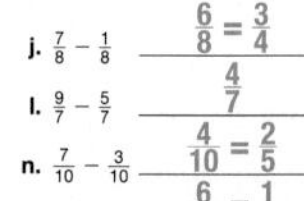

i. $\frac{9}{15} - \frac{5}{15}$ $\frac{4}{15}$ j. $\frac{7}{8} - \frac{1}{8}$ $\frac{6}{8} = \frac{3}{4}$

k. $\frac{4}{5} - \frac{3}{5}$ $\frac{1}{5}$ l. $\frac{9}{7} - \frac{5}{7}$ $\frac{4}{7}$

m. $\frac{3}{4} - \frac{1}{4}$ $\frac{2}{4} = \frac{1}{2}$ n. $\frac{7}{10} - \frac{3}{10}$ $\frac{4}{10} = \frac{2}{5}$

o. $\frac{6}{7} - \frac{3}{7}$ $\frac{3}{7}$ p. $\frac{11}{12} - \frac{5}{12}$ $\frac{6}{12} = \frac{1}{2}$

32. **Test Prep** Choose the correct answer for $\frac{3}{10} + \frac{3}{10}$. D

Ⓐ $\frac{3}{20}$ Ⓑ $\frac{3}{10}$ Ⓒ $\frac{6}{20}$ Ⓓ $\frac{3}{5}$

33. **Geography** About $\frac{3}{50}$ of the earth's surface is covered with land that can be farmed. $\frac{12}{50}$ is desert, tundra, ice, or mountains. $\frac{35}{50}$ is liquid. What fraction of the earth's surface is not covered with water? $\frac{3}{10}$

Problem Solving and Reasoning

34. **Communicate** Galen added $\frac{3}{5}$ and $\frac{1}{5}$. His answer was $\frac{4}{10}$. Explain why Galen's answer does not make sense. What is the correct answer?

35. Journal Explain why you add the numerators in a fraction addition problem, but not the denominators.

36. **Choose a Strategy** Sandra makes bracelets, necklaces, and chokers using leather string. A bracelet requires $\frac{7}{12}$ ft of string, and a necklace requires $\frac{22}{12}$ ft. She has $\frac{81}{12}$ ft, which is exactly enough to make 3 bracelets, 2 necklaces, and 1 choker. How much string does each choker require? Explain.

37. **Communicate** For the equation $\frac{3}{11} + \frac{x}{y} = \frac{10}{11}$, name two values for both x and y that will make the equation true. Explain your reasoning.

Problem Solving
STRATEGIES
- Look for a Pattern
- Make an Organized List
- Make a Table
- Guess and Check
- Work Backward
- Use Logical Reasoning
- Draw a Diagram
- Solve a Simpler Problem

Mixed Review

Find the perimeter for each figure. *[Lesson 4-1]*

38. 28 ft

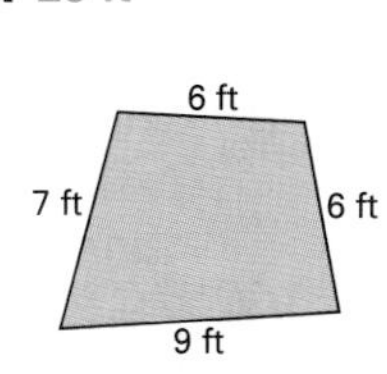

39. 16

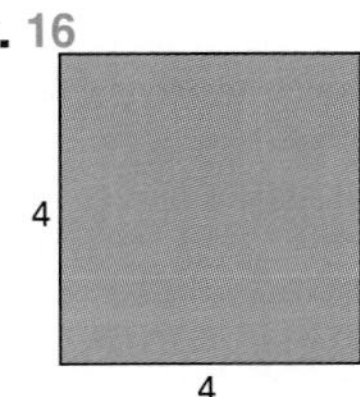

40. 17.5

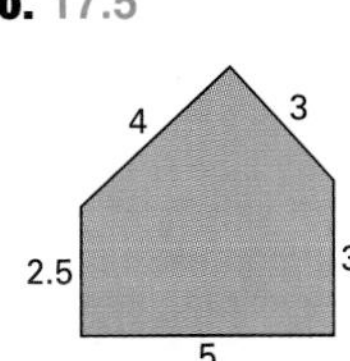

41. 31

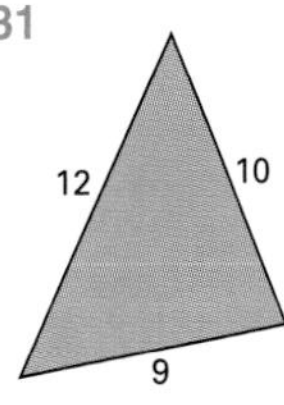

Find the next three numbers in the pattern. *[Lesson 2-9]*

42. 47, 51, 55, 59, 63, ... 67, 71, 75

43. 12, 13, 15, 18, 22, 27, ... 33, 40, 48

PROBLEM SOLVING 6-1

Exercise Notes

Exercise 32

Test Prep Note that for A, only denominators were added, and for C, both numerators and denominators were added.

Exercise Answers

34. He added the numerators together and the denominators together. The correct answer is $\frac{4}{5}$.

35. Possible answer: The whole is divided into pieces. The denominator always represents the number of pieces in one whole, which does not change.

36. $\frac{16}{12}$ or $\frac{4}{3}$ ft; $\frac{7}{12} + \frac{7}{12} + \frac{7}{12} + \frac{22}{12} + \frac{22}{12} + x = \frac{81}{12}$.

37. Possible answer: $x = 7$, $y = 11$; $x = 14$, $y = 22$; $\frac{3}{11} + \frac{7}{11} = \frac{10}{11}$; $\frac{3}{11} + \frac{14}{22} = \frac{10}{11}$.

Alternate Assessment

You may want to use the *Interactive CD-ROM Journal* with this assessment.

Journal Have students write a paragraph in their journals explaining with an example how to add and subtract fractions with like denominators.

Quick Quiz

Find each sum or difference.

1. $\frac{3}{8} + \frac{7}{8}$ $1\frac{1}{4}$
2. $\frac{5}{6} + \frac{5}{6}$ $1\frac{2}{3}$
3. $\frac{7}{12} + \frac{1}{12}$ $\frac{2}{3}$
4. $\frac{11}{12} - \frac{5}{12}$ $\frac{1}{2}$
5. $\frac{13}{20} - \frac{7}{20}$ $\frac{3}{10}$

Available on Daily Transparency 6-1

PROBLEM SOLVING

Name ____________

Guided Problem Solving 6-1

GPS PROBLEM 36, STUDENT PAGE 327

Sandra makes bracelets, necklaces, and chokers using leather string. A bracelet requires $\frac{7}{12}$ ft of string, and a necklace requires $\frac{22}{12}$. She has $\frac{81}{12}$ ft, which is exactly enough to make 3 bracelets, 2 necklaces, and 1 choker. How much string does each choker require? Explain.

Understand

1. Circle what you are asked to find.
2. How much leather string does Sandra have? $\frac{81}{12}$ feet
3. Underline the amount of string needed to make a bracelet and a necklace.

Plan

4. Which operation will you use to find the amount of string needed to make 3 bracelets? Addition. 2 necklaces? Addition.
5. Which operation will you use to find the string left over after making the bracelets and necklaces? Subtraction.

Solve

6. Write a number sentence showing the amount of string needed to make 3 bracelets. $\frac{7}{12} + \frac{7}{12} + \frac{7}{12} = \frac{21}{12}$
7. How much string is needed to make 2 necklaces? $\frac{44}{12}$ feet
8. How much string is needed to make 3 bracelets and 2 necklaces? $\frac{65}{12}$ feet
9. How much string will Sandra have left to make one choker? Explain. $\frac{16}{12}$ feet
Find string needed for 3 bracelets and 2 necklaces.
String left is amount needed to make 1 choker.

Look Back

10. What other operation could you have used to find the amount of string needed to make 3 bracelets? Multiplication.

SOLVE ANOTHER PROBLEM

Sandra also makes belts. She has $\frac{92}{12}$ feet of string, which is enough to make 2 bracelets, 2 necklaces, and 1 belt. A bracelet requires $\frac{7}{12}$ feet and a necklace requires $\frac{22}{12}$ feet of string. How much string does each belt require?

ENRICHMENT

Name ____________

Extend Your Thinking 6-1

Visual Thinking

You may wish to use toothpicks or other items of equal length to model each puzzle and help you find the solution.

1. Which 4 line segments could be removed to leave four identical triangles? Draw an "X" through the segments you would remove.

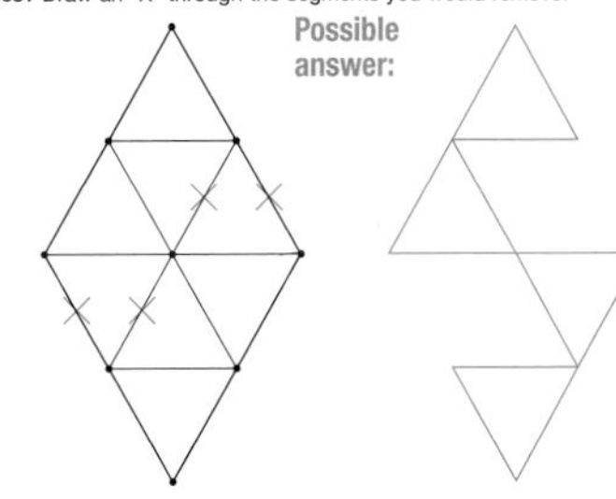

2. Move two line segments and add one more line segment to make two diamonds. Draw an "X" through the segments you would remove and draw in the segments you would add.

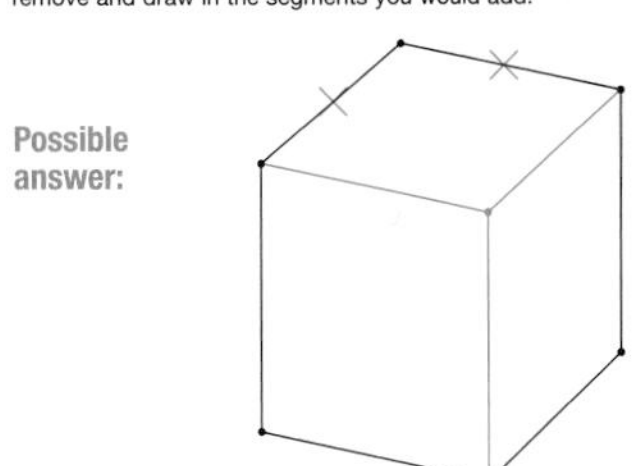

Lesson Organizer

Objective

- Add and subtract fractions with unlike denominators.

Vocabulary

- Unlike denominators, least common denominator (LCD)

Materials

- Explore: Fraction Bars

NCTM Standards

- 1–4, 6, 7

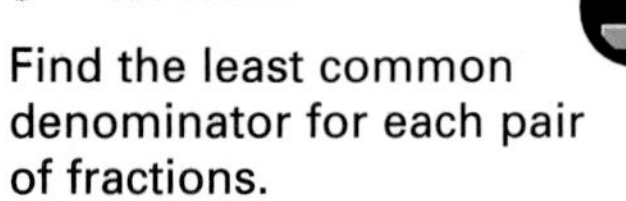

Review

Find the least common denominator for each pair of fractions.

1. $\frac{2}{3}, \frac{7}{8}$ 24
2. $\frac{5}{6}, \frac{8}{9}$ 18
3. $\frac{3}{4}, \frac{5}{16}$ 16
4. $\frac{3}{8}, \frac{7}{12}$ 24
5. $\frac{3}{5}, \frac{1}{4}$ 20

Available on Daily Transparency 6-2

1 Introduce

Explore

You may wish to use Teaching Tool Transparency 14: Fraction Bars and Lesson Enhancement Transparencies 26 and 27 with this lesson.

The Point
Students use Fraction Bars to model addition and subtraction of fractions with different denominators.

Ongoing Assessment
Circulate throughout the class and check that students are able to model the operations correctly.

For Groups That Finish Early
Use Fraction Bars to add or subtract these fractions.

$\frac{3}{4} + \frac{1}{2}$ $1\frac{1}{4}$ $\frac{3}{4} - \frac{1}{3}$ $\frac{5}{12}$

$\frac{5}{6} + \frac{1}{4}$ $1\frac{1}{12}$ $\frac{2}{3} - \frac{1}{6}$ $\frac{1}{2}$

6-2 Adding and Subtracting Fractions with Unlike Denominators

You'll Learn ...

- to add and subtract fractions with unlike denominators

... How It's Used

Composers often work with fractional amounts that have different denominators.

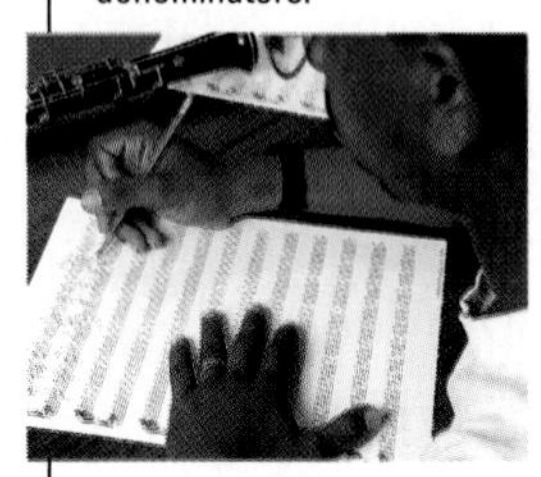

Vocabulary

unlike denominators

least common denominator (LCD)

▶ Lesson Link You have added and subtracted fractions with the same denominator. Now you will work with fractions that have different denominators. ◀

Explore Fractions with Unlike Denominators

Fraction Action

Materials: Fraction Bars®

Adding Fractions with Unlike Denominators

$\frac{1}{2} + \frac{1}{3} = \frac{5}{6}$

- Draw and label a model of the first fraction.
- Draw and label a model of the second fraction next to the first fraction.
- Underneath the first two pictures, draw and label a picture of a fraction that has the same length as the first two models combined.

1. Model these problems.

a. $\frac{1}{3} + \frac{1}{4}$ **b.** $\frac{1}{4} + \frac{3}{6}$ **c.** $\frac{1}{2} + \frac{1}{6}$ **d.** $\frac{1}{3} + \frac{2}{6}$

Subtracting Fractions with Unlike Denominators

- Draw and label a model of the first fraction.
- Under the first model, draw and label a model of the second fraction.
- Next to the second model, draw and label a fraction that equals the difference between the first and second models.

$\frac{1}{2}$

$\frac{1}{3}$ $\frac{1}{6}$

2. Model these problems.

a. $\frac{1}{2} - \frac{1}{6}$ **b.** $\frac{1}{3} - \frac{1}{4}$ **c.** $\frac{2}{3} - \frac{1}{4}$ **d.** $\frac{5}{6} - \frac{3}{4}$

3. In what way is adding fractions with different denominators different from adding fractions with the same denominator?

4. How are the numerators in these problems related to the numerators in the answers?

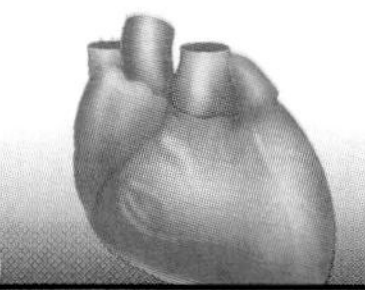

MEETING INDIVIDUAL NEEDS

Resources

- 6-2 Practice
- 6-2 Reteaching
- 6-2 Problem Solving
- 6-2 Enrichment
- 6-2 Daily Transparency
  - Problem of the Day
  - Review
  - Quick Quiz
- Teaching Tool Transparencies 2, 3, 14
- Lesson Enhancement Transparencies 26, 27
- Technology Master 27

Learning Modalities

Logical Use a yardstick and ask students whether the sum of 1 foot and 3 inches is 4 feet or 4 inches. Ask them to describe how they would find the correct sum, and relate the process to writing fractions with their common denominator in order to add them.

Verbal Having students say the fractions out loud may help them to distinguish the denominators.

Inclusion

If students find it difficult to use the least common denominator, allow some latitude in their choices of common denominators and praise their efforts.

Have students add new vocabulary with examples to their reference books.

Learn Fractions with Unlike Denominators

Fractions with like denominators are easy to add and subtract because they represent pieces of the same size. Fractions with different denominators, or **unlike denominators**, are not as easy to work with because they represent pieces of different sizes.

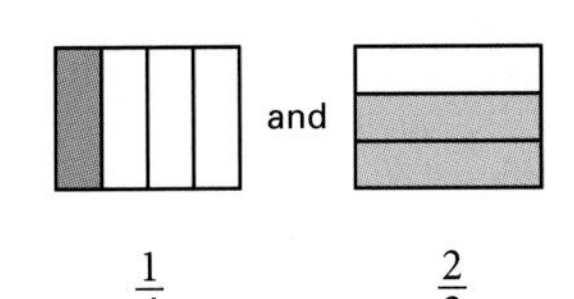

$\frac{1}{4}$ and $\frac{2}{3}$

In order to add or subtract fractions with unlike denominators, you need to change them to equivalent fractions with the same denominator. As you saw before, one way to do this is to multiply the numerator and the denominator of each fraction by the denominator of the other fraction.

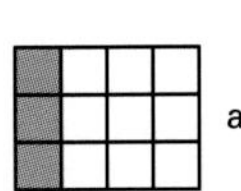 and 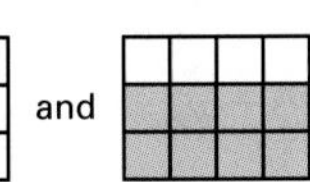

$\frac{1 \times \mathbf{3}}{4 \times \mathbf{3}} = \frac{3}{12}$ $\quad$ $\frac{2 \times \mathbf{4}}{3 \times \mathbf{4}} = \frac{8}{12}$

Example 1

Dwayne is playing Count Dracula in the school production of *Dracula.* He still has to memorize $\frac{3}{4}$ of his lines. If he memorizes $\frac{1}{3}$ of them today, what fraction of his lines will he have left to memorize?

$\frac{3}{4} - \frac{1}{3}$ Write an expression for the problem.

$\frac{3}{4} = \frac{3 \times 3}{4 \times 3} = \frac{9}{12}$ Multiply numerator and denominator by 3.

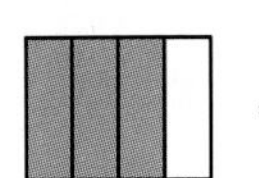 = 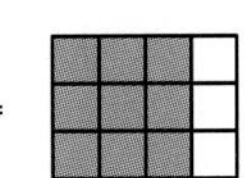

$\frac{1}{3} = \frac{1 \times 4}{3 \times 4} = \frac{4}{12}$ Multiply numerator and denominator by 4.

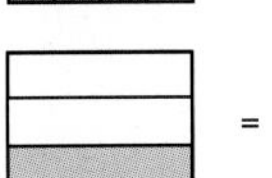 = 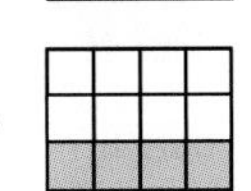

$\frac{3}{4} - \frac{1}{3} = \frac{9}{12} - \frac{4}{12}$ Rewrite the expression using equivalent fractions.

$= \frac{9-4}{12} = \frac{5}{12}$ Subtract.

He will have $\frac{5}{12}$ of his lines left to memorize.

Try It

Simplify. **a.** $\frac{1}{2} + \frac{1}{3}$ $\frac{5}{6}$ **b.** $\frac{5}{6} - \frac{1}{3}$ $\frac{1}{2}$ **c.** $\frac{1}{4} + \frac{3}{5}$ $\frac{17}{20}$ **d.** $\frac{3}{5} - \frac{1}{2}$ $\frac{1}{10}$

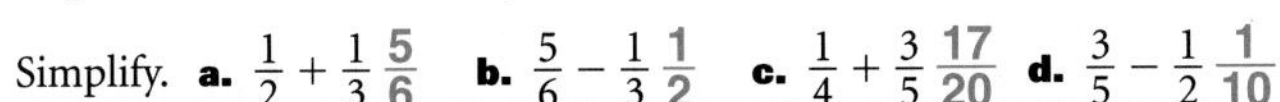
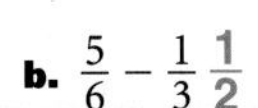
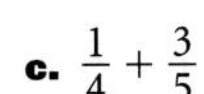

Literature Link

In 1897, Bram Stoker wrote *Dracula,* the story of a vampire who drank human blood to survive. This was not the first published story about vampires, but it's one of the most famous.

MATH EVERY DAY

Problem of the Day

From this block of postage stamps, how many ways can you choose two connected stamps? Three connected stamps? Four connected stamps? Five connected stamps?

Two connected stamps, 6 ways; Three stamps, 7 ways; Four stamps, 6 ways; Five stamps, 4 ways
Additional answers are provided in the transparency package.

Available on Daily Transparency 6-2

An Extension is provided in the transparency package.

Fact of the Day

When refrigerated, whole blood can be stored for 21 to 49 days, but its components, such as red blood cells or plasma, can be frozen and stored for several years.

Mental Math

Do these mentally.

1. $\frac{1}{6} + \frac{3}{6}$ $\frac{4}{6}$, or $\frac{2}{3}$
2. $\frac{7}{12} + \frac{5}{12}$ $\frac{12}{12}$, or 1
3. $\frac{3}{4} - \frac{1}{4}$ $\frac{2}{4}$, or $\frac{1}{2}$
4. $\frac{7}{10} - \frac{3}{10}$ $\frac{4}{10}$, or $\frac{2}{5}$

Answers for Explore

1. a. $\frac{1}{3}$ | $\frac{1}{4}$; $\frac{1}{12}$ $\frac{1}{12}$ $\frac{1}{12}$ $\frac{1}{12}$ $\frac{1}{12}$ $\frac{1}{12}$ $\frac{1}{12}$
   b. $\frac{1}{4}$ | $\frac{3}{6}$; $\frac{3}{4}$
   c. $\frac{1}{2}$ | $\frac{1}{6}$; $\frac{2}{3}$
   d. $\frac{1}{3}$ | $\frac{2}{6}$; $\frac{2}{3}$
2. a. $\frac{1}{2}$; $\frac{1}{6}$ | $\frac{1}{3}$
   b. $\frac{1}{3}$; $\frac{1}{4}$ | $\frac{1}{12}$
   c. $\frac{2}{3}$; $\frac{1}{4}$ | $\frac{1}{12}$ $\frac{1}{12}$ $\frac{1}{12}$ $\frac{1}{12}$ $\frac{1}{12}$
   d. $\frac{5}{6}$; $\frac{3}{4}$ | $\frac{1}{12}$
3. The fractions must be changed to equivalent fractions with the same denominator before adding or subtracting.
4. The numerators in the problem are both factors of the numerator in the answer.

2 Teach

Learn

Alternate Examples

1. For baking, Pat needs $\frac{2}{3}$ of a cup of flour and $\frac{3}{4}$ of a cup of flour. How much flour does Pat need?

$\frac{2}{3} = \frac{2 \times 4}{3 \times 4} = \frac{8}{12}$

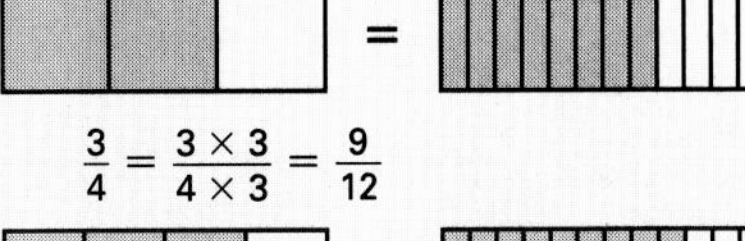

$\frac{3}{4} = \frac{3 \times 3}{4 \times 3} = \frac{9}{12}$

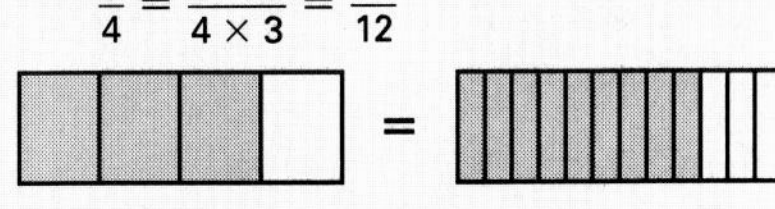

$\frac{2}{3} + \frac{3}{4} = \frac{8}{12} + \frac{9}{12}$

$= \frac{8+9}{12} = \frac{17}{12}$ or $1\frac{5}{12}$

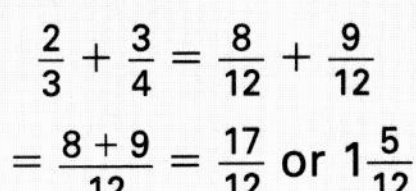

Pat needs $1\frac{5}{12}$ cups of flour.

Alternate Examples

2. About $\frac{9}{100}$ of the population has B-positive blood and about $\frac{1}{50}$ of the population has B-negative blood. What fraction of the population has type B blood?

   The least common denominator of 50 and 100 is 100. Only the first fraction needs to be changed to an equivalent fraction.

   $$\frac{1}{50} = \frac{1 \times 2}{50 \times 2} = \frac{2}{100}$$

   $$\frac{9}{100} + \frac{2}{100} = \frac{9+2}{100} = \frac{11}{100}$$

   $\frac{11}{100}$ of the population have type B blood.

3. What is $\frac{7}{12} - \frac{3}{8}$?

   The least common multiple of 12 and 8 is 24.

   $$\frac{7}{12} = \frac{7 \times 2}{12 \times 2} = \frac{14}{24}$$

   $$\frac{3}{8} = \frac{3 \times 3}{8 \times 3} = \frac{9}{24}$$

   $$\frac{14}{24} - \frac{9}{24} = \frac{14-9}{24} = \frac{5}{24}$$

3 Practice and Assess

Check

Watch for students who are unable to find the least common denominator.

Answers for Check Your Understanding

1. Possible answer: You need to add or subtract groups of the same size.
2. Possible answer: When the denominators have no common factors.

Sometimes it is easier to find the least common multiple of the two denominators and convert both fractions to that denominator. In fractions, this number is known as the **least common denominator**.

▶ Science Link

There are three cat blood types: A, B, and AB. There are eight human blood types: A+, A−, B+, B−, AB+, AB−, O+, and O−.

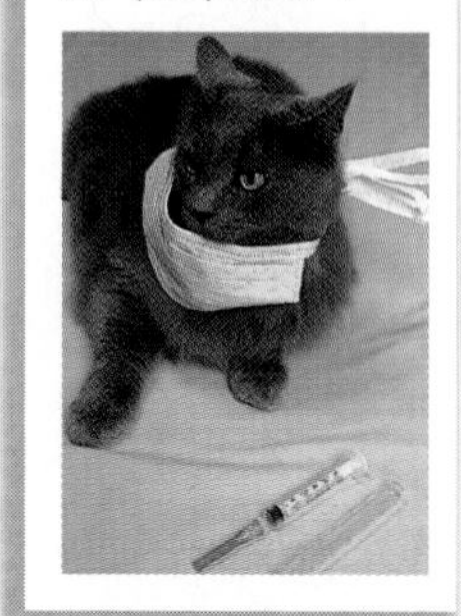

Examples

2 $\frac{73}{100}$ of all cats have type A blood. $\frac{13}{50}$ have type B blood. What fraction has either type A blood or type B blood?

The least common denominator of 50 and 100 is 100. Only the second fraction needs to be changed to an equivalent fraction.

$$\frac{13}{50} = \frac{13 \times 2}{50 \times 2} = \frac{26}{100}$$ Multiply numerator and denominator by 2.

$$\frac{73}{100} + \frac{26}{100} = \frac{73 + 26}{100}$$ Add.

$$= \frac{99}{100}$$

$\frac{99}{100}$ of all cats have either type A or type B blood.

3 What is $\frac{3}{10} - \frac{1}{4}$?

The least common multiple of 10 and 4 is 20.

$$\frac{3}{10} = \frac{3 \times 2}{10 \times 2} = \frac{6}{20}$$ Multiply top and bottom by 2.

$$\frac{1}{4} = \frac{1 \times 5}{4 \times 5} = \frac{5}{20}$$ Multiply top and bottom by 5.

$$\frac{6}{20} - \frac{5}{20} = \frac{6-5}{20} = \frac{1}{20}$$ Subtract.

Try It

Simplify. **a.** $\frac{3}{4} - \frac{1}{2}$ $\frac{1}{4}$ **b.** $\frac{1}{3} + \frac{2}{6}$ $\frac{2}{3}$ **c.** $\frac{5}{6} - \frac{2}{15}$ $\frac{7}{10}$ **d.** $\frac{5}{9} + \frac{1}{6}$ $\frac{13}{18}$

Check Your Understanding

1. Why is it necessary for fractions to have like denominators before you add or subtract them?

2. When is it easier to add fractions using the least common denominator instead of any common denominator?

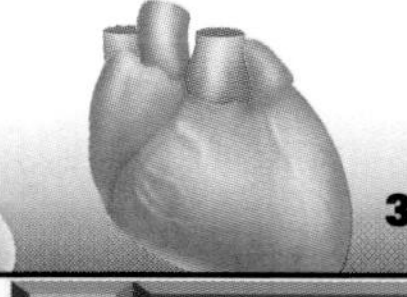

MEETING MIDDLE SCHOOL CLASSROOM NEEDS

Tips from Middle School Teachers

I use egg cartons to illustrate addition and subtraction of fractions with both like and unlike denominators of 2, 3, 4, 6, and 12. We first discuss the equivalent fractions and then proceed to the computations.

Team Teaching

You might ask the language-arts teacher to discuss with their students stories and movies about Dracula and other vampires.

Literature Connection

Like Dracula, vampires in legends are ghosts that rise from their graves at night and suck the blood of living people. People bitten by vampires become vampires themselves. To keep a vampire from rising from its grave, someone must drive a stake through its heart.

6-2 Exercises and Applications

Practice and Apply

1. **Getting Started** Name a common denominator for each pair. Possible answers:

   a. $\frac{1}{2}, \frac{1}{3}$ 6 **b.** $\frac{2}{3}, \frac{3}{6}$ 18 **c.** $\frac{3}{4}, \frac{5}{8}$ 8 **d.** $\frac{6}{7}, \frac{9}{11}$ 77 **e.** $\frac{4}{6}, \frac{4}{8}$ 24

Simplify. Write each answer in lowest terms.

2. $\frac{3}{5} + \frac{1}{4}$ $\frac{17}{20}$ 3. $\frac{5}{12} - \frac{1}{6}$ $\frac{1}{4}$ 4. $\frac{1}{2} + \frac{1}{3}$ $\frac{5}{6}$ 5. $\frac{3}{4} - \frac{7}{12}$ $\frac{1}{6}$ 6. $\frac{9}{10} - \frac{1}{2}$ $\frac{2}{5}$

7. $\frac{3}{4} + \frac{1}{2}$ $\frac{5}{4}$ 8. $\frac{7}{8} - \frac{5}{6}$ $\frac{1}{24}$ 9. $\frac{1}{4} + \frac{5}{7}$ $\frac{27}{28}$ 10. $\frac{4}{11} + \frac{4}{44}$ $\frac{5}{11}$ 11. $\frac{7}{6} - \frac{3}{5}$ $\frac{17}{30}$

12. $\frac{5}{8} + \frac{3}{4}$ $\frac{11}{8}$ 13. $\frac{3}{10} + \frac{3}{4}$ $\frac{21}{20}$ 14. $\frac{3}{9} + \frac{3}{2}$ $\frac{11}{6}$ 15. $\frac{19}{25} - \frac{3}{5}$ $\frac{4}{25}$ 16. $\frac{9}{13} - \frac{9}{26}$ $\frac{9}{26}$

Find the missing numerators.

17. $\frac{2}{5} + \frac{7}{10} = \frac{?}{10} + \frac{?}{10}$ 4, 7 18. $\frac{3}{4} + \frac{5}{6} = \frac{?}{12} + \frac{?}{12}$ 9, 10 19. $\frac{5}{8} - \frac{1}{6} = \frac{?}{24} - \frac{?}{24}$ 15, 4

20. $\frac{3}{8} + \frac{1}{2} = \frac{?}{8} + \frac{?}{8}$ 3, 4 21. $\frac{4}{9} - \frac{1}{3} = \frac{?}{9} - \frac{?}{9}$ 4, 3 22. $\frac{3}{4} - \frac{1}{3} = \frac{?}{36} - \frac{?}{36}$ 27, 12

23. **Science** Most of the cells in your blood are either red blood cells, white blood cells, or platelets. When you cut yourself, blood platelets help the blood to clot so that you don't bleed to death. Platelets can survive for $\frac{10}{14}$ of a week. White blood cells can survive for more than $\frac{126}{21}$ weeks. How much longer is the life span of a white blood cell? $\frac{37}{7}$ weeks

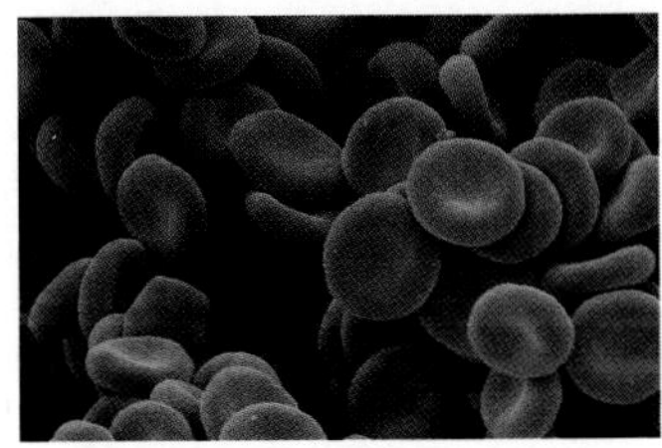

Red blood cells

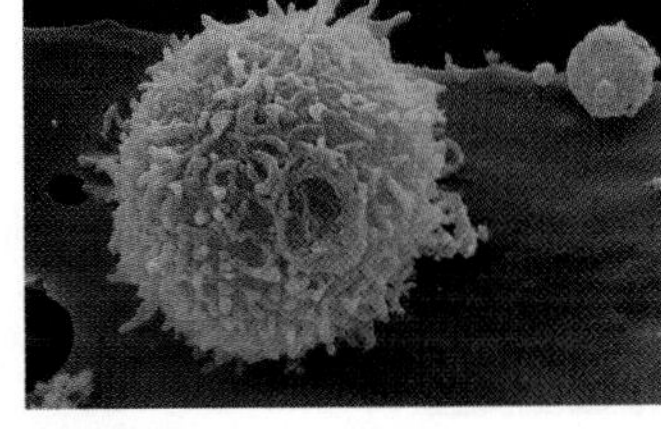

White blood cell

24. **Test Prep** Sam has a science test on Thursday. On Monday, he studied $\frac{2}{9}$ of the material. On Tuesday he studied $\frac{1}{3}$. How much material has he already reviewed? B

   Ⓐ $\frac{3}{12}$ Ⓑ $\frac{5}{9}$ Ⓒ $\frac{7}{9}$ Ⓓ $\frac{3}{3}$

PRACTICE 6-2

6-2 Exercises and Applications

Assignment Guide

- **Basic**
  1–21 odds, 24–27, 30–34 evens
- **Average**
  1–23 odds, 24–27, 30–34 evens
- **Enriched**
  2–34 evens

Exercise Notes

Exercises 2–16

Error Prevention If students' answers do not agree with those given, remind them to reduce all answers to lowest terms, and to give mixed numbers as improper fractions.

Exercise 23

Science Platelets are a type of blood cell that are neither red nor white.

Reteaching

Activity

Materials: Play money: nickels, dimes, quarters, half-dollars

- What fraction of a dollar is a nickel? $\frac{1}{20}$ A dime? $\frac{1}{10}$ A quarter? $\frac{1}{4}$ A half-dollar? $\frac{1}{2}$
- Use play money to add or subtract fractions with denominators of 2, 4, 10, and 20, even if the denominators are not the same.
- To add $\frac{3}{10}$ and $\frac{1}{4}$, think of 3 dimes being added to 1 quarter. The sum is 55¢, which is 11 nickels, or $\frac{11}{20}$ of a dollar.
- Use play money to find each answer.
  1. $\frac{3}{4} - \frac{3}{10}$ $\frac{9}{20}$
  2. $\frac{7}{10} + \frac{1}{2}$ $1\frac{1}{5}$
  3. $\frac{1}{4} + \frac{9}{10}$ $1\frac{3}{20}$
  4. $\frac{9}{10} - \frac{3}{4}$ $\frac{3}{20}$

PRACTICE

Name ______________________

Practice 6-2

Adding and Subtracting Fractions with Unlike Denominators

Simplify. Write each answer in lowest terms.

1. $\frac{3}{5} - \frac{1}{3}$ $\frac{4}{15}$ 2. $\frac{1}{2} + \frac{7}{22}$ $\frac{9}{11}$ 3. $\frac{9}{16} - \frac{1}{8}$ $\frac{7}{16}$ 4. $\frac{3}{5} - \frac{4}{9}$ $\frac{7}{45}$
5. $\frac{1}{5} - \frac{1}{7}$ $\frac{2}{35}$ 6. $\frac{11}{24} + \frac{1}{3}$ $\frac{19}{24}$ 7. $\frac{1}{3} - \frac{1}{10}$ $\frac{7}{30}$ 8. $\frac{7}{10} - \frac{3}{5}$ $\frac{1}{10}$
9. $\frac{8}{9} - \frac{7}{12}$ $\frac{11}{36}$ 10. $\frac{5}{6} - \frac{1}{2}$ $\frac{1}{3}$ 11. $\frac{7}{10} + \frac{2}{25}$ $\frac{39}{50}$ 12. $\frac{4}{5} + \frac{1}{10}$ $\frac{9}{10}$
13. $\frac{5}{8} - \frac{1}{3}$ $\frac{7}{24}$ 14. $\frac{1}{6} + \frac{9}{16}$ $\frac{35}{48}$ 15. $\frac{1}{2} + \frac{5}{11}$ $\frac{21}{22}$ 16. $\frac{1}{6} + \frac{17}{24}$ $\frac{7}{8}$
17. $\frac{1}{7} + \frac{2}{3}$ $\frac{17}{21}$ 18. $\frac{1}{5} + \frac{3}{5}$ $\frac{4}{5}$ 19. $\frac{1}{7} - \frac{1}{9}$ $\frac{2}{63}$ 20. $\frac{5}{7} - \frac{1}{2}$ $\frac{3}{14}$
21. $\frac{1}{2} - \frac{5}{11}$ $\frac{1}{22}$ 22. $\frac{1}{9} + \frac{2}{3}$ $\frac{7}{9}$ 23. $\frac{1}{4} - \frac{1}{11}$ $\frac{7}{44}$ 24. $\frac{5}{13} + \frac{2}{5}$ $\frac{51}{65}$
25. $\frac{5}{6} - \frac{4}{15}$ $\frac{17}{30}$ 26. $\frac{13}{14} - \frac{1}{2}$ $\frac{3}{7}$ 27. $\frac{7}{8} - \frac{1}{2}$ $\frac{3}{8}$ 28. $\frac{1}{4} + \frac{3}{10}$ $\frac{11}{20}$
29. $\frac{1}{5} - \frac{1}{13}$ $\frac{8}{65}$ 30. $\frac{1}{5} + \frac{1}{6}$ $\frac{11}{30}$ 31. $\frac{2}{7} + \frac{1}{3}$ $\frac{13}{21}$ 32. $\frac{6}{25} - \frac{1}{10}$ $\frac{7}{50}$
33. $\frac{14}{15} - \frac{2}{3}$ $\frac{4}{15}$ 34. $\frac{14}{15} - \frac{7}{10}$ $\frac{7}{30}$ 35. $\frac{4}{5} + \frac{1}{25}$ $\frac{21}{25}$ 36. $\frac{1}{6} + \frac{3}{10}$ $\frac{7}{15}$

Find the missing numerators.

37. $\frac{5}{6} + \frac{4}{7} = \frac{35}{42} + \frac{24}{42}$ 38. $\frac{1}{5} - \frac{1}{14} = \frac{14}{70} - \frac{5}{70}$ 39. $\frac{3}{4} - \frac{5}{9} = \frac{27}{36} - \frac{20}{36}$
40. $\frac{3}{5} + \frac{3}{7} = \frac{21}{35} + \frac{15}{35}$ 41. $\frac{4}{9} - \frac{2}{5} = \frac{20}{45} - \frac{18}{45}$ 42. $\frac{1}{8} + \frac{5}{6} = \frac{3}{24} + \frac{20}{24}$
43. $\frac{4}{5} - \frac{3}{20} = \frac{16}{20} - \frac{3}{20}$ 44. $\frac{2}{3} - \frac{1}{15} = \frac{10}{15} - \frac{1}{15}$ 45. $\frac{4}{9} + \frac{1}{3} = \frac{4}{9} + \frac{3}{9}$
46. $\frac{5}{6} - \frac{2}{15} = \frac{25}{30} - \frac{4}{30}$ 47. $\frac{1}{4} + \frac{3}{7} = \frac{7}{28} + \frac{12}{28}$ 48. $\frac{5}{6} - \frac{3}{4} = \frac{10}{12} - \frac{9}{12}$

49. Randy spends $\frac{1}{3}$ of his week sleeping and $\frac{5}{21}$ of his week working. What fraction of the week is left for other activities? $\frac{3}{7}$

50. **Geography** The three states with the largest areas are Alaska ($\frac{4}{25}$ of U.S. area), Texas ($\frac{2}{27}$ of U.S. area), and California ($\frac{2}{45}$ of U.S. area). What fraction of U.S. area do these states make up altogether? $\frac{188}{675}$

RETEACHING

Name ______________________

Alternative Lesson 6-2

Adding and Subtracting Fractions with Unlike Denominators

Fractions with different denominators, or **unlike denominators,** represent pieces of different sizes. In order to add or subtract fractions with unlike denominators, you need to change them to equivalent fractions with the same denominator.

You can find equivalent fractions by either multiplying or dividing the numerator and the denominator of a fraction by the same nonzero number. The **least common denominator** of two fractions is the least common multiple of the two denominators.

Example

Simplify $\frac{3}{4} - \frac{1}{2}$.

Find the least common denominator for $\frac{3}{4}$ and $\frac{1}{2}$ by listing multiples of both denominators.

Multiples of 4: **4**, 8, 12, 16
Multiples of 2: 2, **4**, 6, 8

The least common multiple of 4 and 2 is 4. So, 4 is also the least common denominator. Only $\frac{1}{2}$ needs to be changed to an equivalent fraction.

Multiply numerator and denominator by 2 to make the denominator 4. $\frac{1}{2} = \frac{1 \times 2}{2 \times 2} = \frac{2}{4}$

Rewrite the expression using equivalent fractions. $\frac{3}{4} - \frac{1}{2} = \frac{3}{4} - \frac{2}{4}$

Subtract. $\frac{3 - 2}{4} = \frac{1}{4}$

Since $\frac{1}{4}$ is in lowest terms, $\frac{3}{4} - \frac{1}{2} = \frac{1}{4}$.

Try It Simplify $\frac{5}{12} + \frac{1}{4}$.

a. Find the least common multiple of 12 and 4. 12

b. Write as equivalent fractions. $\frac{5}{12} = \frac{5}{12}$ $\frac{1}{4} = \frac{3}{12}$

c. Rewrite the expression. $\frac{5}{12} + \frac{3}{12}$

d. Add. Write in lowest terms. $\frac{5}{12} + \frac{3}{12} = \frac{8}{12} = \frac{2}{3}$

Simplify.

e. $\frac{5}{6} - \frac{2}{3}$ $\frac{1}{6}$ f. $\frac{3}{8} + \frac{1}{4}$ $\frac{5}{8}$ g. $\frac{2}{3} - \frac{1}{5}$ $\frac{7}{15}$
h. $\frac{1}{12} + \frac{2}{3}$ $\frac{9}{12} = \frac{3}{4}$ i. $\frac{3}{5} - \frac{1}{10}$ $\frac{5}{10} = \frac{1}{2}$ j. $\frac{7}{10} - \frac{1}{4}$ $\frac{9}{20}$

Exercise Notes

■ Exercise 27

Problem-Solving Tip You may wish to use Teaching Tool Transparencies 2 and 3: Guided Problem Solving, pages 1–2.

Exercise Answers

26. $2\frac{29}{40}$ quarts; $\frac{3}{8} + \frac{3}{2} + \frac{1}{10} + \frac{3}{4} = x$.

27. $\frac{11}{12}$ of the way; $\frac{1}{3} - \frac{1}{4} + x = 1$.

28. Least number of equal slices to cut is the LCD of 8, 4, 3, and 6, which is 24. $\frac{1}{8} + \frac{1}{4} + \frac{1}{3} + \frac{1}{6} = \frac{3}{24} + \frac{6}{24} + \frac{8}{24} + \frac{4}{24} = \frac{21}{24}$; There are 3 slices left over.

29. $\frac{1}{2}, \frac{7}{12}, \frac{2}{3}$; Add $\frac{1}{12}$ to each preceding number.

Alternate Assessment

Portfolio Have students select examples of their work which best exemplify the concepts of this lesson and add them to their portfolios.

► Quick Quiz

Find each sum or difference.

1. $\frac{3}{8} + \frac{5}{6}$ $1\frac{5}{24}$
2. $\frac{3}{4} + \frac{7}{10}$ $1\frac{9}{20}$
3. $\frac{1}{5} + \frac{2}{3}$ $\frac{13}{15}$
4. $\frac{11}{12} - \frac{3}{4}$ $\frac{1}{6}$
5. $\frac{7}{8} - \frac{2}{3}$ $\frac{5}{24}$

Available on Daily Transparency 6-2

25. Science When you are at rest, the fraction of total blood that flows to the skeletal muscles is about $\frac{1}{6}$. The fraction of total blood that flows to the skeletal muscles is $\frac{5}{7}$ when you are exercising. What is the difference between the two amounts of blood? $\frac{23}{42}$

Problem Solving and Reasoning

26. Critical Thinking GPS A recipe for fruit punch calls for $\frac{3}{8}$ of a quart of lemon drink, $\frac{3}{2}$ of a quart of orange juice, $\frac{1}{10}$ of a quart of cranberry juice, and $\frac{3}{4}$ of a quart of soda water. How large a container is needed for the punch? Explain.

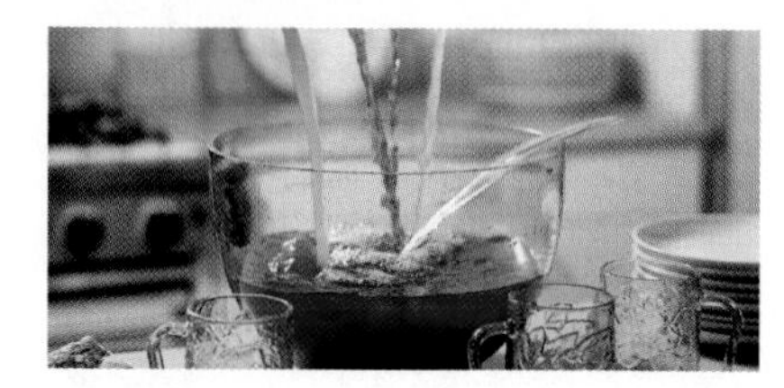

27. Choose a Strategy Denzel had walked $\frac{1}{3}$ of the way to school when he realized he had dropped a book. He turned around, and had covered $\frac{1}{4}$ of the distance between home and school before finding it. What fraction of the total distance between home and school did Denzel now have to walk? Explain.

Problem Solving STRATEGIES

- Look for a Pattern
- Make an Organized List
- Make a Table
- Guess and Check
- Work Backward
- Use Logical Reasoning
- Draw a Diagram
- Solve a Simpler Problem

28. Critical Thinking Four people are sharing a pizza. Ana would like to eat $\frac{1}{8}$, Jon wants $\frac{1}{4}$, Yi wants $\frac{1}{3}$, and Lisa would like $\frac{1}{6}$. What is the least number of slices of the same size that must be cut for each person to get what he or she wants? How much pizza is left over? Explain.

29. Critical Thinking Find the next 3 numbers in the pattern: $\frac{1}{12}, \frac{1}{6}, \frac{1}{4}, \frac{1}{3}, \frac{5}{12}, \ldots$ Explain how you found them.

Mixed Review

PROBLEM SOLVING 6-2

Find the area of each shape. *[Lesson 4-4]*

30. 70

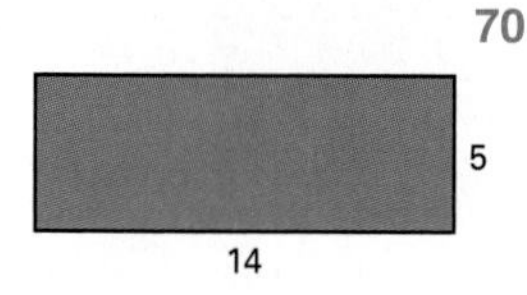

31. 49

7
7

32. 6

0.5
12

Write an expression to describe each situation. *[Lesson 2-10]*

33. Henri had h hens. Each laid 4 eggs. How many eggs did Henri have? $4h$

34. Julia read b books last week and 2 books this week. How many books did Julia read? $b + 2$

PROBLEM SOLVING

Name ____________________

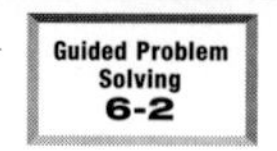

Guided Problem Solving 6-2

GPS **PROBLEM 26, STUDENT PAGE 332**

A recipe for fruit punch calls for $\frac{3}{8}$ of a quart of lemon drink, $\frac{3}{2}$ of a quart of orange juice, $\frac{1}{10}$ of a quart of cranberry juice, and $\frac{3}{4}$ of a quart of soda water. How large a container is needed for the punch? Explain.

— Understand — Possible answers: Items 7 and 8

1. Underline the quantity for each ingredient in the punch.

— Plan —

2. What is the least common denominator for the ingredients? 40
3. Write an equivalent fraction using the least common denominator.
   a. $\frac{3}{8}$ $\frac{15}{40}$ **b.** $\frac{3}{2}$ $\frac{60}{40}$ **c.** $\frac{1}{10}$ $\frac{4}{40}$ **d.** $\frac{3}{4}$ $\frac{30}{40}$
4. Which operation will you use to find the total quantity of punch? Addition.
5. Which of the following is a reasonable answer? C
   a. less than 1 qt **b.** about 1 qt **c.** more than 1 qt

— Solve —

6. How much punch does the recipe make? $\frac{109}{40} = 2\frac{29}{40}$ qt
7. Think about how much liquid most pitchers and punch bowls hold. What is a reasonable size container for the punch? Explain. 3 qt; $2\frac{1}{2}$ qt is too small. Other sizes would be too large.

— Look Back —

8. What should you do if the size container you chose in Item 7 does *not* fall within the range you chose for Item 5? Check estimate and calculations to find errors.

SOLVE ANOTHER PROBLEM

A recipe for party mix calls for $\frac{3}{4}$ of a cup of cereal, $\frac{1}{4}$ of a cup of peanuts, $\frac{5}{8}$ of a cup of pretzels, and $\frac{1}{2}$ of a cup of crackers. How many cups are in the mix? How large a container is needed? Explain. Possible answer: $\frac{17}{8} = 2\frac{1}{8}$ c; $2\frac{1}{2}$ c container since 2 c is too small.

ENRICHMENT

Name ____________________

Extend Your Thinking 6-2

Critical Thinking

You can use multiplication to find sums and differences of fractions! Each of the examples below shows the same way to find $\frac{3}{4} - \frac{1}{2}$.

Find the cross products. Then write the sum (if adding) or difference (if subtracting) over the product of the denominators.

$$\frac{3}{4} \times \frac{1}{2} = \frac{(3 \times 2) - (4 \times 1)}{4 \times 2} = \frac{6-4}{8} = \frac{2}{8} = \frac{1}{4}$$

This can be written algebraically as

$$\frac{a}{b} - \frac{c}{d} = \frac{(a \times d) - (b \times c)}{b \times d}$$

and $$\frac{a}{b} + \frac{c}{d} = \frac{(a \times d) + (b \times c)}{b \times d}.$$

Write the fractions in the boxes. Multiply the denominator of each fraction by the numerator of the other fraction.

6 − 4

3 × 2	6	4	4 × 1	
	3	1	2	Subtract: 6 − 4
	4	2	8	Multiply: 4 × 2

so, $\frac{3}{4} - \frac{1}{2} = \frac{2}{8} = \frac{1}{4}$

Subtract (or add) the products to find the numerator of the difference (or sum).

Multiply the two denominators to find the denominator of the difference (or sum).

Use cross products or boxes to find each sum or difference. Simplify if necessary.

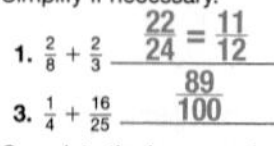

1. $\frac{2}{8} + \frac{2}{3}$ $\frac{22}{24} = \frac{11}{12}$
2. $\frac{5}{6} - \frac{3}{4}$ $\frac{2}{24} = \frac{1}{12}$
3. $\frac{1}{4} + \frac{16}{25}$ $\frac{89}{100}$
4. $\frac{13}{15} - \frac{3}{4}$ $\frac{7}{60}$

Complete the boxes and write the answer in the blank. Simplify if necessary.

5. $\frac{2}{3} + \frac{1}{5} =$ $\frac{13}{15}$
6. $\frac{9}{10} - \frac{5}{8} =$ $\frac{22}{80} = \frac{11}{40}$
7. $\frac{5}{9} + \frac{3}{7} =$ $\frac{62}{63}$

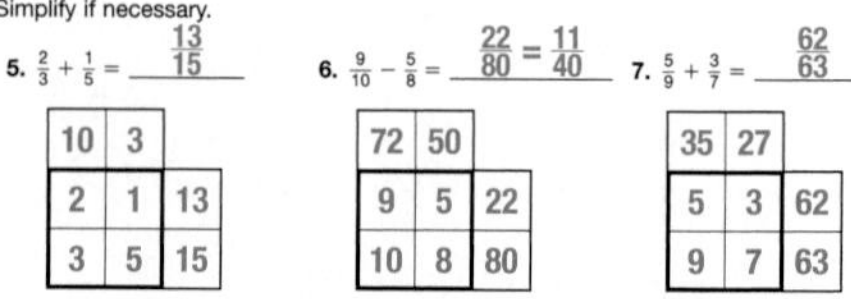

10	3	
2	1	13
3	5	15

72	50	
9	5	22
10	8	80

35	27	
5	3	62
9	7	63

8. How are these methods alike? Which do you prefer? Why? Possible answer: They use the same procedure to find the answer; the boxes procedure is easier to remember.

TECHNOLOGY

Using a Fraction Calculator • Finding Fraction Sums and Differences

Problem: What is the sum of $\frac{7}{17} + \frac{16}{29}$?

Sometimes, fractions involve large numbers that are not easy to work with. A fraction calculator can help you add or subtract the fractions.

1. **Type in the numerator of the first fraction, and then press the [/] button.**
2. **Type in the denominator of the first fraction, and then press the [+] button.**
3. **Type in the numerator of the second fraction, and then press the [/] button.**
4. **Type in the denominator of the second fraction, and then press the [=] button.**

Solution: The answer is $\frac{475}{493}$.

TRY IT

a. What is $\frac{5}{23} + \frac{14}{37}$?

b. What is $\frac{18}{21} - \frac{4}{41}$?

ON YOUR OWN

- What does the calculator display show if the sum of two fractions is bigger than 1?
- The sum of the fractions $\frac{45}{51} + \frac{67}{91}$ has a denominator bigger than 1000. What does the calculator do when the answer has a four-digit denominator?
- How can you find the sum of two fractions with a non-fraction calculator?

Technology

Using a Fraction Calculator • Finding Fraction Sums and Differences

The Point

Students learn how to use a fraction calculator to add and subtract fractions.

Materials

Calculator with fractional capabilities

Resources

Teaching Tool Transparency 24: Fraction Calculator

About the Page

- Some calculators have the [Ab/c] key that performs operations with fractions.
- Some of the newer calculators will perform operations as decimals and convert decimals to fractions, as well as perform operations as fractions and convert them to decimals.

Ask ...

- What process does the calculator go through to add or subtract fractions? Finding a common denominator, creating equivalent fractions with the common denominator, then adding or subtracting the numerators, and reducing to lowest terms.
- How does your calculator enable you to work with fractions?

Answers for Try It

a. $\frac{507}{851}$

b. $\frac{218}{287}$

On Your Own

In the first question, calculators with the [Ab/c] key will show an improper fraction as a mixed number.

Answers for On Your Own

- It shows an improper fraction.
- It converts the answer to a decimal.
- Possible answers: Convert to decimals; Find a common denominator.

6-3 Lesson Organizer

Objective

- Solve equations by adding and subtracting fractions.

NCTM Standards

- 1–4, 9

Review

Use mental math to solve each equation.

1. $x + 5 = 12$ $x = 7$
2. $16 - y = 7$ $y = 9$
3. $a - 5 = 8$ $a = 13$
4. $9 + n = 18$ $n = 9$
5. $c - 4 = 10$ $c = 14$

Available on Daily Transparency 6-3

1 Introduce

Explore

You may wish to use Lesson Enhancement Transparency 28 with **Explore**.

The Point

Students use mental math and logical reasoning to solve missing-addend problems involving fractions with different denominators.

Ongoing Assessment

Check that students understand that they need to use the information in the first table in order to complete the second table.

For Groups That Finish Early

Find the sum of the amounts of blood in the heart, arteries, and veins. $\frac{17}{20}$ Find the sum of the amounts of blood in the arteries, veins, and capillaries. $\frac{16}{20}$, or $\frac{4}{5}$

Follow Up

If students experience difficulty with Step 3, encourage them to express the fractions using the least common denominator of 20 before trying to order the fractions.

6-3 Solving Fraction Equations: Addition and Subtraction

You'll Learn ...

- to solve equations by adding and subtracting fractions

... How It's Used

Scientists on Antarctica use fraction equations to convert temperatures between Celsius and Fahrenheit.

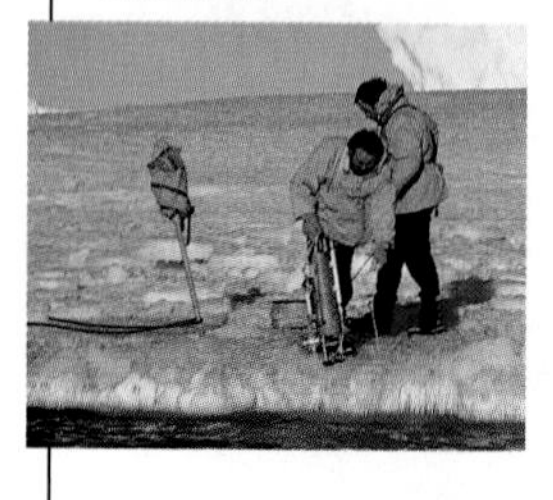

► Lesson Link You have solved simple equations with whole numbers. You have also learned to add and subtract fractions. Now you will combine these ideas as you learn to solve equations by adding and subtracting fractions. ◄

Explore Fraction Equations: Addition and Subtraction

Where's the Blood?

When the body is at rest, blood is distributed throughout the circulatory system as shown.

Organ	Fraction of Blood	Organ	Fraction of Blood
Capillaries	$\frac{1}{20}$	Systemic arteries	$\frac{1}{10}$
Heart	$\frac{1}{10}$	Systemic veins	$\frac{13}{20}$
Lungs	$\frac{1}{10}$		

A cardiologist prepared the table below by adding together the blood from two different parts of the circulatory system. Unfortunately, the data in the second column was accidentally deleted.

Organ 1	Organ 2	Sum	Organ 1	Organ 2	Sum
Heart	???	$\frac{2}{10}$	Heart	???	$\frac{15}{20}$
Lungs	???	$\frac{3}{20}$	Veins	???	$\frac{14}{20}$
Arteries	???	$\frac{15}{20}$	Lungs	???	$\frac{2}{10}$

1. For each line in the second table, find the amount of blood in Organ 2. Write down which of the organs from the first table Organ 2 could be. If there is more than one possible answer, list all of them.
2. Would it be easier if all of the fractions had the same denominator or if all of the fractions had different denominators? Explain.
3. Which organ from the first table has the most blood? The least? How can you tell?

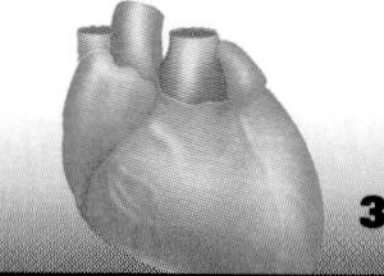

MEETING INDIVIDUAL NEEDS

Resources

- **6-3** Practice
- **6-3** Reteaching
- **6-3** Problem Solving
- **6-3** Enrichment
- **6-3** Daily Transparency
  - Problem of the Day
  - Review
  - Quick Quiz
- Lesson Enhancement Transparency 28
- Technology Master 28
- Chapter 6 Project Master

Learning Modalities

Logical Review with the class the mental-math strategies for solving addition and subtraction equations. On the chalkboard, write a variety of simple equations involving whole numbers, such as $x + 7 = 12$ and $18 - y = 9$. Elicit phrasing of questions such as, "What number plus 7 equals 12?" and "18 minus what number equals 9?"

Social Have students work with a partner to complete **Explore**. Students should explain to their partners how they decided what Organ 2 could be.

Challenge

Have students work in groups of three or four to solve these equations.

1. $\frac{2}{7} + \frac{1}{7} + x = \frac{6}{7}$ $x = \frac{3}{7}$
2. $\frac{4}{13} + x + \frac{2}{13} = \frac{10}{13}$ $x = \frac{4}{13}$
3. $\frac{1}{9} + \frac{4}{9} + \frac{2}{9} + x = 1$ $x = \frac{2}{9}$
4. $\frac{3}{10} + \frac{1}{10} + x = \frac{2}{5}$ $x = 0$

Learn Fraction Equations: Addition and Subtraction

Recall that you can solve addition and subtraction equations with whole numbers and decimals by using mental math. The same method can work for solving equations with fractions.

Examples

1 Solve $x - \frac{2}{8} = \frac{5}{8}$.

$x - \frac{2}{8} = \frac{5}{8}$ Read as "What number minus $\frac{2}{8}$ equals $\frac{5}{8}$?"

$\mathbf{\frac{7}{8}} - \frac{2}{8} = \frac{5}{8}$ Use mental math.

$\frac{5}{8} = \frac{5}{8}$ ✓ Check to see that the equation is true.

x is equal to $\frac{7}{8}$.

2 Kevin had to write a report about the human eye. He wrote $\frac{3}{11}$ of the report on Monday. By Tuesday night, he had written a total of $\frac{7}{11}$ of the report. How much of the report did he write on Tuesday?

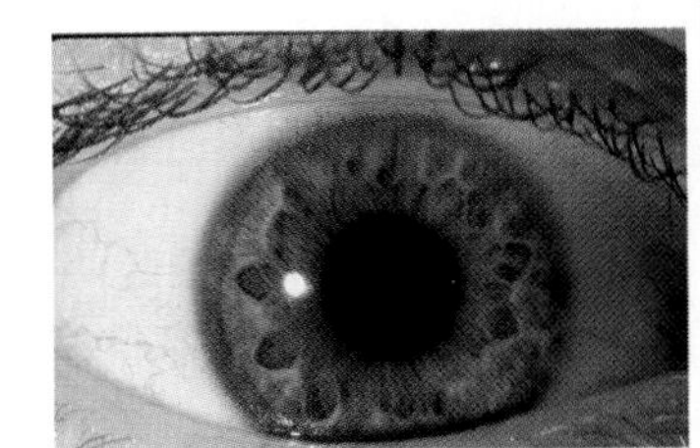

$\frac{3}{11} + x = \frac{7}{11}$ Read as "$\frac{3}{11}$ plus what number equals $\frac{7}{11}$?"

$\frac{3}{11} + \mathbf{\frac{4}{11}} = \frac{7}{11}$ Use mental math.

$\frac{7}{11} = \frac{7}{11}$ ✓ Check to see that the equation is true.

He wrote $\frac{4}{11}$ of the report on Tuesday.

Try It

Solve.

a. $\frac{2}{9} + x = \frac{8}{9}$ $\frac{2}{3}$ **b.** $\frac{15}{3} - x = \frac{7}{3}$ $\frac{8}{3}$ **c.** $\frac{1}{4} + x = \frac{5}{4}$ 1

Problem Solving TIP

Since all of the denominators are the same, you can rewrite this as a simpler problem: $x - 2 = 5$.

▶ Science Link

The light from a camera flash can light up the blood vessels in your retina. This is why some people in photographs have red eyes.

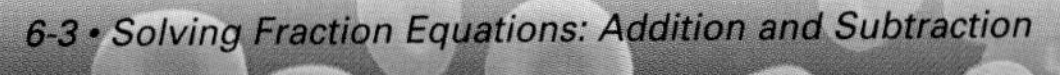

MATH EVERY DAY

▶ Problem of the Day

Each member of Jeremy's class voted on their favorite type of music. Classical music received 7 votes, and country music received 8 votes. Rock music received 6 more votes than the runner-up. Rock music accounted for $\frac{7}{16}$ of all the votes cast. Jazz music received the rest of the votes. How large is the class? How many votes did each type of music get? 32 students; classical-7 votes; country-8 votes; rock, 14 votes; jazz, 3 votes

Available on Daily Transparency 6-3

An Extension is provided in the transparency package.

Fact of the Day

There are 10 billion capillaries in your body. Each capillary is only $\frac{1}{2500}$ inch across.

Mental Math

Solve each equation mentally.

1. $\frac{1}{6} + a = \frac{4}{6}$ $a = \frac{3}{6}$, or $\frac{1}{2}$
2. $\frac{7}{12} - n = \frac{5}{12}$ $n = \frac{2}{12}$, or $\frac{1}{6}$
3. $y - \frac{1}{4} = \frac{1}{4}$ $y = \frac{2}{4}$, or $\frac{1}{2}$
4. $\frac{3}{10} + c = \frac{7}{10}$ $c = \frac{4}{10}$, or $\frac{2}{5}$

Answers for Explore

1. Row 1: $\frac{1}{10}$; Lungs, systemic arteries

   Row 2: $\frac{1}{20}$; Capillaries

   Row 3: $\frac{13}{20}$; Systemic veins

   Row 4: $\frac{13}{20}$; Systemic veins

   Row 5: $\frac{1}{20}$; Capillaries

   Row 6: $\frac{1}{10}$; Heart, systemic arteries
2. Same denominator; It is necessary to have the same denominator before adding or subtracting fractions.
3. Systemic veins have the most; Capillaries the least. Convert each fraction to an equivalent fraction with a denominator of 20. Then compare numerators.

2 Teach

Learn

Alternate Examples

1. Solve $x - \frac{6}{13} = \frac{5}{13}$.

   $x - \frac{6}{13} = \frac{5}{13}$

   $\mathbf{\frac{11}{13}} - \frac{6}{13} = \frac{5}{13}$

   $\frac{5}{13} = \frac{5}{13}$ ✓

   x is equal to $\frac{11}{13}$.
2. Monica had to read a book about the circulatory system. She read $\frac{1}{5}$ of the book on Saturday. By Sunday night she had read a total of $\frac{4}{5}$ of the book. How much of the book did she read on Sunday?

   $\frac{1}{5} + b = \frac{4}{5}$

   $\frac{1}{5} + \mathbf{\frac{3}{5}} = \frac{4}{5}$

   $\frac{4}{5} = \frac{4}{5}$ ✓

   She read $\frac{3}{5}$ of the book on Sunday.

Alternate Examples

3. Together, water and proteins make up $\frac{3}{4}$ of total body weight. If water accounts for $\frac{3}{5}$ of total body weight, what fraction of body weight is proteins? $\frac{3}{5} + p = \frac{3}{4}$

$$\frac{3}{5} = \frac{3 \times 4}{5 \times 4} = \frac{12}{20}$$
$$\frac{3}{4} = \frac{3 \times 5}{4 \times 5} = \frac{15}{20}$$
$$\frac{12}{20} + p = \frac{15}{20}$$
$$\frac{12}{20} + \mathbf{\frac{3}{20}} = \frac{15}{20}$$

$\frac{3}{20}$ of body weight is proteins.

4. Solve $x - \frac{5}{6} = \frac{1}{3}$.
The least common denominator of 6 and 3 is 6.

$$\frac{1}{3} = \frac{1 \times 2}{3 \times 2} = \frac{2}{6}$$
$$x - \frac{5}{6} = \frac{2}{6}$$
$$\mathbf{\frac{7}{6}} - \frac{5}{6} = \frac{2}{6}$$
$$x = \frac{7}{6}$$

3 Practice and Assess

Check

Be sure that students can solve these addition and subtraction equations mentally and that they can express the fractions with the least common denominator. Encourage them to give their solutions as statements including a variable.

Answers for Check Your Understanding

1. Possible answer: The denominator stays the same and the numerators are added or subtracted.
2. In the expression, x can be any value. In the equation, x must equal $\frac{1}{3}$.
3. Substitute the answer for the variable in the original equation and simplify. If the result is a true equation, the answer is correct.

Some equations involve fractions with unlike denominators. To solve these equations, you need to change the fractions to equivalent fractions with like denominators.

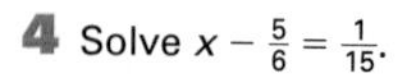

Science Link

Red blood cells are important because they carry oxygen from the lungs to the other organs in your body.

Examples

3 $\frac{43}{100}$ of your blood is made up of only red blood cells. $\frac{9}{20}$ of your blood is made up of red and white blood cells. What fraction of your blood is made up of only white blood cells?

$\frac{9}{20} = \frac{9 \times 5}{20 \times 5} = \frac{45}{100}$ — Change to an equivalent fraction.

$x + \frac{43}{100} = \frac{45}{100}$ — Read as "What number plus $\frac{43}{100}$ equals $\frac{45}{100}$?"

$\mathbf{\frac{2}{100}} + \frac{43}{100} = \frac{45}{100}$ — Use mental math.

$\frac{2}{100}$ of your blood is made up of only white blood cells.

4 Solve $x - \frac{5}{6} = \frac{1}{15}$.

The least common denominator of 6 and 15 is 30.

$\frac{5}{6} = \frac{5 \times 5}{6 \times 5} = \frac{25}{30}$

$\frac{1}{15} = \frac{1 \times 2}{15 \times 2} = \frac{2}{30}$ — Change to equivalent fractions.

$x - \frac{25}{30} = \frac{2}{30}$ — Read as "What number minus $\frac{25}{30}$ equals $\frac{2}{30}$?"

$\mathbf{\frac{27}{30}} - \frac{25}{30} = \frac{2}{30}$ — Use mental math.

$x = \frac{27}{30}$

MENTAL MATH

Sometimes the least common multiple of two numbers is the product of the two numbers. But if the numbers share a prime factor, the least common multiple will be smaller than the product.

Check Your Understanding

1. Why is it necessary to rewrite fraction equations that involve addition or subtraction so that both fractions have the same denominator?
2. How are the x in $\frac{2}{3} - x$ and the x in $\frac{2}{3} - x = \frac{1}{3}$ different?
3. When solving equations, how can you check to see that the answer you got is the correct answer?

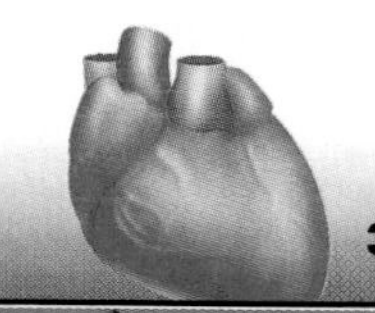

MEETING MIDDLE SCHOOL CLASSROOM NEEDS

Tips from Middle School Teachers

I find that students are often intimidated when they see fractions in equations. To help students, I tell them to think of solving the equation as playing a guess-and-check game. They choose a fraction, substitute it in place of the variable, and see if the equation is true. I remind them not to be discouraged if their first choice is not correct. When they think of solving the equation as a game, they are usually more successful.

Team Teaching

You might ask the science or health teachers to discuss with students the circulatory systems of mammals and other animals.

Health Connection

Frequent participation in aerobic activities can reduce the risk of coronary artery diseases, obesity, and a loss of bone tissue. Aerobic power depends on healthy functioning of the lungs so that oxygen can be supplied to the blood. A strong heart is also necessary to pump blood to the muscles.

6-3 Exercises and Applications

Practice and Apply

1. **Getting Started** Solve.

a. $\frac{2}{5} + p = \frac{7}{5}$ 1 b. $\frac{3}{7} - k = \frac{1}{7}$ $\frac{2}{7}$ c. $w + \frac{4}{9} = \frac{9}{9}$ $\frac{5}{9}$ d. $r - \frac{9}{10} = \frac{3}{10}$ $\frac{6}{5}$

Solve. Write each answer in lowest terms.

2. $\frac{1}{3} + j = \frac{5}{6}$ $\frac{1}{2}$
3. $r + \frac{2}{5} = \frac{7}{10}$ $\frac{3}{10}$
4. $t - \frac{4}{5} = \frac{1}{10}$ $\frac{9}{10}$
5. $v - \frac{1}{2} = \frac{3}{8}$ $\frac{7}{8}$
6. $d + \frac{7}{9} = \frac{8}{9}$ $\frac{1}{9}$
7. $\frac{80}{5} - x = 12$ 4
8. $q - \frac{1}{8} = \frac{3}{4}$ $\frac{7}{8}$
9. $4 - b = \frac{3}{7}$ $\frac{25}{7}$
10. $\frac{17}{100} + a = \frac{67}{100}$ $\frac{1}{2}$
11. $\frac{11}{12} - h = \frac{3}{4}$ $\frac{1}{6}$
12. $g + \frac{1}{8} = \frac{1}{6}$ $\frac{1}{24}$
13. $f - \frac{4}{9} = \frac{6}{3}$ $\frac{22}{9}$
14. $e + \frac{5}{28} = \frac{5}{14}$ $\frac{5}{28}$
15. $\frac{15}{22} - z = \frac{1}{2}$ $\frac{2}{11}$
16. $x - \frac{23}{4} = \frac{24}{3}$ $\frac{55}{4}$
17. $3 + y = \frac{10}{3}$ $\frac{1}{3}$

Write a true equation using the fractions given.

18. $\frac{1}{3}, \frac{2}{3}, 1$
19. $\frac{3}{4}, \frac{1}{2}, \frac{1}{4}$
20. $\frac{5}{6}, \frac{1}{3}, \frac{1}{2}$
21. $\frac{7}{12}, \frac{1}{6}, \frac{5}{12}$
22. $\frac{51}{36}, \frac{5}{6}, \frac{7}{9}$
23. $\frac{14}{18}, \frac{1}{3}, \frac{90}{81}$
24. $\frac{3}{11}, \frac{8}{11}, \frac{5}{11}$
25. $\frac{2}{12}, \frac{13}{15}, \frac{7}{10}$

Write and solve an equation for each situation.

26. At the Blood Research Clinic, Peter and Jen tested $\frac{11}{12}$ of the clinic's blood samples. If Peter tested $\frac{3}{5}$ of the samples, how many did Jen test? $\frac{19}{60}$

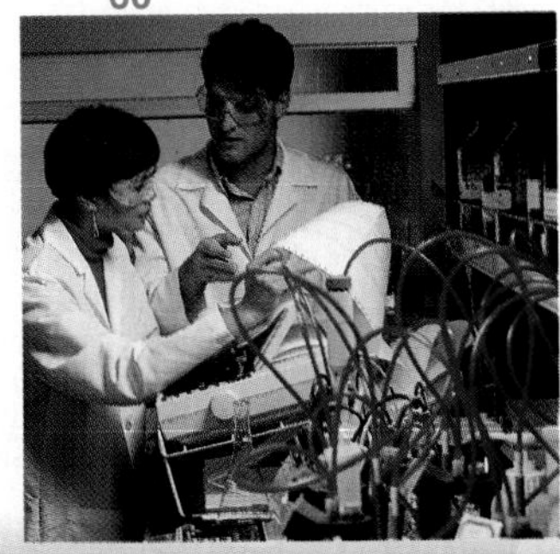

27. Antwon baked a batch of cookies. He and his family ate $\frac{1}{5}$ of the cookies on Monday, and some more cookies on Tuesday. After Tuesday, $\frac{2}{3}$ of the cookies had been eaten. What fraction of the cookies were eaten on Tuesday? $\frac{7}{15}$

28. **Operation Sense** Pam had $\frac{7}{9}$ of a yard of string. After she cut some, she had $\frac{1}{3}$ of a yard left. How much string did Pam cut? $\frac{4}{9}$ yd

29. Marilyn collected $\frac{3}{4}$ of a pound of sea shells. She used some to decorate a picture frame, and she had $\frac{1}{6}$ of a pound left. How many pounds of shells did she use to decorate the frame? $\frac{7}{12}$ lb

PRACTICE 6-3

6-3 Exercises and Applications

Assignment Guide

- **Basic** 1–41 odds
- **Average** 1, 2–28 evens, 29–41 odds
- **Enriched** 2–30 evens, 31–40

Exercise Notes

Exercise 28

Error Prevention If students have trouble writing an equation to describe the situation, suggest that they draw a diagram of the problem.

Exercise Answers

Possible answers for 18–25:

18. $\frac{1}{3} + \frac{2}{3} = 1$
19. $\frac{3}{4} - \frac{1}{4} = \frac{1}{2}$
20. $\frac{1}{3} + \frac{1}{2} = \frac{5}{6}$
21. $\frac{1}{6} + \frac{5}{12} = \frac{7}{12}$
22. $\frac{51}{36} - \frac{5}{6} = \frac{7}{12}$
23. $\frac{90}{81} - \frac{1}{3} = \frac{14}{18}$
24. $\frac{3}{11} + \frac{5}{11} = \frac{8}{11}$
25. $\frac{2}{12} + \frac{7}{10} = \frac{13}{15}$

Reteaching

Activity

Materials: Counters

- Write the equation $x + \frac{3}{8} = \frac{7}{8}$ on a sheet of paper.
- Let each counter represent $\frac{1}{8}$, and place the appropriate number of counters above each fraction.
- How many counters must be added to the 3 counters to equal 7 counters? 4 counters
- If each counter represents $\frac{1}{8}$, what is the value of x? $x = \frac{4}{8}$, or $\frac{1}{2}$
- Repeat the process with the following equations.

1. $y - \frac{5}{12} = \frac{1}{12}$ $y = \frac{6}{12}$, or $\frac{1}{2}$
2. $\frac{5}{6} - a = \frac{1}{6}$ $a = \frac{4}{6}$, or $\frac{2}{3}$
3. $r + \frac{3}{10} = \frac{11}{10}$ $r = \frac{8}{10}$, or $\frac{4}{5}$

PRACTICE

Name ____________

Practice 6-3

Solving Fraction Equations: Addition and Subtraction

Solve. Write each answer in lowest terms.

1. $\frac{5}{17} + a = \frac{8}{17}$ $a = \frac{3}{17}$
2. $\frac{2}{7} + g = \frac{5}{7}$ $g = \frac{3}{7}$
3. $u - \frac{1}{2} = \frac{1}{10}$ $u = \frac{3}{5}$
4. $\frac{7}{8} - v = \frac{13}{16}$ $v = \frac{1}{16}$
5. $\frac{4}{7} - w = \frac{6}{35}$ $w = \frac{2}{5}$
6. $n - \frac{1}{5} = \frac{3}{10}$ $n = \frac{1}{2}$
7. $f + \frac{7}{22} = \frac{13}{22}$ $f = \frac{3}{11}$
8. $\frac{7}{9} - a = \frac{1}{36}$ $a = \frac{3}{4}$
9. $z - \frac{1}{6} = \frac{1}{6}$ $z = \frac{1}{3}$
10. $g + \frac{1}{4} = \frac{7}{16}$ $g = \frac{3}{16}$
11. $\frac{5}{6} + w = \frac{17}{18}$ $w = \frac{1}{9}$
12. $\frac{3}{8} - f = \frac{1}{24}$ $f = \frac{1}{3}$

Write a true equation using the fractions given. **Possible answers:**

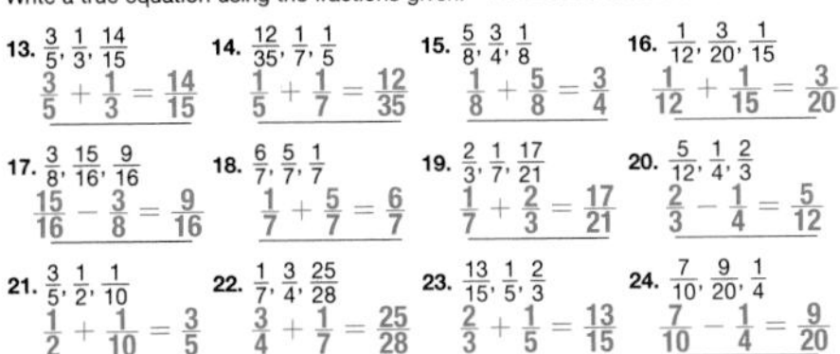

13. $\frac{3}{5}, \frac{1}{3}, \frac{14}{15}$ $\frac{3}{5} + \frac{1}{3} = \frac{14}{15}$
14. $\frac{12}{35}, \frac{1}{7}, \frac{1}{5}$ $\frac{1}{5} + \frac{1}{7} = \frac{12}{35}$
15. $\frac{5}{8}, \frac{3}{4}, \frac{1}{8}$ $\frac{1}{8} + \frac{5}{8} = \frac{3}{4}$
16. $\frac{1}{12}, \frac{3}{20}, \frac{1}{15}$ $\frac{1}{12} + \frac{1}{15} = \frac{3}{20}$
17. $\frac{3}{8}, \frac{15}{16}, \frac{9}{16}$ $\frac{15}{16} - \frac{3}{8} = \frac{9}{16}$
18. $\frac{6}{7}, \frac{5}{7}, \frac{1}{7}$ $\frac{1}{7} + \frac{5}{7} = \frac{6}{7}$
19. $\frac{2}{3}, \frac{1}{7}, \frac{17}{21}$ $\frac{1}{7} + \frac{2}{3} = \frac{17}{21}$
20. $\frac{5}{12}, \frac{1}{4}, \frac{2}{3}$ $\frac{2}{3} - \frac{1}{4} = \frac{5}{12}$
21. $\frac{3}{5}, \frac{1}{2}, \frac{1}{10}$ $\frac{1}{2} + \frac{1}{10} = \frac{3}{5}$
22. $\frac{1}{7}, \frac{3}{4}, \frac{25}{28}$ $\frac{3}{4} + \frac{1}{7} = \frac{25}{28}$
23. $\frac{13}{15}, \frac{1}{5}, \frac{2}{3}$ $\frac{2}{3} + \frac{1}{5} = \frac{13}{15}$
24. $\frac{7}{10}, \frac{9}{20}, \frac{1}{4}$ $\frac{7}{10} - \frac{1}{4} = \frac{9}{20}$

Write and solve an equation for the given situation.

25. Lori and Fraz ate $\frac{7}{12}$ of a pizza. If Lori ate $\frac{1}{3}$ of the pizza, how much of it did Fraz eat?
Possible answer: $\frac{1}{3} + x = \frac{7}{12}$; $\frac{1}{4}$

26. Irene's gas tank was $\frac{9}{10}$ full when she left her house, and it was $\frac{7}{15}$ full when she arrived for her vacation. What fraction of a tank of gas did she use driving there?
Possible answer: $\frac{9}{10} - x = \frac{7}{15}$; $\frac{13}{30}$

RETEACHING

Name ____________

Alternative Lesson 6-3

Solving Fraction Equations: Addition and Subtraction

You can use mental math to solve addition and subtraction equations involving fractions with like denominators. To solve equations involving fractions with unlike denominators, you need to change the fractions to equivalent fractions with like denominators.

Example

Solve $x - \frac{3}{8} = \frac{5}{16}$.

Use 16 as the LCD (least common denominator). Change $\frac{3}{8}$ to an equivalent fraction. $\frac{3}{8} = \frac{3 \times 2}{8 \times 2} = \frac{6}{16}$

Read as "What number minus $\frac{6}{16}$ equals $\frac{5}{16}$?" $x - \frac{6}{16} = \frac{5}{16}$

Use mental math. $\frac{11}{16} - \frac{6}{16} = \frac{5}{16}$

Check to see that the equation is true. $\frac{5}{16} = \frac{5}{16}$ ✓

So, $x = \frac{11}{16}$.

Try It Solve each equation. Write each answer in the lowest terms.

a. $a + \frac{1}{5} = \frac{4}{5}$

What number plus $\frac{1}{5}$ equals $\frac{4}{5}$? $\frac{3}{5}$ So, $a = \frac{3}{5}$.

Show that the equation is true. $\frac{3}{5} + \frac{1}{5} = \frac{4}{5}$; $\frac{4}{5} = \frac{4}{5}$ ✓

b. $k - \frac{1}{3} = \frac{2}{9}$

What is the least common multiple of 3 and 9? 9

Rewrite the equation using like denominators. $k - \frac{3}{9} = \frac{2}{9}$

What number minus $\frac{3}{9}$ equals $\frac{2}{9}$? $\frac{5}{9}$ So, $k = \frac{5}{9}$

Show that the equation is true. $\frac{5}{9} - \frac{3}{9} = \frac{2}{9}$; $\frac{2}{9} = \frac{2}{9}$ ✓

c. $\frac{1}{4} + x = \frac{3}{4}$ $x = \frac{2}{4} = \frac{1}{2}$

d. $y - \frac{5}{8} = \frac{1}{8}$ $y = \frac{6}{8} = \frac{3}{4}$

e. $\frac{7}{10} - c = \frac{2}{5}$ $c = \frac{3}{10}$

f. $\frac{5}{12} + r = \frac{7}{3}$ $r = \frac{23}{12} = 1\frac{11}{12}$

g. $\frac{1}{12} + b = \frac{1}{4}$ $b = \frac{2}{12} = \frac{1}{6}$

h. $s - \frac{1}{2} = \frac{1}{6}$ $s = \frac{4}{6} = \frac{2}{3}$

i. $d + \frac{1}{3} = \frac{7}{12}$ $d = \frac{3}{12} = \frac{1}{4}$

j. $\frac{5}{6} - f = \frac{7}{12}$ $f = \frac{3}{12} = \frac{1}{4}$

k. $s + \frac{3}{8} = \frac{3}{4}$ $s = \frac{3}{8}$

l. $t - \frac{3}{10} = \frac{5}{8}$ $t = \frac{37}{40}$

Exercise Notes

■ Exercise 33

Problem-Solving Tip Students may solve this problem by first solving a simpler problem. Suggest they use 10 instead of $\frac{10}{4}$ and 3 instead of $\frac{3}{4}$.

Project Process

You may want to have students use Chapter 6 Project Master.

Exercise Answers

32. Possible answer: $\frac{1}{2} + p = \frac{3}{4}$; $p = \frac{1}{4}$. $\frac{1}{4}$ of a whole plus $\frac{1}{2}$ of the same whole is $\frac{3}{4}$ of the whole.

33. $\frac{1}{2}$ yd; Solve the equation: $\frac{10}{4} = \frac{3}{4} + \frac{3}{4} + x + x$.

34. Possible answer: A board $\frac{26}{20}$ ft long is cut in two pieces with one piece equal to $\frac{7}{10}$ ft. What is the length of the other piece? $\frac{7}{10} + y = \frac{26}{20}$, $\frac{14}{20} + y = \frac{26}{20}$, $y = \frac{12}{20}$, or $\frac{3}{5}$ ft.

35. x represents the whole fraction in the first equation; x represents the numerator of the fraction in the second equation.

Alternate Assessment

Interview Have students explain how they solve addition and subtraction equations involving fractions. Have them supply examples and detail the steps used.

▶ Quick Quiz

Solve each equation.

1. $a - \frac{3}{5} = \frac{7}{10}$ $a = \frac{13}{10}$, or $1\frac{3}{10}$
2. $x + \frac{1}{3} = \frac{11}{12}$ $x = \frac{7}{12}$
3. $\frac{2}{3} - y = \frac{1}{6}$ $y = \frac{1}{2}$
4. $\frac{3}{8} + n = \frac{1}{2}$ $n = \frac{1}{8}$

Available on Daily Transparency 6-3

---

30. Science A blood bank estimates that $\frac{3}{10}$ of the blood on hand is type O blood. It anticipates a need for $\frac{9}{20}$ of the blood to be type O. How much more type O blood is needed? $\frac{3}{20}$

31. **Test Prep** At the Sierra Road Inn, $\frac{7}{11}$ of the parking lot was full. Choose an equation that shows how much of the lot was empty. A

Ⓐ $\frac{7}{11} + x = 1$ Ⓑ $\frac{7}{11} - x = 1$ Ⓒ $x - \frac{7}{11} = 1$

Problem Solving and Reasoning

32.  Write an equation using unlike denominators that you can solve using mental math. Explain how you would use mental math to solve it.

33. Critical Thinking GPS The perimeter of the lid to Janice's rectangular jewelry box is $\frac{10}{4}$ of a yard. If the longer sides are $\frac{3}{4}$ of a yard, how long are the shorter sides? Explain.

34. Communicate Write a problem that could be solved with the equation $\frac{7}{10} + y = \frac{26}{20}$. Explain how you created the problem and solve it.

35. Communicate Explain the difference in the use of x in $\frac{1}{3} + x = \frac{4}{5}$ and in $\frac{1}{3} + \frac{x}{5} = \frac{4}{5}$.

Mixed Review

Find the area of each parallelogram. *[Lesson 4-5]*

36. 40

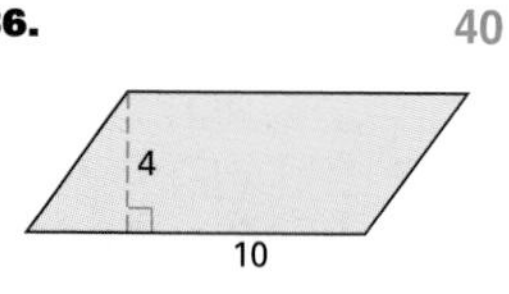

37. 60

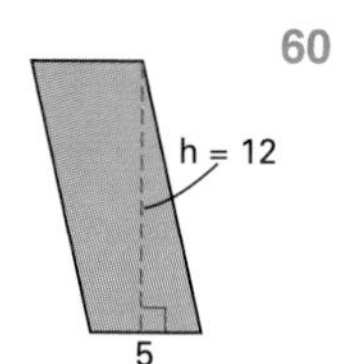

38. 287

7
41

State if the equation is true for the given value of the variable. *[Lesson 2-12]*

39. $x + 17 = 50$; $x = 43$ No **40.** $5j = 60$; $j = 14$ No **41.** $21 - k = 14$; $k = 7$ Yes

Project Progress

Make a table for each of your recipes. In the first column, list the number of servings and amounts of ingredients in the original recipe. In the second column, list half the amounts listed in the first column. In the third column, list double the amounts in the first column.

Problem Solving
Understand
Plan
Solve
Look Back

PROBLEM SOLVING 6-3

PROBLEM SOLVING

Name ______

Guided Problem Solving 6-3

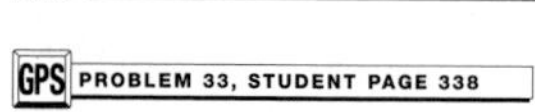

GPS PROBLEM 33, STUDENT PAGE 338

The perimeter of the lid to Janice's rectangular jewelry box is $\frac{10}{4}$ of a yard. If the longer sides are $\frac{3}{4}$ of a yard, how long are the shorter sides? Explain.

— Understand —

1. Circle the perimeter and underline the length of one side of the lid.
2. How do you find the perimeter? Add the length of the four sides.

— Plan —

3. Draw a picture of the jewelry box. Label the longer sides.

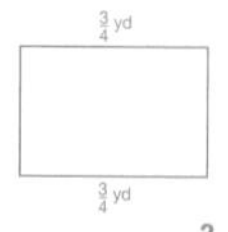

4. Write an equation to find the length of the two longer sides. $\frac{3}{4} + \frac{3}{4} = \frac{6}{4}$
5. Use your answer to Item 4 to write an equation showing the length of the two shorter sides. $\frac{10}{4} - \frac{6}{4} = \frac{4}{4}$

— Solve —

6. The sum of two fractions equals your answer to Item 5. The denominator of each of the two fractions will be 4.

   Use Guess and Check to find each numerator. Each numerator is 2.

7. What is the length of each shorter side? $\frac{2}{4} = \frac{1}{2}$ yd
8. Explain Perimeter less length of two longer sides equals length of two shorter sides. Find half of that difference.

— Look Back —

9. What is a different way to find the answer? Possible answer: Divide perimeter by 2. Subtract the length of longer side.

SOLVE ANOTHER PROBLEM

The perimeter of the lid to a rectangular box is $\frac{14}{6}$ of a yard. If the longer sides are $\frac{5}{6}$ of a yard, how long are the shorter sides? Explain. $\frac{2}{6} = \frac{1}{3}$ yd; $\frac{5}{6} + \frac{5}{6} = \frac{10}{6}$; $\frac{14}{6} - \frac{10}{6} = \frac{4}{6}$; $\frac{2}{6} + \frac{2}{6} = \frac{4}{6}$

ENRICHMENT

Name ______

Extend Your Thinking 6-3

Critical Thinking

Use mental math to solve each equation. It may help to rewrite each equation with a common denominator and solve.

Solve $\frac{y}{3} + \frac{1}{2} = \frac{5}{6}$.

Let ? represent $\frac{y}{3}$. $? + \frac{1}{2} = \frac{5}{6}$

Rewrite with a common denominator. A common denominator of 2, 3, and 6 is 6. $? + \frac{3}{6} = \frac{5}{6}$

Use mental math to solve the equation. $? = \frac{2}{6}$

Rewrite your answer as an equivalent fraction with 3 as the denominator. $\frac{y}{3} = \frac{2}{6}$

Solve for y. $y = 1$

Check your equation. $\frac{y}{3} + \frac{1}{2} \stackrel{?}{=} \frac{5}{6}$; $\frac{1}{3} + \frac{1}{2} \stackrel{?}{=} \frac{5}{6}$; $\frac{2}{6} + \frac{3}{6} = \frac{5}{6}$ √

Solve. Then check your equation.

1. $\frac{1}{8} + \frac{g}{4} = \frac{5}{8}$ $g =$ 2 $\frac{1}{8} + \frac{2}{4} = \frac{1}{8} + \frac{4}{8} = \frac{5}{8}$
2. $\frac{h}{2} - \frac{1}{4} = \frac{1}{4}$ $h =$ 1 $\frac{1}{2} - \frac{1}{4} = \frac{2}{4} - \frac{1}{4} = \frac{1}{4}$
3. $\frac{2}{a} + \frac{1}{4} = \frac{1}{2}$ $a =$ 8 $\frac{2}{8} + \frac{1}{4} = \frac{1}{4} + \frac{1}{4} = \frac{2}{4} = \frac{1}{2}$
4. $\frac{4}{5} - \frac{b}{3} = \frac{2}{15}$ $b =$ 2 $\frac{4}{5} - \frac{2}{3} = \frac{12}{15} - \frac{10}{15} = \frac{2}{15}$
5. $\frac{c}{16} + \frac{1}{2} = \frac{7}{8}$ $c =$ 6 $\frac{6}{16} + \frac{1}{2} = \frac{6}{16} + \frac{8}{16} = \frac{14}{16} = \frac{7}{8}$
6. $\frac{9}{10} - \frac{d}{2} = \frac{2}{5}$ $d =$ 1 $\frac{9}{10} - \frac{1}{2} = \frac{9}{10} - \frac{5}{10} = \frac{4}{10} = \frac{2}{5}$
7. $\frac{e}{6} + \frac{e}{6} = \frac{2}{3}$ $e =$ 2 $\frac{2}{6} + \frac{2}{6} = \frac{4}{6} = \frac{2}{3}$
8. $\frac{3}{f} - \frac{1}{3} = \frac{5}{12}$ $f =$ 4 $\frac{3}{4} - \frac{1}{3} = \frac{9}{12} - \frac{4}{12} = \frac{5}{12}$
9. $\frac{1}{m} + \frac{3}{4} = \frac{11}{12}$ $m =$ 6 $\frac{1}{6} + \frac{3}{4} = \frac{2}{12} + \frac{9}{12} = \frac{11}{12}$
10. $\frac{5}{n} - \frac{1}{4} = \frac{3}{8}$ $n =$ 8 $\frac{5}{8} - \frac{1}{4} = \frac{5}{8} - \frac{2}{8} = \frac{3}{8}$

Section 6A Connect

In this section, you've learned how to add and subtract different types of fractions. Now you'll use that knowledge to prepare information about different types of blood.

What's Your Type?

Every person has only one blood type. A person who needs a blood transfusion cannot receive blood from just anyone. The blood must be a certain type, or complications could arise, and the person could even die. The data from the American Red Cross shows what fraction of the population has each of the eight blood types.

A+	A−	B+	B−	AB+	AB−	0+	0−
$\frac{17}{50}$	$\frac{3}{50}$	$\frac{2}{25}$	$\frac{3}{200}$	$\frac{1}{25}$	$\frac{1}{200}$	$\frac{39}{100}$	$\frac{7}{100}$

The following table lists the types of blood that a person of each blood type can receive.

Patient Type	Can RECEIVE types...	Patient Type	Can RECEIVE types...
A+	A+, A−, 0+, 0−	AB+	A+, A−, B+, B−, AB+, AB−, 0+, 0−
A−	A−, 0−	AB−	A−, B−, AB−, 0−
B+	B+, B−, 0+, 0−	0+	0+, 0−
B−	B−, 0−	0−	0−

1. Determine the fraction of the population from which each patient type can receive blood.
2. If a person can receive a large number of blood types, can that person receive blood from a larger fraction of the population? Explain.
3. People with O− blood are known as "universal donors." Why do you think they are called this?
4. A "universal recipient" is a person who can receive blood from anyone, regardless of their blood type. What fraction of the population are universal recipients? Explain.

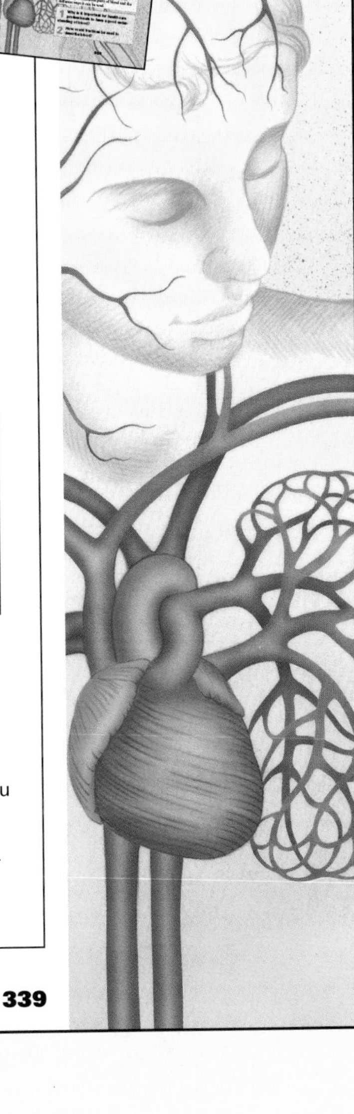

6A Connect

What's Your Type?

The Point

In *What's Your Type?* on page 323, students discussed blood types. Now they will use addition and subtraction of fractions to build a chart of blood types.

About the Page

- Discuss the chart of blood types with the class. If students know their own blood type, ask them what fraction of the population shares their blood type.
- Remind students that they need to refer to both charts to answer the questions.
- Tell students that these four main blood groups have several subgroups. Therefore, the blood of both donor and recipient is carefully tested before a transfusion in an effort to prevent serious reactions.

Ongoing Assessment

Check that students understand that they need to add to determine the fraction of the population from which each patient type can receive blood.

Extension

The blood types are based on the absence or presence of two factors in the red cells. Have students determine what the designations A, B, AB, and O mean. Type A contains only Factor A, Type B contains only Factor B, Type AB contains both Factors A and B, Type O contains neither Factor A nor Factor B.

Answers for Connect

1. A+: $\frac{43}{50}$; A−: $\frac{13}{100}$; B+: $\frac{111}{200}$; B−: $\frac{17}{200}$; AB+: 1; AB−: $\frac{3}{20}$; O+: $\frac{23}{50}$; O−: $\frac{7}{100}$.
2. No; A+, B+, and AB− can all receive four types of blood, but AB− can only receive from a small fraction of the population.
3. Everybody can receive O− blood.
4. $\frac{1}{25}$; It's the people who are AB+.

6A Review

Review Correlation

Item(s)	Lesson(s)
1–4	6-1
5–14	6-2
15–23	6-3
24	6-2

Test Prep

Test-Taking Tip

Tell students that they may need to reduce a fraction to lowest terms after completing the necessary computations. In this case, students may complete the subtraction correctly, but they will not find the correct difference as an answer choice unless they reduce the answer to lowest terms.

Section 6A Review

Simplify. Write each answer in lowest terms.

1. $\frac{3}{11} + \frac{5}{11}$ $\frac{8}{11}$ **2.** $\frac{3}{5} - \frac{1}{5}$ $\frac{2}{5}$ **3.** $\frac{1}{8} + \frac{3}{8}$ $\frac{1}{2}$ **4.** $\frac{9}{10} - \frac{6}{10}$ $\frac{3}{10}$

5. $\frac{3}{4} + \frac{3}{5}$ $\frac{27}{20}$ **6.** $\frac{5}{8} + \frac{2}{5}$ $\frac{41}{40}$ **7.** $\frac{1}{4} + \frac{1}{6}$ $\frac{5}{12}$ **8.** $\frac{4}{5} - \frac{1}{4}$ $\frac{11}{20}$

9. $\frac{5}{9} - \frac{1}{3}$ $\frac{2}{9}$ **10.** $\frac{1}{3} - \frac{1}{4}$ $\frac{1}{12}$ **11.** $\frac{7}{10} + \frac{1}{4}$ $\frac{19}{20}$ **12.** $\frac{5}{6} - \frac{3}{8}$ $\frac{11}{24}$

13. Industry Newspaper ads are available in sizes that are a fraction of a page: $\frac{1}{8}$, $\frac{1}{4}$, $\frac{1}{2}$, and $\frac{3}{4}$. Find a combination of ads that will take up a whole page. Explain your reasoning. Possible answer: one $\frac{1}{4}$, one $\frac{1}{2}$, two $\frac{1}{8}$; Explanations may vary.

14. Health A cup of milk contains $\frac{11}{100}$ of the daily USDA cholesterol allowance. A serving of cooked chicken contains $\frac{19}{75}$ of this allowance. If you eat a serving of cooked chicken and drink a cup of milk, what fraction of your USDA cholesterol allowance have you had? $\frac{109}{300}$

15. When counting the amount of blood at the hospital blood bank, Christine determined that about $\frac{2}{5}$ of the blood was type O and about $\frac{1}{4}$ of the blood was type A. What fraction of the blood is neither type O nor type A? $\frac{7}{21}$

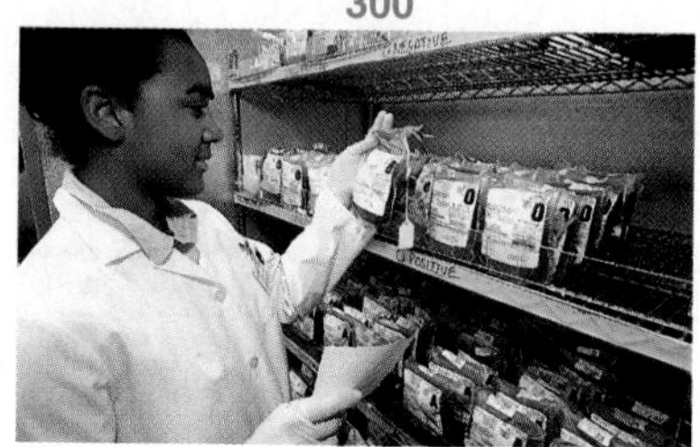

Solve. Write each answer in lowest terms.

16. $\frac{5}{9} - x = \frac{11}{36}$ $\frac{1}{4}$ **17.** $j + \frac{1}{3} = \frac{7}{12}$ $\frac{1}{4}$ **18.** $\frac{7}{10} + w = \frac{9}{10}$ $\frac{1}{5}$ **19.** $t - \frac{1}{2} = \frac{1}{4}$ $\frac{3}{4}$

20. $y + \frac{1}{10} = \frac{4}{5}$ $\frac{7}{10}$ **21.** $\frac{3}{4} - z = \frac{1}{12}$ $\frac{2}{3}$ **22.** $r - \frac{1}{3} = \frac{4}{15}$ $\frac{3}{5}$ **23.** $\frac{5}{6} + p = \frac{29}{24}$ $\frac{3}{8}$

REVIEW 6A

Test Prep

After simplifying an expression, write the fraction in lowest terms.

24. Choose the correct solution to $\frac{5}{12} - \frac{1}{6}$. A

Ⓐ $\frac{1}{4}$ Ⓑ $\frac{1}{3}$ Ⓒ $\frac{2}{3}$ Ⓓ $\frac{5}{6}$

Resources

Practice Masters
Section 6A Review

Assessment Sourcebook
Quiz 6A

TestWorks
Test and Practice Software

PRACTICE

Name ____________

Practice

Section 6A Review

Simplify. Write each answer in lowest terms.

1. $\frac{12}{15} - \frac{1}{15}$ $\frac{11}{15}$ 2. $\frac{11}{20} + \frac{7}{20}$ $\frac{9}{10}$ 3. $\frac{2}{3} - \frac{1}{3}$ $\frac{1}{3}$ 4. $\frac{4}{6} - \frac{2}{6}$ $\frac{1}{3}$

5. $\frac{6}{11} - \frac{2}{11}$ $\frac{4}{11}$ 6. $\frac{4}{7} - \frac{1}{7}$ $\frac{3}{7}$ 7. $\frac{12}{13} + \frac{6}{13}$ $\frac{18}{13}$ 8. $\frac{18}{20} - \frac{3}{20}$ $\frac{3}{4}$

9. $\frac{1}{3} + \frac{3}{7}$ $\frac{16}{21}$ 10. $\frac{1}{10} + \frac{1}{2}$ $\frac{3}{5}$ 11. $\frac{1}{2} + \frac{1}{3}$ $\frac{5}{6}$ 12. $\frac{21}{25} - \frac{1}{2}$ $\frac{17}{50}$

13. $\frac{6}{7} - \frac{3}{4}$ $\frac{3}{28}$ 14. $\frac{5}{7} - \frac{1}{3}$ $\frac{8}{21}$ 15. $\frac{1}{2} + \frac{3}{8}$ $\frac{7}{8}$ 16. $\frac{3}{10} - \frac{1}{8}$ $\frac{7}{40}$

17. $\frac{2}{3} - \frac{1}{6}$ $\frac{1}{2}$ 18. $\frac{3}{5} + \frac{1}{3}$ $\frac{14}{15}$ 19. $\frac{1}{2} + \frac{1}{6}$ $\frac{2}{3}$ 20. $\frac{2}{3} + \frac{1}{8}$ $\frac{19}{24}$

21. **Career** Lorenzo's job consists of filing, typing, and answering telephones. He spends $\frac{1}{6}$ of his time filing and $\frac{5}{8}$ of his time typing. What fraction of his time does he spend answering telephones? $\frac{5}{24}$

22. About $\frac{1}{6}$ of Rhode Island's population lives in Providence, and $\frac{1}{12}$ of the state's population lives in Warwick. What fraction of the state's population lives in these two cities combined? $\frac{1}{4}$

Solve.

23. $k - \frac{5}{11} = \frac{1}{22}$ $k = \frac{1}{2}$ 24. $\frac{7}{10} - s = \frac{1}{30}$ $s = \frac{2}{3}$ 25. $f - \frac{3}{4} = \frac{1}{36}$ $f = \frac{7}{9}$ 26. $c + \frac{2}{3} = \frac{23}{30}$ $c = \frac{1}{10}$

27. $\frac{5}{7} - d = \frac{13}{21}$ $d = \frac{2}{21}$ 28. $\frac{1}{6} + p = \frac{13}{30}$ $p = \frac{4}{15}$ 29. $\frac{1}{5} + c = \frac{2}{5}$ $c = \frac{1}{5}$ 30. $w + \frac{17}{20} = \frac{14}{15}$ $w = \frac{1}{12}$

31. The largest maze ever created had the shape of a rectangle with base 500 ft and height 252 ft. Find the area of the maze. *[Lesson 4-4]* 126,000 ft^2

32. Beth and Carlos are riding on two different Ferris wheels at the park. Beth's Ferris wheel rotates once every 90 seconds, and Carlos' Ferris wheel rotates once every 75 seconds. If Beth and Carlos are both at the bottom of the wheel now, when is the next time they will both be at the bottom? In 450 seconds

Adding and Subtracting Mixed Numbers

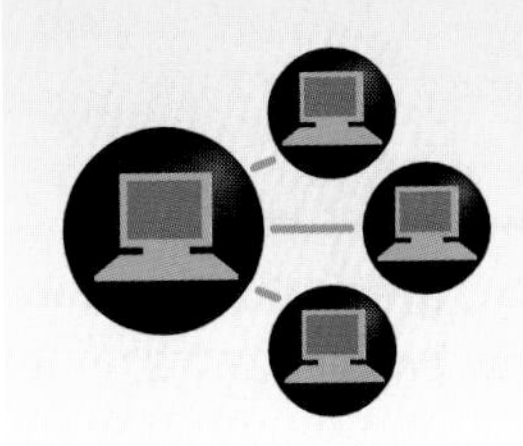

Visit www.teacher.mathsurf.com for links to lesson plans from teachers and other professionals, NCTM information, and other sites.

LESSON PLANNING GUIDE

Student Edition / Ancillaries*

LESSON		MATERIALS	VOCABULARY	DAILY	OTHER
	Section 6B Opener				
6-4	**Estimation: Sums and Differences of Mixed Numbers**			6-4	Teaching Tool Trans. 5 Lesson Enhancement Trans. 29
6-5	**Adding Mixed Numbers**	Fraction Bars®		6-5	Teaching Tool Trans. 14 Lesson Enhancement Trans. 30 Technology Master 29
6-6	**Subtracting Mixed Numbers**	Fraction Bars®		6-6	Teaching Tool Trans. 14 Lesson Enhancement Trans. 31 Technology Master 30 Ch. 6 Project Master *Interactive CD-ROM Lesson*
	Connect				Interdisc. Team Teaching 6B
	Review				Practice 6B; Quiz 6B; *TestWorks*
	Extend Key Ideas				
	Chapter 6 Summary and Review				
	Chapter 6 Assessment				Ch. 6 Tests Forms A–F *TestWorks*; Ch. 6 Letter Home
	Cumulative Review, Chapters 1–6				Cumulative Review Ch. 1–6 Quarterly Test Ch. 1–6

* Daily Ancillaries include Practice, Reteaching, Problem Solving, Enrichment, and Daily Transparency. Teaching Tool Transparencies are in *Teacher's Toolkits*. Lesson Enhancement Transparencies are in *Overhead Transparency Package*.

SKILLS TRACE

LESSON	SKILL	FIRST INTRODUCED GR. 4	GR. 5	GR. 6	DEVELOP	PRACTICE/ APPLY	REVIEW
6-4	Estimating sums and differences of mixed numbers.			✘ p. 342	pp. 342–343	pp. 344–345	pp. 356, 359, 429
6-5	Adding mixed numbers.		✘		pp. 346–347	pp. 348–349	pp. 356, 359, 431
6-6	Subtracting mixed numbers.		✘		pp. 350–352	pp. 353–354	pp. 356, 359, 435

CONNECTED MATHEMATICS

Investigation 4 in the unit *Bits and Pieces II (Using Rational Numbers)*, from the **Connected Mathematics** series, can be used with Section 6B.

INTERDISCIPLINARY TEAM TEACHING

Math and Social Studies

(Worksheet pages 31–32: Teacher pages T31–T32)

In this lesson, students solve woodworking problems by adding and subtracting mixed numbers.

Name ____________________ *Math and Social Studies*

MEASURE TWICE, CUT ONCE

Solve woodworking problems by adding and subtracting mixed numbers.

Throughout history, people have used wood to make many things, such as weapons, furniture, and houses. Close your eyes and visualize all the things in your home that are made of wood. Think about the people who constructed these things. They needed special skills and knowledge to work with wood. They had to know how to read blueprints, understand the characteristics of different kinds of wood, use a variety of manual and electric tools, and apply mathematical skills.

Nearly every type of woodworking project requires that woodworkers measure materials. Measuring very often includes mixed numbers; for example, a piece of lumber that is $4\frac{1}{2}$ feet long, a wooden rod that has a diameter of $1\frac{1}{8}$ inches, or a cabinet door that is $16\frac{3}{4}$ inches wide. There are two major types of woodworkers: carpenters and furniture makers. Carpentry is the oldest of the woodworking crafts. Almost all of the major construction done on and in houses is accomplished by carpenters. Carpenters construct the skeletons of houses. They also make window frames, windows, door frames, doors, and wood trim. Carpenters who work inside houses install paneling, cabinets, stairs, and some wood trim. Carpenters use their math skills to calculate amounts and dimensions of lumber, the sizes of rooms, and building dimensions.

One of the main tasks of furniture makers is joinery. The techniques of joinery used today were perfected centuries ago. Joinery is the craft of making wooden joints. A joint is an almost invisible connection of two pieces of wood that has the greatest possible strength. Accurate measuring is a requirement for making perfect joints.

If a wooden joint is well made, it will last a very long time. Valuable antique furniture has wooden joints that are just as strong and beautiful as they were when they were created a hundred or more years ago. Joinery skills are also important to the building of musical instruments, such as pianos and violins.

Norm Abram, a master carpenter who stars on the woodworking show "New Yankee Workshop," says that tape measures vary. The longer they are used, the more they stretch. To avoid embarrassing errors, Abram suggests that woodworkers use the same tape measure throughout a project. But what might happen if two carpenters were working on the same job with different tape measures?

1. Two carpenters are constructing a long storage building. Each uses his own tape measure. An inch on Carpenter A's very old tape measure is really $1\frac{1}{32}$ inches. An inch on Carpenter B's tape measure is really $1\frac{1}{64}$ inches. Carpenter A measures a piece of wood and finds it to be 15 inches long. It is really $15\frac{15}{32}$ inches long. Carpenter B measures another piece of wood and finds it to be 15 inches long. It is really $15\frac{15}{64}$ inches long. If the two carpenters put their pieces of wood end to end, how much off the desired length of 30 feet will the total length of wood be?

   $\frac{45}{64}$ inches

Name ____________________ *Math and Social Studies*

2. A carpenter is installing stairs in a new home. Each step is supposed to be $7\frac{1}{8}$ inches wide. The carpenter measures several of the steps and discovers that they are all $8\frac{1}{16}$ inches wide. She puts the boards back into their crates to return them to the lumber mill. How many inches must the width of each board be reduced?

   $\frac{15}{16}$ inch

3. The owner of a house decides to install wood flooring. He discovers that one type of wood flooring called strip flooring is available in widths from $1\frac{1}{2}$ to $3\frac{1}{4}$ inches. He chooses a width that is exactly in the middle of the largest and smallest choices. What does he choose?

   $2\frac{3}{8}$ inches

4. A woman decides to build a spice rack. She draws a design of the rack with dimensions based on the size of the spice jars and the number of jars that she plans to put on the rack. Then the woman draws a side view of the rack to help her decide the points at which she will drive the nails to hold each of the rack's seven shelves. The first nail will be driven $\frac{1}{4}$ inch from the top of the rack. The second nail will be driven $5\frac{3}{4}$ inches from the top of the rack.

   a. How much space will be between the first and second nails?

   $5\frac{1}{2}$ inches

   b. If the woman continues to drive nails the same distance apart, how far will the seventh shelf be from the first? It may help to draw a diagram.

   33 inches

5. Of what value might a fraction calculator be to a carpenter?

   See below.

6. a. What kinds of measuring have you observed or done outside of school?

   See below.

   b. How have math skills been important to the measuring you have observed or done?

   See below.

7. Try building your own special model. Here are some guidelines:
   - Use any material—wood, metal, cardboard, etc., to construct a three-dimensional model of an historical object.
   - The model can be any size and serve any practical purpose. Ideas include Egyptian or Aztec pyramids, Greek or Roman temples, or other famous buildings.
   - Use the same measuring device throughout the project.
   - Provide a sketch of your model with dimensions.
   - Provide a list of your references and/or describe any help you received in building the model.

   Choose a partner and exchange your models and sketches. Measure each other's models using your own measuring devices. How did your measurements compare with those shown on your partner's sketch?

Answers

5. Students' responses will vary. Students may say that it would speed the carpenter's work and make it more accurate.
6. a. Students' responses will vary. Students may suggest building projects at home, sewing, cooking, and measuring their height.

   b. Students may say that their measuring often employs math skills such as adding, subtracting, multiplying, and dividing whole numbers, fractions, or mixed numbers.
7. Answers will vary. Students should note that different measuring devices could result in different measurements. Inconsistent measurements could result in an unsafe or unsturdy structure. Teachers can assess a model's structure based on choice of materials, sturdiness, practicality, creativity, proportions, clarity, and completeness of sketches, and references/assistance.

BIBLIOGRAPHY

FOR TEACHERS

Willoughby, Stephen. *Mathematics Education for a Changing World*. Alexandria, VA: ASCD, 1990.

Room, Adrian, ed. *Guinness Book of Numbers*. New York, NY: Sterling, 1990.

Spangler, David. *Math for Real Kids*. Glenview, IL: Good Year Books, 1997.

FOR STUDENTS

Flint, David. *Weather and Climate: Experiments with Geography*. New York, NY: Watts, 1991.

Knapp, Brian J. *Flood*. Austin, TX: Steck-Vaughn Library, 1990.

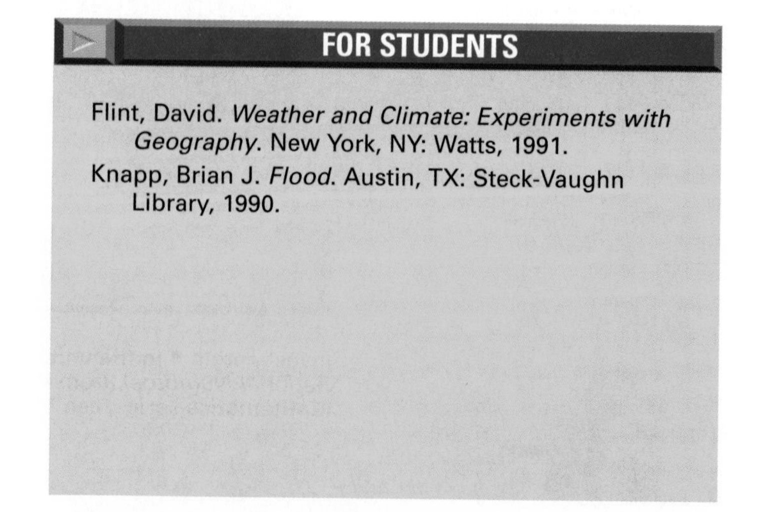

SECTION 6B

Adding and Subtracting Mixed Numbers

▶ Science Link ▶ Geography Link ▶ www.mathsurf.com/6/ch6/floods

Deep Waters Still Run

Police Report
Date: July 17
Filed by: Officer Arlene Smith

When the Parker family returned from vacation, their house was not as they had left it. The piano had been moved to the kitchen. The books in the living room were severely damaged. The car left in the garage would no longer start.

All the doors and windows were locked. There was no sign of forced entry. The only clue was found by the Parkers' daughter. It was a ball of ants.

Have you figured out who committed the crime? If you think it was Mother Nature, you're right. The Parkers weren't crime victims. They were flood victims.

Floods are one of the most powerful forces of nature. They bring great benefits, and they can cause great damage. Mixed numbers are one of the most powerful ideas in mathematics. They can be used to help predict floods, and help people prepare for floods.

1 What kind of damage can a flood cause?

2 How can a flood be a good thing?

3 How could mixed numbers be used to predict and prepare for floods?

341

Where are we now?

In Section 6A, students used addition and subtraction of fractions to solve equations.

They learned how to

- add and subtract fractions with like denominators.
- add and subtract fractions with unlike denominators.
- solve equations by adding and subtracting fractions.

Where are we going?

In Section 6B, students will

- use rounding to estimate sums and differences of mixed numbers.
- add mixed numbers.
- subtract mixed numbers.

Theme: Floods

World Wide Web

If your class has access to the World Wide Web, you might want to use the information found at the Web site address given. The interdisciplinary links relate to topics discussed in this section.

About the Page

This page introduces the theme of the section, floods, and discusses floods as a powerful force of nature.

Ask ...

- What causes a flood? Too much rain or snow melting in a short period of time; Rising rivers or creeks; Tidal waves.
- How could a flood be beneficial? By carrying top soil; By irrigating the land.

Extensions

The following activities do not require access to the World Wide Web.

Science
During a flood, ants will cling to one another in an attempt to save the colony from being separated and destroyed. As the ants cling to each other, they form the shape of a ball capable of floating in flood conditions. Have students research other unusual animal behavior during floods.

Geography
There have been many great floods throughout history in all parts of the world. Ask students to find out where and when some of the great floods occurred. Have students find their locations on the map.

Answers for Questions

1. Knocking down houses and trees, destroying crops, causing power outages.
2. Some people use controlled floods to fertilize or water crops.
3. To measure water levels.

Connect

On page 355, students analyze the principal causes of floods.

Lesson Organizer

Objective

- Estimate sums and differences of mixed numbers.

NCTM Standards

- 1–7

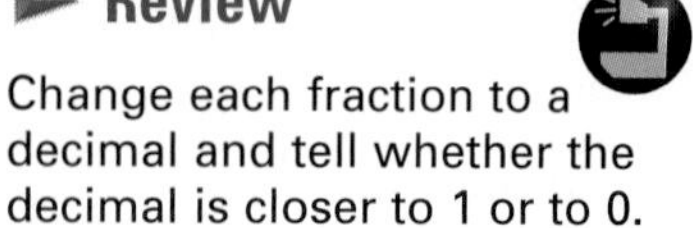

Review

Change each fraction to a decimal and tell whether the decimal is closer to 1 or to 0.

1. $\frac{3}{4}$ 0.75, 1
2. $\frac{5}{12}$ $0.41\overline{6}$, 0
3. $\frac{7}{8}$ 0.875, 1
4. $\frac{5}{6}$ $0.8\overline{3}$, 1
5. $\frac{3}{16}$ 0.1875, 0

Available on Daily Transparency 6-4

1 Introduce

Explore

You may wish to use Teaching Tool Transparency 5: Number Lines and Lesson Enhancement Transparency 29 with this lesson.

The Point
Students read fractional data from a graph and develop intuitive methods of estimating the relationships between those fractions and given fractions.

Ongoing Assessment
Be sure that students can see the relationships among the numbers in the graph and the numbers listed in Step 2.

For Groups That Finish Early
Arrange the mixed numbers in Step 2 in order from least to greatest. $10\frac{6}{7}$, $12\frac{2}{3}$, $22\frac{3}{5}$, $30\frac{1}{11}$, $48\frac{1}{4}$, $50\frac{1}{2}$.

Answers for Explore

1. Knox Landing, Donaldsonville, Red River Landing = Chalmette, New Orleans, Baton Rouge
2. a. Knox Landing; b. New Orleans; c. Donaldsonville; d. Baton Rouge; e. New Orleans; f. Red River Crossing.

6-4 Estimation: Sums and Differences of Mixed Numbers

You'll Learn ...

- to estimate sums and differences of mixed numbers

... How It's Used

Day care providers use estimates of mixed numbers when ordering supplies.

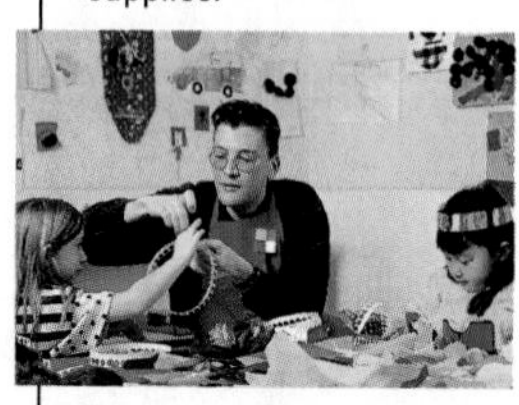

▶ Lesson Link In earlier lessons, you used rounding to make estimates with whole numbers and fractions. Now you'll use rounding to estimate sums and differences of mixed numbers. ◀

Explore Mixed Number Estimation

Breaking the Banks

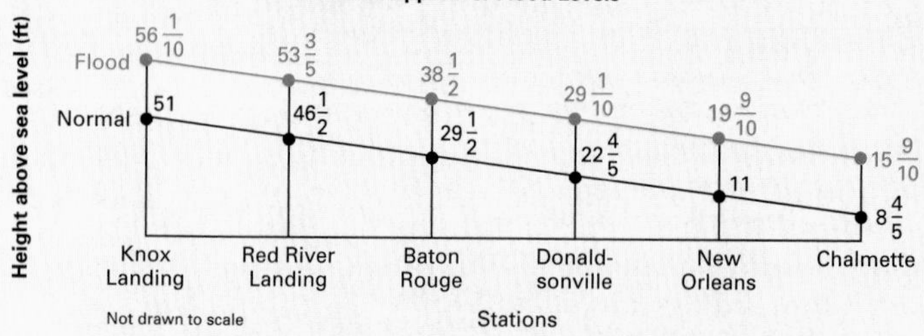

The black line in the diagram lists the normal level of the river at 6 recording stations on the Mississippi River in Louisiana. The red line gives the river's highest level during the 1974 flood.

1. Rank the stations by the amount of flooding at the station. The first station should be where the flood level was closest to the normal level. The last station should be where the flood level was farthest from the normal level.
2. Each number represents the normal level of the river in between two of the stations. Which station is each point closest to?

   a. $50\frac{1}{2}$ **b.** $12\frac{2}{3}$ **c.** $22\frac{3}{5}$ **d.** $30\frac{1}{11}$ **e.** $10\frac{6}{7}$ **f.** $48\frac{1}{4}$

▶ Geography Link
The source of the Mississippi River is Lake Itasca, Minnesota. The mouth is in Louisiana, south of New Orleans.

Learn Estimation: Mixed Numbers

Recall that a *mixed number* contains a whole number and a fraction. You can estimate sums and differences of mixed numbers by rounding each number to the nearest whole number.

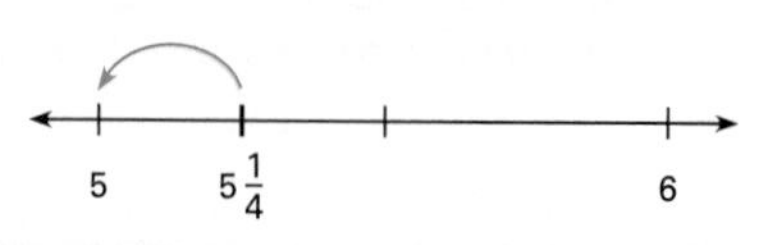

MEETING INDIVIDUAL NEEDS

Resources

- **6-4** Practice
- **6-4** Reteaching
- **6-4** Problem Solving
- **6-4** Enrichment
- **6-4** Daily Transparency
  - Problem of the Day
  - Review
  - Quick Quiz
- Teaching Tool Transparency 5
- Lesson Enhancement Transparency 29

Learning Modalities

Visual Using number lines marked in fractions will help students to identify fractions that are less than, equal to, or greater than $\frac{1}{2}$.

Verbal Have students name a fraction with a denominator of 5 that is greater than $\frac{1}{2}$. Then ask them to name a fraction with a denominator of 12 that is greater than $\frac{1}{2}$. Repeat the question using different denominators until students can verbalize the pattern they notice.

Inclusion

Materials: Graph paper

Have students use graph paper to draw a number line and represent fractions between 0 and 1. Include fractions like the following on the number line: $\frac{1}{12}, \frac{1}{6}, \frac{1}{4}, \frac{1}{3}, \frac{5}{12}, \frac{1}{2}, \frac{7}{12}, \frac{2}{3}, \frac{3}{4}, \frac{4}{5}, \frac{11}{12}$. Students may include other fractions too. Have students refer to this graph to help them determine when to round up or down.

To round a mixed number, look at the fractional part of the mixed number.

Drop the fraction and leave the whole number unchanged if the fractional part is less than $\frac{1}{2}$.

Round up to the next whole number if the fractional part is $\frac{1}{2}$ or greater.

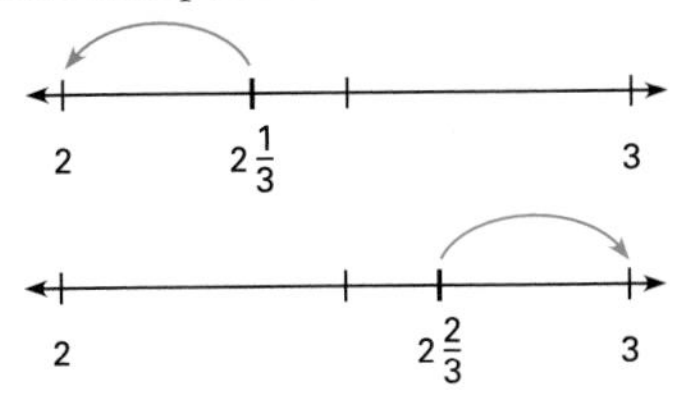

Remember

To round a whole number, look at the digit to the right of the place-value digit in question. If it is less than 5, round down. If it is 5 or greater, round up. [Page 71]

Examples

Round the mean annual rainfall amounts to the nearest inch.

1 Lagos, Nigeria: $72\frac{3}{8}$ in.

The numerator of the fraction, 3, is less than half the denominator, 8. Therefore, $\frac{3}{8} < \frac{1}{2}$.

$72\frac{3}{8}$ rounds down to 72.

2 Athens, Greece: $17\frac{13}{16}$ in.

The numerator of the fraction, 13, is more than half the denominator, 16. Therefore, $\frac{13}{16} > \frac{1}{2}$.

$17\frac{13}{16}$ rounds up to 18.

3 Estimate the sum:

$4\frac{1}{3} + 6\frac{3}{4}$

Round: $4\frac{1}{3} \rightarrow 4$

$6\frac{3}{4} \rightarrow 7$

Estimate: $4 + 7 = 11$

4 Estimate the difference:

$9\frac{1}{2} - 6\frac{9}{10}$

Round: $9\frac{1}{2} \rightarrow 10$

$6\frac{9}{10} \rightarrow 7$

Estimate: $10 - 7 = 3$

Geography Link

Lagos, Nigeria, is the second most populated city in Africa. Cairo, Egypt, is the first.

Try It

Round to the nearest whole number. **a.** $6\frac{2}{7}$ 6 **b.** $1\frac{1}{2}$ 2 **c.** $3\frac{5}{8}$ 4

d. Estimate the sum: $3\frac{1}{2} + 11\frac{7}{8}$ 16 **e.** Estimate the difference: $8\frac{2}{3} - 1\frac{4}{9}$ 8

Check Your Understanding

1. How is rounding mixed numbers like rounding fractions?
2. Describe methods you can use to tell if a fraction is greater than, equal to, or less than $\frac{1}{2}$.
3. Describe a situation where it might be a good idea to round a mixed number up to the next whole number, even if the number would normally be rounded down.

2 Teach

Learn

Alternate Examples

Round the mean annual rainfall amount to the nearest inch.

1. Las Vegas, Nevada: $4\frac{1}{5}$ in.
   $\frac{1}{5} < \frac{1}{2}$
   $4\frac{1}{5}$ rounds down to 4.
2. Mount Washington, New Hampshire: $89\frac{9}{10}$ in.
   $\frac{9}{10} > \frac{1}{2}$
   $89\frac{9}{10}$ rounds up to 90.
3. Estimate the sum: $5\frac{2}{3} + 8\frac{1}{4}$.
   Round: $5\frac{2}{3} \rightarrow 6$
   $8\frac{1}{4} \rightarrow 8$
   Estimate: $6 + 8 = 14$
4. Estimate the difference: $7\frac{3}{8} - 4\frac{11}{12}$.
   Round: $7\frac{3}{8} \rightarrow 7$
   $4\frac{11}{12} \rightarrow 5$
   Estimate: $7 - 5 = 2$

3 Practice and Assess

Check

Answers for Check Your Understanding

1. Round up if fraction is $\frac{1}{2}$ or greater, round down if fraction is less than $\frac{1}{2}$.
2. Possible answer: Determine if the numerator is less than, equal to, or greater than half of the denominator.
3. Possible answer: How many dollar bills should you bring to the store for an item that costs $2\frac{3}{8}$ dollars? \$3

MATH EVERY DAY

Problem of the Day

The Pappas family have three flower boxes on their patio. Each box holds 20 pounds of soil. They bought three 25-lb bags of top soil to fill the boxes. How many bags did they actually use? Write as a mixed number.

$2\frac{2}{5}$ bags

Available on Daily Transparency 6-4

An Extension is provided in the transparency package.

Fact of the Day

April 13, 1992, is the anniversary of the Great Chicago Flood. Water from the Chicago River filled the freight tunnels and basements of downtown buildings.

Mental Math

Name a fraction that is

1. equal to $\frac{1}{2}$. $\frac{4}{8}$
2. greater than $\frac{1}{2}$. $\frac{7}{9}$
3. less than $\frac{1}{2}$. $\frac{3}{7}$

Possible answers are given.

6-4 Exercises and Applications

Assignment Guide

- Basic
  2–38 evens, 42, 43, 46–60 evens
- Average
  2–42 evens, 43–46, 47–61 odds
- Enriched
  2–20 evens, 30–46, 47–61 odds

Exercise Notes

Exercises 1–21

Extension Have students check some of their estimates by writing the fractions as decimals. You may wish to have students use calculators.

Reteaching

Activity

Materials: Fraction Bars

- Use Fraction Bars for a variety of fractions to determine whether fractions are less than, equal to, or greater than $\frac{1}{2}$.
- Arrange the Fraction Bars in order, starting with halves, as shown.

$\frac{1}{2}$						$\frac{1}{2}$					
$\frac{1}{3}$				$\frac{1}{3}$				$\frac{1}{3}$			
$\frac{1}{4}$			$\frac{1}{4}$			$\frac{1}{4}$			$\frac{1}{4}$		
$\frac{1}{8}$		$\frac{1}{8}$	$\frac{1}{8}$		$\frac{1}{8}$	$\frac{1}{8}$		$\frac{1}{8}$	$\frac{1}{8}$		$\frac{1}{8}$
$\frac{1}{12}$	$\frac{1}{12}$	$\frac{1}{12}$	$\frac{1}{12}$	$\frac{1}{12}$	$\frac{1}{12}$	$\frac{1}{12}$	$\frac{1}{12}$	$\frac{1}{12}$	$\frac{1}{12}$	$\frac{1}{12}$	$\frac{1}{12}$

- Tell how each fraction compares with $\frac{1}{2}$.

1. $\frac{3}{4}$ > 2. $\frac{7}{8}$ > 3. $\frac{7}{12}$ >
4. $\frac{5}{12}$ < 5. $\frac{1}{3}$ < 6. $\frac{6}{12}$ =
7. $\frac{9}{12}$ > 8. $\frac{2}{3}$ > 9. $\frac{3}{8}$ <

6-4 Exercises and Applications

Practice and Apply

Getting Started State whether each fraction is closer to 0 or to 1.

1. $\frac{3}{7}$ 0 **2.** $\frac{9}{15}$ 1 **3.** $\frac{5}{8}$ 1 **4.** $\frac{7}{10}$ 1 **5.** $\frac{11}{16}$ 1 **6.** $\frac{2}{9}$ 0

Round to the nearest whole number.

7. $4\frac{3}{8}$ 4 **8.** $3\frac{1}{9}$ 3 **9.** $4\frac{7}{10}$ 5 **10.** $12\frac{1}{5}$ 12 **11.** $25\frac{3}{5}$ 26

12. $1\frac{6}{12}$ 2 **13.** $33\frac{4}{8}$ 34 **14.** $11\frac{7}{9}$ 12 **15.** $8\frac{4}{9}$ 8 **16.** $65\frac{5}{10}$ 66

17. $6\frac{2}{3}$ 7 **18.** $5\frac{1}{5}$ 5 **19.** $2\frac{2}{7}$ 2 **20.** $7\frac{12}{96}$ 7 **21.** $18\frac{34}{101}$ 18

Estimate.

22. $10\frac{11}{20} - 3\frac{6}{25}$ 8 **23.** $1\frac{2}{9} + 8\frac{1}{4}$ 9 **24.** $7\frac{5}{6} - 5\frac{12}{13}$ 2 **25.** $4\frac{3}{7} + 3\frac{1}{5}$ 7

26. $4\frac{1}{3} + 7\frac{3}{4} + 2\frac{8}{9}$ 15 **27.** $11\frac{5}{8} - 4\frac{1}{6}$ 8 **28.** $3\frac{1}{9} + 4\frac{1}{8} + 7\frac{1}{5}$ 14 **29.** $7\frac{5}{8} - 2\frac{4}{5}$ 5

30. $9\frac{1}{9} - 3\frac{1}{3}$ 6 **31.** $12\frac{1}{2} + 7\frac{3}{7} + 5\frac{5}{8}$ 26 **32.** $8\frac{7}{10} - 1\frac{1}{2}$ 7 **33.** $3\frac{2}{5} + 12\frac{1}{6}$ 15

34. $10\frac{3}{5} + 5\frac{2}{3}$ 17 **35.** $22\frac{5}{12} - 2\frac{3}{5}$ 19 **36.** $13\frac{1}{10} + 8\frac{1}{8}$ 21 **37.** $\frac{1}{10} + 7\frac{2}{13}$ 7

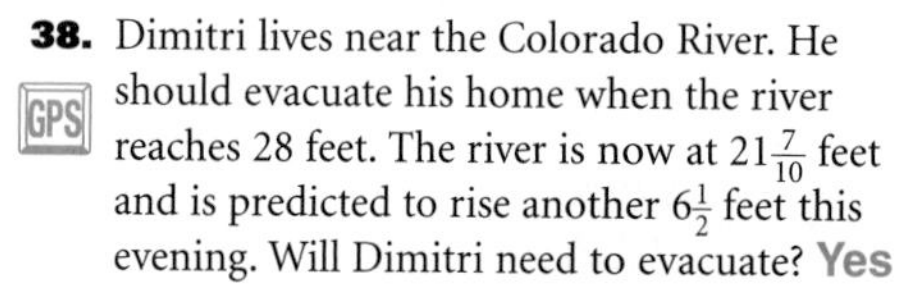

38. GPS Dimitri lives near the Colorado River. He should evacuate his home when the river reaches 28 feet. The river is now at $21\frac{7}{10}$ feet and is predicted to rise another $6\frac{1}{2}$ feet this evening. Will Dimitri need to evacuate? Yes

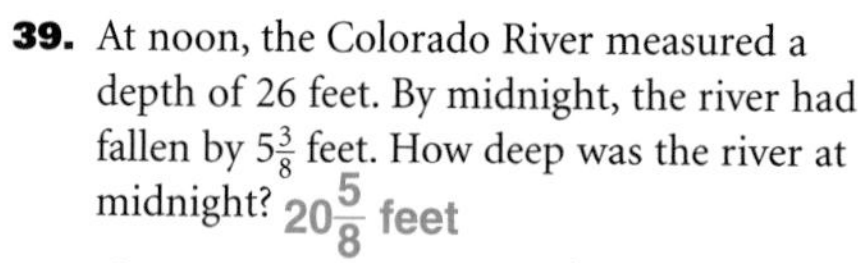

39. At noon, the Colorado River measured a depth of 26 feet. By midnight, the river had fallen by $5\frac{3}{8}$ feet. How deep was the river at midnight? $20\frac{5}{8}$ feet

40. Shannon and Kelly want $14\frac{1}{2}$ feet of rope for a game of tug of war. Shannon has an $8\frac{1}{4}$ foot length of rope. Kelly has a $5\frac{2}{3}$ foot length of rope. If they tie the two ropes together, will it be long enough? No

PRACTICE 6-4

PRACTICE

Name ______________________

Practice 6-4

Estimation: Sums and Differences of Mixed Numbers

Round to the nearest whole number.

1. $2\frac{4}{5}$ 3 2. $11\frac{13}{24}$ 12 3. $19\frac{19}{36}$ 20 4. $9\frac{21}{34}$ 10
5. $2\frac{1}{9}$ 2 6. $8\frac{4}{11}$ 8 7. $15\frac{1}{2}$ 16 8. $17\frac{5}{21}$ 17
9. $9\frac{5}{9}$ 10 10. $4\frac{4}{5}$ 5 11. $5\frac{7}{20}$ 5 12. $2\frac{2}{9}$ 2
13. $6\frac{8}{23}$ 6 14. $3\frac{1}{7}$ 3 15. $6\frac{1}{2}$ 7 16. $13\frac{6}{7}$ 14

Estimate.

17. $1\frac{1}{7} + 6\frac{5}{6}$ 8 18. $9\frac{7}{24} - 7\frac{5}{6}$ 1 19. $19\frac{4}{7} + 7\frac{1}{3}$ 27
20. $14\frac{4}{5} + 1\frac{3}{8}$ 16 21. $20\frac{1}{15} - 15\frac{2}{5}$ 5 22. $4\frac{1}{30} + 2\frac{5}{6} + 3\frac{5}{7}$ 11
23. $7\frac{1}{2} + 6\frac{5}{6}$ 15 24. $4\frac{2}{5} + 2\frac{7}{10}$ 7 25. $12\frac{17}{18} - 1\frac{1}{2}$ 11
26. $16\frac{5}{8} - 2\frac{1}{2}$ 14 27. $9\frac{2}{3} + 3\frac{7}{8} + 4\frac{1}{3}$ 18 28. $6\frac{8}{15} - 1\frac{1}{3}$ 6
29. $11\frac{7}{24} + 10\frac{1}{12}$ 21 30. $5\frac{3}{8} + 1\frac{11}{24}$ 6 31. $11\frac{2}{9} + 4\frac{4}{9} + 8\frac{1}{7}$ 23
32. $3\frac{1}{2} + 9\frac{10}{17}$ 14 33. $3\frac{23}{24} - 1\frac{1}{3}$ 3 34. $12\frac{22}{25} - 11\frac{4}{5}$ 1
35. $7\frac{1}{20} - 4\frac{9}{20}$ 3 36. $1\frac{1}{3} + 14\frac{2}{3}$ 16 37. $9\frac{5}{18} - 4\frac{1}{2}$ 4
38. $23\frac{23}{24} - 21\frac{3}{8}$ 3 39. $1\frac{7}{12} + 9\frac{1}{6}$ 11 40. $11\frac{5}{16} + 11\frac{1}{2}$ 23
41. $6\frac{8}{23} + 5\frac{2}{23}$ 11 42. $9\frac{1}{2} + 8\frac{10}{11}$ 19 43. $5\frac{5}{9} + 5\frac{1}{2}$ 12
44. $20\frac{23}{30} - 8\frac{3}{5}$ 12 45. $24\frac{3}{5} - 17\frac{17}{20}$ 7 46. $12\frac{1}{2} + 3\frac{3}{7} + 2\frac{8}{9}$ 19
47. $15\frac{7}{12} + 11\frac{5}{8}$ 28 48. $2\frac{2}{7} + 1\frac{5}{6}$ 4 49. $19\frac{2}{5} + 5\frac{7}{9}$ 25

50. Bob's punch bowl holds 9 cups. He plans to make a punch using $7\frac{1}{3}$ cups of water and $2\frac{1}{2}$ cups of juice concentrate. Does he need a larger bowl? Yes

51. On Monday, Stephanie bought some stock for $\$36\frac{5}{8}$ per share. Her stock went up 2 on Tuesday, up $1\frac{1}{4}$ on Wednesday, up $3\frac{9}{16}$ on Thursday, and was unchanged on Friday. Estimate the price on Friday. About $44

RETEACHING

Name ______________________

Alternative Lesson 6-4

Estimation: Sums and Differences of Mixed Numbers

A *mixed number* is a number like $6\frac{3}{8}$ that contains a whole number and a fraction. You can estimate sums and differences of mixed numbers by rounding each mixed number to the nearest whole number.

To round a mixed number, look at the fractional part of the mixed number. Drop the fraction and leave the whole number unchanged if the fractional part is less than $\frac{1}{2}$. Round up to the next whole number if the fractional part is $\frac{1}{2}$ or greater.

Example 1

Round $4\frac{1}{3}$ to the nearest whole number.

The numerator of the fraction, 1, is less than half the denominator. So, $\frac{1}{3}$ is less than $\frac{1}{2}$. Drop the fraction.

Round $4\frac{1}{3}$ down to 4.

Try It Round to the nearest whole number.

a. $1\frac{3}{4}$ 3 is more than half of 4, so $1\frac{3}{4}$ rounds to 2.

b. $8\frac{1}{8}$ 8 c. $2\frac{1}{3}$ 2 d. $14\frac{4}{6}$ 15 e. $9\frac{4}{8}$ 10

Example 2

Estimate $1\frac{1}{4} + 3\frac{7}{8}$.

Round each number to the nearest whole number by comparing the numerator to the denominator.

Since 1 is less than half of 4, drop the fraction. $1\frac{1}{4} \rightarrow 1$
Since 7 is more than half of 8, round to the next whole number. $3\frac{7}{8} \rightarrow 4$

Estimate by adding the two whole numbers: 1 + 4 = 5.

An estimate of the sum of $1\frac{1}{4} + 3\frac{7}{8}$ is 5.

Try It Estimate.

f. $4\frac{5}{8} - 2\frac{1}{3}$ Round $4\frac{5}{8}$. 5 Round $2\frac{1}{3}$. 2 Estimate. 3

g. $9\frac{4}{5} - 3\frac{1}{2}$ 6 h. $11\frac{3}{4} + 4\frac{2}{11}$ 16

i. $7\frac{5}{9} - 4\frac{7}{10}$ 3 j. $6\frac{3}{8} + 5\frac{6}{12}$ 12

k. $8\frac{3}{8} - 7\frac{1}{5}$ 1 l. $17\frac{5}{6} - 10\frac{1}{8}$ 8

41. Number Sense Estimate the median of $5\frac{3}{4}, 5\frac{1}{3}, 3\frac{1}{4}, 1\frac{7}{8}, 6\frac{1}{10}, 1\frac{1}{5}, 7\frac{1}{9}, 3\frac{8}{9}$. $4\frac{1}{2}$

42. Test Prep Estimate Eduardo's time in a triathlon if it takes him $\frac{3}{4}$ of an hour to complete the swim, $1\frac{1}{3}$ hours to complete the bike ride, and $1\frac{1}{12}$ hours for the run. C

Ⓐ 1 hour Ⓑ 2 hours Ⓒ 3 hours Ⓓ 4 hours

43. Use the chart to estimate the total weekly rainfall. 7 inches

Day	Sunday	Monday	Tuesday	Wednesday	Thursday	Friday	Saturday
Rainfall (in.)	0	$1\frac{1}{2}$	$1\frac{9}{10}$	0	$2\frac{3}{10}$	$\frac{3}{11}$	$1\frac{3}{7}$

Problem Solving and Reasoning

44. Critical Thinking Estimate the value of x. Explain what you did.

a. $7\frac{1}{4} + x = 10\frac{1}{5}$ **b.** $9\frac{5}{8} - x = 3\frac{1}{2}$ **c.** $x + 7\frac{1}{10} = 15\frac{4}{5}$

45. Communicate Compare rounding mixed numbers by rounding to the nearest whole number with rounding mixed numbers by always rounding up. Which is easier? Which is more accurate? Explain.

46. Critical Thinking At the county fair, Brian entered his frog Horton in the frog jumping contest. Horton's first jump was $10\frac{7}{8}$ feet. His second was $11\frac{1}{5}$ feet, and his third was $9\frac{4}{5}$ feet. Estimate the average length of Horton's jumps. Explain.

Mixed Review

Find the area. *[Lesson 4-6]*

47. 5

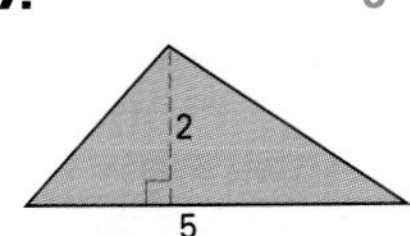

48. 21

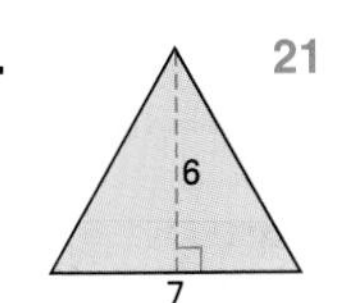

49. 16 in²

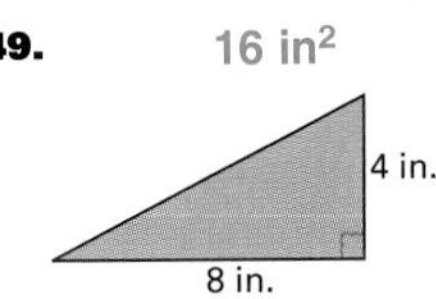

Solve. *[Lesson 2-13]*

50. $m + 22 = 43$ 21 **51.** $n - 11 = 10$ 21 **52.** $15 + v = 27$ 12 **53.** $44 - x = 12$ 32

54. $12b = 36$ 3 **55.** $\frac{x}{2} = 4$ 8 **56.** $3c = 15$ 5 **57.** $\frac{e}{11} = 2$ 22

58. $5z = 35$ 7 **59.** $j + 7 = 13$ 6 **60.** $14 - f = 10$ 4 **61.** $\frac{40}{x} = 8$ 5

PROBLEM SOLVING

Name ______________________

Guided Problem Solving 6-4

GPS PROBLEM 38, STUDENT PAGE 344

Dimitri lives near the Colorado River. He should evacuate his home when the river reaches 28 feet. The river is now at $21\frac{7}{10}$ feet and is predicted to rise another $6\frac{1}{2}$ feet this evening. Will Dimitri need to evacuate?

Possible answers: Items 4, 6, and 9

— Understand —

1. Dimitri should evacuate when the river reaches what level? 28 ft
2. What is the level of the river now? $21\frac{7}{10}$ ft
3. How much is the river predicted to rise this evening? Another $6\frac{1}{2}$ ft

— Plan —

4. Will you use addition or subtraction to decide whether or not Dimitri will need to evacuate? Addition.
5. To round a mixed number, should you drop the fraction if it is more than $\frac{1}{2}$ or if it is less than $\frac{1}{2}$? Less than $\frac{1}{2}$.

— Solve —

6. Round the mixed numbers. Write an equation to tell how high the river will be if it rises as much as predicted. $22 + 7 = 29$
7. Will the river reach 28 feet? Yes.
8. Write a sentence to tell whether or not Dimitri will need to evacuate. Dimitri will need to evacuate since 29 ft is higher than 28 ft.

— Look Back —

9. Could you draw a picture to help you find the answer? Explain. Yes, it could help one visualize the height of the river.

SOLVE ANOTHER PROBLEM

Suppose Dimitri will need to evacuate when the river reaches 30 feet. The river is predicted to rise $5\frac{7}{12}$ feet from its present level of $21\frac{7}{10}$ feet. Will he need to evacuate? No, 28 < 30.

ENRICHMENT

Name ______________________

Extend Your Thinking 6-4

Patterns in Geometry

Graph fractions on a grid by plotting the numerator as x and the denominator as y. For example, the fraction $\frac{1}{3}$ can be plotted as the point (1, 3). Move one space to the right and three spaces up to plot the point.

Possible answers: Items 1-6

1. Write four fractions that are equivalent to $\frac{1}{3}$. $\frac{2}{6}, \frac{3}{9}, \frac{4}{12}, \frac{5}{15}$
2. Plot the equivalent fractions from Question 1.

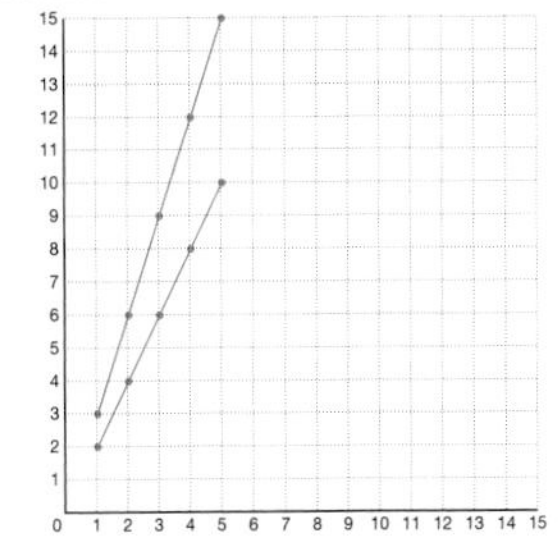

3. Connect the points. Describe the pattern that the graph makes. Points form a line segment, and each point is one space right and three spaces up from the prior point.
4. Predict the pattern that will be made by fractions equivalent to $\frac{1}{2}$. Points will form a line segment, and each point is one space right and two spaces up from the prior point.
5. Write four fractions equivalent to $\frac{1}{2}$. Plot the five fractions on the grid above. Then connect the points. $\frac{2}{4}, \frac{3}{6}, \frac{4}{8}, \frac{5}{10}$
6. Compare the two graphs to find another pattern. The greater the difference between the numerator and denominator, the steeper the line.

Exercise Notes

■ Exercise 41

Error Prevention Be sure that students recall that for a set of data, the median is the middle number.

Exercise Answers

44. a. 3; b. 6; c. 9; Rounded the mixed numbers to whole numbers and then solved the equation.
45. Always rounding up is easier because it does not require determining if the fraction part is greater than, equal to, or less than $\frac{1}{2}$. Rounding to the nearest whole number is more accurate because you will round up or down depending on the fraction.
46. Possible answer: About 11 ft; Estimate the lengths: 11, 11, 10. Add and divide by 3 to get the average.

Alternate Assessment

Performance Have students write three mixed numbers they would round up and three mixed numbers they would round down. Then ask for volunteers to explain what mixed numbers they selected and why.

▶ Quick Quiz

Estimate each sum or difference.

1. $1\frac{1}{2} + \frac{3}{4}$ 3
2. $5\frac{1}{3} - 4\frac{7}{8}$ 0
3. $6\frac{1}{4} - 1\frac{2}{3}$ 4
4. $2\frac{11}{12} + 4\frac{9}{10}$ 8
5. $8\frac{6}{7} + 1\frac{1}{9}$ 10

Available on Daily Transparency 6-4

Lesson Organizer

Objective

- Add mixed numbers.

Materials

- Explore: Fraction Bars

NCTM Standards

- 1–2, 4, 6, 7

► Review

Find each sum. Give improper fractions as mixed numbers.

1. $\frac{5}{6} + \frac{1}{3}$ $1\frac{1}{6}$
2. $\frac{3}{8} + \frac{1}{4}$ $\frac{5}{8}$
3. $\frac{2}{5} + \frac{9}{10}$ $1\frac{3}{10}$
4. $\frac{1}{6} + \frac{5}{8}$ $\frac{19}{24}$
5. $\frac{2}{5} + \frac{3}{4}$ $1\frac{3}{20}$

Available on Daily Transparency 6-5

► Lesson Link

Ask students to describe situations in which they might need to find exact sums of mixed numbers.

1 Introduce

Explore

You may wish to use Teaching Tool Transparency 14: Fraction Bars and Lesson Enhancement Transparency 30 with this lesson.

The Point

Students use Fraction Bars to model addition of mixed numbers with like and unlike denominators.

Ongoing Assessment

Check that students are using the Fraction Bars correctly to model the sums in Step 1. Ask them to give each sum as a mixed number.

a. $3\frac{3}{4}$; b. $3\frac{1}{6}$; c. $3\frac{1}{2}$; d. 4

For Groups That Finish Early

Use Fraction Bars to model the following.

$1\frac{2}{3} + 2\frac{2}{3}$ $4\frac{1}{3}$

$1\frac{1}{4} + 1\frac{5}{8}$ $2\frac{7}{8}$

6-5 Adding Mixed Numbers

You'll Learn ...

- to add mixed numbers

... How It's Used

Farmers add mixed numbers when working with rainfall data.

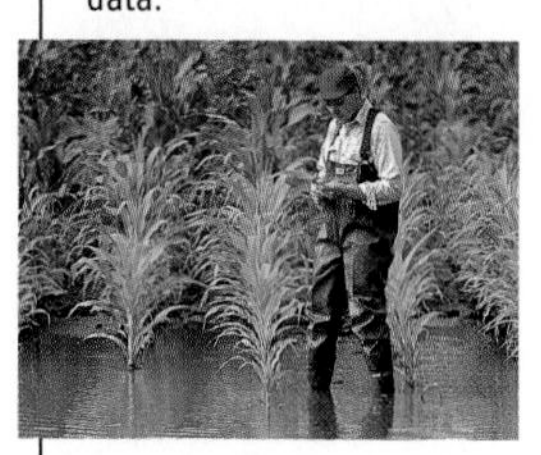

► Lesson Link In the last lesson, you estimated sums of mixed numbers. Now you'll learn how to find mixed number sums exactly. ◄

Explore Adding Mixed Numbers

Another Fine Mix!

Materials: Fraction Bars®

Adding Mixed Numbers

- Draw and label the whole number for the first mixed number.
- Next to that, draw and label the fraction for the first number.
- Next to that, draw and label the whole number for the second mixed number.
- Next to that, draw and label the fraction for the second number.
- Using a whole number and a fraction less than 1, describe the model.

$1\frac{3}{4} + 1\frac{1}{2} = 3\frac{1}{4}$

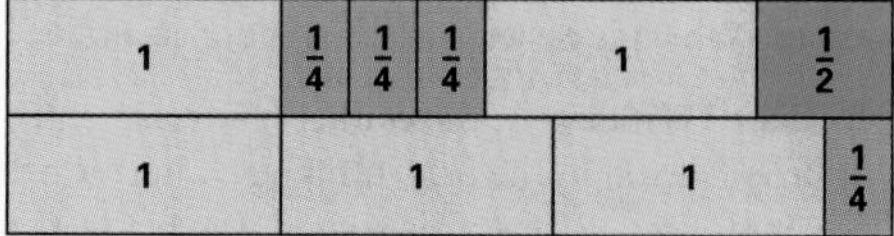

1. Model each problem.

   a. $1\frac{1}{4} + 2\frac{1}{2}$ b. $1\frac{2}{3} + 1\frac{3}{6}$ c. $1\frac{3}{8} + 2\frac{1}{8}$ d. $1\frac{3}{6} + 2\frac{1}{2}$

2. Does the whole number in the answer always equal the sum of the two whole numbers in the problem? Explain.
3. Is the sum of two mixed numbers always a mixed number? Explain.

Learn Adding Mixed Numbers

To add mixed numbers: $5\frac{2}{3} + 1\frac{1}{4}$

1. Add the whole numbers. $5 + 1 = 6$
2. Add the fractions. $\frac{2}{3} + \frac{1}{4} = \frac{8+3}{12} = \frac{11}{12}$
3. Put the two parts together. $= 6\frac{11}{12}$

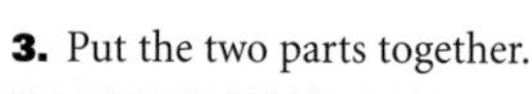

MEETING INDIVIDUAL NEEDS

Resources

6-5 Practice
6-5 Reteaching
6-5 Problem Solving
6-5 Enrichment
6-5 Daily Transparency
  Problem of the Day
  Review
  Quick Quiz
Teaching Tool Transparency 14
Lesson Enhancement Transparency 30
Technology Master 29

Learning Modalities

Visual Encourage students to reproduce as carefully as possible the models they construct with the Fraction Bars in order to get the correct sums.

Kinesthetic Working with concrete models such as pattern blocks and Fraction Bars will add to students' understanding of renaming sums that contain improper fractions.

Inclusion

Many steps are involved when adding mixed numbers. Instead of asking students to do a computation and give an answer, ask students to do only one step of the process and give the result of that step. Then have students report the results of subsequent steps in the same manner. Working step-by-step will allow students to locate errors and clarify the procedure. When breaking down steps, be consistent in the way the steps are written. Allow enough space so that the steps do not become visually confusing. Also, extra space will help students with fine motor difficulties.

If the sum of the fractions is an improper fraction, you may need to rewrite it as a mixed number, and add the whole number parts together.

Examples

1 Add: $1\frac{1}{3} + 2\frac{1}{2}$

Estimate: $1 + 3 = 4$

$$\begin{array}{rcr} 1\frac{1}{3} & = & 1\frac{2}{6} \\ +2\frac{1}{2} & = & +2\frac{3}{6} \\ \hline & & 3\frac{5}{6} \end{array}$$

Rewrite the fractions using the LCD of 6.

Add whole numbers and add fractions. Compare with the estimate.

You can also find the sum using a model.

1	$\frac{1}{3}$	1	1	$\frac{1}{2}$
1	1	1	$\frac{1}{6}$ $\frac{1}{6}$ $\frac{1}{6}$ $\frac{1}{6}$ $\frac{1}{6}$	

2 During the 1993 flood, the Mississippi River rose to $27\frac{9}{10}$ feet. Then it rose another $3\frac{3}{5}$ feet. Find the river's final height.

Estimate: $28 + 4 = 32$

$$\begin{array}{rcr} 27\frac{9}{10} & = & 27\frac{9}{10} \\ +3\frac{3}{5} & = & +3\frac{6}{10} \\ \hline & & 30\frac{15}{10} \end{array}$$

Rewrite the fractions using the LCD of 10.

Add whole numbers and add fractions.

$= 30 + 1\frac{5}{10}$ Rewrite the improper fraction as a mixed number.

$= 31\frac{5}{10}$, or $31\frac{1}{2}$ Add and write in lowest terms.

The final height was $31\frac{1}{2}$ feet.

Try It

Add. **a.** $6 + 2\frac{3}{4}$ $8\frac{3}{4}$ **b.** $1\frac{1}{2} + 3\frac{1}{4}$ $4\frac{3}{4}$ **c.** $3\frac{7}{8} + 2\frac{5}{8}$ $6\frac{1}{2}$ **d.** $4\frac{7}{12} + 2\frac{5}{6}$ $7\frac{5}{12}$

▶ Language Link

The word "Mississippi" comes from the Native American Algonquin language. It means "Father of Waters."

(detail) Currier & Ives, n/ath. & James. "On The St. Lawrence Indian Encampment." Library of Congress, Washington, DC.

Check Your Understanding

1. Could you add mixed numbers by first changing them to decimals? Explain your answer.
2. When adding the fractional parts of mixed numbers, why do you sometimes need to rewrite the fraction sum?

MATH EVERY DAY

▶ Problem of the Day

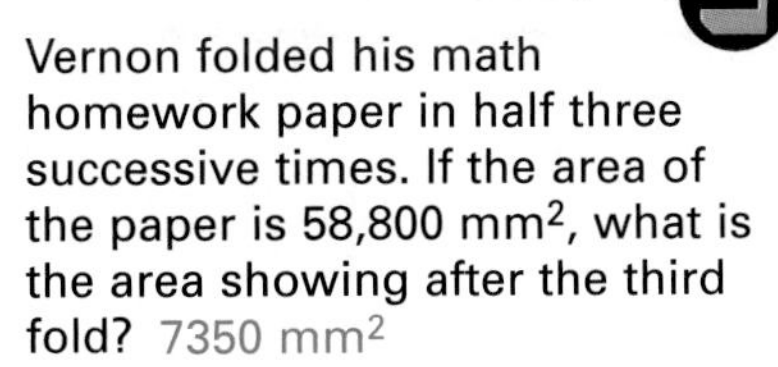

Vernon folded his math homework paper in half three successive times. If the area of the paper is 58,800 mm², what is the area showing after the third fold? 7350 mm²

Available on Daily Transparency 6-5

An Extension is provided in the transparency package.

Fact of the Day

In 1993, floodwaters covered 8 million acres of land in the Midwest. Almost 70,000 people were left homeless.

Mental Math

Find each sum mentally.

1. 5.1 + 3.2 8.3
2. 8.6 + 9 17.6
3. 5 + 3.7 8.7
4. 2.4 + 5.3 7.7
5. 6 + 7.9 13.9

Answers for Explore

1. See page C4.
2. No; If the sum of the fraction parts is greater than 1, the whole number in the answer will be greater than the sum of those in the problem.
3. No; If the sum of the fractions is a whole number, the answer will be a whole number.

2 Teach

Learn

Relate the adding of mixed numbers to the addition of decimals greater than 1.

Alternate Examples

1. Add: $2\frac{1}{4} + 1\frac{2}{3}$

   Estimate: $2 + 2 = 4$

   $$\begin{array}{rcr} 2\frac{1}{4} & = & 2\frac{3}{12} \\ +1\frac{2}{3} & = & +1\frac{8}{12} \\ \hline & & 3\frac{11}{12} \end{array}$$

2. The tide in Boston has a range $3\frac{2}{3}$ feet greater than that of the tide in San Francisco. The range in San Francisco is $5\frac{5}{6}$ feet. Find the range of the tide in Boston.

   Estimate $4 + 6 = 10$

   $$\begin{array}{rcr} 3\frac{2}{3} & = & 3\frac{4}{6} \\ +5\frac{5}{6} & = & +5\frac{5}{6} \\ \hline & & 8\frac{9}{6} \end{array}$$

   $= 9\frac{3}{6}$, or $9\frac{1}{2}$

   The range of the tide in Boston is $9\frac{1}{2}$ feet.

3 Practice and Assess

Check

Answers for Check Your Understanding

1. Yes; The whole number represents the digits to the left of the decimal point, and the fraction represents the digits to the right.
2. Possible answer: The fraction sum may need to be rewritten because it is greater than 1.

Assignment Guide

- **Basic** 1–29 odds, 30–32, 35–45 odds
- **Average** 1–29 odds, 30–35, 38–44 evens
- **Enriched** 4–28 evens, 29–37, 38–44 evens

Exercise Notes

Exercises 5–28

Estimation You might ask students to estimate the sums and compare them with their actual answers.

Exercise 30

Sports As of 1996, the world record for the women's 4 × 100-meter relay was 41.37 seconds, set by an East German team on October 6, 1985. The 4 × 100-meter relay record time for American women as of 1996 was 41.49 seconds.

Reteaching

Activity

Materials: Play money

- You can use play money to add mixed numbers with different denominators.
- What fraction of a dollar is a nickel? $\frac{1}{20}$ A dime? $\frac{1}{10}$ A quarter? $\frac{1}{4}$ A half-dollar? $\frac{1}{2}$
- To add $2\frac{1}{4}$ and $3\frac{3}{10}$, think of adding 2 dollars and one quarter and 3 dollars and 3 dimes. The sum of the dollars is 5. The sum of the coins is 55¢, which is 11 nickels, or $\frac{11}{20}$ of a dollar. The sum is $5\frac{11}{20}$.
- You could also exchange the quarter and the dimes to nickels first. How many nickels are in 1 quarter? 5 nickels How many nickels are in 3 dimes? 6 nickels Is the sum still 11 nickels, or $\frac{11}{20}$? Yes
- Use play money to find the following sums.
  1. $1\frac{1}{4} + \frac{7}{10}$ $1\frac{19}{20}$
  2. $3\frac{1}{10} + 2\frac{1}{2}$ $5\frac{6}{10}$ or $5\frac{3}{5}$
  3. $3\frac{1}{4} + \frac{3}{10}$ $3\frac{11}{20}$

6-5 Exercises and Applications

Practice and Apply

Getting Started Add.

1. $6 + 5\frac{2}{3}$ $11\frac{2}{3}$
2. $8 + 7\frac{3}{8}$ $15\frac{3}{8}$
3. $4\frac{1}{2} + 2$ $6\frac{1}{2}$
4. $3\frac{6}{7} + 9$ $12\frac{6}{7}$

Add. Write each answer as a whole or mixed number in lowest terms.

5. $5\frac{1}{3} + 4\frac{2}{6}$ $9\frac{2}{3}$
6. $6\frac{1}{2} + 2\frac{5}{6}$ $9\frac{1}{3}$
7. $35 + 27\frac{3}{4}$ $62\frac{3}{4}$
8. $47\frac{1}{2} + 49\frac{3}{7}$ $96\frac{13}{14}$
9. $8\frac{2}{4} + 2\frac{1}{2}$ 11
10. $12\frac{3}{5} + 3\frac{4}{5}$ $16\frac{2}{5}$
11. $1\frac{7}{8} + 3\frac{5}{6}$ $5\frac{17}{24}$
12. $9\frac{3}{7} + 1\frac{2}{7}$ $10\frac{5}{7}$
13. $1\frac{3}{5} + 5\frac{1}{5}$ $6\frac{4}{5}$
14. $3\frac{4}{5} + 15$ $18\frac{4}{5}$
15. $8\frac{2}{9} + 7\frac{2}{3}$ $15\frac{8}{9}$
16. $22\frac{3}{4} + 19\frac{2}{5}$ $42\frac{3}{20}$
17. $7\frac{4}{9} + 5\frac{2}{3}$ $13\frac{1}{9}$
18. $45\frac{3}{4} + 21\frac{7}{8}$ $67\frac{5}{8}$
19. $1\frac{3}{10} + 12\frac{4}{5}$ $14\frac{1}{10}$
20. $2\frac{4}{5} + 3\frac{1}{2}$ $6\frac{3}{10}$
21. $9\frac{3}{7} + 12\frac{1}{3}$ $21\frac{16}{21}$
22. $12\frac{2}{3} + 7\frac{5}{8}$ $20\frac{7}{24}$
23. $3\frac{3}{8} + 4\frac{5}{8}$ 8
24. $8\frac{2}{3} + 8\frac{3}{4}$ $17\frac{5}{12}$
25. $9\frac{7}{9} + 32$ $41\frac{7}{9}$
26. $7\frac{1}{3} + 2\frac{2}{3}$ 10
27. $42\frac{1}{6} + 9\frac{11}{12}$ $52\frac{1}{12}$
28. $93\frac{1}{12} + 7$ $100\frac{1}{12}$

29. **Career** The U.S. Geological Survey measured the depth of a Rio Grande River channel during flooding. The difference between the highest and lowest depths was $9\frac{3}{4}$ feet. If the lowest reading was $28\frac{1}{2}$ feet, what was the highest reading? $38\frac{1}{4}$

30. **Test Prep** Samantha ran her part of a 400-meter relay in $1\frac{1}{2}$ minutes. Juana ran in $1\frac{1}{3}$ minutes, Anna in $1\frac{3}{8}$, and Adrienne in $1\frac{1}{4}$. How long did it take their team to run the race? B

    Ⓐ $4\frac{11}{24}$ min. Ⓑ $5\frac{11}{24}$ min. Ⓒ $13\frac{1}{24}$ min. Ⓓ 4 min.

PRACTICE 6-5

PRACTICE

Name ____________

Practice 6-5

Adding Mixed Numbers

Add. Write the answer as a whole or mixed number in lowest terms.

1. $13\frac{1}{5} + 5\frac{3}{5}$ $18\frac{4}{5}$
2. $7\frac{2}{5} + 1\frac{2}{3}$ $9\frac{1}{15}$
3. $9\frac{20}{23} + 14$ $23\frac{20}{23}$
4. $6 + 14\frac{1}{2}$ $20\frac{1}{2}$
5. $4 + 9\frac{5}{17}$ $13\frac{5}{17}$
6. $3\frac{16}{19} + 7$ $10\frac{16}{19}$
7. $10\frac{13}{15} + 4\frac{13}{15}$ $15\frac{11}{15}$
8. $2 + 16\frac{5}{19}$ $18\frac{5}{19}$
9. $6\frac{1}{7} + 19\frac{2}{5}$ $25\frac{19}{35}$
10. $15\frac{1}{2} + 17\frac{1}{7}$ $32\frac{9}{14}$
11. $22\frac{1}{6} + 10\frac{4}{5}$ $32\frac{29}{30}$
12. $10\frac{1}{4} + 7\frac{3}{4}$ 18
13. $1\frac{4}{5} + 3\frac{5}{6}$ $5\frac{19}{30}$
14. $11\frac{10}{11} + 5$ $16\frac{10}{11}$
15. $11\frac{3}{8} + 16\frac{3}{4}$ $28\frac{1}{8}$
16. $11\frac{4}{5} + 2\frac{13}{15}$ $14\frac{2}{3}$
17. $16\frac{4}{15} + 8\frac{13}{15}$ $25\frac{2}{15}$
18. $3\frac{7}{12} + 6\frac{17}{24}$ $10\frac{7}{24}$
19. $3\frac{1}{15} + 4\frac{3}{5}$ $7\frac{2}{3}$
20. $4\frac{1}{3} + 7\frac{5}{13}$ $11\frac{28}{39}$
21. $1\frac{3}{8} + 10$ $11\frac{3}{8}$
22. $12\frac{1}{8} + 1\frac{1}{3}$ $13\frac{11}{24}$
23. $8\frac{7}{15} + 3\frac{5}{9}$ $12\frac{1}{45}$
24. $2\frac{21}{22} + 5\frac{1}{2}$ $8\frac{5}{11}$
25. $5\frac{5}{12} + 10\frac{11}{24}$ $15\frac{7}{8}$
26. $18 + 8\frac{11}{13}$ $26\frac{11}{13}$
27. $3\frac{3}{7} + 1\frac{1}{2}$ $4\frac{13}{14}$

Use the table for Exercises 28–30.

U.S. Immigrants, 1820–1993 (millions)				
Europe	Asia	North America, Central America	South America	Africa, Oceania, Other
$37\frac{11}{20}$	$7\frac{1}{20}$	$13\frac{11}{20}$	$1\frac{4}{10}$	$1\frac{1}{50}$

28. How many people immigrated from Europe? 37,550,000
29. How many people immigrated from Asia and South America combined? 8,450,000
30. What was the total number of immigrants? 60,570,000
31. A cake recipe calls for $2\frac{1}{3}$ cups of milk plus enough water to make $3\frac{1}{4}$ cups of liquid. How much water is used in the recipe? $\frac{11}{12}$ cup

RETEACHING

Name ____________

Alternative Lesson 6-5

Adding Mixed Numbers

Just as you can add whole numbers and add fractions, you can add mixed numbers. To add mixed numbers:

1. Add the whole numbers.
2. Add the fractions.
3. Put the two parts together.

If the sum of the fractions is an improper fraction, you may need to rewrite it as a mixed number and add the whole number parts together.

Example

Add $1\frac{1}{2} + 3\frac{5}{6}$. Write the sum as a whole or mixed number in lowest terms.

Rewrite the fractions using their LCD 6. $1\frac{1}{2} \rightarrow 1\frac{3}{6}$; $+3\frac{5}{6} \rightarrow +3\frac{5}{6}$

Add the whole numbers. Then add the fractions. $4\frac{8}{6}$

Rewrite the improper fraction as a mixed number. $4 + 1\frac{2}{6}$

Add the whole number parts. Write the sum in lowest terms. $5\frac{2}{6} = 5\frac{1}{3}$

So, $1\frac{1}{2} + 3\frac{5}{6} = 5\frac{1}{3}$.

Try It Add. Write each sum as a whole or mixed number in lowest terms.

a. $8\frac{1}{5} + 12\frac{3}{5}$ The fractions have like denominators.

Add the whole numbers. $8 + 12 = 20$ Add the fractions. $\frac{1}{5} + \frac{3}{5} = \frac{4}{5}$

Add the two parts. $20 + \frac{4}{5} = 20\frac{4}{5}$

b. $12\frac{3}{4} + 3\frac{1}{2}$ Rewrite using the LCD. $12\frac{3}{4} + 3\frac{2}{4}$

Add the whole numbers. $12 + 3 = 15$ Add the fractions. $\frac{3}{4} + \frac{2}{4} = \frac{5}{4}$

Rewrite as mixed number. $1\frac{1}{4}$

Add the whole number parts. Write the sum in lowest terms. $16\frac{1}{4}$

c. $4\frac{7}{8} + 2\frac{3}{4}$ $7\frac{5}{8}$

d. $5\frac{2}{3} + 7\frac{1}{12}$ $12\frac{3}{4}$

e. $1\frac{1}{2} + 1\frac{1}{2}$ 3

f. $2\frac{2}{5} + 3\frac{2}{5}$ $5\frac{4}{5}$

g. $4\frac{1}{6} + 2\frac{2}{3}$ $6\frac{5}{6}$

h. $3\frac{5}{8} + 5\frac{3}{4}$ $9\frac{3}{8}$

i. $6\frac{1}{4} + 7\frac{5}{6}$ $14\frac{1}{12}$

j. $9\frac{2}{9} + 7\frac{2}{3}$ $16\frac{8}{9}$

Use the table for Exercises 31–33.

Damages from 1984 Lower Mississippi River Flood (millions of dollars)				
Urban Development	Rural Development	Agricultural Crops	Government and Utilities	Miscellaneous
$5\frac{1}{4}$	$5\frac{1}{2}$	$1\frac{2}{3}$	$2\frac{4}{5}$	$\frac{2}{3}$

31. How much damage was done to Urban and Rural Development? $10\frac{3}{4}$ millions of dollars

32. How much damage was done to Government and Utilities, and to Miscellaneous? $3\frac{7}{15}$ millions of dollars

33. What was the total damage? $15\frac{53}{60}$ millions of dollars

Problem Solving and Reasoning

34. Communicate Describe a situation where you use addition and would want to write $7\frac{5}{3}$ as $8\frac{2}{3}$. Explain your reasoning.

36. Journal Describe some similarities and differences between adding with whole numbers and adding with mixed numbers.

35. Choose a Strategy GPS The combined area of Shapes A and B is $4\frac{2}{3}$ m². The area of Shape B is $1\frac{1}{3}$ m² more than the area of Shape A. Find the areas of both shapes.

Problem Solving STRATEGIES

- Look for a Pattern
- Make an Organized List
- Make a Table
- Guess and Check
- Work Backward
- Use Logical Reasoning
- Draw a Diagram
- Solve a Simpler Problem

Mixed Review

Find the circumference of each object. *[Lesson 4-7]*

37. 9.42 ft 62.8 in. 113.04 in.

3 ft. 10 in. 18 in.

Write in standard form. *[Lesson 3-6]*

38. 3.1×10^3 3100 **39.** 4.27×10^5 427,000 **40.** 5.45×10^7 54,500,000 **41.** 1.124×10^6 1,124,000

42. 7.11×10^4 71,100 **43.** 9.0×10^9 9,000,000,000 **44.** 2.22×10^3 2220 **45.** 6.663×10^{11} 666,300,000,000

PROBLEM SOLVING 6-5

Exercise Notes

Exercise 35

Problem-Solving Tip Working backward, guessing and checking, and drawing a diagram are all strategies that could be used to solve this problem.

Exercise 37

Error Prevention You may need to remind students that the formula for the circumference of a circle is $C = 2\pi r$.

Exercise Answers

34. Possible answer: Jen has $5\frac{2}{3}$ buckets of green beads, $2\frac{1}{3}$ red, and $\frac{2}{3}$ yellow. When she combines the beads, how many full buckets will she have? If the answer is left as $7\frac{5}{3}$, it would seem as if she has 7 full buckets, but she really has 8.

35. A: $1\frac{2}{3}$m²; B: 3m²

36. Possible answer: Similarities: Both involve whole numbers; When adding the whole numbers, grouping is used the same way. Differences: Adding mixed numbers involves fractions; Mixed numbers can be written in lowest terms.

Alternate Assessment

You may want to use the *Interactive CD-ROM Journal* with this assessment.

Journal Have students write an example and explain how they would add two mixed numbers.

Quick Quiz

Find each sum.

1. $1\frac{1}{2} + \frac{3}{4}$ $2\frac{1}{4}$
2. $5\frac{1}{3} + 4\frac{7}{8}$ $10\frac{5}{24}$
3. $6\frac{1}{4} + 1\frac{2}{3}$ $7\frac{11}{12}$
4. $2\frac{11}{12} + 4\frac{5}{6}$ $7\frac{3}{4}$
5. $8\frac{3}{4} + 1\frac{5}{6}$ $10\frac{7}{12}$

Available on Daily Transparency 6-5

PROBLEM SOLVING

Name ______

Guided Problem Solving 6-5

GPS PROBLEM 35, STUDENT PAGE 349

The combined area of Shapes A and B is $4\frac{2}{3}$ m². The area of Shape B is $1\frac{1}{3}$ m² more than the area of Shape A. Find the areas of both shapes.

— Understand —

1. What are you asked to find? Areas of Shapes A and B.
2. What is the combined area of the shapes? $4\frac{2}{3}$ m²
3. How much larger is Shape B than Shape A? $1\frac{1}{3}$ m²

— Plan —

The diagram represents the combined area of the two shapes. Use the diagram to answer the questions.

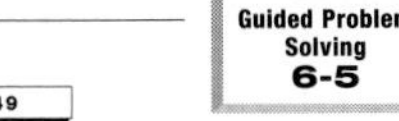

4. Write a "B" in the sections of the diagram that are equal to difference in the areas of Shape B and Shape A.
5. With the difference accounted for, the area of Shape A equals the area of Shape B. Write an "A" for Shape A and a "B" for Shape B in the remaining sections.

— Solve —

6. Use the sections labeled "A" in the diagram to write the area of Shape A. $1\frac{2}{3}$ m²
7. Use the sections labeled "B" in the diagram to write the area of Shape B. 3 m²

— Look Back —

8. Write and solve an addition equation to check your answer. $1\frac{2}{3} + 3 = 4\frac{2}{3}$

SOLVE ANOTHER PROBLEM

The combined area of Shapes C and D is $8\frac{3}{4}$ in². The area of Shape D is $2\frac{1}{4}$ in² more than the area of Shape C. Find the areas of both shapes.
Shape C: $3\frac{1}{4}$ in²; Shape D: $5\frac{1}{2}$ in².

ENRICHMENT

Name ______

Extend Your Thinking 6-5

Decision Making Possible answers: 1-4.

You want to make a meat loaf. The only measuring cups in the house measure $\frac{1}{8}$ c and $\frac{1}{4}$ c. There are only $\frac{1}{8}$, $\frac{1}{4}$, and $\frac{1}{2}$ teaspoon measuring spoons. Since you don't want to continually wash and dry the measuring cups, you want to use certain ones for dry ingredients and the rest for wet ingredients.

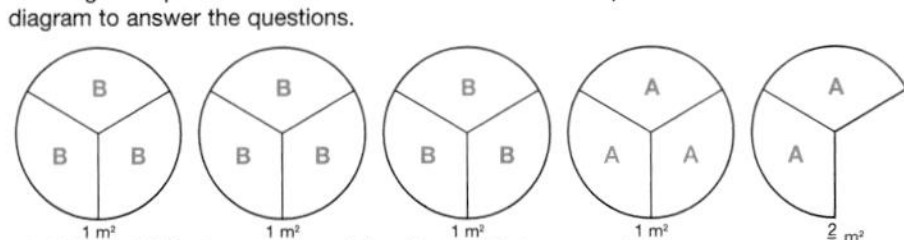

Meat Loaf

	Topping
$\frac{1}{2}$ lb ground beef W	2 tsp mustard W
$\frac{1}{2}$ c catsup W	$\frac{1}{4}$ c catsup W
2 eggs W	2 tsp brown sugar D
$\frac{1}{4}$ c tomato juice W	
$\frac{3}{4}$ c bran cereal D	
$1\frac{1}{2}$ tsp onion flakes D	
$\frac{1}{2}$ tsp Worcestershire sauce W	
$\frac{1}{2}$ tsp salt D	
$\frac{1}{8}$ tsp pepper D	

Mix ingredients in column 1. Place in 9 × 5 pan. Combine topping ingredients. Spread over meat loaf. Bake at 400°F for 45 minutes.

1. Identify the dry and wet ingredients in the recipe by placing a D beside the dry ingredients and a W beside the wet ingredients.
2. Which measuring cups and spoons will you use only for dry ingredients? Which for wet ingredients?
Dry: $\frac{1}{8}$ c, $\frac{1}{8}$ tsp, $\frac{1}{4}$ tsp; Wet: $\frac{1}{4}$ c, $\frac{1}{2}$ tsp
3. Show how you will measure each quantity using the measuring cups you decided to use in Question 2.
$\frac{1}{4}$ c juice; $(\frac{1}{8}+\frac{1}{8}+\frac{1}{8}+\frac{1}{8}+\frac{1}{8}+\frac{1}{8})$ c cereal; $(\frac{1}{4}+\frac{1}{4}+\frac{1}{4}+\frac{1}{4}+\frac{1}{4}+\frac{1}{4})$ tsp onion; $\frac{1}{2}$ tsp Worcestershire sauce; $(\frac{1}{4}+\frac{1}{4})$ tsp salt; $\frac{1}{8}$ tsp pepper; $(\frac{1}{2}+\frac{1}{2}+\frac{1}{2}+\frac{1}{2})$ tsp mustard; $(\frac{1}{4}+\frac{1}{4})$ c catsup; $(\frac{1}{4}+\frac{1}{4}+\frac{1}{4}+\frac{1}{4}+\frac{1}{4}+\frac{1}{4}+\frac{1}{4}+\frac{1}{4})$ tsp brown sugar.
4. Rewrite the recipe so that it makes two meat loaves.
1 lb beef; 1 c catsup; 4 eggs; $\frac{1}{2}$ c juice; $1\frac{1}{2}$ c cereal; 3 tsp onion; 1 tsp Worcest. sauce; 1 tsp salt; $\frac{1}{4}$ tsp pepper; 4 tsp mustard; $\frac{1}{2}$ c catsup; 4 tsp brown sugar.

INTERACTIVE LESSON

6-6 Lesson Organizer

Objective

- Subtract mixed numbers.

Materials

- Explore: Fraction Bars

NCTM Standards

- 1–4, 6, 7, 9

Review

Find each difference.

1. $\frac{5}{6} - \frac{1}{3}$ $\frac{1}{2}$
2. $\frac{3}{8} - \frac{1}{4}$ $\frac{1}{8}$
3. $\frac{7}{10} - \frac{2}{5}$ $\frac{3}{10}$
4. $\frac{5}{8} - \frac{1}{6}$ $\frac{11}{24}$
5. $\frac{4}{5} - \frac{3}{4}$ $\frac{1}{20}$

Available on Daily Transparency 6-6

1 Introduce

Explore

You may wish to use Teaching Tool Transparency 14: Fraction Bars and Lesson Enhancement Transparency 31 with this lesson.

The Point
Students use Fraction Bars to model subtraction of mixed numbers with like and unlike denominators.

Ongoing Assessment
Check that students are using the Fraction Bars correctly to model the differences in Step 1.

For Groups That Finish Early
Have each person in your pair write a subtraction problem. Use Fraction Bars to model each difference.

6-6 Subtracting Mixed Numbers

You'll Learn ...

- to subtract mixed numbers

... How It's Used

Carpenters subtract mixed numbers when determining the amount of lumber needed to finish a project.

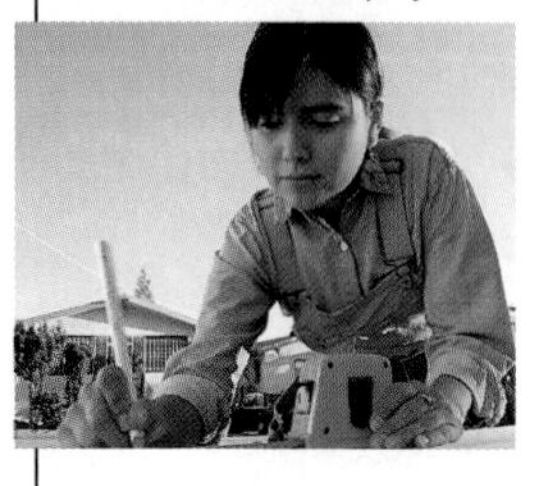

▶ Lesson Link You've seen that regrouping may be necessary when you add mixed numbers. You may also need to regroup to subtract mixed numbers. ◀

Explore Subtracting Mixed Numbers

What Difference Does It Make?

Materials: Fraction Bars®

$2\frac{1}{4} - 1\frac{1}{2} = \frac{3}{4}$

1	1	$\frac{1}{4}$		
1	$\frac{1}{2}$	$\frac{1}{4}$	$\frac{1}{4}$	$\frac{1}{4}$

Subtracting Mixed Numbers

- Draw and label the whole number for the first mixed number.
- Next to that, draw and label the fraction for the first number.
- Below the first whole number, draw and label the whole number for the second mixed number.
- Next to that, draw and label the fraction for the second number.
- Next to the second mixed-number model, draw and label a model that equals the difference between the first and second model.

1. Model these problems.

a. $2\frac{3}{4} - 1\frac{1}{4}$ **b.** $3\frac{2}{3} - 1\frac{1}{6}$ **c.** $2 - \frac{3}{4}$ **d.** $4\frac{1}{4} - 1\frac{1}{2}$ **e.** $4\frac{3}{8} - 3\frac{3}{4}$

2. Can you subtract two mixed numbers if the fraction in the second mixed number is larger than the fraction in the first mixed number? Explain.

3. If one mixed number is subtracted from another mixed number, is the difference always a mixed number? Explain.

Learn Subtracting Mixed Numbers

When subtracting whole numbers, you sometimes have a digit in the second number that's larger than the digit in the same place value in the first number. In order to subtract, you need to "borrow," using the digit to the left.

$$\begin{array}{r} {\scriptstyle 6\,1} \\ 72 \\ -\,18 \\ \hline 54 \end{array}$$

MEETING INDIVIDUAL NEEDS

Resources

6-6 Practice
6-6 Reteaching
6-6 Problem Solving
6-6 Enrichment
6-6 Daily Transparency
 Problem of the Day
 Review
 Quick Quiz
Teaching Tool Transparency 14
Lesson Enhancement Transparency 31
Technology Master 30
Chapter 6 Project Master

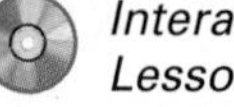

Interactive CD-ROM Lesson

Learning Modalities

Logical Relate the subtraction of mixed numbers to the subtraction of decimals greater than 1. Sometimes the fraction being subtracted is larger than the fraction being subtracted from. Explain that this corresponds to regrouping, or "borrowing," which is used when subtracting decimals.

Kinesthetic Use pattern blocks and Fraction Bars to help students understand the process of borrowing when the fractional part of the mixed number to be subtracted is greater than the fractional part to be subtracted from.

English Language Development

Pair students with limited English ability with English speakers to work on the exercises in this lesson. Have students take turns explaining to each other how they answered the questions. Students will increase their ability to describe their mathematical thinking through the modeling of the English speakers and by verbalizing mathematical explanations.

You can use a similar process when subtracting mixed numbers.

$9\frac{1}{5} - 4\frac{4}{5} = ?$ $\qquad$ $7 - 2\frac{1}{3} = ?$

1. Borrow 1 from the whole number. $\qquad 8\frac{1}{5} + 1 \qquad 6 + 1$
2. Rewrite the 1 as a fraction with the same numerator and denominator. $\qquad 8\frac{1}{5} + \frac{5}{5} \qquad 6 + \frac{3}{3}$
3. If borrowing with a mixed number, add the fractions together. $\qquad 8\frac{6}{5} - 4\frac{4}{5} = 4\frac{2}{5} \qquad 6\frac{3}{3} - 2\frac{1}{3} = 4\frac{2}{3}$

Examples

1 Subtract $7\frac{2}{9} - 3\frac{2}{3}$.

$7\frac{2}{9} = 6 + 1\frac{2}{9} = 6 + \frac{11}{9} = 6\frac{11}{9}$ Borrow from whole number.

$-3\frac{2}{3} = \qquad -3\frac{6}{9}$ Rewrite with a common denominator.

$= 3\frac{5}{9}$ Subtract.

2 Prior to the construction of the Aswan Dam, Egypt's Nile River flooded its banks each summer, fertilizing nearby fields. If the river rose 3 feet above flood level, then fell $1\frac{5}{12}$ feet, find the final height of the river.

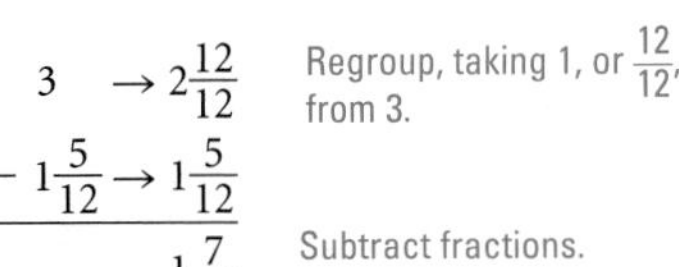

$3 \rightarrow 2\frac{12}{12}$ Regroup, taking 1, or $\frac{12}{12}$, from 3.

$-1\frac{5}{12} \rightarrow 1\frac{5}{12}$

$1\frac{7}{12}$ Subtract fractions. Subtract whole numbers.

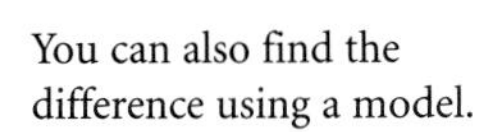

You can also find the difference using a model.

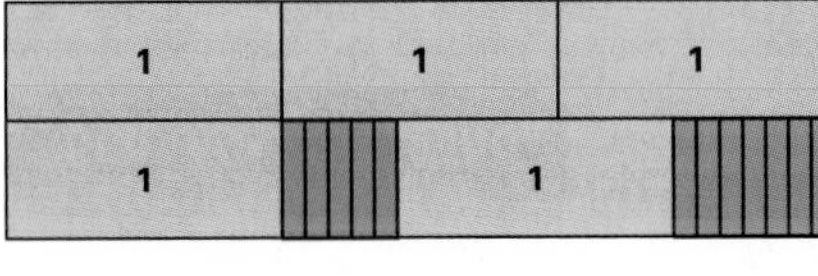
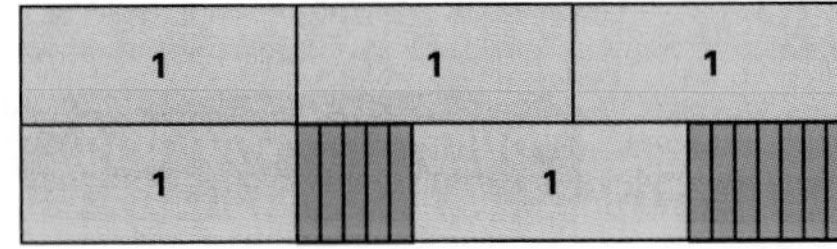

The river's height was $1\frac{7}{12}$ feet above flood level.

Try It

Subtract. **a.** $6\frac{1}{5} - 2\frac{4}{5}$ $3\frac{2}{5}$ **b.** $8\frac{1}{2} - 3\frac{2}{3}$ $4\frac{5}{6}$ **c.** $12 - 9\frac{5}{9}$ $2\frac{4}{9}$

History Link

Dams are often constructed to control floods. The oldest known dam was built on the Nile River in Kosheish, Egypt, in 2900 B.C.

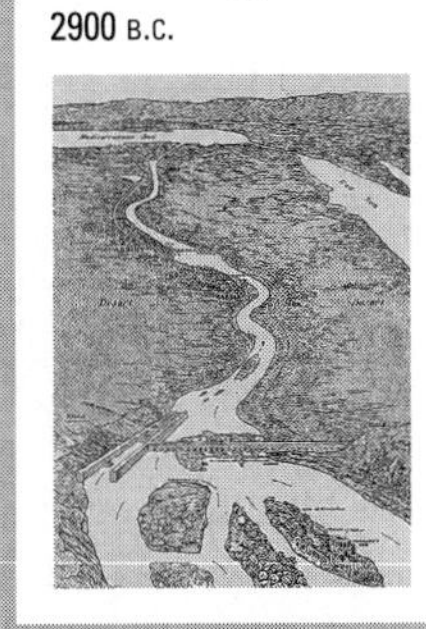

MATH EVERY DAY

Problem of the Day

The earthen mounds located near Epps, Louisiana, are one of the earliest known Native American settlements in North America. It took about 3 million hours to construct the mounds. How many people would it take to build a replica in one year if each worker works a forty-hour week for fifty weeks? 1500 people

Available on Daily Transparency 6-6

An Extension is provided in the transparency package.

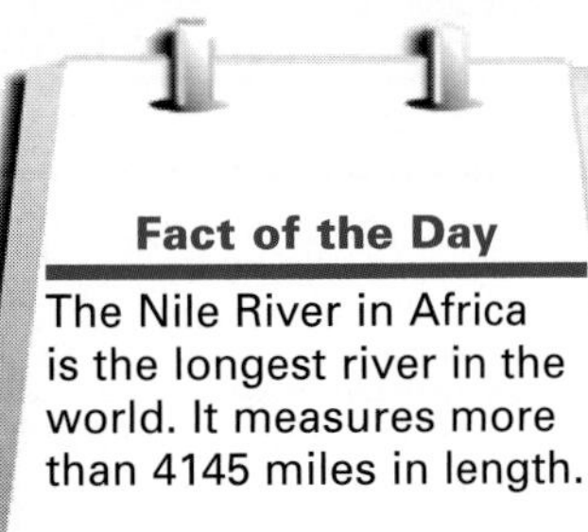

Fact of the Day

The Nile River in Africa is the longest river in the world. It measures more than 4145 miles in length.

Mental Math

Find each difference mentally.

1. 5.8 − 3.2 2.6
2. 8.6 − 5 3.6
3. 4.8 − 0.7 4.1
4. 2.4 − 1.3 1.1
5. 7.9 − 6 1.9

Answers for Explore

1. a. b. c. d. e. (models)
2. Yes; "Borrow" one whole from the first mixed number and add it to the fraction to make it an improper fraction.
3. No; If the fractions are the same, the answer will be a whole number. If the answer is less than 1, it will be a proper fraction.

2 Teach

Learn

Alternate Examples

1. Subtract $2\frac{1}{4} - 1\frac{2}{3}$.

$2\frac{1}{4} = 2\frac{3}{12} = 1 + 1\frac{3}{12} = 1 + \frac{15}{12} = 1\frac{15}{12}$

$-1\frac{2}{3} = \qquad -1\frac{8}{12}$

$\frac{7}{12}$

2. The tide in Portland, Maine, has a range of 9 feet, while the tide in Sandy Hook, New Jersey, has a range of $4\frac{2}{3}$ feet.

How much greater is the range in Portland than that in Sandy Hook?

$9 \rightarrow 8\frac{3}{3}$

$-4\frac{2}{3} \rightarrow 4\frac{2}{3}$

$4\frac{1}{3}$

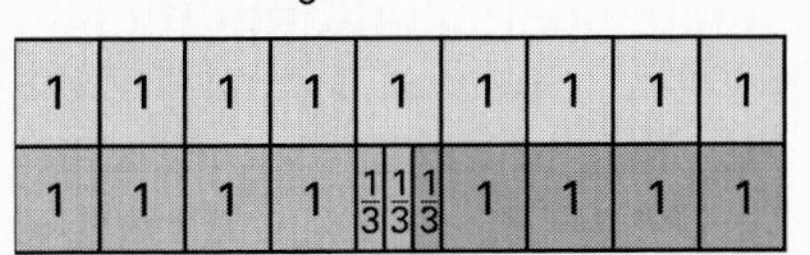

The range of the tide in Portland is $4\frac{1}{3}$ feet greater than that in Sandy Hook.

Students see two methods for subtracting mixed numbers with borrowing. In one case, the numbers are subtracted using regrouping. In the other case, the mixed numbers are changed to improper fractions and the difference is calculated with these fractions.

Answers for What Do You Think?

1. Fractions must have the same denominator before they can be subtracted; The least common denominator is easier to work with than other common denominators.
2. Zack's method would be faster; He would only have to subtract.

3 Practice and Assess

Check

Answers for Check Your Understanding

1. Possible answer: Use the $A^b/_c$ key.
2. Possible answer: The method is the same except when subtracting mixed numbers there is a fraction part to consider.
3. Possible answer: When you need to subtract a fraction from it.

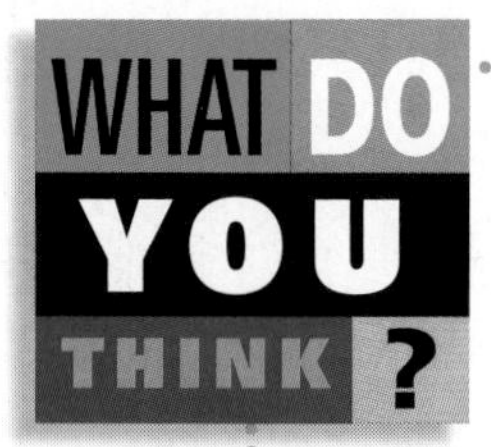

Dams are used to control floods by storing water during heavy rains. During a rainy spell, the height of the water behind a dam rose from $14\frac{5}{6}$ ft to $19\frac{2}{3}$ ft.

Zack and Tyreka wanted to know how much the water had risen.

Zack thought ...

I'll subtract fraction from fraction and whole number from whole number.

$19\frac{2}{3} = 19\frac{4}{6}$ Rewrite using the LCD.

$= 18\frac{10}{6}$ Regroup.

$19\frac{2}{3} = 18\frac{10}{6}$

$-14\frac{5}{6} = 14\frac{5}{6}$

$4\frac{5}{6}$

The water rose $4\frac{5}{6}$ feet.

Tyreka thought...

I'll subtract by rewriting the mixed numbers as improper fractions.

$19\frac{2}{3} = \frac{59}{3} = \frac{118}{6}$ Rewrite using the LCD.

$-14\frac{5}{6} = \frac{89}{6}$

$\frac{29}{6}$

$\frac{29}{6} = 4\frac{5}{6}$ Rewrite as mixed number.

The water rose $4\frac{5}{6}$ feet.

What do 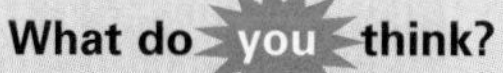

think?

1. Why did both Zack and Tyreka use the least common denominator?
2. If the mixed numbers didn't involve borrowing, would one method be faster than the other? Explain.

Check Your Understanding

1. How could you use a calculator to subtract mixed numbers?
2. How is subtracting mixed numbers like subtracting whole numbers?
3. In a subtraction problem, when might you need to convert a whole number into a mixed number?

MEETING MIDDLE SCHOOL CLASSROOM NEEDS

Tips from Middle School Teachers

Throughout the teaching of fraction concepts and fraction computation, I allow students to use their calculators, not only to check their work but also to reinforce their understanding.

Team Teaching

Ask the science teacher to discuss the uses of dams for the production of hydroelectric power and the provision of flood control.

Geography Connection

One of the largest dams in the world is the Tarbela Dam in Pakistan. Completed in 1976, its volume is 121,720 cubic meters. The largest dam in the United States is the New Cornelia Tailings Dam in Arizona, completed in 1973, with a volume of 209,500 cubic meters.

6-6 Exercises and Applications

Practice and Apply

Getting Started Subtract.

1. $6\frac{3}{4} - 4$ $2\frac{3}{4}$ **2.** $7\frac{7}{8} - 2$ $5\frac{7}{8}$ **3.** $12\frac{1}{2} - 10$ $2\frac{1}{2}$ **4.** $3\frac{4}{5} - 2$ $1\frac{4}{5}$

Subtract. Write each answer as a whole or mixed number in lowest terms.

5. $7\frac{1}{2} - 6\frac{1}{4}$ $1\frac{1}{4}$ **6.** $7\frac{2}{9} - 6\frac{1}{3}$ $\frac{8}{9}$ **7.** $2\frac{1}{4} - 1\frac{1}{2}$ $\frac{3}{4}$ **8.** $9\frac{1}{6} - 4\frac{2}{3}$ $4\frac{1}{2}$

9. $1\frac{1}{3} - \frac{2}{3}$ $\frac{2}{3}$ **10.** $4\frac{5}{6} - 2\frac{1}{6}$ $2\frac{2}{3}$ **11.** $2\frac{1}{6} - 1\frac{1}{8}$ $1\frac{1}{24}$ **12.** $5\frac{1}{5} - 3\frac{2}{3}$ $1\frac{8}{15}$

13. $9\frac{7}{8} - 1\frac{6}{8}$ $8\frac{1}{8}$ **14.** $4\frac{1}{3} - 3\frac{1}{4}$ $1\frac{1}{12}$ **15.** $7\frac{3}{5} - 4\frac{2}{5}$ $3\frac{1}{5}$ **16.** $10\frac{7}{10} - 4\frac{4}{5}$ $5\frac{9}{10}$

17. $6\frac{3}{4} - 2\frac{1}{5}$ $4\frac{11}{20}$ **18.** $3\frac{2}{3} - \frac{2}{3}$ 3 **19.** $1\frac{1}{4} - \frac{1}{2}$ $\frac{3}{4}$ **20.** $2\frac{1}{6} - 1\frac{1}{2}$ $\frac{2}{3}$

21. $6\frac{4}{5} - 3\frac{1}{5}$ $3\frac{3}{5}$ **22.** $7\frac{1}{2} - 1\frac{3}{4}$ $5\frac{3}{4}$ **23.** $8\frac{5}{7} - 2\frac{1}{4}$ $6\frac{13}{28}$ **24.** $4\frac{1}{8} - 1\frac{5}{9}$ $2\frac{41}{72}$

25. Helen and Joe expected the stream near their house to rise to 9 feet when the snow melted. It only rose to $7\frac{4}{5}$ feet. By how much was their prediction off? $1\frac{1}{5}$ ft

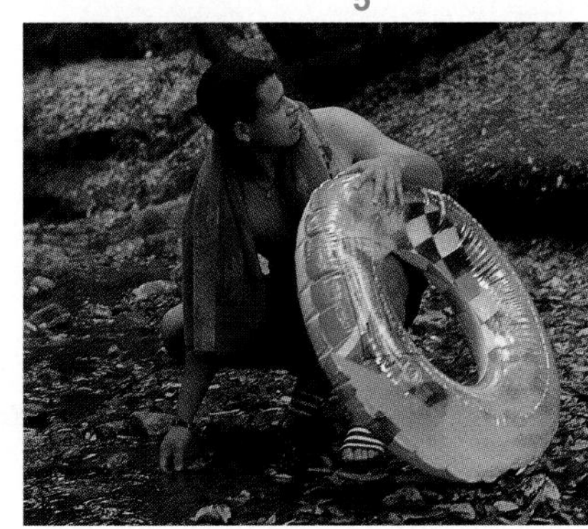

26. Algebra A large financial institution trading on the New York Stock Exchange listed its highest selling price in the last year at $80\frac{3}{8}$ points. The difference between its highest and lowest prices was $26\frac{1}{2}$ points. Write and solve an equation to find the lowest selling price. $80\frac{3}{8} - x = 26\frac{1}{2}$; $53\frac{7}{8}$

GPS

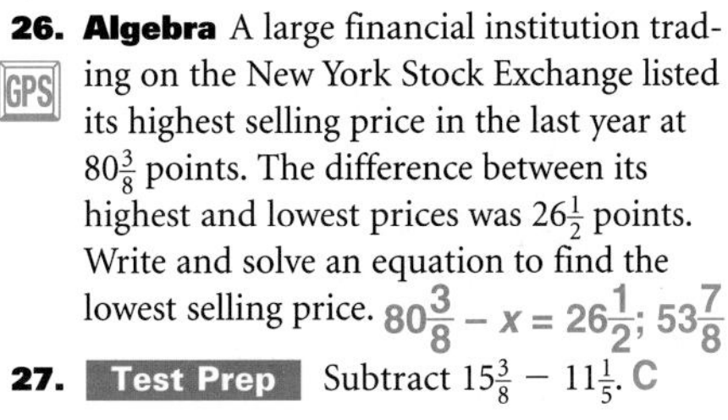

27. Test Prep Subtract $15\frac{3}{8} - 11\frac{1}{5}$. C

Ⓐ $1\frac{67}{40}$ Ⓑ $3\frac{7}{10}$

Ⓒ $4\frac{7}{40}$ Ⓓ $4\frac{2}{3}$

28. Wahn has a box of macaroni and cheese that contains 6 servings. He plans to eat $3\frac{1}{3}$ servings. How many servings will be left? $2\frac{2}{3}$

PRACTICE 6-6

PRACTICE

Name ______________________

Practice 6-6

Subtracting Mixed Numbers

Subtract. Write the answer as a whole or mixed number in lowest terms.

1. $5\frac{2}{7} - 4\frac{2}{3}$ $\frac{13}{21}$ **2.** $15\frac{7}{10} - 12\frac{2}{5}$ $3\frac{3}{10}$ **3.** $7\frac{1}{3} - 4\frac{1}{18}$ $3\frac{5}{18}$ **4.** $2\frac{3}{8} - 2\frac{5}{16}$ $\frac{1}{16}$

5. $8\frac{5}{8} - 4\frac{7}{24}$ $4\frac{1}{3}$ **6.** $10\frac{1}{3} - 4\frac{5}{6}$ $5\frac{1}{2}$ **7.** $9\frac{2}{3} - 1\frac{1}{10}$ $8\frac{17}{30}$ **8.** $12\frac{3}{11} - 8\frac{5}{11}$ $3\frac{9}{11}$

9. $5\frac{1}{6} - 2\frac{5}{6}$ $2\frac{1}{3}$ **10.** $9\frac{4}{5} - 7\frac{2}{5}$ $2\frac{2}{5}$ **11.** $6 - 1\frac{2}{19}$ $4\frac{17}{19}$ **12.** $3\frac{2}{3} - 1\frac{8}{15}$ $2\frac{2}{15}$

13. $10\frac{4}{5} - 1\frac{14}{25}$ $9\frac{6}{25}$ **14.** $8\frac{4}{7} - 1\frac{1}{2}$ $7\frac{1}{14}$ **15.** $2\frac{1}{2} - 1\frac{19}{21}$ $\frac{25}{42}$ **16.** $12\frac{3}{4} - 5\frac{1}{7}$ $7\frac{17}{28}$

17. $7\frac{4}{5} - 2\frac{5}{8}$ $5\frac{7}{40}$ **18.** $10\frac{17}{21} - 1\frac{5}{7}$ $9\frac{2}{21}$ **19.** $10\frac{7}{18} - 4\frac{1}{3}$ $6\frac{1}{18}$ **20.** $15\frac{11}{14} - 14\frac{1}{7}$ $1\frac{9}{14}$

21. $3\frac{5}{8} - 1\frac{9}{10}$ $1\frac{29}{40}$ **22.** $7\frac{5}{6} - 6\frac{5}{7}$ $1\frac{5}{42}$ **23.** $5\frac{1}{9} - 1\frac{4}{9}$ $3\frac{2}{3}$ **24.** $8\frac{4}{5} - 3\frac{13}{20}$ $5\frac{3}{20}$

Use the circle graph for Exercises 25–27.

25. What fraction of U.S. public schools are elementary schools? $\frac{25}{36}$

26. What fraction of U.S. schools are colleges, universities, or in the "other" category? $\frac{2}{27}$

27. What fraction of U.S. schools are secondary schools? $\frac{25}{108}$

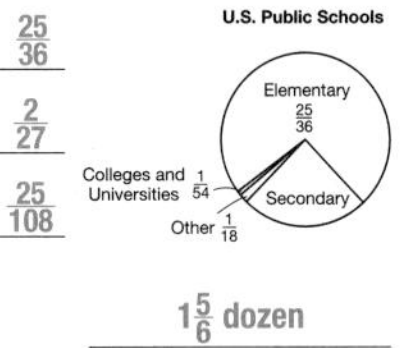

28. Jessie baked $6\frac{1}{2}$ dozen cookies for a bake sale, and $4\frac{2}{3}$ dozen of the cookies were sold. How many dozen cookies were left over? $1\frac{5}{6}$ dozen

RETEACHING

Name ______________________

Alternative Lesson 6-6

Subtracting Mixed Numbers

Just as you can subtract whole numbers and fractions, you can subtract mixed numbers. If the fraction to be subtracted is larger than the other fraction, you must rename part of the whole number as a fraction. Remember that 1 equals a fraction with the same number as the numerator and denominator.

Example 1

Rename $4\frac{2}{3}$ as $3\frac{\square}{\square}$.

Rename 4 as $3 + \frac{3}{3}$ and add to $\frac{2}{3}$: $3 + \frac{3}{3} + \frac{2}{3} = 3\frac{5}{3}$.

So, $4\frac{2}{3} = 3\frac{5}{3}$.

Try It Rename each number.

a. $2\frac{4}{5} = 1\frac{\square}{5}$ $1\frac{9}{5}$ **b.** $10\frac{1}{2} = 9\frac{\square}{2}$ $9\frac{3}{2}$ **c.** $16\frac{5}{8} = 15\frac{\square}{8}$ $15\frac{13}{8}$

Example 2

Subtract $8\frac{1}{3} - 2\frac{5}{6}$. Write the answer as a whole or mixed number in lowest terms.

Rewrite fractions using LCD. LCD is 6.		Rename $8\frac{2}{6}$ as $7 + \frac{6}{6} + \frac{2}{6}$, or $7\frac{8}{6}$.	Subtract the whole numbers.	Subtract the fractions.
$8\frac{1}{3} - 2\frac{5}{6}$ →	$8\frac{2}{6} - 2\frac{5}{6}$ →	$7\frac{8}{6} - 2\frac{5}{6}$ →	$7\frac{8}{6} - 2\frac{5}{6}$ = 5 →	$7\frac{8}{6} - 2\frac{5}{6} = 5\frac{3}{6}$

Write the difference as a mixed number in lowest terms. $5\frac{3}{6} = 5\frac{1}{2}$

So, $8\frac{1}{3} - 2\frac{5}{6} = 5\frac{1}{2}$.

Try It Subtract. Write each difference as a whole or mixed number in lowest terms.

d. $7\frac{1}{5} - 2\frac{3}{5}$

Rename $7\frac{1}{5}$. $7\frac{1}{5} = 6\frac{\square}{5}$. $6\frac{6}{5}$ Subtract the whole numbers. 4

Subtract the fractions. $\frac{3}{5}$ Write the difference. $4\frac{3}{5}$

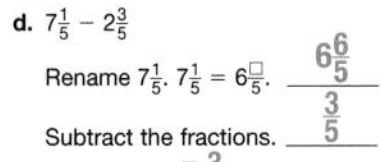

e. $14\frac{3}{5} - 7\frac{3}{10}$ $7\frac{3}{10}$ **f.** $6\frac{1}{4} - 2\frac{3}{4}$ $3\frac{1}{2}$

g. $9\frac{2}{3} - 5\frac{3}{4}$ $3\frac{11}{12}$ **h.** $10 - 3\frac{5}{6}$ $6\frac{1}{6}$

i. $5\frac{7}{8} - 2\frac{1}{4}$ $3\frac{5}{8}$ **j.** $8\frac{1}{5} - 7\frac{3}{4}$ $\frac{9}{20}$

k. $10\frac{5}{9} - 6\frac{2}{3}$ $3\frac{8}{9}$ **l.** $12 - 5\frac{3}{5}$ $6\frac{2}{5}$

m. $15\frac{2}{3} - 15\frac{1}{6}$ $\frac{1}{2}$ **n.** $20\frac{5}{8} - \frac{3}{4}$ $19\frac{7}{8}$

6-6 Exercises and Applications

Assignment Guide

- **Basic**
  1–25 odds, 26, 27, 33–41 odds
- **Average**
  2–26 evens, 27–41 odds
- **Enriched**
  2–26 evens, 27–33, 34–40 evens

Exercise Notes

Exercises 1–4

Error Prevention Have students note that each exercise involves subtracting a whole number from a mixed number. Therefore, they do not need to regroup before they subtract.

Reteaching

Activity

Materials: Play money

- You learned how to use play money to add mixed numbers, now you will use play money to subtract mixed numbers.
- To subtract $2\frac{1}{4}$ from $3\frac{3}{10}$, think of $2\frac{1}{4}$ as 2 dollars and 1 quarter and $3\frac{3}{10}$ as 3 dollars and 3 dimes.
- When 1 quarter is subtracted from 3 dimes, the difference is 1 nickel, which is $\frac{1}{20}$ of a dollar.
- When 2 dollars is subtracted from 3 dollars, the difference is 1 dollar. So the difference is \$1.05, or $1\frac{1}{20}$.
- Use play money to find each difference. You might have to exchange dollars for coins in order to subtract.

1. $3\frac{3}{4} - \frac{9}{10}$ $2\frac{17}{20}$
2. $2\frac{1}{4} - 1\frac{7}{10}$ $\frac{11}{20}$
3. $3 - 1\frac{3}{4}$ $1\frac{1}{4}$

Exercise Notes

■ **Exercises 34–36**

Error Prevention You may need to review the area formulas for rectangles, triangles, and circles with the students.

Project Progress

You may want to have students use Chapter 6 Project Master.

Exercise Answers

31. Possible answer: $x = y = 1$; $x = y = 2$; $x = y = 3$; Any values where $x = y$. If x and y are equal, the fraction part becomes 0.

33. Possible answer: The method is similar. You subtract the whole numbers from each other. However, when subtracting mixed numbers, there is a fraction part to consider.

Alternate Assessment

Self Assessment Have students describe what they find most difficult about subtracting mixed numbers.

Quick Quiz

Find each difference.

1. $1\frac{1}{2} - \frac{3}{4}$ $\frac{3}{4}$
2. $5\frac{1}{3} - 4\frac{7}{8}$ $\frac{11}{24}$
3. $6 - \frac{2}{3}$ $5\frac{1}{3}$
4. $4\frac{5}{6} - 2\frac{11}{12}$ $1\frac{11}{12}$
5. $8\frac{3}{4} - 2\frac{1}{6}$ $6\frac{7}{12}$

Available on Daily Transparency 6-6

Health **The cirlcle graph shows the number of hours Kente spends playing sports. Use the graph for Exercises 29 and 30.**

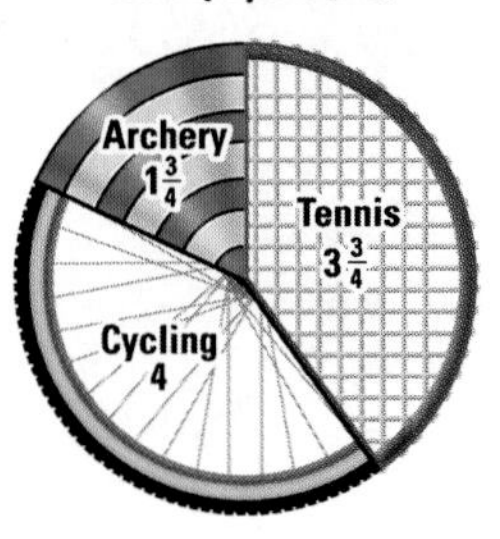

29. How many more hours did Kente spend cycling than practicing archery? $2\frac{1}{4}$ hr

30. Kente predicted that he would play tennis for 7 hours during the week. By how much was his prediction off? $3\frac{1}{4}$ hr

Problem Solving and Reasoning

31. Critical Thinking $5\frac{x}{11} - 2\frac{y}{11}$ = a whole number. List three possible values for x and y. Explain.

32. Critical Thinking If you change one of the digits in $3\frac{1}{4} + 2\frac{5}{8}$ to a 9, and you want to get the smallest possible answer, which digit should you change? 4

33. Journal Describe some similarities and differences between subtracting with whole numbers and subtracting with mixed numbers.

Mixed Review

Find the areas of the shapes. *[Lesson 4-9]*

34. 63

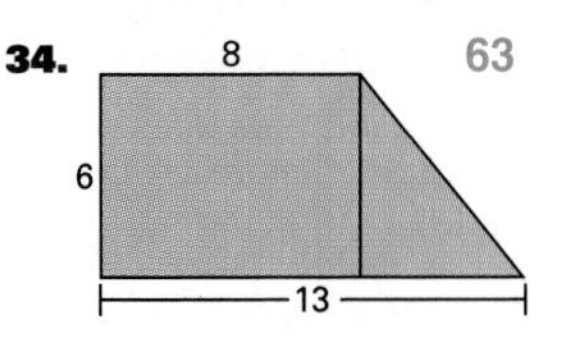

35. 54.2325

36. 33 ft²

Write each number in scientific notation. *[Lesson 3-4]*

37. 340,000 3.4×10^5 **38.** 47,500 4.75×10^4 **39.** 5,000,000 5×10^6 **40.** 4000 4×10^3 **41.** 6,200,000 6.2×10^6

Project Progress

Complete the columns in your recipe tables. Organize the tables into a cookbook. Illustrate your book with pictures of the foods or the animals that the recipes are designed for.

Problem Solving
Understand
Plan
Solve
Look Back

PROBLEM SOLVING 6-6

PROBLEM SOLVING

Name ______________________

Guided Problem Solving 6-6

GPS PROBLEM 26, STUDENT PAGE 353

A large financial institution trading on the New York Stock Exchange listed its highest selling price in the last year at $80\frac{3}{8}$ points. The difference between its highest and lowest prices was $26\frac{1}{2}$ points. Write and solve an equation to find the lowest selling price.

— Understand —

1. What is the highest selling price of the stock? $80\frac{3}{8}$ points.
2. What is the difference between its highest and lowest prices? $26\frac{1}{2}$ points.

— Plan —

3. What is the least common denominator for $\frac{3}{8}$ and $\frac{1}{2}$? 8
4. Write the prices using the least common denominator.
   a. Highest selling price $80\frac{3}{8}$ b. Difference in selling price $26\frac{4}{8}$
5. Which operation will you use to find the difference? Subtraction.
6. When you write the equation, which variable will you use to represent the value of the lowest selling price of the stock? Possible answer: x

— Solve —

7. Write an equation to find the lowest selling price. $80\frac{3}{8} - x = 26\frac{4}{8}$
8. Solve the equation. What is the lowest selling price? $53\frac{7}{8}$

— Look Back —

9. Write an equation that will find the lowest selling price using another operation.
   $26\frac{4}{8} + x = 80\frac{3}{8}$

SOLVE ANOTHER PROBLEM

The highest selling price of the stock was $75\frac{3}{4}$. The difference between its highest and lowest prices was $18\frac{1}{8}$. Write and solve an equation to find the lowest selling price.
$57\frac{5}{8}$; $75\frac{3}{4} - 18\frac{1}{8} = x$; $x = 57\frac{5}{8}$

ENRICHMENT

Name ______________________

Extend Your Thinking 6-6

Visual Thinking

Circle the figure in each set that does **not** belong.

1.

Inside figure shares a vertex with outside figure.

2.
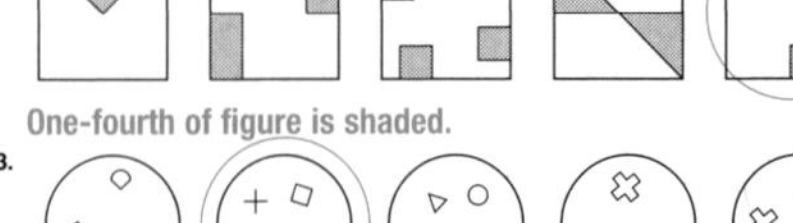
One-fourth of figure is shaded.

3.
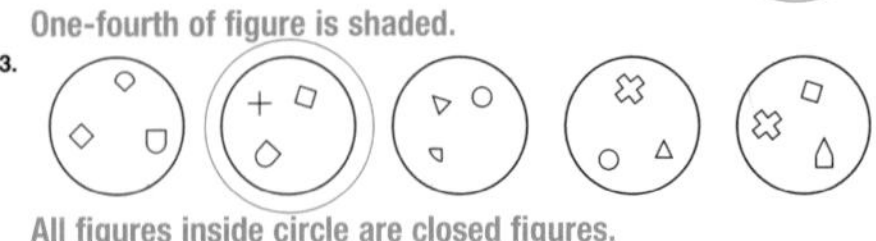
All figures inside circle are closed figures.

4.

All triangles have at least two sides of equal length.

5.
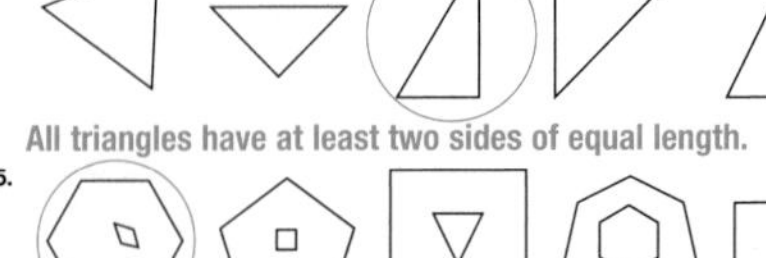
Inside figure has one less side than outside figure.

6.
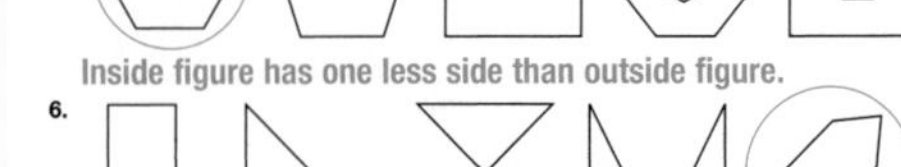
Figures are one-half of same size square.

Section 6B Connect

In this section, you've learned how to add and subtract mixed numbers. In the following investigation, you'll use mixed numbers as you look at two of the main causes of floods.

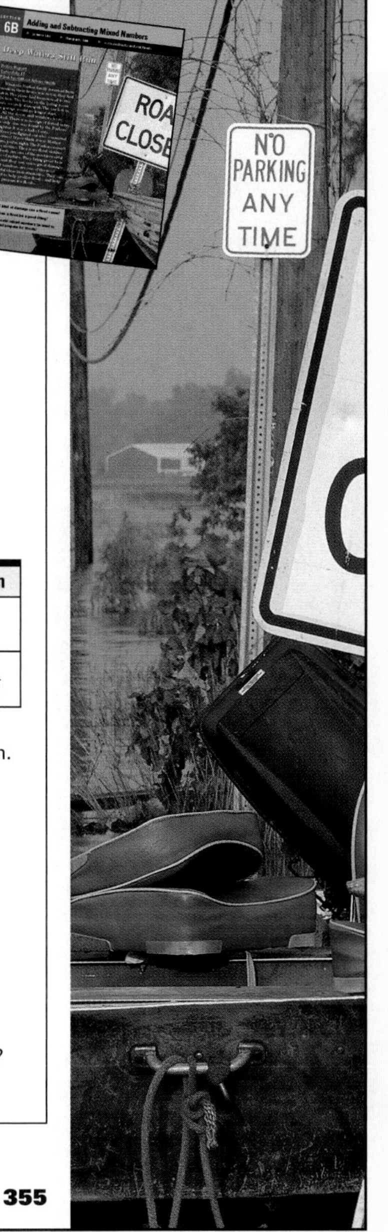

Deep Waters Still Run

Each winter, snow falls in the Sunset Mountains. Each spring, the snow melts and flows into the Wolverine River. The Wolverine River will flood in July if *both* of the following conditions are met:

a. The total amount of precipitation (rain or snow) during December, January, February, and March is greater than 30 inches.

b. The total amount of time during April, May, and June when air temperatures exceed 90°F is greater than $11\frac{1}{2}$ days.

The table gives data for November 1994 to June 1995.

	Nov	Dec	Jan	Feb	Mar	Apr	May	Jun
Precipitation (in.)	$3\frac{3}{4}$	$6\frac{1}{12}$	$8\frac{3}{4}$	$9\frac{5}{6}$	$6\frac{2}{3}$	$1\frac{1}{2}$	$1\frac{5}{12}$	$\frac{5}{8}$
Days over 90°	0	0	0	0	$1\frac{3}{5}$	$2\frac{4}{5}$	$3\frac{3}{10}$	$4\frac{1}{2}$

1. Estimate the amount of precipitation from December through March.

2. Estimate the number of days over 90°F from April through June.

3. Do your estimates indicate that the river will flood in July? Explain.

4. Find the exact amount of precipitation from December through March.

5. Find the exact number of days over 90°F from April through June.

6. Do your exact figures indicate that the river will flood in July? Explain.

7. Why does temperature affect the possibility that the river will flood? What other factors might affect the possibility?

355

6B Connect

Deep Waters Still Run

The Point

In *Deep Waters Still Run* on page 341, students discussed floods as a powerful force of nature. Now they will use mixed numbers to analyze two principal causes of floods.

About the Page

- Discuss with your students why both precipitation and high temperatures must occur to cause a river to flood.
- Ask students why they think high spring temperatures increase the likelihood of a flood. Possible answer: Higher temperatures increase the rapidity of the snow melt.
- Review the chart with students to ensure that students understand the information shown.

Ongoing Assessment

Check that students have added the fractions correctly to determine the exact amount of precipitation and the exact number of days of temperatures over 90°F.

Extension

There was enough precipitation in the winter but there were not enough days of high temperatures in the spring to cause a flood in 1995. How many more days of temperatures over 90°F would have caused flooding that year? At least $\frac{9}{10}$ of a day more.

Answers for Connect

1. 32 in.
2. 11 days
3. No; The estimate of days that the air temperature exceeded 90°F is less than $11\frac{1}{2}$.
4. $31\frac{1}{3}$ in.
5. $10\frac{3}{5}$ days
6. No; The air temperature exceeded 90°F for less than $11\frac{1}{2}$ days.
7. Possible answer: The higher the temperature, the more snow that melts. Other factors: Size of dams; Blockages in rivers; How fast the snow melts.

6B Review

Review Correlation

Item(s)	Lesson(s)
1	6-6
2	6-5
3	6-2
4, 5	6-6
6	6-1
7	6-5
8	6-2
9	6-5
10–13	6-6
14	6-5
15	6-6
16	6-5
17	6-3
18	6-5, 6-6
19	6-4
20–22	6-5

Test Prep

Test-Taking Tip

Tell students to watch for two answers that are really the same. For example, in Question 21, $\frac{8}{3} = 2\frac{2}{3}$, so the choice can be narrowed down to C or D.

Answers for Review

1. $1\frac{3}{5}$ 2. $22\frac{4}{7}$

3. $\frac{17}{45}$ 4. $4\frac{1}{2}$

5. $3\frac{5}{9}$ 6. $1\frac{4}{11}$

7. $111\frac{11}{24}$ 8. $\frac{27}{40}$

9. 7 10. $2\frac{1}{6}$

11. $4\frac{2}{3}$ 12. $3\frac{1}{4}$

13. $\frac{1}{18}$ 14. $14\frac{3}{10}$

15. $3\frac{1}{4}$ 16. $3\frac{11}{12}$

17. $\frac{1}{21}$ 18. Selecas; $\frac{7}{60}$ gallon

19. 6 hours 20. $5\frac{11}{12}$

21. D 22. D

Section 6B Review

Simplify. Write each answer in lowest terms.

1. $4\frac{1}{5} - 2\frac{3}{5}$ **2.** $15 + 7\frac{4}{7}$ **3.** $\frac{7}{9} - \frac{2}{5}$ **4.** $12\frac{7}{8} - 8\frac{3}{8}$

5. $6\frac{1}{3} - 2\frac{7}{9}$ **6.** $\frac{9}{11} + \frac{6}{11}$ **7.** $33\frac{1}{3} + 78\frac{1}{8}$ **8.** $\frac{4}{5} - \frac{1}{8}$

9. $2\frac{1}{3} + 3\frac{5}{3}$ **10.** $6\frac{5}{6} - 4\frac{2}{3}$ **11.** $20 - 15\frac{1}{3}$ **12.** $11\frac{7}{8} - 8\frac{5}{8}$

13. $2\frac{4}{18} - 2\frac{3}{18}$ **14.** $3\frac{4}{5} + 10\frac{1}{2}$ **15.** $6\frac{3}{4} - 3\frac{1}{2}$ **16.** $1\frac{5}{8} + 2\frac{7}{24}$

17. During the 1973 Mississippi River flood, the Fifth Army Corps of Engineers used a number of vehicles to help with the disaster. $\frac{5}{7}$ were Jeeps. $\frac{5}{21}$ were tank trucks. What fraction were neither Jeeps nor tank trucks?

18. Rob and Thomas Lin and Helen and Sarah Seleca spent an afternoon painting a house. Rob used $3\frac{1}{3}$ gallons of paint. Sarah used $4\frac{1}{4}$. Thomas used $5\frac{3}{5}$. Helen used $4\frac{4}{5}$. Did the Lins or the Selecas use more paint? How much more?

19. Estimation Steve plans to do chores for $1\frac{1}{3}$ hours, homework for $2\frac{1}{4}$ hours, and play basketball for $2\frac{3}{4}$ hours. Estimate the amount of time this will take.

20. Robyn ran $2\frac{2}{3}$ miles in the morning and $3\frac{1}{4}$ miles after school. How many miles did she run all together?

REVIEW 6B

Test Prep

In order to eliminate answers, first determine if the answer is a mixed number or a whole number.

21. Choose the correct answer. $5\frac{2}{6} + 2\frac{2}{3}$

Ⓐ $\frac{8}{3}$ Ⓑ $2\frac{2}{3}$ Ⓒ 7 Ⓓ 8

22. Choose the correct answer. $5\frac{3}{4} + 3\frac{3}{4}$

Ⓐ 2 Ⓑ $8\frac{1}{2}$ Ⓒ 9 Ⓓ $9\frac{1}{2}$

Resources

Practice Masters
Section 6B Review

Assessment Sourcebook
Quiz 6B

TestWorks
Test and Practice Software

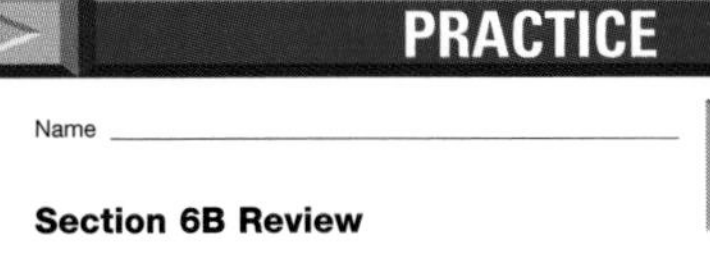

PRACTICE

Name ______________________

Practice

Section 6B Review

Simplify. Write each answer in lowest terms.

1. $6 - 1\frac{3}{14}$ $4\frac{11}{14}$ 2. $3\frac{1}{6} - 1\frac{7}{9}$ $1\frac{7}{18}$ 3. $3 + 5\frac{7}{16}$ $8\frac{7}{16}$ 4. $10\frac{1}{4} + 17\frac{1}{4}$ $27\frac{1}{2}$

5. $7 + 4\frac{2}{5}$ $11\frac{2}{5}$ 6. $8\frac{5}{17} + 1\frac{2}{17}$ $9\frac{7}{17}$ 7. $23\frac{3}{5} - 13\frac{2}{7}$ $10\frac{11}{35}$ 8. $10 - 7\frac{13}{16}$ $2\frac{3}{16}$

9. $12\frac{3}{7} + 3\frac{2}{3}$ $16\frac{2}{21}$ 10. $9\frac{1}{2} - 6\frac{4}{9}$ $3\frac{1}{18}$ 11. $2\frac{2}{3} + 5\frac{1}{12}$ $7\frac{3}{4}$ 12. $3\frac{1}{5} + 1\frac{7}{8}$ $5\frac{3}{40}$

13. $2\frac{1}{9} + 10$ $12\frac{1}{9}$ 14. $2\frac{4}{5} + 4\frac{4}{7}$ $7\frac{13}{35}$ 15. $6\frac{11}{20} - 4\frac{9}{10}$ $1\frac{13}{20}$ 16. $20\frac{5}{6} + 6\frac{2}{7}$ $27\frac{5}{42}$

17. At Paul's Pet Palace, $\frac{3}{16}$ of the animals are dogs and $\frac{5}{24}$ of the animals are cats. What fraction of the animals are neither dogs nor cats? $\frac{19}{48}$

18. At a school music festival, Judy played saxophone for $2\frac{2}{3}$ hours, Carol sang for $1\frac{3}{4}$ hours, Bob played saxophone for $1\frac{1}{4}$ hours, and Ross sang for $2\frac{3}{8}$ hours.

a. Who had more time, the saxophone players or the singers? Singers

b. How much more? $\frac{5}{24}$ hours (or $12\frac{1}{2}$ minutes)

19. Steve bought $2\frac{3}{4}$ lb of broccoli, $1\frac{1}{3}$ lb of carrots, and $\frac{7}{8}$ lb of cauliflower. Estimate the total amount of vegetables. About 5 lb

20. The average commute time for workers in New York is 30.6 minutes. This is 4.2 minutes longer than the average time in Los Angeles. Set up an equation and solve to find the average time in Los Angeles. *[Lesson 3-12]*

Possible answer: $30.6 = x + 4.2$; 26.4 minutes

21. A typical drink coaster is about 0.045 inches thick. Write this amount as a fraction in lowest terms. *[Lesson 5-7]* $\frac{9}{200}$ in.

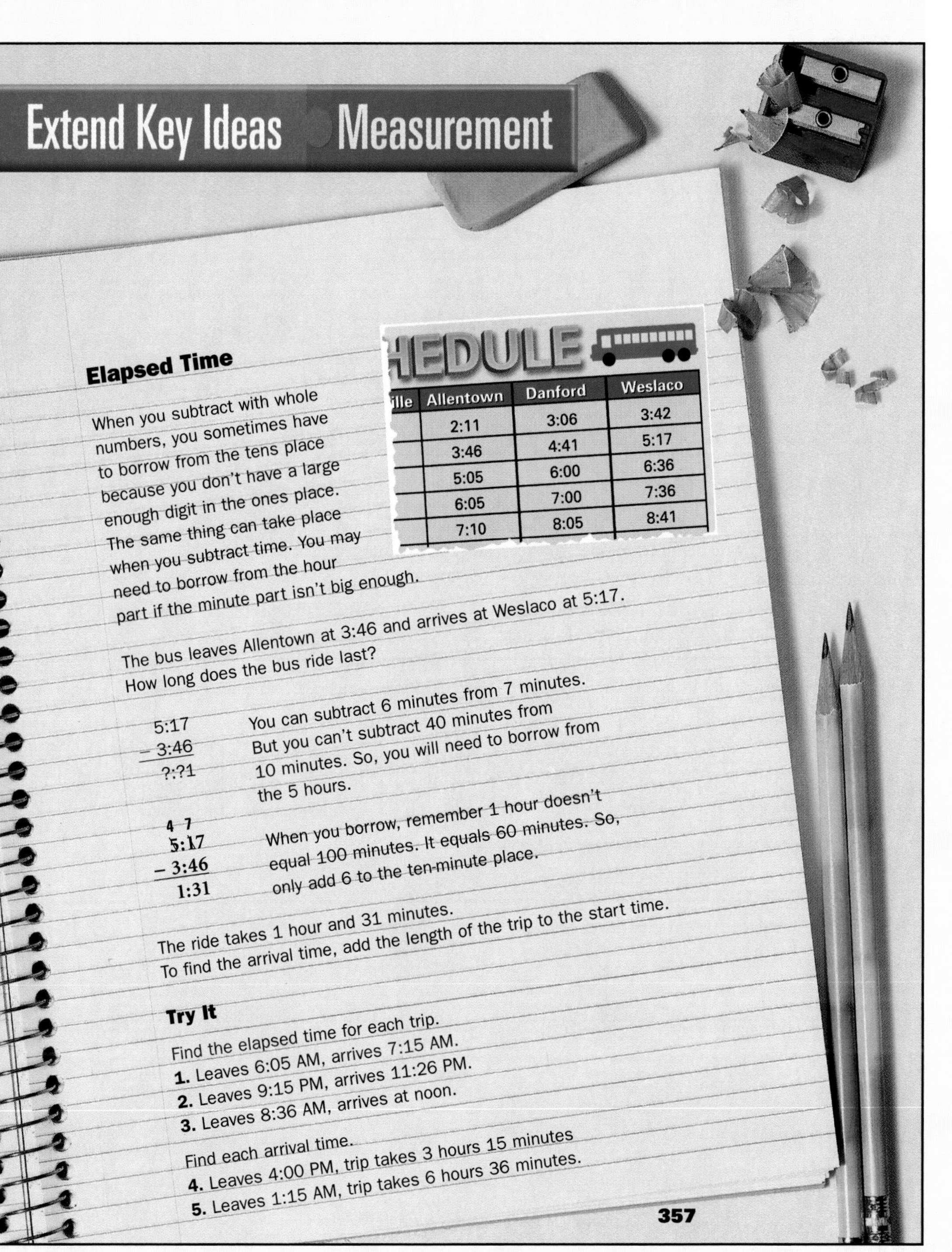

Extend Key Ideas Measurement

Elapsed Time

When you subtract with whole numbers, you sometimes have to borrow from the tens place because you don't have a large enough digit in the ones place. The same thing can take place when you subtract time. You may need to borrow from the hour part if the minute part isn't big enough.

HEDULE

ille	Allentown	Danford	Weslaco
	2:11	3:06	3:42
	3:46	4:41	5:17
	5:05	6:00	6:36
	6:05	7:00	7:36
	7:10	8:05	8:41

The bus leaves Allentown at 3:46 and arrives at Weslaco at 5:17. How long does the bus ride last?

5:17
− 3:46
?:?1

You can subtract 6 minutes from 7 minutes. But you can't subtract 40 minutes from 10 minutes. So, you will need to borrow from the 5 hours.

4 7
5:17
− 3:46
1:31

When you borrow, remember 1 hour doesn't equal 100 minutes. It equals 60 minutes. So, only add 6 to the ten-minute place.

The ride takes 1 hour and 31 minutes. To find the arrival time, add the length of the trip to the start time.

Try It

Find the elapsed time for each trip.

1. Leaves 6:05 AM, arrives 7:15 AM.
2. Leaves 9:15 PM, arrives 11:26 PM.
3. Leaves 8:36 AM, arrives at noon.

Find each arrival time.

4. Leaves 4:00 PM, trip takes 3 hours 15 minutes
5. Leaves 1:15 AM, trip takes 6 hours 36 minutes.

357

Elapsed Time

The Point

Students calculate elapsed time by subtracting hours and minutes.

About the Page

- Students may want to borrow by just adding a 1 in front of the digit in the borrowing column. Point out that this works only because of the place value and what is being borrowed. Thus, 1 hour may be traded for 60 minutes.
- Students may find it easier to figure elapsed time using the "counting on" method. Start with the earlier time and count on until the later time is reached.

Ask ...

- Explain the borrowing for 8:21 P.M. − 5:34 P.M. Borrow from the 2, leaving 1. Add 10 to the 1, making 11, since the borrow is 10 minutes. Borrow 1 hour from 8, leaving 7. Add 6 to the remaining 1, making 7, since 1 hour is 6 10-minute units. The difference is 2 hours and 47 minutes.
- How could you check your answer? Add the calculated elapsed time to the arrival time. The result should be the original departure time.

Extension

Find the elapsed time for each trip.

1. Leaves 10:30 A.M., arrives 4:38 P.M. 6 hours, 8 minutes
2. Leaves 11:16 P.M., arrives 8:43 A.M. 9 hours, 27 minutes

Find each arrival time.

1. Leaves 5:15 P.M., trip takes 10 hours, 13 minutes. 3:28 A.M.
2. Leaves 6:15 A.M., trip takes 2 hours, 45 minutes. 9:00 A.M.

Answers for Try It

1. 1 hour, 10 minutes
2. 2 hours, 11 minutes
3. 3 hours, 24 minutes
4. 7:15 P.M.
5. 7:51 A.M.

Chapter 6 Summary and Review

Review Correlation

Item(s)	Lesson(s)
1	6-1
2–5	6-2
6–10	6-1
11–17	6-2
18–20	6-3
21–30	6-4
31	6-6
32, 33	6-5
34–36	6-6
37	6-5
38, 39	6-6
40	6-5
41, 42	6-6
43–45	6-5

For additional review, see page 667.

Chapter 6 Summary and Review

Graphic Organizer

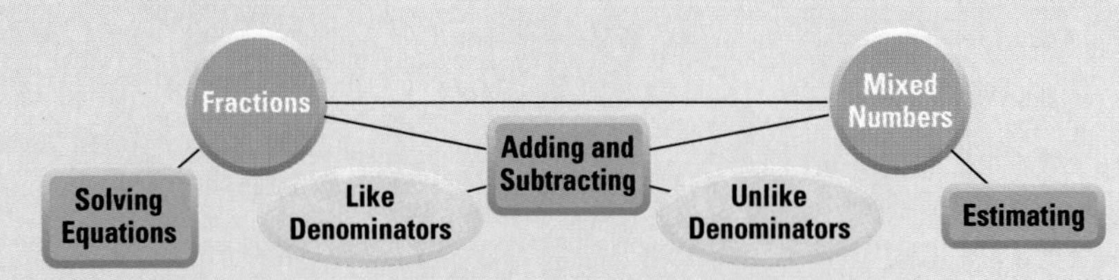

Section 6A Adding and Subtracting Fractions

Summary

- You can add or subtract fractions with **like denominators** by adding or subtracting their numerators. You keep the same denominator because you are adding or subtracting pieces of the same size.
- If the fractions have **unlike denominators,** you must change the fractions to equivalent fractions with like denominators. It is sometimes faster to change to equivalent fractions using the **least common denominator.**
- You can add or subtract fractions to solve fraction equations.

Review

1. Write the problem this model represents. $\frac{1}{5} + \frac{3}{5} = \frac{4}{5}$

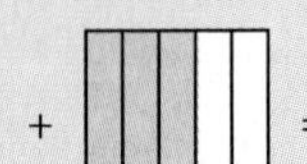

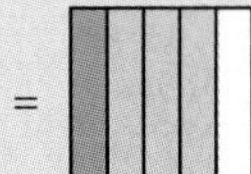

Name the least common denominator of each pair.

2. $\frac{1}{3}, \frac{1}{12}$ 12 **3.** $\frac{1}{4}, \frac{1}{7}$ 28 **4.** $\frac{1}{6}, \frac{1}{10}$ 30 **5.** $\frac{1}{9}, \frac{1}{21}$ 63

Add or subtract. Write each answer in lowest terms.

6. $\frac{5}{7} - \frac{3}{7}$ $\frac{2}{7}$ **7.** $\frac{3}{15} + \frac{8}{15}$ $\frac{11}{15}$ **8.** $\frac{5}{12} + \frac{7}{12}$ 1 **9.** $\frac{3}{5} - \frac{2}{5}$ $\frac{1}{5}$

10. $\frac{7}{8} + \frac{3}{8}$ $1\frac{1}{4}$ **11.** $\frac{11}{14} - \frac{5}{7}$ $\frac{1}{14}$ **12.** $\frac{2}{3} + \frac{1}{2}$ $1\frac{1}{6}$ **13.** $\frac{1}{3} - \frac{1}{5}$ $\frac{2}{15}$

14. $\frac{2}{11} + \frac{1}{2}$ $\frac{15}{22}$ **15.** $\frac{5}{6} + \frac{1}{7}$ $\frac{41}{42}$ **16.** $\frac{7}{8} - \frac{2}{3}$ $\frac{5}{24}$ **17.** $\frac{7}{8} - \frac{7}{9}$ $\frac{7}{72}$

Solve each equation.

18. $\frac{3}{13} + x = \frac{12}{13}$ $\frac{9}{13}$ **19.** $y - \frac{1}{4} = \frac{1}{2}$ $\frac{3}{4}$ **20.** $z + \frac{1}{5} = \frac{9}{10}$ $\frac{7}{10}$

Resources

Practice Masters
Cumulative Review Chapters 1–6

Assessment Sourcebook
Quarterly Test Chapters 1–6

PRACTICE

Name ____________

Practice

Cumulative Review Chapters 1–6

Evaluate each expression. *[Lesson 2-8]*

1. $7 - 12 \div 3$ 3 **2.** $7 \times 4 + 8$ 36 **3.** $16 \div 2 \times 4$ 32

4. $5 \times (3 - 1)$ 10 **5.** $18 - (5 - 2)$ 15 **6.** $(7 - 4)^2$ 9

7. $6 + 4 \times 5$ 26 **8.** $10 - 2^2$ 6 **9.** $21 \div 3 + 4$ 11

10. $8 - 2 \times 3$ 2 **11.** $(7 + 2) \times 5$ 45 **12.** $2 \times (6 - 1)^2$ 50

Write each number in scientific notation. *[Lesson 3-4]*

13. 38,600 3.86×10^4 **14.** 1,420 1.42×10^3 **15.** 3,800,000 3.8×10^6 **16.** 41,500,000 4.15×10^7

17. 6,700,000,000 6.7×10^9 **18.** 17 million 1.7×10^7 **19.** 128 thousand 1.28×10^5 **20.** 7 billion 7×10^9

Find the perimeter. *[Lesson 4-1]*

21. 28 ft **22.** 43 cm **23.** 23.2 m **24.** 116 in.

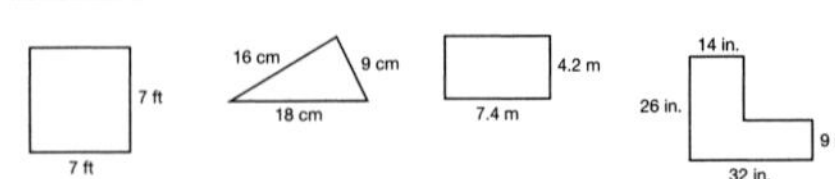

Find the LCM of each pair. *[Lesson 5-3]*

25. 5, 12 60 **26.** 40, 30 120 **27.** 8, 7 56 **28.** 18, 30 90

29. 10, 8 40 **30.** 6, 3 6 **31.** 18, 21 126 **32.** 36, 18 36

Simplify. *[Lesson 6-2]*

33. $\frac{2}{3} + \frac{1}{8}$ $\frac{19}{24}$ **34.** $\frac{1}{6} + \frac{1}{5}$ $\frac{11}{30}$ **35.** $\frac{4}{5} - \frac{4}{7}$ $\frac{8}{35}$

36. $\frac{7}{13} + \frac{1}{3}$ $\frac{34}{39}$ **37.** $\frac{5}{8} + \frac{1}{12}$ $\frac{17}{24}$ **38.** $\frac{2}{3} - \frac{1}{5}$ $\frac{7}{15}$

39. $\frac{13}{20} + \frac{1}{10}$ $\frac{3}{4}$ **40.** $\frac{7}{9} - \frac{5}{7}$ $\frac{4}{63}$ **41.** $\frac{1}{2} - \frac{1}{16}$ $\frac{7}{16}$

Chapter 6 Summary and Review

Section 6B Adding and Subtracting Mixed Numbers

Summary

- You can estimate sums and differences of mixed numbers by rounding each mixed number to the nearest whole number. To find the nearest whole number, you must decide if the fractional part of the mixed number is more or less than one-half.
- You add mixed numbers by adding the fractions and whole numbers separately. If there is an improper fraction in the sum, you will need to regroup the mixed number.
- You subtract mixed numbers by subtracting the fractions and whole numbers separately. You may need to borrow from the whole number and increase the fractional part of the first mixed number in order to subtract.

Review

Round each mixed number to the nearest whole number.

21. $3\frac{3}{8}$ 3 **22.** $4\frac{4}{7}$ 5 **23.** $1\frac{1}{2}$ 2

24. $78\frac{11}{16}$ 79 **25.** $\frac{5}{9}$ 1 **26.** $13\frac{8}{11}$ 14

Estimate each sum or difference.

27. $7\frac{1}{2} + 11\frac{5}{8}$ 20 **28.** $5\frac{1}{3} - 2\frac{5}{7}$ 2 **29.** $3\frac{7}{16} - 1\frac{4}{9}$ 2 **30.** $4\frac{2}{3} - 1\frac{4}{9}$ 3

31. A flag maker wants to attach a $15\frac{3}{4}$-inch tassel on the side of a flag. He has an $18\frac{1}{2}$-inch tassel. How much must he trim off the tassel in order to use it on the flag? $2\frac{3}{4}$ in.

Simplify each expression.

32. $3\frac{3}{5} + 2\frac{1}{5}$ $5\frac{4}{5}$ **33.** $5\frac{1}{6} + 8\frac{1}{2}$ $13\frac{2}{3}$ **34.** $7\frac{7}{8} - 3\frac{1}{8}$ $4\frac{3}{4}$ **35.** $6\frac{12}{17} - 6\frac{5}{17}$ $\frac{7}{17}$

36. $11\frac{5}{11} - 2\frac{5}{8}$ $8\frac{73}{88}$ **37.** $2\frac{3}{7} + 11$ $13\frac{3}{7}$ **38.** $3\frac{2}{3} - 1\frac{1}{2}$ $2\frac{1}{6}$ **39.** $24 - 7\frac{2}{9}$ $16\frac{7}{9}$

40. $6 + 3\frac{2}{3}$ $9\frac{2}{3}$ **41.** $7\frac{1}{4} - 4\frac{5}{12}$ $2\frac{5}{6}$ **42.** $31\frac{4}{7} - 2\frac{5}{7}$ $28\frac{6}{7}$ **43.** $11\frac{5}{11} + 2\frac{6}{11}$ 14

Find the perimeter of each figure.

44.

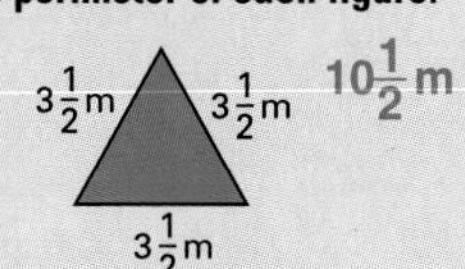

$10\frac{1}{2}$ m

45.

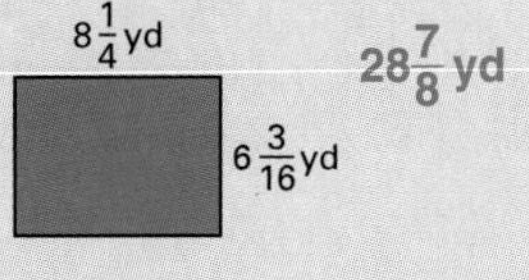

$28\frac{7}{8}$ yd

Chapter 6 Assessment

Assessment Correlation

Item(s)	Lesson(s)
1–4	6-2
5–9	6-1
10–16	6-2
17–20	6-3
21–24	6-4
25	6-5
26	6-6
27, 28	6-5
29–31	6-6
32	6-5
33, 34	6-6
35	6-5
36, 37	6-6
38	6-5

Answers for Performance Task

a. Possible answers: $4\frac{1}{3}$, $3\frac{4}{3}$, $2\frac{7}{3}$.

b. Possible answers: $5\frac{2}{5}$, $4\frac{7}{5}$, $3\frac{12}{5}$.

c. Possible answers: $7\frac{3}{10}$, $6\frac{13}{10}$, $5\frac{23}{10}$.

Chapter 6 Assessment

Find the least common multiple of each number pair.

1. 5, 6 **30** **2.** 12, 15 **60** **3.** 5, 20 **20** **4.** 30, 35 **210**

Add or subtract. Write each answer in lowest terms.

5. $\frac{8}{9} - \frac{2}{9}$ $\frac{2}{3}$ **6.** $\frac{4}{17} + \frac{7}{17}$ $\frac{11}{17}$ **7.** $\frac{6}{11} + \frac{8}{11}$ $\frac{14}{11}$ **8.** $\frac{3}{8} - \frac{1}{8}$ $\frac{1}{4}$

9. $\frac{5}{6} + \frac{5}{6}$ $\frac{5}{3}$ **10.** $\frac{10}{12} - \frac{3}{6}$ $\frac{1}{3}$ **11.** $\frac{1}{3} + \frac{1}{2}$ $\frac{5}{6}$ **12.** $\frac{1}{2} - \frac{1}{7}$ $\frac{5}{14}$

13. $\frac{4}{15} + \frac{1}{2}$ $\frac{23}{30}$ **14.** $\frac{3}{4} + \frac{9}{10}$ $\frac{33}{20}$ **15.** $\frac{3}{5} - \frac{3}{8}$ $\frac{9}{40}$ **16.** $\frac{3}{4} - \frac{2}{9}$ $\frac{19}{36}$

Solve each equation.

17. $\frac{7}{15} + w = \frac{9}{15}$ $\frac{2}{15}$ **18.** $k - \frac{1}{5} = \frac{3}{10}$ $\frac{1}{2}$ **19.** $x + \frac{1}{4} = \frac{5}{7}$ $\frac{13}{28}$

20. Maria and John volunteered to fill sandbags to strengthen a dike during the flood. John filled $8\frac{1}{2}$ bags. They filled a total of 25. Write an equation to find how many bags Maria filled, and then solve it. $8\frac{1}{2} + x = 25$; $16\frac{1}{2}$

Estimate each sum or difference.

21. $3\frac{1}{3} + 6\frac{7}{11}$ 10 **22.** $11\frac{1}{2} - 7\frac{3}{5}$ 4 **23.** $8\frac{10}{21} - 2\frac{1}{19}$ 6 **24.** $5\frac{4}{5} - 5\frac{4}{10}$ 1

25. Find the sum of $9\frac{3}{5}$ and $4\frac{4}{5}$. $14\frac{2}{5}$

26. Find the difference between $11\frac{8}{11}$ and $7\frac{5}{11}$. $4\frac{3}{11}$

Simplify each expression.

27. $2\frac{1}{5} + 5\frac{3}{5}$ $7\frac{4}{5}$ **28.** $8\frac{1}{8} + 7\frac{1}{10}$ $15\frac{9}{40}$ **29.** $6\frac{6}{8} - 3\frac{5}{8}$ $3\frac{1}{8}$ **30.** $11\frac{10}{13} - 6\frac{4}{13}$ $5\frac{6}{13}$

31. $2\frac{9}{10} - 2\frac{2}{5}$ $\frac{1}{2}$ **32.** $11\frac{4}{9} + 3$ $14\frac{4}{9}$ **33.** $12\frac{2}{3} - 1\frac{1}{2}$ $11\frac{1}{6}$ **34.** $17 - 9\frac{5}{7}$ $7\frac{2}{7}$

35. $3 + 9\frac{1}{4}$ $12\frac{1}{4}$ **36.** $13\frac{1}{3} - 10\frac{7}{8}$ $2\frac{11}{24}$ **37.** $50\frac{1}{8} - 16\frac{7}{9}$ $33\frac{25}{72}$ **38.** $10\frac{5}{10} + 13\frac{5}{10}$ 24

Performance Task

Notice that $5\frac{3}{7}$, $4\frac{10}{7}$, and $3\frac{17}{7}$ all equal $\frac{38}{7}$. For each improper fraction, find three equivalent mixed numbers with the same denominators.

a. $\frac{13}{3}$ **b.** $\frac{27}{5}$ **c.** $\frac{73}{10}$

Resources

Assessment Sourcebook

Chapter 6 Tests
- Forms A and B (free response)
- Form C (multiple choice)
- Form D (performance assessment)
- Form E (mixed response)
- Form F (cumulative chapter test)

TestWorks
Test and Practice Software

Home and Community Connections
- Letter Home for Chapter 6 in English and Spanish

Cumulative Review Chapters 1-6 — Test Prep

Multiple Choice

Choose the best answer.

1. What age and height does point B represent? *[Lesson 1-3]* A

Age and Height

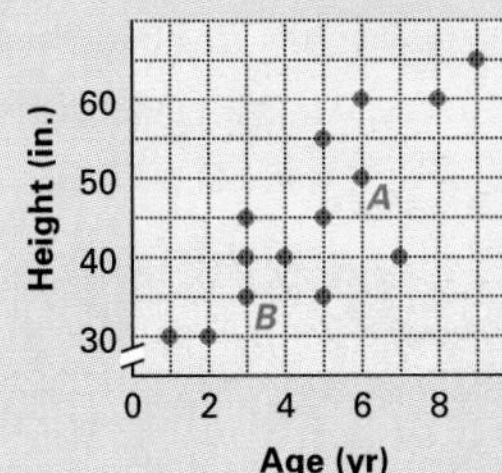

Ⓐ 3 yrs, 35 in. Ⓑ 3 yrs, 40 in.
Ⓒ 4 yrs, 40 in. Ⓓ None of these

2. Find the median of the data in the stem-and-leaf plot. *[Lesson 1-7]* C

Stem	Leaf
2	2 3 6
3	4 4 8 9 9
4	1 1 1 3 7

Ⓐ 1 Ⓑ 36 Ⓒ 39 Ⓓ None of these

3. Simplify 1025×4. *[Lesson 2-5]* C

Ⓐ 500 Ⓑ 1100
Ⓒ 4100 Ⓓ None of these

4. Which of the following would you represent with a variable? *[Lesson 2-10]* D

Ⓐ number of feet in a mile
Ⓑ number of dimes in a dollar
Ⓒ number of letters in your first name
Ⓓ number of jackets sold each day

5. Which expression represents 4,500,000 in scientific notation? *[Lesson 3-4]* B

Ⓐ 4.5×10^5 Ⓑ 4.5×10^6
Ⓒ 45×10^5 Ⓓ 45×10^6

6. Joyce cut a 1.75-inch piece of cord off the end of a cord 8.5-inch long. What length of cord was left? *[Lesson 3-6]* A

Ⓐ 6.75 in. Ⓑ 7.75 in.
Ⓒ 7.85 in. Ⓓ 10.25 in.

7. Simplify $67.5 \div 0.25$. *[Lesson 3-11]* D

Ⓐ 23 Ⓑ 27 Ⓒ 230 Ⓓ 270

8. What is the area of a rectangle 3 ft long and 7 ft wide? *[Lesson 4-4]* D

Ⓐ 10 ft Ⓑ 10 ft^2 Ⓒ 21 ft Ⓓ 21 ft^2

9. Find the area of the figure. *[Lesson 4-9]* C

Ⓐ 20 ft^2
Ⓑ 24 ft
Ⓒ 24 ft^2
Ⓓ None of these

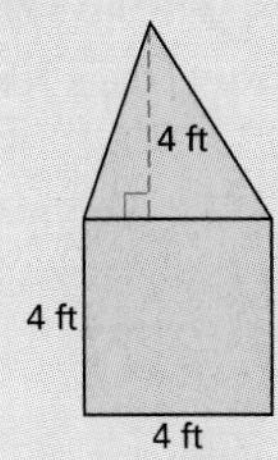

10. Find the prime factorization of 78. *[Lesson 5-2]* C

Ⓐ 2×34 Ⓑ $70 + 8$
Ⓒ $2 \times 3 \times 13$ Ⓓ 2×39

11. Write $\frac{63}{252}$ in lowest terms. *[Lesson 5-5]* B

Ⓐ $\frac{7}{28}$ Ⓑ $\frac{1}{4}$ Ⓒ $\frac{9}{84}$ Ⓓ None of these

12. Write $10\frac{3}{5}$ as a decimal. *[Lesson 5-7]* C

Ⓐ 106 Ⓑ 50.3 Ⓒ 10.6 Ⓓ 10.06

Cumulative Review Test Prep

About Multiple-Choice Tests

The Cumulative Review found at the end of Chapters 2, 4, 6, 8, 10, and 12 can be used to prepare students for standardized tests.

Students sometimes do not perform as well on standardized tests as they do on other tests. There may be several reasons for this related to the format and content of the test.

- **Format**
Students may have limited experience with multiple-choice tests. For some questions, such tests are harder because having options may confuse the students.

- **Content**
A standardized test may cover a broader range of content than normally covered on a test, and the relative emphasis given to various strands may be different than given in class. Also, some questions may assess general aptitude or thinking skills and not include specific pieces of mathematical content.

It is important to not let the differences between standardized tests and other tests shake your students' confidence.

Chapter 7

The information on these pages shows how fractions are used in real-life situations.

World Wide Web

If your class has access to the World Wide Web, you might want to use the information found at the Web site addresses given.

Extensions

The following activities do not require access to the World Wide Web.

Entertainment
Suggest that students investigate the different weight categories in weight lifting and the weights lifted at the last Olympics.

People of the World
Have students work in groups of four to find the number of people per square mile in India. Then have them compare that number with similar statistics for the United States and one other country of their choice.

Arts & Literature
Crazy Horse was an extraordinary military leader of the Oglala band of the Teton Lakota/Dakota nation. Ask students to research Crazy Horse and his times.

Science
Ask students how old the sample would be if it is only $\frac{1}{8}$ radioactive. 17,190 years old Have students investigate how scientists use carbon dating to determine the age of items discovered.

Social Studies
Ask students to determine how long Louis XIV and Franklin D. Roosevelt each led his country. Discuss the differences between how a monarch and a president assume office. Louis XIV, 72 years; Roosevelt, 12 years. The monarch is born into his or her role, whereas the President is elected.

7 Multiplying and Dividing Fractions

Entertainment Link
www.mathsurf.com/6/ch7/ent

Arts & Literature Link
www.mathsurf.com/6/ch7/arts

Entertainment

At the 1996 Centennial Olympic Games in Atlanta, Naim Suleymanoglu of Turkey won the gold medal in the 141-pound division of weightlifting by lifting 413 pounds. This was over $2\frac{3}{4}$ times his own body weight.

People of the World

One out of every 6 people in the world lives in India. With a world population of 5,423,000,000 people, there are about 900,000,000 people in India.

Arts & Literature

Upon completion, the statue of Chief Crazy Horse at Thunderhead Mountain, South Dakota, will be the largest free-standing statue in the world at 563 feet tall. The model of the statue on display is $\frac{1}{34}$ the size of the final statue.

362

TEACHER TALK

Meet Allison Harris

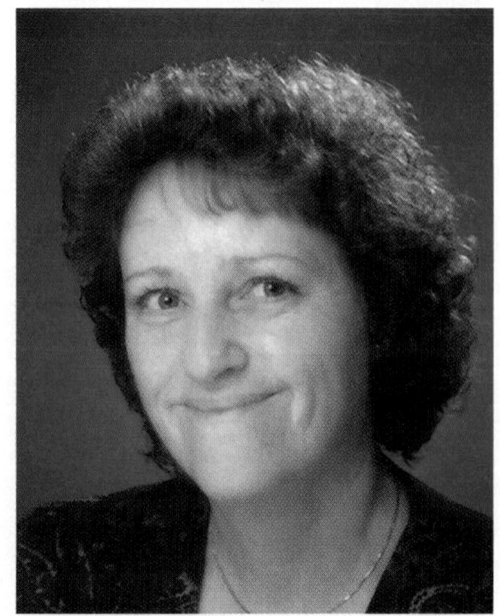

Seattle Public Schools
Seattle, Washington

I like to relate the division of fractions to what students already know about the division of whole numbers. If I present the question, "How many children could get 3 bagels each if I have a dozen bagels?" students may approach the solution by seeing that they can subtract 3 from 12 a total of 4 times. If I change my question to "How many children could get $1\frac{1}{2}$ bagels?" some students will see that the same strategy can be applied. Others will reason that $1\frac{1}{2}$ is half of 3 and construct their solution from that insight. I challenge students to draw a sketch or diagram to illustrate their thinking. Constructing intuitive solutions through sketches, diagrams, and discussions helps students justify the answers they get when they use the standard algorithm for division with fractions.

STUDENT RESOURCES

CONTENTS

Answers

1. $40
2. June
3. No, because the points do not lie near any straight line.
4. $11\frac{1}{2}$
5.

Score	Tally	Frequency
Under 70	II	2
70–79	~~IIII~~ II	7
80–89	~~IIII~~ I	6
90–100	~~IIII~~	5

6.

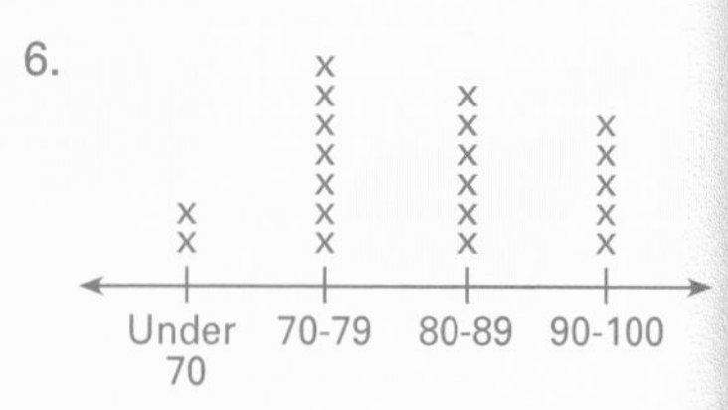

7.

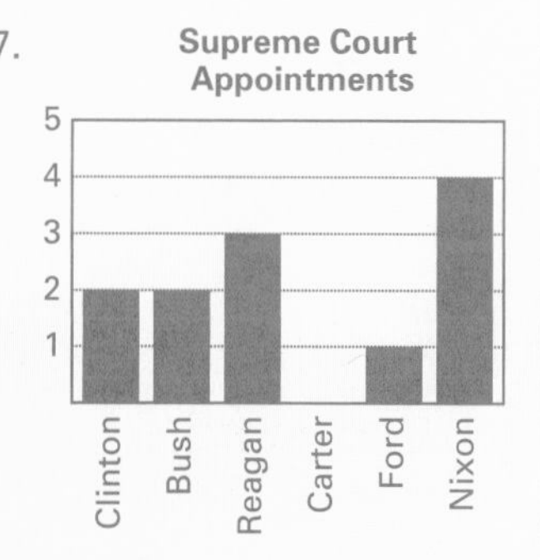

8.

Stem	Leaf
3	7 9
4	0 1 2 2 2 3 3 4 5 7 8
5	1 4 6

9. Median: 740.5; Mode: none; Mean: 790.7
10. The mean, because one outlier can dramatically change the total of the data, which will dramatically change the mean.

Chapter Review

Chapter 1 Review

1. How much was spent on clothes and entertainment?

Tara's Budget

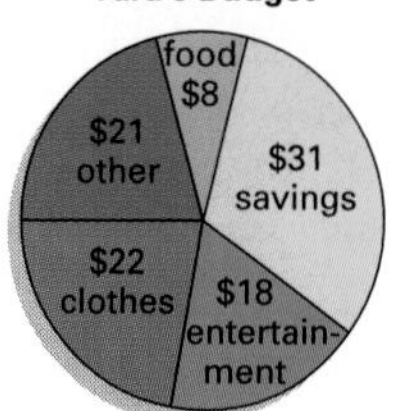

2. In which month did the sales of hot dogs increase the most when compared to the month before?

Hot Dogs Sold

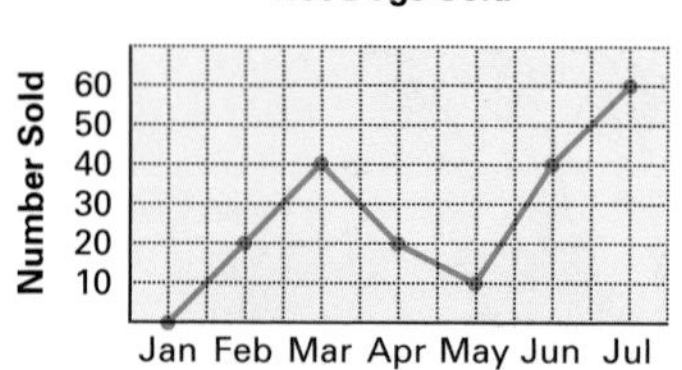

3. Does the scatter-plot show a trend? Explain.

Price of Car and Number of Doors

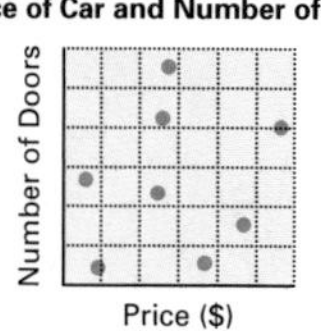

4. A pictograph's key shows that a symbol equals 10 bicycles. How many symbols would be needed to represent 115 bicycles?

Use the Science Test Scores data to answer Exercises 5 and 6.

5. Use tallies to make a frequency chart of test scores in these groups: under 70; 70–79; 80–89; 90–100.

6. Use the test score data to make a line plot.

Science Test Scores									
86	72	98	79	84	63	72	86	89	72
98	92	75	81	76	93	94	88	64	77

7. Make a bar graph using the number of Supreme Court Justices appointed by these Presidents: Clinton, 2; Bush, 2; Reagan, 3; Carter, 0; Ford, 1; and Nixon, 4.

8. Make a stem-and-leaf diagram for the following data: 43, 41, 56, 37, 42, 48, 45, 43, 51, 54, 39, 44, 42, 47, 42, 40.

9. Find the median, mode, and mean for these stolen-base records: Henderson, 1117; Brock, 938; Cobb, 892; Raines, 777; Collins, 743; Carey, 738; Wagner, 703; Morgan, 689; Wilson, 661; and Campaneris, 649.

10. For any data set, which of the three measures (mean, median, or mode) is most likely to be affected by an outlier? Explain.

Chapter 2 Review

1. Give the place value of 4 in 2,549,013.
2. Write 81,294,537 in word form.
3. Round 81,294,537 to the given place: **a.** Thousands **b.** Millions
4. Use > or < and compare 593,293 and 593,392.
5. Order from least to greatest: 3,192,536; 31,925,006; 3,492,426
6. Give the base and exponent of 13^6.
7. Write 6^5 in expanded form.
8. Write 3 squared in exponential notation.
9. Write each in standard form:
   a. 7^2 **b.** 8 cubed **c.** 12^1 **d.** 5 to the fourth power

Use mental math to solve each problem.

10. $170 + 30 + 64 + 36$
11. 8×303
12. 40×700
13. $54{,}000 \div 60$

Use estimation to solve each problem.

14. $592 - 128$
15. $4518 + 3179$
16. 47×712
17. $152 \times 9 \times 12$

Use the order of operations to solve each problem.

18. $7 \times 8 \div 2 + 3$
19. $(11 - 5)^2 \div 3 \times 7$

Find the next three numbers for each pattern.

20. 53, 49, 45, 41, 37, ...
21. 24, 36, 35, 47, 46, ...
22. State whether each phrase describes a constant or a variable.
    a. The number of quarters in a dollar
    b. The number of quarters in your pocket

Evaluate each expression for $x = 3, 5,$ and 7.

23. $3x$
24. $x + 9$
25. Julio bought a roll of film with n pictures. He took 18 of them. Write an expression for the number of pictures left on the roll of film.
26. Is the equation $24 - x = 15$ true for $x = 9$? For $x = 11$?
27. Solve for x: **a.** $x + 6 = 27$ **b.** $\frac{x}{3} = 6$

Chapter 2 Review

Answers

1. Ten thousands
2. Eighty-one million, two hundred ninety-four thousand, five hundred thirty-seven
3. a. 81,295,000
   b. 81,000,000
4. Possible answer: 593,293 < 593,392
5. 3,192,536; 3,492,426; 31,925,006
6. Base: 13; Exponent: 6
7. $6 \times 6 \times 6 \times 6 \times 6$
8. 3^2
9. a. 49 b. 512
   c. 12 d. 625
10. 300
11. 2424
12. 28,000
13. 900
14. 460
15. 7500
16. 35,000
17. 15,200
18. 31
19. 84
20. 33, 29, 25
21. 58, 57, 69
22. a. Constant
    b. Variable
23. 9, 15, 21
24. 12, 14, 16
25. $n - 18$
26. Yes; no
27. a. 21
    b. 18

Answers

1. a. 0.041
   b. 0.4
2. 1 cm; 1.4 cm
3. 0.693
4. 3.3, because 3.34 is 0.04 away from 3.3, but 0.06 away from 3.4.
5. 4.179 > 4.0182 > 4.018
6. 1.799×10^7
7. 100
8. 360
9. 96
10. 3
11. 430.33
12. 8.743
13. 29.93
14. 4
15. About 2.8
16. a. $h = 19.5$
    b. $x = 13.3$
17. 0.0368
18. 49,100
19. 0.83
20. 638,000
21. $k = 0.7$
22. $n = 4.5$

Chapter 3 Review

1. Show each number in decimal form.

a. 41 thousandths

b.

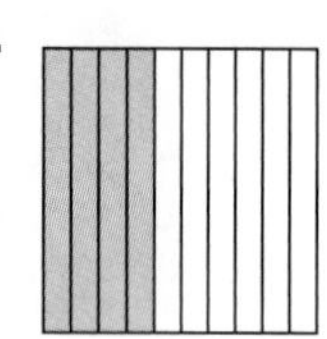

2. Give the fly's length to the nearest centimeter; the nearest tenth of a centimeter.

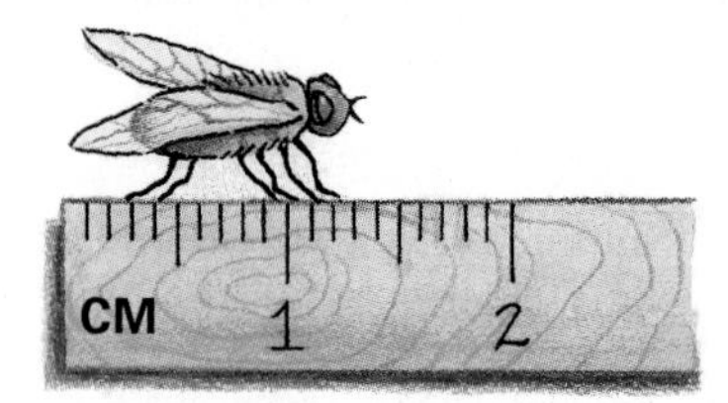

3. Round 0.6927 to the thousandths place.

4. On a ruler, is 3.34 closer to 3.3 or 3.4? Explain.

5. Use the < symbol to order the decimals from greatest to least: 4.018; 4.179; and 4.0182

6. The state of New York has a population of about 17,990,000. Write this number in scientific notation.

Estimate.

7. $29.21 + 72.4$ **8.** $451.8 - 93.507$ **9.** 15.9×6 **10.** $46.4 \div 15$

Simplify.

11. $8.4 + 421.93$ **12.** $11.03 - 2.287$ **13.** 7.3×4.1 **14.** $10.8 \div 2.7$

15. The star Arcturus is about 10.3 light-years from Earth. The star Vega is about 7.5 light-years from Earth. How many more light-years away from Earth is Arcturus?

16. Solve.

a. $h - 7.2 = 12.3$ **b.** $x + 6 = 19.3$

Simplify.

17. 3.68×0.01 **18.** $4.91 \times 10{,}000$ **19.** $83 \div 100$ **20.** $638 \div 0.001$

Solve.

21. $0.5k = 0.35$ **22.** $\frac{n}{0.9} = 5$

Answers

1. 15.6 cm
2. 11.352 in.
3. 6.2 m
4. 0.174
5. 5
6. 104
7. 20
8. 24,913
9. 2800
10. 150 m; 15,000 cm
11. 2958 in^2
12. 570 m^2
13. 204 ft^2
14. 156.25 m^2
15. 7.5 ft^2
16. 30 in.
17. a. 37.68 mm
    b. 113.04 mm^2
18. 451.17 units^2

Chapter 4 Review

Find the perimeter of each figure.

1.

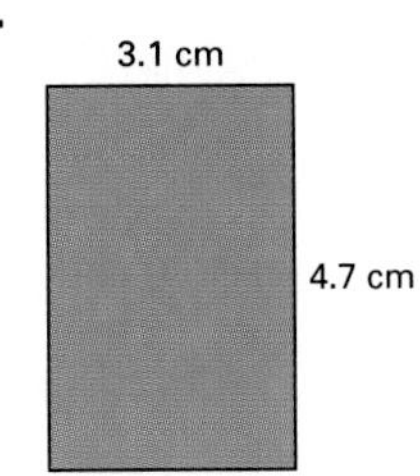

2.

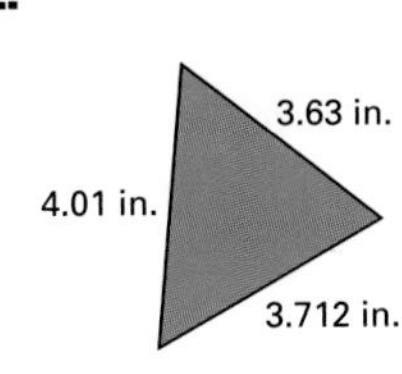

3.

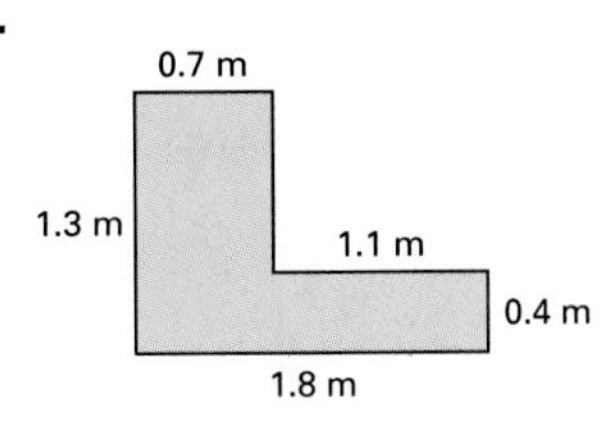

Use powers of 10 or conversion factors to find each measure.

4. 174 g = ☐ kg **5.** 60 in. = ☐ ft **6.** 6.5 lb = ☐ oz

7. 5 gal = ☐ qt **8.** 24.913 km = ☐ m **9.** 2.8 kg = ☐ g

10. A rectangular swimming pool is 25 m by 50 m. What is the perimeter of the pool in meters? In centimeters?

Find the area of each figure.

11.

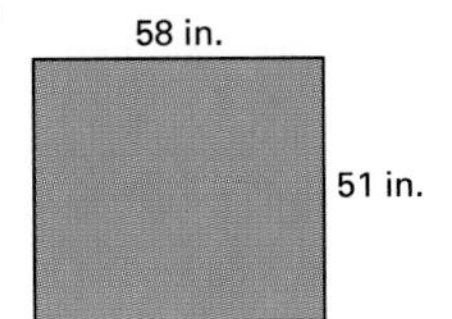

12.

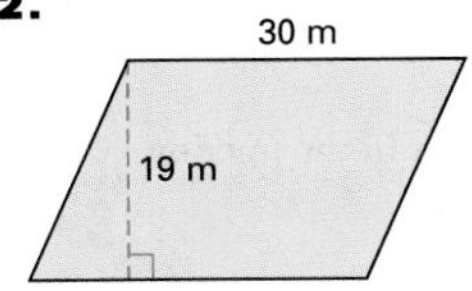

13.

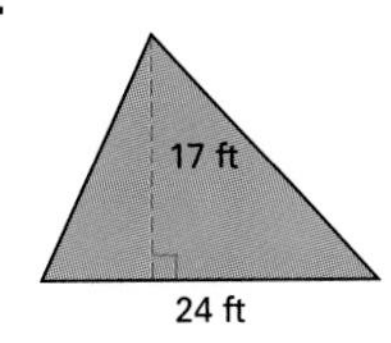

14. What is the area of a square with a side 12.5 m long?

15. What is the area of a rectangular desktop that is 2.5 ft long and 3 ft wide?

16. Find the base of a triangle whose height is 8.4 in. and area is 126 in^2.

17. The diameter of a circle is 12 mm.

a. Find the circumference. Use 3.14 for π.

b. Find its area.

18. Find the area of the irregular shape.

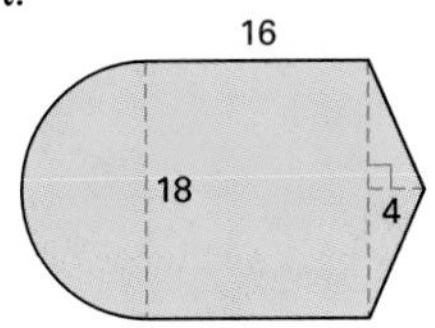

Chapter 5 Review

Answers

1. Divisible by 2 only
2. Divisible by 2, 3, 5, 6, and 10
3. Divisible by 2, 3, 5, 6, 9, and 10
4. Divisible by 2, 3, 5, 6, and 10
5. Composite: $2 \times 2 \times 19$
6. Prime
7. Composite: $3 \times 3 \times 3 \times 3 \times 3$
8. Composite: 5×17
9. 168
10. 105
11. $\frac{3}{7}$
12. $\frac{11}{24}$
13. 7 is the numerator; 12 is the denominator.
14. $\frac{3}{4}$
15. $\frac{3}{8}$
16. $\frac{2}{7}$
17. $\frac{7}{8}$
18. $8\frac{3}{5}$
19. $\frac{23}{6}$
20. $6\frac{1}{4}$
21. $\frac{51}{7}$
22. 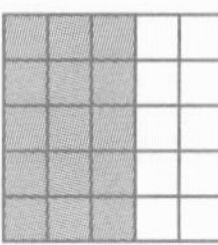

    Possible answer: $\frac{15}{25}$
23. $\frac{15}{4}$ in., $6\frac{1}{3}$ in., $\frac{15}{2}$ in., $7\frac{3}{4}$ in.
24. 0.875
25. $0.1\overline{6}$
26. 3.25
27. 2.8

Chapter 5 Review

Test each number for divisibility by 2, 3, 5, 6, 9, and 10.

1. 104 **2.** 660 **3.** 450 **4.** 1200

Label each number as prime or composite. If it is composite, find its prime factorization.

5. 76 **6.** 101 **7.** 243 **8.** 85

Find the least common multiple for each number pair.

9. 14, 24 **10.** 21, 35

What fraction does the shaded part of each model represent?

11.

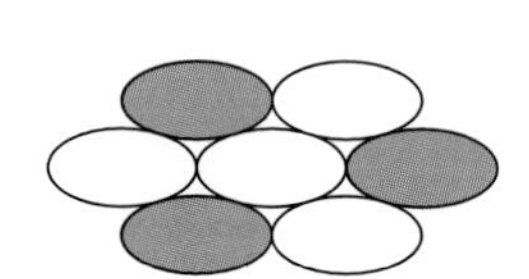

12.

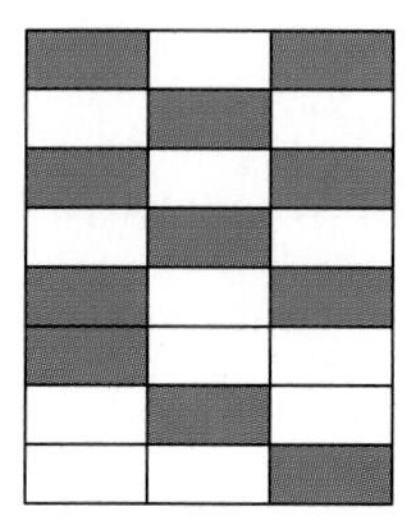

13. Identify the numerator and denominator in the fraction $\frac{7}{12}$.

Write each fraction in lowest terms.

14. $\frac{45}{60}$ **15.** $\frac{48}{128}$ **16.** $\frac{18}{63}$ **17.** $\frac{420}{480}$

Rewrite each as a mixed number or as an improper fraction.

18. $\frac{43}{5}$ **19.** $3\frac{5}{6}$ **20.** $\frac{25}{4}$ **21.** $7\frac{2}{7}$

22. Draw a model of the fraction $\frac{3}{5}$ and name an equivalent fraction.

23. Four drawings have heights of $6\frac{1}{3}$, $\frac{15}{2}$, $7\frac{3}{4}$, and $\frac{15}{4}$ inches. List their heights in order from shortest to tallest.

Rewrite each fraction as a decimal.

24. $\frac{7}{8}$ **25.** $\frac{1}{6}$ **26.** $\frac{13}{4}$ **27.** $\frac{14}{5}$

Chapter 6 Review

1. Write the equation this model represents.

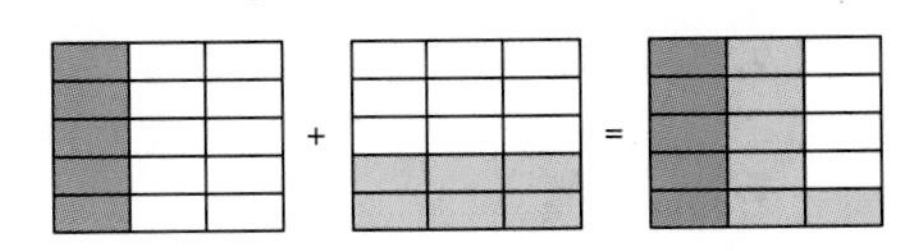

Find the least common multiple of each number pair.

2. 5, 8 3. 6, 24 4. 10, 14 5. 12, 27

Add or subtract. Write each answer in lowest terms.

6. $\frac{8}{9} - \frac{5}{9}$ 7. $\frac{3}{8} + \frac{9}{8}$ 8. $\frac{2}{11} + \frac{7}{11}$ 9. $\frac{5}{6} - \frac{1}{6}$

10. $\frac{3}{19} + \frac{14}{19}$ 11. $\frac{7}{16} - \frac{1}{4}$ 12. $\frac{7}{8} + \frac{1}{3}$ 13. $\frac{4}{7} - \frac{1}{2}$

14. $\frac{7}{9} + \frac{3}{4}$ 15. $\frac{1}{6} + \frac{9}{10}$ 16. $\frac{6}{7} - \frac{4}{5}$ 17. $\frac{3}{4} - \frac{3}{5}$

Solve each equation.

18. $\frac{4}{15} + y = \frac{13}{15}$ 19. $x - \frac{3}{10} = \frac{1}{5}$ 20. $t + \frac{1}{4} = \frac{7}{8}$

Round each mixed number to the nearest whole number.

21. $7\frac{4}{5}$ 22. $12\frac{1}{2}$ 23. $23\frac{9}{19}$ 24. $\frac{6}{11}$

Estimate each sum or difference.

25. $6\frac{3}{4} + 3\frac{1}{8}$ 26. $11\frac{1}{5} - 5\frac{2}{7}$ 27. $4\frac{7}{15} + 1\frac{2}{5}$ 28. $8\frac{4}{5} - 2\frac{5}{11}$

29. Find the sum of $2\frac{7}{9}$ and $5\frac{1}{9}$. 30. Find the difference between $12\frac{10}{13}$ and $4\frac{2}{13}$.

31. Elena wanted to tie a $37\frac{1}{2}$ in. ribbon on a gift. She had a $42\frac{1}{4}$ in. ribbon. How much would she need to trim off the ribbon in order to use it on the gift?

Simplify each expression.

32. $2\frac{3}{4} + 5\frac{1}{4}$ 33. $7\frac{1}{8} + 4\frac{1}{3}$ 34. $10\frac{7}{9} - 3\frac{2}{9}$ 35. $5\frac{11}{16} - 4\frac{3}{16}$

36. $7\frac{4}{15} - 5\frac{1}{9}$ 37. $8\frac{2}{5} + 7$ 38. $6\frac{4}{5} - 2\frac{1}{3}$ 39. $19 - 4\frac{7}{12}$

CHAPTER 6 REVIEW

Answers

1. $\frac{1}{3} + \frac{2}{5} = \frac{11}{15}$
2. 40
3. 24
4. 70
5. 108
6. $\frac{1}{3}$
7. $\frac{3}{2}$
8. $\frac{9}{11}$
9. $\frac{2}{3}$
10. $\frac{17}{19}$
11. $\frac{3}{16}$
12. $\frac{29}{24}$
13. $\frac{1}{14}$
14. $\frac{55}{36}$
15. $\frac{16}{15}$
16. $\frac{2}{35}$
17. $\frac{3}{20}$
18. $y = \frac{3}{5}$
19. $x = \frac{1}{2}$
20. $t = \frac{5}{8}$
21. 8
22. 13
23. 23
24. 1
25. 10
26. 6
27. 6
28. 7
29. $7\frac{8}{9}$
30. $8\frac{8}{13}$
31. $4\frac{3}{4}$ in.
32. 8
33. $11\frac{11}{24}$
34. $7\frac{5}{9}$
35. $1\frac{1}{2}$
36. $2\frac{7}{45}$
37. $15\frac{2}{5}$
38. $4\frac{7}{15}$
39. $14\frac{5}{12}$

CHAPTER REVIEW

Answers

1. $3 \times \frac{3}{5} = 1\frac{4}{5}$
2. 28
3. 4
4. $\frac{12}{5}$
5. $\frac{9}{56}$
6. $\frac{4}{9}$
7. $\frac{3}{40}$
8. $\frac{5}{36}$
9. $\frac{184}{65}$
10. $\frac{72}{32}$
11. 9
12. $\frac{5}{12}$ mi
13. Yes, because a mixed number is always greater than 1.
14. $5 \times \frac{4}{5} = 4$
15. $\frac{11}{4}$
16. $\frac{1}{5}$
17. $\frac{16}{3}$
18. $\frac{5}{18}$
19. $\frac{25}{42}$
20. $\frac{5}{2}$
21. $\frac{5}{36}$
22. $\frac{1}{32}$
23. $\frac{1}{24}$
24. $\frac{5}{21}$
25. No
26. No
27. Yes
28. $x = \frac{5}{4}$
29. $t = 1$
30. $j = \frac{2}{7}$
31. $h = \frac{7}{8}$

CHAPTER REVIEW

Chapter 7 Review

CHAPTER 7 REVIEW

1. Write the problem the model represents.

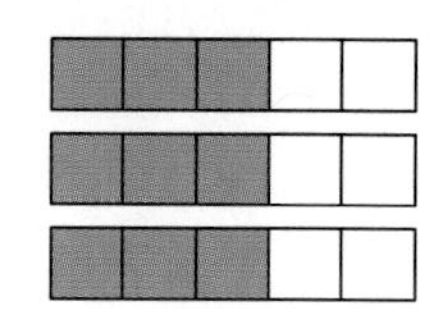

Estimate.

2. $3\frac{1}{2} \times 7\frac{1}{8}$

3. $15\frac{5}{7} \div 3\frac{3}{4}$

Simplify.

4. $\frac{2}{5} \times 6$ **5.** $\frac{3}{7} \times \frac{3}{8}$ **6.** $\frac{2}{3} \times \frac{2}{3}$ **7.** $\frac{3}{10} \times \frac{1}{4}$

8. $\frac{1}{6} \times \frac{5}{6}$ **9.** $4\frac{3}{5} \times \frac{8}{13}$ **10.** $1\frac{1}{4} \times 1\frac{7}{8}$ **11.** $2\frac{7}{10} \times 3\frac{1}{3}$

12. The distance between Joaquin's house and the store is $1\frac{1}{4}$ miles. If he walks $\frac{1}{3}$ of the way to the store, how far has he walked?

13. Is the product of two mixed numbers always larger than either number? Explain.

14. Write the equation that the model represents.

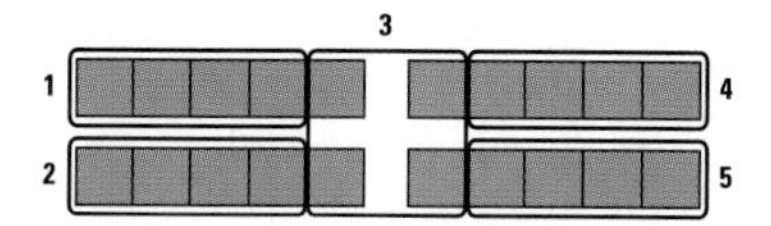

State the reciprocal.

15. $\frac{4}{11}$ **16.** 5

Simplify.

17. $4 \div \frac{3}{4}$ **18.** $\frac{1}{3} \div \frac{6}{5}$ **19.** $\frac{10}{7} \div \frac{12}{5}$ **20.** $\frac{5}{8} \div \frac{1}{4}$

21. $\frac{5}{9} \div 4$ **22.** $\frac{1}{4} \div 8$ **23.** $\frac{3}{12} \div 6$ **24.** $\frac{5}{6} \div 3\frac{1}{2}$

For each equation, state if the given value will make the equation true.

25. $\frac{3}{4}u = \frac{3}{10}$; $u = \frac{3}{5}$ **26.** $t \div \frac{1}{4} = \frac{5}{3}$; $t = \frac{20}{3}$ **27.** $\frac{5}{6}r = \frac{25}{36}$; $r = \frac{5}{6}$

Solve.

28. $\frac{2}{3}x = \frac{5}{6}$ **29.** $\frac{3}{4}t = \frac{15}{20}$ **30.** $\frac{4}{5}j = \frac{8}{35}$ **31.** $\frac{3}{10}h = \frac{21}{80}$

Chapter 8 Review

1. Draw and label a segment with end points *C* and *D*.
2. Draw and label an acute angle through points *A*, *B*, and *C* with *B* as the vertex.
3. Which angle sum has the same number of degrees as a right angle, two complementary angles or two supplementary angles?
4. Draw and label:
   a. Two rays that are perpendicular
   b. *AB*
5. Classify the triangle whose angles measure 73°, 24°, and 83°.
6. What kind of triangle has two sides with length 4 cm and one side with length 5 cm?
7. Which quadrilaterals have two pairs of parallel sides?
8. Explain why all squares are rectangles, but not all rectangles are squares.

Tell whether each transformation is a reflection, translation, or rotation.

9. 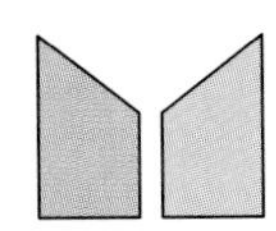

10. 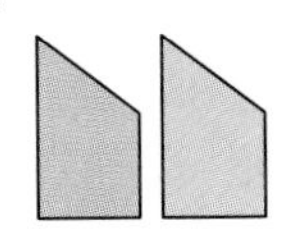

11. 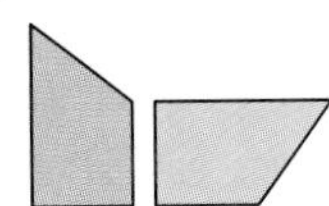

12. Are the figures in Exercises 9–11 congruent? Explain.
13. Trace the figure and draw its reflection over the line.

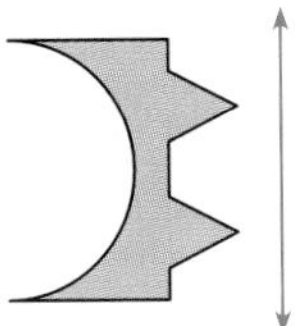

14. Tell whether the figure has line symmetry. If it does, draw its line(s) of symmetry.

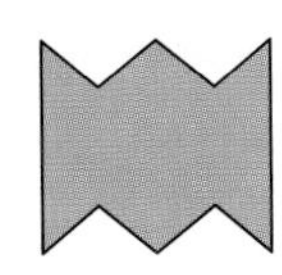

15. Give the number of degrees and the direction the figure has been rotated.

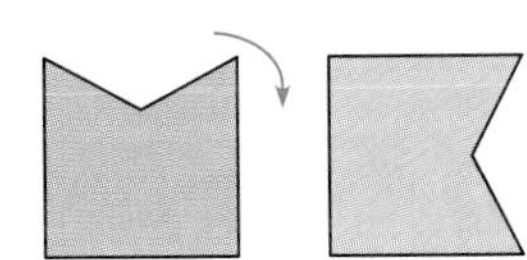

16. What is the least rotation that will land the rectangle on top of itself?

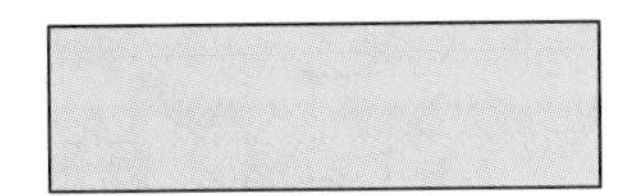

17. If a figure has rotational symmetry, can it also have line symmetry? Explain.
18. Do all parallelograms tessellate? If not, what type of parallelograms tessellate?

Chapter 8 Review

Answers

1. Possible answer:

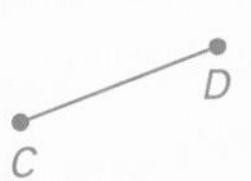

2. Possible answer:

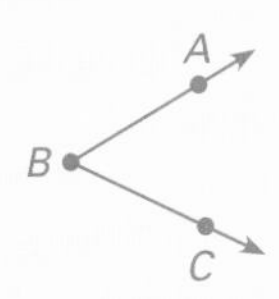

3. Two complementary angles
4. Possible answers:

a. b.

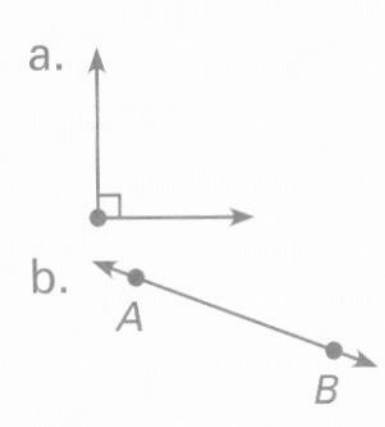

5. Acute triangle
6. Isosceles triangle
7. Parallelograms
8. All squares have 4 right angles and 4 congruent sides, but not all rectangles have 4 congruent sides.
9. Reflection
10. Translation
11. Rotation
12. Yes, since the size and shape of the polygon remains unchanged in each case.
13.

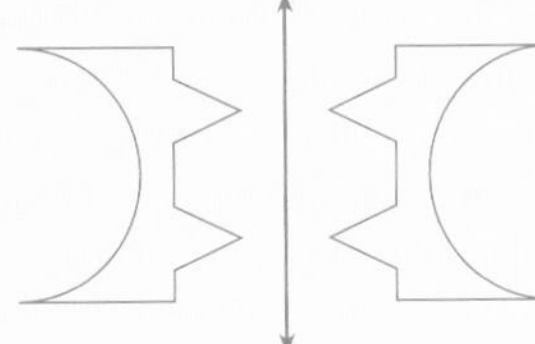

14. Yes

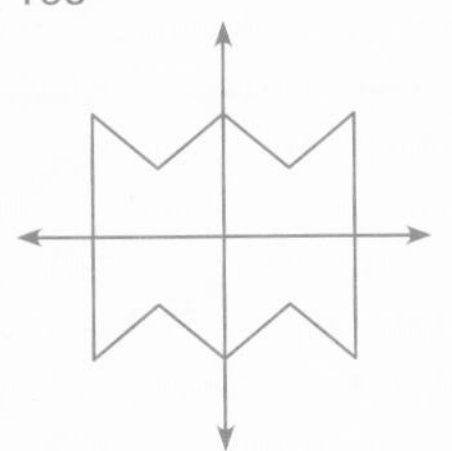

15. 90° clockwise
16. 180°
17. Yes; Example: A square
18. Yes

Answers

1. –4 –2 0 2 4 6

2. −5
3. Negative
4. Positive
5. 3 − 4 = −1
6. 2 − 7 = −5
7. −12
8. −4
9. 7
10. −15
11. 7
12. −5
13. 0
14. −40
15. 36
16. −21
17. −6
18. 5
19. (2, −7)
20. III
21. a. (3, 0)
    b. (0, −3)
22.

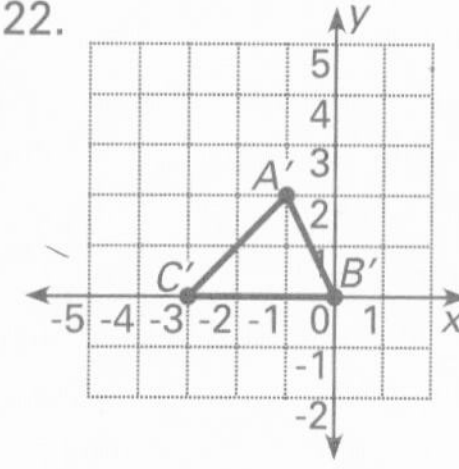

$A(-1, 2)$, $B(0, 0)$, $C(-3, 0)$

23. $Q'(5, 1)$, $R'(5, 3)$, $S'(1, 3)$, $T'(1, 1)$

24. a.

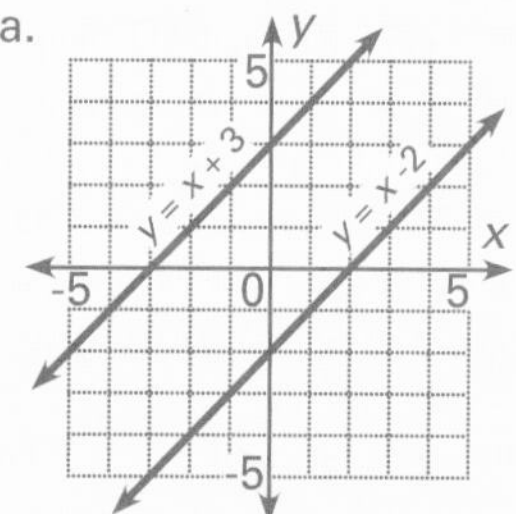

b. Because the lines are parallel, if one line is moved up or down and right or left it will coincide with the other line.

Chapter 9 Review

1. Locate the integers −3, 2, −5, 6, 1, and −1 on a number line.

2. What is the closest integer to the right of $-5\frac{2}{3}$ on a number line?

3. Is the product of one positive and one negative number a positive or negative value?

4. Is the quotient of two negative numbers positive or negative?

Write the equation that is shown by each model.

5.

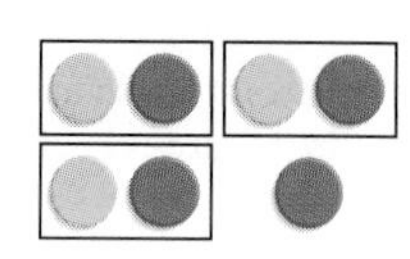

6.

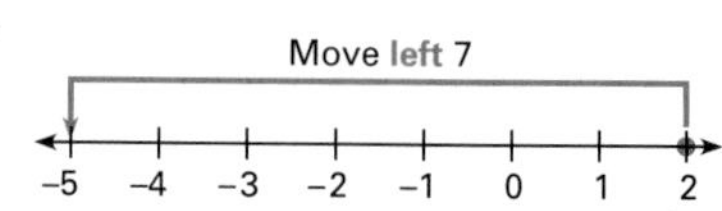

Simplify.

7. $-3 + (-9)$	**8.** $2 + (-6)$	**9.** $-4 + 11$
10. $-7 - 8$	**11.** $5 - (-2)$	**12.** $-6 - (-1)$
13. $-7 - (-7)$	**14.** $8 \times (-5)$	**15.** $-4 \times (-9)$
16. -7×3	**17.** $-24 \div 4$	**18.** $-45 \div (-9)$

19. Name the ordered pair for the point 2 units to the right of the origin and 7 units down.

20. Name the quadrant where the point $(-1, -4)$ is located.

21. Name a point the same *distance* from the origin as (0, 3) and located:

a. On the *x*-axis **b.** On the *y*-axis

22. Create $A'B'C'$ by translating the triangle ABC 3 units to the left and 2 units down. Give the coordinates of A', B', and C'.

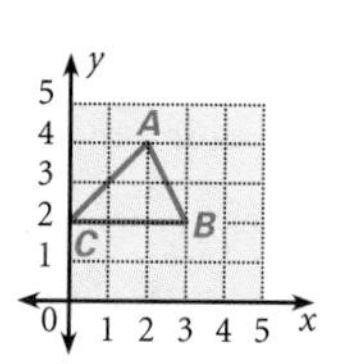

23. Rectangle $QRST$ has coordinates $Q(-5, 1)$, $R(-5, 3)$, $S(-1, 3)$, and $T(-1, 1)$. If $QRST$ is reflected across the y-axis, name the coordinates of Q', R', S', and T'.

24. a. Graph the equations $y = x - 2$ and $y = x + 3$ on the same coordinate grid.

b. Explain why one of the graphs is a translation of the other.

Chapter 10 Review

1. Show three ways to write the ratio of four lemons to seven limes.
2. Write the ratio $\frac{35}{60}$ in lowest terms.
3. Each bag contains 8 red marbles and 11 blue marbles. If there are 4 bags, what is the ratio in lowest terms:
   - a. Of red marbles to blue marbles?
   - b. Of blue marbles to red marbles?
   - c. Of red marbles to total marbles?
   - d. Of bags to marbles?
4. According to the graph, what is the ratio of fiction books to nonfiction books? Of fiction books to total books?

Library Books

Fiction: 4 book symbols

Nonfiction: 5 book symbols and a half symbol

1 book symbol = 200 books

5. Which of the following ratios is *not* equal to the ratio 8 to 24?

   Ⓐ $\frac{5}{15}$ Ⓑ $\frac{30}{10}$ Ⓒ 7:21 Ⓓ $\frac{1}{3}$

6. Which of the following is not a rate?

   Ⓐ $\frac{5 \text{ ft}}{4 \text{ sec}}$ Ⓑ $\frac{4 \text{ ft}}{1 \text{ sec}}$ Ⓒ $\frac{4 \text{ sec}}{5 \text{ ft}}$ Ⓓ $\frac{4 \text{ sec}}{5 \text{ sec}}$

7. Use a table to find four equal rates that describe boiling 2 gallons of water in 4 minutes.
8. What is the unit rate of a car's travel time if the car travels 240 miles in 5 hours?
9. Can the ratios $\frac{5 \text{ mi}}{8 \text{ s}}$ and $\frac{35 \text{ s}}{56 \text{ mi}}$ form a proportion? Explain.
10. Solve for a: $\frac{6}{15} = \frac{4}{a}$.
11. Apples cost $1.20 per pound. How much do 40 oz of apples cost?
12. Explain why the two triangles are similar.

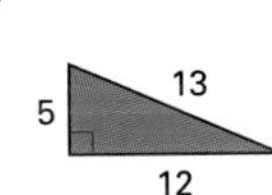

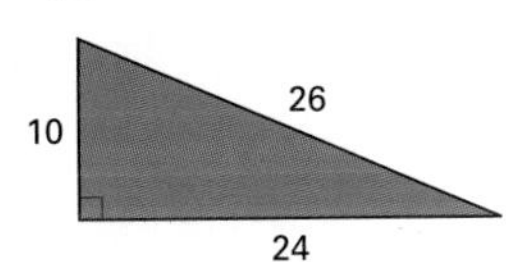

Write each percent as a ratio of a number to 100, as a fraction in lowest terms, and as a decimal.

13. 60% 14. 12% 15. 45% 16. 52%

17. In Denver, Colorado, in 1990, 23% of the population was Latino. If the total population was 467,610, about how many Latino people lived in Denver?

Chapter 10 Review

Answers

1. 4 to 7, 4:7, $\frac{4}{7}$
2. $\frac{7}{12}$
3. a. $\frac{8}{11}$ b. $\frac{11}{8}$ c. $\frac{8}{19}$ d. $\frac{1}{19}$
4. $\frac{8}{11}$; $\frac{8}{19}$
5. B
6. D
7. Possible answer: $\frac{0.5 \text{ gal}}{1 \text{ min}} = \frac{1 \text{ gal}}{2 \text{ min}} = \frac{3 \text{ gal}}{6 \text{ min}} = \frac{4 \text{ gal}}{8 \text{ min}}$
8. 48 mi/hr
9. No, because the units are reversed.
10. $a = 10$
11. $3.00
12. Each side on the larger one is twice as long as the corresponding side on the smaller one.
13. 60:100, $\frac{3}{5}$, 0.6
14. $\frac{12}{100}$, $\frac{3}{25}$; 0.12
15. $\frac{45}{100}$, $\frac{9}{20}$, 0.45
16. $\frac{52}{100}$, $\frac{13}{25}$, 0.52
17. 107,550

Chapter 11 Review

Answers

1. Sphere
2. Triangular prism; 5 faces, 9 edges, 6 vertices
3. Cone
4. 192 m^2
5. 326.56 ft^2
6. 214 cm^2
7. Front Side Top
8. 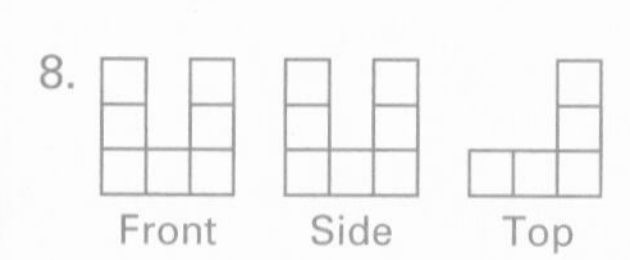

9. 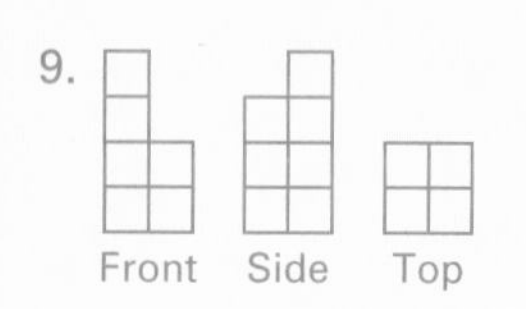

10. 280 $units^3$
11. 1232 ft^3
12. 216 cm^3
13. 87.92 $in.^2$

Chapter 11 Review

Classify each solid. If it is a polyhedron, state the number of faces, edges, and vertices.

1. 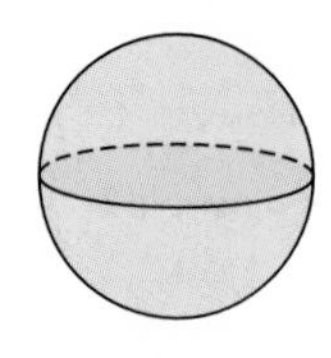

2. 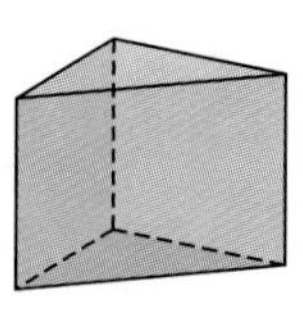

3. 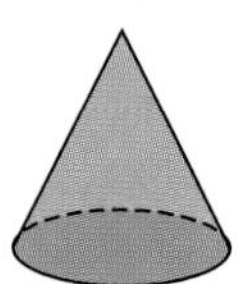

Find the surface area of each figure. Use 3.14 for π.

4. 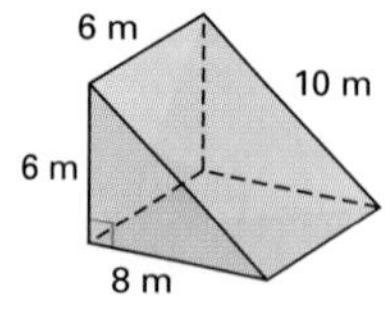

5. 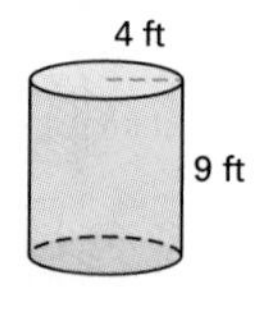

6. 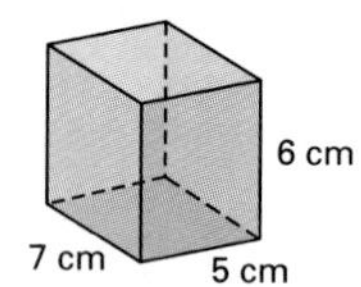

For each solid, draw the front view, the side view, and the top view.

7. 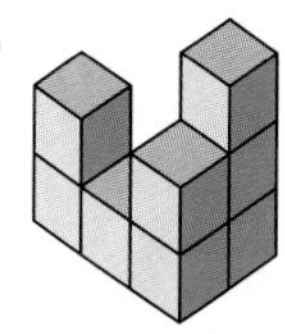

8. 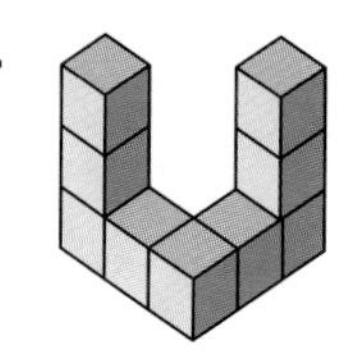

9. 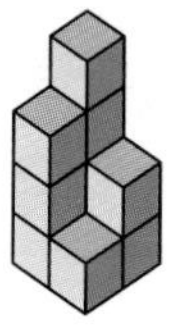

Find each volume.

10. 

11. 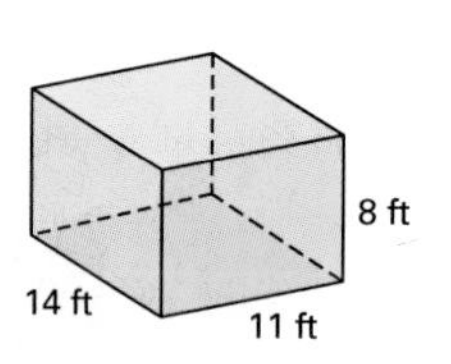

12. 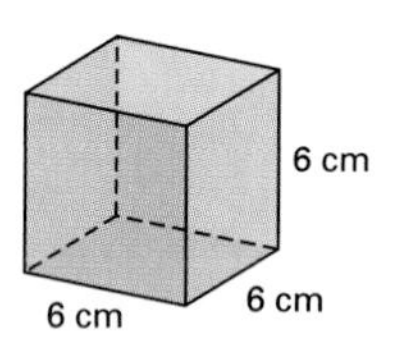

13. The Veggie Soup Co. sells its soup in cans like the one pictured. Find the surface area of the can. Use 3.14 for π.

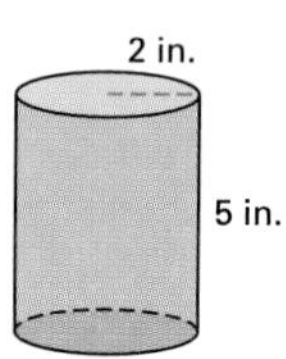

Chapter 12 Review

1. Estimate the probability of choosing a person at random whose birthday falls on a Monday next year.

2. If $P(\text{event}) = \frac{2}{3}$, what is the probability that the event will not occur?

3. Michiko bought 12 eggs. Three of them were brown. One was spotted. The rest were white. If she chooses an egg at random, what are the chances she will choose a white or brown egg?

4. In one neighborhood, 30 out of 45 people surveyed said they read at least one book each week. Predict how many of the 600 people in the neighborhood read at least one book each week.

5. A spinner has 6 equal sections labeled A, B, C, D, E, and F.

a. What is the probability of landing in the "B" section?

b. What is the probability of *not* landing in "B" section?

6. Estimate the probability of hitting the shaded area with a dart.

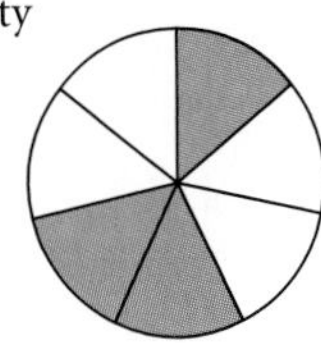

7. Complete a tree diagram that shows how many different kinds of lunches can be made if there are 4 kinds of sandwiches (tuna, peanut butter, turkey, and cheese); 2 kinds of snacks (chips and fruit); and 3 kinds of drinks (milk, juice, and soda.)

8. Use multiplication to find the possible number of stereo systems that could be assembled using one each of 3 tuners, 5 compact disc players, 4 cassette players, and 3 amplifiers.

9. If you spin both of the spinners, how many possible outcomes are there?

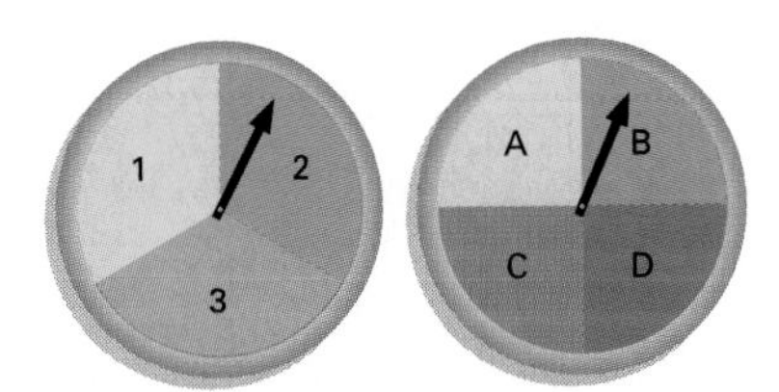

10. What is the probability of spinning A or B on Spinner 1 and an odd number on Spinner 2?

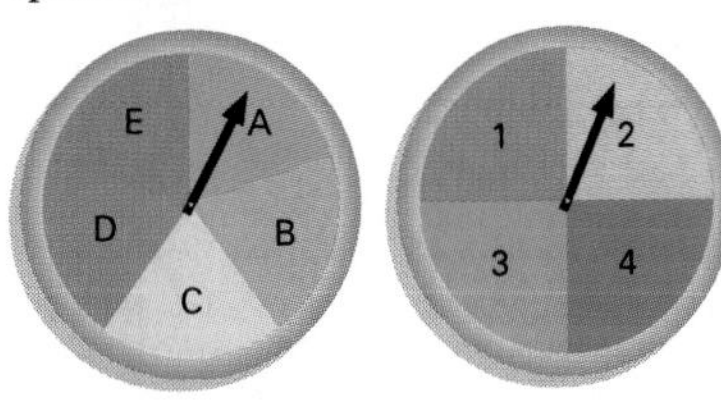

11. Emily rolls one six-sided number cube twice. What is the probability that she rolls an even number and then a 5?

12. What is the probability of flipping three coins and getting all heads?

13. Player A and Player B each roll a number cube. If the sum of the two numbers is greater than 5, Player A wins. Otherwise, Player B wins. Is the game fair? Explain.

Answers

1. $\frac{1}{7}$
2. $\frac{1}{3}$
3. $\frac{11}{12}$
4. 400
5. a. $\frac{1}{6}$
   b. $\frac{5}{6}$
6. $\frac{3}{7}$
7. See below left for tree diagram.
8. 180
9. 12
10. $\frac{1}{5}$
11. $\frac{1}{12}$
12. $\frac{1}{8}$
13. No. Player A's chance of winning is $\frac{13}{18}$, and Player B's chance is $\frac{5}{18}$.

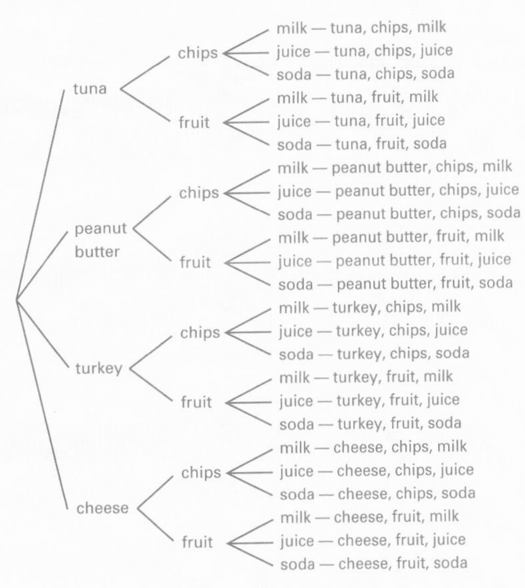

24 different kinds of lunches

Geometric Formulas

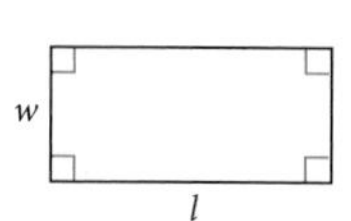

Rectangle
Area: $A = lw$
Perimeter: $p = 2l + 2w$

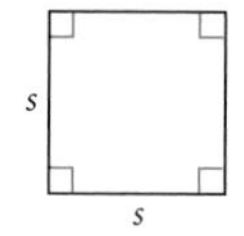

Square
Area: $A = s^2$
Perimeter: $p = 4s$

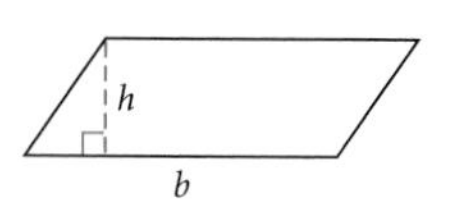

Parallelogram
Area: $A = bh$

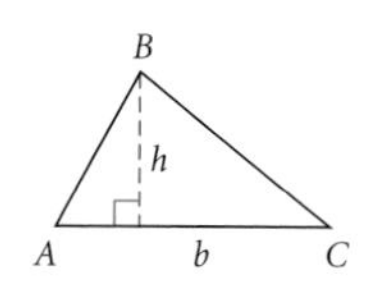

Triangle
Area: $A = \frac{1}{2}bh$
$m\angle A + m\angle B + m\angle C = 180°$

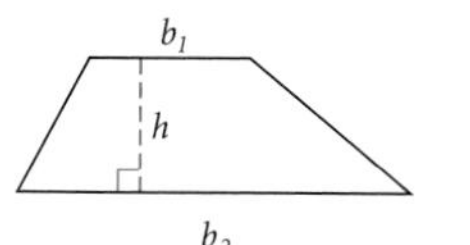

Trapezoid
Area: $A = \frac{1}{2}h(b_1 + b_2)$

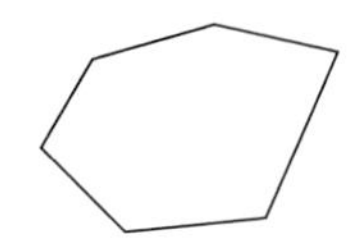

Polygon
Sum of angle measures for n-sided polygon: $S = (n - 2)180°$
Perimeter: sum of measures of all sides

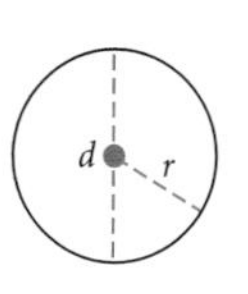

Circle
Area: $A = \pi r^2$
Circumference: $C = \pi d = 2\pi r$

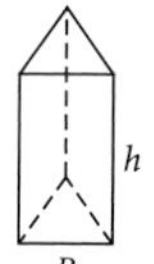

Prism
Volume: $V = Bh$
Surface Area: $SA = ph + 2B$

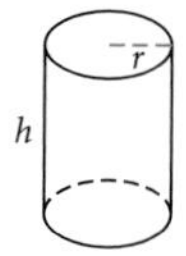

Cylinder
Volume: $V = \pi r^2 h$
Surface Area: $SA = 2\pi rh + 2\pi r^2$

TABLES

TABLES

Measurement Conversion Factors

Metric Measures of Length

1000 meters (m) = 1 kilometer (km)
100 centimeters (cm) = 1 m
10 decimeters (dm) = 1 m
1000 millimeters (mm) = 1 m
10 cm = 1 decimeter (dm)
10 mm = 1 cm

Area

100 square millimeters (mm^2) = 1 square centimeter (cm^2)
10,000 cm^2 = 1 square meter (m^2)
10,000 m^2 = 1 hectare (ha)

Volume

1000 cubic millimeters (mm^3) = 1 cubic centimeter (cm^3)
1000 cm^3 = 1 cubic decimeter (dm^3)
1,000,000 cm^3 = 1 cubic meter (m^3)

Capacity

1000 milliliters (mL) = 1 liter (L)
1000 L = 1 kiloliter (kL)

Mass

1000 kilograms (kg) = 1 metric ton (t)
1000 grams (g) = 1 kg
1000 milligrams (mg) = 1 g

Temperatures in Degrees Celsius (°C)

0°C = freezing point of water
37°C = normal body temperature
100°C = boiling point of water

Time

60 seconds (sec) = 1 minute (min)
60 min = 1 hour (hr)
24 hr = 1 day

Customary Measures of Length

12 inches (in.) = 1 foot (ft)
3 ft = 1 yard (yd)
36 in. = 1 yd
5280 ft = 1 mile (mi)
1760 yd = 1 mi
6076 ft = 1 nautical mile

Area

144 square inches (in^2) = 1 square foot (ft^2)
9 ft^2 = 1 square yard (yd^2)
43,560 sq ft^2 = 1 acre (A)

Volume

1728 cubic inches (cu in.) = 1 cubic foot (cu ft)
27 cu ft = 1 cubic yard (cu yard)

Capacity

8 fluid ounces (fl oz) = 1 cup (c)
2 c = 1 pint (pt)
2 pt = 1 quart (qt)
4 qt = 1 gallon (gal)

Weight

16 ounces (oz) = 1 pound (lb)
2000 lb = 1 ton (T)

Temperatures in Degrees Fahrenheit (°F)

32°F = freezing point of water
98.6°F = normal body temperature
212°F = boiling point of water

TABLES

TABLES

Symbols

TABLES

$+$	plus or positive
$-$	minus or negative
$\cdot$	times
$\times$	times
$\div$	divided by
$\pm$	positive or negative
$=$	is equal to
$\neq$	is not equal to
$<$	is less than
$>$	is greater than
$\leq$	is less than or equal to
$\geq$	is greater than or equal to
$\approx$	is approximately equal to
%	percent
$a{:}b$	the ratio of a to b, or $\frac{a}{b}$
$\cong$	is congruent to
$\sim$	is similar to
$^\circ$	degree(s)
$\overleftrightarrow{AB}$	line containing points A and B
$\overline{AB}$	line segment with endpoints A and B
$\overrightarrow{AB}$	ray with endpoint A and containing B
$\llcorner$	right angle
$\perp$	is perpendicular to
$\parallel$	is parallel to
AB	length of $\overline{AB}$; distance between A and B
$\triangle ABC$	triangle with vertices A, B, and C
$\angle ABC$	angle with sides $\overrightarrow{BA}$ and $\overrightarrow{BC}$
$\angle B$	angle with vertex B
$m\angle ABC$	measure of angle ABC
$'$	prime
a^n	the nth power of a
$\lvert x \rvert$	absolute value of x
$\sqrt{x}$	principal square root of x
π	pi (approximately 3.1416)
(a, b)	ordered pair with x-coordinate a and y-coordinate b
$P(A)$	the probability of event A
$n!$	n factorial

Glossary

acute angle An angle smaller than a right angle. [p. 413]

acute triangle A triangle with three acute angles. [p. 424]

addend A number added to one or more others.

addition An operation that gives the total number when two or more numbers are put together.

algebra A branch of mathematics in which arithmetic relations are explored using letter symbols to represent numbers.

algebraic expression An expression that contains at least one variable. Example: $n - 7$.

angle Two rays with the same endpoint. [p. 412]

area The amount of surface a figure covers. [p. 229]

Associative Property The fact that changing the grouping of addends or factors does not change the sum or product. Example: $(5 + 3) + 7 = 15$ and $5 + (3 + 7) = 15$. [p. 87]

average See mean.

axes See x-axis and y-axis.

bar graph A graph using vertical or horizontal bars to display numerical information. [p. 7]

base [of an exponent] A number multiplied by itself the number of times shown by an exponent. Example: $6^2 = 6 \times 6$, where 6 is the base and 2 is the exponent. [p. 78]; [of a figure] On a two-dimensional figure, the distance across the bottom. [p. 230] On a prism, one of the two parallel and congruent faces. [p. 580]

binary number system A base-2 place value system. [p. 201]

bisect Dividing a geometric figure into two equal parts. [p. 459]

box-and-whisker plot A graph showing the shape of a data set. [p. 57]

capacity The volume of a figure, given in terms of liquid measure.

center The point at the exact middle of a circle.

centi- A prefix meaning $\frac{1}{100}$. [p. 216]

circle See examples below. [p. 246]

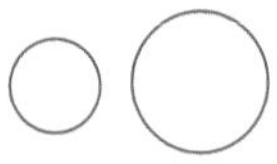

circle graph A round graph that uses different-sized wedges to show how portions of a set of data compare with the whole set. [p. 8]

circumference The perimeter of a circle. [p. 246]

clockwise The direction of rotation when the top of a figure turns to the right. [p. 448]

clustering An estimation method where numbers that are approximately equal are treated as if they were equal. Example: $26 + 24 + 23$ is about $25 + 25 + 25$, or 3×25. [p. 91]

common denominator A denominator that is the same in two fractions. [p. 309]

common factor A number that is a factor of two different numbers. Example: 4 is a common factor of 8 and 12.

common multiple A number that is a multiple of each of two given numbers. Example: 44 is a common multiple of 2 and 11. [p. 281]

Commutative Property The fact that changing the order of addends or factors does not change the sum or product. Example: $4 \times 7 = 28$ and $7 \times 4 = 28$. [p. 87]

compatible numbers Pairs of numbers that can be computed easily. Example: $30 + 70$. [p. 86]

compensation Choosing numbers close to the numbers in a problem, and then adjusting the answer to compensate for the numbers chosen. [p. 87]

complementary angles Two angles whose measures add up to 90°. [p. 417]

composite number A whole number greater than 1 that is not prime. [p. 276]

compound event A combination of two or more single events. Example: getting heads on a coin toss and then rolling 4 with a number cube. [p. 647]

cone See example below. [p. 581]

congruent Having the same size and shape. [p. 444]

constant A quantity that does not change. [p. 111]

GLOSSARY

GLOSSARY

677

conversion factor The number of measurement units that another unit is equal to. Example: to convert inches to feet, divide by the conversion factor 12 (12 inches = 1 foot). [p. 222]

coordinate One of the numbers in an ordered pair. [p. 489]

coordinate plane A set of lines used to locate points in a plane. [p. 489]

counterclockwise The direction of rotation when the top of a figure turns to the left. [p. 448]

cross product For two ratios, the product of the top value from one and the bottom value from the other. [p. 530]

cube A prism whose faces are all squares of the same size. [p. 581]

cubed Raised to the power of 3. Example: 2 cubed = $2^3 = 8$. [p. 79]

cubic unit A unit measuring volume, consisting of a cube with edges one unit long. [p. 606]

customary system (of measurement) The measurement system often used in the United States, using inches, feet, miles, ounces, pounds, quarts, gallons, etc.

cylinder See example below. [p. 581]

deca- A prefix meaning 10. Example: the decameter = 10 meters. [p. 217]

decagon A polygon with 10 sides. [p. 433]

deci- A prefix meaning $\frac{1}{10}$. Example: the decimeter = 0.1 meter. [p. 217]

decimal system A base-10 place value system.

degree A unit of angle measure, $\frac{1}{360}$ of a complete circle. [p. 417]

denominator The bottom number in a fraction, telling how many parts the whole is divided into. [p. 289]

diameter A line connecting two points on a circle and passing through the circle's center. [p. 246]

difference The result of subtracting one number from another. [p. 114]

digit The symbols used to write the numerals 0, 1, 2, 3, 4, 5, 6, 7, 8, and 9.

Distributive Property The fact that numbers can be broken into smaller numbers for calculating. Example: $(32 \times 5) = (30 + 2) \times 5 = (30 \times 5) + (2 \times 5) = 160$. [p. 87]

dividend A number being divided by another number. Example: in $5 \div 3$, 5 is the dividend. [p. 185]

divisible Can be divided by another number without leaving a remainder. Example: 18 is divisible by 6. [p. 271]

division An operation that tells how many equal sets or how many in each equal set.

divisor A number that another number is being divided by. Example: in $4 \div 9$, 9 is the divisor. [p. 185]

dodecagon A polygon with 12 sides. [p. 433]

edge The line where two faces of a solid come together. [p. 580]

endpoint A point at the end of a segment or ray. [p. 409]

equality A mathematical relation of being exactly the same.

equation A mathematical sentence stating that two expressions are equal. Example: $14 = 2x$. [p. 119]

equilateral triangle A triangle with three sides of the same length. [p. 428]

equivalent fractions Two fractions naming the same amount. [p. 289]

estimate An approximation for the result of a calculation.

Euler's formula A formula about edges, faces, and vertices of polyhedrons stating: $E = F + V - 2$. [p. 617]

evaluate To find the number that an algebraic expression names.

even number A whole number that has 0, 2, 4, 6, or 8 in the ones place.

event The particular outcome one is looking at in a probability experiment. [p. 627]

expanded form A way of writing an exponential number showing all of the factors individually. Example: $9 \times 9 \times 9$. [p. 79]

experiment A situation that can turn out in more than one way. [p. 626]

exponent A raised number telling how many times another number, the base, is being multiplied by itself. Example: $9^3 = 9 \times 9 \times 9$, where 3 is the exponent and 9 is the base. [p. 78]

exponential notation A way of writing repeated multiplication of a number using exponents. Example: 9^3. [p. 78]

expression A mathematical phrase containing variables, constants, and operation symbols. Example: $12 - x$. [p. 111]

face A flat surface on a solid. [p. 580]

factor A number that divides another number without remainder. Example: 6 is a factor of 42. [p. 78]

GLOSSARY

678

factor tree A diagram showing how a composite number breaks down into its prime factors. [p. 276]

fair game A game in which each player has the same probability of winning. [p. 651]

flip See *reflection.*

foot A unit in the customary system of measurement equal to 12 inches. [p. 221]

formula A rule showing relationships among quantities. Example: $A = bh$.

fraction A number describing part of a whole when the whole is cut into equal pieces. [p. 288]

frequency chart A table listing each value that appears in a data set followed by the number of times it appears. [p. 25]

front-end estimation An estimation method where only the first digit of each number is used for computation, and the result is adjusted based on the remaining digits. [p. 91]

gallon A unit in the customary system of measurement equal to 4 quarts. [p. 221]

geometry A branch of mathematics in which the relations between points, lines, figures, and solids are explored.

gram The basic unit of mass in the metric system. [p. 215]

graph A diagram that shows information in an organized way.

greatest common factor (GCF) The greatest whole number that divides two whole numbers. Example: 16 is the GCF of 32 and 48. [p. 295]

hecto- A prefix meaning 100. Example: the hectometer = 100 meters. [p. 217]

height The distance along a figure that is perpendicular to the base. [p. 230]

heptagon A polygon with 7 sides. [p. 433]

hexagon A polygon with 6 sides. [p. 433]

horizontal axis The horizontal line of the two lines on which a graph is built. [p. 29]

improper fraction A fraction whose numerator is greater than or equal to its denominator. Example: $\frac{22}{7}$. [p. 298]

inch A unit of length in the customary measurement system. [p. 221]

inequality A statement that two expressions are not equal. Example: $7 > 5$.

integers The set of positive whole numbers, their opposites, and 0: ... −3, −2, −1, 0, 1, 2, 3, ... [p. 469]

intersect To cross through the same point. [p. 409]

interval One of the equal-sized divisions on a bar graph scale. [p. 29]

isosceles triangle A triangle with exactly two sides of the same length. [p. 428]

kilo- A prefix meaning 1000. [p. 216]

least common denominator (LCD) The least common multiple (LCM) of two denominators. Example: 30 is the LCD of $\frac{1}{6}$ and $\frac{1}{15}$. [p. 330]

least common multiple (LCM) The smallest multiple common to two numbers. Example: 60 is the LCM of 10 and 12. [p. 281]

like denominators Denominators that are the same in two fractions. [p. 325]

line A one-dimensional figure that extends forever in both directions. [p. 409]

line graph A graph in which a line shows changes in data, often over time. [p. 8]

line of symmetry The imaginary "mirror" in line symmetry.

line plot A plot that shows the shape of a data set by stacking ×'s above each value on a number line. [p. 26]

line symmetry The ability of a figure to be folded into congruent halves. [p. 444]

liter The basic unit of volume in the metric system. [p. 215]

lowest terms The name for a fractional amount where the numerator and denominator have a greatest common factor of 1. [p. 294]

mass The amount of matter that something contains.

mean The sum of the values in a data set divided by the number of values. [p. 47]

median The middle value in a data set when the values are listed from lowest to highest. [p. 42]

mental math Performing calculations in your mind, without using pencil and paper or a calculator.

meter The basic unit of length in the metric system. [p. 215]

metric system (of measurement) A system of measurements used to describe how long, heavy, or big something is. [p. 215]

mile A unit in the customary system of measurement equal to 5280 feet. [p. 221]

milli- A prefix meaning $\frac{1}{1000}$. [p. 216]

mixed number A number combining a whole number with a fraction. Example: $2\frac{7}{8}$. [p. 298]

mode One of the values appearing most often in a data set. [p. 42]

GLOSSARY

679

GLOSSARY

multiple The product of a given number and any whole number. [p. 281]

multiplication An operation that combines two numbers, called factors, to give one number, called the product.

negative numbers Numbers less than 0. [p. 469]

net A flat pattern that can be folded into a solid. [p. 581]

nonagon A polygon with 9 sides. [p. 433]

number line A line that shows numbers in order.

number-word form A way of writing a number using digits and words. Example: 45 trillion. [p. 67]

numeral A symbol for a number.

numerator The top number in a fraction, telling how many parts of the whole are being named. [p. 289]

obtuse angle An angle greater than a right angle but smaller than a straight angle. [p. 413]

obtuse triangle A triangle with an obtuse angle. [p. 424]

octagon A polygon with 8 sides. [p. 433]

odd number A whole number that has 1, 3, 5, 7, or 9 in the ones place.

odds A ratio expressing the chances of an event happening that compares the number of favorable to unfavorable outcomes. [p. 657]

operation A mathematical procedure. Examples: addition, subtraction, multiplication, division.

opposite The integer on the opposite side of zero from a given number, but at the same distance from zero. Example: 7 and −7 are opposites of each other. [p. 472]

order of operations The rules telling what order to do operations in: (1) simplify inside parentheses, (2) simplify exponents, (3) multiply and divide from left to right, and (4) add and subtract from left to right. [p. 99]

ordered pair A pair of numbers, such as (3, −7), used to locate a point on a coordinate plane. [p. 489]

origin The point (0, 0), where the x- and y-axes of a coordinate plane intersect. [p. 489]

ounce A unit of weight in the customary measurement system. [p. 221]

outcome One of the ways an experiment can turn out. [p. 626]

outlier A number very different from the other numbers in a data set. [p. 51]

parallel Two lines, segments, or rays that do not cross, no matter how far they extend. [p. 409]

parallelogram A four-sided figure whose opposite sides are parallel and of the same length. [p. 234]

pentagon A polygon with 5 sides. [p. 433]

percent A ratio comparing a part to a whole using the number 100. The percent is the number of hundredths that the part is equal to. [p. 550]

perimeter The distance around the outside of a figure. [p. 210]

perpendicular Two lines are perpendicular if they cross at right angles. [p. 409]

pi (π) For any circle, the ratio of the circumference divided by the diameter. Pi equals 3.14159265... . [p. 247]

pictograph A graph using symbols to represent data. [p. 7]

place value The multiple of ten telling how much a digit represents. Example: in 374, the 7 is in the tens place. [p. 66]

polygon A closed figure made of line segments. [p. 432]

polyhedron A solid consisting entirely of flat faces. [p. 580]

positive numbers Numbers greater than 0. [p. 469]

pound A unit in the customary system of measurement equal to 16 ounces. [p. 221]

power An exponent. [p. 79]

prime factorization The set of primes whose product is a given composite. Example: $70 = 2 \times 5 \times 7$. [p. 276]

prime number A whole number greater than 1 with exactly two whole positive factors: 1 and itself. Examples: 2, 3, 5, 7, 11, ... [p. 276]

prism A polyhedron that has two faces congruent and parallel. See examples below. [p. 580]

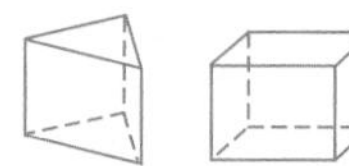

probability A ratio of the number of ways an event can happen to the total number of possible outcomes. [p. 627]

product The result of multiplying numbers. [p. 114]

proportion A pair of equal ratios. [p. 531]

protractor A tool that measures angles. [p. 417]

pyramid A solid with one base and whose other sides are all triangles. See examples below. [p. 581]

680

quadrants The four regions into which the two axes of a coordinate grid divide the plane. [p. 489]

quadrilateral A polygon with 4 sides. [p. 433]

quart A unit of volume in the customary measurement system. [p. 221]

quotient The result of dividing one number by another. [p. 114]

radius A line from the center of a circle to any point on the circle. [p. 246]

range The difference between the highest and lowest values in a data set. [p. 30]

rate A ratio in which two quantities with different units of measure are compared. Example: 18 dollars per 2 hours. [p. 523]

ratio A comparison of two quantities, often written as a fraction. [p. 515]

ray A part of a line that has one endpoint and extends forever in the other direction. [p. 409]

reciprocal A fraction whose numerator and denominator have been switched. [p. 383]

rectangle A parallelogram with opposite sides the same length and all angles measuring 90°.[p. 437]

reflection The mirror image of a figure that has been "flipped" over a line. [p. 444]

regular polygon A polygon whose sides and angles all have the same measure. [p. 433]

remainder The number less than the divisor that remains after the division process is completed.

repeating decimal A decimal number that repeats a pattern of digits continuously on the right. Example: 6.141414 ... . [p. 304]

rhombus A parallelogram with all sides the same length. [p. 437]

right angle An angle like the corner of an index card. It measures 90°. [pp. 230, 413]

right triangle A triangle with a right angle. [p. 424]

rotation The image of a figure that has been "turned," as if on a wheel. [p. 448]

rotational symmetry The ability of a figure to be rotated less than a full circle and exactly match its original image. [p. 449]

rounding Adjusting a number to make it more convenient to use, according to a given place value. Example: 2571 rounded to the nearest hundred is 2600. [p. 71]

sample A set of data used to predict how a particular situation might happen. [p. 631]

scale The "ruler" that measures the heights of the bars in a bar graph. [p. 29]

scalene triangle A triangle with no sides of equal length. [p. 428]

scatterplot A graph showing paired data values. [p. 17]

scientific notation Writing a number as the product of a decimal and a power of 10. Example: $350 = 3.50 \times 10^2$. [p. 153]

segment Part of a line, with two endpoints. [p. 409]

side Each of the rays forming an angle. [p. 412]

similar Figures having the same shape but possibly different sizes. [p. 543]

slide See *translation.*

solid A three-dimensional figure. [p. 580]

sphere See example below. [p. 582]

square A quadrilateral with all sides the same length and all angles measuring 90°. [p. 437]

square centimeter The area of a square with 1-centimeter sides. [p. 229]

square inch The area of a square with 1-inch sides. [p. 229]

square root The length of one side of a square with an area equal to a given number. [p. 261]

squared Raised to the power of 2. Example: 3 squared = $3^2 = 9$. [p. 79]

standard form A way of writing a number using digits. Example: 45,000,000,000,000. [p. 67]

stem-and-leaf diagram A graph showing the shape of a data set by breaking each value into a "stem" part and a "leaf" part. [p. 35]

straight angle An angle formed by two rays pointing in opposite directions. [p. 413]

subtraction An operation that tells the difference between two numbers, or how many are left when some are taken away.

sum The result of adding numbers. [p. 114]

supplementary angles Two angles whose measures add up to 180°. [p. 417]

surface area (SA) The sum of the areas of each face of a polyhedron. [p. 584]

symmetry See *line symmetry* and *rotational symmetry.*

T-table A table showing corresponding x- and y-values for an equation. [p. 499]

tally marks Marks used to organize a large set of data. Each mark indicates one time a value appears in the data set. [p. 25]

GLOSSARY

681

terminating decimal A decimal number that ends on the right. [p. 304]

tessellation A pattern of congruent shapes covering a surface without gaps or overlaps. [p. 454]

translation The image of a figure that has been slid to a new position without flipping or turning. [p. 453]

trapezoid A quadrilateral with exactly two sides parallel. [p. 437]

tree diagram A branching, tree-like diagram showing all possible outcomes of a situation. [p. 642]

trend A relationship between two sets of data that shows up as a pattern in a scatterplot. [p. 18]

triangle A closed figure made from three line segments. [p. 424]

turn See *rotation.*

unfair game A game in which not all players have the same probability of winning. [p. 651]

unit One of something. An amount or quantity used as a standard of measurement.

unit fraction A fraction with a numerator of 1.

unit rate A rate in which the second number in the comparison is one unit. Example: 25 gallons per minute. [p. 524]

unlike denominators Denominators that are different in two fractions. [p. 329]

variable A quantity that can change or vary, often represented with a letter. [p. 111]

Venn diagram A diagram that uses regions to show relationships between sets of things. [p. 315]

vertex The common endpoint of two rays forming an angle. Plural: vertices. [p. 412]

vertical axis The vertical line of the two lines on which a graph is built. [p. 29]

volume The number of cubic units an object contains. [p. 606]

weight A measure of the force that gravity exerts on a body.

whole number Any number in the set {0, 1, 2, 3, 4, ... }.

word form A way of writing a number using only words. Example: forty-five trillion. [p. 67]

***x*-axis** The horizontal axis on a coordinate plane. [p. 489]

***x*-coordinate** The first number in an ordered pair, locating a point on the *x*-axis of a coordinate plane. [p. 489]

***y*-axis** The vertical axis on a coordinate plane. [p. 489]

***y*-coordinate** The second number in an ordered pair, locating a point on the *y*-axis of a coordinate plane. [p. 489]

yard A unit in the customary system of measurement equal to 3 feet. [p. 221]

zero pair A number and its opposite. Example: 7 + (−7).

GLOSSARY
682

Selected Answers

Chapter 1

1-1 Try It (Example 2)

a. 200 m **b.** 800

1-1 Try It (Example 4)

a. 1993 **b.** Interactive TV

1-1 Exercises & Applications

1. Pictograph **3.** Circle graph **5.** 11–50 m; 51–100 m **7.** 3 **9.** $37 **11.** Medical, clothes; other, transportation; housing **13.** 64,000,000 sq mi **17.** 6 million **21.** 5106 **23.** 8022 **25.** 90 **27.** 806 **29.** 694 **31.** 630 **33.** 433 **35.** 790 **37.** 1000 **39.** 1586 **41.** 600 **43.** 1056

1-2 Try It

a. Possible answer: It looks like Crispies sells almost as much cereal as Crunchies, but there is $9 million difference. **b.** Possible answer: It looks like Pete's Pizza pays twice as much as Prize Pizza, but they only pay 50 cents more.

1-2 Exercises & Applications

3. 30 yr; 70 yr **5.** B **7.** Twice; $1\frac{1}{2}$ **9.** Mouse: 300; robin: 600 **11.** 2 million **15.** Two hundred four **17.** Nine hundred thirteen **19.** Eight thousand nine hundred twelve **21.** One thousand forty-five **23.** 614 **25.** 772 **27.** 71 **29.** 306

1-3 Try It

a. (80, 40) **b.** (100, 45) **c.** (125, 32) **d.** (160, 22) **e.** (200, 20)

1-3 Exercises & Applications

1. a. 15 right, 600 up **b.** 600 lb, 15 ft **3. a.** 20 right, 3000 up **b.** 3000 lb, 20 ft **5.** No trend **7.** A **11.** 24; 51 **15.** 6606 **17.** 8900 **19.** 4329 **21.** 1888

Section 1A Review

3. 3 million **5.** Yes **7.** The daily garbage per person increases.

1-4 Try It (Example 1)

a.

History	Frequency
Test Scores	
Under 60	1
60–69	3
70–79	4
80–89	7
90–100	5

b. 7; 4

1-4 Try It (Example 2)

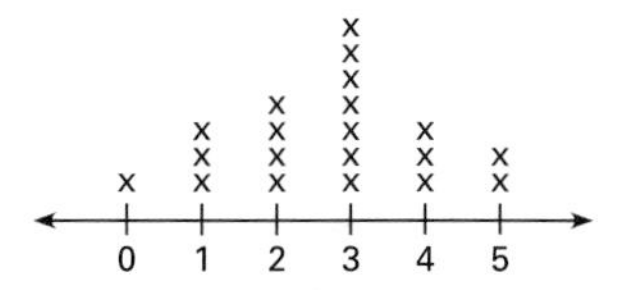

The line plot shows that 3 is the most common number of phone calls, 0 is the least common, and 1 and 4 appear with the same frequency.

1-4 Exercises & Applications

1.

a.

1	IIII
2	I
3	III
4	III
5	I
6	I
7	I
10	I

b.

13	I
17	I
18	I
19	II
20	IIII
21	II
22	II
23	I

c.

1500	I
2000	II
2500	I
3500	I
4000	II
5000	I
6000	I
6500	I

3.

Shoes in Closet

Shoes	Frequency
2	5
4	6
6	9
8	13
10	16
12	18

11. Two hundred seventeen **13.** Six hundred sixteen **23.** 25 **25.** 21 **27.** 11 **29.** 19 **31.** 24 R2 or 24.7

1-5 Try It

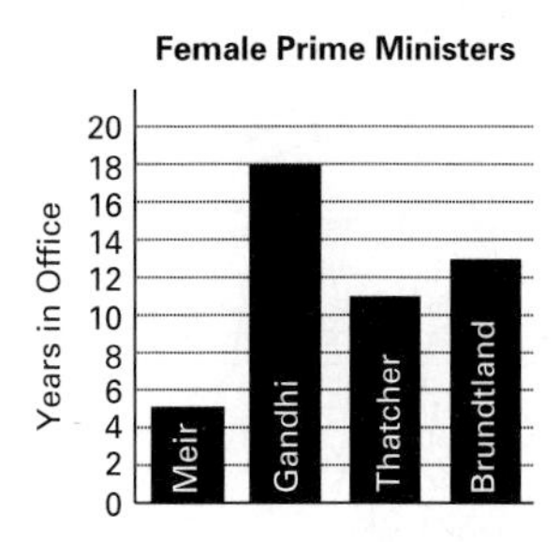

1-5 Exercises & Applications

1. a. Range 13, interval 2 **b.** Range 90, interval 25
3.

Calories Burned per Hour

Calories burned: 0, 200, 250, 300, 350, 400

Activity: Bicycling (5.5 mph), Lawn mowing, Raking leaves, Walking (2 mph)

5. a. The first graph has range 40, interval 20. The second has range 40, interval 10. **7.** 8587 **9.** 718,530 **11.** 32,717 **13.** 3594 **15.** 153,885 **17.** 13,991

1-6 Try It

Stem	Leaf
9	0 3 3 5 7
10	0 1 5 8 8
11	3 4 5 8
12	4 6 8 8
13	0 0 3 3 6
14	1 1 2 3 4 6 8

SELECTED ANSWERS

SELECTED ANSWERS

683

1-6 Exercises & Applications

1. a.

Stem	Leaf
1	8 9 0 9
2	7 9
3	8 2 6
4	2 0 7 2

b.

Stem	Leaf
1	0 8 9 9
2	7 9
3	2 6 8
4	0 2 2 7

5. 52 **7.** A **11.** There will be more leaves in the 5 stem. **13.** 1152 **15.** 1360 **17.** 193 **19.** 158

Section 1B Review

1.

No. of Elections Lost	Frequency
1	13
2	3
3	2

3.

Stem	Leaf
1	5 5 7 8 9
2	2 3 3 3 3 4
3	2 2

1-7 Try It

a. 108 **b.** No mode

1-7 Exercises & Applications

1. a. Median $4, mode $10 **b.** Median 19, modes 12 and 54 **c.** Median 86, mode 82 **d.** Median 306, no mode **3.** 36 **5.** Median 12, mode 10 **7.** Median 11, mode 13 **9.** Median 21, modes 13 and 31 **11.** Median 10, no mode **13.** Median, mode 28 **21.** 2204 **23.** 8918 **25.** 5436 **27.** 32,760 **29.** 48,256 **31.** 517,176 **33.** 95,207 **35.** Basketball **37.** 15 pairs

1-8 Try It

a. $14.39 **b.** 1.5

1-8 Exercises & Applications

1. $5 **3.** 5 **5.** 11.81 seconds **7.** 3.63 **9.** D **13.** It doesn't change. **15.** 51 R4 or ≈ 51.57 **17.** 88 R5 or 88.625 **19.** 40 R2 or ≈ 40.15 **21.** 49 **23.** 11 **25.** 23 **27.** 3

1-9 Try It

With the outlier: Median 21, no mode, mean 28; Without the outlier: Median 19, no mode, mean 18.29

1-9 Exercises & Applications

1. 56 **3.** 0 **5.** 3 **7.** 70 **9. a.** With the outlier: Mean 287.4, median 287, mode 287; Without the outlier: Mean 286.25, median 286.5, modes 287. **11. a.** Mean 74.8, median 82, mode 82 **b.** Mean 69.64, median 82, mode 82 **13.** 1687 **15.** 34 R1 or 34.11 **17.** 83,210 **19.** 30 R14 or ≈ 30.47 **21.** 5

Section 1C Review

1. Mean 4.81, median 5, modes 5 and 1 **3.** Mean 15.07, median 12, modes 10 and 25 **5.** The mean **7.** C

Chapter 1 Summary & Review

1. 80 blue jackets **2.** 270 mi
3.

Box of Souvenirs	Tally Marks	Frequency
Flags	~~IIII~~	5
White House models	III	3
Posters	IIII	4
Uncle Sam hats	I	1

4.

	Flags	White House model	Posters	Hats
X's	5	3	4	1

5.

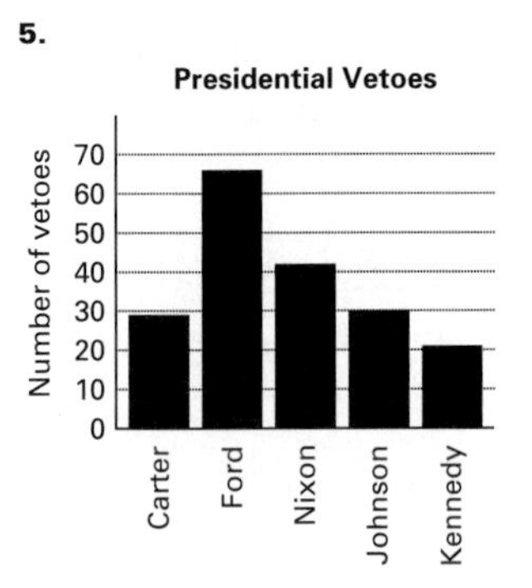

6. Stems will be 0 through 9. Leaves will be 2, 4, 6, and 8 for the row opposite the zero stem and leaves of 0, 2, 4, 6, and 8 for each row opposite the 1 through 9 stems. **7.** Median, 563; Mode, 521; Mean, 591.91 or ≈ 592 **8.** The mean

Chapter 2

2-1 Try It

a. Ten-millions **b.** Nineteen million, eight hundred eighty-eight thousand, eight hundred **c.** 5,020,000,000,300

2-1 Exercises & Applications

1. Ones **3.** Ten-thousands **5.** Millions **7.** Thousands **9.** Thirty million, eighty thousand, seven hundred five **11.** Eight thousand, two hundred thirty-five **13.** Seven thousand, ninety-eight **15.** Fifty-six million, fifty-six thousand, five hundred sixty **17.** 93 million **19.** 888 million **21.** 2 billion, 791 million **23.** 52,000,000 **25.** 560,000,000 **27.** 9000 **29.** 321,000 **31.** 42,006,000 **33.** 9,020,000,000,030 **35.** 81,500 **37.** Thousand **39.** Billion **45.** D **47.** 3,666,200,000 **49.** 14 **51.** 1.9

2-2 Try It

a. 70,000 **b.** 74,000 **c.** 74,000

2-2 Exercises & Applications

1. a. 4 **b.** Less than 5 **c.** Leave it the same because the next digit is less than 5. **d.** 1,370,000 **3.** 90,000 **5.** 740 **7.** 3,900,000 **9.** 23,000 **11.** Two billion, seven hundred fifty-eight million, five hundred thirty thousand, nine hundred twenty-eight **13.** B **17.** 9 buses

2-3 Try It

a. 98,419; 138,417; 146,416 **b.** 190,000 $<$ 198,000

2-3 Exercises & Applications

1. $>$ **3.** $<$ **5.** $<$ **7.** $<$ **9.** 5678; 5687; 5768 **11.** 20,002; 20,200;

SELECTED ANSWERS

684

22,000 **13.** 10 hundred; 10 million; 1 trillion **15.** 6 hundred; 62 thousand; 29 billion **17.** D **19.** The diameter at the equator is greater. **21.** Calcutta, Rio de Janeiro, Buenos Aires **23.** 268,356,000 $>$ 261,931,000 **29.** 29,297

2-4 Try It

a. 12^4 **b.** $5 \times 5 \times 5 \times 5 \times 5 \times 5$ **c.** 81 **d.** 161,051

2-4 Exercises & Applications

1. a. 4 **b.** 7 **c.** 4; 7 **d.** 4^7 **3.** 9^5 **5.** 79^2 **7.** $7^2 \times 3^2$ **9.** 36^1 **11.** 25×25 **13.** $200 \times 200 \times 200 \times 200$ **15.** $7 \times 7 \times 7 \times 7 \times 7 \times 7 \times 7$ **17.** $3 \times 3 \times 3 \times 3$ **19.** $5 \times 5 \times 5 \times 5 \times 5 \times 5 \times 5 \times 5$ **21.** $9 \times 9 \times 9 \times 9 \times 9 \times 9 \times 9 \times 9$ **23.** 125 **25.** 243 **27.** 1 **29.** 256 **31.** 729 **33.** 8^6: base 8, exponent 6, 262,144; 3^5: base 3, exponent 5, 243. **35.** $>$ **37.** $<$ **39. b.** 2^{50} cells **41.** 6

Section 2A Review

1. 16; 20 **3.** 100,000; 100,000 **5.** 81; 100 **7. a.** 864°F **9.** 7,000; 17,000; 19,000; 19,000; 20,000; 23,000; 29,000 **11.** = **13.** $<$ **15.** $>$ **19.** C

2-5 Try It

a. 1,200,000 **b.** 300 **c.** 183 **d.** 347 **e.** 1300 **f.** 351 **g.** 174 **h.** 714

2-5 Exercises & Applications

1. a. 240 **b.** 24,000 **c.** 2,400,000 **d.** 24,000,000 **e.** 70 **f.** 70 **g.** 7 **h.** 7 **3.** 565 **5.** 1100 **7.** 40 **9.** 147 **11.** 50 **13.** 900 **15.** 124 **17.** 693 **19.** 534 **21.** 3500 **23.** 35,000 **25.** 7,200,000 **27.** 290 **29.** 2858 **31.** 166 **33.** 200 **35.** 336 **37.** 525 **39.** 50 **41.** 174 **43.** 777 **45.** $105 **47.** 50 yards **51.** $2.20; No **53.** 335,728,642 **57.** Three million, ninety-three thousand, two **59.** 73,259 **61.** 2,674,445 **63.** 61,236 **65.** 2,146,337

2-6 Try It

a. 1600 **b.** 2000 **c.** 900

2-6 Exercises & Applications

1. a. ≈ 740; ≈ 740 **b.** ≈ 1200; ≈ 1200 **c.** $\approx 72{,}000$; $\approx 73{,}000$ **d.** ≈ 1000; ≈ 990 **3–21.** Possible answers are given: **3.** ≈ 3000 **5.** ≈ 500 **7.** ≈ 325 **9.** $\approx 3{,}300{,}000$ **11.** ≈ 1000 **13.** $\approx 600{,}000$ **15.** $\approx 18{,}000$ **17.** ≈ 70 **19.** $\approx 19{,}000{,}000$ **21.** ≈ 250 **23.** ≈ 120 in. **25.** $\approx 99{,}000{,}000$; $\approx 98{,}400{,}000$ **27.** D **31.** 7,000,000 **33.** 400,000,000 **35.** $695.86 **37.** $16,402.44

2-7 Try It (Examples 1–2)

a. 24,000 **b.** 200

2-7 Try It (Examples 3–4)

a. 600 **b.** 7

2-7 Exercises & Applications

Possible answers: **1. a.** 2400 **b.** 400 **c.** 35,000 **d.** 30 **e.** 7 **f.** 300 **g.** 1000 **h.** 120,000 **3.** 56,000,000 **5.** 25,000 **7.** 1700 **9.** 20 **11.** 15,000 **13.** 4000 **15.** 100 **17.** 350,000 **19.** 6 **21.** 14,000 **23.** 40 **25.** 560 **27.** 50 **29.** 300 **31.** 2 **33.** 100,000 **35.** Under **37.** 60,000 **39.** C **43.** $<$ **45.** $<$ **47.** $<$ **49.** 10; 356; 383; 1009; 1023 **51.** 12,140 **53.** 18,240 **55.** 252 **57.** 3120 **59.** 144 **61.** 2142

2-8 Try It

a. 25 **b.** 1 **c.** 3 **d.** 48

2-8 Exercises & Applications

1. a. Multiplication **b.** Addition **c.** Division **d.** Simplify exponents **e.** Subtraction **f.** Multiplication **g.** Subtraction **h.** Subtraction **3.** 56 **5.** 8 **7.** 48 **9.** 27 **11.** 0 **13.** 120 **15.** 27 **17.** 300 **19.** 10 **21.** 0 **23.** 5 **25.** 20 **27.** 33 **29.** 1 **31.** 66 **33.** 8200 **35.** 190 **37.** $20 \times (15 - 2) = 260$ **39.** $2 \times (6^2 - 8) = 56$ **41.** $(12 + 10) \div 11 = 2$ **43.** $(5 + 4) \div 3 = 3$ **45.** B **47.** $(4 \times 7 - 2 + 1.96) \div 2 = 13.98$ **51.** 100,000 **53.** 4096 **55.** 38,416 **57.** $2^7 = 128$ **59.** 62,103 **61.** 1,921,899,992

2-9 Try It

a. 30 **b.** 10

2-9 Exercises & Applications

1. a. Add **b.** Add **c.** Subtract **d.** Subtract **e.** Subtract **f.** Subtract **g.** Subtract **h.** Add **3.** Add 3 **5.** Add 13 **7.** Subtract 1 **9.** Add 11 **11.** Subtract 29 **13.** Subtract 8 **15.** Add 15 **17.** Add 58 **19.** 271, 266, 260 **21.** 76, 70, 64 **23.** 1010, 1028, 1049 **25.** 10, 9, 11 **27.** 125, 180, 245 **29.** 1131, 1135, 1139 **31.** 332, 348, 301 **33.** $22 **35.** 550 **41.** 166 **43.** 1661 **45.** 205 **47.** 6 **49.** $121.68 **51.** $185,295.50 **53.** $23.80 **55.** $1453.32

Section 2B Review

1. 60,000 **3.** 879 **5.** 4000 **7–17.** Possible answers: **7.** 30,000 **9.** 300 **11.** 17,000 **13.** 30 **15.** 23,000 **17.** 1600 **19.** C **21.** D **23.** E **25.** B

2-10 Try It

a. 21, 28, 35 **b.** 12, 11, 10 **c.** 20, 15, 12 **d.** 26, 27, 28

2-10 Exercises & Applications

1. a. Constant **b.** Variable **c.** Variable **d.** Constant **e.** Variable **f.** Variable **3.** 9, 10, 11 **5.** 12, 18, 24 **7.** 14, 15, 16 **9.** 16, 24, 32 **11.** 17, 18, 19 **13.** 18, 13, 9 **15.** 17, 15, 11 **17.** 15, 9, 5 **19.** 6, 8, 12 **21.** 3, 5, 9 **23.** 6, 10, 18 **25.** 9, 25, 81 **27.** 28, 14, 8 **29.** 6, 12, 21 **31.** 10, 20, 35 **33.** 8, 16, 28 **35.** 29, 31, 34 **37.** 14, 16, 19 **39.** Number of stars: 13, 26, 39, 52, $13w$ **41.** A **43. a.** ii **b.** i **c.** iii **45.** 7000 **47.** 35,000 **49.** 6400 **51.** 64, 8, 384 **53.** 24, 30

2-11 Try It

a. $c + 8$ **b.** $\frac{n}{9}$ **c.** $r + 5$ **d.** $7x$

2-11 Exercises & Applications

1. A **3.** F **5.** $10q$ **7.** $6d$ **9.** $s - 3$ **11.** $20v$ **13.** $y - 3$ **15.** $n - 5$ **17.** $n - 4$ **19.** $\frac{x}{8}$ **21.** $4 + s$

SELECTED ANSWERS

685

SELECTED ANSWERS

23. $t - 146$ degrees **25.** $22{,}278 - m$ square miles **29. a.** $x + x + x + x$ or $4x$ **b.** $x + 2 + x + 2 + x + 2 + x + 2$ or $4x + 8$ **c.** $x + 3 + x + 3 + x + 3 + x + 3$ or $4x + 12$ **31.** ≈ 800 **33.** $\approx 250{,}000$ **35.** ≈ 2 **37.** ≈ 3 **39.** 122 **41.** 319 **43.** 78 **45.** 4332

2-12 Try It

a. No **b.** No **c.** Yes

2-12 Exercises & Applications

1. a. True **b.** False **c.** False **d.** True **e.** False **f.** False **g.** True **h.** False **i.** True **j.** True **3.** No **5.** Yes **7.** Yes **9.** No **11.** Yes **13.** No **15.** No **17.** Yes **19.** Yes **21.** $\frac{12}{p} = 3$ **23.** $1600 + x = 3212$ **25.** $84 + d = 88$ **27.** $75 - b = 26$ **29.** No **33.** $555 \div 111 = 5$ **35.** $1536 \div 48 = 32$ **37.** $546 \div 13 = 42$ **39.** $1978 \div 86 = 23$ **41.** $8 \times 8 = 64$ **43.** $4 \times 8 = 32$ **45.** $63 \times 56 = 3528$ **47.** $87 \times 12 = 1044$ **49.** 13; 14; 15 **51.** 36; 18; 12 **53.** 6; 12; 18 **55.** 30; 15; 10 **57.** 8; 9; 10

2-13 Try It

a. $a = 15$ **b.** $b = 63$ **c.** $c = 22$ **d.** $d = 48$

2-13 Exercises & Applications

1. Less **3.** Less **5.** Less **7.** Greater **9.** Greater **11.** 2 **13.** 8 **15.** 8 **17.** 10 **19.** 22; 26; 31; 43 **21.** $j = 1.2$ **23.** $k = 6$ **25.** $v = 6$ **27.** $n = 8$ **29.** $z = 80$ **31.** $g = 5$ **33.** $k = 9$ **35.** $r = 168$ **37.** B **39.** 1000 ft/hr **41.** 1038 m **43.** It must decrease by 2. **45.** $200 - 151 = 49$ **47.** $43 + 10 = 53$ **49.** $159{,}000 + 21{,}000 = 180{,}000$

Section 2C Review

1. Constant **3.** $\frac{d}{4}$ **5.** $16m$ **7.** $\frac{d}{17}$ **9.** ≈ 9000 **11.** ≈ 60 **13.** 17 **15.** 220 **17.** 4 **19.** 12 **21.** No **23.** $x = 22$ **25.** $x = 5$ **27.** 5000 ft **29.** D

Chapter 2 Summary & Review

1. Thousands **2.** Twenty-nine million, one hundred fifty-eight thousand, six hundred forty-seven **3. a.** 29,160,000 **b.** 29,000,000 **4.** $129{,}058{,}647 < 129{,}186{,}000$ **5.** 4,067,338; 4,567,238; 40,098,001 **6.** Base 5, exponent 9 **7.** $7 \times 7 \times 7$ **8.** 8^2 **9. a.** 16 **b.** 8 **c.** 10,000 **d.** 9 **e.** 121 **10.** 400 **11.** 1224 **12.** 900,000 **13.** 700 **14. a.** 300 **b.** 11,000 **15. a.** 5 **b.** 750 **16.** 9 **17.** 351 **18.** 29, 22, 15 **19.** 126, 141, 156 **20.** 12, 18, 24 **21.** 4, 3, 2 **22.** $\frac{m}{11}$ **23.** Yes; No **24. a.** $x = 61$ **b.** $x = 116$

Cumulative Review Chapters 1–2

1. C **2.** B **3.** D **4.** B **5.** A **6.** B **7.** D **8.** A **9.** D **10.** C **11.** A **12.** C **13.** B **14.** D **15.** C

Chapter 3

3-1 Try It

a. 0.81 **b.** 0.4

c. **d.**

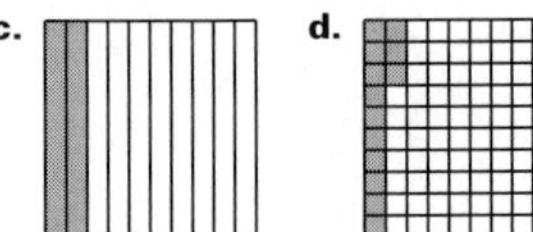

e. Three and fifty-one thousandths **f.** One hundred seventy-one thousandths **g.** Forty-seven hundredths **h.** Eight and one tenth **i.** 0.09 **j.** 2.101

3-1 Exercises & Applications

1. a. 0.6 **b.** 0.43 **c.** 0.312 **d.** 0.9 **e.** 0.097 **f.** 0.08 **3.** 0.78 **5.** 2.45

7. **9.**

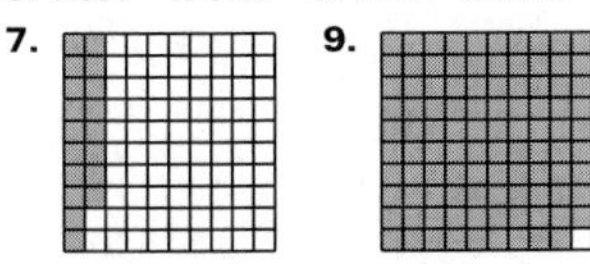

13. 1.067 **15.** 0.08 **17.** 0.2 **19.** 0.015 **21.** Sixty-seven hundredths **23.** Eight and six hundred eleven thousandths **25.** Twelve and six thousandths **27.** Ten and forty-eight hundredths **29.** B **31.** Possible answer: 3.608 **33.** Infinitely many **37.** 11; 8; 5 **39.** 1; 8; 11 **41.** 17; 15; 1 **43.** 416 **45.** 3 **47.** 356 **49.** 2

3-2 Try It (Examples 1–2)

a. 0.8 **b.** 7.05 **c.** 3.462 **d.** 1.9 cm

3-2 Try It (Example 3)

a. 3 cm; 2.5 cm **b.** 13 cm; 13.1 cm

3-2 Exercises & Applications

1. a. 1 **b.** 3 **c.** 3 **d.** 0 **e.** 1 **f.** 2 **3.** 5.8 **5.** 0.472 **7.** 4.3 **9.** 0.100 **11.** 33.5 **13.** 16.13 **15.** 7.30 **17.** 88 **19.** 7.3 **21.** 8.2 **23.** 0.7893 **25.** 60 **27.** 1000 cm **29.** 2 cm; 2.2 cm **31.** 5 cm; 5.4 cm **33.** 3 cm; 2.5 cm **35.** 6 cm; 55 mm **43.** $12 + k$

3-3 Try It (Examples 1–2)

a. $>$ **b.** $>$ **c.** $>$ **d.** $<$

3-3 Try It (Example 3)

1.009, 1.08, 1.6, 1.725, 1.74

3-3 Exercises & Applications

1. a. 0.280 **b.** 1.4500 **c.** 1.670 **d.** 0.3000 **3.** $=$ **5.** $>$ **7.** $=$ **9.** $<$ **11.** $<$ **13.** $<$ **15.** $<$ **17.** $<$ **19.** 0.675 **21.** 27.939, 27.946, 27.948 **23.** 1.23, 1.5, 2.64 **25.** 2.84, 2.96, 3.02 **27.** 3.107, 30.17, 31.07, 31.7, 310.7 **29.** A **31.** Angela and Temeca **33.** Possible answer: 8.743 **37.** True **39.** False

3-4 Try It

a. 30,000 **b.** 90,620,000,000 **c.** 5.2×10^4 **d.** 1.74×10^9

3-4 Exercises & Applications

1. a. 4 **b.** 5 **c.** 3 **3.** 75,000 **5.** 200,000 **7.** 8,890,000 **9.** 2,459,000,000,000 **11.** 445,600,000,000 **13.** 6,900,000,000 **15.** 370,000 **17.** 57,000,000 **19.** 50,000; 100,000 **21.** 5×10^3 **23.** 1.6×10^5 **25.** 7.9×10^9 **27.** 5.1×10^7 **29.** 6×10^{12} **31.** 5×10^2 **33.** 1.2×10^7 **35.** D **39.** 3.65 **41.** Median: 7; modes: 5, 7, 8 **43.** 10 **45.** 12

Section 3A Review

1. 0.7 **3.** 26.5 **5.** 2 cm **7.** 0.1 **9.** 2.42 **11.** 7.0 **13. a.** KB: 1000; MB: 1,000,000; GB: 1,000,000,000 **b.** 2.4×10^9 **15.** 120,000,000 **17.** 560,000 **19.** 4.5×10^{10} **21.** 6.78×10^6 **23.** 6×10^7 **25.** 5.69×10^4 **27.** A

3-5 Try It

a. $34 **b.** 35 **c.** 630 **d.** 8

3-5 Exercises & Applications

1. a. 50 **b.** 25 **c.** 10 **d.** 5 **3–33.** Possible answers given. **3.** $2 **5.** 5 **7.** 9 **9.** 300 **11.** $240 **13.** 6 **15.** 43 **17.** 73 **19.** 164 **21.** 1800 **23.** $2 **25.** 6 **27.** 8100 **29.** 900 **31.** 11 **33.** 5 **35.** About $700 **37.** Yes **39.** About 3 km **45.** 65.625 **47.** 0.32 **49.** 0.789 **51.** 0.05

3-6 Try It

a. 8.617 **b.** 3.957 **c.** 7.573 **d.** 2.85

3-6 Exercises & Applications

1. a. i **b.** ii **c.** i **3.** 46.906 **5.** 8.4 **7.** $11.25 **9.** 25.904 **11.** 66.2284 **13.** 0.061 **15.** $10.01 **17.** 14.38 **19.** 442.1822 **21.** 41.69 **23.** 4.947 **25.** 15.678 **27.** 42.63 **29.** $76.57 **31.** 104.67 **33.** D **43.** 5.998 **45.** 35 **47.** 0.2

3-7 Try It

a. $x = 10.1$ **b.** $n = 10.6$ **c.** $j = 5.1$ **d.** $p = 2.2$

3-7 Exercises & Applications

1. a. True **b.** False **c.** True **d.** False **3.** $d = 0.4$ **5.** $x = 8.1$ **7.** $u = \$2.37$ **9.** $w = 28.2$ **11.** $a = 1.22$ **13.** $c = 0.02$ **15.** $f = \$3.25$ **17.** $i = 87.7$ **19.** $m = 0.088$ **21.** $w = 2.32$ **23.** $z = 60$ **25.** $t = 0.67$ **27.** $g =$ 12.1 cm **29.** A **31.** $\$26.49 + \$18.50 = s; s = \$44.99$ **37.** 0.123, 0.672, 1.784

Section 3B Review

1. 2.7 cm **3.** 3.3 cm **5.** 2.5 **7.** 0.88 **9.** 0.03 **11.** 28.4 **13.** 5.161 **15.** 13.776 cm **17.** $x = 24.05$ **19.** $n = 17.5$

3-8 Try It

a. 4.8 **b.** 4.2 **c.** 117.756 **d.** 62

3-8 Exercises & Applications

1. a. i **b.** ii **c.** i **3.** 34.12 **5.** 24.032 **7.** 872.83 **9.** 357.8 **11.** 52.2 **13.** 872.3 **15.** $603.05 **17.** 12.865 **19.** 80.7 **21.** 3850 **23.** $2539 **25.** $6 **27.** C **29.** Yes **33.** 34,790,001; 34,890,000; 34,891,000 **35.** 5540 **37.** 14,200 **39.** 928,000 **41.** 1,932,000

3-9 Try It

a. 9.44 **b.** 146.72 **c.** 0.0369 **d.** 56.77 **e.** 0.21 **f.** 0.6

3-9 Exercises & Applications

1. a. i **b.** i **c.** ii **3.** 0.9591 **5.** 8.19541 **7.** 4238.01 **9.** 0.068 **11.** 0.0065 **13.** 0.00425 **15.** 38.86 **17.** 23.22 **19.** 0.546 **21.** 54.288 **23.** 0.7496 **25.** 0.775 **27.** 4.232 **29.** $2; $2.12 **31.** < **33.** = **35.** C **41.** 7 **43.** 29 **45.** 2 **47.** 143 **49.** 3 **51.** 3 **53.** 10 **55.** 40

3-10 Try It

a. 19.3 **b.** 0.89 **c.** 0.1085 **d.** 0.262 **e.** 0.003012 **f.** 4.5

3-10 Exercises & Applications

1. a. i **b.** i **c.** i **3.** 5.87 **5.** 0.994 **7.** 0.0258 **9.** 1.548 **11.** 3.254 **13.** 0.013 **15.** 0.084 **17.** 1.24 **19.** 49.75 **21.** 22.476 **23.** 18.96 **25.** 0.407 **27.** 0.67 **29.** 9.4 **31.** 137.667 mi **37.** 73, 78, 79 **39.** 23, 17, 10 **41.** 33, 30, 27 **43.** 52.07 **45.** 0.007 **47.** 3.53 **49.** 6.999

3-11 Exercises & Applications

1. a. ii **b.** ii **c.** i **3.** 2.8 **5.** 0.4 **7.** 4.79 **9.** 1.09 **11.** 8 **13.** 0.07 **15.** 6.1 **17.** 9.87 **19.** 1.94 **21.** 42 **23.** 3.7 **25.** 0.6 **27.** 500 **29.** 14.74 mi per day **31.** A **33.** 21,900 **37.** $15 \times 15 \times 15$ **49.** $e = 8.1$ **51.** $g = 1.2$ **53.** $j = 1.3$

3-12 Try It

a. $j = 0.7$ **b.** $w = 6$ **c.** $t = 5.5$ **d.** $f = 0.49$

3-12 Exercises & Applications

1. a. 1000 **b.** 100 **c.** 0.1 **d.** 0.1 **3.** $e = 0.63$ **5.** $r = 50$ **7.** $w = 0.02$ **9.** $s = 114.49$ **11.** $u = 45$ **13.** $q =$ 12.5 **15.** $h = 6$ **17.** $n = 0.07$ **19.** $v = 10.8$ **21.** $k = 0.08$ **23.** $j = 0.14$ **25.** $u = 0.02$ **27.** $8.3d = 83$; 10 days **29.** $\frac{t}{9} = 0.08$; 0.72 kg **31.** $465 - x = 165.3$; 299.7 kg **33.** 36 **37.** Greek pasta salad **39.** 8.7 **41.** 21.8 **43.** 54.06

Section 3C Review

1. 5,600,000 **3.** 400,000,000 **5.** 122,000 **7.** 16,000,000,000 **9.** 23.5 **11.** 250 **13.** 20.6 **15.** 60.02 **17.** 2.04 **19.** 310.75 **21.** 3.6 **23.** 2.793 **25.** 10.78 km **27.** $u = 142.2$ **29.** $n = 50$ **31.** $s = 24.31$ **33.** $v = 830$ **35.** $0.36 **37.** B

Chapter 3 Summary & Review

1. a. 0.25 **b.** 0.7 **2. a.** 5.6 **b.** 0.8 **3. a.** > **b.** < **4. a.** 71,600 **b.** 395,000 **5.** ≈ 700; 729.36 **6.** ≈ 270; 262.277 **7.** 65.92 **8.** 4.4 < 4.876 **9.** 6.4 mm **10. a.** $t = 4.6$ **b.** $k = 13.5$ **11.** ≈ 120; 128.8 **12.** ≈ 12; 13.25 **13.** ≈ 1; 0.893 **14.** ≈ 2; 2.2 **15.** 0.04533 **16.** 751 **17.** 0.367 **18.** 3.1

Chapter 4

4-1 Try It

a. 27 **b.** 46

4-1 Exercises & Applications

1. 180 cm **3.** 100 in. **5.** 8 cm **7.** 16 in. **9.** $a = 9$ in.; $b = 3$ in. **11.** $f = 12$ mm; $g = 26$ mm **13.** A **19.** 90 milliseconds **21.** 5.6×10^4

SELECTED ANSWERS

687

23. 2×10^{12} **25.** 1.6×10^3 **27.** 9.456×10^7

4-2 Try It (Example 1)

a. km **b.** cm **c.** kg **d.** L

4-2 Try It (Examples 2–3)

a. 7360 **b.** 8 **c.** 0.325

4-2 Exercises & Applications

1. 1 kilometer **3.** 1 meter **5.** 1 centimeter **7.** Kilogram **9.** Kilometer **11.** Gram **13.** 0.09 **15.** 100 **17.** 0.00788 **19.** 4.2 **21.** 0.005 **23.** 131 **25.** 267,000 **27.** 42,900 **31.** B **33.** 480 mm; 48 cm; 0.48 m **35.** 562 cm **37.** 103 **39.** 45,000,000,000 **41.** 45,612 **43.** 0.55 **45.** 0.067 **47.** 0.4 **49.** 0.02 **51.** 0.008

4-3 Try It (Example 1)

a. Miles **b.** Pounds **c.** Quarts

4-3 Try It (Examples 2–3)

a. 28 **b.** 4 **c.** 10,560

4-3 Exercises & Applications

1. 3 ft **3.** 8 ft **5.** 5 ft **7.** 21 **9.** 12 **11.** 32 **13.** 36 **15.** 384 **17.** 21,120 **19.** 7040 **21.** 72 in.; 6 ft **23.** 24 oz **25.** D **31.** 60 points; A and D **33.** B and C **35.** 1.06, 1.34, 1.36, 1.66 **37.** 0.0349, 0.56, 0.678, 0.982 **39.** 66.3, 67.1, 67.4, 67.5, 68.3

Section 4A Review

1. 35.6 cm **3.** 3120 cm **5.** 32,000 cm **7.** 42,240 ft **9.** 60 ft **11.** 8000 **13.** 38,000,000 **15.** 29 **17.** A

4-4 Try It (Example 2)

a. 14 in^2 **b.** 12 cm^2 **c.** 28 ft^2

4-4 Try It (Examples 3–4)

a. 20 in^2 **b.** 54 cm^2 **c.** 28 yd^2

4-4 Exercises & Applications

1. 25 **3.** 24 **5.** 24 cm **7.** 27 ft^2 **9.** 1.2 km^2 **11.** 132 mm^2 **13.** C **15.** 4 cm^2 **17.** 1 cm^2 **19.** 720 in^2 **21.** C **23. a.** 12,800 ft^2 **25.** $60,000 **27.** The mean **29.** 70 **31.** 28 **33.** 5 **35.** 143

4-5 Try It

a. 18 **b.** 198 mm^2

4-5 Exercises & Applications

1. 35 **3.** 24 **5.** 44 cm^2 **7.** 5.52 km^2 **9.** 0.07 in^2 **11.** 7500 m^2 **13.** 84 yd^2 **15.** 266.07 cm^2 **17.** 1,000,000 km^2 **19.** 50,830 mi^2 **21.** 14.57 m^2 **25. a.** 2.36 m^2 **b.** 384 in^2 **c.** 132 mm^2 **d.** 456 mm^2 **27.** 81 **29.** 144 **31.** 64 **33.** 1 **35.** 2,097,152 **37.** 5,764,801 **39.** 1.913 **41.** 232.47 **43.** 6.8

4-6 Try It

a. 6 **b.** 4.75 yd^2 **c.** 1.75 in^2

4-6 Exercises & Applications

1. 15 **3.** 6 **5.** 45 cm^2 **7.** 2,466,000 km^2 **9.** 1581 yd^2 **11.** 260 **13.** 27 in^2 **15.** 31.5 in^2 **17.** 1440 **21.** 52 **23.** 6^5 **25.** 7^4 **27.** 10^4 **29.** $3^4 \times 8$

Section 4B Review

1. 48 in^2 **3.** 0.935 yd^2 **5.** Yes **7.** 96 **9.** 3.2 **11.** 48 in. **13.** 110 mm

4-7 Try It

a. 37.68 cm **b.** 23.9 ft **c.** 18.84 ft **d.** 25.16 cm

4-7 Exercises & Applications

1. True **3.** False **5.** 43.96 cm **7.** 37.68 mm **9.** 9 **11.** 7.5 yd; 15 yd **13.** 5.5 m; 34.54 m **15.** 9.3 **17.** 6.28 cm **19.** 0.83 m **23.** 42 **25.** 11,658 **27.** $3 \times 3 \times 3 \times 3 \times 3$ **29.** $9 \times 9 \times 9 \times 9 \times 9 \times 9$ **31.** $12 \times 12 \times 12 \times 12 \times 12$ **33.** $6 \times 6 \times 6$ **35.** $13 \times 13 \times 13 \times 13 \times 13 \times 13 \times 13 \times 13 \times 13 \times 13 \times 13$ **37.** 900 **39.** 10 **41.** 200 **43.** $6

4-8 Try It

a. 1133.54 cm^2 **b.** 3.14 in^2

4-8 Exercises & Applications

1. True **3.** False **5.** 803.84 yd^2 **7.** 12.56 ft^2 **9.** 128.6144 ft^2 **11.** 907.46 ft^2 **13.** 7850 mm^2 **15.** 1.1304 mi^2 **17.** 1.3 km; 5.4 km^2 **19.** 0.5 mm; 0.8 mm^2 **21.** 0.2 mi; 0.1 mi^2 **23.** 2.9 m; 25.8 m^2 **25.** 1.32665 yd^2 **27.** C **29.** A **31.** 144 ft^2 **33. a.** C, B, D, A **35.** No **37.** 75 **39.** 240 **41.** 1600 **43.** 800,000

4-9 Exercises & Applications

1. Rectangle, semicircle **3.** Semicircle, rectangle **5.** 34.8125 **7.** 450 ft^2 **9.** $\approx$ 31.8 cm^2 **11.** 412,090.5 mi^2 **15.** 289.56 ft^2 **17.** 21 **19.** 134 **21.** 24 **23.** 6 **25.** 7 **27.** 8.02 **29.** 162.5 **31.** 5.3

Section 4C Review

1. 12,000 **3.** 9.2 **5.** A: 43.2 mm^2; P: 28 mm **7.** A: 0.5024 km^2; C: 2.512 km **9.** A: 153.86 in^2; C: 43.96 in. **11.** A: 119.065 $units^2$; P: 42.71 units **13.** The perimeter of the square

Chapter 4 Summary & Review

1. 33.6 **2.** 4.14 **3.** 2.407 **4.** 5300 **5.** 73 **6.** 48 **7.** 14 **8.** 11,726 **9.** 0.432 **10.** $18.\overline{3}$ ft **11.** 19,200 ft^2 **12.** 1200 cm^2 **13.** 75 ft^2 **14.** 56.25 mm^2 **15.** 21 ft^2 **16.** 30 ft **17. a.** 9.42 yd **b.** 7.065 yd^2 **18.** 167.13 sq. units

Cumulative Review Chapters 1–4

1. B **2.** A **3.** C **4.** B **5.** D **6.** B **7.** C **8.** A **9.** B **10.** D **11.** A **12.** A

Chapter 5

5-1 Try It

a. 3 **b.** 5 **c.** 2, 3, 6, 9 **d.** 3, 5 **e.** 2, 3, 5, 6, 9, 10

5-1 Exercises & Applications

1. a. 2 **b.** 2 **c.** 5 **d.** 2, 5, 10 **e.** 5 **f.** 2, 5, 10 **3.** 5 **5.** 3, 9 **7.** 2, 5, 10

SELECTED ANSWERS

688

9. 2, 3, 6 **11.** 2, 3, 5, 6, 9, 10 **13.** 2, 3, 5, 6, 9, 10 **15.** 2 **17.** 3, 5, 9 **19.** 2 **21.** 2, 3, 6 **23.** 2, 3, 5, 6, 10 **25.** 2, 3, 6 **27.** 3, 5 **29.** 5 **31.** 2, 3, 6 **33.** Yes **35.** No **37.** No **39.** Yes **41.** Yes **43.** Yes **45.** No **47.** Yes **49.** No **51.** No **53.** Yes **55.** Yes **57.** **a.** No **b.** No **c.** No **d.** Yes **e.** Yes **59.** No **61.** **a.** 2, 5, 10 **b.** 2, 5, 10 **c.** 2, 5, 10 **73.** 16 **75.** 4.86 **77.** 6.8 **79.** 13.6

5-2 Try It

a. $2^2 \times 3$ **b.** $2^2 \times 5$ **c.** $2^2 \times 3^2$ **d.** $3^2 \times 5$ **e.** $2 \times 3 \times 5 \times 7$

5-2 Exercises & Applications

1. **a.** 5×3 **b.** 11×3 **c.** 7×2 **d.** 7×3 **e.** 2×3 **f.** 5×7 **3.** Prime **5.** Composite **7.** Composite **9.** 5^2 **11.** 5×19 **13.** 5^3 **15.** 2×3 **17.** $2^3 \times 11$ **19.** $2^3 \times 3^2$ **21.** $2^2 \times 3^2 \times 19$ **23.** $2^2 \times 3 \times 5$ **25.** $3 \times 5 \times 7$ **27.** $2^4 \times 3$ **29.** 5×17 **31.** 2×3^4 **33.** $3 \times 5 \times 11$ **35.** $2^2 \times 3^2 \times 13$ **37.** $2 \times 3 \times 7$ **39.** Composite **41.** 101, 103, 107, 109 **43.** 41, 43, 47, 53, 59, 61, 67, 71, 73, 79 **49.** 5,700,000 **51.** 5,890,000,000 **53.** 1.2 **55.** 0.25 **57.** 0.25 **59.** 0.5

5-3 Try It (Examples 1–2)

a. 35 **b.** 30 **c.** 20 **d.** 45

5-3 Try It (Example 3)

a. 18 **b.** 8 **c.** 100 **d.** 60 **e.** 55 **f.** 30 **g.** 54 **h.** 1297

5-3 Exercises & Applications

1. **a.** 3, 6, 9, 12, 15 **b.** 10, 20, 30, 40, 50 **c.** 11, 22, 33, 44, 55 **d.** 8, 16, 24, 32, 40 **e.** 4, 8, 12, 16, 20 **f.** 5, 10, 15, 20, 25 **3.** 5, 10, 15 **5.** 60, 120, 180 **7.** 42, 84, 126 **9.** 8, 16, 24 **11.** 16, 32, 48 **13.** 28, 56, 84 **15.** 33 **17.** 65 **19.** 10 **21.** 12 **23.** 42 **25.** 42 **27.** 20 **29.** 14 **31.** 15 **33.** Every 60 minutes **35.** D **37.** Every 12 days **39.** March 2 **41.** 150 **43.** $>$ **45.** $>$ **47.** 2000

Section 5A Review

1. No **3.** Yes **5.** No **7.** Yes **9.** Yes **11.** Yes **13.** $2^2 \times 19$ **15.** 2×11 **17.** $2^2 \times 3$ **19.** $2 \times 3 \times 19$ **21.** 73 is prime **23.** 3^4 **25.** 2, 4, 6, 8, 10, 12, 14 **27.** 7, 14, 21, 28, 35, 42, 49 **29.** 0, 0, 0, 0, 0, 0, 0 **31.** 6 **33.** 18 **35.** 20 **37.** 1998, 2000, 2002, 2004 **39.** 585

5-4 Try It

a. $\frac{6}{11}$ are red; $\frac{5}{11}$ are not. **b.** $\frac{7}{8}$; $\frac{14}{16}$

5-4 Exercises & Applications

1. **a.** $\frac{1}{2}$ **b.** $\frac{1}{4}$ **c.** $\frac{5}{8}$ **d.** $\frac{3}{4}$ **3–19.** Possible equivalent fractions: **3.** $\frac{14}{18}$ **5.** $\frac{24}{34}$ **7.** $\frac{4}{6}$ **9.** $\frac{1}{2}$ **11.** $\frac{2}{5}$ **13.** $\frac{6}{16}$ **15.** $\frac{12}{16}$ **17.** $\frac{4}{8}$ **19.** $\frac{18}{20}$ **21.** $\frac{2}{9}$ **23.** B **25.** $\frac{6}{7}$ **27.** $\frac{8}{28}$ or $\frac{2}{7}$ **29.** $\frac{10}{16}$ in. or $\frac{5}{8}$ in. **31.** a, b **33.** 101.9 **35.** 48.3 **37.** 9 **39.** $n = 100$ **41.** $h = 2$

5-5 Try It

Possible answers for a–c: **a.** $\frac{3}{5}, \frac{12}{20}$ **b.** $\frac{4}{5}, \frac{24}{30}$ **c.** $\frac{1}{3}, \frac{14}{42}$ **d.** 5 **e.** 2 **f.** 9 **g.** $\frac{4}{5}$ **h.** $\frac{3}{4}$ **i.** $\frac{2}{3}$

5-5 Exercises & Applications

1. **a.** Yes **b.** No **c.** Yes **d.** Yes **e.** No **f.** Yes **3–13.** Possible answers given. **3.** $\frac{2}{6}, \frac{1}{3}$ **5.** $\frac{2}{12}, \frac{3}{18}$ **7.** $\frac{3}{7}, \frac{18}{42}$ **9.** $\frac{2}{5}, \frac{20}{50}$ **11.** $\frac{1}{3}, \frac{22}{66}$ **13.** $\frac{8}{18}, \frac{20}{45}$ **15.** $\frac{1}{5}$ **17.** $\frac{1}{3}$ **19.** $\frac{4}{5}$ **21.** $\frac{3}{5}$ **23.** $\frac{1}{6}$ **25.** $\frac{2}{3}$ **27.** $\frac{1}{4}$ **29.** $\frac{1}{6}$ **31.** $\frac{1}{6}$ **33.** 5 **35.** 2 **37.** 1 **39.** 8 **41.** 10 **43.** 4 **45.** 9 **47.** 4 **49.** 3 **51.** C **59.** 25 kg **61.** Flyweight and Cruiserweight; 40 kg

5-6 Try It

a. $4\frac{2}{3}$ **b.** $2\frac{8}{9}$ **c.** $8\frac{3}{4}$ **d.** $\frac{11}{6}$ **e.** $\frac{33}{8}$ **f.** $\frac{13}{5}$

5-6 Exercises & Applications

1. **a.** Proper **b.** Improper **c.** Improper **d.** Proper **e.** Improper **f.** Improper **3.** $\frac{14}{5}$ **5.** $\frac{10}{3}$ **7.** $\frac{14}{4}$ **9.** $\frac{14}{5}$ **11.** $\frac{31}{10}$ **13.** $\frac{33}{12}$ **15.** $2\frac{4}{5}$ **17.** $5\frac{1}{2}$ **19.** $2\frac{7}{8}$ **21.** $9\frac{9}{10}$ **23.** $100\frac{5}{8}$ **25.** $2\frac{7}{11}$ **27.** $\frac{31}{8}$ **29.** Yes **31.** 12 **39.** 10,560 **41.** 9 **43.** 26,400 **45.** 30

5-7 Try It

a. $\frac{4}{5}$ **b.** $\frac{6}{25}$ **c.** $\frac{3}{8}$ **d.** 0.2; Terminates **e.** 0.65; Terminates **f.** $0.\overline{36}$; Repeats

5-7 Exercises & Applications

1. **a.** $\frac{3}{10}$ **b.** $\frac{7}{10}$ **c.** $\frac{11}{100}$ **d.** $\frac{37}{100}$ **e.** $\frac{121}{1000}$ **f.** $\frac{333}{1000}$ **3.** $0.\overline{14}$ **5.** $1.\overline{345}$ **7.** $0.\overline{18}$; Repeats **9.** 0.45; Terminates **11.** 0.28; Terminates **13.** $0.\overline{6}$; Repeats **15.** 2.5; Terminates **17.** 1.25; Terminates **19.** 0.72; Terminates **21.** 0.75; Terminates **23.** 0.5; Terminates **25.** $\frac{2}{5}$ **27.** $\frac{11}{25}$ **29.** $\frac{67}{100}$ **31.** $\frac{7}{20}$ **33.** $\frac{13}{25}$ **35.** $\frac{24}{125}$ **37.** $\frac{7}{10}$ **39.** $\frac{16}{125}$ **41.** $\frac{22}{25}$ **43.** $\frac{1}{8}$ in., $\frac{1}{4}$ in., $\frac{3}{8}$ in., $\frac{1}{2}$ in., $\frac{5}{8}$ in., $\frac{3}{4}$ in., $\frac{7}{8}$ in. **45.** D **47.** $0.\overline{02}$; $0.\overline{37}$ **51.** 600 **53.** 2040 **55.** 15,000 **57.** 102

5-8 Try It

a. $\frac{7}{16}$ **b.** $\frac{5}{6}$ **c.** $\frac{8}{11}$

5-8 Exercises & Applications

1. **a.** $<$ **b.** $>$ **c.** $<$ **d.** $>$ **e.** $<$ **f.** $<$ **3.** 24; $>$ **5.** 6; $<$ **7.** 4; $=$ **9.** 132; $<$ **11.** 33; $<$ **13.** 2; $=$ **15.** $\frac{4}{8} < \frac{7}{9} < \frac{5}{6}$ **17.** $\frac{3}{11} < \frac{11}{11} < \frac{11}{3}$ **19.** $\frac{4}{7} < \frac{4}{6} < \frac{4}{5}$ **21.** $\frac{2}{7} < \frac{3}{8} < \frac{3}{5}$ **23.** $\frac{2}{33} < \frac{3}{22} < \frac{10}{11}$ **25.** $\frac{1}{6} < \frac{7}{36} < \frac{13}{4}$ **27.** $\frac{7}{8}, \frac{10}{16}, \frac{3}{8}, \frac{10}{32}, \frac{1}{4}, \frac{2}{16}$ **29.** Renaldo **35.** 0; 4; 6 **37.** 198; 110; 90 **39.** 35; 63; 77 **41.** 8; 4; 2

SELECTED ANSWERS

689

SELECTED ANSWERS

Section 5B Review

1. Yes; 3^3 **3.** No; 2^5 **5.** Yes; $2^4 \times 3$ **7.** $\frac{1}{2}$; numerator 1; denominator 2 **9.** $\frac{3}{8}$; numerator 3; denominator 8 **11.** $\frac{3}{4}$; 0.75 **13.** $\frac{1}{3}$; $0.\overline{3}$ **15.** $\frac{1}{2}$; 0.5 **17.** $3\frac{2}{10} = 3\frac{1}{5}$ **19.** $\frac{39}{5}$ **21.** $8\frac{2}{5}$ **23.** Beverly; Tom and Maye

Chapter 5 Summary & Review

1. 2, 3, 6, and 9 **2.** 2 **3.** 2, 3, 5, 6, and 10 **4.** 3 and 5 **5.** Composite **6.** Prime **7.** Composite **8.** Composite **9.** 108 **10.** 126 **11.** $\frac{5}{8}$ **12.** $\frac{4}{6}$ or $\frac{2}{3}$ **13.** The numerator is 11, the denominator is 3. **14.** $\frac{2}{3}$ **15.** $\frac{1}{8}$ **16.** $\frac{1}{6}$ **17.** $\frac{4}{5}$ **18.** $4\frac{1}{4}$ **19.** $\frac{43}{5}$ **20.** $6\frac{5}{7}$ **21.** $\frac{26}{9}$ **22.** $\frac{7}{8}$ in., $1\frac{1}{4}$ in., $2\frac{3}{4}$ in., $\frac{7}{2}$ in. **23.** $0.\overline{6}$ **24.** 5.5 **25.** 0.375 **26.** 1.4 **27.** $\frac{1}{20}$ **28.** $3\frac{4}{5}$ **29.** $\frac{5}{8}$ **30.** $2\frac{23}{1000}$

Chapter 6

6-1 Try It

a. $\frac{7}{10}$ **b.** $\frac{2}{7}$ **c.** $\frac{17}{2}$ **d.** 0

6-1 Exercises & Applications

1. a. Yes **b.** Yes **c.** No **d.** No **e.** Yes **3.** $\frac{1}{10}$ **5.** 2 **7.** $\frac{1}{3}$ **9.** $\frac{1}{2}$ **11.** $\frac{1}{6}$ **13.** $\frac{4}{9}$ **15.** $\frac{6}{13}$ **17.** = **19.** > **21.** < **23.** > **25.** > **27.** $\frac{7}{13}$ **29.** $\frac{4}{17}$ **31.** $\frac{9}{20}$ **33.** $\frac{3}{10}$ **39.** 16 **41.** 31 **43.** 33, 40, 48

6-2 Try It (Example 1)

a. $\frac{5}{6}$ **b.** $\frac{1}{2}$ **c.** $\frac{17}{20}$ **d.** $\frac{1}{10}$

6-2 Try It (Examples 2–3)

a. $\frac{1}{4}$ **b.** $\frac{2}{3}$ **c.** $\frac{7}{10}$ **d.** $\frac{13}{18}$

6-2 Exercises & Applications

1. Possible answers: **a.** 6 **b.** 18 **c.** 8 **d.** 77 **e.** 24 **3.** $\frac{1}{4}$ **5.** $\frac{1}{6}$ **7.** $\frac{5}{4}$ **9.** $\frac{27}{28}$ **11.** $\frac{17}{30}$ **13.** $\frac{21}{20}$ **15.** $\frac{4}{25}$ **17.** 4, 7 **19.** 15, 4 **21.** 4, 3 **23.** $\frac{37}{7}$ weeks **25.** $\frac{23}{42}$ **27.** $\frac{11}{12}$ **29.** $\frac{1}{2}, \frac{7}{12}, \frac{2}{3}$ **31.** 49 **33.** $4h$

6-3 Try It

a. $\frac{2}{3}$ **b.** $\frac{8}{3}$ **c.** 1

6-3 Exercises & Applications

1. a. 1 **b.** $\frac{2}{7}$ **c.** $\frac{5}{9}$ **d.** $\frac{6}{5}$ **3.** $\frac{3}{10}$ **5.** $\frac{7}{8}$ **7.** 4 **9.** $\frac{25}{7}$ **11.** $\frac{1}{6}$ **13.** $\frac{22}{9}$ **15.** $\frac{2}{11}$ **17.** $\frac{1}{3}$ **19–25.** Possible answers given. **19.** $\frac{3}{4} - \frac{1}{4} = \frac{1}{2}$ **21.** $\frac{1}{6} + \frac{5}{12} = \frac{7}{12}$ **23.** $\frac{90}{81} - \frac{1}{3} = \frac{14}{18}$ **25.** $\frac{2}{12} + \frac{7}{10} = \frac{13}{15}$ **27.** $\frac{7}{15}$ **29.** $\frac{7}{12}$ lb **31.** A **33.** $\frac{1}{2}$ yard **37.** 60 **39.** No **41.** Yes

Section 6A Review

1. $\frac{8}{11}$ **3.** $\frac{1}{2}$ **5.** $\frac{27}{20}$ **7.** $\frac{5}{12}$ **9.** $\frac{2}{9}$ **11.** $\frac{19}{20}$ **15.** $\frac{7}{20}$ **17.** $\frac{1}{4}$ **19.** $\frac{3}{4}$ **21.** $\frac{2}{3}$ **23.** $\frac{3}{8}$

6-4 Try It

a. 6 **b.** 2 **c.** 4 **d.** 16 **e.** 8

6-4 Exercises & Applications

1. 0 **3.** 1 **5.** 1 **7.** 4 **9.** 5 **11.** 26 **13.** 34 **15.** 8 **17.** 7 **19.** 2 **21.** 18 **23.** 9 **25.** 7 **27.** 8 **29.** 5 **31.** 26 **33.** 15 **35.** 19 **37.** 7 **39.** $20\frac{5}{8}$ ft **41.** $4\frac{1}{2}$ **43.** 7 inches **47.** 5 **49.** 16 in^2 **51.** 21 **53.** 32 **55.** 8 **57.** 22 **59.** 6 **61.** 5

6-5 Try It

a. $8\frac{3}{4}$ **b.** $4\frac{3}{4}$ **c.** $6\frac{1}{2}$ **d.** $7\frac{5}{12}$

6-5 Exercises & Applications

1. $11\frac{2}{3}$ **3.** $6\frac{1}{2}$ **5.** $9\frac{2}{3}$ **7.** $62\frac{3}{4}$ **9.** 11 **11.** $5\frac{17}{24}$ **13.** $6\frac{4}{5}$ **15.** $15\frac{8}{9}$ **17.** $13\frac{1}{9}$ **19.** $14\frac{1}{10}$ **21.** $21\frac{16}{21}$ **23.** 8 **25.** $41\frac{7}{9}$ **27.** $52\frac{1}{12}$ **29.** $38\frac{1}{4}$ ft **31.** $10\frac{3}{4}$ millions of dollars **33.** $15\frac{53}{60}$ millions of dollars **35.** A: $1\frac{2}{3}$ m^2; B: 3 m^2 **37.** 9.42 ft; 62.8 in.; 113.04 in. **39.** 427,000 **41.** 1,124,000 **43.** 9,000,000,000 **45.** 666,300,000,000

6-6 Try It

a. $3\frac{2}{5}$ **b.** $4\frac{5}{6}$ **c.** $2\frac{4}{9}$

6-6 Exercises & Applications

1. $2\frac{3}{4}$ **3.** $2\frac{1}{2}$ **5.** $1\frac{1}{4}$ **7.** $\frac{1}{2}$ **9.** $\frac{2}{3}$ **11.** $1\frac{1}{24}$ **13.** $8\frac{1}{8}$ **15.** $3\frac{1}{5}$ **17.** $4\frac{11}{20}$ **19.** $\frac{3}{4}$ **21.** $3\frac{3}{5}$ **23.** $6\frac{13}{28}$ **25.** $1\frac{1}{5}$ ft **27.** C **29.** $2\frac{1}{4}$ hr **35.** 54.2325 **37.** 3.4×10^5 **39.** 5×10^6 **41.** 6.2×10^6

Section 6B Review

1. $1\frac{3}{5}$ **3.** $\frac{17}{45}$ **5.** $3\frac{5}{9}$ **7.** $111\frac{11}{24}$ **9.** 7 **11.** $4\frac{2}{3}$ **13.** $\frac{1}{18}$ **15.** $3\frac{1}{4}$ **17.** $\frac{1}{21}$ **19.** 6 hours **21.** D

Chapter 6 Summary & Review

1. $\frac{1}{5} + \frac{3}{5} = \frac{4}{5}$ **2.** 12 **3.** 28 **4.** 30 **5.** 63 **6.** $\frac{2}{7}$ **7.** $\frac{11}{15}$ **8.** 1 **9.** $\frac{1}{5}$ **10.** $1\frac{1}{4}$ **11.** $\frac{1}{14}$ **12.** $1\frac{1}{6}$ **13.** $\frac{2}{15}$ **14.** $\frac{15}{22}$ **15.** $\frac{41}{42}$ **16.** $\frac{5}{24}$ **17.** $\frac{7}{72}$ **18.** $\frac{9}{13}$ **19.** $\frac{3}{4}$ **20.** $\frac{7}{10}$ **21.** 3 **22.** 5 **23.** 2 **24.** 79 **25.** 1 **26.** 14 **27.** 20 **28.** 2 **29.** 2 **30.** 3 **31.** $2\frac{3}{4}$ in. **32.** $5\frac{4}{5}$ **33.** $13\frac{2}{3}$ **34.** $4\frac{3}{4}$ **35.** $\frac{7}{17}$ **36.** $8\frac{73}{88}$ **37.** $13\frac{3}{7}$ **38.** $2\frac{1}{6}$ **39.** $16\frac{7}{9}$ **40.** $9\frac{2}{3}$ **41.** $2\frac{5}{6}$ **42.** $28\frac{6}{7}$ **43.** 14 **44.** $10\frac{1}{2}$ m **45.** $28\frac{7}{8}$ yd

Cumulative Review Chapters 1–6

1. A **2.** C **3.** C **4.** D **5.** B **6.** A **7.** D **8.** D **9.** C **10.** C **11.** B **12.** C

Chapter 7

7-1 Try It

a. 15 **b.** 3 **c.** 3 **d.** 1

7-1 Exercises & Applications

1. 5 **3.** 6 **5.** 9 **7.** 15 **9.** 50 **11.** 12 **13.** 72 **15.** 60 **17.** 35 **19.** 28 **21.** 12 **23.** 40 **25.** 30 **27.** 20 **29.** 6 **31.** A **33.** No **35.** 3 **39.** 800 **41.** 97.6 **43.** 0.453 **45.** No **47.** No **49.** Yes **51.** Yes **53.** No **55.** Yes

7-2 Try It

a. $2\frac{2}{3}$ **b.** $5\frac{1}{4}$ **c.** 8 **d.** 25

7-2 Exercises & Applications

1. $3 \times \frac{3}{5}$ **3.** $4 \times \frac{2}{3}$ **5.** $\frac{2}{3}$ **7.** $\frac{3}{5}$ **9.** $6\frac{2}{3}$ **11.** 2 **13.** $1\frac{1}{2}$ **15.** $6\frac{3}{5}$ **17.** $2\frac{2}{9}$ **19.** $5\frac{2}{5}$ **21.** $4\frac{3}{4}$ **23.** $12\frac{5}{6}$ **25.** $9\frac{3}{5}$ **27.** 27 **31.** $2\frac{1}{4}$ lb rice and $1\frac{1}{2}$ lb sugar **33.** 28 years **37.** 98 **39.** 8 **41.** 17 **43.** $3^2 \times 7$ **45.** 17 **47.** 3×19

7-3 Try It

a. $\frac{12}{35}$ **b.** $1\frac{1}{3}$ **c.** $2\frac{8}{21}$ **d.** $\frac{2}{45}$

7-3 Exercises & Applications

1. $\frac{2}{3} \times \frac{2}{4} = \frac{4}{12}$ **3.** $\frac{5}{6} \times \frac{3}{10} = \frac{15}{60}$ **5.** $\frac{2}{7}$ **7.** $\frac{21}{40}$ **9.** $3\frac{59}{105}$ **11.** $\frac{78}{187}$ **13.** $8\frac{3}{10}$ **15.** $\frac{13}{60}$ **17.** $1\frac{146}{169}$ **19.** $1\frac{5}{14}$ **21.** $\frac{11}{42}$ **23.** $\frac{3}{64}$ **25.** $\frac{36}{121}$ **27.** $2\frac{32}{49}$ **29.** $6\frac{1}{4}$ ft **31.** $\frac{1}{8}$ cup sugar, $\frac{1}{8}$ cup flour, and $\frac{7}{8}$ cup water **37.** 126,720 **39.** 190,080 **41.** 63,360 **43.** 6 **45.** 8 **47.** 35 **49.** 72 **51.** 29 **53.** 9

Section 7A Review

1. 3 **3.** 30 **5.** 2 **7.** 11 **9.** 3 oz wax; $19\frac{1}{2}$ tbs oil; 9 tbs water; $\frac{3}{4}$ tsp borax **11.** Yes **13.** $1\frac{2}{3}$ **15.** D

7-4 Try It

a. $6\frac{2}{3}$ **b.** $1\frac{3}{4}$ **c.** $2\frac{6}{17}$ **d.** 5

7-4 Exercises & Applications

1. $\frac{7}{5}$ **3.** $\frac{9}{2}$ **5.** 4 **7.** 9 **9.** $3\frac{1}{2}$ **11.** $11\frac{1}{4}$ **13.** $1\frac{3}{29}$ **15.** $1\frac{7}{23}$ **17.** $3\frac{3}{10}$ **19.** 40 **21.** $3\frac{9}{13}$ **23.** $\frac{9}{32}$ **25.** $10\frac{1}{2}$ **27.** $1\frac{9}{13}$ **29.** $\frac{9}{34}$ **31.** B **33.** 30 **35. a.** About $3\frac{1}{2}$ **b.** 2 **c.** About 11 **37.** No **39.** 896 **41.** 400 **43.** 160

7-5 Try It

a. $1\frac{7}{25}$ **b.** $1\frac{1}{2}$ **c.** $\frac{1}{10}$ **d.** $\frac{1}{25}$

7-5 Exercises & Applications

1. $\frac{2}{3} \div \frac{1}{6} = 4$ **3.** $\frac{1}{3} \div \frac{2}{12} = 2$ **5.** $\frac{2}{5}$ **7.** 7 **9.** $1\frac{1}{4}$ **11.** $\frac{20}{189}$ **13.** $\frac{2}{31}$ **15.** $\frac{5}{16}$ **17.** 10 **19.** 8 **21.** $\frac{4}{25}$ **23.** $\frac{19}{41}$ **25.** 7 **27.** B **29. a.** 9 **b.** 108 **35.** $r = 8$ cm; $d = 16$ cm **37.** $r = 4$ mm; $d = 8$ mm **39.** $\frac{6}{10}$ **41.** $\frac{2}{8}$

7-6 Try It (Example 2)

a. 6 **b.** $\frac{5}{4}$ **c.** 12

7-6 Try It (Example 4)

a. 2 **b.** $\frac{7}{2}$ **c.** $1\frac{1}{2}$

7-6 Exercises & Applications

1. Yes **3.** No **5.** $\frac{24}{133}$ **7.** 15 **9.** $\frac{3}{4}$ **11.** 2 **13.** $125\frac{1}{45}$ **15.** $2\frac{13}{25}$ **17.** 68 **19.** $1\frac{1}{3}$ **21.** $1\frac{1}{4}$ **23.** $6\frac{6}{7}$ **33. a.** 256 **b.** 7000 **c.** 240 **d.** 5760 Possible answers for 35–39: **35.** $\frac{9}{24}$; $\frac{6}{16}$ **37.** $\frac{1}{2}$; $\frac{2}{4}$ **39.** $\frac{22}{28}$; $\frac{33}{42}$ **41.** 3 **43.** 1

Section 7B Review

1. 8 **3.** $7\frac{1}{2}$ **5.** $2\frac{4}{7}$ **7.** $4\frac{17}{22}$ **9.** 50 **11.** 13 **13.** 4 **15.** $v = 32$ **17.** $x = 2$ **19.** $p = \frac{2}{5}$ **21.** $u = 1\frac{3}{5}$ **25.** 3 gallons **27.** A

Chapter 7 Summary & Review

1. $2 \times \frac{5}{7} = \frac{10}{7}$ **2.** ≈ 14 **3.** ≈ 5 **4.** $\frac{3}{32}$ **5.** $\frac{1}{81}$ **6.** $\frac{4}{15}$ **7.** $\frac{12}{49}$ **8.** 25 **9.** 2 **10.** $11\frac{1}{4}$ **11.** $10\frac{5}{9}$ **12.** $1\frac{1}{4}$ cups **13.** No **14.** $4 \div \frac{2}{3} = 6$ **15.** $\frac{8}{5}$ **16.** $\frac{1}{3}$ **17.** $4\frac{1}{2}$ **18.** $\frac{5}{6}$ **19.** $\frac{9}{35}$ **20.** $\frac{8}{35}$ **21.** $\frac{3}{28}$ **22.** $\frac{4}{63}$ **23.** $\frac{1}{40}$ **24.** $\frac{7}{22}$ **25.** Yes **26.** Yes **27.** No **28.** No **29.** $x = \frac{3}{2}$ **30.** $m = \frac{3}{4}$ **31.** $w = \frac{7}{30}$ **32.** $q = \frac{7}{3}$ **33.** 10 pieces

Chapter 8

8-1 Exercises & Applications

1. Ray **3.** Ray **5.** Line **13.** Parallel **15.** Parallel **17.** Intersecting **19.** Perpendicular **31.** $1\frac{2}{3}$ **33.** $2\frac{1}{3}$ **35.** $3\frac{1}{2}$ **37.** $1\frac{4}{5}$ **39.** $1\frac{1}{2}$ **41.** $2\frac{2}{5}$ **43.** 1 **45.** $1\frac{3}{5}$ **47.** $1\frac{1}{4}$ **49.** $1\frac{2}{3}$ **51.** 1

8-2 Try It

a. Straight **b.** Right **c.** Obtuse **d.** Acute

8-2 Exercises & Applications

1. I **3.** B **5.** Obtuse **7.** Acute **9.** Acute **11.** Right **13.** $\angle ABC$, $\angle CBA$, $\angle B$ **15.** $\angle GHI$, $\angle IHG$, $\angle H$ **21.** Obtuse **23.** Straight **25.** Acute **29.** 6 **31.** Acute **33.** $\frac{33}{5}$ **35.** $\frac{7}{2}$ **37.** $\frac{119}{11}$ **39.** $\frac{39}{4}$ **41.** $\frac{13}{6}$ **43.** $\frac{27}{7}$ **45.** $1\frac{19}{36}$ **47.** $1\frac{1}{3}$ **49.** $\frac{3}{8}$ **51.** $\frac{1}{2}$ **53.** $\frac{9}{11}$

SELECTED ANSWERS

691

8-3 Exercises & Applications

1. Greater than **3.** Less than **5.** 72° **7.** 135° **9.** 180° **11.** 55° **15.** Obtuse **17.** Obtuse **19.** 11° **21.** 87° **23.** 128° **25.** 90° **29.** B **33.** 0.5 **35.** 0.25 **37.** $0.\overline{3}$ **39.** $0.\overline{4}$ **41.** $0.\overline{54}$ **43.** 1.0 **45.** $\frac{1}{24}$ **47.** $1\frac{25}{66}$ **49.** $\frac{5}{72}$ **51.** $\frac{9}{10}$

Section 8A Review

1. Parallel **3.** Nonintersecting **5.** Right **7.** Obtuse **9.** 37°; C = 53°; S = 143° **11.** 75°; C = 15°; S = 105° **13.** A

8-4 Try It

a. 39°; Right **b.** 122°; Obtuse

8-4 Exercises & Applications

1. 40° **3.** 80° **5.** 100° **7.** Acute **9.** Obtuse **11.** Right **13.** Obtuse **15.** Acute **17.** Right **19.** 66°, 56°, 58° **21.** 43°, 112°, 25° **23.** 77°, 45°, 58° **25.** 79°, 60°, 41° **27.** 31° **29.** 5° **31.** 90° **33.** Yes; Acute **35.** Yes; Obtuse **37.** 30°, 43°, 107° **41.** 28° **43.** $\frac{39}{50}$ **45.** $\frac{9}{10}$ **47.** $\frac{18}{25}$ **49.** $\frac{69}{500}$ **51.** $\frac{3}{8}$ **53.** $\frac{999}{1000}$ **55.** 5 **57.** 16 **59.** 5 **61.** 5

8-5 Try It

a. Yes **b.** No **c.** No

8-5 Exercises & Applications

1. 4 m **3.** 20 ft **5.** 9 yd **7.** Scalene **9.** Isosceles **11.** Equilateral **13.** Scalene **15.** Scalene **17.** Equilateral **19.** Yes **21.** Yes **23.** No **25.** Yes **27.** Scalene **29.** No **31.** Right scalene **33.** Obtuse scalene **35.** Yes **37.** Right scalene triangles **39.** $>$ **41.** $=$ **43.** $11\frac{4}{15}$ **45.** $23\frac{1}{2}$ **47.** $11\frac{17}{35}$ **49.** $7\frac{23}{35}$

8-6 Try It

a. Regular quadrilateral **b.** Irregular triangle **c.** Irregular pentagon

8-6 Exercises & Applications

1. Not closed **3.** Not closed **5.** Regular pentagon **7.** Irregular hexagon **9.** Regular quadrilateral **11.** Regular octagon **19.** Octagon **21.** Pentagon **23.** Triangle **25.** Quadrilateral **27.** 8 **29.** 40 in. **33.** $\frac{4}{5}, \frac{7}{8}, \frac{8}{9}$ **35.** $\frac{6}{9}, \frac{6}{6}, \frac{9}{6}$ **37.** $\frac{1}{4}, \frac{1}{3}, \frac{1}{2}$ **39.** $\frac{6}{7}, \frac{9}{8}, \frac{7}{6}$ **41.** $1\frac{27}{35}$ **43.** $\frac{1}{8}$ **45.** $3\frac{11}{56}$ **47.** $6\frac{4}{9}$ **49.** $4\frac{9}{28}$

8-7 Try It

a. False **b.** True **c.** Trapezoid, quadrilateral

8-7 Exercises & Applications

1. 2 **3.** 2 **5.** False **7.** True **23.** A **25.** Yes **31.** $>$ **33.** $>$ **35.** $=$ **37.** $<$ **39.** $=$ **41.** $>$ **43.** 29.4 **45.** 226.8 **47.** 48.23 **49.** 0.4

Section 8B Review

1. $\angle JAH$, $\angle HAJ$, $\angle A$ **3.** $\angle IPK$, $\angle KPI$, $\angle P$ **5.** 24° **7.** 135° **9.** 128° **11.** Scalene; 57° **13.** Scalene; 18° **19.** Rhombus, parallelogram, irregular quadrilateral, polygon **21.** Trapezoid, irregular quadrilateral, polygon

8-8 Try It

a. No **b.** Yes **c.** Yes

8-8 Exercises & Applications

1. **3.**

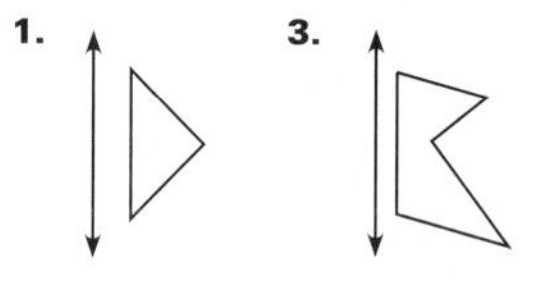

5. Not symmetric **7.** Not symmetric **9.** Yes **11.** Yes **13.** Yes **17.** 2 **19.** Octagon **23.** $\frac{2}{3}$, 0.75, $\frac{7}{9}$ **25.** 1.1, $\frac{7}{6}$, 1.167 **27.** $\frac{1}{3}$, 1.3, $\frac{3}{1}$ **29.** 0.25, $\frac{2}{5}$, 2.5 **31.** 30.528 **33.** 4.3792 **35.** 17.29 **37.** 3.96

8-9 Try It

a. 90° counterclockwise **b.** 270° clockwise **c.** 2

8-9 Exercises & Application

1. **3.**

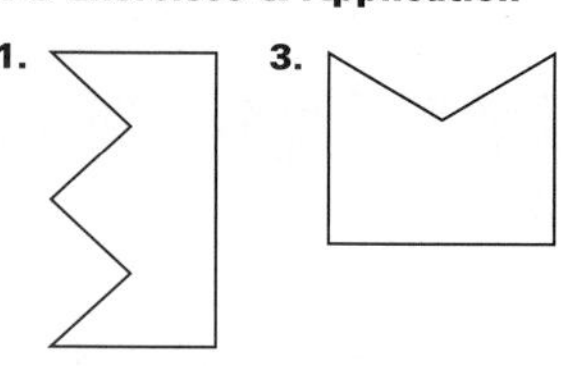

5. 360° **7.** 180° **13.** 45° **15.** 180° **17.** 90° **19.** 72° **25.** 3.55 **27.** 0.13 **29.** 0.06 **31.** 2.37 **33.** 18.2 **35.** 2.69 **37.** 14.2 **39.** 7

8-10 Try It

Yes

8-10 Exercises & Applications

1. No **3.** Yes **7.** Yes **9.** No **11.** No **13.** Yes **15.** Hexagon **17.** Yes **21.** 28 cm **23.** 26 mm **25.** 3100 **27.** 56 **29.** 0.106

Section 8C Review

7. Obtuse, 110°, 40°, 30° **9.** Acute, 65°, 65°, 50° **11.** Regular octagon; Yes; 16 **13.** Irregular triangle; No **15.** Yes **17.** No **19.** 104° **21.** 81° **23.** 90° **25.** C

Chapter 8 Summary & Review

1.

2.

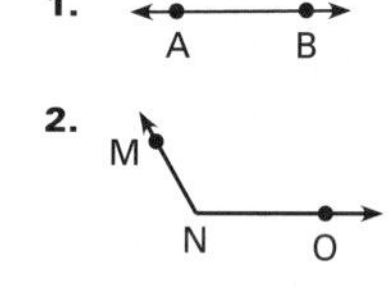

3. a.

b.

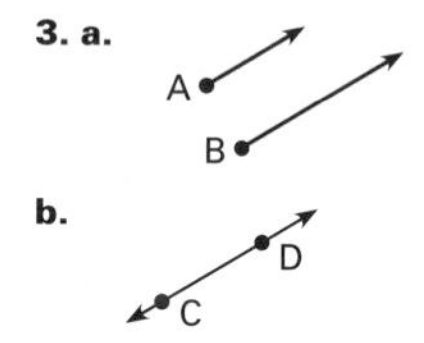

4. Acute triangle **5.** All rectangles are parallelograms because their opposite sides have the same

lengths and are parallel. But some parallelograms do not have all 90° angles, which rectangles must have.
6. Translation **7.** Reflection
8. Rotation **9.** Yes. The figures have the same size and shape.
10.

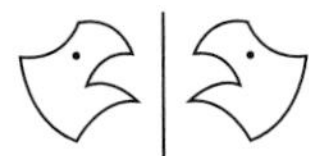

11. Symmetric

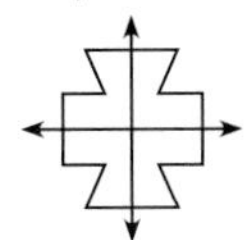

12. 90° clockwise

Cumulative Review
Chapters 1–8

1. B **2.** A **3.** B **4.** C **5.** A **6.** A
7. D **8.** C **9.** A **10.** B **11.** C
12. B **13.** C **14.** D **15.** A

Chapter 9

9-1 Try It

a. 4° **b.** −6° **c.** −10, −3, 0, 1, 7, 10

9-1 Exercises & Applications

1. Yes **3.** Yes **5.** Yes
7–11.

-5 -4 -3 -2 -1 0 1 2 3

13. > **15.** < **17.** > **19.** >
21. > **23.** 3, 2, −4, −5 **25.** 13, −16, −56, −78 **27.** 16, 12, 0, −10
29. 19, 17, 16, −18 **31.** −114
33. 62 **35.** −7 **37.** −213, −211, −107, −76, −52 **39.** −12, 22
41. −20, −15, −5, −4, −3, −2, −1
47. 14 **49.** 1 **51.** 44 **53.** 180
55. Intersecting **57.** Perpendicular
59. Perpendicular **61.** Intersecting

9-2 Try It

a. 10 **b.** −8 **c.** 1 **d.** 0 **e.** 7 **f.** 6
g. 3 **h.** −3

9-2 Exercises & Applications

1. 8 + (−5) = 3 **3.** 3 + (−1) = 2
5. −12 **7.** 40 **9.** 1589
11. Negative **13.** Positive
15. Zero **17.** Negative
19. Negative **21.** −12 **23.** −2
25. 6 **27.** −12 **29.** −17 **31.** 1
33. 2 **35.** −6 **37.** 13 **39.** −14
41. 9 **43.** −1 **45.** −31 **47.** −14
49. 0 **51.** Opposite of 211 **55.** B
57. Yes **59.** $34\frac{1}{2}$ **61.** 1 **63.** $6\frac{2}{3}$
65. 50 **67.** Right **69.** Acute

9-3 Try It (Examples 1–2)

a. −2 **b.** −8 **c.** 4 **d.** −1

9-3 Try It (Example 3)

a. 17 **b.** 5 **c.** 26 **d.** −11

9-3 Exercises & Applications

1. −2 − 4 = −6 **3.** −4 − 2 = −6
5. −5 − (−2) = −3 **7.** −9 **9.** 9
11. 12 **13.** 2 **15.** −11 **17.** 19
19. −20 **21.** −11 **23.** −8 **25.** 13
27. −5 **29.** 20 **31.** −13 **33.** 22
35. 11 **37.** 30,300 ft **39.** 16 feet
41. 65° **43. b.** 33 and 26 **45.** 116°
47. 87° **49.** $4\frac{3}{5}$ **51.** $2\frac{3}{40}$

9-4 Try It

a. −36 **b.** 90 **c.** 60 **d.** −10
e. −4 **f.** 3 **g.** −5 **h.** 3

9-4 Exercises & Applications

1. Negative **3.** Negative
5. Negative **7.** 9 **9.** 100 **11.** −12
13. 18 **15.** −20 **17.** −48
19. −32 **21.** −2 **23.** −4 **25.** −7
27. −20 **29.** −2 **31.** −7 **33.** −8
35. 3 **37.** −12; 2; 0; −4; −2; −4, −3, 12 **39.** −2; −3; 0; 3, 3; 3, 2; 9, 3, 3 **43.** His actual average is −3.
45. $4\frac{2}{3}$ **47.** $9\frac{1}{3}$ **49.** 28 **51.** $2\frac{1}{22}$
53. 73 **55.** 11

Section 9A Review

1. −63 **3.** −1 **5.** −4 **7.** 2 **9.** −9
11. −42 **13.** −1 **15.** −2 **17.** −6
19. 10 **21.** −40 **23.** 24 **25.** −23
27. Lost 12 yards **29.** −4°C **31.** D

9-5 Try It

a. $A(2, 1)$; $B(3, -4)$; $C(0, 5)$; $D(-1, 2)$; $E(4, 0)$; $F(1, -3)$; $G(2, -3)$
b.

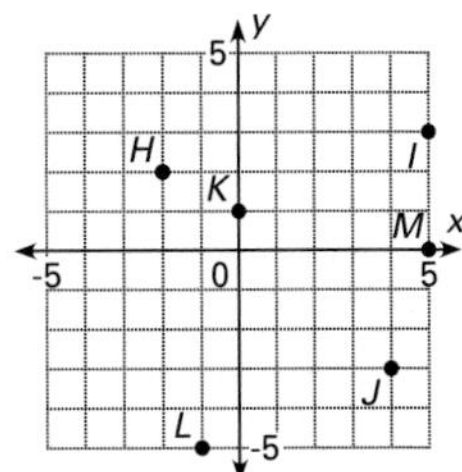

9-5 Exercises & Applications

1. I **3.** III **5.** (−5, 4) **7.** (−3, −2)
9. I **11.** IV **13.** IV **25.** Start at the origin. Go left 35 units and down 18 units. **27.** Start at the origin. Go right 4 units and up 10 units.
29. Start at the origin. Go right 88 units and down 23 units.
31. a. 1 (300, 100); 2 (400, 300); 3 (0, 400)
33. a.

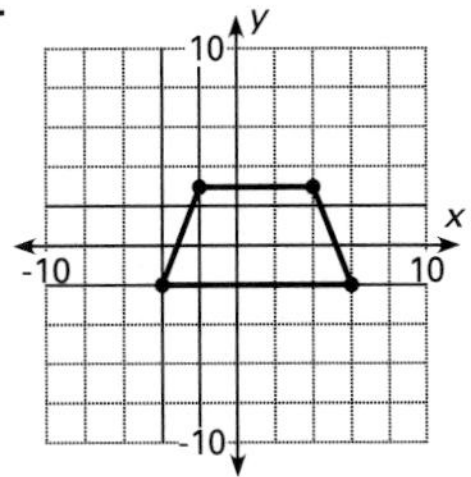

b. Trapezoid, quadrilateral, irregular polygon **35.** (10, 8) **37.** $\frac{147}{256}$
39. $2\frac{13}{144}$ **41.** Yes **43.** Yes

9-6 Try It (Example 1)

$L'(1, -2)$; $M'(2, 0)$; $N'(6, -3)$

9-6 Try It (Example 2)

$X'(-1, -1)$; $Y'(-3, 4)$; $Z'(-5, 1)$

9-6 Exercises & Applications

1. (4, 6) **3.** (7, 4) **5.** (−3, 6)
7. $P'(5, 3)$ **9.** $P'(3, 5)$ **11.** $P'(2, 2)$

SELECTED ANSWERS

693

13.

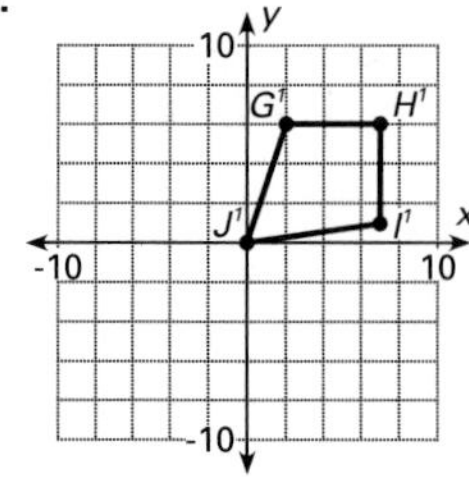

17. c. $R'(2, 3)$, $S'(4, 5)$, $T'(7, 1)$ **19.** 6 right and 8 up **21.** $A'(2, 3)$, $B'(-1, 3)$, $C'(-1, 3)$, $D'(2, -3)$ **25.** $p = 4\frac{2}{5}$ **27.** $e = \frac{9}{8}$ **29.** Irregular heptagon or polygon **31.** Irregular quadrilateral

9-7 Try It

a.

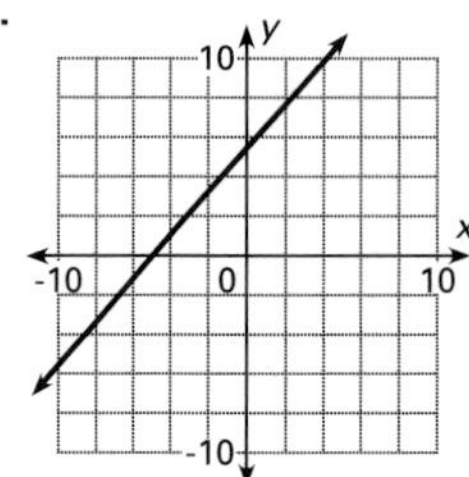

b.

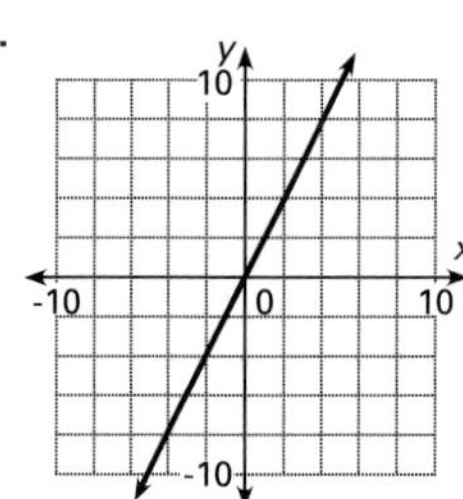

c.

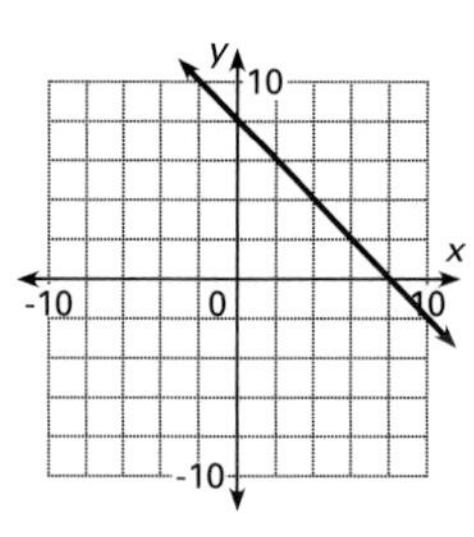

d.

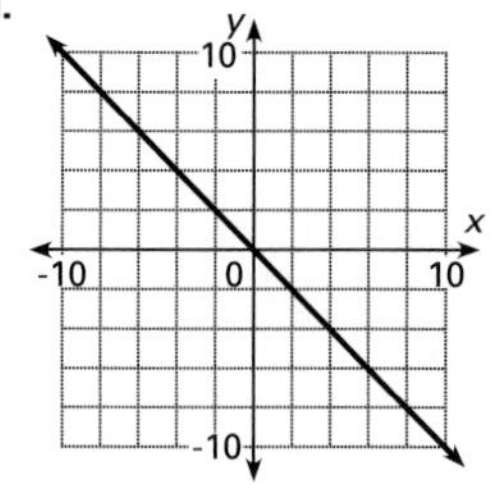

9-7 Exercises & Applications

1. a–d.

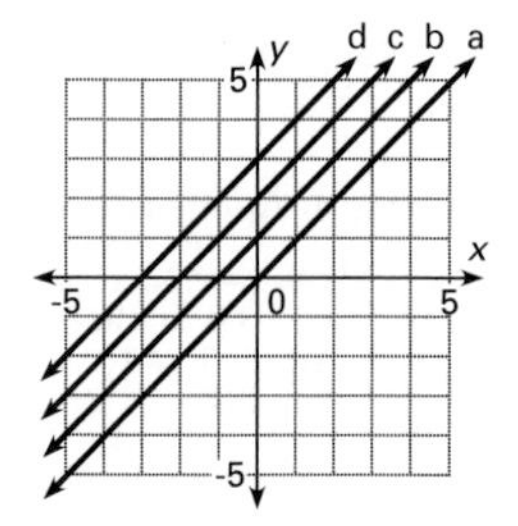

The lines are parallel.

Possible answers for 3–5:

3.

x	y
-2	25
-1	26
0	27
1	28
2	29

5.

x	y
-2	100
-1	50
0	0
1	-50
2	-100

7.

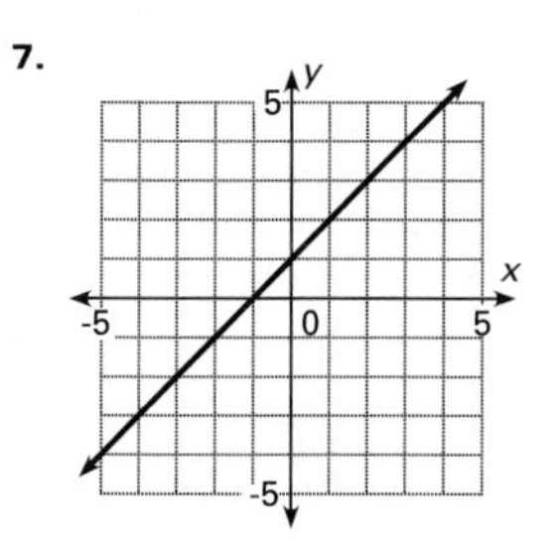

19.

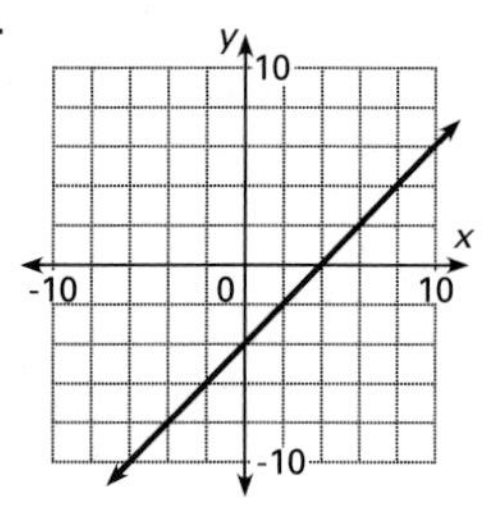

27. 43 **29.** -7 **31.** -2 **39.** 864 **41.** 36 **43.** 9

Section 9B Review

1. 8 **3.** -12 **5.** -10 **7.** 35 **9.** 5 **11.** $A(-3, 2)$, $B(2, 1)$, $C(-2, -2)$, $D(1, -1)$ **13.** $(-2, 1)$ **15.** $(4, 4)$

17.

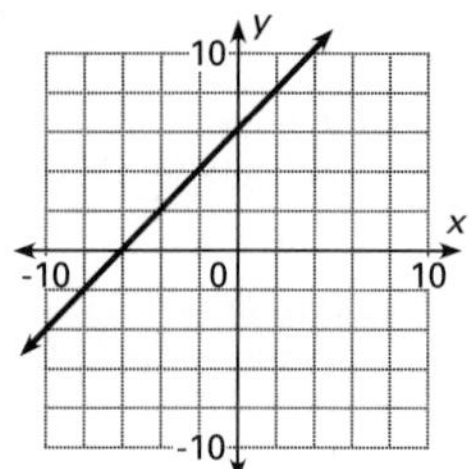

19.

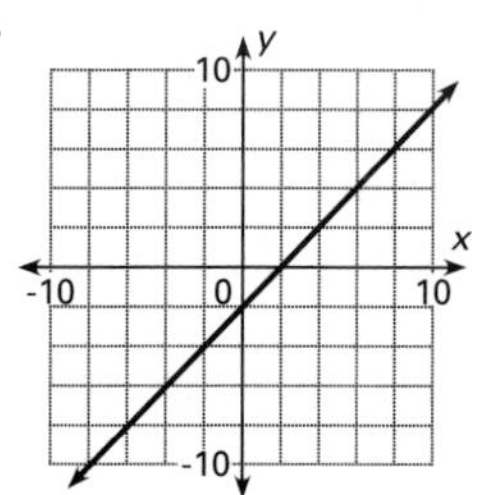

21. (2, 2), (2, 4), (4, 2), (4, 4) **23.** A

Chapter 9 Summary & Review

1.

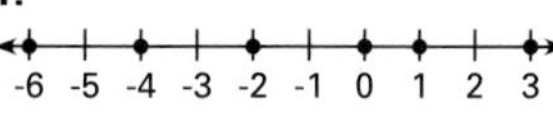

2. -3 **3.** Negative **4.** Positive **5.** $4 + (-5) = -1$ or $4 - 5 = -1$ **6.** $2 + (-4) = -2$ or $2 - 4 = -2$ **7.** 4 **8.** -6 **9.** 2 **10.** 0 **11.** -6 **12.** -10 **13.** 0 **14.** 28 **15.** -21

SELECTED ANSWERS

694

16. 36 **17.** −8 **18.** 3 **19.** (−6, −5) **20.** Quadrant II **21. a.** (5, 0) **b.** (0, 5) or (0, −5) **22.** $R'(-4, -2)$, $S'(-3, -4)$, $T'(-2, -2)$ **23.** $A'(0, 2)$; $B'(3, 2)$; $C'(3, 0)$; $D'(0, 0)$

24. a.

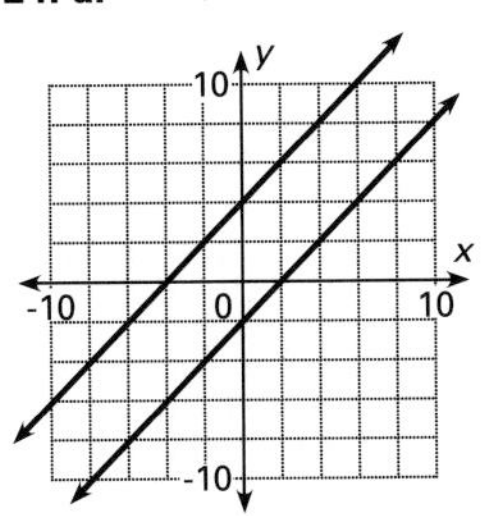

b. Each point on the upper line has been translated down 3 units to create the lower line.

Chapter 10

10-1 Try It

a. 2:5 **b.** 1:2

10-1 Exercises & Applications

1. Yes **3.** Yes **5.** No **7.** 3:2 **9.** 2:3 **11. a.** 20:9 **b.** 9:29 **13.** 3:8; $\frac{3}{8}$; 3 to 8 **15.** 1:7; $\frac{1}{7}$; 1 to 7 **17.** 24:49 **19.** Turtles **21.** Turtles to dogs **23.** You can't tell **25.** Yes **27.** No **29.** 9 in. **31.** 2 km

10-2 Try It

Possible answers: **a.** 10:18; 15:27 **b.** $\frac{6}{16}$, $\frac{9}{24}$ **c.** 3 to 5; 6 to 10 **d.** 2:26; 3:39 **e.** 24:8; 3:1

10-2 Exercises & Applications

1. Yes **3.** Yes **5.** No Possible answers for 7–17: **7.** 8 to 10; 12 to 15 **9.** 6:4; 3:2 **11.** $\frac{2}{3}$, $\frac{16}{24}$ **13.** $\frac{1}{2}$, $\frac{2}{4}$ **15.** $\frac{2}{16}$, $\frac{3}{24}$ **17.** $\frac{6}{8}$, $\frac{12}{16}$ **19.** Yes **21.** Yes **25.** A Possible answers for 27: **27.** 14:20; 28:40; 21:30 **29.** Men: 8, 12; Women: 5; 20 **31.** 19 **33.** 180° **35.** 360° **37.** 20 unit² **39.** 36 cm² **41.** 15.75 m²

10-3 Try It

Possible answers: About 0.44 mi in 1 min; 18 miles in 41 min; About 7 mi in 16 min; 72 mi in 164 min

10-3 Exercises & Applications

1. Yes **3.** No **5.** Yes **7.** No Possible answers for 9–11: **9.** 7 mi/hr, 21 mi/3 hr **11.** $\frac{15\text{ j.j.}}{20\text{ sec}}$, $\frac{3\text{ j.j.}}{4\text{ sec}}$ Possible answer for 13: **13.** An ostrich runs 5 miles in 10 minutes. **15.** About 25 mi **17.** Orange **19.** D **21.** $2\frac{1}{2}$ hours **25.** Yes **27.** No **29.** 2.4 m² **31.** 0.12 cm² **31.** 120,000 mi²

Section 10A Review

1. 23:30 **3.** Possible answer: $\frac{3\text{ red}}{5\text{ blue}}$, $\frac{3\text{ red}}{4\text{ green}}$, $\frac{3\text{ red}}{7\text{ red or green}}$, $\frac{1\text{ red}}{3\text{ blue or green}}$, $\frac{1\text{ red}}{4\text{ total}}$ **5.** Possible answers: 3:8, 12:32, 15:40 **7.** 1:3 **9.** Possible answer: $\frac{3\text{ blue stones}}{28\text{ stones}}$ **11.** D

10-4 Try It

a. Yes **b.** No **c.** No **d.** Yes

10-4 Exercises & Applications

1. a. II **b.** III **c.** I **d.** IV **3.** No **5.** No **7.** No **9.** No **11.** No **13.** Yes **15.** b **17.** c **19.** Yes **21.** D **23.** Ms. Lee and Mrs. Nieto **25.** You use multiplication to see if the cross products are equal. **27.** $3 \times 2 = 6$, but $8 \times 2 \neq 9.5$. **29.** 55, 31, −13, −55 **31.** −9, −17, −31, −53 **33.** 44, 41, −14, −41 **35.** 133, 0, −100, −178 **37.** 4.2 **39.** $r = 4.4$ yd; $d = 8.8$ yd

10-5 Try It

a. 9 **b.** 10 **c.** 1.5 **d.** 7.2

10-5 Exercises & Applications

1. $9x = 36$ **3.** $44j = 275$ **5.** $16s = 56$ **7.** 12 **9.** 25 **11.** $16.\overline{5}$ **13.** 0.96 **15.** 6 **17.** 3 **19.** $2.\overline{6}$ **21.** 3.6 **23.** 154 **25.** $23.\overline{3}$ **27.** 12 **29.** $5\frac{1}{3}$ ft **31.** A **33.** 6 **35.** Greater than **37.** −18 **39.** −6 **41.** 12.56 cm² **43.** 153.86 cm²

10-6 Try It

a. 3600 ft/min **b.** $2.80

10-6 Exercises & Applications

1. 3 **3.** 7 **5.** 8 **7.** 2 houses/mi **9.** $5\frac{1}{6}$ holes/in² **11.** 0.6 waves/sec **13.** 3 slices/person **15.** $\frac{1}{3}$ m/hr **17.** 0.5 cup/serving **19.** 1.5 turtles/mi² **21.** 7.5 m/sec **23.** 252 mi **25.** 2.2 points **27.** 9 drips **29.** 1.2 apples **31.** $\frac{70\text{ apples}}{6\text{ baskets}} = \frac{x}{3}$ baskets; $x = 35$ apples **33.** 3 pounds for 72¢ **35.** $0.58\overline{3}$ ft, or $\frac{7}{12}$ ft **41.** −17 **43.** 14 **45.** 4 **47.** 13 **49.** 34 **51.** 33.25 in² **53.** 154 mm²

10-7 Try It

6

10-7 Exercises & Applications

1. Congruent **3.** Neither **5.** $A = B = C = 1$ mm **7.** $A = C = 0.625$ yd, $B = 0.5$ yd **9.** 12.5 m **11. a.** 1000 mi; 675 mi; 1667.5 mi **b.** Yes **13.** 25 ft or 64 ft **15.** No; Yes **17.** −21 **19.** 16 **21.** −70 **23.** 26 **25.** 12 **27.** Yes **29.** No **31.** Yes **33.** Yes **35.** Yes **37.** Yes

Section 10B Review

1. Possible answers: $\frac{5\text{ cm}}{2\text{ sec}}$, $\frac{2.5\text{ cm}}{1\text{ sec}}$, $\frac{10\text{ cm}}{4\text{ sec}}$ **3.** $0.65/min **5.** 0.6 commercials/min **7.** 50.4 **9.** $0.30 **11.** 5 **13.** $A = 4.\overline{6}$, $B = 3$, $C = 7$ **15.** B

10-8 Try It

a. 25% **b.** 75%

10-8 Exercises & Applications

1. Greater **3.** Less **5.** Less **7.** 50% **9.** 25% **11.** 50% **13.** 74% **15.** About 12%; About 88% **17.** India, Myanmar, Other **19.** 25% **21. a.** 89% **b.** No **23.** Yes **25.** Yes **33.** 5^2 **35.** 5×19 **37.** 5^3 **39.** 2×3 **41.** $2^3 \times 11$ **43.** $2^3 \times 3^2$

SELECTED ANSWERS

695

10-9 Try It

a. 20% **b.** 70%

10-9 Exercises & Applications

1. 50% **3.** 40% **5.** 25% **7.** 70% **9.** 33% **11.** 25% **13.** 10% **15.** 50% **17.** 75% **19.** 60% **21.** 1% **23.** 7% **25.** C **27.** 33% **29.** $\frac{7}{200}$ **31.** 66% are not **37.** 6 **39.** 12 **41.** 10 **43.** 30 **45.** 42 **47.** 6

10-10 Try It

a. $\frac{83}{100}$; 0.83 **b.** $\frac{7}{100}$; 0.07 **c.** 37.5%

10-10 Exercises & Applications

1. 0.37 **3.** 1.0 **5.** 0.1 **7.** 2.34 **9.** 0.673 **11.** 0.8887 **13.** $\frac{14}{25}$ **15.** $\frac{3}{4}$ **17.** $1\frac{1}{2}$ **19.** $\frac{89}{100}$ **21.** $\frac{9}{10}$ **23.** $2\frac{17}{50}$ **25.** 84% **27.** 4% **29.** 110% **31.** 85% **33.** 53% **35.** 30% **37.** 56% **39.** 48% **41.** 75% **43.** 67.5% **45.** 33.3% **47.** 38% **49.** 40%, $\frac{2}{5}$, 0.4 **51.** 50%, $\frac{4}{8}$, 0.5 **53.** $66.\overline{6}$% **55.** C **57.** $\frac{27}{200}$

10-11 Try It (Example 2)

a. 611 **b.** 133

10-11 Try It (Example 3)

a. 70 **b.** 50,000

10-11 Exercises & Applications

1. 50 **3.** 2 **5.** 22.1 **7.** 18.48 **9.** 104.94 **11.** 54.3 **13.** 22.44 **15.** 0.376 **17.** 15.2 **19.** ≈ $2.75 **21.** 6.12 **23.** 8.51 **25.** 250 **27.** 200 **29.** 88 **31.** 176 **33.** 20 or more **35.** $36,720 **37.** 249 **39.** $90.00 **41.** Probably Gloria **43.** About 62 points **47.** $\frac{1}{5}$ **49.** $\frac{1}{3}$ **51.** $\frac{4}{5}$ **53.** $\frac{3}{5}$ **55.** $\frac{1}{6}$ **57.** $\frac{2}{3}$ **59.** $1\frac{1}{5}$ **61.** $3\frac{1}{3}$ **63.** $2\frac{2}{7}$ **65.** $\frac{47}{4}$ **67.** $8\frac{1}{8}$ **69.** $\frac{119}{12}$

Section 10C Review

1. a. 3:4 **b.** $\frac{3}{4}$; 0.75 lettuce/carrot **c.** ≈ 57.14% **3.** Yes **5.** Yes **7.** 4 **9.** 10 **11.** 1200 **13.** *A* and *C* = 0.2 in.; *B* = 0.3 in. **15.** 28.86 **17.** 17.52 **19.** Possible answers: **a.** 85% **b.** 60% **21.** 95%; 60%

Chapter 10 Summary & Review

1. 6:11, 6 to 11, $\frac{6}{11}$ **2.** $\frac{3}{4}$ **3. a.** 10 to 1 **b.** 1 to 10 **c.** 5 to 1 **d.** 2 to 1 **4.** 3 to 4; 3 to 7 **5.** A **6.** B **7.** No **8.** 15 **9.** $4.32 **10.** Possible answer: The ratios of all the matching sides are equal. The angle measures are equal. **11.** $\frac{35}{100}$, $\frac{7}{20}$, 0.35 **12.** $\frac{20}{100}$, $\frac{1}{5}$, 0.2 **13.** $\frac{8}{100}$, $\frac{2}{25}$, 0.08 **14.** $\frac{75}{100}$, $\frac{3}{4}$, 0.75 **15.** ≈ 4,680,998 people **16.** Possible answer: $\frac{6}{4}$, $\frac{12}{8}$, $\frac{18}{12}$, $\frac{24}{16}$ **17.** $\frac{1.5 \text{ min}}{1 \text{ mi}}$

Cumulative Review Chapters 1–10

1. D **2.** B **3.** A **4.** C **5.** C **6.** B **7.** D **8.** A **9.** B **10.** C **11.** A **12.** D **13.** C **14.** A

Chapter 11

11-1 Exercises & Applications

1. Triangles and squares or rectangles **3.** Squares or rectangles **5.** Sphere **7.** Triangular prism; 6 vertices, 9 edges, 5 faces **9.** Cylinder **11.** Cone **17.** Rectangular prisms **19.** Spheres **25.** No; No; No **27.** 100 to 10 **29.** 2.5 **31.** 0.75 **33.** $0.8\overline{3}$

11-2 Try It

a. 6 faces: All rectangles **b.** 272 units^2

11-2 Exercises & Applications

1. 12 units^2 **3.** 18 units^2 **5.** 24 cm^2; Cube or rectangular prism **7.** 60 units^2; Triangular prism **9.** 6 faces: All rectangles; 310 ft^2 **13.** 5 faces: 2 triangles, 3 rectangles; 112.4 in^2 **15.** D **19.** Sometimes; No Possible answers for 21–25: **21.** 3:12, 2:8 **23.** 14 to 18, 21 to 27 **25.** 6:16, 9:24 **27.** $\frac{1}{6}$, $\frac{5}{6}$, 6.7 **29.** $\frac{1}{3}$, $\frac{3}{3}$, 3.3

11-3 Try It

a. 358 units^2 **b.** 96 units^2 **c.** 380 units^2

11-3 Exercises & Applications

1. 6 cm^2 **3.** 96 m^2 **5.** 48 ft^2 **7.** 268 units^2 **9.** 34.56 mm^2 **11.** 109.8 cm^2 **13.** 13.5 cm^2 **15.** C **17.** 1128 in^2 **19.** Yes **21.** No **23.** $\frac{1}{6}$ **25.** $\frac{13}{28}$ **27.** $\frac{10}{63}$

11-4 Exercises & Applications

1. 15.7 cm **3.** 6.28 ft **5.** 61.23 m^2 **7.** 17.27 in^2 **9.** 150.72 ft^2 **11.** 747.32 units^2 **13.** 266.9 units^2 **15. a.** 42.39 in^2 **b.** 56.52 in^2 **17.** C **19.** 37.68 in^2 **21.** No **23.** No **25.** No **27.** Yes **29.** No **31.** 124 **33.** 18.72 **35.** 13.5 **37.** 18.48

Section 11A Review

1. Sphere **3.** Triangular prism; 6 vertices, 9 edges, 5 faces **5.** Cube or rectangular prism; 8 vertices, 12 edges, 6 faces **9.** 54 ft^2 **11.** 8800 cm^2

11-5 Try It

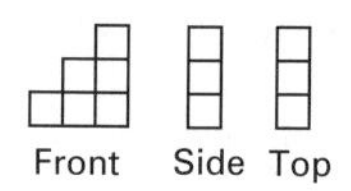

11-5 Exercises & Applications

1. 5 **3.** 12 **13.** 36 **15. a.** 7 **b.** 5.1 cm **c.** 6.8 cm **17. a.** No **b.** No **21.** $f = 48$ **23.** $r = 3$ **25.** 156% **27.** 55% **29.** 28% **31.** $\frac{67}{100}$ **33.** $2\frac{1}{2}$ **35.** $\frac{1}{100}$

11-6 Try It

a. 8 units^3 **b.** 48 units^3 **c.** 16 units^3 **d.** 225 units^3

SELECTED ANSWERS

696

11-6 Exercises & Applications

1. 10 units^3 **3.** 21 units^3 **5.** 360 units^3 **7.** 64 units^3 **9.** 60 units^3 **11.** 60 **13.** Yes **15.** 4 ways **17.** 3 mi per min **19.** 5 bananas per dollar **21.** $0.31\overline{6}$ m per sec **23.** 4.5 worms per in^2 **25.** About 20% **27.** About 20%

11-7 Try It

a. 105 in^2 **b.** 18 in.

11-7 Exercises & Applications

1. 125 in^3 **3.** 343 ft^3 **5.** 72 yd^3 **7.** 910 m^3 **9.** 480 units^3 **11.** 74.088 in^3 **13.** 2907 m^3 **15.** B **17.** About 12 inches deep **19.** $A = 32$ ft, $B = 64$ ft **21.** $33.\overline{3}$% **23.** 40%

Section 11B Review

1. Rectangular prism; 8 vertices, 12 edges, 6 faces **3.** Triangular prism; 6 vertices, 9 edges, 5 faces **5.** \$16.39

7.

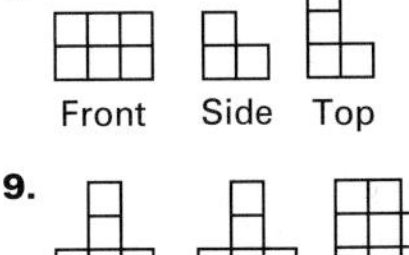

9.

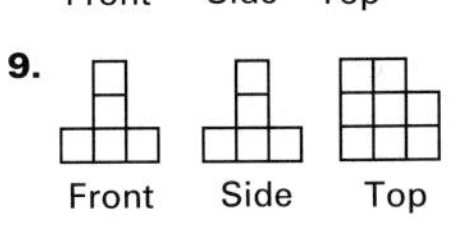

Chapter 11 Summary & Review

1. Triangular prism; 5 faces, 9 edges, 6 vertices. **2.** Sphere **3.** Rectangular pyramid; 5 faces, 8 edges, 5 vertices. **4.** 310 in^2 **5.** 340 units^2 **6.** 80.07 mm^2

7.

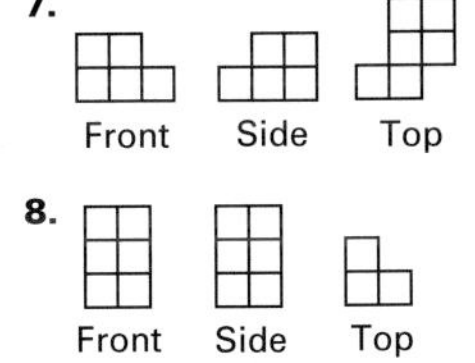

8.

Front Side Top

9. 80 units^3 **10.** 240 cm^3 **11.** 0.36 units^3 **12.** 477.28 in^2

Chapter 12

12-1 Try It

a. i. $\frac{3}{8}$ **ii.** 0 **b. i.** $\frac{1}{2}$ **ii.** $\frac{3}{5}$

12-1 Exercises & Applications

1. 2 **3.** 6 **5.** $\frac{1}{10}$ **7.** $\frac{1}{10}$ **9.** 0 **11.** $\frac{1}{2}$ **13.** $\frac{1}{6}$ **15.** $\frac{5}{6}$ **17.** $\frac{1}{6}$ **19.** $\frac{1}{3}$ **21.** Both are $\frac{1}{8}$ **23.** $\frac{1}{5}$ **25.** Will occur **27.** $\frac{9}{32}$ **29.** No; No **33.** Rectangular prism **35.** Cylinder **37.** 31.74 cm^2 **39.** 708 ft^2

12-2 Try It

a. $\frac{13}{61}$ **b.** $\frac{51}{61}$

12-2 Exercises & Applications

1. Yes **3.** No **5.** 3 **7.** $\frac{17}{20}$ **9.** 67 **11.** 16 **13.** May; $\frac{181}{826} \approx 0.22$ **15.** Yes **17.** The numbers are considerably above average. **19.** First figure **21.** 482.8 in^2

12-3 Try It

50%

12-3 Exercises & Applications

1. 9 square units **3.** 30% **5.** 25% **7.** 37.5% **9.** 50% **11.** A **21.** 18 units^3 **23.** 16 units^3

Section 12A Review

1. $\frac{1}{6}$ **3.** 0 **5.** $\frac{5}{6}$ **7.** $\frac{5}{8}$ **9.** 1 **11.** C **13.** 1000 **15.** B

12-4 Try It

a. Possibilities are: chocolate, hot fudge; chocolate, butterscotch; vanilla, hot fudge; vanilla butterscotch; mint, hot fudge; mint, butterscotch. **b.** 16

12-4 Exercises & Applications

1. 12 outcomes **5.** D **7. a.** 6 **b.** $\frac{1}{3}$ **9.** 45,697,600 **13.** 12; 12 **15.** 24 in^2 **17.** $\frac{3}{10}$ **19.** $\frac{1}{5}$ **21.** $\frac{2}{5}$

12-5 Try It

$\frac{1}{3}$

12-5 Exercises & Applications

1. a. 6 **b.** 216 **c.** 1 **d.** 1 **e.** $\frac{1}{216}$ **3.** $\frac{1}{9}$ **5.** $\frac{4}{27}$ **7.** $\frac{1}{27}$ **9.** About $\frac{1}{32}$ **11.** $\frac{1}{16}$ **13.** $P(\text{same}) = \frac{1}{6}$; $P(\text{different}) = \frac{5}{6}$ **15.** Winning both the 50-yard dash and the hurdles. **17.** $\frac{5}{51}$ **21.** #2

12-6 Try It

a. No; If Player A always chooses 1, Player A will always win. If the numbers are chosen at random, Player B has a greater chance of winning. **b.** Yes

12-6 Exercises & Applications

1. b. $\frac{13}{18}$ **c.** $\frac{5}{18}$ **d.** No; Player A has a greater chance of winning. **3.** Fair **5.** Unfair; Edna **7.** Yes; He got each number about the same amount of times. **9.** Unfair

Section 12B Review

1. a. 8 **b.** $\frac{1}{8}$ **3.** $\frac{1}{16}$ **5. a.** 42,875 **b.** $\frac{1}{42{,}875}$ **7.** No; $P(\text{A win}) = \frac{3}{8}$, $P(\text{B win}) = \frac{5}{8}$

Chapter 12 Summary & Review

1. About $\frac{1}{4}$ **2.** It is likely to occur. **3.** $\frac{3}{7}$ **4.** 16 **5.** About $\frac{1}{4}$ **6.** 24 outfits **7.** 180 **8.** 8 **9.** $\frac{1}{3}$ **10.** $\frac{1}{36}$ **11.** $\frac{1}{16}$ **12.** Yes **13.** No

Cumulative Review Chapters 1–12

1. C **2.** B **3.** D **4.** A **5.** A **6.** D **7.** C **8.** D **9.** B **10.** B **11.** C **12.** B **13.** A **14.** A

SELECTED ANSWERS

697

Photographs

Cover/Spine: Uniphoto Picture Agency, Inc.

Front Matter **iii** GHP Studio* **iii (background)** John Banagan/The Image Bank **v-xvi T** GHP Studio* **xviii L** Cheryl Fenton* **xviii R** George Hunter/Tony Stone Images **xix T** Parker/Boon Productions and Dorey Sparre Photography* **xix B** Ken Karp,* Dennis Geaney* & Parker/Boon Productions and Dorey Sparre Photography* **xxii** Jean-Marc Giboux/Liaison International **xxiii** Pictor/Uniphoto Picture Agency **xxiv** Ken Karp* **xxv** Fridmar Damm/Leo de Wys Inc. **xxvi** John Lund/Tony Stone Images **xxvii** Robie Price* **xxviii** Mark C. Burnett/Stock, Boston

Chapter 1 **2–3 (background)** Ralph Mercer/Tony Stone Images **2 TR (frame)** John Michael/International Stock Photo **2 TR (inset)** Christopher Liu/China Stock **2 BR** NASA/Stock, Boston **2 BL** Robie Price* **3** ZEFA/The Stock Market **4 B** Soames Summerhays/Photo Researchers **4 T** Ed R. Degginger/Photo Researchers **5** Robie Price* **6** Douglas Faulkner/Photo Researchers **8** Blake/Reuters/Corbis-Bettmann **10** Damien Lovegrove/SPL/Photo Researchers **11 L** Marc Chamberlain/Tony Stone Images **11 R** Geoffrey Nilsen Photography* **12** Jeff Rotman **14** W. Gregory Brown/Animals, Animals **15** Bob Daemmrich/Stock, Boston **16** Pete Saloutos/The Stock Market **17** David Hall/Photo Researchers **18 T** David Madison/Bruce Coleman Inc. **18 B** Dr. Nigel Smith/Earth Scenes **19 T** Paul Humann/Jeff Rotman Photography **19 B** Geoffrey Nilsen Photography* **20** Lee F. Snyder/Photo Researchers **21** Robie Price* **23 L** Joseph Nettis/Stock, Boston **23 R** Jon Feingersh/The Stock Market **24** Ron Chapple/FPG International **26 R** UPI/Corbis-Bettmann **26 L** Portrait by Ellis Sawyer/FPG International **28** from HERBLOCK: A CARTOONIST'S LIFE (Macmillan Publishing, 1993) **29** Owen Franken/Stock, Boston **31 BLC** Popperfoto/Archive Photos **31 BR** Ron Thomas/Reuters/Corbis-Bettmann **31 BRC** Mark Reinstein/FPG International **31 T** Worldsat International Inc./SPL/Photo Researchers **31 BL** FPG International **32** Robert Frerck/Tony Stone Images **33** Geoffrey Nilsen Photography* **34 R** Win McNamee/Reuters/Corbis-Bettmann **34 L** Jeffrey Sylvester/FPG International **35** AFP/Archive Photos **36 L** Dennis Geaney* **36 R** Parker/Boon Productions and Dorey Sparre Photography* **37** Corbis-Bettmann **38** Archive Photos **39** Jon Feingersh/The Stock Market **40 B** © 89 Mug Shots/The Stock Market **40 T** Geoffrey Nilsen Photography* **41 T** Geoffrey Nilsen Photography* **41 B** Geoffrey Nilsen Photography* **41 (inset)** Mississippi Valley State University **42** Shelley Gazin/The Image Works **43** Bill Reitzel **45** Kevin Lamarque/Reuters/Corbis-Bettmann **46 TL** Berenguier & Jerrican/Photo Researchers **46 TR** Robie Price* **46 B** Geoffrey Nilsen Photography* **47** Paul Souders/Allsport **48 T** Dennis Geaney* **48 B** Al Bello/Allsport **49** Gail Shumway/FPG International **51** Tim DeFrisco/Allsport **52** Otto Rogge/The Stock Market **53** Robie Price* **54** Brad Mangin/Duomo **55 BL** National Baseball Hall of Fame © Topps **55 TL** Geoffrey Nilsen Photography* **55 TR** Geoffrey Nilsen Photography* **55 BR** Geoffrey Nilsen Photography* **56** Popperfoto/Archive Photos **57** Geoffrey Nilsen Photography* **61 T** Stewart L. Craig, Jr./Bruce Coleman Inc. **61 C** Robie Price* **61 B** Geoffrey Nilsen Photography*

Chapter 2 **62–63 (background)** Comstock **62 TL** Erich Lessing/Art Resource, NY **62 TR** David Frazier/Science Source/Photo Researchers **62 B** Cheryl Fenton* **63 T** Robert Fried/Stock, Boston **63 B** Cheryl Fenton* **64 T** Mark Gamba/The Stock Market **64 B** John Terence Turner/FPG International **65 T** Rob Lewine/The Stock Market **65 B** NASA **66 T** Alan Carey/The Image Works **68** Frank Rossotto/The Stock Market **69 L** NASA/Science Source/Photo Researchers **69 R** NASA/Lunar & Planetary Inst. **70** Robert Houser/Comstock **72 L** Lunar & Planetary Inst. **72 R** NASA/ESA/Tom Stack & Associates **73** Robie Price* **74** Tim Flach/Tony Stone Images **75** Lunar & Planetary Institute **77** Sovfoto/Eastfoto **78** Gabe Palmer/Mugshots/The Stock Market **79 T** NASA/JPL/TSADO/Tom Stack & Associates **79 B** NASA **80 L** Parker/Boon Productions and Dorey Sparre Photography* **80 R** Dennis Geaney* **81** NASA/JPL/TSADO/Tom Stack & Associates **82** NIBSC/SPL/Photo Researchers **82 (inset)** CNRI/SPL/Photo Researchers **83 T** Rob Lewine/The Stock Market **83 B** NASA **84** NASA/Mark Marten/Photo Researchers **86 L** Mike Malyszko/FPG International **87** Underwood Collection/Corbis-Bettmann **88** Geoffrey Nilsen Photography* **89** Carl Yarbrough/Uniphoto Picture Agency **90 L** Billy Hustace/Tony Stone Images **90 R** Geoffrey Nilsen Photography* **93** Geoffrey Nilsen Photography* **94 L** John Coletti/Tony Stone Images **94 R** Geoffrey Nilsen Photography* **95** Bob Daemmrich/The Image Works **96 R** Fujifotos **97 T** Geoffrey Nilsen Photography* **97 C** Robie Price* **98 L** Lawrence Migdale/Stock, Boston **98 R** Hewlett Packard **100** Robie Price* **101** Geoffrey Nilsen Photography* **102 TL** Stephen Frisch/Stock, Boston **102 TR** Robie Price* **102 B** Gregory Sams/SPL/Photo Researchers **104 L** Ken Karp* **104 R** Parker/Boon Productions and Dorey Sparre Photography* **105** Anne Dowie* **106** IFA-Bildesteam/Uniphoto Picture Agency **107 L** Geoffrey Nilsen Photography* **108** Anne Dowie* **109** Barry E. Parker/Bruce Coleman Inc. **110 L** Jon Feingersh/Stock, Boston **110 R** Steve Starr/Stock, Boston **113** Martin Rogers/Stock, Boston **114 L** Anne Dowie* **114 R** Robie Price* **115** Topham/The Image Works **116** Eric A. Wessman/Stock, Boston **117** ©1986 Carmen Lomas Garza, photo by Wolfgang Dietze **118** Jeff Lepore/Photo Researchers **119** Mark Gamba/The Stock Market **120** Navaswan/FPG International **122** Lawrence Migdale/Photo Researchers **123** Brian Parker/Tom Stack & Associates **125** Monteath C./Hedgehog House N. Zeal./Explorer/Photo Researchers **127** Barry E. Parker/Bruce Coleman Inc. **127 TL** Peter David/Photo Researchers **127 BL** Richard Pasley/Stock, Boston **128** Thomas Kitchin/Tom Stack & Associates **129** Geoffrey Nilsen Photography*

Chapter 3 **134–135 (background)** Superstock **134 L** Steven E. Sutton/Duomo **134 TR** J. P. Courau/DDB Stock Photo **134 BR** Stuart Cohen/Comstock **135 T** Cheryl Fenton* **135 B** Kimimasa Mayama/UPI/Corbis-Bettmann **136 T** Anne Dowie* **136 B** Jane Burton/Bruce Coleman Inc. **137** Robie Price* **137 (insets)** Stephen Cooper/Tony Stone Images **138** Doug Wechsler/Earth Scenes **139** G. C. Kelley/Photo Researchers **140** Andrew Syred/SPL/Photo Researchers **141** Popperfoto/Archive Photos **142 L** Gabe Palmer/Mugshots/The Stock Market **142 R** Robie Price* **143 L** Ray Coleman/Photo Researchers **143 R** John Fennell/Bruce Coleman Inc. **144 T** Geoffrey Nilsen Photography* **144 C** Geoffrey Nilsen Photography* **144 B** Rod Planck/Tony Stone Images **145 L** Geoffrey Nilsen Photography* **145 R** Parker/Boon Productions and Dorey Sparre Photography* **146 L** Gilbert S. Grant/Photo Researchers **146 R** John Gerlach/Animals, Animals **148** David Madison **149** Jan C. Taylor/Bruce Coleman Inc. **150 L** Ken Karp* **150 R** Dennis Geaney* **151 L** James H. Carmichael, Jr. /Photo Researchers **151 R** L. West /National Audubon Society/Photo Researchers **152** Bob Llewellyn/Uniphoto Picture Agency **153** ATC Productions 1993/The Stock Market **155 T** Astrid & Hanns-Frieder Michler/SPL/Photo Researchers **155 B** Kim Taylor/Bruce Coleman Inc. **156** Geoffrey Nilsen Photography* **157 L** James Carmichael/Bruce Coleman Inc. **157 R** Robie Price* **158 TL** Buddy Mays/FPG International **158 TR** Buddy Mays/FPG International **158 B** David Parker/SPL/Photo Researchers **159** Robie Price* **160** Martin Rogers/Tony Stone Images **161** Geoffrey Nilsen Photography* **162** Geoffrey Nilsen Photography* **163** Robie Price* **164** Jeff Albertson/Stock, Boston **165** Anne Dowie* **166 L** Ken Karp* **166 R** Dennis Geaney* **167** Jeff Greenberg/The Image Works **168 T** Anne Dowie* **169** Robie Price* **170** Robie Price* **171** Robie Price* **172 T** Geoffrey Nilsen Photography* **172 B** Robie Price* **173** Robie Price* **174** Geoffrey Nilsen Photography* **175** Western History Department/Denver Public Library **176** Terry Qing/FPG International **177** Antman Archive/The Image Works **178** Corbis-Bettmann **180** Ron Cronin **181** Bill Stormont/The Stock Market **184 T** Geoffrey Nilsen Photography* **184 B** Robie Price* **185** Geoffrey Nilsen Photography* **187** Jon Feingersh/The Stock Market **188** McLaughlin Historical File 1/FPG International **189** Doug Pensinger/Allsport **190** Laima Driskis/Stock, Boston **192 L** Parker/Boon Productions and Dorey Sparre Photography* **192 R** Ken Karp* **194** Western History Department/Denver Public Library **195** Shaw McCutcheon/Bruce Coleman Inc. **196** Western History Department/Denver Public Library **197** Richard Price/FPG International **199** Western History Department/Denver Public Library **200** Alan Carey/The Image Works **201** Geoffrey Nilsen Photography* **205 T** Uniphoto Picture Agency **205 CL** Geoffrey Nilsen Photography* **205 TCR** Roy Morsch/The Stock Market **205 BL** Bob Daemmrich/Stock, Boston **205 BCR** Lawrence Migdale/Stock, Boston

Chapter 4 **206–207 (background)** Marc Romanelli/The Image Bank **206 T** Matthew Borkoski/Stock, Boston **206 L** Louis S. Glanzman/National Geographic Image Collection **206 B** Anne Dowie* **207 TL** Michael Macor/San Francisco Chronicle **207 TR** Richard Martin/Agency Vandystadt/Allsport **207 BL** Prim & Ray Manley/Superstock **207 BR** NASA **208 T** Jack Zehrt/FPG International **208 (background)** NASA/SPL/Photo Researchers **208 BL** NASA **208 BC** NASA/The Image Works **208 BR** Owen Franken/Stock, Boston **209** John Elk/Stock, Boston **210** Robie Price* **211** Michael Thompson/Comstock **212 L** Parker/Boon Productions and Dorey Sparre Photography* **212 R** Dennis Geaney* **213** Robie Price* **214** Jerry Wachter/Photo Researchers **215** Donald Carroll/The Image Bank **216** Chuck Place/The Image Bank **217** Andy Snyder/San Francisco Zoo **218 T** Robie Price* **218 C** Robie Price* **218 B** Steve Dunwell/The Image Bank

219 T Telegraph Colour Library/FPG International **219 B** Norman O. Tomalin/Bruce Coleman Inc. **220** Robie Price* **221** Geoffrey Nilsen Photography* **222** Robie Price* **223 T** Anne Dowie* **223 B** Robie Price* **224** Susan Kuklin/Photo Researchers **225 CL** Yellow Dog Prods./The Image Bank **225 R** John Elk/Stock, Boston **225 BL** Ted Russell/The Image Bank **227 (foregound)** Cheryl Fenton* **227** Kunio Owaki/The Stock Market **228** Julie Houck/Stock, Boston **230** Robie Price **231** NMAA, Smithsonian Institution/Art Resource, NY **233** Comstock **236** Geoffrey Nilsen Photography* **237** Anne Dowie* **239 L** Ken Karp* **239 R** Ken Karp* **241** Robie Price* **243 (foreground)** Cheryl Fenton* **243** Kunio Owaki/The Stock Market **246** Pictor/Uniphoto Picture Agency **247 BL** Robie Price* **247 BR** Robie Price* **248 TR** Arthur Tilley/FPG International **248 BL** Cheryl Fenton* **248 BR** David Sams/Stock, Boston **249 R** FPG International **250** Walter Iooss/The Image Bank **251 BL** Cheryl Fenton* **251 BR** Cheryl Fenton* **252 L** Georg Gerster/Comstock **253** James Carmichael/The Image Bank **254** James Blank/The Stock Market **256 L** Dennis Geaney* **256 R** Parker/Boon Productions and Dorey Sparre Photography* **257 TL** Mark Antman/The Image Works **257 TLC** Cheryl Fenton* **257 TRC** Cheryl Fenton* **257 TR** Andrea Pistolesi/The Image Bank **257 BL** Cheryl Fenton* **257 BR** Cheryl Fenton* **259 TL** Corbis-Bettmann **259 CL** Corbis-Bettmann **261** Geoffrey Nilsen Photography*

Chapter 5 **266–267 (background)** Pierre-Yves Goavec/The Image Bank **266 L** Geoffrey Nilsen Photography* **266 R** Kevin Schafer/Tony Stone Images **267 T** Cheryl Fenton* **267 B** Ellen Beach/Bruce Coleman Inc. **268** Robie Price* **69** NASA **270** Dennis O'Clair/Tony Stone Images **272** Peggy and Ronald Barnett/The Stock Market **274 T** FPG International **274 BL** George Hunter/Tony Stone Images **274 BR** ET Archive/Superstock **275** RLC Trust/Superstock **277 L** Ken Karp* **277 R** Parker/Boon Productions and Dorey Sparre Photography* **279** M. Fischer/Art Resource, NY **280** Pekka Parviainen/SPL/Photo Researchers **281** The Cartoon Bank, Inc. **282 T** Pat Lanza Field/Bruce Coleman Inc. **282 B** Superstock **283** Robie Price* **284** Anne Dowie* **285** NASA **286** Photri/The Stock Market **287** Cheryl Fenton* **288** Robie Price* **289** Cheryl Fenton* **290** Cheryl Fenton* **292** Geoffrey Nilsen Photography* **293** Anne Dowie* **296** Cheryl Fenton* **297** AKG/Superstock **298** Anne Dowie* **300** Robie Price* **301** Anne Dowie* **302** Lee Snider/The Image Works **303** Geoffrey Nilsen Photography* **304 B** Superstock **304 T** M. Greenlar/The Image Works **305** Cheryl Fenton* **308 T** Anne Dowie* **308 B** Cheryl Fenton* **309** Cheryl Fenton* **310** Parker/Boon Productions and Dorey Sparre Photography* **312 L** V. Rouse/Southern Card & Novelty, Inc. **312 R** Rindy Nyberg/Southern Card & Novelty, Inc. **313** Cheryl Fenton* **314** Robie Price* **315** Geoffrey Nilsen Photography* **319** Larry Gatz/The Image Bank

Chapter 6 **320–321 (background)** John Elk/Stock, Boston **320 L** Snowdon/Hoyer/Focus/Woodfin Camp & Associates **320 TR** Robie Price* **320 BR** Jane Grushow/Grant Heilman Photography **321 T** Townsend P. Dickinson/Comstock **321 B** Tom Till/Tony Stone Images **322 T** Hans Pfletschinger/Peter Arnold, Inc. **322 BL** Myron J. Dorf/The Stock Market **322 BR** Cheryl Fenton* **324** Geoffrey Nilsen Photography* **325** AP/Wide World Photos **327** Pictos/Uniphoto Picture Agency **328** Anne Dowie* **329** Robie Price* **330** Anne Dowie* **331** David Scharf **332** Geoffrey Nilsen Photography* **333** Texas Instruments **334** Dave Watts/Tom Stack & Associates **335 L** SIU/Peter Arnold, Inc. **335 R** Robie Price* **337** Jay Freis/The Image Bank **338** Larry Mulvehill/Photo Researchers **340** Michael Tamborrino/FPG International **341** Tom Dietrich/Tony Stone Images **342** Kevin Horan/Tony Stone Images **343** Owen Franken/Stock, Boston **344** Tom Till/DRK Photo **346** Peter Beck/The Stock Market **347** Library of Congress/Superstock **348 L** Thomas Dimock/The Stock Market **348** R Lori Adamski Peek/Tony Stone Images **349** MacTavish/Comstock **350** Robie Price* **351 L** Bob Burch/Bruce Coleman Inc. **351 R** Culver Pictures **352** Parker/Boon Productions and Dorey Sparre Photography* **353** Anne Dowie* **355** Tom Dietrich/Tony Stone Images **356** UPI/Corbis-Bettmann **357** Geoffrey Nilsen Photography*

Chapter 7 **362–363 (background)** Geoffrey Nilsen Photography* **362 TL** Dimitri Messinis/Agence France/Corbis-Bettmann **362 TR** Michele Burgess/The Stock Market **362 BL** Bill Bachmann/The Image Works **362 BR** Ken Cole/Earth Scenes **363 T** David Woodfall/Tony Stone Images **363 BL** Culver Pictures **363 BR** Draeger/Culver Pictures **364** Bruce M. Herman/Photo Researchers **365** Lawrence Migdale/Stock, Boston **365 (background)** Jeff Schultz/AlaskaStock **366** Grant Heilman Photography **367** R. Dahlquist/Superstock **368** George F. Godfrey/Earth Scenes **369 L** Archive Photos **369 R** Kunio Owaki/The Stock Market **370** M. Timothy O'Keefe/Bruce Coleman Inc. **371** Robert A. Tyrrell **372 L** Dennis Geaney* **372 R** Ken Karp* **373** Geoffrey Nilsen Photography* **374 L** Renee Stockdale/Animals, Animals **374 R** Karl & Kay Ammann/Bruce Coleman Inc. **375** David Hundley/The Stock Market **376** James Carmichael/Bruce Coleman Inc. **377** James H. Robinson/Photo Researchers **378** Robie Price* **379** Lawrence Migdale/Stock, Boston **379 (background)** Jeff Schultz/AlaskaStock **380** Akos Szilvasi/Stock, Boston **381** Steve Liss/People Weekly **381 (inset)** Stanley Tretick/People Weekly **382** Dean Siracusa/FPG International **383** Larry Brownstein/Rainbow **384** Parker/Boon Productions and Dorey Sparre Photography* **385** Kwok Leung Paul Lau/Liaison International **386** Robie Price* **387** John Eastcott/The Image Works **388 L** Culver Pictures **388 R** Simon Bruty/Allsport **389** Robie Price* **390** Geoffrey Nilsen Photography* **391** Texas Instruments **392** Stephen Frisch/Stock, Boston **393** Cheryl Fenton* **395** Geoffrey Nilsen Photography* **396** Bob Daemmrich/Stock, Boston **397 R** Steve Liss/People Weekly **397 L** The MIT Museum **398** Jack Daniels/Tony Stone Images **399** Geoffrey Nilsen Photography **403 TL** Cheryl Fenton* **403 TR** Bruce Wilson/Tony Stone Images **403 BL** Henry Ausloos/Animals, Animals **403 BR** David Madison

Chapter 8 **404–405 (background)** Bruce Hands/Comstock **404 T** Derek Berwin/The Image Bank **404 C** Art Resource, NY **404 B** Corbis-Bettmann **405 T** John David Fleck/Liaison International **405 BL** William Johnson/Stock, Boston **405 BR** Kim Taylor/Bruce Coleman Inc. **406 T** Cheryl Fenton* **406 BL** Robie Price* **406 BC** Robie Price* **406 BR** Robie Price* **407** Cheryl Fenton* **408** Steven H. Begleiter/Uniphoto Picture Agency **409** Cheryl Fenton* **410** Cheryl Fenton* **411** Bob Llewellyn/Uniphoto Picture Agency **412 L** Bob Daemmrich/The Image Works **412 R** Cheryl Fenton* **416** Ilene Perlman/Stock, Boston **418 T** Pascal Rondeau/Allsport USA **418 C** Ken Karp* **418 B** Parker/Boon Productions and Dorey Sparre Photography* **419** Cheryl Fenton* **421** Cheryl Fenton* **423** Cheryl Fenton* **424** Bard Wrisley/Liaison International **425** Cheryl Fenton* **427** Cheryl Fenton* **428** Pierre Boulat/Woodfin Camp & Associates **430** Cheryl Fenton* **431** Jenny Thomas* **432** Comstock **433** Cheryl Fenton* **434 L** Eduardo Garcia/FPG International **434 CL** Peter Menzel/Stock, Boston **434 CR** Archive Photos **434 R** S. Vidler/Superstock. **435 T** Dave B. Fleetham/Tom Stack & Associates **435 BL** Cheryl Fenton* **435 BC** Cheryl Fenton* **435 BR** Cheryl Fenton* **436** Bill Gallery/Stock, Boston **438** Archive Photos **441** Cheryl Fenton* **443** Adam Woolfitt/Woodfin Camp & Associates **444** Art Wolfe/Tony Stone Images **445** ©1994, Asian Art Museum of San Francisco **446 TL** Chris Arend/Tony Stone Images **446 TLC** Barry L. Runk/Grant Heilman Photography **446 TCR** Carl Zeiss/Bruce Coleman Inc. **446 TR** Noble Stock/International Stock Photo **446 B** Robert Fried/Stock, Boston **447** Wolfgang Kaehler/Liaison International **448** Bill Lyons/Liaison International **450 T** Richard Pasley/Liaison International **450 C** Parker/Boon Productions and Dorey Sparre Photography* **450 B** Parker/Boon Productions and Dorey Sparre Photography* **451** ©1994, Asian Art Museum of San Francisco **452** Will & Deni McIntyre/Tony Stone Images **453** Robie Price* **454** Barry Brukoff/Woodfin Camp & Associates **455 T** Sylvain Grandadam/Tony Stone Images **455 CL** A.K.G. Berlin/Superstock **455 CC** Cheryl Fenton* **455 CR** Wolfgang Kaehler/Liaison International **455 B** Bruce Hands/Comstock **456 T** Arvind Garg/Liaison International **456 B** Oddo & Sinibaldi/The Stock Market **457** Adam Woolfitt/Woodfin Camp & Associates **459** Geoffrey Nilsen Photography **462** Henryk T. Kaiser/Uniphoto Picture Agency

Chapter 9 **464–465 (background)** Gary & Vivian Chapman/The Image Bank **464 T** Bonnie Schiffman **464 B** Joe McBride/Tony Stone Images **465 T** John Lawrence/Tony Stone Images **465 B** Robie Price* **466** Cheryl Fenton* **467** Cheryl Fenton* **468 TL** James Elness/Comstock **468 TC** Parker/Boon Productions and Dorey Sparre Photography* **468 TR** Ken Karp* **468 BL** Parker/Boon Productions and Dorey Sparre Photography* **468 BC** Parker/Boon Productions and Dorey Sparre Photography* **468 BR** Dennis Geaney* **469 L** Charles Thatcher/Tony Stone Images **469 R** Glyn Kirk/Tony Stone Images **470** Chris & Donna McLaughlin/The Stock Market **471** Telegraph Colour Library/FPG International **472** Lambert/Archive Photos **473** Michael Collier/Stock, Boston **474** Ken Chernus/FPG International **475** Ken Karp* **476** Bob Daemmrich/The Image Works **477** Lawrence Migdale/Tony Stone Images **478** Ken Karp* **479** Comstock **481** John Eastcott-Yva Momatiuk/Stock, Boston **484** Don Smetzer/Tony Stone Images **485 L** Laurance B. Aluppy/FPG International **485 R** Cheryl Fenton* **487** Cheryl Fenton* **488** Bruce Silverstein/FPG International **493** Telegraph Colour Library/FPG International **494** Robert DiGiacomo/Comstock **496** Robie Price* **498** Ted Horowitz/The Stock Market

500 Parker/Boon Productions and Dorey Sparre Photography* **501** Ken Karp* **502** Jeffry Myers/Stock, Boston **503** Cheryl Fenton* **505** Geoffrey Nilsen Photography* **509 L** Andrew Unangst/The Image Bank **509 R** Gary S. Chapman/The Image Bank

Chapter 10 **510–511 (background)** Harald Sund/The Image Bank **510 TL** Steve Vidler/Superstock **510 C** Superstock **510 B** Chris Arend/AlaskaStock **511 B** Superstock **511 T** Cheryl Fenton* **512 T** C. M. Fitch/Superstock **512 BL** Patricia J.Bruno/Positive Images **512 BR** Margaret Hensel/Positive Images **513** Superstock **514** Bill Bachmann/Stock, Boston **515 T** Cheryl Fenton* **515 B** Ken Karp* **516 T** Gary Irving/Tony Stone Images **516 B** Cheryl Fenton* **518** Ken Karp* **519** Robie Price* **520** Parker/Boon Productions and Dorey Sparre Photography* **522** Stan Osolinski/Tony Stone Images **523 TL** Ken Karp* **523 TR** Cary S.Wolinsky/Stock, Boston **523 B** Jack Daniels/Tony Stone Images **525** Kent Knudson/Stock, Boston **527** Superstock **528** Cheryl Fenton* **529** Scott Barrow/Superstock **530** Cary Wolinsky/Stock, Boston **531** Christian Michaels/FPG International **532** Jonathan Wright/Bruce Coleman Inc. **534 T** Liaison International **534 BL** Ken Karp* **534 BR** Rafael Macia/Photo Researchers **535** Russell D.Curtis/Photo Researchers **536 L** Mike Nazzaschi/Stock, Boston **536 R** S. L. Craig, Jr./ Bruce Coleman Inc. **537** Jack S. Grove/Tom Stack & Associates **538** Superstock **539** Paul Harris/Tony Stone Images **540** Dennis Geaney* **541** Robert Frerck/Tony Stone Images **542** Robie Price* **543** John Eastcott-Yva Momatiuk/Stock, Boston **545 L** Superstock **545 R** FPG International **547 L** Jerry Jacka Photography **547 CL** Jerry Jacka Photography **547 C** Ron Sanford/Tony Stone Images **547 CR** Chris Arend/AlaskaStock **547 R** Scott Barrow/Superstock **548** Jeff Gnass/The Stock Market **549 (background)** Art Wolfe/Tony Stone Images **549 T** Nancy Adams/Tom Stack & Associates **549 C** David M. Dennis/Tom Stack & Associates **549 BL** Roy Toft/Tom Stack & Associates **549 BR** Gregory G.Dimijian/Photo Researchers **550 L** Superstock **550 C** Ken Karp* **550 R** Ken Karp* **554** Spencer Grant/FPG International **555** Robie Price* **556 L** Fritz Prenzel/Animals, Animals **556 R** John Cancalosi/Stock, Boston **558** Superstock **559** Jeff Lepore/Photo Researchers **560 T** P. Curto/U.P./ Bruce Coleman Inc. **560 C** Parker/Boon Productions and Dorey Sparre Photography* **560 B** Parker/Boon Productions and Dorey Sparre Photography* **562** David Austen/Stock, Boston **563** Keith Wood/Tony Stone Images **564** Philippe Plailly/Eurelios/SPL/Photo Researchers **565** Ken Karp* **566 T** Cheryl Fenton* **566 B** Robert A. Tyrell **569 CR** Stuart Westmorland/Tony Stone Images **569 BL** Art Wolfe/Tony Stone Images **569 TR** Art Wolfe/ Tony Stone Images **569 BC** Rodolpho Machado/ Nexus/DDB Stock Photo **569 BR** Gail Shumway/ FPG International **571** Geoffrey Nilsen Photography*

Chapter 11 **576–577 (background)** Geoffrey Nilsen Photography* **576 TL** Mark Segal/Tony Stone Images **576 TR** Christie's Image, London/Superstock **576 BL** Geoffrey Nilsen Photography* **576 BR** Ken Karp* **577 T** Superstock **577 B** Sylvain Grandadam/Tony Stone Images **578 T** B. Cavedo/Superstock **578 B** Ken Karp* **579** Geoffrey Nilsen Photography* **580** Richard Pasley/Stock, Boston **581 L** Corbis-Bettmann **581 C** Cheryl Fenton* **581 R** C. G. Maxwell/National Audubon Society/Photo Researchers **583 L** Joseph Nettis/Stock, Boston **583 R** National Gallery of Art, photo by Philip A. Charles **584** John Blaustein/Liaison International **585** Geoffrey Nilsen Photography* **586** Cheryl Fenton* **587** Geoffrey Nilsen Photography* **588** Superstock **592** Alan Carey/The Image Works **593** Robie Price* **595 L** Ken Karp* **595 R** Dennis Geaney* **596** Geoffrey Nilsen Photography* **599 L** Cheryl Fenton* **599 R** Geoffrey Nilsen Photography* **601** Mike Severns/Tony Stone Images **602** Alfred Pasieka/SPL/Photo Researchers **606** Frank Siteman/Tony Stone Images **607** Jane Burton/Bruce Coleman Inc. **608** Cheryl Fenton* **610** Michael Fisher/Custom Medical Stock **611** Robie Price* **612** Parker/Boon Productions and Dorey Sparre Photography* **613** Jeff Hunter/The Image Bank **614** Jeff Rotman/Tony Stone Images **615 L** Jeffrey Sylvester/FPG International **615 R** Mike Severns/Tony Stone Images **617** Geoffrey Nilsen Photography* **621 T** Robie Price* **621 B** Cheryl Fenton*

Chapter 12 **622–623 (background)** Cheryl Fenton* **622 T** Ken Karp* **622 B** Cheryl Fenton* **623 T** Cheryl Fenton* **623 B** Ken Karp* **624 T** Cheryl Fenton* **624 B** Rafael Macia/Photo Researchers **625** Paul & Lindamarie Ambrose/FPG International **626** Chuck Keeler/Tony Stone Images **627** Ken Karp* **628** Cheryl Fenton* **629** ChinaStock **630 L** John Coletti/Stock, Boston **630 R** Ken Karp* **631** George B. Fry III* **632** Warren Bolster/Tony Stone Images **633** NASA/GSFC/Science Source/Photo Researchers **635** Philippe Brylak/Liaison International **636** Howard Bluestein/Photo Researchers **639** Paul & Lindamarie Ambrose/FPG International **640** Ralph H. Wetmore II/Tony Stone Images **641** Cheryl Fenton* **642** Louis Bencze/Tony Stone Images **644 L** Dennis Geaney* **644 R** Ken Karp* **645** Cheryl Fenton* **646 T** Bob Daemmrich/Stock, Boston **646 B** Robie Price* **647** Ken Karp* **649** Cheryl Fenton* **650** George B. Fry III* **651 L** Ken Karp* **651 R** Michael Stuckey/Comstock **654** Ken Karp* **655** Cheryl Fenton* **656** Robie Price* **657** Geoffrey Nilsen Photography* **659** Cheryl Fenton*

*Photographs provided expressly for Scott Foresman-Addison Wesley.

Illustrations

Jenny Ahrens: **407a, 409g, 410o, 412a, 419n** Christine Benjamin: **142b, 205a, 223b, 518b, 664b** Ken Bowser: **538c, 584a** Barbara Friedman: **160a, 191a** Cynthia Gamo: **118a** Joe Heiner Studio: all icons and borders Barbara Hoopes Ambler: **622b** Marlene Howerton: **345d** Dave Jonason: **597a** Jane McCreary: **515b, 517a** Patrick Merewether: **273a, 524a** Karen Minot: **319d, 285a** Andrew Muonio: **23c, 61e, 70a, 225a, 255c** Bill Pasini: **179d, 183d, 186a, 235l, 258d, 439a, 545i, 554e, 557b, 565b, 567a** Matt Perry: **421a, 532b, 545j, 545k** Precision Graphics: All illustrative artwork throughout: all generated electronically Bill Rieser: **284a, 292a, 297b, 301a, 319b, 591d** Rob Schuster: **9a, 22a, 22d, 24a, 29b, 42a, 44a, 66a, 76a, 96b, 116a, 120b, 148a, 168b, 195a, 198b, 238d, 241b, 244e, 260i, 278a, 291e, 299a, 320c, 320d, 349a, 354a, 357a, 366a, 372e, 379a, 379b, 380a, 385b, 386a, 429a, 441a, 465a, 470b, 480e, 484a, 485a, 508c, 514a, 519e, 521a, 527c, 552b, 582q,r,s, 589c, 590a, 597i, 621a, 633f, 649b, 652b** Bob Ting: **492a, 503a, 509b, 571a** Joe Van Der Bos: **73c, 240l, 243a, 258b** Tom Ward: **7a, 16b, 37a, 38a, 74a, 92a** Sarah Woodward: **323a** Rose Zgodzinski: **525m, 563a, 592a**

SCOPE AND SEQUENCE

CONTENTS

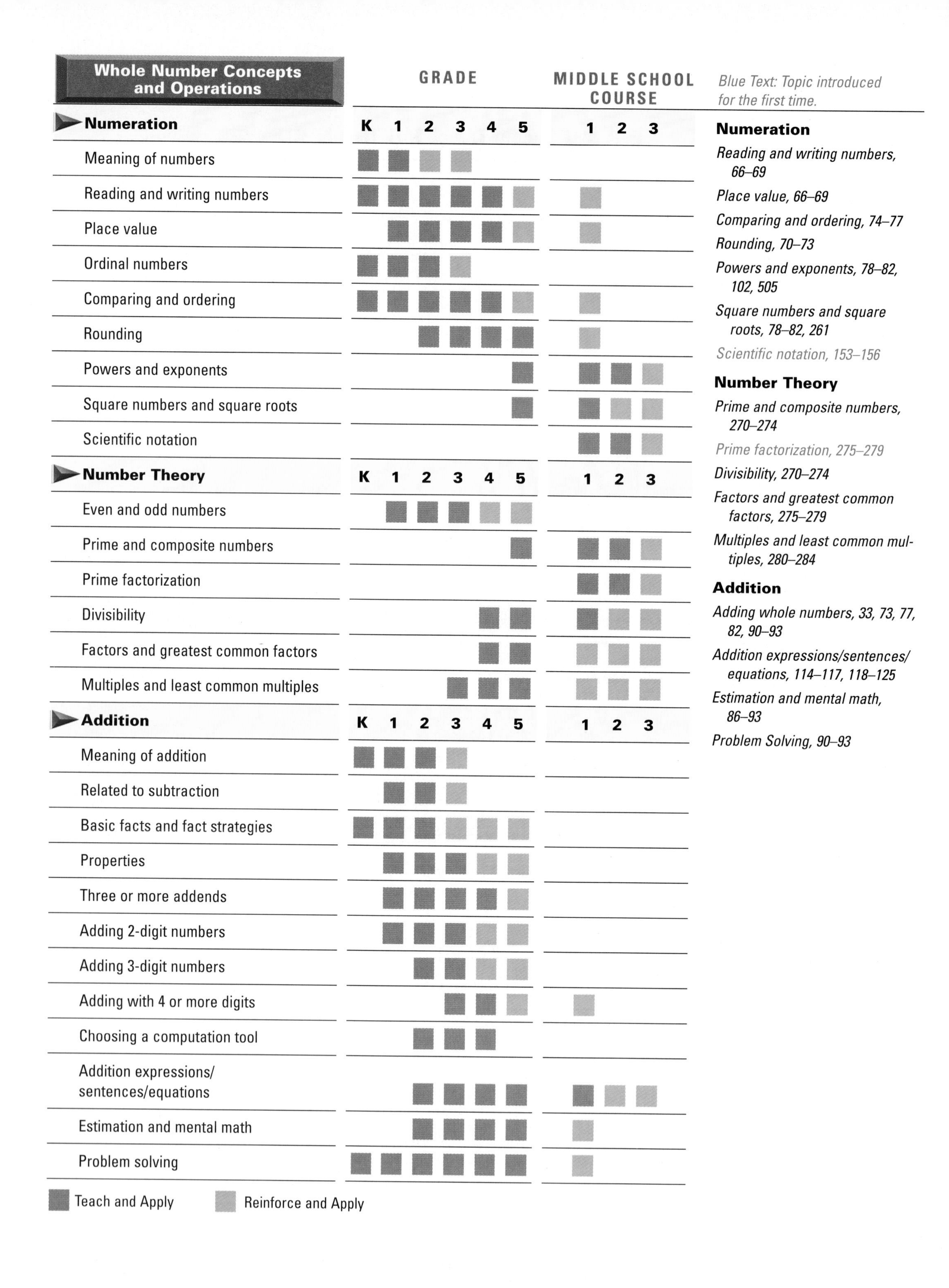

Whole Number Concepts and Operations

Numeration	GRADE K	1	2	3	4	5	MIDDLE SCHOOL COURSE 1	2	3
Meaning of numbers	Teach and Apply	Teach and Apply	Reinforce and Apply	Reinforce and Apply					
Reading and writing numbers	Teach and Apply	Teach and Apply	Teach and Apply	Teach and Apply	Teach and Apply	Reinforce and Apply	Reinforce and Apply		
Place value		Teach and Apply	Teach and Apply	Teach and Apply	Teach and Apply	Reinforce and Apply	Reinforce and Apply		
Ordinal numbers	Teach and Apply	Teach and Apply	Teach and Apply	Reinforce and Apply					
Comparing and ordering	Teach and Apply	Teach and Apply	Teach and Apply	Teach and Apply	Teach and Apply	Reinforce and Apply	Reinforce and Apply		
Rounding			Teach and Apply	Teach and Apply	Teach and Apply	Teach and Apply	Reinforce and Apply		
Powers and exponents						Teach and Apply	Teach and Apply	Teach and Apply	Reinforce and Apply
Square numbers and square roots						Teach and Apply	Teach and Apply	Reinforce and Apply	Reinforce and Apply
Scientific notation							Teach and Apply	Teach and Apply	Reinforce and Apply

Number Theory	K	1	2	3	4	5	1	2	3
Even and odd numbers		Teach and Apply	Teach and Apply	Teach and Apply	Reinforce and Apply	Reinforce and Apply			
Prime and composite numbers						Teach and Apply	Teach and Apply	Teach and Apply	Reinforce and Apply
Prime factorization							Teach and Apply	Teach and Apply	Reinforce and Apply
Divisibility					Teach and Apply	Teach and Apply	Teach and Apply	Reinforce and Apply	Reinforce and Apply
Factors and greatest common factors					Teach and Apply	Teach and Apply	Reinforce and Apply	Reinforce and Apply	Reinforce and Apply
Multiples and least common multiples				Teach and Apply	Teach and Apply	Teach and Apply	Reinforce and Apply	Reinforce and Apply	Reinforce and Apply

Addition	K	1	2	3	4	5	1	2	3
Meaning of addition	Teach and Apply	Teach and Apply	Teach and Apply	Reinforce and Apply					
Related to subtraction		Teach and Apply	Teach and Apply	Reinforce and Apply					
Basic facts and fact strategies	Teach and Apply	Teach and Apply	Teach and Apply	Reinforce and Apply	Reinforce and Apply	Reinforce and Apply			
Properties		Teach and Apply	Teach and Apply	Teach and Apply	Reinforce and Apply	Reinforce and Apply			
Three or more addends		Teach and Apply	Teach and Apply	Teach and Apply	Teach and Apply	Reinforce and Apply			
Adding 2-digit numbers		Teach and Apply	Teach and Apply	Teach and Apply	Reinforce and Apply	Reinforce and Apply			
Adding 3-digit numbers			Teach and Apply	Teach and Apply	Reinforce and Apply	Reinforce and Apply			
Adding with 4 or more digits				Teach and Apply	Teach and Apply	Reinforce and Apply	Reinforce and Apply		
Choosing a computation tool			Teach and Apply	Teach and Apply	Teach and Apply				
Addition expressions/ sentences/equations			Teach and Apply	Teach and Apply	Teach and Apply	Teach and Apply	Teach and Apply	Reinforce and Apply	Reinforce and Apply
Estimation and mental math			Teach and Apply	Teach and Apply	Teach and Apply	Teach and Apply	Reinforce and Apply		
Problem solving	Teach and Apply	Teach and Apply	Teach and Apply	Teach and Apply	Teach and Apply	Teach and Apply	Reinforce and Apply		

■ Teach and Apply ■ Reinforce and Apply

Blue Text: Topic introduced for the first time.

Numeration

Reading and writing numbers, 66–69
Place value, 66–69
Comparing and ordering, 74–77
Rounding, 70–73
Powers and exponents, 78–82, 102, 505
Square numbers and square roots, 78–82, 261
Scientific notation, 153–156

Number Theory

Prime and composite numbers, 270–274
Prime factorization, 275–279
Divisibility, 270–274
Factors and greatest common factors, 275–279
Multiples and least common multiples, 280–284

Addition

Adding whole numbers, 33, 73, 77, 82, 90–93
Addition expressions/sentences/equations, 114–117, 118–125
Estimation and mental math, 86–93
Problem Solving, 90–93

Whole Number Concepts and Operations (cont'd)

GRADE / **MIDDLE SCHOOL COURSE**

Blue Text: Topic introduced for the first time.

Subtraction	K	1	2	3	4	5	MS 1	MS 2	MS 3
Meaning of subtraction	■	■	■	□					
Related to addition		■	■	□					
Basic facts and fact strategies	■	■	■	□	□	□			
Properties		■	■	■	□	□			
Subtracting 2-digit numbers		■	■	■	□	□			
Subtracting 3-digit numbers			■	■	■	□			
Subtracting with 4 or more digits				■	■	□	□		
Choosing a computation tool			■	■	■				
Subtraction expressions/ sentences/equations				■	■	■	■	□	□
Estimation and mental math			■	■	■	■	□		
Problem solving	■	■	■	■	■	■	□		

Multiplication	K	1	2	3	4	5	MS 1	MS 2	MS 3
Meaning of multiplication			■	■	□				
Related to addition/division			■	■	□				
Basic facts and fact strategies			■	■	■	□			
Properties			■	■	■	■			
By a 1-digit number				■	■	■			
By multiples of 10 and 100				■	■	■			
By a multi-digit number				■	■	■	□		
Choosing a computation tool					■	■			
Multiplication expressions/ sentences/equations				■	■	■	■	□	□
Estimation and mental math				■	■	■	■		
Problem solving			■	■	■	■	■		

Division	K	1	2	3	4	5	MS 1	MS 2	MS 3
Meaning of division			■	■	■	□			
Related to subtraction/multiplication				■	■	□			
Basic facts and fact strategies				■	■	□			
Properties				■	■	■			
By a 1-digit divisor				■	■	■	□		
By multiples of 10 and 100				■	■	■	□		
By a multi-digit divisor					■	■	■		
Division expressions/sentences/equations				■	■	■	■	□	□
Estimation and mental math				■	■	■	■		
Problem solving			■	■	■	■	■		

■ Teach and Apply □ Reinforce and Apply

Subtraction

Subtracting whole numbers, 33, 90–93

Subtraction expressions/sentences/equations, 114–117, 118–125

Estimation and mental math, 86–93

Problem Solving, 90–93

Multiplication

Multiplying whole numbers, 20, 38, 45, 94–97

Multiplication expressions/sentences/equations, 114–117, 118–125

Estimation and mental math, 86–89, 94–97

Problem Solving, 94–97

Division

Dividing whole numbers, 38, 49, 94–97

Division expressions/sentences/equations, 114–117, 118–125

Estimation and mental math, 86–89, 90–93, 94–97

Problem Solving, 94–97

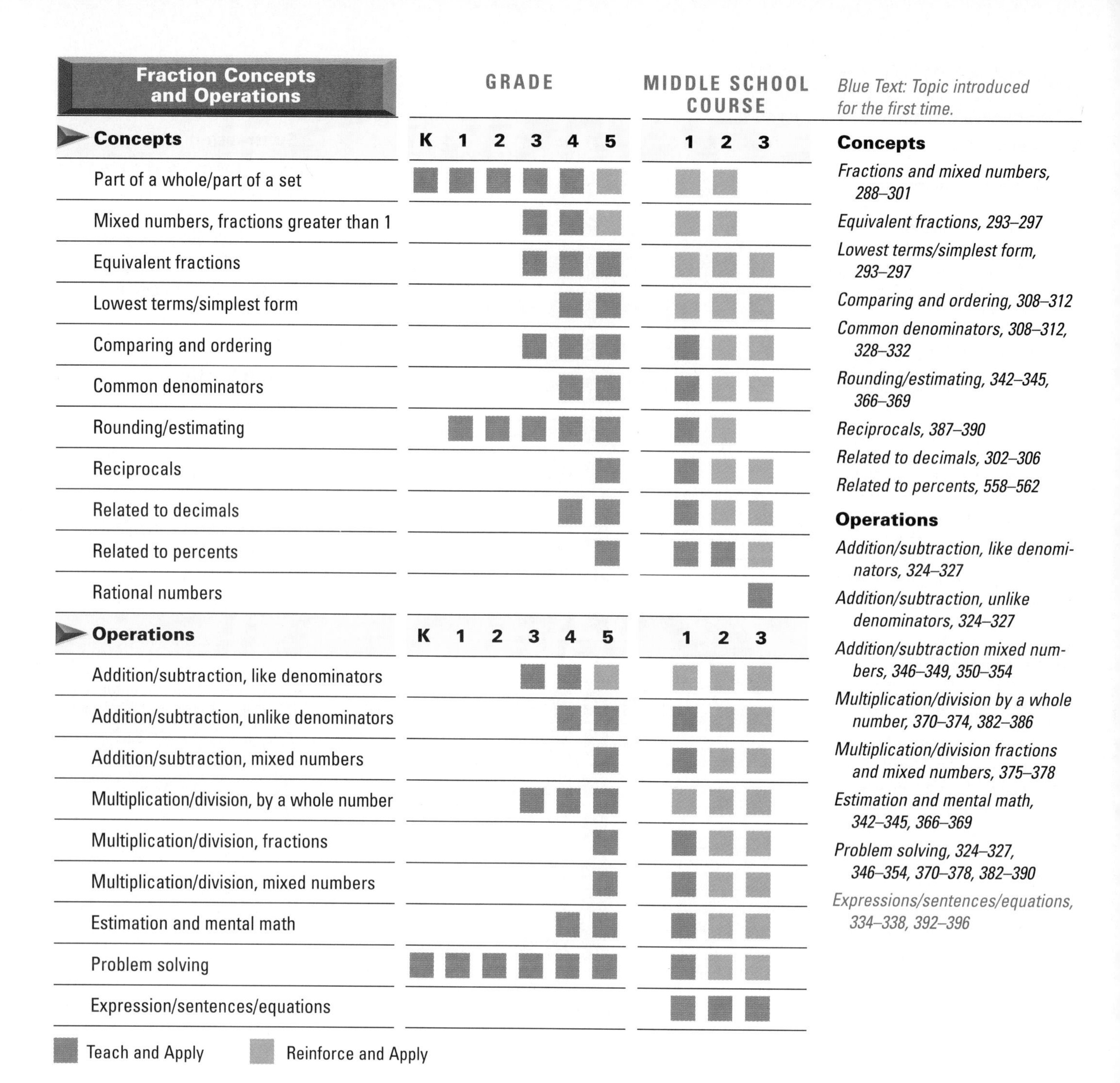

Fraction Concepts and Operations

	GRADE						MIDDLE SCHOOL COURSE		
Concepts	K	1	2	3	4	5	1	2	3
Part of a whole/part of a set	T	T	T	T	T	R	R	R	
Mixed numbers, fractions greater than 1				T	T	R	R	R	
Equivalent fractions				T	T	T	R	R	R
Lowest terms/simplest form					T	T	R	R	R
Comparing and ordering				T	T	T	T	R	R
Common denominators					T	T	T	R	R
Rounding/estimating		T	T	T	T	T	T	R	
Reciprocals						T	T	R	R
Related to decimals					T	T	T	R	R
Related to percents						T	T	T	R
Rational numbers									T
Operations	K	1	2	3	4	5	1	2	3
Addition/subtraction, like denominators				T	T	R	R	R	R
Addition/subtraction, unlike denominators					T	T	T	R	R
Addition/subtraction, mixed numbers						T	T	R	R
Multiplication/division, by a whole number				T	T	T	R	R	R
Multiplication/division, fractions						T	T	R	R
Multiplication/division, mixed numbers						T	T	R	R
Estimation and mental math					T	T	T	R	R
Problem solving	T	T	T	T	T	T	T	R	R
Expression/sentences/equations							T	T	T

T = Teach and Apply   R = Reinforce and Apply

Blue Text: Topic introduced for the first time.

Concepts

Fractions and mixed numbers, 288–301

Equivalent fractions, 293–297

Lowest terms/simplest form, 293–297

Comparing and ordering, 308–312

Common denominators, 308–312, 328–332

Rounding/estimating, 342–345, 366–369

Reciprocals, 387–390

Related to decimals, 302–306

Related to percents, 558–562

Operations

Addition/subtraction, like denominators, 324–327

Addition/subtraction, unlike denominators, 324–327

Addition/subtraction mixed numbers, 346–349, 350–354

Multiplication/division by a whole number, 370–374, 382–386

Multiplication/division fractions and mixed numbers, 375–378

Estimation and mental math, 342–345, 366–369

Problem solving, 324–327, 346–354, 370–378, 382–390

Expressions/sentences/equations, 334–338, 392–396

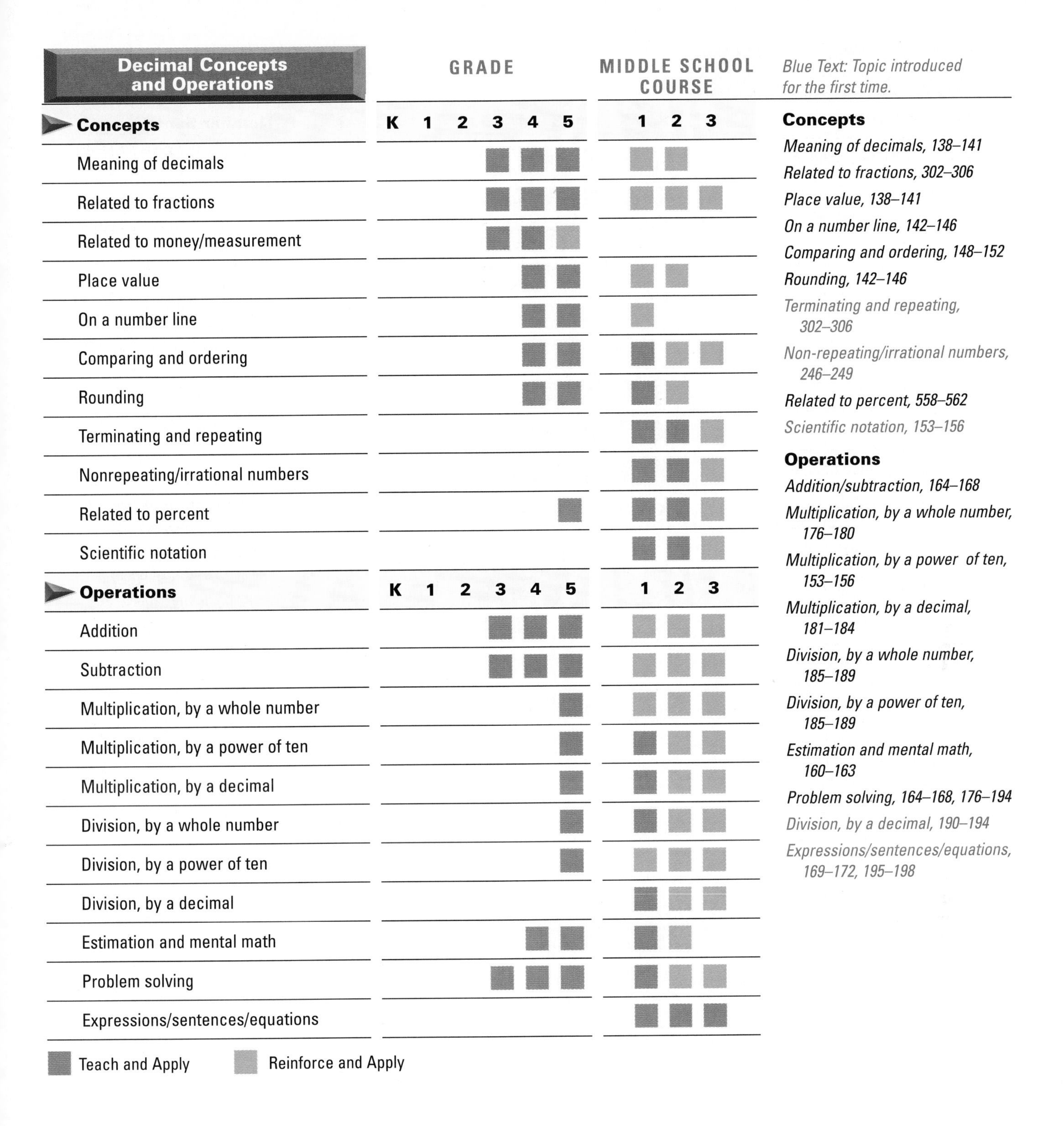

Decimal Concepts and Operations

	GRADE						MIDDLE SCHOOL COURSE		
Concepts	**K**	**1**	**2**	**3**	**4**	**5**	**1**	**2**	**3**
Meaning of decimals				■	■	■	□	□	
Related to fractions				■	■	■	□	□	□
Related to money/measurement				■	■	□			
Place value					■	■	□	□	
On a number line					■	■	□		
Comparing and ordering					■	■	■	□	□
Rounding					■	■	■	□	
Terminating and repeating							■	■	□
Nonrepeating/irrational numbers							■	■	□
Related to percent						■	■	■	□
Scientific notation							■	■	□
Operations	**K**	**1**	**2**	**3**	**4**	**5**	**1**	**2**	**3**
Addition				■	■	■	□	□	□
Subtraction				■	■	■	□	□	□
Multiplication, by a whole number						■	□	□	□
Multiplication, by a power of ten						■	■	□	□
Multiplication, by a decimal						■	■	□	□
Division, by a whole number						■	■	□	□
Division, by a power of ten						■	□	□	□
Division, by a decimal							■	□	□
Estimation and mental math					■	■	■	□	
Problem solving				■	■	■	■	□	□
Expressions/sentences/equations							■	■	■

■ Teach and Apply □ Reinforce and Apply

Blue Text: Topic introduced for the first time.

Concepts

Meaning of decimals, 138–141
Related to fractions, 302–306
Place value, 138–141
On a number line, 142–146
Comparing and ordering, 148–152
Rounding, 142–146
Terminating and repeating, 302–306
Non-repeating/irrational numbers, 246–249
Related to percent, 558–562
Scientific notation, 153–156

Operations

Addition/subtraction, 164–168
Multiplication, by a whole number, 176–180
Multiplication, by a power of ten, 153–156
Multiplication, by a decimal, 181–184
Division, by a whole number, 185–189
Division, by a power of ten, 185–189
Estimation and mental math, 160–163
Problem solving, 164–168, 176–194
Division, by a decimal, 190–194
Expressions/sentences/equations, 169–172, 195–198

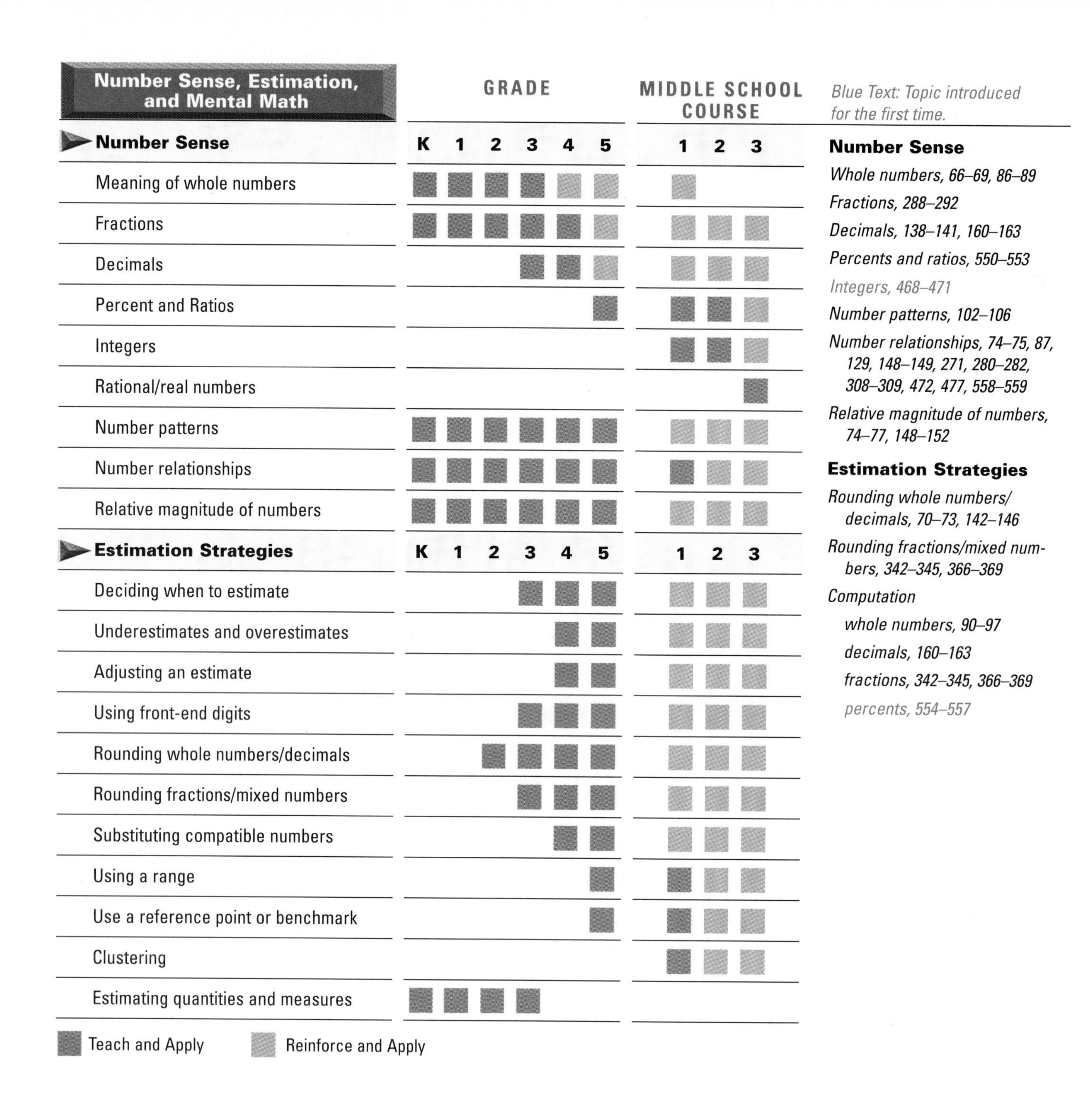

Number Sense, Estimation, and Mental Math

■ = Teach and Apply; □ = Reinforce and Apply

	GRADE K	GRADE 1	GRADE 2	GRADE 3	GRADE 4	GRADE 5	MIDDLE SCHOOL COURSE 1	MIDDLE SCHOOL COURSE 2	MIDDLE SCHOOL COURSE 3
Number Sense	**K**	**1**	**2**	**3**	**4**	**5**	**1**	**2**	**3**
Meaning of whole numbers	■	■	■	■	□	□	□		
Fractions	■	■	■	■	■	□	□	□	□
Decimals				■	■	□	□	□	□
Percent and Ratios						■	■	■	□
Integers							■	■	□
Rational/real numbers									■
Number patterns	■	■	■	■	■	■	□	□	□
Number relationships	■	■	■	■	■	■	■	□	□
Relative magnitude of numbers	■	■	■	■	■	■	□	□	□
Estimation Strategies	**K**	**1**	**2**	**3**	**4**	**5**	**1**	**2**	**3**
Deciding when to estimate				■	■	■	□	□	□
Underestimates and overestimates					■	■	□	□	□
Adjusting an estimate					■	■	□	□	□
Using front-end digits				■	■	■	□	□	□
Rounding whole numbers/decimals			■	■	■	■	□	□	□
Rounding fractions/mixed numbers				■	■	■	□	□	□
Substituting compatible numbers					■	■	□	□	□
Using a range						■	■	□	□
Use a reference point or benchmark						■	■	□	□
Clustering							■	□	□
Estimating quantities and measures	■	■	■	■					

■ Teach and Apply   □ Reinforce and Apply

Blue Text: Topic introduced for the first time.

Number Sense

Whole numbers, 66–69, 86–89

Fractions, 288–292

Decimals, 138–141, 160–163

Percents and ratios, 550–553

Integers, 468–471

Number patterns, 102–106

Number relationships, 74–75, 87, 129, 148–149, 271, 280–282, 308–309, 472, 477, 558–559

Relative magnitude of numbers, 74–77, 148–152

Estimation Strategies

Rounding whole numbers/ decimals, 70–73, 142–146

Rounding fractions/mixed numbers, 342–345, 366–369

Computation

whole numbers, 90–97

decimals, 160–163

fractions, 342–345, 366–369

percents, 554–557

Number Sense, Estimation, and Mental Math (cont'd)

Blue Text: Topic introduced for the first time.

Mental Math Strategies	Grade K	Grade 1	Grade 2	Grade 3	Grade 4	Grade 5	Middle School Course 1	Middle School Course 2	Middle School Course 3
Basic-fact strategies: add and subtract									
Count on/count back	■	■	■						
Use turnaround facts		■	■						
Add with doubles/doubles plus one		■	■						
Make ten	■	■	■						
Use doubles to subtract		■	■						
Think addition to subtract		■	■	□	□	□			
Use families of facts		■	■	□	□	□			
Basic-fact strategies: multiply and divide									
Skip count	■	■	■	□	□				
Multiply in any order			■	■	■				
Use doubling				■	■				
Use known facts				■	■				
Use patterns				■	■	□			
Think multiplication to divide				■	□	□			
Mental-computation strategies									
Multiply/divide by 10, 100, 1,000				■	■	□	□	□	□
Use properties and patterns		■	■	■	■	□	□	□	□
Break apart numbers					■	□	□	□	□
Compatible numbers				■	■	□	□	□	□
Compensation						■	■	□	□
with Fractions				■	■	■	■	□	□
with Percents						■	■	□	□

■ Teach and Apply   □ Reinforce and Apply

Mental Math Strategies

Mental–computation strategies

Whole numbers, 86–89, 90–109

Decimals, 160–163

Fractions, 342–345, 366–369

Percents, 554–557

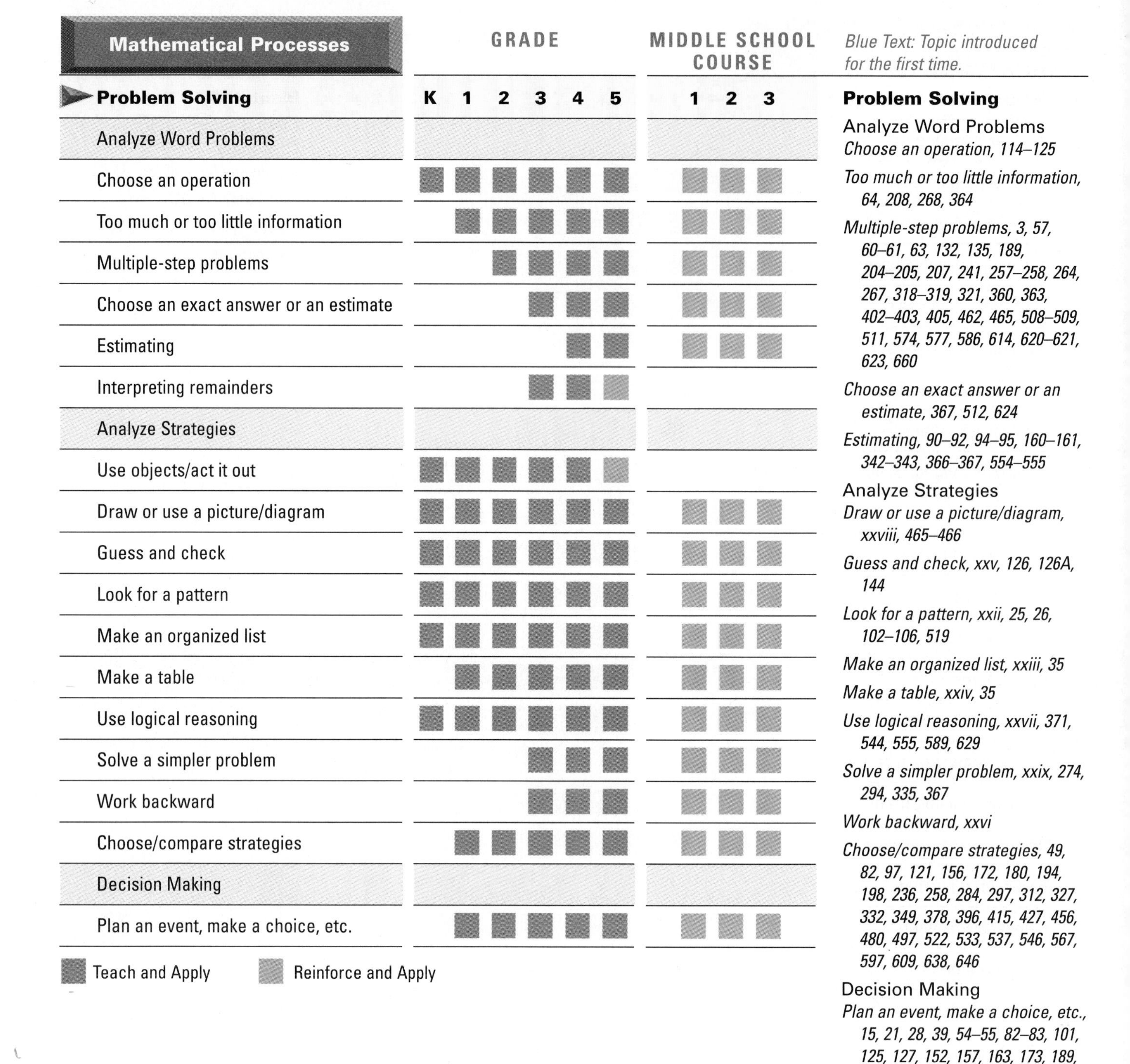

Mathematical Processes

Problem Solving	GRADE K	1	2	3	4	5	MIDDLE SCHOOL COURSE 1	2	3
Analyze Word Problems									
Choose an operation	■	■	■	■	■	■	□	□	□
Too much or too little information		■	■	■	■	■	□	□	□
Multiple-step problems			■	■	■	■	□	□	□
Choose an exact answer or an estimate				■	■	■	□	□	□
Estimating					■	■	□	□	□
Interpreting remainders				■	■	□			
Analyze Strategies									
Use objects/act it out	■	■	■	■	■	□			
Draw or use a picture/diagram	■	■	■	■	■	■	□	□	□
Guess and check	■	■	■	■	■	■	□	□	□
Look for a pattern	■	■	■	■	■	■	□	□	□
Make an organized list	■	■	■	■	■	■	□	□	□
Make a table		■	■	■	■	■	□	□	□
Use logical reasoning	■	■	■	■	■	■	□	□	□
Solve a simpler problem				■	■	■	□	□	□
Work backward				■	■	■	□	□	□
Choose/compare strategies		■	■	■	■	■	□	□	□
Decision Making									
Plan an event, make a choice, etc.		■	■	■	■	■	□	□	□

■ Teach and Apply □ Reinforce and Apply

Blue Text: Topic introduced for the first time.

Problem Solving

Analyze Word Problems

Choose an operation, 114–125

Too much or too little information, 64, 208, 268, 364

Multiple-step problems, 3, 57, 60–61, 63, 132, 135, 189, 204–205, 207, 241, 257–258, 264, 267, 318–319, 321, 360, 363, 402–403, 405, 462, 465, 508–509, 511, 574, 577, 586, 614, 620–621, 623, 660

Choose an exact answer or an estimate, 367, 512, 624

Estimating, 90–92, 94–95, 160–161, 342–343, 366–367, 554–555

Analyze Strategies

Draw or use a picture/diagram, xxviii, 465–466

Guess and check, xxv, 126, 126A, 144

Look for a pattern, xxii, 25, 26, 102–106, 519

Make an organized list, xxiii, 35

Make a table, xxiv, 35

Use logical reasoning, xxvii, 371, 544, 555, 589, 629

Solve a simpler problem, xxix, 274, 294, 335, 367

Work backward, xxvi

Choose/compare strategies, 49, 82, 97, 121, 156, 172, 180, 194, 198, 236, 258, 284, 297, 312, 327, 332, 349, 378, 396, 415, 427, 456, 480, 497, 522, 533, 537, 546, 567, 597, 609, 638, 646

Decision Making

Plan an event, make a choice, etc., 15, 21, 28, 39, 54–55, 82–83, 101, 125, 127, 152, 157, 163, 173, 189, 199, 214, 225, 241, 243, 249, 259, 285, 313, 338–339, 354–355, 378–379, 386, 431, 484–485, 502, 526–527, 546–547, 562, 569, 587, 599, 614–615, 638–639, 654–655

Mathematical Processes (cont'd)

Blue Text: Topic introduced for the first time.

Problem Solving (cont'd)	Grade K	Grade 1	Grade 2	Grade 3	Grade 4	Grade 5	Middle School Course 1	Course 2	Course 3
Problem-Solving Guide/Checklist									
Understand									
Determine what you know			T	T	T	R	R	R	R
Use data from pictures, graphs, ...			T	T	T	R	R	R	R
Tell what you need to find out					T	R	R	R	R
Plan									
Choose an operation/strategy			T	T	T	R	R	R	R
Chose a computation method			T	T	T	R	R	R	R
Estimate the answer				T	T	T	R	R	R
Solve									
Carry out the plan			T	T	T	R	R	R	R
Try another strategy if needed			T	T	T	R	R	R	R
Give the answer			T	T	T	R	R	R	R
Look Back									
Check your answer			T	T	T	R	R	R	R
Check reasonableness of answer				T	T	T	R	R	R
Be sure the question is answered			T	T	T	R	R	R	R

Reasoning	Grade K	Grade 1	Grade 2	Grade 3	Grade 4	Grade 5	Middle School Course 1	Course 2	Course 3
Critical Thinking, Logical Reasoning									
Classifying/sorting	T	T	T	T	T	T	R	R	R
Comparing/contrasting	T	T	T	R	R	R	R	R	R
Finding/extending/using patterns	T	T	T	T	T	T	R	R	R
Making generalizations	T	T	T	T	T	T	R	R	R
Drawing conclusions	T	T	T	T	T	T	R	R	R
Making/testing conjectures		T	T	T	T	T	R	R	R
Explaining/justifying answers					T	T	R	R	R
Visual and Creative Thinking									
Visual patterns	T	T	T	T	T	T	R	R	R
Spatial reasoning	T	T	T	T	T	T	R	R	R
Solve nonroutine problems				T	T	T	R	R	R
Generate problems				T	T	T	R	R	R
Develop alternative ways to solve problems						T	R	R	R

T = Teach and Apply; R = Reinforce and Apply

Problem Solving

Problem-Solving Guide/Checklist

Use problem-solving guidelines, xx–xxi, 4, 15, 28, 54, 64, 82, 101, 125, 136, 152, 163, 189, 208, 214, 241, 249, 268, 279, 301, 322, 338, 354, 364, 378, 386, 406, 420, 431, 456, 466, 484, 502, 512, 526, 546, 562, 578, 587, 614, 624, 638, 654

Reasoning

Critical Thinking, Logical Reasoning

Classifying/sorting, 408–409, 413–414, 424–427, 430, 434, 580–583, 586

Comparing/contrasting, 74–77, 148–151, 308–310, 470, 631

Finding/extending/using patterns, 20, 87, 102–105, 129, 201, 236, 483, 604

Making generalizations, 102–106, 129, 141, 176, 181, 201, 222, 237, 246, 250, 275, 328, 346, 350, 416, 424, 478, 502, 532, 546, 562

Drawing conclusions, 43, 46, 66, 185, 346, 350, 432, 472, 606

Making/testing conjectures, 78, 98, 153, 308, 481, 630, 647

Explaining/justifying answers, 6, 21, 29, 31, 42–43, 46–47, 52, 55, 57, 60–61, 66, 74–75, 80, 92, 94–95, 119, 122–123, 148, 157, 169–170, 178, 182, 185–186, 199, 201, 213, 215, 218, 225, 233–234, 237, 254, 256–257, 273, 275, 282, 288, 290, 294, 298, 302, 305, 310, 324, 334, 346, 350, 366, 372, 377, 382, 387, 409, 416, 451, 469, 472–473, 481, 490, 498, 500, 514, 521, 530, 535, 538, 543–544, 555, 582, 588, 591, 603, 606–607, 612, 631, 642, 644, 660

Visual and Creative Thinking

Visual patterns, 129, 210, 237, 275, 454–455

Spatial reasoning, 129, 210, 237, 275, 454–455

Solve non-routine problems, 3, 60–61, 63, 132, 135, 204–205, 207, 264, 267, 318–319, 321, 360, 363, 402–403, 405, 462, 465, 508–509, 511, 574, 577, 620–621, 623, 660

Generate problems, 45, 48, 107, 170, 184, 192, 195–196, 198, 338

Develop alternative ways to solve problems, 379, 391, 412, 440, 591

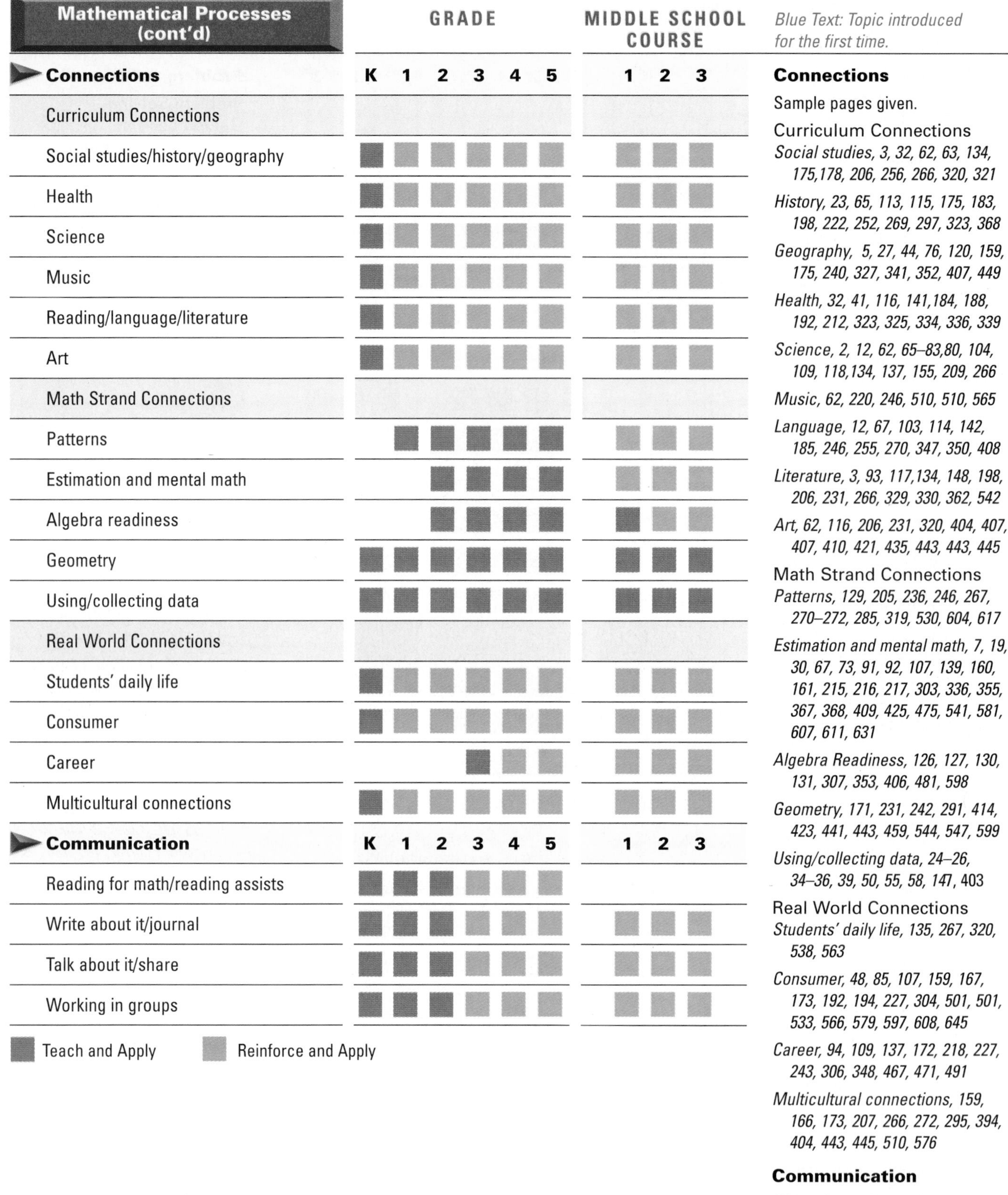

Mathematical Processes (cont'd)	GRADE						MIDDLE SCHOOL COURSE		
Connections	**K**	**1**	**2**	**3**	**4**	**5**	**1**	**2**	**3**
Curriculum Connections									
Social studies/history/geography	■	□	□	□	□	□	□	□	□
Health	■	□	□	□	□	□	□	□	□
Science	■	□	□	□	□	□	□	□	□
Music	■	□	□	□	□	□	□	□	□
Reading/language/literature	■	□	□	□	□	□	□	□	□
Art	■	□	□	□	□	□	□	□	□
Math Strand Connections									
Patterns		■	■	■	■	■	□	□	□
Estimation and mental math			■	■	■	■	□	□	□
Algebra readiness			■	■	■	■	■	□	□
Geometry	■	■	■	■	■	■	■	■	■
Using/collecting data	■	■	■	■	■	■	■	■	■
Real World Connections									
Students' daily life	■	□	□	□	□	□	□	□	□
Consumer	■	□	□	□	□	□	□	□	□
Career				■	□	□	□	□	□
Multicultural connections	■	□	□	□	□	□	□	□	□
Communication	**K**	**1**	**2**	**3**	**4**	**5**	**1**	**2**	**3**
Reading for math/reading assists	■	■	■	□	□	□			
Write about it/journal	■	■	■	□	□	□	□	□	□
Talk about it/share	■	■	■	□	□	□	□	□	□
Working in groups	■	■	■	□	□	□	□	□	□

■ Teach and Apply □ Reinforce and Apply

Blue Text: Topic introduced for the first time.

Connections

Sample pages given.

Curriculum Connections

Social studies, 3, 32, 62, 63, 134, 175,178, 206, 256, 266, 320, 321

History, 23, 65, 113, 115, 175, 183, 198, 222, 252, 269, 297, 323, 368

Geography, 5, 27, 44, 76, 120, 159, 175, 240, 327, 341, 352, 407, 449

Health, 32, 41, 116, 141,184, 188, 192, 212, 323, 325, 334, 336, 339

Science, 2, 12, 62, 65–83,80, 104, 109, 118,134, 137, 155, 209, 266

Music, 62, 220, 246, 510, 510, 565

Language, 12, 67, 103, 114, 142, 185, 246, 255, 270, 347, 350, 408

Literature, 3, 93, 117,134, 148, 198, 206, 231, 266, 329, 330, 362, 542

Art, 62, 116, 206, 231, 320, 404, 407, 407, 410, 421, 435, 443, 443, 445

Math Strand Connections

Patterns, 129, 205, 236, 246, 267, 270–272, 285, 319, 530, 604, 617

Estimation and mental math, 7, 19, 30, 67, 73, 91, 92, 107, 139, 160, 161, 215, 216, 217, 303, 336, 355, 367, 368, 409, 425, 475, 541, 581, 607, 611, 631

Algebra Readiness, 126, 127, 130, 131, 307, 353, 406, 481, 598

Geometry, 171, 231, 242, 291, 414, 423, 441, 443, 459, 544, 547, 599

Using/collecting data, 24–26, 34–36, 39, 50, 55, 58, 147, 403

Real World Connections

Students' daily life, 135, 267, 320, 538, 563

Consumer, 48, 85, 107, 159, 167, 173, 192, 194, 227, 304, 501, 501, 533, 566, 579, 597, 608, 645

Career, 94, 109, 137, 172, 218, 227, 243, 306, 348, 467, 471, 491

Multicultural connections, 159, 166, 173, 207, 266, 272, 295, 394, 404, 443, 445, 510, 576

Communication

Write about it/journal, 10, 64, 73, 84, 89, 136, 146, 189, 208, 268, 284, 364, 369, 406, 420, 427, 466, 512, 527, 569, 578, 583, 624

Talk about it/share, 150, 277, 352, 372, 396, 415, 553, 560, 583, 587, 605

Working in groups, 34, 46, 74, 142, 233, 250, 280, 295

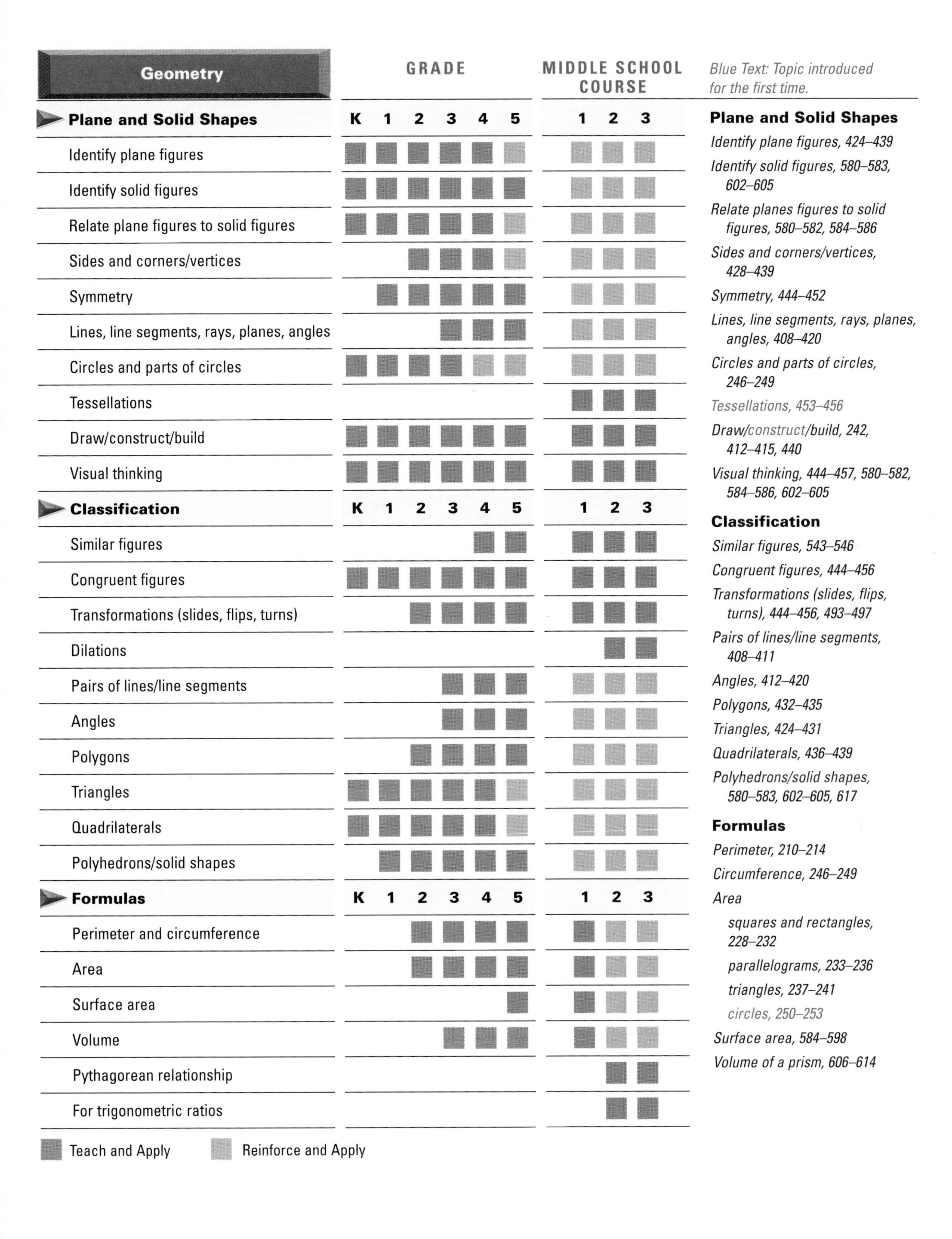

Geometry

Plane and Solid Shapes	Grade K	Grade 1	Grade 2	Grade 3	Grade 4	Grade 5	Middle School Course 1	Middle School Course 2	Middle School Course 3
Identify plane figures	T	T	T	T	T	R	R	R	R
Identify solid figures	T	T	T	T	T	T	R	R	R
Relate plane figures to solid figures	T	T	T	T	T	R	R	R	R
Sides and corners/vertices			T	T	T	R	R	R	R
Symmetry		T	T	T	T	T	R	R	R
Lines, line segments, rays, planes, angles				T	T	T	R	R	R
Circles and parts of circles	T	T	T	T	R	R	R	R	R
Tessellations							T	T	T
Draw/construct/build	T	T	T	T	T	T	T	T	T
Visual thinking	T	T	T	T	T	T	T	T	T
Classification	**K**	**1**	**2**	**3**	**4**	**5**	**1**	**2**	**3**
Similar figures					T	T	T	T	T
Congruent figures	T	T	T	T	T	T	T	T	T
Transformations (slides, flips, turns)			T	T	T	T	T	T	T
Dilations								T	T
Pairs of lines/line segments				T	T	T	R	R	R
Angles				T	T	T	R	R	R
Polygons			T	T	T	T	R	R	R
Triangles	T	T	T	T	T	R	R	R	R
Quadrilaterals	T	T	T	T	T	R	R	R	R
Polyhedrons/solid shapes		T	T	T	T	T	R	R	R
Formulas	**K**	**1**	**2**	**3**	**4**	**5**	**1**	**2**	**3**
Perimeter and circumference			T	T	T	T	T	R	R
Area			T	T	T	T	T	R	R
Surface area						T	T	R	R
Volume				T	T	T	T	R	R
Pythagorean relationship								T	T
For trigonometric ratios								T	T

T = Teach and Apply; R = Reinforce and Apply

Blue Text: Topic introduced for the first time.

Plane and Solid Shapes

Identify plane figures, 424–439
Identify solid figures, 580–583, 602–605
Relate planes figures to solid figures, 580–582, 584–586
Sides and corners/vertices, 428–439
Symmetry, 444–452
Lines, line segments, rays, planes, angles, 408–420
Circles and parts of circles, 246–249
Tessellations, 453–456
Draw/construct/build, 242, 412–415, 440
Visual thinking, 444–457, 580–582, 584–586, 602–605

Classification

Similar figures, 543–546
Congruent figures, 444–456
Transformations (slides, flips, turns), 444–456, 493–497
Pairs of lines/line segments, 408–411
Angles, 412–420
Polygons, 432–435
Triangles, 424–431
Quadrilaterals, 436–439
Polyhedrons/solid shapes, 580–583, 602–605, 617

Formulas

Perimeter, 210–214
Circumference, 246–249
Area
squares and rectangles, 228–232
parallelograms, 233–236
triangles, 237–241
circles, 250–253
Surface area, 584–598
Volume of a prism, 606–614

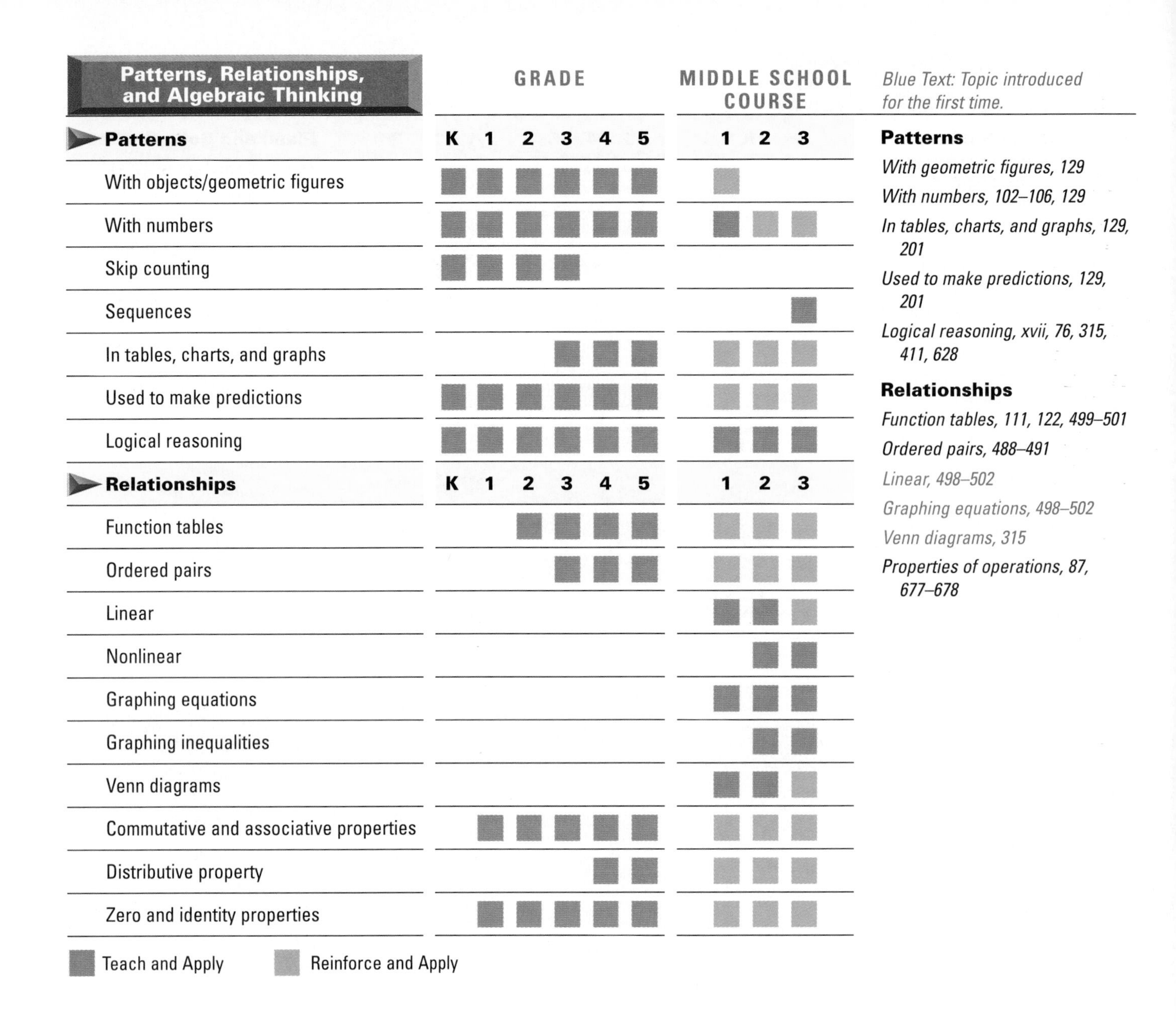

Patterns, Relationships, and Algebraic Thinking

	GRADE K	1	2	3	4	5	MIDDLE SCHOOL COURSE 1	2	3
Patterns	**K**	**1**	**2**	**3**	**4**	**5**	**1**	**2**	**3**
With objects/geometric figures	■	■	■	■	■	■	□		
With numbers	■	■	■	■	■	■	■	□	□
Skip counting	■	■	■	■					
Sequences									■
In tables, charts, and graphs				■	■	■	□	□	□
Used to make predictions	■	■	■	■	■	■	□	□	□
Logical reasoning	■	■	■	■	■	■	■	■	■
Relationships	**K**	**1**	**2**	**3**	**4**	**5**	**1**	**2**	**3**
Function tables			■	■	■	■	□	□	□
Ordered pairs				■	■	■	□	□	□
Linear							■	■	□
Nonlinear								■	■
Graphing equations							■	■	■
Graphing inequalities								■	■
Venn diagrams							■	■	□
Commutative and associative properties		■	■	■	■	■	□	□	□
Distributive property					■	■	□	□	□
Zero and identity properties		■	■	■	■	■	□	□	□

■ Teach and Apply □ Reinforce and Apply

Blue Text: Topic introduced for the first time.

Patterns

With geometric figures, 129

With numbers, 102–106, 129

In tables, charts, and graphs, 129, 201

Used to make predictions, 129, 201

Logical reasoning, xvii, 76, 315, 411, 628

Relationships

Function tables, 111, 122, 499–501

Ordered pairs, 488–491

Linear, 498–502

Graphing equations, 498–502

Venn diagrams, 315

Properties of operations, 87, 677–678

SCOPE AND SEQUENCE

Patterns, Relationships, and Algebraic Thinking (cont'd)

Algebraic Thinking	GRADE K	1	2	3	4	5	MIDDLE SCHOOL COURSE 1	2	3
Expressions, Equations, Inequalities									
Missing numbers and number sentences			■	■	■				
Variables						■	■	■	□
Writing/evaluating expressions						■	■	■	□
Writing/simplifying polynomials									■
Order of operations						■	■	□	□
Solving/writing for addition/subtraction							■	■	□
Solving/writing for multiplication/division							■	■	□
Solving/writing two-step equations								■	■
Solving/writing inequalities								■	■
Graphing equations							■	■	■
Graphing inequalities									■
Systems of equations/inequalities									■
Related to formulas						■	■	□	□
Integers									
Writing and reading							■	□	□
On a number line							■	□	□
Comparing and ordering							■	■	□
Opposites							■	■	□
Absolute value								■	□
Adding and subtracting							■	■	■
Multiplying and dividing							■	■	■
Graphing in four quadrants							■	■	■
Solving equations								■	■
Rational and Real Numbers									
Computing with rational numbers									■
Repeating and nonrepeating decimals							■	□	□
Exponents and powers							■	□	□
Squares and square roots							■	■	□
Irrational and real numbers							■	■	■

■ Teach and Apply   □ Reinforce and Apply

Blue Text: Topic introduced for the first time.

Algebraic Thinking

Expressions, Equations, Inequalities

Variables, 110–113

Writing/evaluating expressions, 114–117

Order of operations, 98–101

Solving/writing for addition/subtraction, 118–125, 169–172, 334–338

Solving/writing for multiplication/division, 118–125, 195–198, 392–396

Graphing equations, 498–502

Related to formulas, 228–241, 250–253, 588–592, 610–614

Integers

Writing and reading, 468–471

On a number line, 468–471

Comparing and ordering, 468–471

Opposites, 468–471

Adding and subtracting, 472–475, 476–480

Multiplying and dividing, 481–484

Graphing in four quadrants, 488–491

Rational and Real Numbers

Repeating and nonrepeating decimals, 302–306

Exponents and powers, 78–82, 505

Squares and square roots, 261

Irrational and real numbers, 246–249

Measurement, Time, and Money

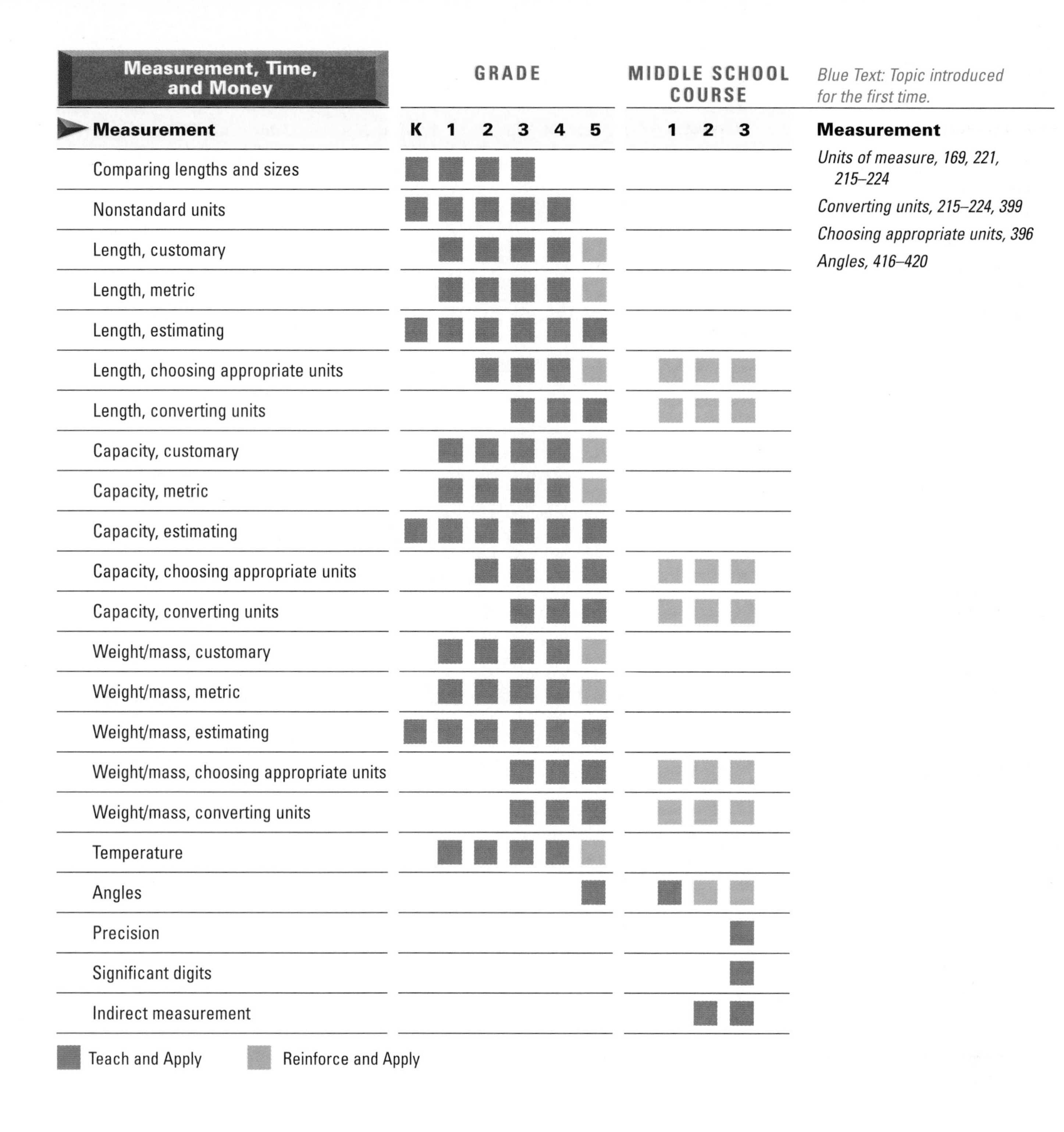

Measurement	GRADE K	1	2	3	4	5	MIDDLE SCHOOL COURSE 1	2	3
Comparing lengths and sizes	■	■	■	■					
Nonstandard units	■	■	■	■	■				
Length, customary		■	■	■	■	□			
Length, metric		■	■	■	■	□			
Length, estimating	■	■	■	■	■	■			
Length, choosing appropriate units			■	■	■	□	□	□	□
Length, converting units				■	■	■	□	□	□
Capacity, customary		■	■	■	■	□			
Capacity, metric		■	■	■	■	□			
Capacity, estimating	■	■	■	■	■	■			
Capacity, choosing appropriate units			■	■	■	■	□	□	□
Capacity, converting units				■	■	■	□	□	□
Weight/mass, customary		■	■	■	■	□			
Weight/mass, metric		■	■	■	■	□			
Weight/mass, estimating	■	■	■	■	■	■			
Weight/mass, choosing appropriate units				■	■	■	□	□	□
Weight/mass, converting units				■	■	■	□	□	□
Temperature		■	■	■	■	□			
Angles						■	■	□	□
Precision									■
Significant digits									■
Indirect measurement								■	■

■ Teach and Apply   □ Reinforce and Apply

Blue Text: Topic introduced for the first time.

Measurement

Units of measure, 169, 221, 215–224

Converting units, 215–224, 399

Choosing appropriate units, 396

Angles, 416–420

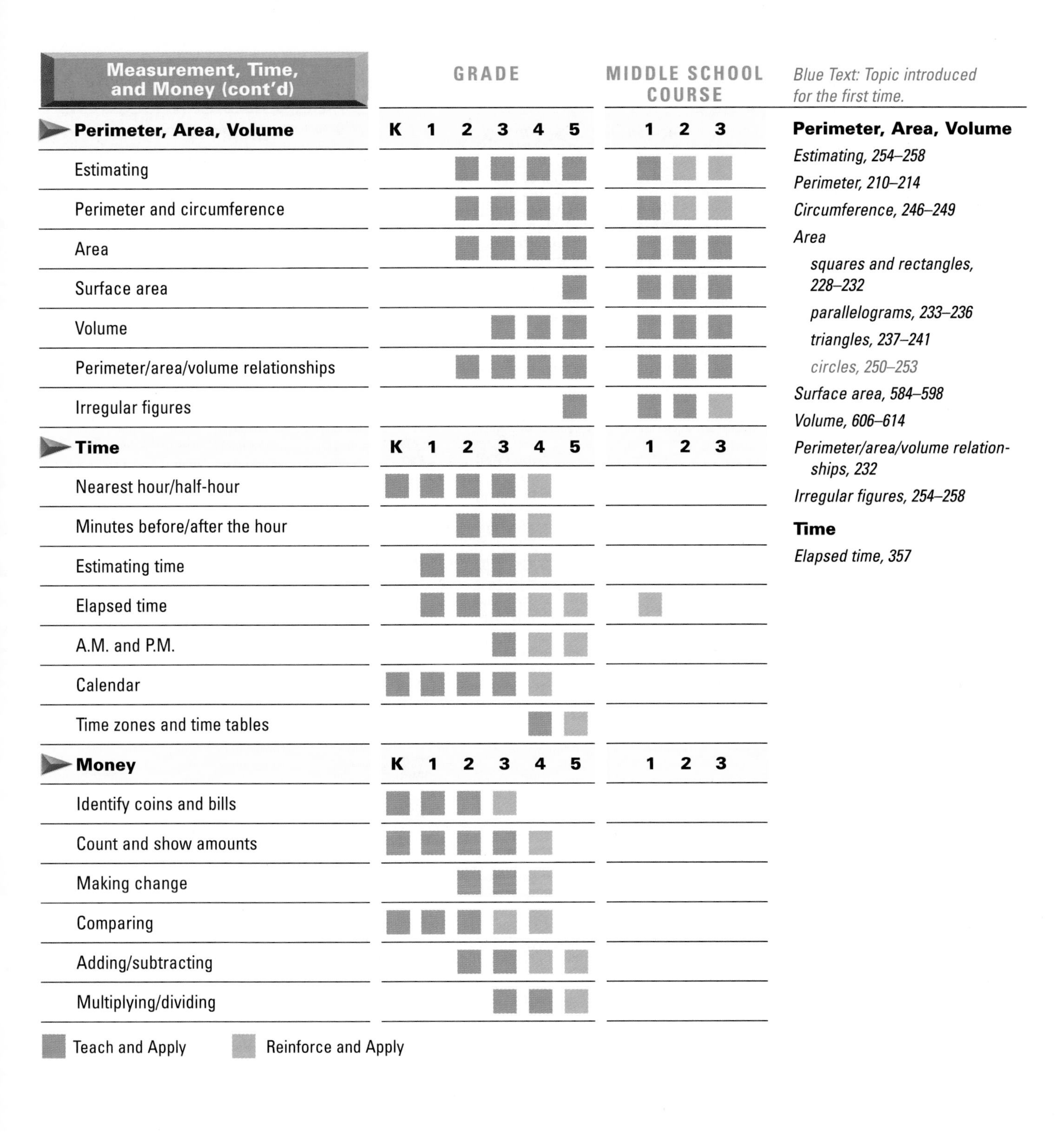

Measurement, Time, and Money (cont'd)

■ = Teach and Apply; □ = Reinforce and Apply

Perimeter, Area, Volume	Grade K	1	2	3	4	5	Middle School Course 1	2	3
Estimating			■	■	■	■	■	□	□
Perimeter and circumference			■	■	■	■	■	□	□
Area			■	■	■	■	■	■	■
Surface area						■	■	■	■
Volume				■	■	■	■	■	■
Perimeter/area/volume relationships			■	■	■	■	■	■	■
Irregular figures						■	■	■	□
Time	**K**	**1**	**2**	**3**	**4**	**5**	**1**	**2**	**3**
Nearest hour/half-hour	■	■	■	■	□				
Minutes before/after the hour			■	■	□				
Estimating time		■	■	■	□				
Elapsed time		■	■	■	□	□	□		
A.M. and P.M.				■	□	□			
Calendar	■	■	■	■	□				
Time zones and time tables					■	□			
Money	**K**	**1**	**2**	**3**	**4**	**5**	**1**	**2**	**3**
Identify coins and bills	■	■	■	□					
Count and show amounts	■	■	■	■	□				
Making change			■	■	□				
Comparing	■	■	■	□	□				
Adding/subtracting			■	■	□	□			
Multiplying/dividing				■	■	□			

■ Teach and Apply □ Reinforce and Apply

Blue Text: Topic introduced for the first time.

Perimeter, Area, Volume

Estimating, 254–258

Perimeter, 210–214

Circumference, 246–249

Area

- *squares and rectangles, 228–232*
- *parallelograms, 233–236*
- *triangles, 237–241*
- *circles, 250–253*

Surface area, 584–598

Volume, 606–614

Perimeter/area/volume relationships, 232

Irregular figures, 254–258

Time

Elapsed time, 357

SCOPE AND SEQUENCE

Data, Statistics, and Probability

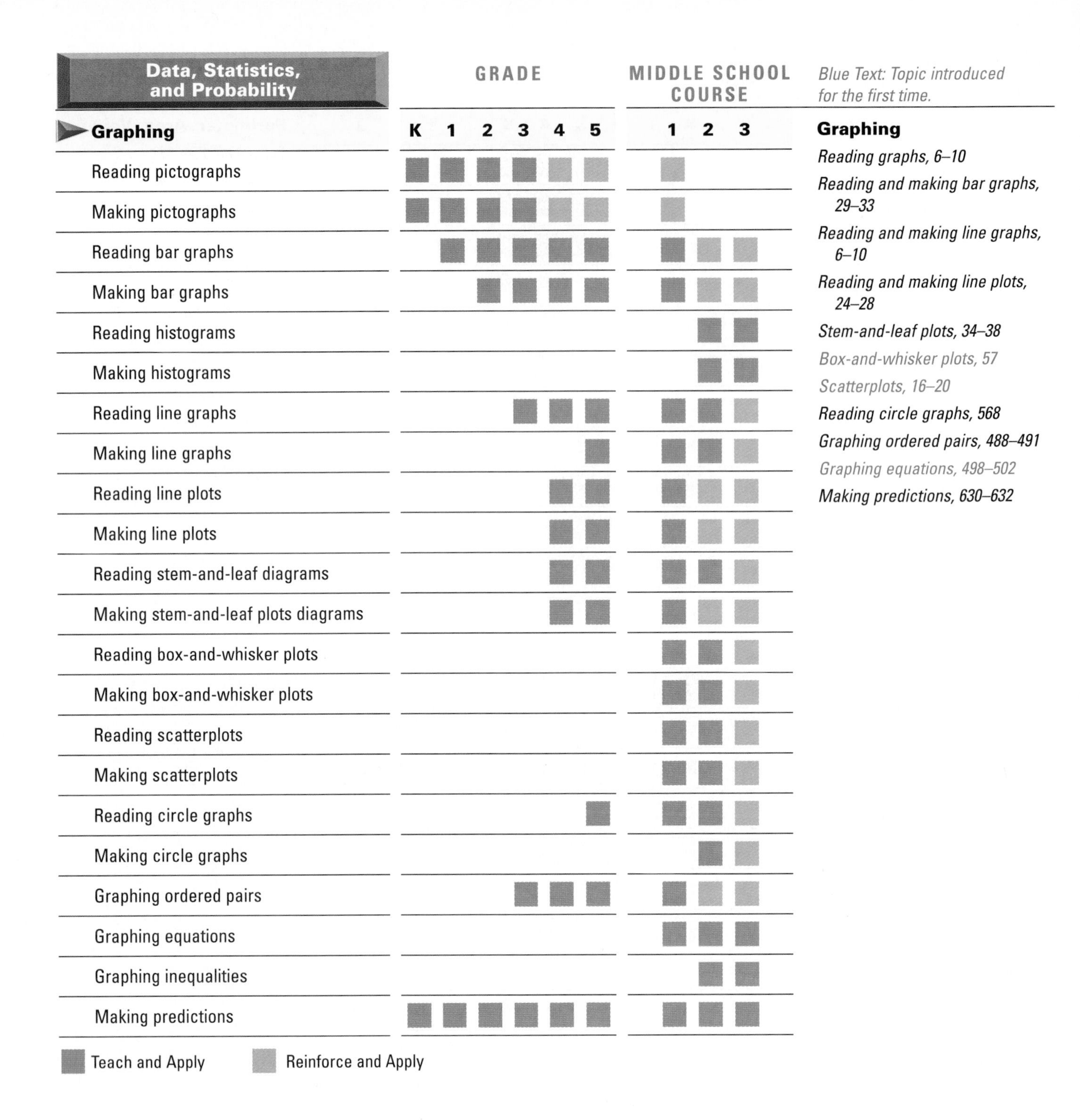

Graphing	GRADE K	GRADE 1	GRADE 2	GRADE 3	GRADE 4	GRADE 5	MIDDLE SCHOOL COURSE 1	MIDDLE SCHOOL COURSE 2	MIDDLE SCHOOL COURSE 3
Reading pictographs	■	■	■	■	□	□	□		
Making pictographs	■	■	■	■	□	□	□		
Reading bar graphs		■	■	■	■	■	■	□	□
Making bar graphs			■	■	■	■	■	□	□
Reading histograms								■	■
Making histograms								■	■
Reading line graphs				■	■	■	■	■	□
Making line graphs						■	■	■	□
Reading line plots					■	■	■	□	□
Making line plots					■	■	■	□	□
Reading stem-and-leaf diagrams					■	■	■	■	□
Making stem-and-leaf plots diagrams					■	■	■	□	□
Reading box-and-whisker plots							■	■	□
Making box-and-whisker plots							■	■	□
Reading scatterplots							■	■	□
Making scatterplots							■	■	□
Reading circle graphs						■	■	■	□
Making circle graphs								■	□
Graphing ordered pairs				■	■	■	■	□	□
Graphing equations							■	■	■
Graphing inequalities								■	■
Making predictions	■	■	■	■	■	■	■	■	■

■ Teach and Apply   □ Reinforce and Apply

Blue Text: Topic introduced for the first time.

Graphing

Reading graphs, 6–10

Reading and making bar graphs, 29–33

Reading and making line graphs, 6–10

Reading and making line plots, 24–28

Stem-and-leaf plots, 34–38

Box-and-whisker plots, 57

Scatterplots, 16–20

Reading circle graphs, 568

Graphing ordered pairs, 488–491

Graphing equations, 498–502

Making predictions, 630–632

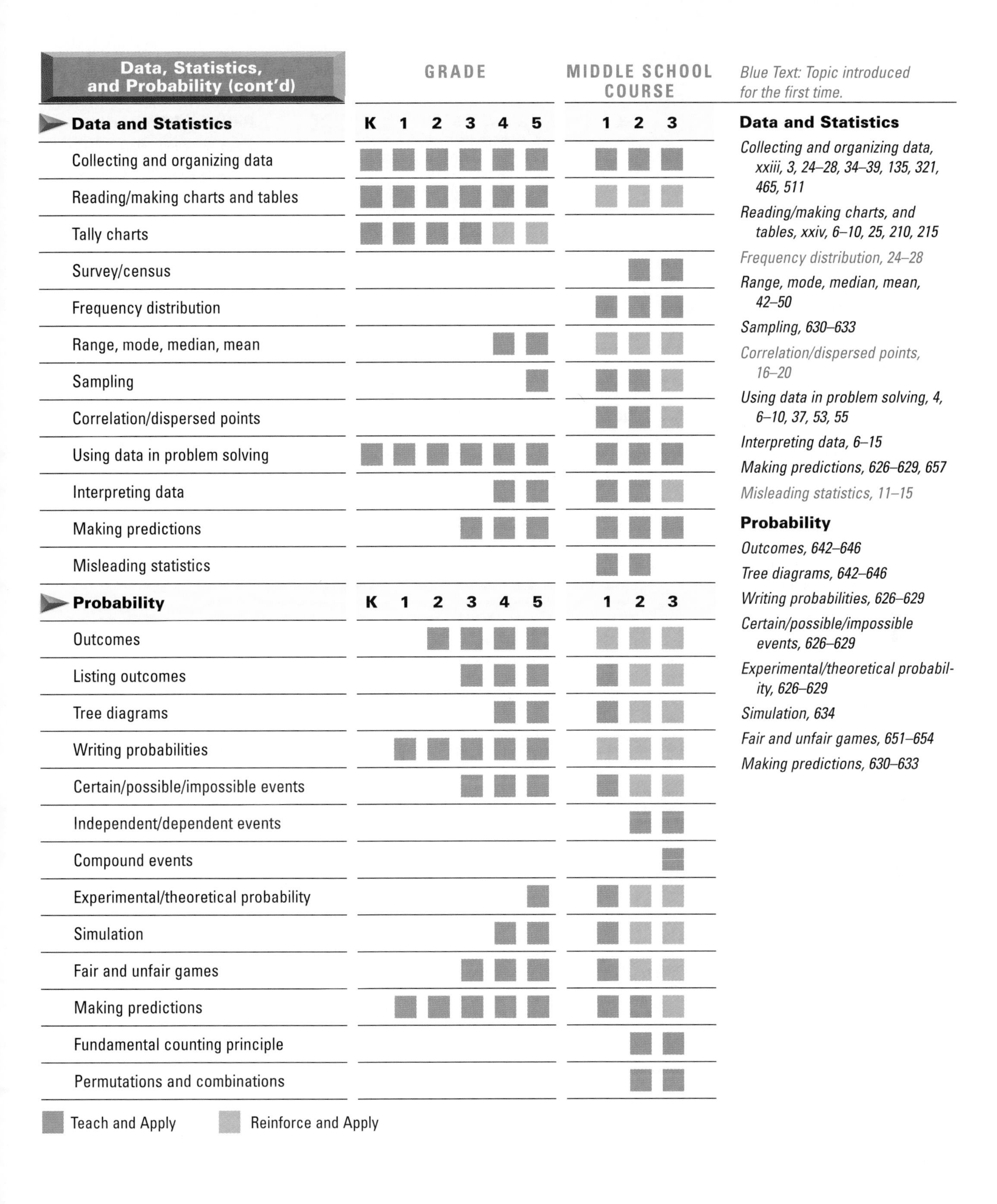

Data, Statistics, and Probability (cont'd)

	GRADE						MIDDLE SCHOOL COURSE		
Data and Statistics	**K**	**1**	**2**	**3**	**4**	**5**	**1**	**2**	**3**
Collecting and organizing data	■	■	■	■	■	■	■	■	■
Reading/making charts and tables	■	■	■	■	■	■	□	□	□
Tally charts	■	■	■	■	□	□			
Survey/census								■	■
Frequency distribution							■	■	■
Range, mode, median, mean					■	■	□	□	□
Sampling						■	■	■	□
Correlation/dispersed points							■	■	□
Using data in problem solving	■	■	■	■	■	■	■	■	■
Interpreting data					■	■	■	■	□
Making predictions				■	■	■	■	■	■
Misleading statistics							■	■	
Probability	**K**	**1**	**2**	**3**	**4**	**5**	**1**	**2**	**3**
Outcomes			■	■	■	■	□	□	□
Listing outcomes				■	■	■	■	□	□
Tree diagrams					■	■	■	□	□
Writing probabilities		■	■	■	■	■	□	□	□
Certain/possible/impossible events				■	■	■	■	□	□
Independent/dependent events								■	■
Compound events									■
Experimental/theoretical probability						■	■	□	□
Simulation					■	■	■	□	□
Fair and unfair games				■	■	■	■	□	□
Making predictions		■	■	■	■	■	■	■	□
Fundamental counting principle								■	■
Permutations and combinations								■	■

■ Teach and Apply □ Reinforce and Apply

Blue Text: Topic introduced for the first time.

Data and Statistics

Collecting and organizing data, xxiii, 3, 24–28, 34–39, 135, 321, 465, 511

Reading/making charts, and tables, xxiv, 6–10, 25, 210, 215

Frequency distribution, 24–28

Range, mode, median, mean, 42–50

Sampling, 630–633

Correlation/dispersed points, 16–20

Using data in problem solving, 4, 6–10, 37, 53, 55

Interpreting data, 6–15

Making predictions, 626–629, 657

Misleading statistics, 11–15

Probability

Outcomes, 642–646

Tree diagrams, 642–646

Writing probabilities, 626–629

Certain/possible/impossible events, 626–629

Experimental/theoretical probability, 626–629

Simulation, 634

Fair and unfair games, 651–654

Making predictions, 630–633

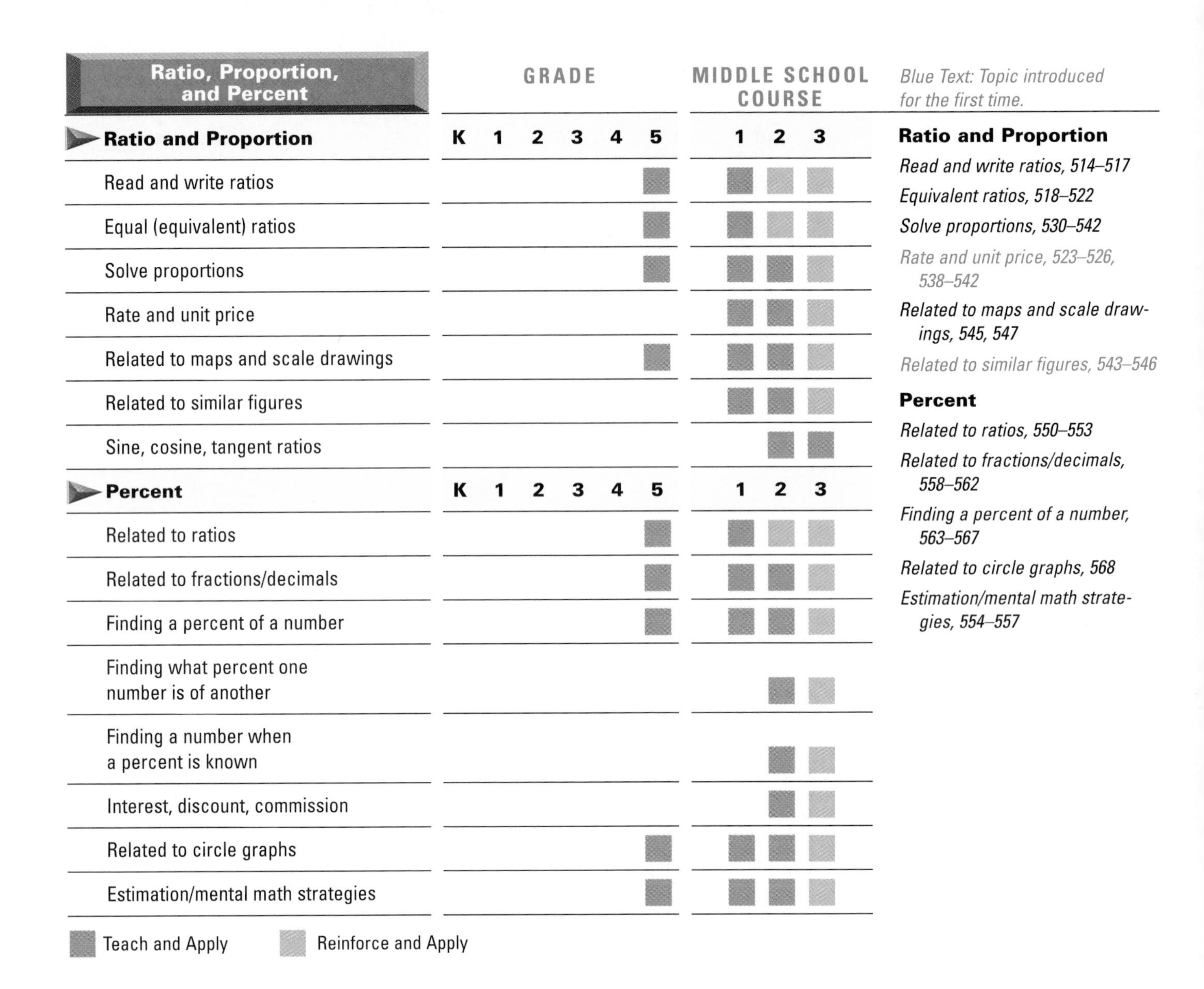

Ratio, Proportion, and Percent

	GRADE						MIDDLE SCHOOL COURSE		
Ratio and Proportion	**K**	**1**	**2**	**3**	**4**	**5**	**1**	**2**	**3**
Read and write ratios						■	■	□	□
Equal (equivalent) ratios						■	■	□	□
Solve proportions						■	■	■	□
Rate and unit price							■	■	□
Related to maps and scale drawings						■	■	■	□
Related to similar figures							■	■	□
Sine, cosine, tangent ratios								■	■
Percent	**K**	**1**	**2**	**3**	**4**	**5**	**1**	**2**	**3**
Related to ratios						■	■	□	□
Related to fractions/decimals						■	■	■	□
Finding a percent of a number						■	■	■	□
Finding what percent one number is of another								■	□
Finding a number when a percent is known								■	□
Interest, discount, commission								■	□
Related to circle graphs						■	■	■	□
Estimation/mental math strategies						■	■	■	□

■ Teach and Apply □ Reinforce and Apply

Blue Text: Topic introduced for the first time.

Ratio and Proportion

Read and write ratios, 514–517

Equivalent ratios, 518–522

Solve proportions, 530–542

Rate and unit price, 523–526, 538–542

Related to maps and scale drawings, 545, 547

Related to similar figures, 543–546

Percent

Related to ratios, 550–553

Related to fractions/decimals, 558–562

Finding a percent of a number, 563–567

Related to circle graphs, 568

Estimation/mental math strategies, 554–557

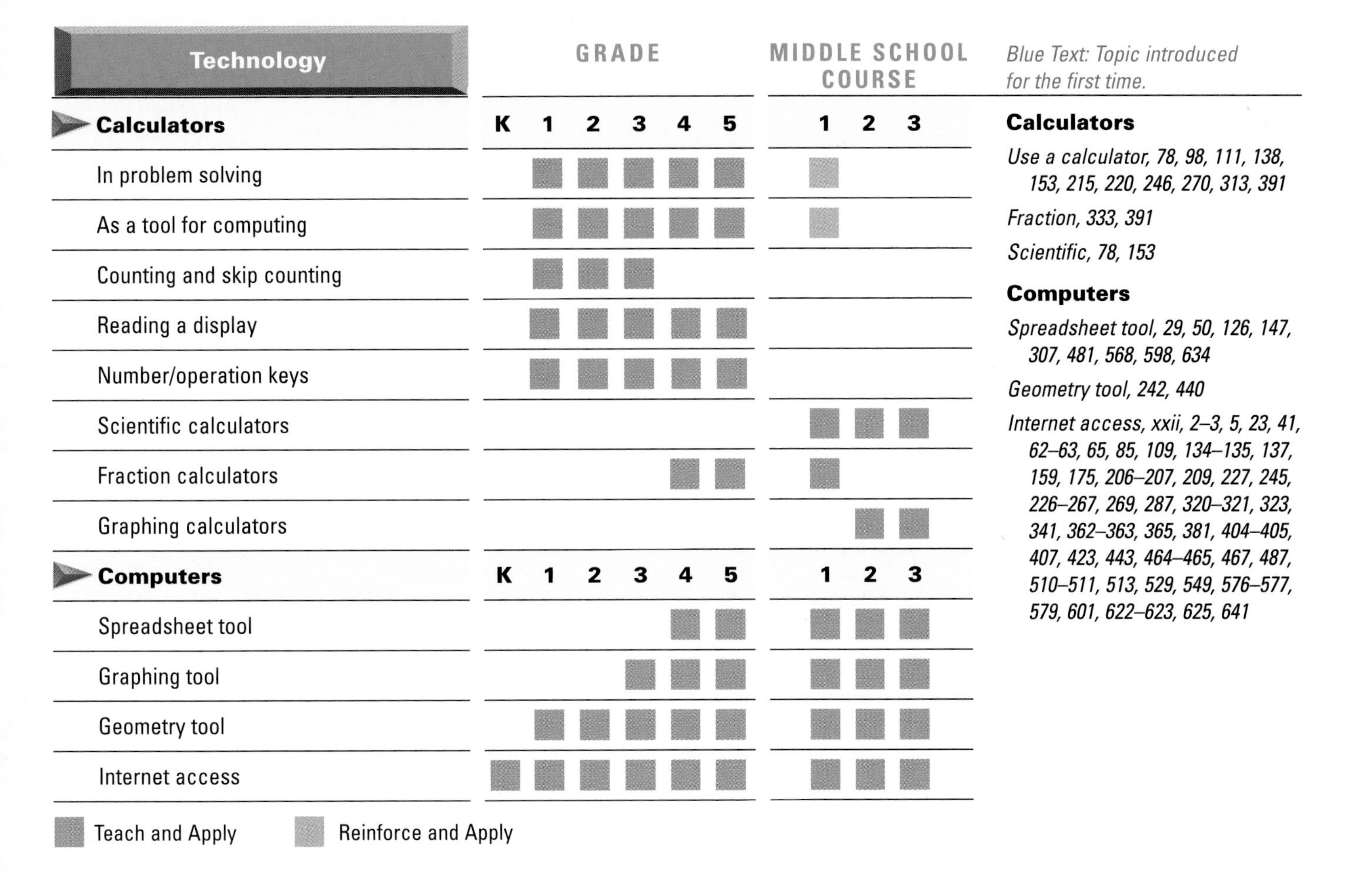

Technology	GRADE K	1	2	3	4	5	MIDDLE SCHOOL COURSE 1	2	3
Calculators	**K**	**1**	**2**	**3**	**4**	**5**	**1**	**2**	**3**
In problem solving		■	■	■	■	■	▒		
As a tool for computing		■	■	■	■	■	▒		
Counting and skip counting		■	■	■					
Reading a display		■	■	■	■	■			
Number/operation keys		■	■	■	■	■			
Scientific calculators							■	■	■
Fraction calculators					■	■	■		
Graphing calculators								■	■
Computers	**K**	**1**	**2**	**3**	**4**	**5**	**1**	**2**	**3**
Spreadsheet tool					■	■	■	■	■
Graphing tool				■	■	■	■	■	■
Geometry tool		■	■	■	■	■	■	■	■
Internet access	■	■	■	■	■	■	■	■	■

■ Teach and Apply ▒ Reinforce and Apply

Blue Text: Topic introduced for the first time.

Calculators

Use a calculator, 78, 98, 111, 138, 153, 215, 220, 246, 270, 313, 391

Fraction, 333, 391

Scientific, 78, 153

Computers

Spreadsheet tool, 29, 50, 126, 147, 307, 481, 568, 598, 634

Geometry tool, 242, 440

Internet access, xxii, 2–3, 5, 23, 41, 62–63, 65, 85, 109, 134–135, 137, 159, 175, 206–207, 209, 227, 245, 226–267, 269, 287, 320–321, 323, 341, 362–363, 365, 381, 404–405, 407, 423, 443, 464–465, 467, 487, 510–511, 513, 529, 549, 576–577, 579, 601, 622–623, 625, 641

CONTENTS

Building a Foundation for Number Sense

TAKE A MOMENT

What does "number sense" mean? Is it important? Does your class have it? How can it be taught? Some people say number sense is a way of thinking that unfolds as students explore the skills and concepts shown at the right. Stress these topics to build number sense—working with numbers, operations, basic facts, and computation in ways that make sense.

NUMBERS

Number Meanings and Uses

- *Concrete and Pictorial Models:* Models for fractions, decimals, integers.
- *Number Uses:* Quantity (5 girls), measurement (5 feet), order (the fifth day)

Number Relationships

- *Breaking Apart Numbers:* 87 = 80 + 7
- *Relative Size of Numbers:* 248 is 2 less than 250, is large compared to 4, and is small compared to 8,000,000.
- *Benchmark Numbers:* 98 is about 100.
- *Number Patterns:* Sequences, figurate numbers, divisibility, etc.

Estimation in Measurement

- *Estimates:* About 200 people, 10 to 20 feet long, about 1/2 eaten
- *Common-Object Benchmarks:* The end of your thumb is about 1 inch.
- *Checking for Sensible Answers:* A person isn't 4 meters tall.

OPERATIONS

Operation Meanings

- *Knowing When to Add or Subtract:* Joining, separating, comparing
- *Knowing When to Multiply or Divide:* Joining or forming equal groups, comparing with "times as many" or "fraction of"

Operation Relationships; Properties

- *Relationships Between Operations:* Multiplication as repeated addition and as the inverse of division
- *Properties:* Commutative, associative, distributive, identity

Effects of Operations

- Ask students if adding and multiplying always result in a larger number.
- Have students multiply two numbers, then explore the effect of doubling one factor, the other factor, both factors.
- Have students add 2 to a number ten times. Then have them multiply the same number by 2 ten times.

Try This Tomorrow

Using the overhead projector, show students some computation exercises for just one minute. Tell them to write down estimates for the answers. Afterwards have students compare their estimates and how they got them.

How would you estimate the number of seats in an auditorium?

Which is greater, 3,523 + 245 or 245 + 3,524?

If $6 \times 452 = 2{,}712$, what is 6×453?

Find $4{,}567 \times 12.8 \times 0 \times 15.47$.

Which is greater, 79/80 or 99/100?

How many different ways can find 5 x 124 in your head?

"Number sense is to using numbers and operations as comprehension is to reading words and sentences."

—John Dossey

BASIC FACTS AND COMPUTATION

Basic Facts

Rapid recall of basic facts is important for estimation, mental math, and computation. Use flash cards, software, fact strategies, etc. as needed to ensure all students know their facts.

Estimation and Mental Computation

Remind students to estimate before calculating an exact answer or when an exact answer isn't needed. Remind them of various estimation and mental-computation strategies.

Estimation Strategies in Computation
Front End 173 + 421 + 348 —> 100 + 400 + 300 = 800. Then add 150 because 73 + 21 + 48 is about 150. 800 + 150 = 950.
Rounding 28.4 – 3.9 —> 28 – 4 = 24. 425 × 28 —> 400 × 30 = 1,200.
Compatible Numbers 1/3 × 187 —> 1/3 × 180 = 60.
Clustering 627 + 658 + 589 + 613 —> 4 × 600 = 2,400.
Benchmark 46 + 38 —> $46 < 50$ and $38 < 50$. $46 + 38 < 100$.

Mental-Computation Strategies
Compensation 57 + 29 —> 57 + 30 = 87. 87 – 1 = 86.
Breaking Apart Numbers 54 + 23 —> 54 + 20 = 74. 74 + 3 = 77. 92 × 6 = (90 × 6) + (2 × 6) = 540 + 12 = 552.
Special Numbers Look for numbers like 1, 10, 100 or 3, 30, 300. 400 × 20 = 8,000. 45 + 30 = 75. 3 + 79 + 7 = 3 + 7 + 79 = 10 + 79 = 89.

Paper-Pencil Computation

If some students have still not mastered paper-pencil computation that you consider important, provide remediation but don't deny them access to other math in the meantime. Let students use calculators as needed to solve problems and learn concepts.

Choosing a Computation Tool

Remind students to try mental math first and don't use calculators instead of mental math. Discuss the choice of calculators or paper and pencil. In real life, the choice may depend on how tedious the computation is, how many computations are needed, etc.

NUMBER SENSE TEACHING TIPS

Encourage Flexibility
People with good number sense use multiple strategies and can use different strategies for the same problem.

Basic-Facts Mastery
Basic-facts mastery is a key to good number sense. When appropriate, work for rapid recall of basic facts.

The Value of Estimation
Stress the value of estimates. Some students see them as wrong answers.

Put Strategies in Perspective
Point out that learning names of strategies for basic facts, mental math, and estimation is not important. Being able to use strategies is what's important.

Scott Foresman - Addison Wesley Math

Number sense is a foundation of the program.

Student Book

- Lessons that focus on the many aspects of number sense including Mental Math, Estimating Sums and Differences, Estimating Products and Quotients, Numerical Patterns, Estimating with Decimals, Estimation: Sums and Differences of Mixed Numbers, Estimating: Products and Quotients of Fractions, Estimating Percents
- Exercises identified as number sense, operation sense, estimation
- Mental math notes in lesson development

Teacher's Edition

- Support for number sense in notes and activities plus special Mental Math or Estimation exercises for every lesson

Ancillaries

- Support for number sense in the program components including the Interactive CD-ROM with a Place-Value Blocks tool and a Fraction Tool.

Keys to Success in Teaching Problem Solving

TAKE A MOMENT

Many teachers ask "What can I do to help my students do better in problem solving?" There's no one simple answer. There may be a variety of reasons why students are struggling. One reason could be that students are simply having difficulty reading the problem and gaining the kind of information they need in order to understand and solve the problem. One of the keys to success in teaching problem solving is helping students learn to "read for math."

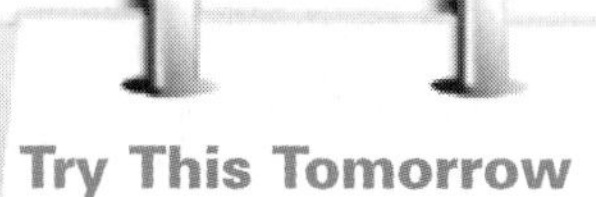

Try This Tomorrow

Give students some word problems and tell them you want to check on how effectively they read the problems. Ask questions to check their understanding of the problems. Then give some more problems and have the students ask such questions.

PROVIDE TOOLS FOR LEARNING THE PROBLEM-SOLVING PROCESS

Problem-Solving Guidelines

Introduce general problem-solving guidelines and use them to provide guided problem solving as needed.

Understand the Problem
- What do you know?
- What do you need to find out?

Develop a Plan
- Have you ever solved a similar problem?
- What strategies can you use?
- What is an estimate for the answer?

Solve the Problem
- Do you need to try another strategy?
- What is the solution?

Look Back
- Did you answer the right question?
- Does your answer make sense?

Problem-Solving Strategies

Introduce problem-solving strategies and show students examples of problems solved using the strategies.

- Look for a Pattern
- Make an Organized List
- Make a Table
- Guess and Check
- Work Backward
- Use Logical Reasoning
- Draw a Diagram
- Solve a Simpler Problem

Within daily lessons at middle school, integrate instruction of problem-solving strategies by:

- Using problems-solving strategies in lesson examples.
- Providing problem-solving tips as a regular part of instruction.

INTEGRATE PROBLEM SOLVING INTO DAILY INSTRUCTION

Teach Through Problem Solving Use real-world contexts. Introduce content with opportunities for students to explore, letting the math emerge during the problem-solving process.

Integrate Problem Solving Into Practice There's no substitute for solving lots of problems. Give routine, nonroutine, and open-ended problems. Do a problem of the day and multi-day projects.

Use Technology to Enhance Problem Solving Use calculators so students can access problems involving real data and can solve more problems in a given period of time.

"All students can think, reason, and solve problems in mathematics."

—Randy Charles

▶ PROBLEM-SOLVING TEACHING TIPS

Model Good Problem Solving
Model the problem solving skills, strategies, and habits you'd like students to have.

Facilitate Class Discussions
Make students responsible for thinking. Listen to them. Ask them to explain what they did. Ask who did it a different way.

Introduce Ideas As Needed
Present math terms, symbols, content, and alternative solutions as needed within an overall role of problem-solving coach.

Assess Problem Solving Holistically
Look at the total work (the process) and not just the answer. Use scoring rubrics.

Reading for Math

Focus on ways that reading problems with math in mind can help students at various phases of the problem-solving process: doing an initial reading to understand the problem, reading to organize information and make a plan, reading to look back and compare the answer to the original problem.

Reading for Math	Is a Key to Success
To Help You Understand	
• Read the problem and then ask yourself questions.	• What is the problem about? What is it asking for?
• Read the problem looking for unnecessary information.	• Read all the data in the problem? Is some not needed?
To Help You Plan	
• As you read, interpret math phrases.	• Look for phrases like 3 more than, twice as long as, half of.
• After you read, identify any missing information.	• Is there data you need that is not stated in the problem?
To Help You Look Back	
• After you get an answer, reread for reasonableness.	• Ask if your answer is too low or too high or close enough.
• Reread to check the rules of the problem.	• Verify that your solution agrees with all the facts.

Scott Foresman - Addison Wesley Math

Problem solving is a foundation of the program.

Teaching the Problem-Solving Process

- A Problem-Solving Handbook in front of the book presents problem-solving guidelines and strategies.
- Problem-Solving Focus pages look at reading the problem, finding unnecessary information, etc.
- Problem-Solving Tips are in lesson development.

Integrating Problem Solving in Instruction

- "Explore" teaches through problem solving.
- Problem-solving exercises are one-step, multiple-step, nonroutine, and include Choose a Strategy.
- Chapter Projects are introduced and revisited.
- Problem of the Day is in the Teacher's Edition and on the Daily Transparencies.
- A Guided Problem Solving blackline master for each lesson provides a step-by-step approach to solving a problem selected from an exercise in the book.
- Calculators are assumed. An Interactive CD-ROM, Wide World of Mathematics for Middle School, and the New Adventures of Jasper Woodbury videodisc provide technology-enhanced problem solving.

Encouraging Helpful Habits and Beliefs

- "What Do You Think" in lessons throughout shows how 2 students solved the same problem and then asks questions about comparing their methods.

ENCOURAGE HELPFUL HABITS AND BELIEFS

Promote Good Problem-Solving Habits

- Perseverance
- Flexibility
- Confidence, risk taking
- Willingness to reflect on one's thinking

Foster Important Beliefs About Problem Solving

- There's more than one way to solve a problem.
- Some problems have more than one solution.

Technology in Math Class: What Are Your Goals?

TAKE A MOMENT

What technology is available to you as you teach math? How do you use it? Whether you have a little or a lot and use it rarely or often, take a moment to think through your technology goals. Start by thinking about your students.

- Write down the year they will turn 21 and the year they'll be 65.
- Think about the math and the technology they will use as adults.
- Now set some goals. What math content will you emphasize and how would you like to use technology in your math class? Use the information at the right to help.

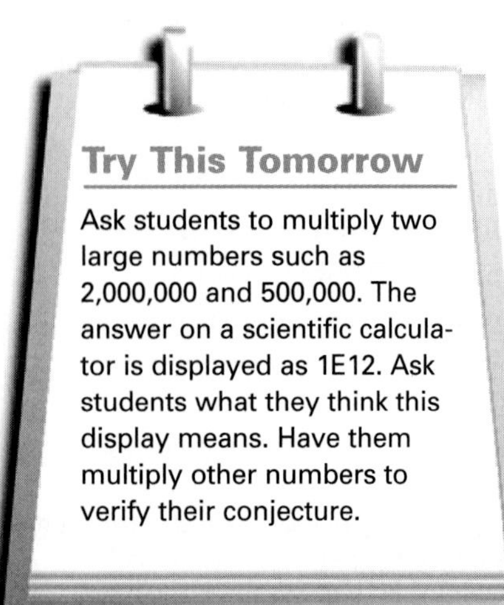

Try This Tomorrow

Ask students to multiply two large numbers such as 2,000,000 and 500,000. The answer on a scientific calculator is displayed as 1E12. Ask students what they think this display means. Have them multiply other numbers to verify their conjecture.

LEARNING WITH TECHNOLOGY

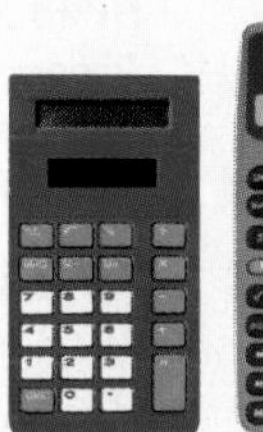

4-Function Calculator

Fraction Calculator

Scientific Calculator

Graphing Calculator

Computer Software

Interactive CD-ROM

www.mathsurf.com

Internet Connections

Learning with Calculators

Calculators as Problem-Solving Tools Calculators save time when students solve problems involving data analysis, areas, number patterns, numerical conjectures, or any tedious computation. Calculators let students spend their time focusing on the problem-solving process.

Calculators as Concept Development Tools While students should not use calculators to do basic facts, mental computation, or simple paper-pencil computation, calculators can help develop other number skills and concepts as shown in the Estimation Target Game below.

Graphing Calculators Graphing calculators can assist learning in statistics and algebra.

ESTIMATION TARGET GAME

One student enters a number and operation and says a target range: enter 8 [×] and say 2000–3000. Another student enters a number and presses [=]. If the answer is within the target range, it's a bull's-eye.

Learning with Computers

Tool Software and Practice Games Computers help students explore and practice math concepts by providing:

- Graphing tools for bar graphs, line graphs, line plots, etc.
- Geometry tools for 2D, 3D work
- Number tools such as a place-value blocks tool and a fraction tool
- Probability tools for simulations
- Spreadsheet tools to explore patterns, relationships, pre-algebra
- Writing tools for journal work
- Practice games for motivation and instant feedback

Interactive, Multimedia CD-ROM For interactive teaching, math tools, sound, movies, and animation.

Internet Connections For worldwide gathering and sharing of data.

Learning with Video

You can bring real-world math into the classroom with:

- Videotape
- Video on CD-ROMs
- Videodisc, digital videodisc
- Other digital video sources

"Technology can open the door to students learning more math than ever before."

—Cathy Seeley

LEARNING ABOUT TECHNOLOGY

Learning About Calculators

Use key sequences like these to help students learn about their calculators.

- Automatic constant: 4 [+] 3 [=] [=] [=] [7, 10, 13]
- Order of operations: 4 [+] 5 [×] 3 [19]
- Memory: 5 [M+] 3 [+] [MR] [=] [8]
- Integer division: 26 [INT÷] 3 [=] [8 R2]

Learning About Computers

Here are some basic computer skills students should learn.

- Starting up; using a floppy disk, CD-ROM, or network
- Finding, opening, and operating a document or program
- Changing, saving, and printing a document; shutdown

Learning About the Internet

Here are some Internet basics.

- Getting on the Internet: you need a computer, a modem to get information, and a browser to display information.
- Getting around the Internet: type a URL to find a "page" (like using an address to find a house); click on hyperlinks (underlined words) to go somewhere else (to "surf"); use a search engine or directory to find information sources.

LEARNING WHEN TO USE TECHNOLOGY

- Teach students that it's not appropriate to use technology as a substitute for thinking or doing basic facts, mental computation, and simple paper-pencil computation. To convince students, have a race between students doing these problems mentally and others using a calculator.

  3 x 5 200 + 500 2 x 800 30 + 10 + 20 100 + 78

- Teach students that it's appropriate to use technology when solving problems and exploring new ideas.
- Stress that technology makes estimation more important, not less, because it's easy to push a wrong button.

TECHNOLOGY FOR TEACHERS

To Plan Use an interactive CD-ROM lesson planner.

To Assess Use test and practice software.

To Present a Lesson Use an overhead display panel or large monitor to show computer screens during presentations.

To Help You Grow Gather and share ideas on the Internet.

TECHNOLOGY TIPS

Managing Calculators

Number the calculators and storage slots for easy distribution and retrieval.

Using Technology Helpers

Ask 3–4 students to volunteer as technology helpers for the class.

Communicating with Others

Find out what technology is available at school and request more that you need. Keep parents informed about how you're using technology and why.

Math/Calculator Discoveries

Students using calculators continue to discover new things about math and about calculators. Have students add their discoveries to a class collection.

Scott Foresman - Addison Wesley Math

The program offers many opportunities to use technology.

Student Book

- Calculators: Scientific calculator assumed, with options for using a fraction calculator; Calculator Hint and Technology Link in examples.
- Computers: Tool software used in Technology pages; Mathsurf Internet site references; opportunities for using spreadsheets in lessons.

Teacher's Edition

- Technology options keyed into chapters and lessons

Ancillaries

- Calculator and computer activities in Technology Masters
- Interactive, multimedia CD-ROM with lessons and tools
- The New Adventures of Jasper Woodbury for problem solving on videodiscs
- Wide World of Mathematics for Middle School on videotape, videodisc, or multimedia CD-ROM
- For teachers: Teacher's Resource Planner CD-ROM to preview ancillaries and plan lessons, *TestWorks:* Test and Practice Software, Mathsurf Internet site for teachers. Also a Mathsurf Internet site for parents.

Working Together to Make Connections in Middle School

TAKE A MOMENT

What are some of the differences between math in school and math in real life? In real life, math problems don't appear in paragraphs on pages next to other pages that focus primarily on math. One way to get closer to real-life math in school is to do interdisciplinary team teaching. It helps students see knowledge as part of an integrated system. It helps them see the "big picture" and the relevance of math to their lives.

Try This Tomorrow

Ask students to name some math topics. Write them on the board. Form small groups. Have each group take a topic and brainstorm uses of that math in other school subjects. Have groups share results and display the results on the wall.

A RANGE OF WAYS TO DO INTERDISCIPLINARY TEAM TEACHING

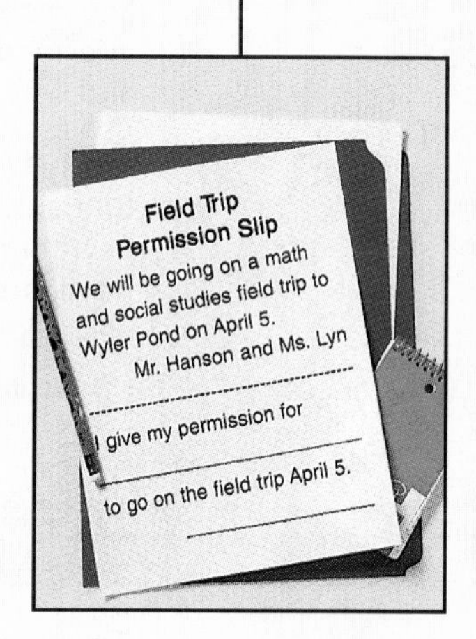

KEEPING IN TOUCH

Two teachers talk during the year and do some activities jointly.

Mr. Hanson teaches math. Ms. Lyn teaches science. At different times during the year, they talk about what they're doing. Once when students were using ratios in sampling in math, the teachers did a field trip to a local pond.

Talking to Colleagues

- Share information. Talk about topics in math that tie into other areas, like measurement in science or symmetry in art.
- Ask what students know about an application you plan to use in math.

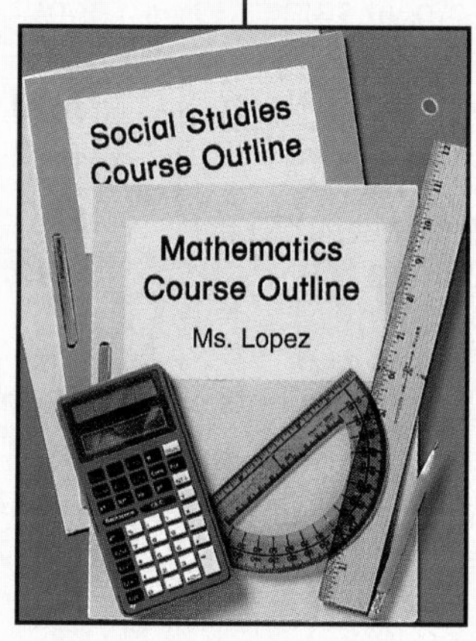

CO-PLANNING

Two teachers plan their courses so that some topics will coincide.

At the beginning of the year, Ms. Lopez, the math teacher, and Miss Kennedy, the social studies teacher, sequence topics in each course. Last year they planned for statistics to be done at the same time that elections were studied.

Planning Courses Together

- Share your course outline and time line with colleagues early.
- Help them see that the sequence of topics in math might not be as flexible as in other subjects.

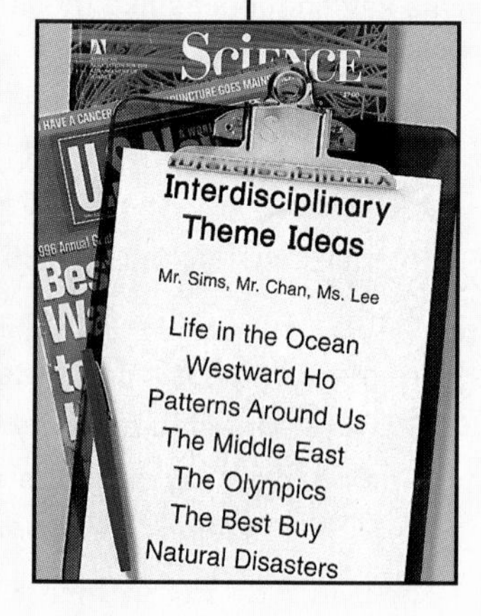

THEMATIC TEACHING

A team of 3 teachers uses themes at specific times during the year.

At Washington Middle School, the math, science, and social studies teachers plan one or more themes they will follow in their courses and when. The team might have a theme run for one week, a few weeks, or longer.

Selecting Themes

- Begin by brainstorming connections between the disciplines. Look for math-rich topics.
- When deciding how long a theme will last, consider students' interest in that topic.

> *"We must choose among the many ways to help students see the connections between math and other disciplines."*
>
> —*Janet Caldwell*

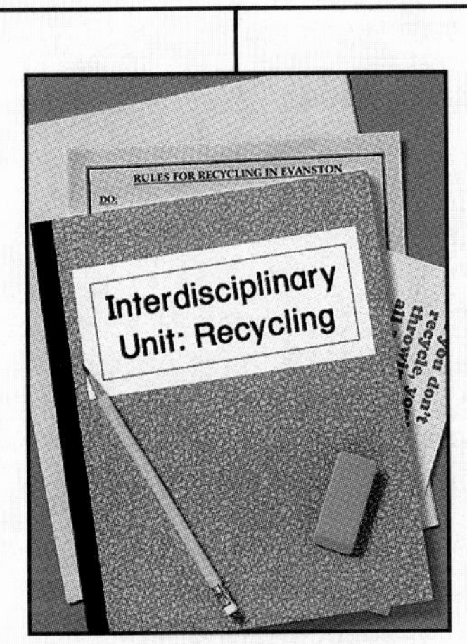

THEMATIC UNITS

A team of 4 teachers use themes ending with investigations/units.

At Ames School, four teachers (math, science, language arts, and social studies) use a theme each quarter and finish with a 1-week investigation/unit. Last year, one unit was on recycling; another was on proportional reasoning.

Planning Thematic Units

- Take advantage of local opportunities: the need for a new parking lot.
- Have each teacher plan one of the units.
- Rotate classes so each teacher sees all students.
- Do portfolio assessment.

CO-TEACHING

Two teachers co-teach a two-subject course to one large class.

Mr. Hasad teaches math. Mrs. Wyler teaches science. They have a first and second period block for combining two classes of students in a large room. They plan one course that covers both math and science content.

Teaching Together

- Plan the course to maximize opportunities for interdisciplinary work.
- Be flexible so you can take advantage of the freedom to adjust content coverage or sequence along the way.

TEAM TEACHING TIPS

Worthwhile Mathematics
Be sure the math involved in an interdisciplinary theme or unit is worthwhile, not just an occasional use of measurement or graphing.

Maximize Student Involvement
One of the biggest benefits of interdisciplinary units is the excitement they generate when students get really involved.

Communication with Other Math Teachers
Coordinate with other math teachers. It's difficult for a science teacher to plan with you if that teacher's students have three other math teachers.

Covering the Math Content
A math topic can be taught before or during its use in a thematic unit. Plan the year so that you feel units enhance, not interrupt, your instruction.

Scott Foresman - Addison Wesley Math

The program provides support for interdisciplinary connections and for team teaching.

Student Book

- Problems related to other disciplines, such as science, social studies, health, are identified.
- Chapter Projects at the beginning of chapters may involve several disciplines.
- Section themes are often interdisciplinary.

Teacher's Edition

- Lesson-specific Team Teaching suggestions are in Meeting Middle School Classroom Needs.
- Block scheduling for an interdisciplinary course is given at the front of each chapter.
- An Interdisciplinary Bulletin Board is shown for each chapter.
- Units in the Connected Mathematics series are keyed to chapters.

Ancillaries

- For each section, a 2-page Interdisciplinary Team Teaching worksheet is provided. It connects math with science/technology, social studies, language arts, or fine arts and typically includes an open-ended activity encouraging further exploration.
- The Home and School Connections booklet includes a Community Project for each chapter.
- The Wide World of Mathematics videodisc, videotape, or CD-ROM is often interdisciplinary.

Fostering a Community of Learners in the Math Classroom

TAKE A MOMENT

Think back to when your students entered your class. Did they have diverse learning styles, cultural backgrounds, socioeconomic backgrounds, levels of English proficiency, and perhaps physical, emotional, or mental challenges? Which of your students are the hardest to reach in math? In our information society, it is a priority for all students to succeed in math. The best way to achieve this is to build a community of learners in the classroom that support each other on the road to achieving math power.

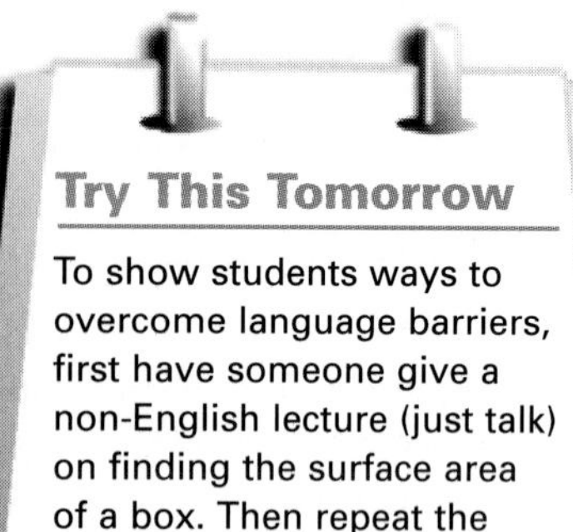

Try This Tomorrow

To show students ways to overcome language barriers, first have someone give a non-English lecture (just talk) on finding the surface area of a box. Then repeat the explanation using drawings, gestures, symbols, props, and interaction.

ESL STUDENTS

"Show me what you mean."

Overcome Language Barriers When You Communicate

- Use real objects, manipulatives, and pictures, especially ones relating to the students' world.
- Use gestures and highlighting.
- Speak slowly in short, simple sentences and enunciate clearly.
- Provide ample repetition; check comprehension frequently.
- When you model, show what to do; don't just say what to do.
- Use tables and diagrams.
- Use "scaffolding;" rephrase what students say to help them be clear.

Vary How Students Communicate

- Have them demonstrate, write, speak, draw, play math games, use computers, and work with parents.
- Pair students with same-language or English-language speakers.

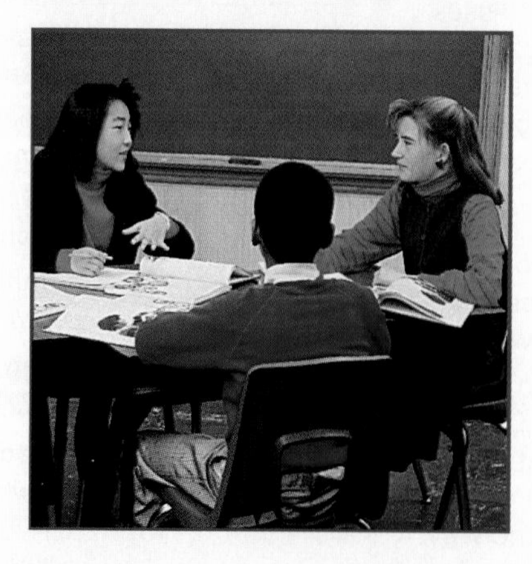

INCLUSION STUDENTS

"Give me more time."

Identify Student Needs

- Learning disabled (LD) students have normal intelligence but have problems with memory, perception, distractibility, and reasoning.
- Low achievers and the educable mentally handicapped (EMH) have problems with memory, attention span, learning rate, and reasoning.
- Students with attention deficit disorder, ADD, are easily distracted.
- Physical and emotional challenges vary: visual, auditory, speech, orthopedic, hyperactive, etc.

Modify Instruction

- Present lessons in a structured manner with regular checkpoints.
- Collaborate with specialized resource teachers about ways to customize instruction.
- Check activities for too many materials, memory skills, or steps.
- Don't deny students opportunities to learn important content; just modify how it's presented based on students' needs.
- Use graphic organizers, a file of math words, real-world links, group and pair work; have one student read to another when needed.
- Assign less; allow more time.
- Vary assessment methods; use students' writing, speaking, and hands-on work to gain insights into their understanding.

"All students must have access to a curriculum that fosters mathematical thinking."

—Freddie Renfro

DIVERSE LEARNING STYLES

"Let me try it my way."

Use Activities That Support Diverse Learning Styles

Learning Style	Learns Through
Verbal	Reading, writing, talking, listening.
Logical	Exploring, questioning, reasoning.
Visual	Drawing, building, designing, creating.
Kinesthetic	Movement, hands-on activities.
Musical	Rhythm, melody, tapping, rapping.
Social	Grouping, team participation, and sharing.
Individual	Thinking, reflecting, goal setting.

GIFTED AND TALENTED STUDENTS

"Give me a challenge."

Provide challenging, interesting problems. Have gifted students work others; then everyone benefits.

AT-RISK STUDENTS

"Give me a chance."

Provide extra encouragement and excitement in school with emphasis on problem solving and critical thinking.

GENDER ISSUES

"Treat me the same way."

Some teachers pay more attention to boys, give them more praise, let them talk more, give them more help, and ask them higher-level questions. Be aware of this issue.

CULTURAL DIVERSITY

"Respect my heritage."

Clarify misconceptions, negative beliefs, and stereotypes. Provide relevant, motivating contexts. Encourage all students to share and celebrate their cultures.

A COMMUNITY OF LEARNERS

An Accepting, Supportive Learning Environment
Create an atmosphere that honors students' unique ideas. Encourage peer coaching as a normal part of the classroom culture.

Observing Students
Provide opportunities for interactions, and then observe to assess students' needs.

Promoting Self Confidence
Many students have been told they aren't good at math. Praise small positive steps that will lead to larger ones.

Teaching Strategies for All
Use a variety of teaching and assessment strategies that are age, gender, and culturally appropriate for all learners.

Scott Foresman - Addison Wesley Math

The program is designed to reach all learners.

Overcoming Language Barriers

- Pictures in the Student book that show what to do
- Vocabulary called out; Language Link for help with non-math words; Study Tips as students read the text
- Activities with manipulatives, technology—not just words
- Varied forms of assessment—not just written
- Mathematics Dictionary
- Multilingual Handbook including a multilingual glossary

Accommodating Varied Abilities, Learning Styles, Backgrounds

- Assignment Guide; daily blackline masters for Practice, Reteaching, Enrichment, Guided Problem Solving
- Inclusion tips and Reteaching activities in lesson notes
- Extend Key Ideas pages; For Groups that Finish Early in lesson notes
- Communicate and Journal exercises, Chapter Project, Work Together in Explore, Your Choice (learning styles), multicultural and gender-sensitive contexts
- Learning Modalities and Diversity ideas in lesson notes

A Teacher's Guide to Assessment: What, How, Why, and When

TAKE A MOMENT

Think about the students in your class. Write down the names of any students for whom you'd like more information about what they know and don't know about mathematics. Then write down two ways you might be able to get that information. Perhaps a different form of assessment would help.

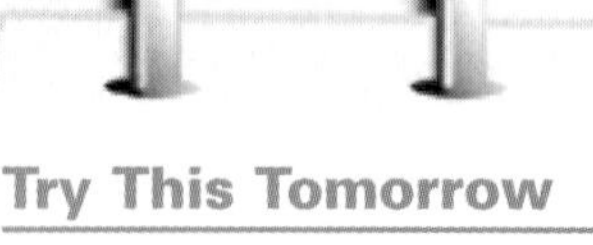

Try This Tomorrow

If you haven't tried all the methods of assessment listed at the right, pick one and try it tomorrow. Then use it at least once more in the next week. The suggestions given in the Assessment Sourcebook can help you get started.

WHAT TO ASSESS

Assess Full Math Power

- Concepts
- Facts
- Skills, procedures
- Problem solving: routine problems, nonroutine problems, open-ended problems, decision making
- Mathematical reasoning and critical thinking

Assess Math Habits and Disposition

- Perseverance
- Flexibility
- Confidence, risk-taking
- Motivation
- Participation
- Cooperation
- Reflection on one's own work and learning

Assess content and approaches that are valuable in the real world; don't just assess what is easy to test.

HOW TO ASSESS

Use a Mix of Student Work

- Oral work: explanations, questions
- Written work: skills, drawings, graphs, explanations of student thinking, written reports
- Work with tools: manipulatives, calculators, computers
- Work with others: partners, small groups, and the whole class

Vary Assessment Methods

- Observation, interview
- Journal of student writing
- Performance tasks scored using assessment rubrics
- Free-response or multiple-choice tests
- Warm-ups; quick checks
- Self assessment, peer assessment
- Portfolio of selected student work

Use a variety of student work and assessment methods that reflect how students learn and how you teach.

T

U

V

W

X

Y

Z

INDEX

D

E

F

INDEX

Page 309

5-8 Answers for Explore

3.

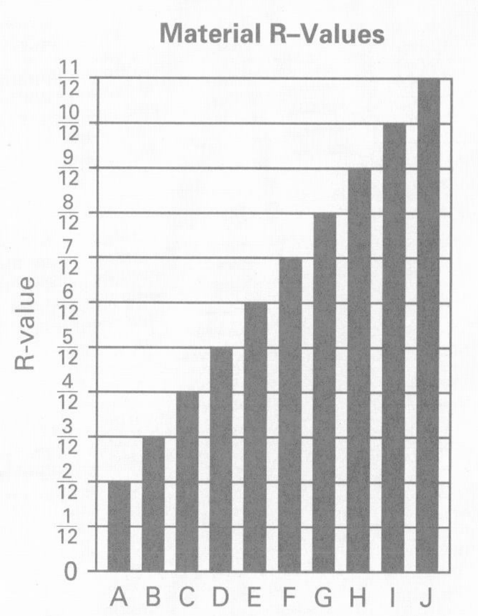

A: stucco
B: common brick
C: lightweight gypsum plaster
D: asphalt roof shingles
E: three-eighths-inch plywood
F: half-inch gypsum board
G: hardwood finish flooring
H: wood bevel siding
I: wood siding shingles
J: wood roof shingles

Page 318

Answer for Performance Task

Coin	No.	Fractions of a Dollar	Value
Nickel	1	1/20	$0.05
	2	2/20 or 1/10	$0.10
	3	3/20	$0.15
	4	4/20 or 1/5	$0.20
	5	5/20 or 1/4	$0.25
	6	6/20 or 3/10	$0.30
	7	7/20	$0.35
	8	8/20 or 2/5	$0.40
	9	9/20	$0.45
	10	10/20 or 1/2	$0.50
	11	11/20	$0.55
	12	12/20 or 3/5	$0.60
	13	13/20	$0.65
	14	14/20 or 7/10	$0.70
	15	15/20 or 3/4	$0.75
	16	16/20 or 4/5	$0.80
	17	17/20	$0.85
	18	18/20 or 9/10	$0.90
	19	19/20	$0.95
	20	20/20 or 1	$1.00
Dime	1	1/10	$0.10
	2	2/10 or 1/5	$0.20
	3	3/10	$0.30
	4	4/10 or 2/5	$0.40
	5	5/10 or 1/2	$0.50
	6	6/10 or 3/5	$0.60
	7	7/10	$0.70
	8	8/10 or 4/5	$0.80
	9	9/10	$0.90
	10	10/10 or 1	$1.00
Quarter	1	1/4	$0.25
	2	2/4 or 1/2	$0.50
	3	3/4	$0.75
	4	4/4 or 1	$1.00
Half-Dollar	1	1/2	$0.50
	2	2/2 or 1	$1.00

Page 347

6-5 Answers for Explore

1. a.

1	$\frac{1}{4}$	1	1	$\frac{1}{2}$
1	1	1	$\frac{3}{4}$	

b.

1	$\frac{1}{3}$	$\frac{1}{3}$	1	$\frac{1}{6}$	$\frac{1}{6}$	$\frac{1}{6}$
1	1	1	$\frac{1}{6}$			

c.

1	$\frac{1}{8}$	$\frac{1}{8}$	$\frac{1}{8}$	1	1	$\frac{1}{8}$
1	1	1	$\frac{1}{2}$			

d.

1	$\frac{1}{6}$	$\frac{1}{6}$	$\frac{1}{6}$	1	1	$\frac{1}{2}$
1	1	1	1			

g. 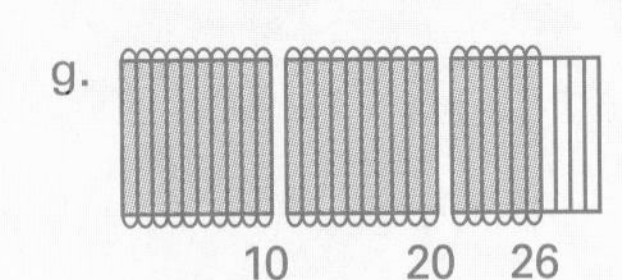

h. 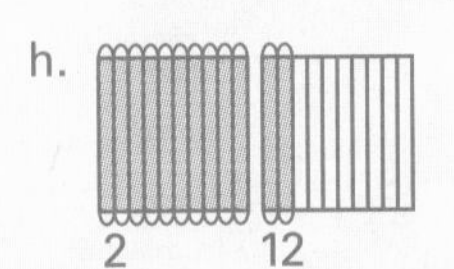

Chapter 5

Page 276

5-2 Answers for Explore

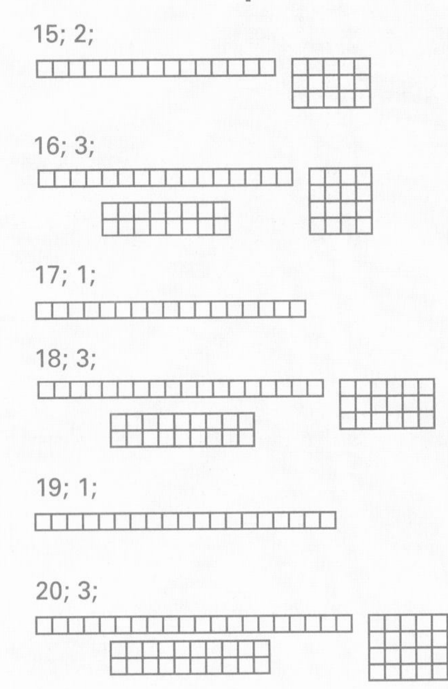

Page 291

5-4 Exercise Answers

7. $\frac{4}{6}$;

8. $\frac{24}{24}$;

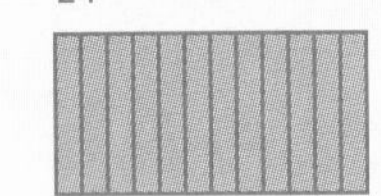

9. $\frac{1}{2}$;

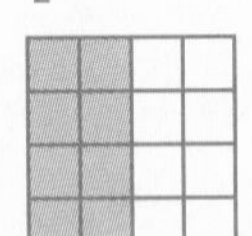

10. $\frac{22}{22}$;

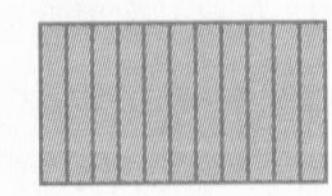

11. $\frac{2}{5}$;

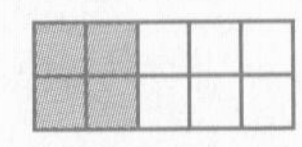

12. $\frac{12}{14}$;

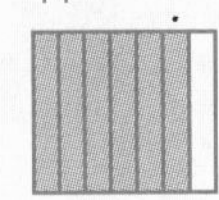

13. $\frac{6}{16}$;

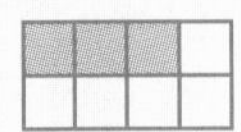

14. $\frac{2}{18}$;

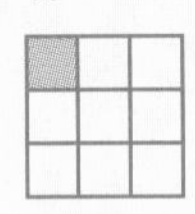

15. $\frac{12}{16}$;

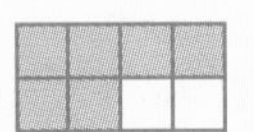

16. $\frac{4}{14}$;

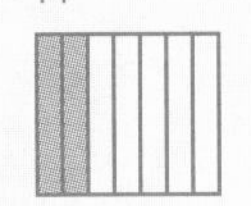

17. $\frac{4}{8}$;

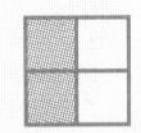

18. $\frac{16}{22}$;

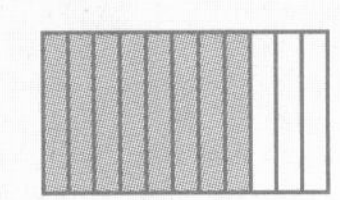

19. $\frac{18}{20}$;

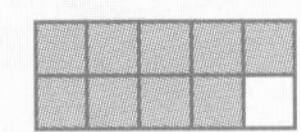

Page 306

5-7 Exercise Answers

59.

60.

61.

62.

63.

64.

48. The graphs are similar because the bars have the same relative height. The graphs are different because one has numbers less than 10 and the other has numbers in the millions.

Page 110

2-10 Answers for Explore

1.

Number of Volumes	Value of Gold	Processing Cost	Profit
1	$ 400	$ 250	$ 150
2	800	500	300
3	1,200	750	450
4	1,600	1,000	600
5	2,000	1,250	750
10	4,000	2,500	1,500
20	8,000	5,000	3,000
50	20,000	12,500	7,500
100	40,000	25,000	15,000

Page 141

3-1 Exercise Answers

34.

Number	Frequency
3	4
4	2
5	2
6	2
7	2
8	1
9	1
10	2
12	1

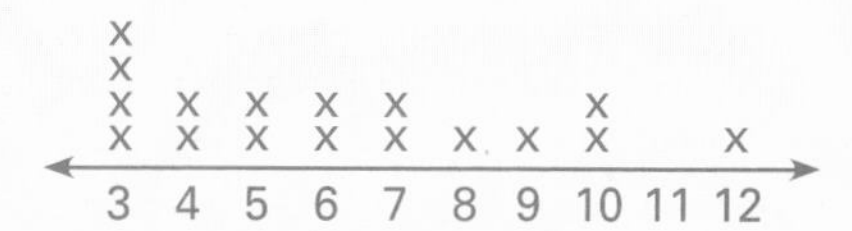

35.

Number	Frequency
10	1
20	2
30	2
40	1
50	3
60	1
70	4
80	2
100	1

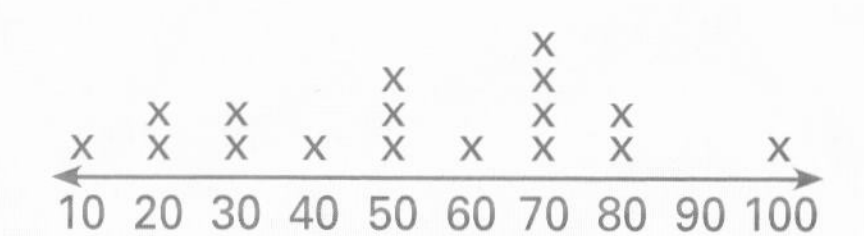

Page 146

3-2 Exercise Answers

41. Juice Cans Sold

Number

Apple Grape Orange Cranberry

Flavor

42.

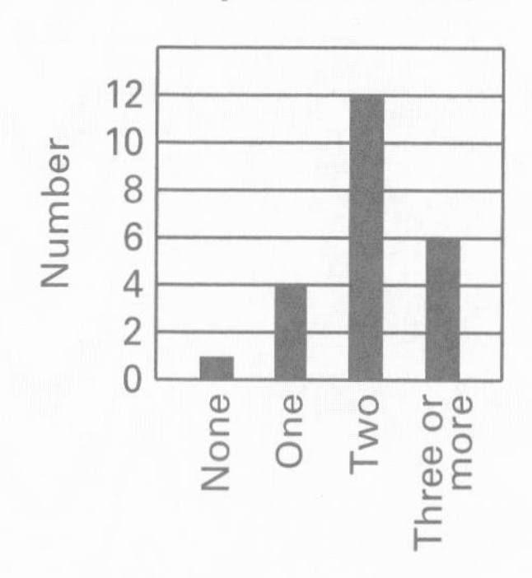

Page 191

3-11 Answers for Explore

1. a. 1 2 3 4 5 6 7 8 9 10

b.

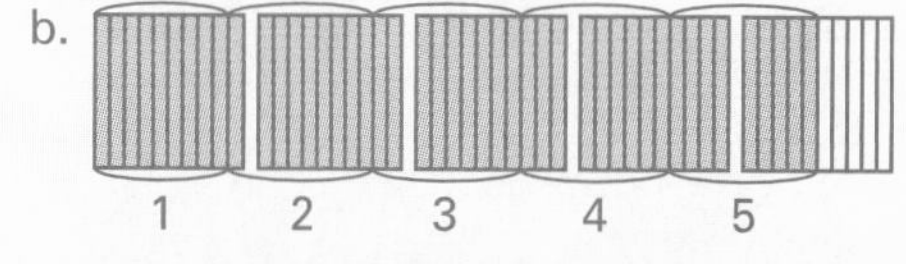

c.

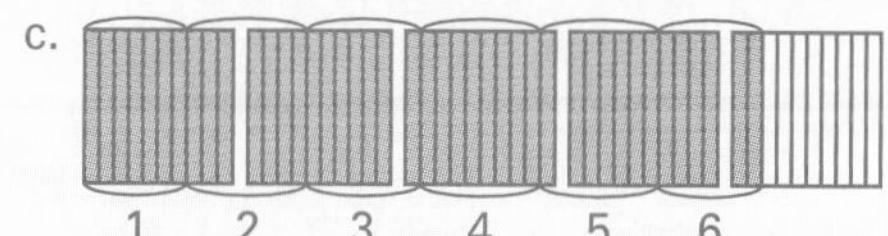

d.

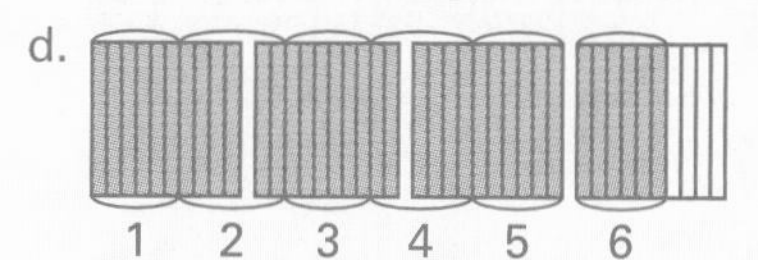

e.

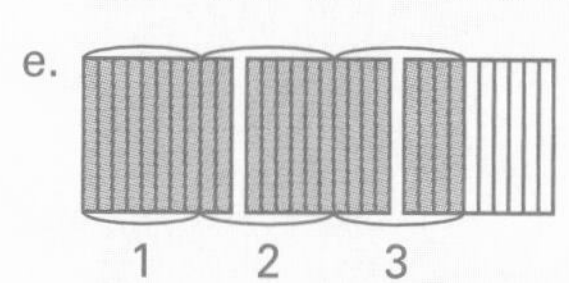

f.

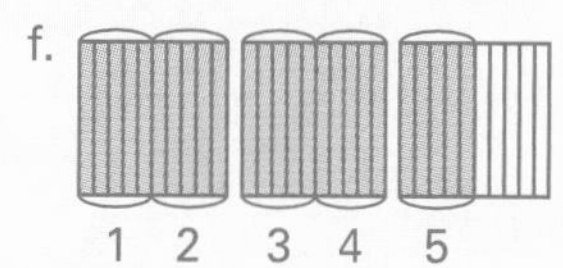

Answer continues on next page.

ADDITIONAL ANSWERS

Additional Answers

Chapter 1

Pages 27–28

1-4 Exercise Answers

3.

No. of Shoes in Closet	Frequency
2	5
4	6
6	9
8	13
10	16
12	18

4.

Hair length (in.)	Frequency
1	1
2	8
3	10
4	5
5	3
6	2
7	1

5.

6.

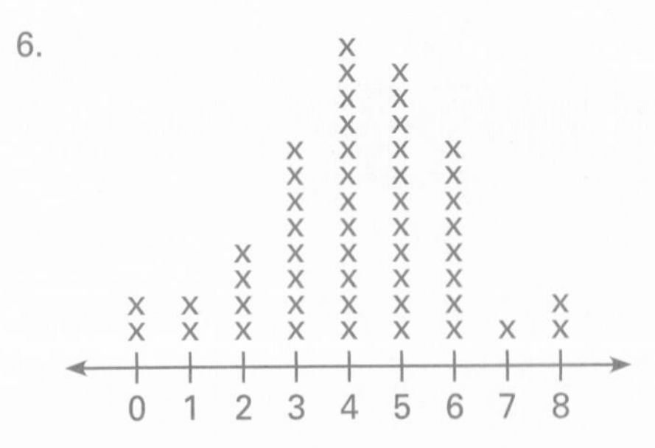

17. Two thousand one hundred forty-three
18. Three thousand seven hundred eighty-one
19. Nine thousand six hundred eleven
20. Five thousand five hundred five
21. Four thousand three hundred two
22. Nine thousand nine hundred thirty-three

Page 40

Answers for 1B Review

3.

Stem	Leaf
1	5 5 7 8 9
2	2 3 3 3 3 4
3	2 2

Possible answers: The most common length is 23 inches; the longest birds are 32 inches and the shortest are 15; most birds are between 15 and 25 inches long.

4. A

Page 61

Suggested Scoring Rubric

It's My Party

Score	Criteria
4	•Provide realistic cost of order. •Logical and precise explanation.
3	•Provides good estimate of cost. •Provides adequate explanation.
2	•Provides rough estimate of cost. •Gives little explanation.
1	•Projected cost is very unrealistic. •Gives no explanation.

Chapter 2

Pages 68–69

2-1 Exercise Answers

11. Eight thousand, two hundred thirty-five
12. Nine million, three hundred three thousand, nine hundred forty-six
13. Seven thousand, ninety-eight
14. Two hundred twenty-two
15. Fifty-six million, fifty-six thousand, five hundred sixty
16. Eight trillion, nine hundred sixty-nine million, one hundred fifty-two thousand, one
17. 93 million
18. 141 million, 500 thousand
19. 888 million
20. 1 billion, 779 million, 500 thousand
21. 2 billion, 791 million
22. 3 billion, 653 million, 500 thousand
48. Possible answers:

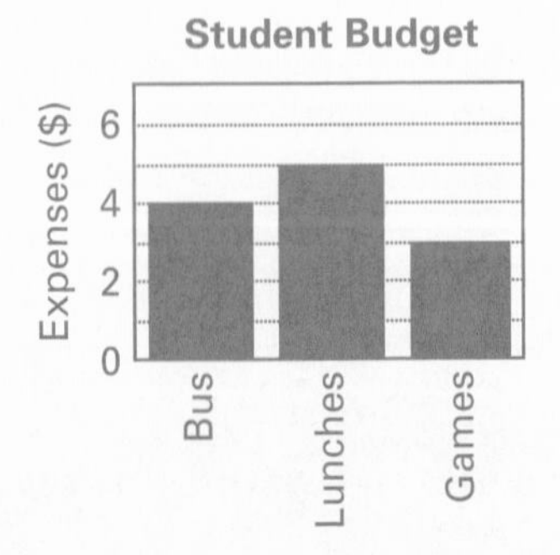

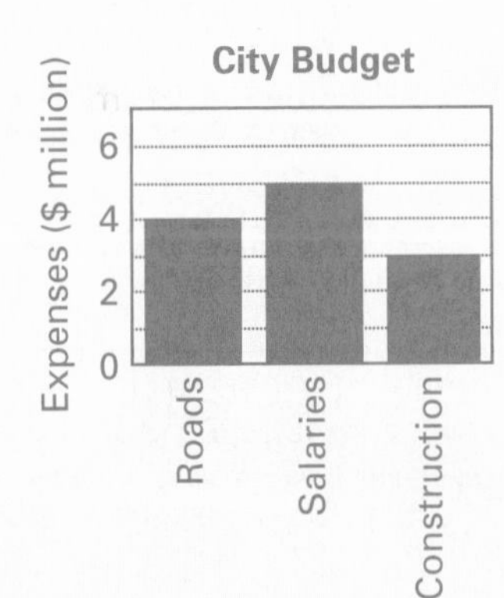

Answer continues on next page.

ADDITIONAL RESOURCES

INSERVICE WORKSHOPS FROM SCOTT FORESMAN-ADDISON WESLEY

At Scott Foresman-Addison Wesley, we offer more than program materials. We also offer our commitment to service with inservice workshops for professional staff development as well as support for implementation of program materials. As part of our ongoing partnership between teacher and publisher, we are at your service. Contact your sales representative to hear how our educational consultants can customize inservice programs to meet your needs.

Northeast	1-800-521-0011
Southwest	1-800-241-3532
Midwest	1-800-535-4391
West	1-800-548-4885
Southwest	1-800-527-2701
In Texas	1-800-441-1438
Web Site	http://www.sf.aw.com

ADDITIONAL RESOURCES

Number Sense

McIntosh, A., B. Reys, R. Reys, and J. Hope. *Number Sense: Simple Effective Number Sense Experiences.* Palo Alto, CA: Dale Seymour Publications, 1996.

Reys, Barbara, et al. *Developing Number Sense in the Middle Grades: Addenda Series, Grades 5–8.* Reston, VA: NCTM, 1991.

Ritchhart, Ron. *Making Numbers Make Sense.* Palo Alto, CA: Dale Seymour Publications, 1993.

Schoen, H. L., and M. J. Zweng, eds. *Estimation and Mental Computation.* Reston, VA: NCTM, 1986.

Sowder, Judith. "Estimation and Number Sense." Grouws, Douglas A. ed. *Handbook of Research on Mathematics Teaching and Learning.* Reston, VA: NCTM, 1992.

Van de Walle, John A. *Elementary and Middle School Mathematics: Teaching Developmentally,* 3rd ed. Reading, MA: Addison Wesley Longman, 1998.

Problem Solving

Charles, Randall, and Frank Lester. *Teaching Problem Solving: What, Why, & How.* Palo Alto, CA: Dale Seymour Publications, 1982.

Charles, Randall, Frank Lester, and Phares O'Daffer. *How to Evaluate Progress in Problem Solving.* Reston, VA: NCTM, 1987.

Charles, Randall, and Edward Silver, eds. *The Teaching and Assessing of Mathematical Problem Solving.* Hillsdale, NJ: Lawrence Erlbaum, 1989.

Dolan, Daniel T., and James Williamson. *Teaching Problem-Solving Strategies.* Palo Alto, CA: Dale Seymour Publications, 1983.

Gibney, T., S. Miering, L. Pikaart, and M. Suydam, eds. *Problem Solving: A Basic Mathematics Goal.* Palo Alto, CA: Dale Seymour Publications, 1980.

Polya, G. *Mathematical Discovery: On Understanding Learning, Teaching Problem Solving.* New York, NY: Wiley, 1962.

Technology

Fey, James T., and Christian R. Hirsch, eds. *Calculators in Mathematics Education.* Reston, VA: NCTM, 1992.

Mathematical Sciences Education Board of the National Research Council. *Reshaping School Mathematics: a Philosophy and Framework for Curriculum.* Washington, DC: National Academy Press, 1990.

Virginia Grant Consortium. *The Educator's Guide to the Internet.* Palo Alto, CA: Dale Seymour Publications, 1997.

Interdisciplinary Team Teaching

Cook, Nancy, and Christine Johnson. *The MESA Series.* Palo Alto, CA: Dale Seymour Publications, 1994–1998.

Lappan, Glenda, James T. Fey, William M. Fitzgerald, Susan N. Friel, and Elizabeth Difanis Phillips. *Connected Mathematics.* Palo Alto, CA: Dale Seymour Publications, 1996.

Diversity

Cech, Maureen. *Global Sense: A Leader's Guide to Games for Change.* Palo Alto, CA: Dale Seymour Publications, 1995.

Perl, Teri. *Math Equals.* Palo Alto, CA: Dale Seymour Publications, 1978.

Reimer, Luetta, and Wilbert Reimer. *Mathematicians Are People, Too.* Palo Alto, CA: Dale Seymour Publications, 1990, 1995.

Skolnick, J, C. Langbort, and L. Day. *How to Encourage Girls in Math and Science.* Palo Alto, CA: Dale Seymour Publications, 1982.

Thornton, Carol A. *Teaching Mathematics to Children with Special Needs.* Palo Alto, CA: Dale Seymour Publications, 1983.

Assessment

Ainsworth, Larry and Jan Christinson. *Student-Generated Rubrics,* Palo Alto, CA: Dale Seymour Publications, 1998.

Barton, James. *Portfolio Assessment* Palo Alto, CA: Dale Seymour Publications, 1996.

Freedman, Robin Lee Harris, *Open-Ended Questioning.* Palo Alto, CA: Dale Seymour Publications, 1993.

Hart, Diane. *Authentic Assessment* Palo Alto, CA: Dale Seymour Publications, 1993.

Stenmark, Jean Kerr, ed. *Mathematics Assessment: Myths, Models, Good Questions, and Practical Suggestions.* Palo Alto, CA: Dale Seymour Publications, 1991.

Other

Burns, Marilyn. *Writing in Math Class.* White Plains, NY: Cuisenaire Company of America, 1995.

Burns, Marilyn. *About Teaching Mathematics.* White Plains, NY: Cuisenaire Company of America, 1992.

Mathematics: for Middle School. Videotapes and discussion guide. White Plains, NY: Cuisenaire Company of America, 1989.

"What we test tells students what we value. What gets inspected is respected."

—Steve Leinwand

ASSESSMENT TIPS

Ongoing Assessment
Carry a clipboard and checklist. Write on self-stick labels to transfer notes. Be a good listener; be nonjudgmental.

Using Assessment Rubrics
Score papers with a colleague at first.

Portfolios
Have students move papers from their work folder to an assessment portfolio at various times.

Changing How You Assess
Don't change everything all at once. Show students criteria and sample work.

WHY AND WHEN TO ASSESS

Assessment Purposes

- Monitor progress against criteria and give students feedback.
- Adjust instruction as needed.
- Do long-term planning.
- Send progress reports or grades home to parents.
- Compare an individual student or a group of students to other students in the district, state, or nation.

Assessment Times

- Ongoing assessment integrated with daily instruction
- End-of-section quizzes
- End-of-chapter tests
- End-of-quarter or semester tests
- Annual district, state, or national tests

Assess primarily to help students grow and to help you plan. Assess on an ongoing basis during instruction.

Scott Foresman - Addison Wesley Math

Here are some of the many built-in assessment options.

Student Book

- Check Your Understanding, Journal, Test Prep exercises (multiple-choice), Test Prep notes, Project Progress
- Chapter Assessment including Performance Assessment
- Cumulative Review (half in multiple-choice format)

Teacher's Edition

- Ongoing Assessment: Error Intervention, Portfolio, Interview, Observation, Journal, Self-Assessment, Performance Assessment in lessons
- Quick Quiz, Project Assessment, Scoring Rubrics
- Standardized Test Correlation in front of each chapter

Ancillaries

- Assessment Sourcebook: Inventory Test, Quizzes, Chapter Tests (free-response, multiple-choice, mixed formats), Cumulative Tests, record forms, assessment tips, . . .
- TestWorks: Test and Practice Software with ready-made and customized tests, free response or multiple choice
- Interactive CD-ROM with a Journal feature